THE COMPLETE

CYBERSPACE
REFERENCE
and
DIRECTORY

**AN ADDRESSING AND UTILIZATION GUIDE TO
THE INTERNET, ELECTRONIC MAIL SYSTEMS,
AND BULLETIN BOARD SYSTEMS**

Other VNR Communications Books . . .

EDI Guide: A Step by Step Approach
by Edward Cannon

NetView: IBM's Network Management Product
by Alfred Charley

Doing Business on the Internet
by Mary J. Cronin

Routing in Today's Internetworks
by Mark Dickie

EDI: A Total Management Guide, 2nd Edition
by Margaret A. Emmelhainz, Ph.D.

Digital Signal Processing in Communications
by Marvin E. Frerking

Broadband Networking
by Lawrence Gasman

Data Communications Test and Troubleshooting, 2nd Edition
by Gilbert Held

Mastering PC Communications Software
by Gilbert Held

Working With NetWare: For Network Supervisors and Users
by Gilbert Held

The Complete Cyberspace Reference and Directory
by Gilbert Held

Low-Cost E-Mail With UUCP: Integrating Unix, DOS, Windows and MAC
by Thomas Wm. Madron

Analyzing DECNET/OSI Phase V
by Carl Malamud

Analyzing Novell Networks
by Carl Malamud

Analyzing Sun Networks
by Carl Malamud

The Handbook of International Connectivity Standards
Edited by Gary R. McClain

Networking NT: Using Windows NT in the Corporate LAN Environment
by Christopher Monro

The Illustrated Network Book: A Graphic Guide to Understanding Computer Networks
by Matthew G. Naugle

Making Telecommuting Happen: A Guide for Telemanagers and Telecommuters
by Jack M. Nilles

JPEG Still Image Data Compression Standard
by William B. Pennebaker and Joan L. Mitchell

X.500 Directory Services: Technology and Deployment
by Sara Radicati

SNA: IBM's Systems Network Architecture
by Stephen J. Randesi and Donald H. Czubek

Using Wireless Communications in Business
by Andrew M. Seybold

Network Topology Optimization
by Roshan Lal Sharma

Communications Standard Dictionary, 2nd Edition
by Martin H. Weik, DSc.

THE COMPLETE

CYBERSPACE REFERENCE
and
DIRECTORY

AN ADDRESSING AND UTILIZATION GUIDE TO THE INTERNET, ELECTRONIC MAIL SYSTEMS, AND BULLETIN BOARD SYSTEMS

Gilbert Held

VAN NOSTRAND REINHOLD
I(T)P A Division of International Thomson Publishing Inc.

New York • Albany • Bonn • Boston • Detroit • London • Madrid • Melbourne
Mexico City • Paris • San Francisco • Singapore • Tokyo • Toronto

Copyright © 1994 by Van Nostrand Reinhold

I(T)P   A division of International Thomson Publishing Inc.
         The ITP logo is a trademark under license

Printed in the United States of America
For more information, contact:

Van Nostrand Reinhold
115 Fifth Avenue
New York, NY 10003

International Thomson Publishing GmbH
Königswinterer Strasse 418
53227 Bonn
Germany

International Thomson Publishing Europe
Berkshire House 168-173
High Holborn
London WCIV 7AA
England

International Thomson Publishing Asia
221 Henderson Road #05-10
Henderson Building
Singapore 0315

Thomas Nelson Australia
102 Dodds Street
South Melbourne, 3205
Victoria, Australia

International Thomson Publishing Japan
Hirakawacho Kyowa Building, 3F
2-2-1 Hirakawacho
Chiyoda-ku, 102 Tokyo
Japan

Nelson Canada
1120 Birchmount Road
Scarborough, Ontario
Canada M1K 5G4

International Thomson Editores
Campos Eliseos 385, Piso 7
Col. Polanco
11560 Mexico D.F. Mexico

1 2 3 4 5 6 7 8 9 10 RRDHB 01 00 99 98 97 96 95 94

Library of Congress Cataloging-in-Publication Data
Held, Gilbert, 1943–
    The Complete Cyberspace Reference and Directory / Gilbert Held.
      p.   cm.
    ISBN 0-442-01913-0
    1. Computer networks—Directories.   2. Electronic mail systems—
    Directories.   3. Computer bulletin boards—Directories.   I. Title.
TK5105.5.H437   1994
384.3'3—dc20   94-17569
                                                CIP

CONTENTS

PREFACE

The purpose of this book is to provide readers with a comprehensive guide to the evolving electronic highway, a term referred to by many persons as cyberspace.

In developing the material for inclusion in this book I recognized that the term cyberspace (or electronic highway) means many things to different people. For some persons the Internet is their electronic highway, while for other persons the use of a bulletin board system or the services of an electronic mail provider represent their electronic highway. Like a conventional highway, the electronic highway has a variety of entrance and exit ramps, which provide users with the ability to route communications in the form of messages and files from one service provider to another. However, unlike the concrete variety highway, in which entrance and exit ramps are normally explicitly marked, the use of cyberspace can represent a challenge when attempting to transfer information to users on a different service from the one you are using. Thus, the key challenge for the development of this book was to provide a sufficient level of information to provide readers with the tools and techniques required to transport information between a variety of electronic messaging services, bulletin board systems and the Internet.

Another important goal of this book was to provide readers with a comprehensive list of electronic addresses from which they can obtain information. Since the information requirements of readers as well as their access to different types of electronic transfer resources can vary considerably the electronic addresses presented in this book were developed to meet those differences between readers. That is, information resources available electronically are grouped alphabetically based upon different electronic addressing methods. This means that readers that are limited to sending electronic mail will obtain a large number of electronic addresses from which they can obtain information to include files sent via electronic mail. Similarly, readers that access a bulletin board system or who have a connection to the Internet via FTP or Telnet will also obtain a significant number of electronic addresses from which they can obtain information electronically.

Recognizing the problem of terminology in which the use of abbreviations, symbols, and terms has become difficult to follow resulted in the development and inclusion of a chapter devoted entirely to terms, definitions and abbreviations. Due to the importance many readers will attach to being able to refer to this material, I decided to place this chapter at the beginning of this book. This will facilitate its use as well as provide readers that like to progress logically through a book with the ability to discover new terms, definitions and abbreviations from the beginning. In doing so you may encounter some terms, definitions and abbreviations that may facilitate future electronic sessions and provide you with the ability to communicate more effectively.

As a professional author I depend upon you, the reader, for feedback. Please feel free to write to me at the publisher's address listed on the back cover of this book concerning any comments you may wish to share with me. If there are other areas of cyberspace you would like to see covered in a second edition, an expansion of an existing area or general comments to wish to share with me please do so.

Gilbert Held
Macon, GA

ACKNOWLEDGMENTS ⎯⎯⎯⎯⎯⎯⎯⎯⎯⎯⎯⎯⎯⎯⎯⎯⎯⎯⎯⎯⎯⎯⎯⎯⎯⎯⎯⎯⎯⎯⎯

The preparation and completion of a book represents an effort which requires the cooperation and assistance of many individuals. This book was even more dependent upon the assistance of persons I met electronically than most books I previously authored due to my desire to provide readers with information concerning bulletin board systems and BBS networks, data whose compilation is beyond the ability of any one individual.

I am extremely grateful for the cooperation and assistance of Mr. Jack Crawford for providing K12Net bulletin board information and node listings, R. Bonnie Anthony for permitting the use of Relaynet node information, Mr. Joe Smolinski for permitting me to incorporate GlobalNet information into the book you are reading, Mr. Ken Sukimoto for the use of his comprehensive 96LIST, Mr. Gary Barr for his RemoteAccess node list and technical support BBS listing, Mr. Bob Breedlove for the use of his comprehensive uSBBS list, and to Mr. Cesar Keller for permission to use the Dream BBS list of Switzerland. To Dr. Anthony and the gentlemen just mentioned, I truly appreciate your cooperation and assistance which was instrumental in providing data which formed a firm foundation for this comprehensive directory of electronic highway resources.

THE COMPLETE

CYBERSPACE REFERENCE
and
DIRECTORY

**AN ADDRESSING AND UTILIZATION GUIDE TO
THE INTERNET, ELECTRONIC MAIL SYSTEMS,
AND BULLETIN BOARD SYSTEMS**

CHAPTER 1

Definitions, Terms, and Abbreviations

The growth in electronic communications resulted in the addition of a considerable number of definitions, terms, and abbreviations used to convey information between users of electronic messagings systems, bulletin boards, and the Internet. In this chapter we focus our attention upon cyberspace terminology, providing definitions of terms, the meaning of many common abbreviations and define symbols used to express the feeling of users, the later commonly referred to as emoticons.

To facilitate the use of information contained in this chapter definitions of terms are based upon the alphabetical order of the term. Similarly, abbreviations are listed in their alphabetical order.

DEFINITIONS OF CYBERSPACE TERMS

Academnet - A network within Russia which connects universities.

Aconet - A research network in Austria.

Address Resolution Protocol (ARP) - A protocol which provides translation of host addresses from Internet addresses to Ethernet addresses.

Administrative Management Domain (ADMD) - Under X.400 addressing the ADMD represents a public messaging service, such as CompuServe or MCI Mail which handles electronic mail between countries and large organizations.

Adonis - A network operated by the Institute for Automated Systems in Moscow which connects computer centers located in the former Soviet Union.

Afrimail - An electronic mail network in Tunisia which has UUCP connections to the rest of the world.

AGFNET - A network consisting of research centers and universities located in Germany.

Alex - Software which provides Internet users with a transparent read capability of remote files at anonymous FTP sites.

Alias - A nickname for a domain or host computer.

Anonymous FTP - A service provided on some computers which enables files to be downloaded by the general Internet community, usually requiring the use of the password GUEST or ANONYMOUS.

AppleLink - Apple Computer Company's electronic mail system.

Application Programming Interface (API) - A standard interface between a communications device and a software application operating on a computer.

Archie - A service which enables the databases of many anonymous FTP sites to be searched. Archie searches can be performed by either complete or partial file names and search results include a listing of anonymous FTP site addresses, directory path, file name and the date Archie last visited the site. Archie was developed at McGill University in Montreal. Archie can be accessed via Telnet, a local archie client, or E-mail.

Ariadne - A research network located in Greece which uses the X.25 protocol.

Aristote - A research network located in France.

ARPANET - The first packet switched network used to connect different types of computer systems. ARPANET was the predecessor to the Internet.

askERIC - A question-answering service for teachers, library media specialists and administrators involved with K–12 education.

Attachment - The process of attaching a file to an electronic message.

Backbone - In a bulletin board system network the series of echo conferences carried in a zone.

Bang - An exclamation point (!) used in a Unix-to-Unix Copy Program (UUCP) electronic mail address.

Bang Path - A series of UUCP nodes mail will pass through to reach a remote user. Node names are separated by exclamation marks nicknamed "bangs." The first node in the path must be on the local system, the second node must be linked to the first, and so on. To reach user1 on sys3 through sys2 if your computer's address is sys1 you would use the following address:

```
sys1!sys2!sys3!user1
```

BBS - Bulletin Board System. BBS software enables a computer to be used for message posting and retrieval, file transfers and similar activity.

Binary File Transfer (BFT) - The transmission of binary files, documents and electronic data exchange information between fax devices.

BITNET - A network which interconnects approximately 3000 computers located at educational institutions throughout the world.

Bogon - Something that is stupid or nonfunctional.

Bounced Mail - Mail that is returned to the originator due to an incorrect E-mail address.

Btoa - A UNIX program which translates Binary files into ASCII.

CDNnet - A Canadian academic network based upon the International Standards Organization Open Systems Interconnection Reference Model.

CITNET - California Institute of Technology electronic mail network.

CIX - Commercial Internet Exchange. A group formed to link commercial providers into an Internet subnet.

ClariNews - A fee based Usenet newsfeed available from ClariNet Communications.

Class I/II - PC fax modem boards that support different fax commands and operate as Group III fax devices.

Client - The host requesting a service.

CompuServe - A fee based information service which provides a connection to the Internet.

CompuServe Mail Hub - A facility of CompuServe which enables users on a local area network operating Novell NetWare Message Handling Service (MHS) software to exchange electronic messages with other MHS users, CompuServe Mail subscribers and users of other E-mail services that can be reached via a CompuServe gateway.

Conference - An interactive discussion forum which enables users to post statements, comments, questions and opinions. Although a conference has a general topic, user comments are not restricted to that topic.

Consultative Committee for International Telegraph and Telephone (CCITT) - An international standards recommending body which sets worldwide communications standards. Now renamed the ITU-TSS.

Cracker - A person who breaks or attempts to break the security of a computer system.

Cyberspace - A term used to reference electronic communications.

Daemon - An agent program which continuously operates on a UNIX server and provides resources to client systems on the network.

DENet - The Danish Ethernet Network which consists of many Ethernet networks in universities connected together by bridges.

Direct Inward Dialing (DID) - Dialing which enables a call to go directly to an office extension without requiring the intervention of an operator.

Domain - The owner or controller of computer resources. In the Internet a domain name consists of a sequence of names or words separated by dots.

Domain Defined Attribute (DDA) - Under X.400 addressing the DDA is a special field that may be required to assist a receiving E-mail system in delivering a message to the intended recipient. Up to four DDAs are allowed per address, with each DDA address entry made up of two parts, a Type and a Value.

Door - Any application which bulletin board software can "shell out" to execute. Most doors provide access to games and databases.

DREnet - A Canadian TCP/IP based network connected to the Internet.

DSIRnet - The Department of Scientific and Industrial Research network in New Zealand.

Easynet - The name of DEC's internal corporate network.

Echo - The transmission of messages between bulletin board systems. A group of bulletin board systems which exchange messages using a predefined format is known as an echo network.

EchoMail - A public message area or conference on a bulletin board system that is "echoed" to other systems in a BBS network. EchoMail is organized into different groups, each with a different topic and the term normally references communications on a FidoNet network. Also a term referring to the electronic transfer of messages between bulletin board systems.

Electronic Data Exchange (EDI) - An international standard for the exchange of debit and credit transactions, such as bank debits, commercial invoices and purchase orders.

Emoticons - Symbols usually sent with electronic mail to express the emotions of normal voice communications.

E-mail - Electronic mail.

EUnet - A subscription-funded research oriented network in Europe.

European Academic Research Network (EARN) - A general purpose computer network connecting universities and research sites throughout Europe, Africa and the Middle East.

FAQ - Frequently Asked Question, references a document containing common questions and their answers.

FidoNet - An amateur network of bulletin board systems that exchange messages electronically.

File Extension - A suffix to a file name which further identifies the contents of the file. Common file extensions include:

.bas	Basic language file
.com	DOS executable file
.exe	DOS executable file
.gif	graphic interchange format
.hqx	Macintosh binhex file; de-binhex with Stuffit, BinHex, or DeHQX
.ps	postscript file
.tar	UNIX tape archive format, unpack using: tar -xvf filename.tar
.Z	UNIX compressed file, decompress using: uncompress filename.Z
.zip	DOS compressed file, compressed via use of PKZIP program

Finger - A TCP/IP application which is used to obtain a list of persons logged onto other hosts or the status of a specific user on another host.

Firewall - Hardware and/or software which limits the exposure of a computer or group of computers to an attack from an external location.

Flame - An electronic mail message or Usenet posting which is violently argumentative.

FOSSIL - Fideo Opus SeaDog Serial Interface Layer. A program which takes over the serial port of a computer in a standard manner, acting as a buffer between some bulletin board system programs and the serial port.

Free-Nets - A computer system connected to a network which provides members of a community with access to local and remote computing resources. Some of the Freenets available for community use, the locations and modem access numbers include:

Computer System	Location	Visitor Logon	Modem Access Number
Big Sky Telegraph	Dillon, MT	bbs	406-683-7680
Buffalo Free-Net	Buffalo, NY	Freeport	716-645-6128
Cleveland Free-Net	Cleveland, OH	n/a	216-368-3888
COIN	Columbia, MO		314-884-7000
Denver Free-Net	Denver, CO	guest	303-270-4865
Heartland Free-Net	Peoria, IL	bbguest	309-674-1100
Lorain County Free-Net	Elyria, OH	guest	216-366-9721
Medina County Free-Net	Medina, OH	guest	216-723-6732
National Capital Free-Net	Ottawa, Canada	guest	613-780-3733
Tallahassee Free-Net	Tallahassee, FL	visitor	904-576-6330
Tristate Online	Cincinnati, OH	visitor	513-579-1990
Victoria Free-Net	Victoria, British Columbia Canada	guest	604-595-2300
Wellington Citynet	Wellington, New Zealand		644-801-3060
Youngstown Free-Net	Youngstown, OH		216-742-3072

Freqing (Freq) - A term or abbreviation for a "file request" for a file from another node in a network. In FidoNet a node user usually freq's a file through mailer software which sends an appropriate request to a distant node that has the desired file.

Frobnicate - To manipulate, adjust or tweak something. Often abbreviated as frob.

Front end mailer - A program that operates on a bulletin board system and which determines if a caller is another computer that wants to exchange mail or a human that wants to access the BBS resources. Usually the mailer transmits the prompt "Press ESC".. and upon receiving an ESC character or the passing of a timeout period considers the caller to be human and gives it the resources of the BBS. Also known as a mailer.

FTP - File Transfer Protocol. The Internet protocol used for transferring files from one computer to another.

FTP Mail Server - A server which permits the retrieval of files via E-mail.

Freenet - An open access, free to use, community computer system.

FYI - For Your Information. A series of documents put out by the Internet NIC which addresses common user questions.

Gateway - A computer that functions as a node in two or more networks, forwarding mail and messages from one network to addresses in the other network.

GlobalNet - A free, electronic amateur bulletin board system network which operates based upon FidoNet technical standards. GlobalNet nodes are located in North America and Europe.

Global Network Navigator (GNN) - An application developed at CERN in Switzerland which provides information about new services available on the Internet, articles about existing services, and an online version of Internet related books. The GNN is a World Wide Web (WWW) based information service.

Gopher - A distributed menuing system developed at the University of Minnesota for information access on the Internet. Gopher servers store a wide range of information, from news and phone books to weather reports and recipes. To access the Gopher system your host must have a Gopher client package.

Grapevine - The name of the Xerox Corporation internal company network.

Group III - A digital facsimile standard promulgated by the CCITT in its recommendation T.4. A Group III fax can transmit a standard page in 30 seconds over the switched telephone network.

High-ASCII - ASCII characters whose values exceed 127. In most bulletin board networks the use of high-ASCII in messages is prohibited since some types of personal computers cannot correctly interpret those characters.

High Energy Physics Network (HEPnet) - A worldwide network used to connect researchers in the field of High Energy Physics.

Horton - A software program which provides an automatic method for creating a directory of e-mail addresses. Users can look up electronic addresses via a search key which can be a fragment of a persons name.

Host - An end-system computer located on a network.

Hub - A bulletin board system that calls another Hub or is called by one or more nodes to transfer mail.

Hypertext - A program which provides non-sequential access to a document. This is normally accomplished by highlighting key words or phrases in the text on a page whose selection brings up a screen with the desired information.

Hytelnet - A hypertext system which contains information about the Internet, such as accessible library catalogs, Freenets, Gophers, bulletin boards, etc.

ID CODE - On the RIME network an ID CODE is used to identify each node in the network. The ID CODE can be up to 12 alphanumeric characters in length and appears at the bottom of every message relayed throughout the network.

Internet - The set of interconnected networks that share the same network address scheme and use the TCP/IP protocol.

Internet Architecture Board (IAB) - A group tasked with addressing Internet technical problems and developing solutions to those problems.

Internet Network Information Center (InterNIC) - A joint NSFnet and NREN information center which provides voice and electronic assistance concerning the Internet.

JNET - A communications program which operates on a DEC VAX computer, providing DEC systems with the ability to communicate with IBM computers via BITNET.

Joint Academic Network (JANET) - A networking organization supported by the Science and Engineering Research Council in the United Kingdom.

Jughead - A database of Gopher links which accepts word searches and allows search results to be used on many remote Gophers.

JUNET - A network of universities in Japan which supports electronic mail and news. JUNET users can be reached via UUCP and the Internet.

JvNCnet - Princeton University's John von Neumann Computer Network which connects universities in the eastern US and Europe.

Kluge - Hardware or software assembled from a variety of parts or modules, usually in haste. A Rube Goldberg device.

Knowbots - A program which functions as a front-end to all of the white pages on the Internet, searching for the information a user enters. Knowbot Information Services of Reston, VA developed the Knowbot concept.

K12NET - A loosely organized network of school based electronic bulletin board systems located throughout North America, Australia and Europe that share curriculum related information, classroom projects and other education related information.

Linkletter - The name of a bimonthly NSFNET newsletter published by Merit Network Information Center.

Listserv - An automated system that contains BITNET discussion lists and acts as both a mail forwarding system and as a file repository.

Login - A sequence of actions at a terminal which enables a user to access the resources of a computer or communications system.

Logout - The termination of a computer or communications session.

Magic Name - A command a bulletin board system is configured to recognize which then provides the requestor with a specific file or set of files.

Mail Reader - Software which enables a user to select unread mail and unread conference messages and have them downloaded for reading off-line. Most mail readers also permit users to create responses off-line and upload them at their convenience.

Mail Reflector - A special type of electronic mailbox which upon receipt of a message resends it to a list of other mailboxes. A mail reflector provides the ability to create a discussion group.

Mailing List - A list of persons or organizational addresses that receive a copy of a message when it is addressed to a mailing list.

Merit - A regional TCP/IP network for the State of Michigan and a mid-level network in NSFNET.

MHS (Message Handling Service) - A personal computer based software system whose primary function is the transportation of messages between application programs. MHS was developed by Action Technologies and Novell acquired full marketing and development rights to MHS for NetWare based LANs. Under MHS each application sends messages to the server's \mhs\mail\snd directory. MHS delivers messages to an application by placing them in the application's assigned directory.

MIDnet - A regional TCP/IP network which covers Nebraska, Iowa, Illinois, Missouri, Arkansas, Oklahoma, and Kansas. MIDnet is also a mid-level network in NSFNET.

MILNET - The military network within the Internet.

Minnesota Regional Network (MRNET) - A NSF regional network which provides communications between the NSFNET and researchers in Minnesota.

Mirror - A term used to reference Internet FTP sites that copy files from other archives every day or so. By accessing a mirror site close to your location you reduce transmission over the Internet

Moderator - A participant who is in charge of a conference. A moderator is responsible for keeping the discussion on track, alleviating fights, and similar functions.

Multicasting - Transmitting a message to more than one site.

Multipurpose Internet Mail Extensions (MIME) - An extension to Internet mail which adds support for the exchange of multipart messages, including binary files.

Multi-User Dungeon (MUD) - A program which enables persons to interact with each other in a simulated environment.

Name Lookup Service (NLS) - An electronic directory service which is designed to respond to external queries for general information about a large group of users. Once installed, NLS can be accessed via finger or whois.

Name Server - A program which provides information about network objects, such as domains and hosts within a domain, by answering queries.

National Center for Science Information Systems (NACSIS) - The operator of a network in Japan known as the Science Information Network which connects many Japanese universities.

National Center for Supercomputer Applications network (NCSAnet) - A regional TCP/IP network which connects users in Illinois, Wisconsin and Indiana. NCSAnet is also a mid-level network in NSFNET.

Native Computer Communications Network (NCCN) - A computer network located in Canada which provides communications for native people.

Netfind - A white pages service which enables a person to query one service and have that service search other databases for addresses matching the originally entered query.

Net.God - A person very visible on a network and who may have played an important role in its development.

NetHub - The home of the RIME network which is located in Bethesda, MD. All Super-Regional Hubs in the RIME network call the NetHub to exchange mail packets.

Netiquette - A term used to indicate proper behavior on a network.

NetMail - A private message transmission capability on FidoNet in which nodes directly communicate with one another on a point-to-point transmission basis. NetMail was originally developed for use by SYSOPS to communicate with one another and is available on some BBSs for regular users.

NETSERV - A file server used for distributing files directly related to the BIT-NET network.

Network - A group of computers connected together to facilitate the transfer of information.

Network Coordinator - In FidoNet the network coordinator is the "host" of the network who is responsible for coordinating FidoNet within the network, distributing nodelists and the FidoNet newsletter to members of the network. The network coordinator is appointed by the regional coordinator.

Network User Identification (NUI) - A combination of an ID and password which enables a value added carrier subscriber to obtain access to an overseas network or host computer attached to the carrier's network.

Node - An intermediate computer that operates as part of a network. On a bulletin board system a node normally calls a hub to exchange mail.

Nodelist - The list of nodes participating in the exchange of messages in a particular bulletin board system network, such as FidoNet or RelayNet. The nodelist defines the topology of the network.

NORDUnet - A network which connects users located in Sweden, Norway, Denmark and Finland. NORDUnet uses DECnet, NJE and TCP/IP protocols.

NorthWestNet - A regional TCP/IP network connecting users in Alaska, Washington, Oregon, Montana, Idaho and North Dakota. NorthWestNet is a mid-level network in NSFNET.

NREN - National Research and Education Network, an eventual successor to NSFnet.

NSFnet - National Science Foundation network. The NSFnet forms the national backbone for the Internet, enabling regional networks to interconnect with one another.

PACNET - An academic network connecting users in Australia, Hong Kong, Korea, Malaysia, Singapore and Indonesia.

Pan-Pacific Education and Communication Experiments by Satellite (PEACESAT) - A project of the University of Hawaii Social Science Research Institute which provides telecommunications services via satellite to the Pacific Basin.

PC Connect - A service of MCI which enables computer modem users to obtain discounted long distance rates when calling distant bulletin board systems.

Pennsylvania Research and Economic Partnership Network (PREPnet) - A mid-level TCP/IP network serving users in Pennsylvania.

Ping - A TCP/IP application in which a packet is transmitted and its echoed response indicates the status of a host or network device.

Point - A computer that is not in a FideoNet nodelist but which communicates in the same manner as a participating nodelist computer. Points are addressed using a boss node nodelist address and the boss node then transfers messages to the point. Points are addressed using the boss node's nodelist address followed by a period (point) and a number.

PostLink - A program used by a RIME bulletin board system node in place of mailer software.

Postmaster - A person responsible for administration of electronic messaging at a site.

Private Management Domain (PRMD) - Under X.400 addressing the PRMD represents a private electronic messaging system that may be connected to a Administrative Management Domain. The PRMD is usually a corporate or government agency E-mail system connected to an ADMD.

Prospero - UNIX software which facilitates the search of archives connected to the Internet. Prospero uses a virtual file system which enables users to transparently view directories and retrieve files.

Protocol - The set of rules followed by two computers when they communicate with one another.

Public message - A message available for reading by all network users.

QWK-format - The format of a file which contains bulletin board system mail from selected conferences that will be transmitted for offline reading. Most BBS's have doors for accessing off-line readers that use the QWK-format.

RFC - Request for Comments. The set of documents which defines the internal operation of the Internet.

Region - In a bulletin board system network a region is a geographic area that contains nodes that exchange messages in a defined manner.

RelayNet International Message Exchange - A bulletin board network which provides participating hubs and nodes with a mechanism to exchange messages through common conference areas that are relayed via a central NetHub.

Request For Discussion (RFD) - A period of time during which comments on a particular subject are solicited.

Resolver - A program which connects user programs to domain name servers.

REUNIR - The name of a university research network connecting sites in France.

RIME - RelayNet International Message Exchange, a multi-tier communications network which exchanges messages among member bulletin board systems.

R/O message-Receiver Only - A message directed to a single individual.

Route - The path that a message takes from its source to its destination.

Routed Message - On a bulletin board system network a message meant to be delivered to a specific board.

San Antonio Technical Research Network (SATIN) - A DECnet based network in San Antonio which is part of THEnet.

San Diego Supercomputer Center Network (SDSCNET) - A regional TCP/IP network which connects sites located in Southern California. SDSCNET is a mid-level network in NSFNET.

Scanner - A program on a bulletin board system which scans the message base for previously entered E-mail and pulls a copy of each message and makes them available to the BBS mailer program.

SENDIT - A telecommunications network for North Dakota educators and students in the K-12 environment.

SESQUINET - A regional TCP/IP network which connects sites in Texas. Sesquinet is a mid-level network in NSFNET.

Server - A computer which shares its resources with other computers. Common resources shared by a server include files and printing facilities.

Simple Mail Transfer Protocol (SMTP) - The Internet standard protocol used for transferring electronic messages from one computer to another.

Site - A node in a bulletin board system network.

Site Number - A number assigned to a site in a bulletin board system network.

Sneaker mail - A term used to reference delivery of messages by the postal service.

Southeastern Universities Research Association network (SURAnet) - A regional TCP/IP network which connects sites in the District of Columbia, Alabama, Delaware, Florida, Georgia, Kentucky, Louisiana, Maryland, Mississippi, North Carolina, South Carolina, Tennessee, Virginia, and West Virginia.

South Pacific Educational And Research Network (SPEARNET) - A network which connects universities located in Australia and New Zealand.

Space Physics Analysis Network (SPAN) - A DECnet based research network which connects NASA users.

Starlink - The name of a network which connects astronomers in the United Kingdom.

Super-Regional Hub - In the RIME network a Super-Regional Hub receives messages from Hubs within a geographic area and calls the NetHub to exchange mail packets on a network basis.

SURFnet - A network which connects research and higher education sites in the Netherlands.

Swedish University Network (SUNET) - A network which connects local and regional networks at universities in Sweden. SUNET supports DECnet, BITNET and TCP/IP protocols.

SWITCH - The national Swiss research network which uses X.25, DECnet, TCP/IP and ISO protocols.

Sysop - (System Operator) - The owner or operator of a bulletin board system.

System Development Network (SDNNET) - A network using the TCP/IP and UUCP protocols which connects locations in the Republic of Korea.

Telemail - The name of the electronic mail service operated by Sprint.

Telnet - The Internet protocol used to create a connection with a remote computer, enabling a user to work on a distant computer as if his or her terminal was directly connected. The format of the telnet command is:

```
        telnet address.domain
    or  telnet address.domain port#
```

telnet port - The port address on a computer which supports remote telnet access. Normally port 23 is the default telnet port.

Terminate and stay resident (TSR) - A program which stays resident in memory after execution and can be repeatedly invoked by pressing a predefined "hot key" combination. After the TSR program functions are completed, pressing of the ESC key or another program defined key causes the program to go back to sleep and restores the original program.

THEnet - A multiprotocol network which connects over 50 sites in the state of Texas. THEnet is managed by the University of Texas Office of Telecommunication Services and was previously known as TEXNET.

Thai Computer Science Network (TCSnet) - A network which connects universities in Thailand.

Thread - A chain of connected messages.

tn3270 - A version of the Telnet program which supports IBM 3270 terminal emulation.

Tosser - A program which takes incoming mail from another bulletin board system and tosses incoming messages into appropriate message areas in the BBS message bases.

Transmission Control Protocol/Internet Protocol (TCP/IP) - A set of protocols used by the Internet to support such services as file transfer (FTP), electronic mail transfer (SMTP), and remote login (telnet).

Trickle - The name of a BITNET mail server package which provides access to anonymous ftp archive sites via E-mail.

Tymnet - The name of a public packet switching network operated by British Telecom.

UFGATE - A program which enables a FIDO compatible bulletin board system to exchange UUCP mail with UUCP sites.

UFGATE site - A FidoNet node which runs UFGATE or equivalent software which enables a Fido BBS to exchange UUCP mail with other UUCP sites.

UNINETT - A network in Norway formed as a result of a joint effort by universities, the PTT, some research institutes and vendors. UNINETT is connected to the Internet and is Norway's part of NORDUnet.

UNIX - A computer operating system developed at AT&T Bell Laboratories in the late 1960's which provides a multi-user, multi-tasking capability. Also a trademark of Unix Systems Laboratories, Inc. which is owned by Novell, Inc.

Unrouted Message - On a bulletin board system network a message sent to every board in the network. Also known as plain mail.

USAN - The name of a network whch connects atmospheric and oceanographic science institutions in the United States. USAN members include the University of Miami, Oregon State University, Penn State, University of Maryland, University of Wisconsin, Institute of Naval Oceanography, the Naval Research Laboratory and the Woods Hole Oceanographic Institute.

Usenet - A network message sharing system that exchanges messages using a standard format. Messages are grouped into categories known as newsgroups.

UUCP - Unix-to-Unix Copy Program.

UUCP network - A loose association of computer systems communicating with each other at specific intervals using the UUCP protocol. UUCP routing is on a store and forward basis based upon the addresses in the bang path.

Uudecode - A utility program which converts an ASCII file which represents binary data back into binary.

Uuencode - A program which encodes a binary file into ASCII code, usually for transmission between two computer systems.

uwho - A program which simplifies access to many whois servers connected to the Internet. The program enables a user to search for an e-mail address without having to know where such information is kept.

Value Added Network (VAN) - A communications network with provides such value added services as reverse billing, speed conversion and store and forward capability in addition to packet switching.

Veronica - An Internet accessible service which maintains an index of titles of gopher items and provides a keyword search of those titles. Veronica is accessed through a gopher client which provides a connection to a Veronica server.

VNET - The name of an internal IBM network which supports the transmission of electronic mail, remote login, and file transfer operations.

Westnet - A regional TCP/IP network which links sites in Arizona, Colorado, New Mexico, Utah and Wyoming. Westnet is a mid-level network in NSFNET.

West Virginia Network for Educational Telecomputing (WVNET) - A network which connects universities in West Virginia. WVNET is connected to SURAnet which provides a connection to Internet.

White Pages - a term used to reference a database that contains basic information about subscribers on a network, such as their name, E-mail address, telephone number and postal address.

WHOIS - A database produced and maintained by the Internet Network Information Center (NIC) which lists both users and sites as well as a term used to reference separate databases maintained by organizations connected to the Internet.

Wide Area Information Service (WAIS) - A distributed text searching system which enables you to search the contents of archives on the Internet for occurrences of specific words. WAIS requires the use of a client program on the local workstation or host to access the system.

Wide Area Network (WAN) - A network which connects geographically separated areas.

Worm - A computer program which replicates itself and may destroy files on a computer.

Xmodem - A half duplex file transfer program with uses a 128-byte field to transport information and a simple checksum for verifying the integrity of data carried in the block.

X Windows - The graphical user-interface used by many UNIX systems.

X.400 - A Consultative Committee for International Telephone and Telegraph standard which facilitates communications between messaging systems.

X.500 - A Consultative Committee for International Telephone and Telegraph standard which defines a directory system used for permitting E-mail users to obtain an E-mail address.

Ymodem - An extension of the Xmodem file transfer protocol which permits multiple files to be transported between locations with the invocation of one command.

ZIP - The extension of a file compressed using PKZIP, a shareware program from PKWare Inc. of Brown Deer, WI. Also a term used to reference compressing a file.

Zmodem - A file transfer protocol which permits simultaneous transmission in both directions and the resumption of transmission from where a previous transmission was suspended due to line noise or another type of interruption.

Zone - In a bulletin board system based network a zone is a large geographic area that can cover one or more countries or continents.

Zone Coordinator - A person responsible for maintaining the nodelist of a zone for a bulletin board based network and sharing that list with other zone coordinators.

Zone Mail Hour (ZMH) - A common hour in a BBS FidoNet network zone when all boards are available for transmitting and receiving NetMail. During the ZMH a BBS does not accept human calls, file requests, or EchoMail transfers.

@ - When used in an Internet address separates a user name or computer name from a domain address, e.g., user@host.

% - When used in an Internet UUCP address acts as a forwarding request, resulting in mail being sent to the address between the % and @ after it is received by the primary address, e.g., user%host1@host2.

! - When used in an Internet address defines the path data flows between addresses on each side of the exclamation point, e.g., host1!host2!user.

:: - When used in an Internet address separates the host and user name. The double colon is primarily used in Digital Equipment Corporation computer networks, e.g., host::user.

E-MAIL, NETWORK AND BULLETIN BOARD SYSTEM (BBS) ABBREVIATIONS

ACSNET	Australian Computer Science Network
ADMD	Administrative Management Domain
AMPRNET	Amateur Packet Radio Network
ARP	Address Resolution Protocol
ARPANET	Advanced Research Project Agency network
AUP	Acceptable Use Policy
BARRNet	Bay Area Regional Research Network (San Francisco)
BCnet	British Columbia network
BFT	Binary File Transfer
BITNET	Because It's Time Network
BITNIC	BITNET Network Information Center
BRB	Be right back
BTW	By the way
CCITT	Consultative Committee for Telephone and Telegraph
CERFNet	California Education and Research Federation Network

CERN	Corporation for Research and Educational Networking
CERT	Computer Emergency Response Team
CHAT	Conversational Hypertext Address Technology
CICNet	Committee on Institutional Cooperation Network
CP	Copy protection
CPM	Characters Per Minute
CPS	Characters Per Second
CFV	Call for votes
CRIM	Computer Research Institute of Montreal
CSIRONET	Commonwealth Scientific and Industrial Research Organization Network (Australia)
CSNET	Computer Science Research Network
DAF	Direct Access Facility
DARPA	Defense Advanced Research Projects Agency
DDA	Domain Defined Attribute
DDN	Defense Data Network
DID	Direct Inward Dialing
EARN	European Academic Research Network
EDI	Electronic Data Interchange
ERIC	Educational Resources Information Center
ESNET	Energy Sciences Network
FTP	File Transfer Protocol
FUBAR	"F...ed" up beyond all recognition
FUnet	Finnish University Network
FWIW	For what it's worth
FYI	For your information
GIF	Graphic Interchange Format file format
gr&d	Grinning, running, and ducking
HARNET	Hong Kong Academic and Research Network
HEANET	Higher Education Authority Network (Ireland)
HEPnet	High Energy Physics network
HHOK	Ha Ha, only kidding
HHOS	Ha Ha, only serious
HST	High Speed Technology referring to modem (tm) of USRobotics
IAB	Internet Architecture Board
IAE	In any event
ILAN	Israeli Academic Network
IMO	In my opinion
IMHO	In my humble opinion
IMR	Internet Monthly Reports

InterNIC	Internet Network Information Center
IOW	In other words
IRC	Internet Relay Chat
JANET	Joint Academic Network
JUGHEAD	Jonzy's Universal Gopher Hierarchy Excavation and Display
LOCUS	Library of Congress Information System
MHS	Message Handling System
MIDnet	Midwestern States Network
MIMI	Multipurpose Internet Mail Extension
MRNET	Minnesota Regional Network
MUD	Multi-User Dungeon
NACSIS	National Center for Science Information Systems
NCCN	Native Computer Communications Network
NCSA	National Center for Supercomputer Applications
NLS	Name Lookup Service
NUI	Network User Identification
NorthWestNet	Northwestern States Network
NSFNET	National Science Foundation Network
OIC	Oh, I see
OTOH	On the other hand
PEACESAT	Pan-Pacific Education and Communication Experiments by Satellite
PITA	Pain in the ...
POT	Plain Old Telephone
POX	Plain Old Fax machine
PPP	Point-to-Point Protocol
PREPnet	Pennsylvania Research and Economic Partnership Network
PRMD	Private Management Domain
RFC	Requests for Comments
RFD	Request For Discussion
RIPE	Reseaux IP Europeans
rof,l	Rolling on floor, laughing
RSN	Real soon now
RTFM	Read the [fine] manual (or message)
SATIN	San Antonio Technical Interchange Network
SDNNET	System Development Network
SDSCnet	San Diego Supercomputer Center network
SLIP	Serial Line IP
SMTP	Simple Mail Transfer Protocol

SNAFU	Situation normal, all "f...d" up
SPAN	Space Physics Analysis Network
SPEARNET	South Pacific Educational And Research Network
SUNET	Swedish University Network
SURAnet	Southeastern Universities Research Association network
SYSOP	System Operator, the person who runs the BBS
TCP/IP	Transmission Control Protocol/Internet Protocol
TIA	Thanks in advance
TSR	Terminate and stay resident program
VAN	Value Added Network
VERONICA	Very Easy Rodent-Oriented Net-Wide Index to Computerized Archives
WAIS	Wide Area Information Service
WAN	Wide Area Network
WRT	With Respect To
WVNET	West Virginia Network for Educational Telecomputing
WYSIWYG	What you see is what you get

EMOTICON SYMBOLS

Emoticon symbols are figures created through the use of different keys on the keyboard. These symbols are used to convey the spirit in which a line of text is typed. Examples of many popular emoticon symbols and their meanings are included in the following table.

Emoticon	*Meaning*
.-]	User has one eye
.-)	User has one eye
:8)	User is a pig
:-i	Semi-smiley
:-]	Smiley blockhead
:-%	User has beard
:-o	User singing national anthem
:-t	User is cross
:-:	User is mutant
:-(	Drama
:-)	Comedy

:-	User is male
:-?	User is smoking a pipe
:-=)	Older user with mustache
:-\	Undecided user
:-p	User is sticking their tongue out (at you!)
:-)'	User tends to drool
:-'|	User has a cold
:-)8	User is well dressed
:-D	User talks too much
:-\	Popeye smiling face, for people who look like Popeye
:-#	User's lips are sealed
:-o	User is bored (yawn)
:-&	User is tongue-tied
:-*	User just ate a sour pickle
:-)-{8	User is a big girl
:-s	User after a BIZARRE comment
:-o	User is surprised
:-|	No expression face, "that comment doesn't phase me"
-:-)	User sports a mohawk and admires Mr. T
:-&	User is tongue-tied
:-9	User licking his or her lips
:-(	Sad
:-`	User spitting out chewing tobacco
:-*	User after eating something bitter
:->	Hey hey
:-E	User has a dental problem
:-X	User is wearing a bow tie
:-0	User is an orator
:-7	User after a wry statement
:-#|	User with bushy mustache
:-@	User face screaming
:-%	User is a banker
:-}	User wears lipstick
:-c	Bummed out Smiley
:-J	I'm being tongue-in-cheek
:-x	"my lips are sealed" Smiley
:-|	"have an ordinary day" Smiley
:-<	Real sad Smiley
:-(	User is crying
:-I	Hmm
:-8(	Condescending stare

:-O	Uh oh
:-Q	User is smoking/smoker
:=)	User has two noses
:=8	User is a baboon
:>	Midget Smiley
:>)	User has a big nose
:%)%	User has acne
:-)))	User is overweight
;-)	Winking Smiley
;-\	Popeye gets his lights punched out
'-)	User only has a left eye, which is closed
(-:	User is left-handed
(-)	User needing a haircut
(:-)	Smiley big-face
(:I	Egghead
{:-)	Smiley with its hair parted in the middle
{(:-)	User is wearing toupee
}(:-(	User, wearing toupee in wind
+-(:-)	User is the pope
+:-)	Smiley priest
*:o)	User is a Bozo
*<I:-)	User is Santa Claus
<:I	Dunce
<|-)=	User is Chinese
=:-)	User is a hosehead
=:-#}	Smiley punk with a mustache
=:-)	Smiley punk-rocker
>-	Female
>:-<	Mad
%-)	User is cross-eyed
#-)	User partied all night
@:I	Turban
:-)	Hee hee
:-D	Ho ho
|-)	User is asleep (boredom)
|-P	Yuk
3:*>	Rudolph the reindeer
3:-o	User is a cow
5:-)	I'm Elvis
8-)	User wears glasses
8-*	Just ate a hot pepper

8:-)	Glasses on forehead
8:]	Normal smiling face except that User is a gorilla
B-)	Horn-rims
B-|	User is wearing cheap sunglasses
o-)	User is a cyclops
L:-)	User just graduated
P-)	User is getting fresh
[:-)	User is listening to Walkman radio
[:|]	User is a robot
CI:-=	I'm Charlie Chaplin
+-:-)	I'm a priest
+-(:-)	I'm the Pope

CHAPTER 2
General UNIX Information and Common Computer Commands

There are a large number of computers using the UNIX operating system that are connected to the Internet or operate as standalone bulletin board systems. Some computers operating UNIX do both, providing the capability of a bulletin board system for users that communicate through the use of modems as well as provide access to their facilities for users that access the computer via an Internet connection. Once a UNIX computer has an Internet connection it may also provide access to the Internet for subscribers reaching the BBS via a modem connection, although some bulletin board systems may restrict such access to paying subscribers. Regardless of the service or access facilities provided you will need to know a core set of UNIX commands to make appropriate use of the computer. The information presented in this chapter was included to provide readers with a reference to the operation and utilization of a core set of UNIX commands.

The UNIX operating system was originally developed by AT&T Bell Laboratories and was primarily used as a research oriented operating system. Since its original development at AT&T Bell Laboratories a number of versions of this operating system were developed, resulting in differences between the commands supported by each operating system and to a small degree the operational result occurring from the execution of some commands. In this chapter most commands are applicable to all versions of UNIX, however, readers are cautioned that one or more commands may not be applicable to some versions of UNIX.

25

THE UNIX PROMPT

Once you successfully login to a UNIX operating system the prompt (%) will be displayed. Commands are entered by typing a series of characters and pressing the <RETURN> key. Almost all UNIX commands are represented by lowercase characters and, since the operating system is case-sensitive commands, entered as uppercase characters will usually not work.

MULTIKEY OPERATORS

Similar to most operating systems UNIX was designed to respond to certain multi-key combinations. The following table lists some of the more popular UNIX multi-key operators and the resulting operation performed by UNIX in response to the entry of the indicated multikey combination.

Multikey Combination	*Operational Result*
<CTRL> + S	Suspend screen output
<CTRL> + Q	Resume screen output
<CTRL> + C	Terminate (break) current program
<CTRL> + X	Erase to beginning of line

THE MAN COMMAND

The man command invokes the UNIX manual facility which is available on most UNIX systems. You can use the manual facility to display information about a UNIX command or topic. You can enter the manual command in one of the following formats:

man -k subject
> where subject is the subject you require information about.
>
> example: man -k directory

man number topic
> where number is the number of the UNIX manual and topic is the topic you require information about. The UNIX manual is divided into the following nine sections:

Section	General Subject Area
1	Commands
2	System Calls
3	Subroutine Libraries
4	File Formats
5	Miscellaneous Facilities
6	GAMES
7	Devices
8	Administration Commands
1	Locally Added Commands

example: man 1 chdir

BASIC UNIX COMMANDS

Command	*Operational Result*
at	execute a command at a specified time.
cat	concatenate files. You can use this command to display the contents of a file. For example, cat pay.txt.
cd	change the current working directory. For example, cd/pay/east makes east the current working directory.
chdir	same as cd.
chgrp	changes the group owner of a file.
chmod	changes the access permissions of a file. The format of this command is: chmod [u,g,o,a][+,-][r,w,x] filename. where: u is user, g is group, o is other user, a is all (uog), + adds permissions, - removes permissions, r indicates read, w indicates write, x is execute only
chown	changes the ownership of a file.
chroot	change the root directory.

Command	*Operational Result*
`compress`	compress a file or file archive producing the file extension `.Z`.
`cp`	copy files. Makes a duplicate of specified files. For example, `cp old.txt new.txt` makes duplicate of `old.txt` which is renamed `new.txt`.
`crypt`	encodes the contents of a file using a user supplied key and decodes a previously encrypted file.
`date`	displays the current date and time.
`df`	displays the number of free blocks for mounted file systems.
`du`	displays disk usage.
`elm`	invokes the electronic mail utility for sending and receiving messages.
`find`	locates files that match a certain criteria.
`help`	displays help information.
`kill`	terminate a process.
`ln`	create a new link (name) for a file. For example, `ln /pay/east jan` first makes the file jan also have the identity first.
`logout`	log off the computer.
`ls`	list all files and directories. For example, `ls /pay/east` will list files in the directory east.
	Add the flag `-a` (all) to list hidden files and the flag `-l` (long) to obtain a long listing which provides information concerning file ownership, file size, and modification ability.
`makekey`	generates an encryption key for use in a program then encrypts a file.
`man`	displays entries from the online manual for the specified command.

Command	Operational Result
mkdir	make (create) new directory. For example, `mk/pay/west` makes the subdirectory under the directory pay.
more	displays the contents of a file one screen at a time.
mv	move (rename) files. For example, `mv name1 name2` renames `name1` as `name2`.
newgrp	changes a user's active membership to a new group.
pack	compresses a file to reduce data storage requirements.
passwd	use to change the password.
pcat	concatenates the contents of several packed files.
pg	displays the contents of a file page-by-page.
ps	displays process status information.
pwd	print (displays) the name of the current working directory.
rm	remove files. For example, `rm pay.txt` deletes the file `pay.txt`.
rmdir	remove directory. The directory to be removed must first have all files within it deleted.
su	temporarily changes a user's ID.
talk	a UNIX utility which enables real time conversation with other users.
tar	create file archive with the extension `.tar`. Use `tar -xf` to extract all files in an archive and `tar -tf` to list the contents of a `.tar` file.
touch	updates the time of last modification for a file or group of files.
uncompress	decompress a file or file archive.
unpack	reconstructs the contents of a previously packed file.
who	displays names of users on the system.
xmodem	transmit a file using Xmodem or a derivative file transfer protocol.

Command format: xmodem parameter filename

where: *parameter*   *result*

parameter	result
c	select Xmodem-CRC protocol
g	select YModem-G protocol
k	select Xmodem-1k protocol
l	do not write to log file
m	select Modem7 batch protocol
ra	select receive Apple (MacIntosh)
rb	select receive binary
rt	select receive text
sa	select send Apple (MacIntosh)
sb	select send binary
st	select send text
w	wait 15 seconds prior to initiating transfer
y	select Ymodem batch protocol

UNIX FILENAMES

UNIX filenames can consist of one to 255 characters in length, with any character except "*", "?", or "/" valid. You cannot start a filename with the dash ("-") character, and the use of the period (".") as the first character in a filename results in the file becoming a hidden file. When accessing a UNIX system from an MSDOS or another type of personal computer to perform file transfer operations, you must comply with the file naming restrictions applicable to your computer. That is, when transferring a file to an MSDOS computer you must use a filename up to eight characters in length with up to three characters in its extension. This means that you may have to rename some files when downloading them from a computer operating UNIX to a computer operating MSDOS or another type of personal computer operating system.

UNIX Wildcards

UNIX supports the use of the "?" and "*" wildcard characters in filenames. This enables a UNIX command to operate upon a group of files.

The "?" wildcard character replaces a single character in a filename. For example, the command: rm pay? would delete all files whose names commence with pay followed by any additional character. Thus, if files pay1, pay2, pay3 exist they would all be deleted by the one command.

The "*" wildcard character replaces any number of characters from the position in the filename to the end of the filename. For example, the command: rm pay*.txt would delete files named pay.txt, payroll.txt, payment.txt, and so on, if they previously existed.

UNIX DIRECTORY STRUCTURE

UNIX has a hierarchical directory structure in which a directory can contain other directories known as subdirectories. Each directory represents a collection of files stored together, typically based upon some common characteristic, such as topic, subject, type of program, user creation, etc. The top of the directory structure is referred to as the root directory, designated by the character "/". That character also functions as a delimiter between different directories to reference a path to a subdirectory or a file within a subdirectory. An example of a possible UNIX directory structure is illustrated below:

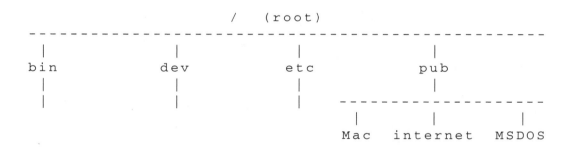

```
                          /    (root)
    ---------------------------------------------------------------
      |              |              |                |
    bin            dev            etc              pub
      |              |              |                |
      |              |              |      --------------------------
                                            |          |          |
                                           Mac    internet     MSDOS
```

The path to a file named ftp.list in the directory internet would be /pub/internet/ftp.list.

One of the more interesting aspects of UNIX is its ability to distinguish between absolute and relative path names. An absolute path name begins with a slash and includes the complete path commencing with the root directory. For example, the path /pub/internet specifies an absolute path from the root directory to the subdirectory "internet" under the directory "pub". The use of a relative path enables you to specify a directory and/or file relative to your current location. For example, if you previously entered the command cd/pub, you could then enter the command cd internet where internet becomes a relative path to your current directory location for changing to a new directory. Note that the use of a relative path name does not require a slash and is used to specify a directory structure relative to the current directory where you are located.

Two special directory identifiers are supported by UNIX, dot (.) and double dot (..). The dot (.) identifier represents the current directory, while double dot (..) represents the parent or next higher directory. You can use either identifier in a UNIX command which references a directory or file. For example, cd .. would result in the parent directory to your current directory becoming the current directory. If you previously entered cd /pub/internet, then entering cd .. would result in pub becoming the current directory.

UNIX FILE PROTECTION

UNIX breaks file protection into three classifications which are indicated below:

Classification	*Description*
user	the owner of the file
group	any user in the same group as the file owner
other	any other user

Within each of the above classifications there are three possible access modes to a file as indicated below:

Access mode	*Description*
r	read access to the file
w	write and delete access to file
x	execute access to the file

If you use the ls command with the -l option the file protections will be displayed as follows: -rwxrwx---. The first character indicates the type of the file. The following three characters indicate the user's access to the file, read (r), write (w), and execute (x). The next group of three characters indicate the group's access rights to the file. The last three characters, shown as dashes in this example, indicate the file access available to other users. To change a file's protection you can use the chmod (change mode) command.

CHAPTER 3

Internet Electronic Mail

In this chapter we turn our attention to a variety of subjects related to the transmission and reception of electronic messages via the Internet. That network, which we reference by using a capital "I," refers to what is now the largest computer network in the world, permitting millions of users throughout the world to communicate with one another.

Currently the Internet ties together over 16,000 individual networks, ranging in scope from departmental local area networks that have a handful of computers to regional networks that may link hundreds to thousands of computers. Collectively, the Internet interconnects in excess of 1.5 million host computers which serve approximately 15 million users.

Although the Internet had its origin as a research and development network, today commercial use as opposed to research represents the fastest-growing sector of the Internet. Numerous commercial organizations provide subscriber access to the Internet and such companies as AT&T, MCI, SPRINT, among others, provide interconnections to the Internet for the transmission and reception of electronic mail which is the focus of this chapter. After reviewing Internet addressing and the structure of electronic mail messages two comprehensive lists of Internet addresses are provided for readers to obtain different types of information. The first list of electronic addresses is presented alphabetically based upon the topic or subject of available information and can be used as a resource for obtaining a variety of information ranging in scope from instructions concerning how to apply for access to different host computers to ways to download files representing documents and journals by electronic mail. Most of the addresses presented in this list respond automatically to a predefined message in the subject field or body of the message and this list includes the keyword or phrase you should include in your message to those automatic answering addresses.

A second list is oriented to providing readers with the electronic addresses of individuals and organizations. That list also indicates the electronic structure required to properly address messages from the Internet to subscribers on other electronic mail services. Due to the large subscriber base of MCI Mail this chapter concludes with a table indicating the three methods by which you can address messages to subscribers of that electronic mail system.

INTERNET ADDRESSING

The general format of an Internet address is based upon whether it is a person's email address or a computer location. The two general formats are indicated below:

> a person's email address: user@organization.domain
>
> a computer's address: name.domain

where:

the user normally references a person's account on a computer which is also commonly referred to as a user ID or userid.

the organization references an organization address within a domain and may include several identifiers tied together via periods (dots) to include a location, computer and site. For example, phys.riscl.msu could reference the physics department's IBM reduced instruction set (IBM RS/6000) computer at Moscow State University.

domain indicates the type of ownership and/or control of the account.

Examples of trailing domains include:

.com   identifies a commercial institution.
.edu   identifies an educational institution.
.gov   identifies a government agency or site.

`.mil`	identifies a military organization.
`.net`	identifies a gateway or administrative host for a network.
`.org`	identifies a private organization.
`.int`	identifies an international organization.

To define the forwarding of a message at its destination use the following format:

user%organization.domain2@organization.domain1

where:

organization.domain1 is the primary address that will forward the message.

organization.domain2 is the ultimate message address.

Other common types of message addressing are indicated below:

`host::user` - Used to address Digital Equipment Corp computer network users.

`host!host2!user` - Used to address a specific routing to a UUCP host.

The internal JANET (UK network connected to the Internet) address components are the opposite of the way they are used in Internet addressing. The order of significance of JANET components are as follows:

`uk`	- the top level domain.
`ac or co`	- for academic community or commercial organization.
`site`	- location.
`dept`	- subsequent components define the computer or a department.

Once the previous components are specified in their order of significance with a "`.`" used as a component separator the persons name is prefixed to the address, using the "`%`" as a name to address separator. For example, gheld in the physics department at Cambridge University with an account on the VAX computer would have the internal JANET address: gheld%uk.ac.cambridge.physics.vax.

When sending mail to JANET users via Internet or Bitnet you must reverse the JANET address so UK is at the end and convert '`%`' to '`@`'. Thus, to address gheld via Internet you would use the address: gheld@vax.physics.cambridge.ac.uk.

ELECTRONIC MAIL MESSAGE STRUCTURE

Each electronic mail message has a specific structure whose entries are based upon the number of locations that forwarded the message and formatting that may be performed by a receiving E-mail system. Figure 3.1 illustrates an E-mail message transmitted from a corporate network via the Internet to CompuServe's InfoPlex E-mail system.

Electronic Mail Programs

There are two key items required to obtain the ability to send and receive mail electronically—an appropriate communications program and an account on an electronic mail service. In this section we will focus our attention upon the basic operation of a few communications programs.

The type of communications program you need to send and receive electronic mail will depend upon the initial or primary electronic mail system you intend to

```
*   Message 1567-313
*   Subj: Chance of e-mail address

    Sender: gbjwspw1@ibmmail.IBMMAIL.COM
    Received: from ibmmail.com by iha.compuserve.com
              (5.67/5.930129sam)
              id AA19614; Thu, 19 Aug 93 05:24:07 -0400
    Message-Id: <9308190924.AA19614@iha.compuserve.com>
    Received: from IBMMAIL.COM by ibmmail.COM (IBM VM SMTP
V2R3) with BSMTP id 9781;
       Thu, 19 Aug 93 05:02:23 EDT
    Date: Thu, 19 Aug 93 05:03:06 EDT
**  From: gbjwspw1@ibmmail.COM
    To: held@wiley.compuserve.com
    Subject: Chance of e-mail address

Note:   * added by CompuServe
        ** indicates actual originator's address
```

Figure 3.1 Sending a Message Via Internet to a Compuserve Account

access. That initial or primary electronic mail system will more than likely have gateways which enable the exchange of mail with other electronic mail systems. For example, if you establish an account on MCI Mail, SprintMail, or CompuServe, each electronic mail service provides gateways which enable the exchange of electronic mail with subscribers of the other two services as well as with persons that have accounts on the Internet. Thus, if one of those three electronic mail providers became your primary electronic mail system you should consider acquiring a communications program that provides you with the ability to communicate with one of those service providers. If your primary service provider was your organization's connection to the Internet you would then want to obtain a communications program which provides you with the ability to send and receive electronic messages via your organization's Internet connection based upon the type of computer system you use.

Since there are a large number of different types of computer systems that can be connected to the Internet we will limit our discussion to two of the most popular types of computers connected to the Internet: DOS and UNIX based machines. However, prior to doing so let's briefly discuss the type of communications software you would normally use to access most commercial electronic mail services, such as CompuServe, MCI Mail, and SprintMail.

Commercial E-mail Service Access

Most commercial electronic mail services transmit and recessive information based upon the use of conventional ASCII on a line-by-line basis, with each line terminated by a Carriage Return and Line Feed. This type of transmission is more commonly referred to as "teletype type" transmission, as it is based upon the line-by-line transmission used by terminals primarily used with early Telex and TWX messaging systems during the 1930's, 1940's and 1950's. To access and exchange mail with those service providers requires a communications program that supports line-by-line transmission. Examples of popular communications programs you can use include Crosstalk, ProcomPlus, BLAST, and Relay Gold, among others. Figure 3.2 illustrates the use of ProcomPlus to access the author's MCI Mail account. Unless ProcomPlus' log or print facility is used, data scrolling off the screen as new information is displayed will be lost or will require a second retrieval to review.

Internet Access

The transmission and reception of electronic mail on the Internet requires the use of a communications program that supports the Simple Mail Transfer

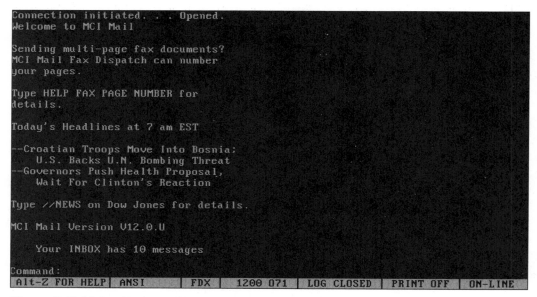

```
Connection initiated. . . Opened.
Welcome to MCI Mail

Sending multi-page fax documents?
MCI Mail Fax Dispatch can number
your pages.

Type HELP FAX PAGE NUMBER for
details.

Today's Headlines at 7 am EST

--Croatian Troops Move Into Bosnia;
    U.S. Backs U.N. Bombing Threat
--Governors Push Health Proposal,
    Wait For Clinton's Reaction

Type //NEWS on Dow Jones for details.

MCI Mail Version V12.0.U

    Your INBOX has 10 messages

Command:
Alt-Z FOR HELP  ANSI       FDX    1200 071   LOG CLOSED   PRINT OFF   ON-LINE
```

Figure 3.2 Using Procom Plus to Access MCI Mail

Protocol (SMTP). In a UNIX environment the native MAIL program supports SMTP and provides you with the ability to transmit and receive electronic messages with other persons that have accounts on that computer or persons scattered throughout the globe that are connected to the Internet.

The UNIX Mail prompt is the ampersign (&) symbol, whose appearance informs you that the program is active and waiting for you to enter a command. Table 3.1 summarizes the more popular UNIX MAIL commands. You can also use the UNIX MAN command to obtain additional information from the UNIX online manual. To do so you would enter MAN MAIL, which would result in a screen-by-screen display of information concerning the MAIL command.

As an alternative to the use of a text based command driven program you can consider using a graphic user interface (GUI) communications program. For DOS computers there are a large number of programs you can consider using. Many of those programs provide access to a full range of Internet application resources, enabling you to send and receive mail, transfer files and connect and operate applications on distant computers. One such communications program is Chameleon™ from NetManage, Inc. of Cupertino, CA.

Chameleon is a versatile communications program that operates under Microsoft Windows. You can operate Chameleon on a computer connected to an Ethernet or Token-Ring network in turn connected to the Internet via a router,

Table 3.1 *Popular UNIX MAIL Program Commands*

Command	Operational Result
.	send message
d [message list]	delete messages
f [message list]	show from lines of messages
h	print out active message headers
m [user list]	mail to specific users
n	go to and type next message
p [message list]	print messages
pre [message list]	make messages go back to system mailbox
q	quit
r [message list]	reply to sender of messages
R [message list]	reply to sender and all recipients of messages
s [message list] file	append messages to file
t [message list]	type messages (same as print)
top [message list]	show top lines of messages
u [message list]	undelete messages
v [message list]	edit messages with display editor
w [message list]	append messages to file, without from line
x	quit, do not change system mailbox
z [-]	display next (previous) page of headers
!	shell escape
~b	enable blind carbon copies
~c	send carbon copy to another recepient
~m	includes current message in your letter
~p	display entire letter
~q	cancel current letter
~r	insert a file into current letter
~v	start in vi editor

or via dial-up through the Serial Line Interface Protocol (SLIP) connection support. Concerning the latter, SLIP provides you with the ability to access Internet through an Internet access provider, such as PSI, or through an existing LAN connected to the Internet even through your computer is not directly connected to the LAN. In the latter situation you would use SLIP to access a workstation on the LAN to obtain a connection to the Internet.

Figure 3.3 illustrates the Chameleon group window displayed on the author's computer after the program was installed on his hard drive. The 13 icons shown in the window represent different Internet applications as well as information files and a customization tool. Since this chapter is primarily concerned with Internet electronic mail we will click on the Chameleon "Mail" icon and reserve a discussion concerning the use of other program applications to future chapters where they are more appropriate to the topic covered.

Figure 3.4 illustrates the main Chameleon mail window once you log into Mail as a user. From this window you can view the contents of previously created messages, examine mail received in your in-box, create messages, reply to a previously received message and forward messages to other persons. In addition, the buttons in the window also provide you with the ability to create a hardcopy of a message and delete messages. Since we want to examine the use of a GUI communications program to create messages let's click on the Create button so we can create and send a mail message.

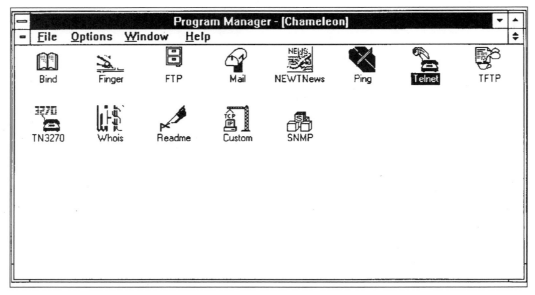

Figure 3.3 Chameleon Group Window Display

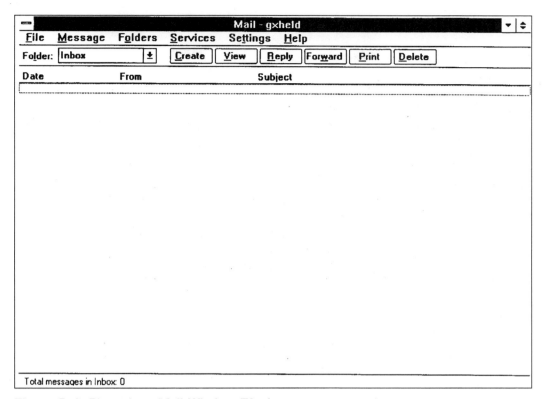

Figure 3.4 Chameleon Mail Window Display

Figure 3.5 illustrates the creation of a short message to the author's friend Fred. Note that several menu items provide you with the ability to easily perform a number of functions on an automatic basis. For example, the Feelings menu allows you to insert the symbols for Happy, Sad, and Wink anywhere in your message by simply selecting the appropriate menu item. Of course, as an alternative you could look up an appropriate emotion symbol previously listed in Chapter 1 and type that symbol into your message.

Internet Information and Information Addresses

If you can send to and receive electronic mail from the Internet you can obtain information to include publications in the form of files that will be transferred to you electronically. Many electronic mail systems to include AT&T Mail,

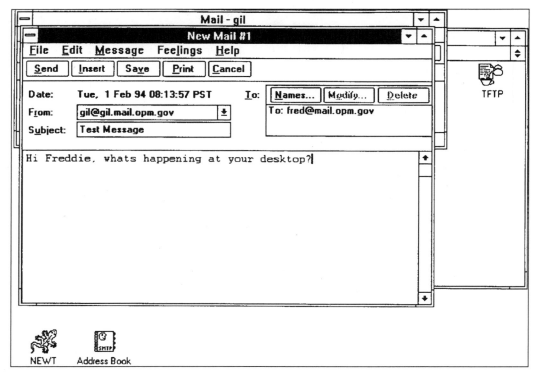

Figure 3.5 Creating a Message with Chameleon Mail Window

CompuServe, MCI Mail, and SprintMail provide an interconnection to the Internet and provides subscribers with the ability to obtain a large variety of information without requiring full Internet access.

The following table lists Internet electronic mail addresses alphabetically based upon the topic or subject of material you can obtain from the indicated address. Readers should note that many addresses include an indication of a predefined message you should place in the subject line or body of your message. Typically the address that requires a predefined message, such as "HELP" or "SEND XXX", represents the electronic location of an automated server which automatically responds to a request. To do so, the server examines incoming messages and looks for a predefined word or sentence at a specific location in the incoming message; hence, you should insure the correct placement of the required word or phrase in your electronic message. Other addresses that do not indicate a requirement for a specific word or phrase in a predefined place in the message may result in a response to your request by a human and you may be able to structure your message to suit your information requirement.

When multiple electronic mail addresses are listed for a particular topic or subject this means that you can send your request to any one of the denoted addresses. However, to reduce network utilization you should first attempt to obtain information from an address located in your country prior to sending a request to an address in another country.

for: ***AARNET Information***
Send E-mail to: aarnet@aarnet.edu.au

for: ***Aberdeen University Library Information***
Send E-mail to: library@uk.ac.aberdeen

for: ***Aberystwyth University Library Information***
Send E-mail to: library@uk.ac.aberystwyth
                 for inter-library loans: interlib@uk.ac.aberystwyth

for: ***Address of a student at a university/college***
Send E-mail to: mail-server@pit-manager.mit.edu
place: SEND USENET/SOC.COLLEGE/Student_Email-address in
                 subject field of message.

for: ***Agricultural information, USDA market news***
Send E-mail to: almanac@ecn.purdue.edu
                 almanac@esusda.gov
                 almanac@orst.edu
                 almanac@ces.ncsu.edu
                 almanac@silo.ucdavis.edu
                 almanac@wisplan.uwex.edu
place: In body of letter:
                   send guide   or
                   send catalog

for: ***Amateur Radio and electronics information***
Send E-mail to: info@arrl.org
place: In body of letter:
                   help
                   info
                     send <filename>

for: ***Andrew Toolkit Information***
Send E-mail to: info-andrew-request@andrew.cmu.edu

for: ***Anonymous host list***
Send E-mail to: anonymous+ping@tygra.michigan.com
                   help@anon.penet.fi
place: HELP in body of message

for: ***ARCHIE server utilization information***
Send E-mail to: archie@archie.mcgill.ca (McGill University, Canada)
                   archie@archie.ac.il (Israel)
                   archie@archie.ans.net (United States)
                   archie@archie.au (Australia)
                   archie@archie.doc.ic.ac.uk (United Kingdom)
                   archie@archie.edvz.uni-linz.ac (Austria)
                   archie@archie.funet.fi (Finland)
                   archie@archie.kr (Korea)
                   archie@archie.luth.se (Sweden)
                   archie@archie.ncu.edu.tw (Taiwan)
                   archie@archie.nz (New Zealand)
                   archie@archie.rediris.es (Spain)
                   archie@archie.rutgers.edu (Rutgers University, US)
                   archie@archie.sogang.ac.kr (Korea)
                   archie@archie.sura.net (United States)
                   archie@archie.switch.ch (Switzerland)
                   archie@archie.th-darmstadt.de (Germany)
                   archie@archie.univie.ac.at (Austria)
                   archie@archie.unl.edu (United States)
                   archie@archie.wide.ad.jp (Japan)
place: HELP in body or subject field of message

for: ***ARCHIE server information***
Send E-mail to: service@nic.ddn.mil
place: in subject field:
                       HELP to obtain list of available commands
                       RFC xxxx to obtain a copy of an RFC
                       RFC INDEX to obtain an index of available RFCs
                       WHOIS name to obtain whois information on name

for: ***askERIC answers to questions***
Send E-mail to: askeric@ericir.syr.edu
place: question you wish answered in body of message

for: ***Aston University Library Information***

Send E-mail to: library@uk.ac.aston
                   for interlibrary loans: ill@uk.ac.aston

for: ***Astronomer listing of names, addresses, fax, telephone numbers***
Send E-mail to: email@srf.ro-greenwich.ac.uk
place: Send Guide in body of message

for: ***AT&T Employee Addresses***
Send E-mail to: lastname@att.com or firstname.lastname.att.com
                   If name is ambiguous a bounce message will be generated which
                   will list several possible matches and appropriate addresses to
                   use.

for: ***Bangor University Library Information***
Send E-mail to: library@uk.ac.bangor
                   for interlibrary loans: ill@uk.ac.bangor

for   ***Bath University Library Information***
Send E-mail to: library@uk.ac.bath.gdr
                   for interlibrary loans: interlib@uk.ac.bath.gdr

for: ***Biological Services (Gene Splicing)***
Send E-mail to: grail@ornl.gov
place: HELP in body of message

for: ***Birmingham University Library Information***
Send E-mail to: library@uk.ac.birmingham

for: ***BITNET discussion lists and related information***
Send E-mail to: LISTSERV@BITNIC.BITNET
place: LIST GLOBAL in body of message for full listing
                   LIST GLOBAL/TOPIC in body of message, where
                   TOPIC is the topic you are interested in.
                   GET BITNET USERHELP in body of message for helpful
                        information on BITNET.
                   GET BITNET INTRO in body of message for information
                        concerning the use of BITNET.
                   INFO DATABASE in body of message for listserv database
                        information.
                   GET NETINFO INDEX in body of message for index of files
                        located at BITNIC.

GET BITNET SERVERS in body of message for list of BITNET servers.

GET MAIL MANNERS in body of message for network etiquette information.

HELP in body of message for general information

for: ***BITNET discussion list subscription***
Send E-mail to: LISTSERV@BITNIC.BITNET
place: SUBSCRIBE LIST YOUR-NAME in body of message

for: ***BITNET discussion list removal***
Send E-mail to: LISTSERV@BITNIC.BITNET
place: UNSUBSCRIBE LIST YOUR-NAME in body of message

for: ***Bristol University Library Information***
Send E-mail to: library@uk.ac.bristol

for: ***Brown University CS Archive Information***
Send E-mail to: redsoft@cs.brown.edu

for: ***California Polytech Institute***
                   Image Processing and OCR Library Information
Send E-mail to: cstaley@polyslo.calpoly.edu

for: ***Cambridge University Library Information***
Send E-mail to: wdsm@uk.ac.cam.ula

for: ***Cancer Information***
Send E-mail to: cancernet@icicb.nci.nih.gov
place: HELP in body of message
                   SPANISH in body of message to receive information in Spanish.

for: ***CCITT Documents***
Send E-mail to: teledoc@itu.arcom.ch
place: HELP in body of message

for: ***City University (UK) Library Information***
Send E-mail to: sb370@uk.ac.city

for: ***Chaos Project at University of Washington***

Send E-mail to: chaos@cs.washington.edu

for: ***Clinton White House Information Releases***
Send E-mail to: clinton-info@campaign92.org
place: RECEIVE ALL in subject line of message

for: ***College email address information***
Send E-mail to: mail-server@rtfm.mit.edu
place: send usenet/soc.college/Student_Email_Address
                    in message body

for: ***Computer Algebra Group Information***
                    University of Passau, Germany
Send E-mail to: alice.fmu.uni-passau.de

for: ***Computer Oriented Abbreviations and Acronyms Glossary***
Send E-mail to: listserv@vm.temple.edu
place: SEND BABEL94A.TXT in body of message

for: ***COSMIC Information Services Information***
                    NASA's Computer Software Management and Information
                       Center at the University of Georgia
Send E-mail to: service@cossack.cosmic.uga.edu

for: ***Cranfield Institute of Technology Library Information***
Send E-mail to: li003a@uk.ac.cranfield

for: ***CREN/CSNET information***
Send E-mail to: info-server@sh.cs.net
place: REQUEST:INFO and TOPIC:ns on separate lines in body of
                    message

for: ***CREN'S Acceptable User Policy***
Send E-mail to: listserv@bitnic.bitnet
place: CREN NET_USE in body of message

for: ***CTILIS Resources Guide***
                    University and Public School Service Listing Primarily
                    for the United Kingdom
Send E-mail to: mailbase@newcastle.ac.uk
place: SEND LIS-INFO CTILIS.RES.GUIDE in body of message

for other information about the server place
HELP, INDEX, LISTS or SEND MAILBASE USERHELP in
message

for: ***Curtin University Library Information***
Send E-mail to: help@cc.curtin.edu.au

for: ***Deakin University Library Information***
Send E-mail to: library@deakin.oz.au

for: ***Dundee Institute of Technology Library Information***
Send E-mail to: lbasec@uk.ac.dundee-tech

for: ***Dundee University Library Information***
Send E-mail to: library@uk.ac.dundee.primeb
                    for interlibrary loans: library@uk.ac.dundee.primeb

for: ***Durham University Library Information***
Send E-mail to: main.library@uk.ac.durham
                    for interlibrary loans: interlibrary.loans@uk.ac.durham

for: ***EARN information***
Send E-mail to: grange%frors12.bitnet@mitvma.mit.edu

for: ***Edinburgh University Library Information***
Send E-mail to: library@uk.ac.edinburgh
                    for interlibrary loans: inter_library_loans@uk.ac.edinburgh

for: ***Electronic journal and newsletter directory***
Send E-mail to: listserv@ottawa.bitnet

for: ***Essex University Library Information***
Send E-mail to: library@uk.ac.essex

for: ***EUnet information***
Send E-mail to: glenn@eu.net

for: ***European Molecular Biology Laboratory Access Information***
Send E-mail to: netserv@embl-heidelberg.de
place: HELP in body of message

for: ***Exeter University Library Information***
Send E-mail to: library@uk.ac.exeter

for: ***Fax transmission via a fax distribution point***
Send E-mail to: tpc.faq@town.hall.org

for: ***FAXiNET commercial service***
Send E-mail to: info@awa.com
place: HELP in body of message

for: ***FAQ documents***
Send E-mail to: mail-server@rtfm.mit.edu
place: HELP in body of message for utilization information or
                     command(s) in body of message for specific information.
                     For example, send usenet/news.answers/-listing-
                     to obtain a list of Usenet newsgroups that have FAQ files.

for: ***FTP via E-mail Information***
Send E-mail to: ftpmail@decwrl.dec.com
                     ftpmail@gatekeeper.dec.com
place: HELP in body of message

for: ***FTP via E-mail***
Send E-mail to: ftpmail@gatekeeper.dec.com
                     place list of FTP commands, one per line, in the body of the
                     message. For example, to retrieve the directory listing of the di-
                     rectory pub at ftp.sura.net:
                             To: ftpmail@gatekeeper.dec.com
                             Subject: (leave blank)
                             connect ftp.sura.net
                             chdir /pub
                             dir
                             quit
                             CTRL-D

for: ***FTPmail Server Utilization***
Send E-mail to: ftpmail@decwrl.dec.com
                     ftpmail@src.doc.ic.ac.uk
                     ftpmail@cs.uow.edu.au
                     ftpmail@grasp1.univ-lyon1.fr
place   HELP in body of message

for: **Georgia Institute of Technology Anonymous FTP Server**
Send E-mail to: sys@eedsp.gatech.edu

for: **Georgia State University FTP Server Information**
Send E-mail to: postmaster@ftp.gsu.edu

for: **Genetics Banks Information**
Send E-mail to: gene-server@bchs.uh.edu
                    retrieve@ncbi.nlm.nih.gov
                    blast@ncbi.nlm.nih.gov (place HELP in body of message)
                      genmark@ford.gatech.edu
                    blocks@howard.fhcrc.org
                    cbrg@inf.ethz.ch (place HELP in body of message)
                    quick@embl-heidelberg.de
                    netserv@embl-heidelberg.de

for: **German anonymous FTP site list**
Send E-mail to: listserv@askhp.ask.uni-karlsruhe.de
place: subscribe ftp-list-de <name, E-mail address> in body of message

for: **Glasgow University Library Information**
Send E-mail to: library@uk.ac.glasgow.vme
                    for interlibrary loans: interlib@uk.ac.glasgow.vme

for: **Global Land Information System Information**
Send E-mail to: glis@glis.cr.usgs.gov

for: **subscribing to gopher-news list**
Send E-mail to: gopher-news-request@boombox.micro.umn.edu

for: **Gopher via E-mail Information**
Send E-mail to: gophermail@ncc.go.jp
place: HELP in body of message

for: **Griffith University Library Information**
Send E-mail to: libblinc@itc.gu.edu.au

for: **HEPnet information**
Send E-mail to: denise@priam.cern

for: **Heriot-Watt University Library Information**

Send E-mail to: library@uk.ac.heriot-watt.cluster

for: **Homebrew Digest Subscription**
Send E-mail to: homebrew-request@hpfcmr.hp.com

for: **Institute for Academic Technology Information**
Send E-mail to: info.iat@mhs.unc.edu
place: HELP in body of message

for: **Internet Address Information (non-military)**
Send E-mail to: whois@whois.internic.net
place: HELP in body of message

for: **Internet Book Reviews**
Send E-mail to: listserv@ubvm.cc.buffalo.edu
place: GET NETTRAIN REVIEWS in body of message

for: **Internet "List of lists" listing of special interest group**
                    mailing lists available on the Internet
Send E-mail to: mail-server@misc.sri.com
place: SEND NETINFO/INTEREST-GROUPS in body of message

for: **Internet Marketing Information from the Internet Company**
Send E-mail to: market@internet.com
place: SEND MARKET INFO in body of message

for: **Internet Monthly Reports (IMRs)**
Send E-mail to: rfc-info@isi.edu
place: Getting Imrs in Subject field, help:ways_to_get-imrs
                    in body of message

for: **Internet Multicast Backbone (MBONE) Information**
Send E-mail to: mbone@isi.edu

for: **Internet Protocol (IP) Address Resolution Information**
Send E-mail to: dns@grasp.insa-lyon.fr
place: HELP in body of message

for: **ITU Telecom Information Exchange Services Account Information**
Send E-mail to: itudoc@itu.ch
place: HELP LIST TIES END in body of message

for: ***InterNIC Directory assistance***
Send E-mail to: mailserv@ds.internic.net
place: HELP in body of message
                       for specific information use the following formats in the body
                           of the message:

                       institution name, us   :to obtain corporate name postal address
                                                   and telephone number

                       institution *,us   :to obtain list of institutions in the US
                                               participating in the X.500 directory project

                       institution -, *   :to obtain a list of ISO 3166 country codes and
                                               names

                       person fname lname, institution, us   :display information for
                                                                   named person

                       file /directory/filename   :request file via email

                       document-by-name filename   :request file via email

                       document-by-keyword keyword   :request list of documents
                           containing indicated keyword

                       whois .lname,fname   :query the whois server for a person

                       whois institution   :query whois server for all persons that work
                                               for institution and all references to named
                                               institution
                       whois help   :retrieve whois user documentation

                       limit xxk   :set the file transfer message size limit to xx k bytes,
                           k=1024

for: ***InterNIC public files***
Send E-mail to: mailserv@rs.internic.net
place: request in subject field

for: ***John Hopkins Genetic Database Access Information***
Send E-mail to: help@welch.jhu.edu
Database: Kent State University Directory of Scholarly Electronic
                           Conferences
Send E-mail to: listserv@kentvm.kent.edu
place: GET FILENAME FILETYPE in body of messsage
                       where Filetype =FILE!, FILE@, ...HQX.

Filename Filetype Description
ACADLIST README   (directory explanation)
ACADSTAC.HQX   (binhexed, self-decompressing,
                HYPERCARD archive of first 7 files -
                Keyword searchable)
ACADCOMP.HQX   (binhexed, self-decompressing,
                HYPERCARD Stack of FILE8 -
                Keyword searchable)
ACADLIST FILE1   (Anthropology- Education)
ACADLIST FILE2   (Geography-Library and Information
                Science)
ACADLIST FILE3   (Linguistics-Political Science)
ACADLIST FILE4   (Psychology-Writing)
ACADLIST FILE5   (Biological Sciences)
ACADLIST FILE6   (Physical Sciences)
ACADLIST FILE7   (Business, Academia, News)
ACADLIST FILE8   (Computer Science, Social, Cultural, and
                Political Aspects of Computing and
                Academic Computing Support)
ACADWHOL HQX   (binhexed self-decompressing Macintosh
                M.S. Word 4.0 document of all 8 files)

for: ***subscription to KIDS children's computer network***
Send E-mail to: joinkids@vms.cis.pitt.edu

for: ***Posting messages to KIDS children's computer network***
Send E-mail to: kids@vms.cis.pitt.edu

for: ***Posting messages to KIDSPHERE children's computer network***
Send E-mail to: kidsphere@vms.cis.pitt.edu

for: ***Knowbot Information Service Information***
Send E-mail to: kis@cnri.reston.va.us
                  netaddress@regulus.cs.bucknell.edu
place: MAN in bodu of message

for: ***Lancaster University Library Information***
Send E-mail to: lba008@uk.ac.lancs.cent1
                  for interlibrary loans: lba005@uk.ac.lancs.cent1

for: ***Leeds University Library Information***

Send E-mail to: library@uk.ac.leeds.ucs.prime1

for: ***Leicester University Library Information***
Send E-mail to: library@uk.ac.leicester.vax
                          for interlibrary loans: interlib@uk.ac.leicester

for: ***Liverpool University Library Information***
Send E-mail to: library@uk.ac.liverpool
                          for interlibrary loans: interlib@uk.ac.liverpool

for: ***listserv commands***
Send E-mail to: LISTSERV@BITNIC.BITNET
place: HELP in body of message

LISTSERV version 1.7f—Most Commonly Used Commands

Info	<topic|?>	Get detailed information files
List	<Detail|Short|Global>	Get a description of all lists
SUBscribe	listname <full_name>	Subscribe to a list
SIGNOFF	listname	Sign off from a list
SIGNOFF	* (NETWIDE	- from all lists on all servers
REView	listname <options>	Review a list
STats	listname <options>	Review list statistics
Query	listname	Query personal distribution options
SET	listname options	Set personal distribution options
INDex	<filelist_name>	Obtain a list of LISTSERV files
GET	filename filetype	Obtain a file from LISTSERV
REGister	full_name|OFF	Tell LISTSERV about your name

For other commands send a request for a complete reference card, or an E-mail message with INFO ? in the body for a list of available documentation files.

for: ***LISTSERV Searching Guide***
Send E-mail to: listserv@ulkyvm.bitnet
place: GET DATABASE SEARCH in body of message

for: ***LISTSERV Tips***
Send E-mail to: listserv@bitnic.bitnet

place: GET LISTSERV TIPS in body of message

for: **London University Central Library Consortium Information**
Send E-mail to: library@uk.ac.ucl

for: **London University British Library of Politics and Economics**
Send E-mail to: library@uk.ac.lse.vax

for: **London University Imperial College of Science Library**
Send E-mail to: library@uk.ac.imperial.cc.vaxa
                    for interlibrary loans: illoans@uk.ac.imperial.cc.vaxa

for: **London University Kings College Library Information**
Send E-mail to: library@uk.ac.kcl.cc.oak
                    for interlibrary loans:
                       Kings College London, Strand: interloans@uk.ac.kcl.cc.oak
                       Kings College London, Chelsa: udylo15@uk.ac.kcl.cc.oak
                       Kings College London, Coleridge: udylo11@uk.ac.kcl.cc.oak
                       Kings College London, Kensington: udyl053@uk.ac.kcl.cc.oak

for: **London University Royal Holloway and Bedford New College**
                    Library Information
Send E-mail to: library@uk.ac.rhbnc.vax
                    for interlibrary loans: uhy009@uk.ac.rhbnc.vax

for: **London University University College Library**
Send E-mail to: library@uk.ac.ucl

for: **Loughborough University of Technology Library Information**
Send E-mail to: library@uk.ac.lut

for: **Mailing-list server for group communications**
Send E-mail to: listserv@uacsc2.albany.edu
place: SEND LISTSERV MEMO in body of message

for: **Manchester University Library Information**
Send E-mail to: ymumlb@uk.ac.umist

for: **Matchmaker by E-mail information**
Send E-mail to: perfect@match.com
place: SEND FORM in body of message

for: ***MERIT Mail Query Server Information***
Send E-mail to: nic-info@nic.merit.edu
place   HELP in body of message for general information
                   INDEX in body of message for summary of directories
                   INDEX XXX, where XXX is directory name for a specific index
                   GET FILENAME in body of message to obtain a specific
                       document

for: ***Military Personnel Address Access Information***
Send E-mail to: service@nic.ddn.mil
place: HELP in body of message

for: ***Movie Database Information***
Send E-mail to: movie@ibmpcug.co.uk
place: HELP in body of message

for: ***NASA Climate Data System Information***
Send E-mail to: ncdsuso@nssdca.gsfc.nasa.gov

for: ***NASA Ocean Data System Information***
Send E-mail to: ral@stans.jpl.nasa.gov
                   eas@stans.jpl.nasa.gov

for: ***NASA Science Internet-Network Information Center***
                   Answers to questions concerning software, files, or
                   general NASA topics.
Send E-mail to: help@nic.nsi.nasa.gov

for: ***National Center for Biotechnology Information***
Send E-mail to: info@ncbi.nlm.nih.gov

for: ***National Center of Supercomputer Applications***
Send E-mail to: stgadmin@ncsa.uiuc.edu for server information
                   pctelnet@ncsa.uiuc.edu for Telnet for PC information
                   mactelnet@ncsa.uiuc.edu for Telnet for Macintosh information
                   softdev@ncsa.uiuc.edu for NCSA software development tools
                   information

for: ***National Information Services and Systems (UK) Library***
                   Information
Send E-mail to: niss@uk.ac.soton.ibm

for: ***National Science and Technology Research Center for Computation and Visualization of Geometric Structures***

Send E-mail to: ftp@geom.umn.edu

for: ***NATO mailing list subscription***

Send E-mail to: listserv@ccl.kuleuven.ac.be

place SUB NATODATA YOURNAME in message

for: ***Netfind Software Release Information***

Send E-mail to: netfind-users-request@cs.colorado.edu

for: ***Network Bibliography***

Send E-mail to: comserve@piecs.bitnet

place: SEND COMPUNET BIBLIO in body of message

for: ***NIC mail services***

Send E-mail to: service@nic.ddn.mil

place: the type of service you want followed by any required arguments in the Subject field. The following service requests are supported:

HELP   for a list of current services.

HOST xxx   for information about host xxx.   WHOIS xxx can also be used to get more details about a host.

IEN nnn   nnn is the IEN number or the word INDEX.

IETF xxx   xxx is a file name.

INDEX   for the master list of available index files.

INTERNET-DRAFTS xxx   xxx is a file name.

NETINFO xxx   xxx is a file name or the word INDEX.

RFC nnn   nnn is the RFC number or the word INDEX.

RFC nnn.PS   to retrieve an available Postscript RFC.

Check RFC INDEX for form of RFC.

FYI nnn   nnn is the FYI number or the word INDEX.

FYI nnn.PS   to retrieve postscript versions of FYI files.

SEND xxx   xxx is a fully specified file name.

WHOIS xxx   Returns information about xxx from the WHOIS service.

Use "WHOIS HELP" for information on how to use WHOIS.

Example SUBJECT lines:

HELP
RFC 822

RFC INDEX
RFC 1119.PS
FYI 1
IETF 1IETF-DESCRIPTION.TXT
INTERNET-DRAFTS 1ID-ABSTRACTS.TXT
NETINFO DOMAIN-TEMPLATE.TXT
SEND RFC: RFC-BY-AUTHOR.TXT
SEND IETF/1WG-SUMMARY.TXT
SEND INTERNET-DRAFTS/DRAFT-IETF-NETDATA-
 NETDATA-00.TXT
HOST DIIS
WHOIS HELD, GILBERT

for: ***Nottingham University Library Information***
Send E-mail to: uazmain@uk.ac.nottingham.ccc.vme

for: ***Occidental College Library Information***
Send E-mail to: infoserv@oxy.edu

for: ***Online Book Initiative Mailing List***
Send E-mail to: obi@world.std.com
place: SUB General Discussion in body of message to subscribe to general discussion mailing list.
SUB ANNOUNCEMENTS in body of message to subscribe to a mailing list of announcement

for: ***Online Public Access Catalogues Services***
Send E-mail to: listserv@itocsivm.csi.it
place: SUBSCRIBE NewNIR-L <your name> in body of message

for: ***Open University Library System Information***
Send E-mail to: library@uk.ac.open.acs.vax

for: ***Oxford University Library Information***
Send E-mail to: olismail@uk.ac.oxford.vax

for: ***PDIAL list produced by Peter Kaminski***
Send E-mail to: info-deli-server@netcom.com
place: SEND PDIAL in body of message

for: ***PEACESAT information***

Send E-mail to: peacesat@elele.peacesat.hawaii.edu

for: **Project Gutenberg Mailing List Subscription**
Send E-mail to: listserv@uiucvmd.bitnet
place: SUB GUTNBERG your-name in body of message

for: **Prospero Information**
Send E-mail to: info-prospero@isi.edu
                    info-prospero@cs.washington.edu

for: **PTT Research (Netherlands) Employee Addresses**
Send E-mail to: whois@research.ptt.nl
place: HELP in body of message

for: **Public Dialup Internet Access List (PDIAL)**
Send E-mail to: kaminski@netcom.com
place: SEND PDIAL in body of message

for: **RadioMail Product Information**
Send E-mail to: info@radiomail.net

for: **RAM Mobile Data Product Information**
Send E-mail to: airmail@ram.com

for: **Reading University Library Information**
Send E-mail to: library@uk.ac.reading.cc.am.cmsy

for: **RFC acquisition information**
Send E-mail to: rfc-info@isi.edu
place: Accessing RFCs in subject field, Help:ways_to_get_rfcs in
                    message body

for: **RFC documents**
Send E-mail to: service@nic.ddn.mil
place: SEND RFC-xxxx.TXT in subject line, with xxxx being
                    the requested RFC number.
Send E-mail to: mailserv@ds.internic.net
place: document-by-name rfcnnnn in body, where nnnn is RFC
                       number
                    file /ftp/rfc/rfcnnnn.yyy in body, where yyy is txt
                    for ASCII or ps for Postscript

help in body to get information on how to use the
mailserver

Send E-mail to: sendrfc@jvnc.net
place: RFCnnnn in Subject field, where nnnn indicates RFC
                 number.
Send E-mail to: rfc-info@isi.edu
place: in body of message the following:
                 Retrieve: RFC
                 Doc-ID: RFCnnnn
                 where nnnn indicates RFC document number
Send E-mail to: info-server@doc.ic.ac.uk
place: wanted in Subject field and a message body of:
                 request sources
                 topic path rfc/rfcnnnn.txt.z
                 request end
                 where nnnn indicates RFC document number
                 Note: to request the RFC Index use the command
                 topic path rfc/rfc-index.txt.z in the above message body

for: **RFC repositories**
Send E-mail to: service@nic.ddn.mil
place: SEND netinfo/ways_to_get_rfcs in Subject field or
                 first line of body of message.

for: **registering name in whois database**
Send E-mail to: registrar@nic.ddn.mil
place: register information in subject line

for: **Restriction Enzyme Database Information**
Send E-mail to: roberts@neb.com
                 macelis@neb.com

for: **Ribosomal Database Project at University of Illinois Information**
Send E-mail to: rdp@mcs.anl.gov

for: **RMIT, Melbourne Australia Anonymous FTP archive information**
Send E-mail to: ftpadmin@cs.rmit.edu.au

for: **The Royal Greenwich Observatory Library Information**
Send E-mail to: library@uk.ac.rgo

for: ***RPI White Pages Server for Persons in Communications Information***
Send E-mail to: comserve@vm.its.rpi.edu
place: HELP in body of message

for: ***Rutgers University FTP Archive Information***
Send E-mail to: bbs@quartz.rutgers.edu

for: ***The Rutherford Appleton Laboratory Library Information***
Send E-mail to: library@uk.ac.rutherford.ibm-b

for: ***St. Andrews University Library Information***
Send E-mail to: library@uk.ac.st-and
                       for circulation system: library@uk.ac.st-andrews

for: ***Science and Technology Information System Information***
Send E-mail to: stis@nsf.gov

for: ***Sheffield University Library Information***
Send E-mail to: library@uk.ac.sheffield.primea
                       for interlibrary loans: lb1ill@uk.ac.sheffield.primea

for: ***Southampton University Library Information***
Send E-mail to: library@uk.ac.soton.ibm

for: ***Strathclyde University Library Information***
Send E-mail to: library@uk.ac.strathclyde.vabx

for: ***Sussex University Library Information***
Send E-mail to: library@uk.ac.sussex.cluster
                       for interlibrary loans: interlib@uk.ac.sussex.cluster

for: ***Swansea University Library Information***
Send E-mail to: mailbox@uk.ac.swansea.library
                       for interlibrary loans: illmail@uk.ac.swan.library

for: ***Thames Polytechnic Library Information***
Send E-mail to: rosalind@uk.ac.thames

for: ***Trickle Mail Server Utilization Information***
Send E-mail to: trickle@awiwuw11.bitnet (Austria)
                       trickle@dktc11.bitnet (Denmark)

                        trickle@banufs11.bitnet (Belgium)
                        trickle@frmop11.bitnet (France)
                        trickle@dtuzdv1.bitnet (Germany)
                        trickle@taunivm.bitnet (Israel)
                        trickle@imipoli.bitnet (Italy)
                        trickle@hearn.bitnet (Netherlands)
                        trickle@eb0ub011.bitnet (Spain)
                        trickle@trearn.bitnet (Turkey)
place: HELP in body of message

for: ***University Claude Bernard***
                        Gopher Server Laboratorie de Biometrie Information
Send E-mail to: gopher@biom3.univ-lyon1.fr

for: ***University of Georgia Artifical Intelligence Archives***
                        File Contributions and Information
Send E-mail to: mcovingt@ai.uga.edu

for: ***University of Melbourne Information***
Send E-mail to: helpdesk@its.unimelb.edu.au

for: ***University of Michigan MERIT Network Information***
Send E-mail to: info@merit.edu

for: ***University of Michigan Software Archive Access Information***
Send E-mail to: mac@mac.archive.umich.edu (Macintosh)
                        atari@atari.archive.umich.edu (Atari)
place: HELP in body of message

for: ***University of New South Wales Library Information***
Send E-mail to: nunlib@libprime.libsys.unsw.oz.au

for: ***University of Pittsburgh FTP Archive Information***
Send E-mail to: query@vms.cis.pitt.edu

for: ***University of Tokyo International Science Network (TISN)***
Send E-mail to: admin@utsun.s.u-tokyo.ac.jp

for: ***Usenet addreess***
Send E-mail to: mail-server@pit-manager.mit.edu   or
                        mail-server@rtfm.mit.edu

place: send usenet-address/name in subject or body of message,
                    with name either first or last name of person whose
                    address you seek.

for: **USENET Postings via E-mail**
Send E-mail to: hierarchy-group-name@cs.utexas.edu
place: Your subject in subject field, your message in body of message

for: **US Department of Agriculture factsheet information guide**
Send E-mail to: almanac@eusda
place: SEND GUIDE in message

for: **US Government Internet online services information**
Send E-mail to: listserv@internic.net
place: SUB nethappenings YOURNAME in message

for: **US Government document information**
Send E-mail to: listserv@psuvm.bitnet
place: SUB GOVDOC-L YOURNAME in message

for: **US State Department travel advisory**
Send E-mail to: ftpbymail@stolaf.edu
place: cd pub/travel-advisories/advisories get NAME
                    where NAME is the lowercase name of the country you
                    want a travel advisory for.

for: **UUCP map entry**
Send E-mail to: dns@grasp.insa-lyon.fr
place: HELP in body of letter or
                    uucp uucp_site in body of letter

for: **whois program utilization information**
Send E-mail to: mailserv@rs.internic.net
place: whois help in subject field

for: **whois search request**
Send E-mail to: service@nic.ddn.mil
place: whois name in subject field

for: **World Wide Web (WWW) General Information**
Send E-mail to: listproc@online.ora.com

place: get gnn-announce/web-info sanders-intro in body of message

for: ***World Wide Web (WWW) GNN Client Software Information***
Send E-mail to: istproc@online.ora.com
place: get gnn-announce/getting-software abc in body of message

for: ***X.500 UNINETT Information***
Send E-mail to: directory@uninett.no
place: HELP in body of message

for: ***York University Library Information***
Send E-mail to: libr1@uk.ac.york.vaxa

INDIVIDUAL AND ORGANIZATIONAL INTERNET ADDRESSES

A2I Communications (Internet access provider)   info@rahul.net

AlterNet   alternet-info@μμnet.μμ.net

AlterNex Brazilian non-government   suporte@ax.apc.org
  organization (NGO) network

America Online information   postmaster@aol.com

America Online user   username@aol.com

Antenna (Netherlands based) network   support@antenna.nl

Applelink information   postmaster@applelink.apple.com

Applelink user   username@applelink.apple.com

Archie information   archie-info@bunyip.com

Argentina Research Network (ARNET)   postmaster@atina.ar

Association for Computing Machinery   acmhelp@acmvm.bitnet

AT&T Mail user   username@attmail.com

Australian Academic and Research Network (AARNet)   aarnet@aarnet.edu.aμ

Austrian Academic Computer Network   domain-admin@cc.univie.ac.at
  (ACOnet)

Baden-Wuettemberg academic and research network (Germany)	belwve-koordination@belwue.de
Bay Area Regional Research Network (BARRNet)	info@barrnet.net
BITNET information	info@bitnic.educom.edu
BITNET user	user%hostsite.bitnet@cunyvm.cuny.edu user%hostsite.bitnet@pucc.princeton.edu user%hostsite.bitnet@wuvmd.wustl.edu

Note: The above represent three gateways available for use.

BMUG user	firstname.lastname@bmug.fidonet.org
Byte Information eXchange (BIT) user	username@dcibix.das.net username@bix.com
BYTE Magazine Letters to the Editor	letters@bytepb.byte.com
California Education and Research Federation Network (CERFnet)	help@cerf.net
Chasque Internet public assess provider (Uruguay)	apoyo@chasque.apc.org
Clarinet electronic publishing network services	info@clarinet.com
Colorado Alliance of Research Libraries	help@carl.org
Colorado SuperNet (Internet access provider serving CO)	info@csn.org
Columbia University Computer Science FTP server information	ftp@ftp.cs.columbia.edu
Communication for North Carolina Education Research and Technology (CONCERT)	info@concert.net
CompuServe information	postmaster@compuserve.com
CompuServe user	xxxxx.xxx@compuserve.com
Computer Emergency Response Team (CERT) Coordination Center	cert@cert.org
Computer Emergency Response Team (CERT) advisory mailing list	cert-advisory-request@cert.org
Computer Professionals for Social Responsibility	cpsr@csli.stanford.edu

Connect user	username@dcjcon.das.net
Danish Eunet Affiliate (DKnet)	pr@denmark.eu.net
Datamation Magazine Letters to the Editor	512-1847@mci.mail.com
Delphi user	username@delphi.com
Deutsches ForshungsNetz (DFN) German Science Network	dfm-verein@dfn.dbp.de
EASYnet Digital Equipment Corporation internal network information	postmaster@dec.com
EasyNet user	username@host.enet.dec.com or username%host.enet@decwrl.com
Egyptian Universities Network	postmaster@cairo.eg
Electronic Frontier Foundation	eff@eff.org
Energy Sciences (ESnet) network	info@es.net
ERNET India academic network subscriber	name@host.org.ernet.in
EUnet	info@eu.net
EUnet - Austria Internet access provider	office@austria.eu.net
EUnet - Belgian Internet access provider	postmaster@belgium.eu.net
EUnet - Finland Internet access provider	helpdesk@eunet.fi
EUnet - Germany Internet access provider	postmaster@germany.eu.net
EUnet - Hungary Internet access provider	postmaster@hungary.eu.net
EUnet - Luxemburg Internet access provider	postmaster@luxemburg.eu.net
EUnet - Norway Internet access provider	info@norway.eu.net
EUnet - Switzerland Internet access provider	info@uenet.ch
EUnet - United Kingdom Internet access provider	postmaster@britain.eu.net
FidoNet user	username@point.node.net.zone.fidonet.com
Finish University and Research Network (FUNET)	postmaster@figbox.funet.fi
Free Software Foundation:	gnu@prep.ai.mit.edu

Genie user	usermailaddress@genie.geis.com
Giant Toad Systems (GTS) UUCP network	postmaster@gts.org
GlasNet Moscow based electronic mail network	support@glas.apc.org
Great Circle Associates	tutorial-info@greatcircle.com
GreenNet	support@gn.apc.org
Hebrew University Social Science Data Archive	magar1@vms.huji.il
Higher Education Authority Network (HEAnet - Ireland)	postmaster@irlearn.ucd.ie
Hong Kong supernet	postmaster@super.hk
IIJ Internet access provider (Japan)	info@iij.ad.jp
InfoWorld Magazine Letters to the Editor	letters@infoworld.com
Institute for Global Communications user	username@igc.org
Interagency (Federal) E-mail User's Working Group	stein.mike@epamail.epa.gov
Intercon Systems Corp. (Internet access provider)	info@intercon.com
Internet Engineering Task Force	ietf-info@isoc.org
Internet Letter	helen@access.diget.com
Internet Network Information Center	info@internic.net

Internet Network Information Center (NIC)
    General user assistance
    Hostname and domain changes and updates
    User registration and WHOIS
    NIC computer operations
    Comments on NIC publications and services
	
	nic@nic.ddn.mil
	hostmaster@nic.ddn.mil
	updates registrar@nic.ddn.mil
	action@nic.ddn.mil
	suggestions@nic.ddn.mil

Internet Research Task Force	isoc@isoc.org
Internet Society	isoc@isoc.org
Internet user	username@host

InterNIC Registration Services
    Host, domain, network changes and updates
    computer operations
	
	hostmaster@internic.net
	action@internic.net

automatic mail service	mailserv@rs.internic.net
Irish EUnet	postmaster@ieunet.ie
Italian Eunet	pr@italy.eu.net
Italian Research and Academic Network	info@mis.garr.it
Janet (Joint Academic Network) UK	janet-liaison-desk@jnt.ac.wk
JUNET	info@junet.ad.jp
Lausanne Univesrsity (Switzerland) network	postmaster@unil.ch
League for Programming Freedom:	league@prep.ai.mit.edu
Los-Nettos California Area Retional Network	los-nettos-request@isi.edu
Matchmaker (MMNet) network	postmaster@ucm.org
MCI Mail user	username@mcimail.com
Michigan State Univesrsity	postmaster@msu.edu
MichNet (Internet access provider serving Michigan)	joden@merit.edu
Missouri Research and Education network	morenic@more.net
MRNet (Minnesota Regional Network)	info@mr.net
MRnet (Internet access provider serving Minnesota)	dfazio@mr.net
NASA Science Internet	naic@nasa.gov
National Public Telecomputing Network	info@nptn.org
NBC Nightly News	nightly@nbc.ge.com
Netherlands EUnet	nlnet@nluug.nl
NevanaNet (Internet access provider serving Nevada)	zitter@nevada.edu
New England Academic and Research Network (NEARmet)	nearnet-join@nic.near.net
New Mexico Technet (Internet access provider serving NM)	reynolds@technet.nm.org
NordNet	support@nn.apc.org
North Dakota Higher Education computer Network user	user@machine.nodak.edu

NorthWestNet	info@nwnet.net
NSFNET	nsfnet-info@merit.edu
NYSERnet (Internet access provider serving New York)	info@nysernet.org
OARnet (Internet access provider serving Ohio)	nic@oar.net
Ohio State University System of Neighboring Networks (SONNET)	nic@osu.edu
PACCOM (Internet access provider serving Hawaii)	torben@foralie.ics.hawaii.edu
PC Link user	username@aol.com
PC Magazine Letters to the Editor	157-9301@mci.com
Ross Perot	71511.460@compuserve.com
PIPEX Internet access provider (UK)	pipex@pipex.net
Portal Communications (Internet access provider)	info@portal.com
PREPnet (Internet access provider serving PA)	twb+@andrew.cmu.edu
Prodigy user	prodigyserviceid@prodigy.com
President Bill Clinton	president@whitehouse.gov
PSCNET (Internet access provider serving NE US)	pscnet-admin@psc.edu
PSILink	psilink.info@psi.com
Purdue University Cyprus Network	cypress-admin@cs.purdue.edu
Red IRIS (Spanish National Research and Academic Network)	info@rediris.es
Relcom-EUnet (Baltic and former Soviet Union Nestwork)	postmaster@ussr.eu.net
SDSCnet (Internet access provider serving CA)	loveep@sds.sdsc.edu
SESQUINET (Internet access provider serving Texas)	farrell@rice.edu
SInet (EUnet in Slovenia)	postmaster@slovenia.eu.net
Sogang University Network	root@ccs.sogang.ac.kr
SprintLink (Internet access provider)	mkiser@icm1.icp.net

SpringMail messaging center	postmaster@sprint.com
SprintMail user	/G=givenname/S=surname/O=organization/ ADMD=SprintMail/C=US@SPRINT.COM

SURAnet

administrative/financial issues	admin@sura.net
Internet resource information	info@sura.net
marketing information	marketing@sura.net
mailing list changes	list-admin@sura.net
network information provision	nic@sura.net
SURAnet principal investigators	sura-pi@sura.net
SURAnet staff	staff@sura.net
technical staff	noc@sura.net
USENET news feed information	news-admin@sura.net

SURFnet (Netherlands)	info@surfnet.nl
SWITCH (Swiss Telecommunications Systems for Higher Education and Research	postmaster@switchich
THAINET (Thailand)	postmaster@chulkn.chula.ac.th
THEnet (Internet access provider serving Texas)	tracy@utexas.edu
University of Illinois at Urbana Campus Network	postmaster@uiuc.edu
UNDPNET (United Nations Development Programme Network)	postmaster@undp.org
University of Pittsburg FTP archive	query@ums.cis.pitt.edu
USENET	info@uunet.uu.net
U.S. House of Representatives:	congress@hr.house.gov

Rep. Jay Dickey	R-AK	jdickey@hr.house.gov
Rep. Sam Gejdenson	D-CT	bozrah@house.hr.gov
Rep. Newt Gingrich	R-GA	georgia6@hr.house.gov
Rep. George Miller	D-CA	georgem@hr.house.gov
Rep. Charlie Rose	D-NC	crose@hr.house.gov
Rep. Peter Stark	D-CA	petemail@hr.house.gov
Rep. Melvin Watt	D-NC	melmail@hr.house.gov

U.S. Supreme Court opinions	aa584@cleveland.freenet.edu
UUCP user	user%host.UUCP@uunet.uu.net

UUNET Communications Services (Internet access provider)	info@uunet.uu.net
UUNET Technologies	info@uunet.uu.net
VERnet (Internet access provider serving Virginia)	jaj@virginia.edu
Vice President Al Gore	vice.president@whitehouse.gov
VNET (IBM internationational network) subscriber information	userid@nodename.vnet.ibm.com msdec@vnet.ibm.com
Westnet (WSester Stations Regional Network)	westnet@spot.colorado.edu
WVNET (Internet access provider serving West VA)	cc011041@wvnvms.wvnet.edu
White House press releases	pjones@sonsite.unc.edu
WiscNet (Internet access provider serving Wisconson)	tad@cs.wis.edu
World Software Tool & Die (Internet access provider)	info@world.std.com
York Univsersity ftp administrator	ftp@ftp.york.ca

The Finger Command

You can often verify an Internet electronic mail address through the use of the Finger command. To do so you would enter the command:

```
finger userid@host
```

Some host sites will return information concerning all users logged onto the system if you enter the finger command at the system prompt. The actual response to a finger command depends upon the site being fingered. Some sites may disable the finger command for security purposes, while other sites may provide such information as the userid, person's name, office location, telephone number, login time and when their mail was last read.

SENDING MAIL VIA INTERNET TO AN MCI MAIL SUBSCRIBER

There are three ways you can address mail to an MCI Mail subscriber:

1. use the unique 7 digit MCI Mail subscriber ID.
   format: ID@mcimail.com   example: 235-8068@mcimail.com

2. use subscriber's MCI Mail username.
   format: username@mcimail.com   example: gheld@mcimail.com
3. use subscriber's MCI Mail registered name.
   format: reg_name@mcimail.com example: gilbert_held@mcimail.com

Note: An underscore (_) must be used to connect the registered name elements in the address.

CHAPTER 4

Internet Commands and Electronic Address Retrieval

The focus of this chapter is upon two related Internet topics. First, we will examine the use of commands supported by computers to perform different Internet related activities, such as obtaining information about a specific user or active users on a computer connected to the Internet, determine the operational status of a computer connected to the Internet, use the mail program for transmitting electronic messages to persons connected to the Internet, and obtain information about registered users at a computer site. Concerning the latter, this chapter concludes with a list of electronic addresses readers can use to determine the electronic mail address and other information from over 100 sites located throughout the world. Although the majority of those sites represent educational institutions, site information for government agencies and commercial organizations is also provided in the table which concludes this chapter. Readers can use the addresses in that table in conjunction with the whois command to obtain electronic mail addresses and other information concerning persons attending or working at different educational institutions or working for different commercial organizations and government agencies.

COMMON INTERNET COMMANDS

The following commands are supported by most computers connected to the Internet. The response to these commands may vary based upon the manner in which they are implemented.

finger - The Finger command provides you with the ability to obtain information concerning a specific user or active users on a system or the retrieval of data concerning a specified topic.

format: finger @sitename

format: finger username@sitename

format: finger topic@sitename

examples:

% finger @msu.edu - to obtain a list of active users at msu.

% finger gheld@msu.edu - to obtain information about user gheld at msu.

% finger ruble@msu.edu - to obtain information on the ruble from msu.

In addition to obtaining information about a specific user or all active users on a computer, you can retrieve a variety of information through the use of Finger. To illustrate a few of the types of information obtainable from the use of Finger we will use the Chameleon graphic user interface program's Finger application.

Figure 4.1 illustrates the use of Finger to access the host address vm1.nodak.edu, searching for users named "Held". this finger site is the north Dakota Higher Education Computer Network (HECN) and the search results provides us with the electronic mail address of a person who is not related to the author. Later in this chapter we will examine the use of the whois command which provides us with another method to determine electronic mail addresses.

When in doubt concerning the use of Finger you can use a username of 'help' to obtain information concerning its' use at a particular site. Figure 4.2 illustrates the results of "fingering" the address vm1.nodak.edu using the username 'help'. Note that the information contained in the Chameleon Finger window provides information concerning its use at HECN.

One of the more interesting uses of Finger is provided by the address we just fingered. That address provides local weather information by fingering the site using the username 'qw'. Figure 4.3 illustrates the use of the Finger command with

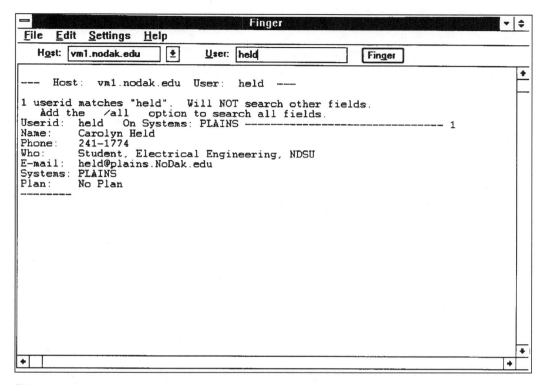

Figure 4.1 Using Finger to Access a Host Address

the username 'qw' when fingering the address vm1.nodak.edu. Note the result of this operation provides you with the weather at 14 cities in North Dakota. So, if you are preparing a trip to North Dakota remember to finger vm1.nodak.edu using a username of qw prior to packing your clothing!

FINGER RETRIEVAL

for:	***Andrew Toolkit Demonstration***
Access method:	finger help@atk.itc.cmu.edu
for:	Auroral and Solar activity information
Access method:	finger aurora@xi.uleth.ca
	finger daily@xi.uleth.ca
	finger solar@xi.uleth.ca

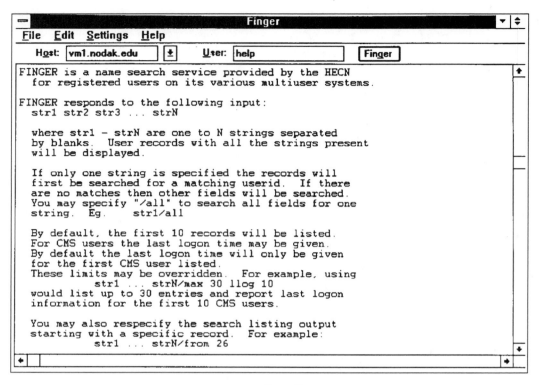

Figure 4.2 Using Finger with Username "help"

| for: | Billboard (Top Pop Music) Charts |
| Access method: | finger buckmr@rpi.edu |

for:	Candy and drink machine information
Access method:	finger coke@cmu.edu
	finger drink@drink.csh.rit.edu
	finger info@drink.csh.rit.edu
	finger graph@drink.csh.rit.edu

| for: | Earthquake Information |
| Access method: | finger quake@geophys.washington.edu |

| for: | FAQs listings |
| Access method: | finger nichol@stavanger.sgp.slb.com |

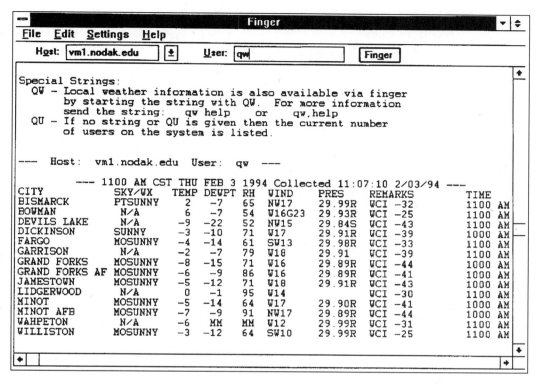

Figure 4.3 Using Finger with Username "qw"

for:	NASA Headline News
Access method:	finger nasanews@space.mit.edu

for:	Nielsen TV Ratings
Access method:	finger normg@halcyon.halcyon.com

for:	Star Trek Quotes
Access method:	finger franklin@ug.cs.dal.ca

mail - The mail command provides you with the ability to compose, edit, send and receive, save and delete electronic messages.

format:	mail sitename
example:	mail gheld@cs.msu.edu

Note: Entering mail by itself brings up the mail prompt (&). At that prompt you can enter the following mail commands, where message list references a list or range of integers or user names separated by spaces. If the message list is omitted the command operates upon the current message.

numeric - to read a specific message

d	[message list]	- delete specified messages
e	[message list]	- edit messages
f	[message list]	- show from lines of messages
h		- print out active message headers
m	[user list]	- mail to specific users
p	[message list]	- print specified messages
pre	[message list]	- make messages go back to system mailbox
q		- quit, saving unresolved messages in mbx
r	[message list]	- reply to sender (only) of message
R	[message list]	- reply to sender and all recipients of specified messages
s	[message list] file	- append message to file
t	[message list]	- type specified messages (same as p)
top	[message list]	- show top line of specified messages
u	[message list]	- undelete specified messages
v	[message list]	- edit specified messages with display editor
w	[message list] file	- append specified messages to file
x		- quit, do not change system mailbox
z		- display next page of headers
–		- display previous page of headers
!		- shell escape
:n		- return to mail (&) prompt
.		- by itself on a line ends a message
~b		- send blind carbon copies
~c		- send a carbon copies
~f		- include current message
~h		- list message headings
~m		- include current message with leading tabs
~p		- display entire message
~q		- cancel the message
~r		- insert file into message
~v		- invoke vi editor, exit with ESC followed by :wq and CR.

ping - The ping command is used to determine the operational status of another computer connected to the Internet.

format: ping sitename

example: % ping msu.edu

The ping command provides you with a mechanism to verify the operational status of a computer connected to the Internet. For example, if you are using WHOIS, FTP or another application and do not receive a response you may wish to ping the address to determine its operational status. Figure 4.4 illustrates the use of the Chameleon Ping application. In this example several sites were "pinged" and a host with the address "deakin.edu.au," which represents a com-

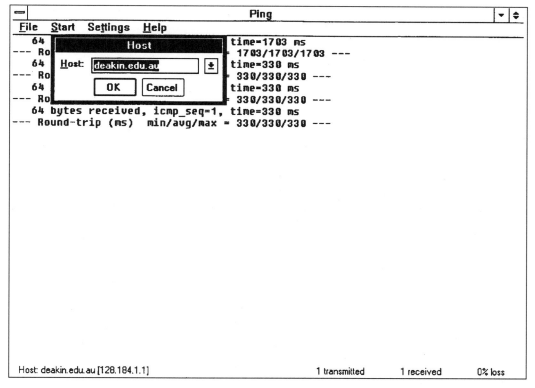

Figure 4.4 Chameleon's Ping Application

puter in Australia, is about to be pinged for a second time. If the pinged computer is operational, it responds to the ping which enables the round trip delay in ms to be displayed. Thus, if you examine the last two lines in Figure 4.4's window you'll note that the transmission of the last ping resulted in the receipt of 64 bytes and the computation of a round trip delay of 330 ms.

talk - The talk command provides you with the ability to interactively communicate with another person.

format:	talk name@sitename
example:	% talk held@msu.edu

Note: Most sites require the entry of CTRL-C to exit talk mode.

whois - The whois command is supported at many computer sites, enabling you to use this command to obtain information about a registered user of the system at a selected site.

format:	whois name@sitename
example:	% whois held@msu.edu

Note: Many implementations of whois require the use of an option or qualifier, such as /HOST for a VMS system and -h for a UNIX system. Other implementations may support wildcard searches.

A UNIX example of the whois command is as follows:

whois - h server-address name-of-person

Through the use of whois you can look up a handle, name, hostname or another field by simply typing in the entry. This results in a very broad search. To narrow the search you can prefix your entry with one or more of the following keywords or their minimum abbreviation which is indicated in CAPS.

To locate only a certain record TYPE	*To search only a specified FIELD*
DOmain GAteway GRoup HOst IMp	HAndle or '!'
MIlnet NEtwork Organization	Mailbox or contains '@'
PErson PSn TAc	NAme or leading '.'

Other WHOIS keywords include:

EXPand or '*'	Show all parts of display without asking.
Full or '='	Show detailed display for each match.
HELp	Enters help program for documentation listing.
PArtial or trailing '.'	Match targets starting with given string.
Q, QUIT or RETURN	Exit WHOIS.
SUBdisplay or '%'	Show users of host, hosts on network.
SUMmary or '$'	Show summary always, even if only one match.

Example: To perform a partial search that matches everything starting with your input Fred you would enter: 'Fred.', which could result in WHOIS listing such matches as 'Fred', 'Frederick', 'Fredericksburg' and so on.

If no whois program is available you may be able to telnet to the indicated server-address using port address 43. For example, telnet server-address 43. Then, type the name of the person on a separate line.

To obtain additional information concerning the use of the whois command at a particular computer site try entering whois help or whois ?.

Readers should note that both whois searches and the response to such searches can vary from site to site. Some whois sites support a Soundex search which displays all names that should be close to the name you are attempting to locate. Other whois sites may perform a pure alphabetic search.

To illustrate the use of whois let's return to Chameleon and use its whois application. Figure 4.5 illustrates the use of whois to access the Case Western Reserve University Whois/Nickname Service whose address is whois.cwru.edu. Note that 'help' was entered in the user field, which provides a GUI equivalent of the text command: whois whois.cwru.eduhelp. After reading the response to the previous whois help request we learn that Case Western Reserve University supports the Soundex search. So, quite naturally the author of this book is inquisitive and wants to determine if any long-lost relatives attend or work at that school. To satisfy this curiosity the entry 'tsxheld' was entered in the user field for a subsequent whois search. The results of that search operation are illustrated in Figure 4.6. Although the author did not find any long-lost relatives the Soundex search listed six similar sounding first or last names.

The HORTON program

A program known as Horton operates on some servers and enables the retrieval of a person's e-mail address by specifying a search_key that can represent a fragment of a person's name or username. The command to use Horton is:

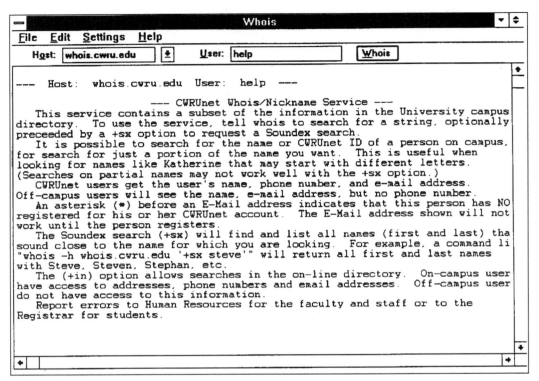

Figure 4.5 Using the Whois Command

whois -h horton_server search_key

where: horton_server is the name of the computer running Horton.

search_key is the fragment of the name or username to use in the search.

Horton returns a list of persons whose name or username match the entered search_key, displayed one per line.

INTERNET WHOIS SERVERS

Organization/Institution or Government Agency	*Server Address*
Association of Research Networks in Iceland	isgate.is
Auburn University	ducserv.duc.auburn.edu

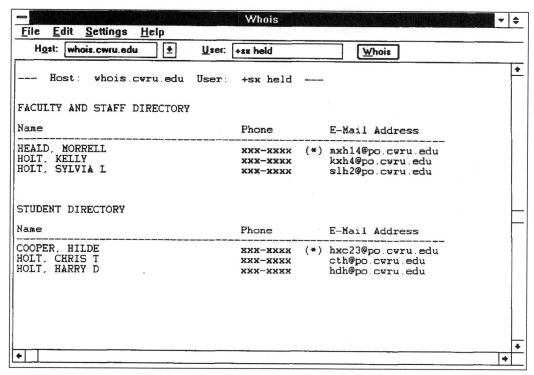

Figure 4.6 Results of a Whois Search Operation

Organization/Institution or Government Agency	Server Address
Australian Academic and Research Network	archie.au
Bates College	whois.bates.edu
Baylor College of Medicine	whois.bcm.tmc.edu
California Institute of Technology	caltech.edu
California Institute of Technology	horton.caltech.edu
California State University - Fresno	csufres.csufresno.edu
California State University - Hayward	csuhayward.edu
California State University - Sacramento	csus.edu
Cambridge Computer Associates	camb.com
Case Western Reserve University	whois.cwru.edu

Organization/Institution or Government Agency	*Server Address*
Chalmers University of Technology (Sweden)	chalmers.se
CITI Lille (France)	whois.citilille.fr
Communications Canada, Federal Department (Canada)	whois.doc.ca
Corporation for National Research Initiatives	info.cnri.reston.va.us
Dana-Farber Cancer Institute	whois.dfci.harvard.edu
Danish Computing Centre for Research and Education	whois.uni-c.dk
Darmstadt University of Technology (Germany)	whois.th-darmstadt.de
DDN Network Information Center	whois.nic.ddn.mil
Deakin University (Australia)	deakin.edu.au
Eindhoven University of Technology (Netherlands)	whois.tue.nl
Energy Sciences Network	wp.es.net
Florida State University	cc.fsu.edu
Foundation of Research and Technology(FORTHnet-Germany)	whois.forthnet.gr
Foundation of Research and Technology(FORTHnet-Germany	wp.forthnet.gr
Gesellschaft fuer Mathematik und Datenverarbe (Germany)	dfnnoc.gmd.de
George Mason University	gmu.edu
Gettysburg College	gettysburg.edu
Gothenburg University Computer Centre	whois.gd.chalmers.se
GTE Laboratories	gte.com
Harvey Mudd College	hmc.edu
Helsinki University of Technology (Finland)	cs.hut.fi
Imperial College (Great Britain)	src.doc.ic.ac.uk
Indiana University	iugate.ucs.indiania.edu
Institute of Automatic Control, Warsaw University	whois.ia.pw.edu.pl
Japan Network Information Center	whois.nic.ad.jp
Jyvaskyla University (Finland)	cc.jyu.fi

Organization/Institution or Government Agency	*Server Address*
Kean College	kean.edu
Keio University (Japan)	whois.cc.keio.ac.jp
Korea Network Information Center	whois.nic.nm.kr
Kutztown University	acad.csv.kutztown.edu
Lawrence Livermore National Laboratory	llnl.gov
Loughborough University (England)	whois.lut.ac.uk
Massachusetts Institute of Technology	mit.edu
Minnesota State University - Winona	vax2.winona.msus.edu
Mississippi State University	whois.msstate.edu
Monash University (Australia)	whois.monash.edu.au
NASA Ames Research Center	x500.arc.nasa.gov
NASA Goddard Space Flight Center	x500.gsfc.nasa.gov
NASA Langley Research Center	larc.nasa.gov
National Center for Software Technology (India)	sangam.ncst.ernet.in
National Energy Research Supercomputer Center	wp.nersc.gov
Naval Research Laboratory	whois.nrl.navy.mil
Network Solutions, Inc. (non-MILNET)	ds.internic.net
Network Solutions, Inc.	whois.internic.net
New Jersey Institute of Technology	earth.njit.edu
New Jersey Intercampus Network	pilot.njin.net
New York University, Courant Institute	acfcluster.nyu.edu
North Carolina State University	whois.ncsu.edu
Northern Arizona University	nau.edu
Occidental College	whois.oxy.edu
Ohio Northern University	austin.onu.edu
Ohio State University	osu.edu

Organization/Institution or Government Agency	*Server Address*
Oregon State University	ph.orst.edu
Oulu University (Finland)	oulu.fi
Pacific Bell	whois.pacbell.com
Pennsylvania State University	info.psu.edu
Performance Systems International	whois.sunquest.com
Queen's University, Kingston (Canada)	whois.queensu.ca
Research IP Europeans (Netherlands)	whois.ripe.net
Rochester Institute of Technology	cs.rit.edu
Rhodes University (South Africa)	hippo.ru.ac.za
Royal Institute of Technology (Sweden)	kth.se
Royal Institute of Technology (Sweden)	othello.admin.kth.se
Rutgers University	whitepages.rutgers.edu
Sandia National Research Laboratories	seda.sandia.gov
San Diego State University	whois.sdsu.edu
SANET (Slovakia)	whois.uakom.sk
Sonoma State University	sonoma.edu
Stanford University	stanford.edu
Stanford University	camis.stanford.edu
Stanford University	hpp.stanford.edu
State University of New York at Binghamton	bingsuns.cc.binghamton.edu
State University of New York at Oswego	oswego.edu
State University of New York at Stony Brook	sunysb.edu
St. John's University	stjohns.edu
SUNET (Swedish University Network)	whois.sunet.se
Sunquest Information Systems	whois.sunquest.com
Swedish Institute of Computer Science (Sweden)	sics.se

Organization/Institution or Government Agency	*Server Address*
SWITCH Teleinformatics Services (Switzerland)	nic.switch.ch
Syracuse University	syr.edu
Texas State Technical College	tstc.edu
Technical Research Center of Finland (Finland)	vtt.fi
Technische Universitaet Chemnitz (Germany)	whois.tu-chemnitz.de
United States Department of Energy	dirsvc.xosi.doe.gov
University of Adelaide (Australia)	whois.adelaide.edu.au
University of Akron	directory.uakron.edu
University of Arizona	ns.arizona.edu
University of Baltimore	ub.umd.edu
University of California at Berkeley	whois.berkeley.edu
University of California at Davis	directory.ucdavis.edu
University of California at Los Angeles	oac.ucla.edu
University of California at Santa Barbara	whois.ucsb.edu
University of California at San Diego	ucsd.edu
University of California at San Francisco	cgl.ucsf.edu
University of Canterbury (New Zealand)	cantsc.canterbury.ac.nz
University of Chicago	uchicago.edu
University of Cincinnati	uc.edu
University of Cincinnati	thor.ece.uc.edu
University Claude Bernard (Lyon, France)	whois.univ-lyon1.fr
University College, Australian Defense Force	sserve.cc.adfa.oz.au
University of Dortmund (Germany)	deins.informatik.uni-dortmund.de
University of Electro-Communications (Japan)	whois.cc.uec.ac.jp
University of Florida	whois.eng.ufl.edu
University of Houston	whois.uh.edu

Organization/Institution or Government Agency	*Server Address*
University of Maryland	umd5.umd.edu
University of Maryland, Baltimore County	umbc.edu
University of Miami, Rosentiel School of Marine and Atmospheric Science	whois.rsmas.miami.edu
University of Minnesota	umn.edu
University of Mississippi	sun1.mcsr.olemiss.edu
University of Natal (South Africa)	whois.und.ac.za
University of Nebraska at Lincoln	ns.unl.edu
University of New Brunswick (Canada)	whois.unb.ca
University of Notre Dame	nd.edu
University of Oregon	whois.uoregon.edu
University of Ottawa (Canada)	panda1.uottawa.ca
University of Pennsylvania	whois.upenn.edu
University of Rochester	whois.cc.rochester.edu
University of San Diego	teetot.acusd.edu
University of Saskatchewan (Canada)	whois.usask.ca
University of Saskatchewan, Engineering (Canada)	dvinci.usask.ca
University of Sydney (Australia)	jethro.ucc.su.oz.au
University of Texas at Austin	x500.utexas.edu
University of Victoria, Physics and Astronomy (Canada)	phys.uvic.ca
University of Virginia	whois.virginia.edu
University of Western Australia (Australia)	uwa.edu.au
University of Western Australia, University College	whois.gu.uwa.edu.au
University of Western Ontario (Canada)	whois.uwo.ca
University of Wisconson	wisc.edu
Victoria University (New Zealand)	directory.vuw.ac.nz

Organization/Institution or Government Agency	*Server Address*
Virginia Institute of Marine Science	whois.vims.edu
Waikato University (New Zealand)	waikato.ac.nz
Wake Forest University	whois.wfu.edu
Warsaw University, EE Faculty (Poland)	whois.elka.pw.edu.pl
Washington University	ibc.wustl.edu
Wirtschaftsuniversitaet Wien (Austria)	whois.wu-wien.ac.at
Worcester Polytechnic Institute	wpi.wpi.edu
York University (Canada)	horton.yorku.ca

CHAPTER 5

The File Transfer Protocol (FTP) and Anonymous FTP Sites

The purpose of this chapter is twofold. First, we will examine how we can establish an FTP connection to a computer connected to the Internet and the use of various FTP commands to facilitate the transfer of files. Using this information as a base we will then view a comprehensive list of anonymous FTP sites from which we can obtain a variety of information.

The term anonymous FTP site references a computer connected to the Internet that was programmed to provide other users with access to its files without requiring those users to first establish an account on the computer. When accessing an anonymous FTP site you will normally login using "anonymous" as your identification, hence the term anonymous FTP. Based upon Internet etiquette, you should use your full Internet mail address as your password. In fact, some anonymous FTP sites will break the connection if you do not use an appropriately formatted Internet address for your information.

When attempting to establish an anonymous FTP session a few sites are programmed to accept "guest" instead of "anonymous" for your login identification. Another item that warrants attention is the ability of some anonymous FTP sites which generate a predefined welcome message to cause client FTP software running on your computer to terminate an FTP session. You can usually suppress the welcome message by prefixing your identification with the dash "-" character. When in doubt, a good rule to follow is to experiment. That is, if you cannot access a desired anonymous FTP site due to a login problem try changing your identifier to "guest". If it appears your session is being terminated before it can start, try prefixing your login with the dash character.

The table of anonymous FTP sites which concludes this chapter is arranged alphabetically by subject or topic and not by FTP site address. Readers should note that, for some topics or subjects, multiple anonymous FTP sites are listed. In such situations you should attempt to access the anonymous FTP site closest to your location or within your country. Doing so reduces potential congestion and resulting transmission delays on international circuits which are normally relatively slow in comparison to intra country circuits and may provide persons that truly require access to distant host computers with improved access.

ESTABLISHING AN FTP CONNECTION

format: ftp siteaddress

example: ftp cs.msu.edu

response: connected to ftp.cs.msu.edu
            Name(ftp.csu.msu.edu):anonymous
            guest login ok, send ident as password
            Password: gheld@cs.msu.gov
            guest login ok
            ftp>

Note: Some FTP client software may crash or hang shortly after login due to informational messages sent by the server. The use of a dash (-) as the first character of your password should then be tried as this will turn off the informational messages generated by many FTP sites.

FTP Commands

acct account-information - Use to send host dependent account information.

ascii - This is the default setting which enables ASCII text file transfers. Computer responds with Type set to A.

binary - Use to enable the transfer of binary files. Computer responds with Type set to I, which signifies Image format.

bye - End the FTP session with a remote computer and return to your computer's system prompt.

cd directory - Change to the specified directory on the remote computer.

cdup - Change to the parent of the current directory on a remote VMS computer.

close - Use to disconnect from a foreign host.

dir - Use to list the current directory on the remote computer.

ebcdic - Use to disconnect from a foreign host.

get filename - Retrieve the specified file to your computer.

help - Obtain a list of FTP commands.

ls - List the contents of the current directory of the remote computer.

locstat - Use to display local status information.

mget filenames - Retrieve the specified list of file names to your computer. This command supports wildcards.For example:

    ftp> mget pay* - gets all files that begin with pay.

mput filenames - Transfer the specified list of filenames from the local to the remote computer. This command supports wildcards. For example:

    ftp> mput *.o puts all files that end with .o.

prompt - Use to turn off the interactive mode.

put filename - Transfer file from local to remote system.

pwd - Print the name of the working directory on the remote computer.

quit - Use to disconnect from the foreign host.

status - Use to check the previously specified file transfer type.

system - Use to obtain the name of the foreign host's operating system.

File Formats

Files at FTP sites can be classified into two major categories—text or binary. Text files are those files that do not contain embedded special non-printable characters. The most common extensions provided for text files are "txt" and "doc".

Binary files contain embedded non-printable characters. The most common examples of binary files are executable and compressed files. Common extensions for binary files include "exe" , "com", "tar", "Z" and "zip". The meaning of each file extension is indicated in the following table:

File Extension   Meaning

.tar   - - UNIX tape archive. Unpack using "tar -xvf filename.tar".

.Z   - - Compressed UNIX file. Uncompress using "uncompress filename.Z".

.zip   - - IBM PC compressed file; unzip using PKUNZIP.EXE

.exe   - - IBM PC executable file which is in binary and non-printable.

.hqx   - - Macintosh binhex file; de-binhex with Stuffit, BinHex, or DeHQX.

.ps   - - PostScript file useful only if you have a printer that supports this file format.

.txt   - - A straight text or ASCII file that does not contain control codes.

When you enter the client FTP program its default file transfer mode is text. Thus, if you want to transfer a binary file you should first change the mode of your client FTP software to support binary file transfer. To do so you would enter "binary" at the FTP prompt as indicated below.

```
ftp> type binary
```

If your FTP client was previously set to binary and you intend to transfer files that have the extension ".doc", ".txt", or ".ps", you should set your file type to ASCII. To do so you would enter "ascii" at the FTP prompt as indicated below.

```
ftp> type ascii
```

As previously noted, all .tar, .Z, .exe, and .zip files require a binary file transfer setting when they are transferred. If you are using FTP, issue the command "binary". If you are using Kermit, issue the command "set file type binary" on both machines.

To restore a tar.Z file which represents an archive that was compressed requires you to have the UNIX "compress" and "uncompress" commands and the "tar" command on your host computer. In addition, your computer's operating system must be compatible with Berkeley UNIX. Once you FTP a tar.Z file to your host you would first use the "uncompress" command to replace the compressed ".Z" file with a copy of the file in its original form prior to it being compressed. For example, if the file name was internetguide-ps.tar.Z, enter the following command:

```
uncompress -v internetguide-ps.tar.Z
```

The operational result of that command is the file "internetguide-ps.tar".

Next, use the "tar -xvf" command to replace the previously archived tar file with the set of directories and files contained in the archive. For example,

```
tar -xvf internetguide.tar
```

might generate the following files:

```
copyright.ps
copyright.txt
introduction.ps
introduction.txt
chapter1.ps
 .  .  .  .  .
```

For additional information concerning the operation of compression and archiving commands you can enter the commands "man compress" and "man tar" to obtain online documentation from the UNIX online manual.

GETTING FILES WITH ANONYMOUS FTP

Through the use of an FTP session you can logon to a system and transfer public files to your computer. The series of events required to do this is listed below:

1. Select the appropriate FTP address and initiate an FTP session using that address.
2. Signon to the distant computer using the password "anonymous"; however, note that some systems require the password "guest".
3. Navigate through the distant computers directory structure using the directory related commands previously listed in Chapter 2 to locate the file or files you need. Use the "cd" command to change directories and "ls" command to list the contents of a directory.

4. Once you locate the desired file use an appropriate file transfer command to transfer the file. For example, to transfer the file "snoopy" to your computer you would enter the FTP command "get snoopy". To transfer multiple files you would use the "mget" command. For example, to transfer the files snoopy, woodstock and bigbert you could enter the following mget command:

```
ftp> mget snoopy woodstock bigbert
```

5. After you completed your FTP session signoff the remote computer by entering the command "bye".

ANONYMOUS FTP RESOURCES

A site connected to Internet which permits other users connected to the network to transfer files to and from their host computer without having to establish an account provides anonymous FTP access. To use an anonymous ftp service you would type the command FTP MACHINE-NAME on your computer, where MACHINE-NAME is the name of the computer you want to connect to. You would then use "anonymous" as the username and provide your E-mail address as the password when the distant computer prompts you for this information. When in doubt concerning the commands supported by the FTP site type HELP.

To find out additional information about a particular site retrieve and display a file typically named README, SITEINFO, or a similar name. This file, which is included in the top directory of many FTP sites may provide you with such information as the primary purpose of the databases contained at the site, method for contacting persons at the site and similar information.

For the access methods listed in the comprehensive table in this chapter, the colon (:) after the ftp address is a separator for the directory and an optional file within a directory you should access. For example, ftp: rs6000.msu.edu:/pub/money/cash.txt indicates you should access the file cash.txt in the /pub/money directory at the ftp address rs6000.msu.edu.

As an alternative to the use of a command based communications program you can consider the use of a graphic user interface program which converts many FTP operations to a simple point-and-click use of the mouse. One such program is Chameleon, whose FTP application provides you with an easy to use interface for transferring files based upon the Internet File Transfer Protocol.

Figure 5.1 illustrates the Chameleon FTP window after the Connect menu was selected to display the connect dialogue box. Note that the host name, username and password were entered in appropriate fields in the Dialogue box to prepare for accessing the SURAnet anonymous FTP server.

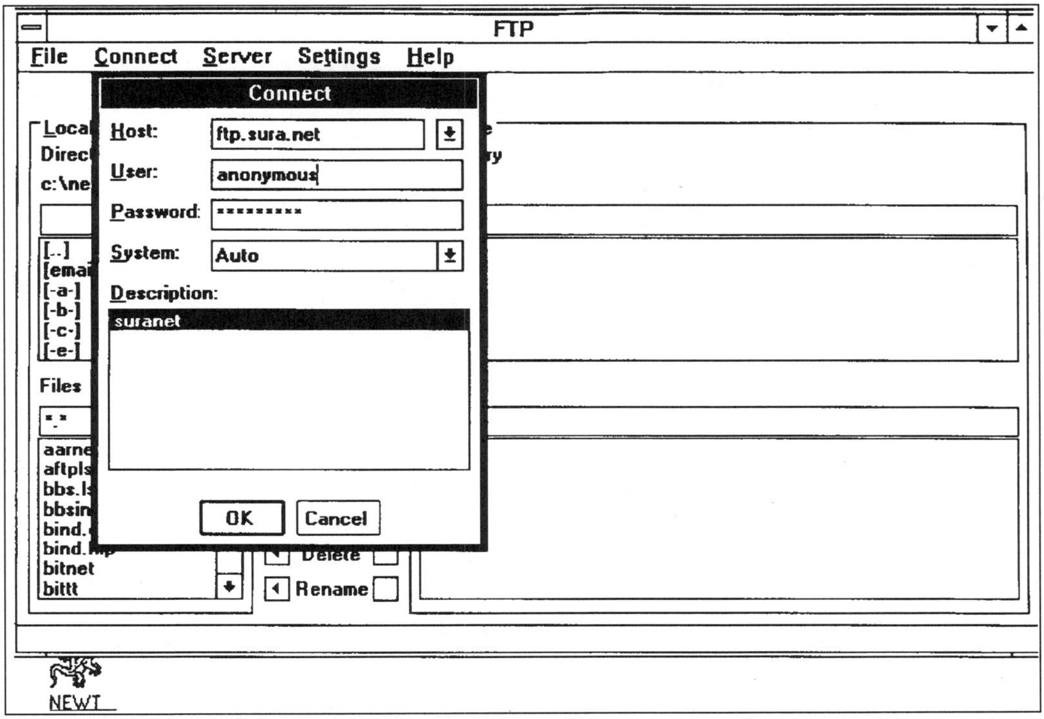

Figure 5.1 Chameleon FTP Window

SURAnet is a major Internet access provider serving the Southeast United States and its anonymous FTP server contains a large amount of most informative information concerning the Internet. To access an anonymous FTP server you enter "anonymous" in the User field and your e-mail address in the Password field. The System field provides you with the ability to define the type of system you are connecting. Chameleon supports a range of computers, varying in scope from IBM MVS mainframes to UNIX, OS/2 and other machines. Normally a selection of Auto is sufficient to access an FTP site. The Description field contains a description of previously defined destinations created from the Settings menu by selecting a 'Connection Profile' option in that menu. Once you define a connection profile you can simply select the connect menu and click on the description name in the connect dialogue box to complete the entries in the fields of that dialogue box. Regardless of the method used to complete the fields, once they are completed you can select the OK button to initiate a connection to the previously designated host system. Figure 5.2 illustrates the Chameleon FTP window upon a successful logon to the SURAnet anonymous FTP server.

In examining Figure 5.2 note that the host address of the connected system is displayed along the top of the Chameleon FTP window. Local files and directories appear on the left side of the FTP window, while remote files and directories are listed on the right side of the window. The dual row of buttons commencing with the label 'Change', with two exceptions, operates upon the local and remote files and directories according to the direction of the arrow in each button. Those exceptions are the Copy and Append buttons whose arrows indicate the direction of file transfers.

Upon login to the SURAnet anonymous FTP server you are positioned at the root directory indicated by the slash (/) under the Remote Directory label in the Chameleon FTP window. To change to the 'pub' director you would simply click on 'pub' to highlight it in inverse video, as shown, and then click on the 'Change' button whose arrow points to the right.

Figure 5.3 illustrates the Chameleon FTP window after we changed to the SURAnet pub directory. Note that the directory window contains a list of new di-

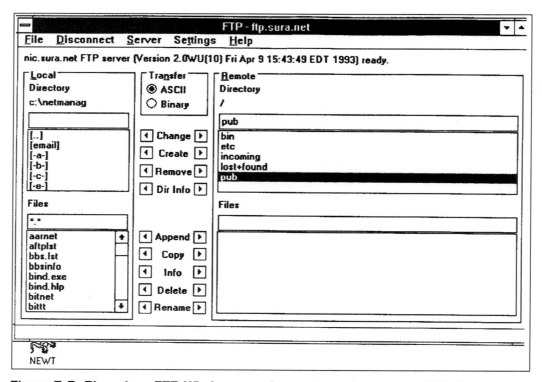

Figure 5.2 Chameleon FTP Window upon Logon to an Anonymous FTP Server

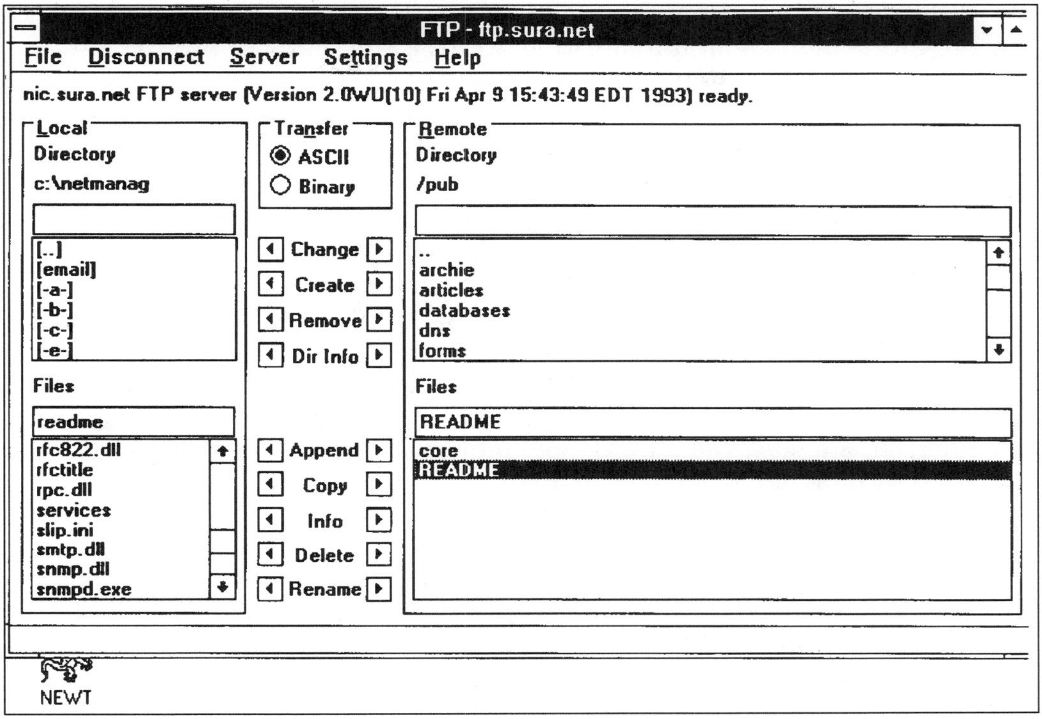

Figure 5.3 Chameleon FTP Window After Changing to SURAnet Pub Directory

rectories which represent subdirectories under the director 'pub'. Also note that the Files window contains the name of two files that are contained in the 'pub' directory, core and README. In Figure 5.3 we selected the README file and entered the same file name in the local Files window on the lower left corner of the FTP window. We did this in preparation for transferring the contents of the README file from the remote host to our computer. Now, all we have to do is click on the Copy button which has an arrow pointing to the left to invoke the file transfer operation.

As illustrated by the previous series of illustrations a GUI communications program can facilitate your communications operations, reducing many functions to a point-and-click operation or series of operations. When exploring FTP sites it is a good idea to transfer files labeled README and WELCOME, as they usually contain information about the site or its directories and files that can be extremely valuable. Some sites have a WELCOME file located in the root directory, while other sites typically have one or more README files located in one or more specific directories under the root directory. The WELCOME file usually provides general information about the site, while README files usually provide information about the contents of the directory in which they are located. However, readers should note that there are not standards regarding the use of information files and many sites do things differently or do not provide any information files, making searches most interesting when you encounter a list of cryptic file names.

Prior to copying a file to your computer it's a good idea to determine its size. Upon occasion, the name of a file may be deceptive and the result of a file transfer operation could result in a megabyte or more of unanticipated data. By clicking on the right Info button you can obtain information about a selected file to include its size. Figure 5.4 illustrates the display of the Chameleon Remote Info window which indicates that the file README contains 3974 bytes of information. Assuming that the selected file has an acceptable file length for transferring to our computer, let's initiate a file transfer operation to illustrate some of the advantages associated with the use of a GUI program.

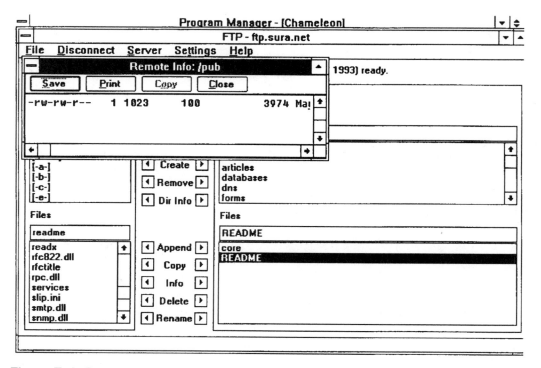

Figure 5.4 Chameleon Remote Info Window

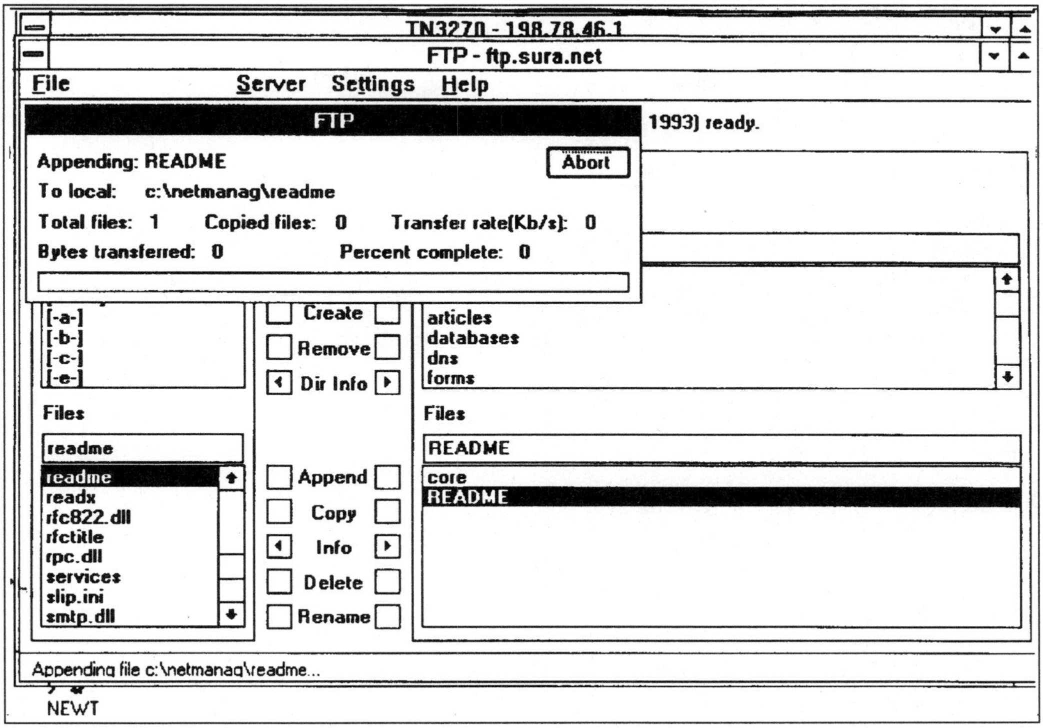

Figure 5.5 Chameleon FTP Window During a File Transfer Operation

Figure 5.5 illustrates the display of the Chameleon FTP window during a file transfer operation. Note that the previously displayed Info window was replaced by the FTP window. In this example, the left Append button was pressed since a previous file named 'readme' was created on the local computer which we want to add to. Thus, the FTP window displays the message "Appending: README". The horizontal bar under the heading "Bytes transferred", which was empty when the screen image was captured, will fill from left to right as the file transfer occurs, providing you with a visual indication of the transfer. In addition, the value to the right of the label "Percent complete" will increase in tandem with the bar under that label being filled from left to right. Thus, this GUI provides both a numeric and visual indication of the progress of the file transfer operation.

FTP Site
Database: AARNET Information
Access method: ftp: sao.aarnet.edu.au

Database: ADA Archive
Access method: ftp: ajpo.sei.cmu.edu
                   ftp: bugs.nose.mil

Database: Agriculture Resources on Internet Guide
Access method: ftp:ftp.ucdavis.edu:/pub/extension/document/ag-guide.ps

Database: Agriculture and Related Sciences Internet/Bitnet Guide
Access method: ftp: ftp.sura.net:/pub/nic/agricultural.list

Database: AIDS Information
Access method: ftp: nifty.andrew.cmu.edu:/pub/qrd/
                   ftp: spdcc.com:/pub/hiv/

Database: AIX/370
Access method: ftp: aix.rpi.edu

Database: Alex Information
Access method: ftp: alex.sp.cs.cmu.edu:/doc/README

Database: Alternet UUNET information
Access method: ftp: uu.net:/uunet-info/

Database: Amiga Computer Software
Access method: ftp: ab20.larc.nasa.gov

Database: Amiga SIG
Access method: ftp: drycas.club.cc.cmu.edu

Database: Andrew Toolkit Consortium Database
                   (Integrated applications to include multi-media printing)
                   Carnegie Mellon University
Access method: ftp: emsworth.andrew.cmu.edu

Database: Anonymous FTP site list
Access method: ftp: pilot.njin.net:/pub/ftp-list/ftp.list

Database: Ansnet information
Access method: ftp: nis.ans.net:/pub/info/

Database: Archie Client Software
Access method: ftp: ashley.cs.widner.edu
                        This site has a collection of the various clients
                        that are available to query the Archie service
                        (finding where things are available via Anonymous FTP).
                   archie-1.4.1.tar.Z   - a command-line client
                   archie-dos.zip   - a CUTCP Archie client for DOS

archie-NeXT.tar.z	- a version of Archie for the NeXT
archie-perl-3.tar.Z	- a client written in Perl
archie-vms.com	- Archie 1.3.1 for VMS, in a DCL .com file
archie.el	- Archie under Emacs; uses ange-ftp
log_archie-pl1.tar.Z	- log an interactive session with an Archie server
one-liner.sh	- a shell script client
xarchie-1.3.tar.Z	- a client for running under Xwindows

Database: Archie Information
Access method: ftp: archie.ans.net:/pub/archie/doc/README

Database: Archie Manual and Introduction Information
Access method: ftp: ftp.sura.net:/pub/nic/archie.manual

Database: Archives
Access method: ftp: ocf.berkeley.edu:/pub/library
                   ftp: wuarchive.wustl.edu (for GIFS)
                   ftp: sounds.sdsu.edu (for sound archive)
                   ftp: archive.umich.edu (Apple, Amiga, MSDOS software)
                   ftp: oak.oakland.edu (for DOS, UNIX software)
                   ftp: quartz.rutgers.edu:/pub/humor (humor)
                   ftp: sumex-aim.stanford.edu (Apple, Amiga, DOS software)
                   ftp: ftp.sura.net:/pub/nic (Internet information)
                   ftp: avahi.inria.fr (France)
                   ftp: aix370.rrz.uni-koeln.de (Germany)
                   ftp: wuarchive.wustl.edu

Database: Artwork
Access method: ftp: sunsite.unc.edu:/pub/multimedia/pictures/

Database: askERIC Information Archive
Access method: ftp: ericir.syr.edu:/pub

Database: Astronomy
Access method: ftp: pulsar.princeton.edu
                   ftp: qiclab.scn.rain.com:/pub/astronomy/
                   ftp: stsci.edu

Database: AT&T Bell Laboratories Annonymous FTP
Access method: att-in.att.com

Database: AT&T 6300 Series Computer Information
Access method: ftp: ames.arc.nasa.gov:pub/MSDOS/ATT/6300/

Database: Atomic Network and related Technology Papers
Access method: ftp: venera.isi.edu:/atomic/

Database: Australian Annonymous FTP Sites
Access method: ftp: aarnet.edu.au
                  ftp: audrey.sait.edu.au
                  ftp: augean.eleceng.adelaide.edu.au
                  ftp: brolga.cc.uq.oz.au
                  ftp: cc.curtin.edu.au
                  ftp: ccadfa.cc.adfa.oz.au
                  ftp: csc2.anu.edu.au
                  ftp: csuvax1.csu.murdoch.edu.au
                  ftp: cujo.curtin.edu.au
                  ftp: draci.cs.uow.edu.ac
                  ftp: extro.ucc.su.oz.au
                  ftp: godzilla.cgl.rmit.oz.au
                  ftp: gondwana.ecr.mu.oz.au
                  ftp: marlin.jcu.edu.au
                  ftp: minnie.cs.adfa.oz.au
                  ftp: sao.aarnet.edu.au
                  ftp: shark.mel.dit.csiro.au
                  ftp: tasman.cc.utas.edu.au
                  ftp: uniwa.uwa.oz.au

Database: Australian Network Sites and Resources Guide
Access method: ftp: aarnet.edu.au:/pub/resource-guide/
                  for network user's guide: pub/user-guide

Database: BABEL: Computer Related Abbreviations and Acronyms
Access method: ftp:ra.msstate.edu:/pub/docs/words-1/Net-Stuff/babel.txt
                  ftp: ftp.temple.edu:/pub/info/help-net/babel93c.txt

Database: BCM Archive Server (Texas Christian University)
Access method: bcm.tmc.edu

                  Categories in the BCM archive-server include:

    public   -- items that are useful to hosts in the tmc.edu do-
                                 main or don't fit any of the other categories
    nfs   -- repository of information and sources about NFS
                                 andPC-NFS   contact   ARCHIVE-MANAGE-
                                 MENT@BCM.TMC.EDU for more information
    unisys   -- respository of information and sources that re-
                                 late to   UNiSYS U-series computers

maps	-- Repository of the latest UUCP maps for the State of Texas
whois	-- Repository of program sources for accessing the BCM WHOIS database
rn	-- rn, the readnews program, includes source kit and patches
pcnfs	-- official archive of information on PC-NFS
nntpclnt	-- nntp client distribution This directory contains sources that will work on Unisys U-series computers
daytime-ddn-1100.shar	-- A simple daytime server for the Unisys 1100 Exec with DDN-1100. UCS C and COBOL are required
ndir.shar	-- The Berkeley directory reading library emulator.
res[1-5].shar	-- The BIND resolver libraries (no name-daemon) for Unisys 5000 computers running NET-5000

Database: Beer Brewing
Access method: ftp: caticsuf.cati.csufresno.edu
                    ftp: sierra.stanford.edu:/pub/homebrew/

Database: Bell Atlantic Anonymous FTP Site
Access method: ftp: ba.com

Database: Bellcore Anonymous FTP Server
Access method: ftp: flash.bellcore.com

Database: Bible Resources List
Access method: ftp: ftp.sura.net:/pub/nic/bible.resources

Database: Online Bible
Access method: ftp: ymir.claremont.edu:/onlinebible/

Database: Bibliographic Record Processing Utilities
Access method: ftp: indri.primate.wisc.edu

Database: Biologists Guide to Internet Resources
Access method: ftp: rtfm.mit.edu:/pub/usenet/news.answers/biology/guide

Database: Biological (Molecular) Software and Data Archive
Access method: ftp: ftp.bio.indiana.edu
                    access and read file Archive.doc for instructions

Database: BITNET Information
Access method: ftp: vax1.umkc.edu

Files and file descriptions at this address:

BITNET_ETHICS.TXT	A brief file on how to use the BITNET network ethically.
BITNET_HELP.TXT	A complete help file on BIT-NET.
BITNET_LISTS.TXT	An up-to-date list of ALL currently known Listserv lists available to the public.
BITNET_SERV.TXT	A summarized yet verbose description on the various services available over BITNET.
ETHERNET_NUMBERS TXT	A list of known Ethernet Addresses.
FTP_COMMANDS.TXT	A descriptive list of all the commands that an anonymous ftp site will accept.
FTP_HELP.TXT	A brief document regarding what FTP is and the basics to use it.
FTP_SITES.TXT	An up-to-date list of sites that accept anonymous FTP.
GNUCHESS.DIR	A VAX/VMS version of Gnuchess with an SMG interface.
GUIDE.TXT	The complete NNSC.NSF.NET Internet Resource Guide.
HITCH_GUIDE.TXT	The Internet and what's available through it.
HOSTS.TXT	A current table of IP hosts according to NIC.DDN.MIL.
INT_LISTS.TXT	A complete list of listserv discussion groups available over the Internet. This list also con-

	tains detailed information about each list, and how to subscribe.
IRG.DIR	The Internet Resource Guide.
MSKERMIT.ZIP	Kermit for the PC.
NET_ADMIN_INTRO .TXT	An introduction to setting up a network and how to maintain it.
NETWORK_READING_LIST .TXT	A list of publications (both free and of charge) containing useful information about networking and existing networks.
NETWORK_INFO.DIR	A sub-directory containing many helpfiles, sitelists, and documentation regarding most of the networks around the world.
NET_DIRECTORY.DIR	A sub-directory containing the "Users' Directory of Computer Networks."
NIST_SECURE_GUIDE .TXT	A manual describing networking's vulnerability to viridae, and how to enhance network security.
SENDMAIL_TUTORIAL .TXT	An E-mail tutorial.
TCP_IP_INTRO.TXT	An introduction to the TCP/IP protocol and its uses.
UNIX_SECURE.TXT	A manual regarding the problems and holes within UNIX security, with special attention paid on how to repair them.
WHAT_IS_FTP.TXT	A short description of what FTP is, and what to do!

Database: BITNET node list
Access method: ftp: vm1.nodak.edu:/bitinfo/Bitnet.lists
                 ftp: vax1.umkc.edu

Database: BLT Library
Access method: ftp: harbor.ecn.purdue.edu

Database: Boston University
Access method: ftp: cs.bu.edu

Database: British Interactive Library Catalogue on JANET
Access method: ftp: ftp.unt.edu:/pub/library/uk.lib
                 ftp:csuvax1.csu.murdoch.edu.au:/pub/library/
                 JANET.OPACs.list

Database: Brown University
Access method: ftp: wilma.cs.brown.edu

Database: List of dialup bulletin board systems
Access method: ftp: wuarchive.wustl.edu:/mirrors/msdos/bblists

Database: Bull Research Kola Project
Access method: ftp: avahi.inria.fr

Database: Internet BBS Listing
Access method: ftp: ftp.sura.net:/pub/nic/bbs.list.xx-xx where xx-xx represents
                 most recent date of publication
                 ftp: casbah.acns.nwu.edu
                 ftp: plains.nodak.edu:/pub/bbs-list.txt/

Database: Bibliographical Guide For Networked Information
Access method: ftp: infolib.murdoch.edu.au:/pub/bib/stanton.bib

Database: Biology (primarily molecular) Software Archive
Access method: ftp: ftp.bio.indiana.edu

Database: C+++
Access method: ftp: sun.soe.clarkson.edu:/pub/C++/

Database: California Institute of Technology
Access method: ftp: csvax.cs.caltech.edu
                 ftp: hamlet.caltech.edu
                 ftp: hobiecat.pcmp.caltech.edu

Database: California Polytech
                 Image Processing and OCR Library
Access method: ftp: polyslo.calpoly.edu

Database: California State Government Information
Access method: ftp: lsl.leg.ca.gov

Database: Campus Wide Information Systems List of CampusSystems and
                    Free-Net BBS
Access method: ftp: ftp.oit.unc.edu:/pub/docs/about-the-net/cwis

Database: Campus Wide Information Systems (CWIS) site list
Access method: ftp: ftp.sura.net:/pub/nic/cwis.list

Database: Canada (CA) Domains
Access method: ftp: relay.cdnnet.ca:/ca-domains/

Database: Center for Electronic Records - National Archives
Access method: ftp: ftp.cu.nih.gov:/NARA_ELECTRONIC/READ.ME

Database: Centre d'information ed d'ArchivageReseau Interordinateus
                    Scientifique Quebecois (RISQ)
Access method: ftp: clouse.crim.ca

Description des differents sujets d'information

/cia/CAnet   contient des informations concernant les
                    reseaux de recherche canadiens

/cia/Internet   contient des informations concernants des
                    reseaux nationals et internationals (surtout
                    Americain) (exemples RFCs, IETF, IAB, re-
                    source guide, ...)

/cia/ca-domain   contient les formulaires d'enregistrement de
                    domaines sous .CA.

/cia/divers   contient des informations generales concer-
                    nant le CIA dont la structure detaillee.

/cia/pub   on retrouve dans ce repertoire differents
                    logiciels du domaine publique.

/cia/risq   information sur le RISQ.

Database: CERFnet information
Access method: ftp: nic.cerf.net:/cerfnet/

Database: Chaos Project Group
Access method: ftp: shrimp.cs.washington.edu:/pub/chaos/

Database: CHAT Clients
Access method: ftp: ftp.santafe.edu:/pub/sig/4m
                  ftp: csd4.csd.uwm.edu:/pub/tjk
                  ftp: cs.bu.edu:/irc/clients

Database: CHAT Information
Access method: ftp: debra.dgbt.ca:/pub/chat/info.page

Database: Chemistry Manuals
Access method: ftp: cscihp.ecst.csuchico.edu:/pub/chemistry/

Database: C Language Library
Access method: ftp: ftp.cac.washington.edu

Database: C Language Tutorial
Access method: ftp: isis.cshl.org

Database: CAD Programs
                  Stanford University Electronics and Technology CAD (SELECT-
                  CAD)
Access method: ftp: sierra.stanford.edu

Database: CCITT V and X Series Documents
Access method: ftp: sunie.sunet.se:/.ccitt/

Database: China News Digest
Access method: ftp: ucbvax.berkeley.edu

Database: Claremont College
Access method: ftp: hmcvax.claremont.edu
                  ftp: pomona.claremont.edu

Database: Clarkson University Software Archive
                  (Primarily MS DOS)
Access method: ftp: sun.soe.clarkson.edu

Database: Clearinghouse for Subject-Oriented Internet Resource Guide
                  Sponsored by University of Michigan
Access method: ftp: una.hh.lib.umich.edu:/inetdirs

Database: Clemson University
Access method: ftp: hubcap.clemson.edu

Database: CNAM Annonymous FTP Server
Access method: ftp: cnam.cnam.fr

Directory	Description
ABU	French texts
Ada	Ada programming language
Astro	Astronomy pictures
Atari	All about Atari computers
Boizumault	Sources for the implementation of Prolog
CNAM	Local literature
CNU	Administrative stuff
Fractals	Fractal pictures
Modulog	Modulog programming language
Network	Misc. about networks
Rfc	Request For Comments of the Internet
VMS	For the VMS operating system
camlada	Teaching exercices in CAML and Ada
incoming	Yes, you can write here

Database: College student e-mail address information
Access method: ftp: rtfm.mit.edu:/pub/usenet/soc.college/Student_Email_Addresses

Database: Colorado SuperNet information
Access method: ftp: csn.org:/csn/reports

Database: Columbia University
Access method: ftp: watsun.cc.columbia.edu
Columbia University Academic Information Systems public file transfer access point, /pub/ftp. You may cd to any of the following areas:

bibliographic	Bibliographic items
bootp	New RFC1395 UNIX bootp server
ccmd	C-language interactive command-parsing package

dj	Automatic backup of network hosts to jukebox
kermit	Kermit communications and file transfer software
misc	Miscellaneous software
mm	Mail Manager (MM) software, C-language version
packet-drivers	The Cyrnwr (nee Clarkson) packet-driver collection
patch	Larry Wall's PATCH program
pcfonts	A large collection of fonts for PCs from Yossi Gil
vms-make	A new Make program for (Open)VMS VAX and AXP
vms-libcmu	Berkeley sockets library for CMU/Tek VMS TCP/IP

Other ftp sites of interest at Columbia University include:

ftp.ctr.columbia.edu:	Center for Telecommunications Research
ftp.cs.columbia.edu:	Computer Science Department
lamont.ldeo.columbia.edu:	Lamont-Doherty Earth Observatory

For the Columbia Appletalk Package (CAP), visit rutgers.edu.
For Xnext, go to foxtrot.ucsd.edu.

Database: Community Networks Information
Access method: ftp: netcom.com:/pub/amcgee/community/communet.msg

Database: Computer Abbreviations
Access method: ftp: ftp.temple.edu:/pub/info/help-net/babe194a.txt

Database: Computers and Academic Freedom Archive
Access method: ftp: ftp.eff.org:/pub/academic/README

Database: Computer Algebra Group
                 University of Passau, Germany
Access method: ftp: alice.fmi.uni-passau.de

Database: Computer Emergency Response Team (CERT)
Access method: ftp: info.cert.org

Database: Computer Networking Bibliography
Access method: ftp: csuvax1.csu.murdoch.edu.au:/pub/library/parker.bib
                    ftp: syr.edu:/networks/doc/netbib.txt

Database: Computer Jargon
Access method: ftp: aeneas.mit.edu:/pub/gnu/jargon-README

Database: CONCERT Network information
Access method: ftp: concert.net:/doc
                    ftp: ncnoc.concert.net

Directories of Interest:

cer   Computer Emergency Response Team advisories and clippings

concert Network stats, maps, etc.

doc   Contains info helpful to network and host admins. Includes CONCERT policy and operating procedure documents.

patches Sun and UCB UNIX patches

pub   Contains CONCERT Network host and subnet registration information and local DECNET infomation

netinfo Information gleaned from the DDN NIC concerning hosts, registration procedures, etc.

rfc   RFCs including postscript versions when available

dist   Software of local interest or locally developed to solve current networking problems

Database: Connection Machine Network Server (CMNS)
                    Massively Parallel Applications
Access method: ftp: cmns-sun.think.com
                    ftp: cmns-mood.think.com

Database: Conservationist Online Resources Guide
Access method: ftp: ftp.sura.net:/pub/nic/conservation-guide.11-93.txt

Database:	CONVEX Users Group
Access method:	ftp: pemrac.space.swri.edu

Database:	Cornell University
Access method:	ftp: helios.tn.cornell.edu

Database:	Cornell University
	School of Electrical Engineering Anonymous FTP
Access method:	ftp: tesla.ee.cornell.edu

Database:	Cryptology
Access method:	ftp: stout.atd.ucar.edu:/pub/Crypto/

Database:	CSRI Technical Reports
Access method:	ftp: csri.toronto.edu

Database:	Curtain University of Technology Annonymous FTP Server
Access method:	ftp: cc.curtin.edu.au

Database:	Cyberspace and Legal Issues
Access method:	ftp: ftp.eff.org:/pub/cud/papers/cyberspace

Database:	Cyberspace FAQ
Access method:	ftp: rtfm.mit.edu:/pub/usenet/news.answers/cyberpunk-faq

Database:	Dartmouth University
Access method:	ftp: dartvax.dartmouth.edu

Database:	Data Compression Program Archives
Access method:	ftp: ftp.cso.uiuc.edu

```
        /pc/exec-pc (ZIP, ARC)
        /pc/local/ (MS DOS)
        /mac/  (Macintosh)
        /amiga/ (Amiga)

ftp: wuarchive.wustl.edu
        /mirrors/msdos/archiver/ (ARC, LHARC, HPACK)
          /filutl/ (DIET)
          /zip/ (PKZIP)
          /mac/ (Macintosh)
          /info-mac/util/
          /unix-c/arc-progs/ (ARC, ZIP)
          /misc/vaxvms/ (UNZIP for VMS)
          /misc/unix/  (UNZIP,  ZOO  for  UNIX,  VMS,
        UNARJ)
```

ftp: sumex-aim.stanford.edu
   /info-mac/util/ (STUFFIT, LITE, COMPACTORPRO)
      /unix/ (UNSIT)
ftp: omnigate.clarkson.edu:/pub/ncsa2.2tn/
ftp: pc.usl.edu:/pub/unix/
ftp: plains.nodak.edu:/pub/appleII/GS/utils/nonGS/pacers/
ftp: vmd.cso.uiuc.edu
ftp: uxc.cso.uiuc.edu:/pub/
ftp: tybalt.caltech.edu:/pub/apple2/shrinkits/
ftp: vmsa.oac.uci.edu
ftp: kuhub.cc.ukans.edu:/LZW/
ftp: akiu.gw.tohoku.ac.jp:/pub/mac/tools/archiver
ftp: brownvm.brown.edu
ftp: atari.archive.umich.edu:/atari/archivers/
ftp: ab20.larc.nasa.gov:/amiga/utils/archivers/
ftp: rascal.ics.utexas.edu:/misc/mac/utilies/
ftp: ftp.lysator.liu.se:/pub/archivers/
ftp: minnie.cs.adfa.oz.au:/archives/
ftp: plains.nodak.edu:/pub/pc/archives/
ftp: turbo.bio.net
ftp: oak.oakland.edu:/pub/msdos/archives/

Database:	Data General Anonymous FTP
	Research Triangle, NC
Access method:	ftp: dg-rtp.dg.com
Database:	Data Research Associates
Access method:	ftp: dra.com
	ftp: ftp.dra.com
Database:	Datmouth Merged Special Interest Group List
Access method:	ftp: dartcms1.dartmouth.edu:/siglists/
Database:	Defense Data Network New User Guide
Access method:	ftp: nic.ddn.mil:/netinfo/nug.doc
Database:	Department of Defense Internet Host Table
Access method:	ftp: bitnic.educom.edu:/anonymu/hosts.txt
Database:	Digital Equipment Alpha Chip Information
Access method:	ftp: sciences.sdsu.edu:/dec-alpha/
	ftp: zaphod.ncsa.uiuc.edu:/DEC_Alpha/

Database: Digital Equipment Corporation Gatekeeper Anonymous
                   FTP archive
Access method: ftp: gatekeeper.dec.com

Database: Diplomacy, Multilateral Conventions
                   Law of Sea, Law of War, Human Rights, Environment
Access method: ftp: jade.tufts.edu:/pub/diplomacy/
                   ftp: fatty.law.cornell.edu
                   ftp: gopher.ciesin.org

Database: Distance Education
Access method: ftp: una.hh.lib.umich.edu:/inetdirsstacks/

Database: Drinking Games
Access method: ftp: sauna.hut.fi:/pub/drinking_games/

Database: Duke University
Access method: ftp: duke.cs.duke.edu

Database: Economic Resources List
Access method: ftp: rtfm.mit.edu:/pub/usenet/sci.econ.research/
                   econ-resources-faq

Database: Educator's E-mail List
Access method: ftp: nic.umass.edu:/pub/ednet/educatrs.lst

Database: Educator's USENET Guide
Access method: ftp: nic.umass.edu:/pub/ednet/edusenet.gde

Database: Electronic Frontier Foundation Information
Access method: ftp: ftp.eff.org:/pub/EFF/about-eff

Database: Electronic Journals and Newsletters Directory
Access method: ftp: csuvax1.csu.murdoch.edu.au:/pub/library/
                   e-journals.dir

Database: Electronic Magazine Archive
Access method: ftp: etext.archive.umich.edu:/pub/Zines/

Database: EMACS Patches
Access method: ftp: rml2.sri.com:/EMACS-PATCHES/

Database: E-mail Student Address Retrival Manual
Access method: ftp:pit-manager.mit.edu:/soc.college/FAQ_College_
                   Email_Addresses

Database: E-mail Services
Access method: ftp: hydra.uwo.ca:/libsoft/email_services.txt

Database: E-mail Understanding
Access method: ftp: ftp.cso.uiuc.edu:/doc/net/uiucnet/vol3no2.txt

Database: E-mail use
Access method: ftp: ftp.sura.net:/pub/nic/network.service.guides/

Database: European History and Culture Electronic Sources List
Access method: ftp: ra.msstate.edu:/pub/docs/history/resources/
                     european.guide

Database: Faces Window based tool for monitoring lists with icons
Access method: ftp: iuvax.es.indiana.edu

Database: Federal Information Resources
Access method: ftp: nic.merit.edu:/omb/INDEX.omb

Database: Federal Information
Access method: ftp: ftp.nwnet.net:/user-docs/government/
                     ftp: is.internic.net:/infosources/internet-info/

Database: Federal Reserve Bank of Boston economic data
Access method: ftp: neeedc.umesbs.maine.edu:/frbb

Database: Free Database Catalog
Access method: ftp: bloom-picayune.mit.edu:/pub/usenet-by-group/
                     comp.answers/free-databases
                     ftp: idiom.berkeley.ca.us:/pub/free-databases

Database: Freenet Information
                     Carleton University, Ottawa, Canada
Access method: ftp: alfred.ccs.carleton.ca:/pub/freenet/
                     ftp: cs.dal.ca:/freenet/

Database: FidoNet Gateway Utilization (UUCP-FidoNet)
Access method: ftp: csn.org:/pub/mail/internet.fidonet

Database: FidoNet News (Newsletter) Archive
Access method: ftp: pit-manager.mit.edu:/pub/usenet/comp.org.fidonet/

Database: FidoNet Node List
Access method: ftp: genome.wi.mit.edu:/wais-sources/fidonet-nodelist.src
                     ftp: asuvax.eas.asu.edu:/stjhmc/nodelist.txt
                     ftp: zeus.ieee.org:/pub/fidonet/

Database: Finnish University and Research Network (FUNET) Software
                     Archive
Access method: ftp: funet.fi

Database: FTP guide
Access method: ftp: ftp.sura.net:/pub/nic/network.service.guides/
                       how.to.ftp.guide

Database: FTP Site List
Access method: ftp: pilot.njin.net:/pub/ftp-list/ftp.list
                       ftp: ugle.unit.no:/ftp-list/

Database: Garbo Archive
Access method: ftp: garbo.uwasa.fi

Database: Gateway Guide for E-mail Transfer
Access method: ftp: cerberus.epa.orst.edu:/pub/misc/bigfun/gateways.txt

Database: General Accounting Office Reports Archive
Access method: ftp: cu.nih.gov:/GAO-REPORTS/

Database: Georgia Institute of Technology
Access method: ftp: vax.eedsp.gatech.edu

Database: Georgia State University
Access method: ftp: cgcr.gsu.edu

Database: German Annonymous FTP Servers
Access method: *location*   *address*

location	address
Aachen:	reze-2.rz.rwth-aachen.de
Aachen:	ftp.informatik.rwth-aachen.de
Aachen:	ftp.dfv.rwth-aachen.de
Aalen:	ftp.fh-aalen.de
Augsburg:	ftp.uni-augsburg.de
Augsburg:	ftp.cc.uni-augsburg.de
Augsburg:	ftp.rz.uni-augsburg.de
Bayreuth:	ftp.uni-bayreuth.de
Berlin:	ftp.artcom.de
Berlin:	ftp.fu-berlin.de
Berlin:	elib.zib-berlin.de
Berlin:	coma.cs.tu-berlin.de
Berlin:	tub.cs.tu-berlin.de
Berlin:	ftp.zrz.tu-berlin.de
Berlin:	ftp.dfn.de
Berlin:	ftp.wtza-berlin.de
Berlin:	netmbx.netmbx.de
Berlin:	ftp.cs.tu-berlin.de
Berlin:	zelator.in-berlin.de

Bielefeld:	ftp.mathematik.uni-bielefeld.de
Bielefeld:	ftp.uni-bielefeld.de
Bochum:	ftp.rz.ruhr-uni-bochum.de
Bonn:	ftp.gmd.de
Bonn:	ftp.cs.uni-bonn.de
Braunschweig:	u8405.bs.ptb.de
Braunschweig:	ftp.tu-bs.de
Braunschweig:	ftp.rz.tu-bs.de
Braunschweig:	bseis.eis.cs.tu-bs.de
Bremen:	wowbagger.zfn.uni-bremen.de
Castrop-Rauxel:	ftp.ins.de
Chemnitz:	ftp.tu-chemnitz.de
Clausthal:	ftp.tu-clausthal.de
Darmstadt:	ftp.darmstadt.gmd.de
Darmstadt:	ftp.th-darmstadt.de
Dortmund:	deins.informatik.uni-dortmund.de
Dortmund:	ftp.germany.eu.net
Dresden:	irz301.inf.tu-dresden.de
Dresden:	rinfo.urz.tu-dresden.de
Duesseldorf:	clio.rz.uni-duesseldorf.de
Duesseldorf:	ftp.novell.de
Duisburg:	ftp.uni-duisburg.de
Duisburg:	du9ds4.uni-duisburg.de
Duisburg:	du9ds4.fb9dv.uni-duisburg.de
Erlangen:	ftp.uni-erlangen.de
Erlangen:	medusa.informatik.uni-erlangen.de
Frankfurt:	ftp.uni-frankfurt.de
Frankfurt:	ftp.physik.uni-frankfurt.de
Freiburg:	ftp.ise.fhg.de
Freiburg:	ftp.informatik.uni-freiburg.de
Freiburg:	ftp.psychologie.uni-freiburg.de
Freiburg:	ftp.uni-freiburg.de
Freiburg:	ftp.ruf.uni-freiburg.de
Giessen:	ftp.hrz.uni-giessen.de
Goettingen:	ftp.gwdg.de
Hamburg:	ftp.desy.de
Hamburg:	ftp.dkrz-hamburg.de
Hamburg:	ftp.informatik.uni-hamburg.de
Hannover:	ftp.rrzn.uni-hannover.de
Heidelberg:	ftp.embl-heidelberg.de
Heidelberg:	statlab.uni-heidelberg.de

Heidelberg:	ftp.urz.uni-heidelberg.de
Heidelberg:	sunserver.embnet.dkfz-heidelberg.de
Ilmenau:	ftp.tu-ilmenau.de
Ilmenau:	metallica.prakinf.tu-ilmenau.de
Jena:	ftp.uni-jena.de
Juelich:	ftp.zam.kfa-juelich.de
Kaiserslautern:	ftp.uni-kl.de
Kaiserslautern:	uranus.mathematik.uni-kl.de
Karlsruhe:	ftp.ask.uni-karlsruhe.de
Karlsruhe:	hpux.ask.uni-karlsruhe.de
Karlsruhe:	ftp.ira.uka.de
Karlsruhe:	ftp.rz.uni-karlsruhe.de
Karlsruhe:	microsrv2.rz.uni-karlsruhe.de
Karlsruhe:	ubkadec2.ubka.uni-karlsruhe.de
Karlsruhe:	ftp.fzi.de
Karlsruhe:	ma2s2.mathematik.uni-karlsruhe.de
Karlsruhe:	ftp.telematik.informatik.uni-karlsruhe.de
Karlsruhe:	smurf.sub.org
Kiel:	ftp.informatik.uni-kiel.de
Kiel:	obelix.informatik.uni-kiel.de
Koeln:	ftp.uni-koeln.de
Koeln:	ftp.rrz.uni-koeln.de
Koeln:	rs1.rrz.uni-koeln.de
Koeln:	ftp.thp.uni-koeln.de
Konstanz:	ftp.rz.uni-konstanz.de
Leipzig:	ftp.rz.uni-leipzig.de
Leipzig:	server2.rz.uni-leipzig.de
Lemgo:	ftp.fh-lippe.de
Mainz:	ftp.uni-mainz.de
Mannheim:	ftp.fht-mannheim.de
Mannheim:	rummelplatz.uni-mannheim.de
Marburg:	ftp.uni-marburg.de
Marburg:	rsrz01.hrz.uni-marburg.de
Marburg:	ftp.wiwi.uni-marburg.de
Muenchen:	ftp.informatik.tu-muenchen.de
Muenchen:	ftp.ecrc.de
Muenchen:	ftp.fgb.mw.tu-muenchen.de
Muenchen:	flop.informatik.tu-muenchen.de
Muenchen:	ftp.informatik.uni-muenchen.de
Muenchen:	dszenger9.informatik.tu-muenchen.de
Muenchen:	ps2zenger1.informatik.tu-muenchen.de

Muenchen:	ftp.bl.physik.tu-muenchen.de
Muenchen:	ftp.bl.physik.uni-muenchen.de
Muenchen:	sally.bl.physik.tu-muenchen.de
Muenchen:	ftp.lrz-muenchen.de
Muenchen:	sunserver.lrz-muenchen.de
Muenster:	ftp.uni-muenster.de
Muenster:	von-neum.uni-muenster.de
Oldenburg:	ftp.uni-oldenburg.de
Oldenburg:	hpux01.hrz.uni-oldenburg.de
Oldenburg:	ftp.informatik.uni-oldenburg.de
Oldenburg:	ftp.ccc.de
Oldenburg:	sol.ccc.de
Osnabrueck:	ftp.rz.uni-osnabrueck.de
Osnabrueck	tethys.rz.uni-osnabrueck.de
Paderborn:	ftp.uni-paderborn.de
Passau:	alice.uni-passau.de
Passau:	ftp.uni-passau.de
Passau:	forwiss.uni-passau.de
Passau:	ftp.forwiss.uni-passau.de
Passau:	ftp.fmi.uni-passau.de
Regensburg:	ftp.uni-regensburg.de
Regensburg:	rrzs3.rz.uni-regensburg.de
Rostock:	ftp.informatik.uni-rostock.de
Rostock:	poel.informatik.uni-rostock.de
Saarbruecken:	coli.uni-sb.de
Saarbruecken:	ftp.cs.uni-sb.de
Saarbruecken:	ftp.rz.uni-sb.de
Saarbruecken:	rzsrv002.rz.uni-sb.de
Saarbruecken:	ftp.math.uni-sb.de
Saarbruecken:	mpi-sb.mpg.de
Stuttgart:	ftp.informatik.uni-stuttgart.de
Stuttgart:	ftp.belwue.de
Stuttgart:	ftp.uni-stuttgart.de
Trier:	ftp.uni-trier.de
Trier:	rzftp.uni-trier.de
Tuebingen:	atlas.physchem.chemie.uni-tuebingen.de
Tuebingen:	softserv.zdv.uni-tuebingen.de
Ulm:	ftp.rz.uni-ulm.de
Ulm :	info.rz.uni-ulm.de
Ulm:	ftp.mathematik.uni-ulm.de
Ulm:	titania.mathematik.uni-ulm.de

Weimar:	ftp.hab-weimar.de
Weimer:	gonzo.hab-weimar.de
Worms:	ftp.worms.fh-rpl.de
Worms:	nibelung.worms.fh.rpl.de
Wuerzburg:	ftp.rz.uni-wuerzburg.de
Wuerzburg:	wrzx03.rz.uni-wuerzburg.de
Zeuthen:	ftp.ifh.de

You can obtain an updated list of anonymous German FTP sites from askhp.ask.uni-karlsruhe.de:/pub/info/ftp.list.de bzw. This list is also obtainable by e-mail to: listserv@askhp.ask.uni-karlsruhe.de. Place in body of message: subscribe ftp-list-de <name, E-mail address>

Database:	GNU Released Software
Access method:	ftp: ftp.gnu.ai.mit.edu:/pub/gnu/
	ftp: prep.ai.mit.edu:/pub/gnu/
	ftp: jaguar.utah.edu:/gnustuff/
Database:	Gopher client software
Access method:	ftp: boombox.micro.umn.edu:/pub/gopher
	ftp: serv1.cl.msu.edu
Database:	Gopher FAQ
Access method:	ftp: pit-manager.mit.edu:/pub/usenet/news.answers/ gopher-faq
	ftp: csc2.anu.edu.au:/gopher/
	ftp: stsci.edu:/software/
Database:	Gopher List by Subject
Access method:	ftp: ftp.einet.net:/pub/gopher-jewels.txt
	hypertext file: gopher-jewels.html
Database:	Gopher Use
Access method:	ftp: ftp.cso.uiuc.edu:/doc/net/uiucnet/vol6no1.txt
	ftp: boombox.micro.umn:/pub/gopher/OOREADME
Database:	Graphics
Access method:	ftp: june.cs.washington.edu:/pub/graphics/
	ftp: kum.kaist.ac.kr:/pub/graph/
	ftp: lut.fi:/pub/graphic.formats/
	ftp: p6xje.ldc.lu.se
	ftp: ugle.unit.no:/pub/graphics/
Database:	Graphix Bibliography Server

Access method: ftp: gatekeeper.dec.com

Database: Greendisk Paperless Environmental Journal Resources
Access method: ftp: csus.edu:/pub/greendisk/contents

Database: Gutenberg (Books in Print) Project
Access method: ftp: mrcnext.cso.uiuc.edu:/pub/etext/
INDEX - for the index
NEW.GUT - general user information

Database: Harvard University
Access method: ftp: harvard.harvard.edu

Database: Project Hermes (US Supreme Court Opinions)
Access method: ftp: ftp.cwru.edu:/hermes/
files: INFO and README.FIRST

Database: Hewlett Packard Corporation HP 48 Archives
Access method: ftp: hpcsos.col.hp.com
ftp: hpcvaaz.cv.hp.com
ftp: hpcvbbs.cv.hp.com
FTP tree availability on hpcsos.col.hp.com, aka col.hp.com.

bin - directories needed by ftpd

dist - contributed software for HP products

mirrors - automatically-maintained mirror images of packages that are normally available from other sites outside HP

misc - random goodies from various places

packet - the KA9Q Internet Protocol Package and related-software for amateur packet radio - most of which is copied from ucsd.edu and sics.se

pub - HP's "upload" directory; files are purged after 14 days.

Database: Historical Documents (Freedom Shrine) maintained by National Public Telecomputing Network (NPTN)
Access method: ftp: nptn.org:/pub/e.texts/freedom.shrine/

Database: History Archive maintained at Mississippi State University
Access method: ftp: ra.msstate.edu:/pub/docs/history/

Database: Holocast Archive
Access method: ftp: ftp.sura.net:/pub/nic/holocaust.archive

Database: Horton Software
Access method: ftp: punisher.caltech.edu:/pub/dank/horton/
          ftp: wuarchive.wustl.edu:/usenet/alt.sources/articles/574
          ftp: ftp.inria.fr:/network/misc/horton-1.8.share.z

Database: HP-UX Archive
Access method: ftp: me10.lbl.gov

Database: Hypermedia and the Internet
Access method: ftp: life.anu.edu.au:/education/hypermedia.html

Database: Hypertext Guide to Internet/Bitnet
Access method: ftp: sunsite.unc.edu:/pub/docs/about-the-
          net/libsoft/hwguide.txt

Database: Hypertext Markup Language Compiler
Access method: ftp: isis.cshl.org

Database: Hytelnet Information
Access method: ftp: access.usask.ca:/pub/hytelnet/README
          ftp: access.usask.ca:/pub/hytelnet/mac/
          ftp: ftp.unt.edu:/library/hytelnxx.ZIP (program)
          hytelnet.mac.sea.hqx (Macintosh)

Database: Images
Access method: ftp: eru.mt.luth.se:/images/
          ftp: ftp.brl.mil:/images/
          ftp: pomona.claremont.edu

Database: Indian Classical Music
Access method: ftp: stolaf.edu:/pub/indian-music/

Database: InfoPop PC-based guide to Internet, CompuServe and
          Bulletin Board Systems
Access method: ftp: ftp.gmu.edu:/pub/library/infopop27.zip

Database: Institut de Recherche en Informatique et Systems aleatoires
          (INRIA/CNRS) Universite de Rennes, Brittany, France
Access method: ftp: inria.inira.fr

Database: Institute for Academic Technology Internet
          Resource Guides
Access method: ftp: gandalf.iat.unc.edu:/guides

Database: Institute of Electrical and Electronic Engineers
Access method: ftp: zeus.ieee.org

Database: Institute for Global Communications
Access method: ftp: igc.apc.org:/pub/

Database: International Connectivity Table by Larry Landweber
Access method: ftp: ftp.cs.wisc.edu:/connectivity_table/

Database: Internet accessible libraries and databases
Access method: ftp: nic.cerf.net:/cerfnet/cerfnet_info/library_catalog/
                   ftp: ariel.unm.edu:/library/internet.library

Database: Internet Access Guide: Introducing The Internet
Access method: ftp: nic.merit.edu:/introducing.the.internet
                   ftp: nic.mr.net:/pub/introducing.the.internet
                   ftp: ftp.nisc.sri.edu:/introducing.the.internet
                   ftp: ftp.hawaii.edu:/mirrors/introducing.the.internet

Database: Internet access providers
Access method: ftp: ftp.nisc.sri.com:/netinfo/internet-access-
                   providers-us.txt
                   ftp: ftp.nisc.sri.com:/netinfo/internet-access-
                   providers-non-us.txt

Database: Internet basic information
Access method: ftp: nnsc.nsf.net:/nsfnet/internet-basics.eric-digest

Database: Internet Bibliography of Training Materials
Access method: ftp: alexia.lis.uiuc.edu:/pub/training.bib

Database: Internet list of information locations
Access method: ftp: ftp.rpi.edu:/pub/communications/internet-cmc

Database: Internet FAQs and Answers
Access method: ftp: rtfm.mit.edu:/pub/usenet/news.answers/internet-ser-
                   vices/faq

Type of Guide	Host FTP Address	Directory/file location
AARNet Guide	aarnet.edu.au	pub/resource-guide/
AARNet User Guide	aarnet.edu.au	pub/user-guide/
CERFNet Guide	nic.cerf.net	cerfnet/cerfnet_info/
DDN New User Guide	nic.ddn.mil	netinfo/nug.doc
Desktop Internet	ftp.uwp.edu	pub/msdos/dir/
Electric Mystics Guide	panda1.uottawa.ca	pub/religion/electric-mystics-guide*

Gold in Networks	nic.merit.edu	documents/fyi/fyi_10.txt
Hitchhikers Guide	nic.merit.edu	documents/rfc/rfc1118.txt
Individual Access	slufxb.slu.edu	pub/millesjg/internet.access
Internet Access	liberty.uc.wlu.edu	pub/lawlib/internet.access
Internet Access Guide	nic.merit.edu	introducing.the.internet/access.guide
Internet Accounting	ftp.sdsc.edu	pub/sdsc/anr/papers/acctng
Internet Basics	nnsc.nsf.net	nsfnet/internet-basics.eric-digest
Internet Books	nic.ddn.mil	rfc
Internet Browser	fatty.law.cornell.edu	pub/LII/Cello/readme.1st
Internet Companion	world.std.com	OBS/The.Internet.Companion/
Internet Course	pilot.njin.net	pub/Internet-course/
Internet Cruise	nic.merit.edu	resources/cruise.*/
Internet Domain Nanes	nic.merit.edu documents/rfc/rfc 1394.txt	
Internet Economics	gopher.econ.lsa. umich.edu pub/ Papers/	
Internet Explorer's Kit	hydra.uwo.ca	libsoft/explorer.doc
Internet Glossary	nic.merit.edu	documents/fyi/fyi_18.txt
Internet Growth	tic.com	matrix/growth/internet/
Internet Guide	vm1.nodak.edu	nnews/guide1.nnews
Internet Health Science	oak.oakland.edu	pub/msdos/windows3/hmatrix.zip
Internet History	umcc.umich.edu	pub/seraphim/doc/nethist8.txt
Internet Hunt	ftp.cni.org	pub/net-guides/i-hunt/
Internet Hunt Gopher	gopher.cic.net	The-Internet-Hunt
Internet Introduction	nic.merit.edu	introducing.the.internet
Internet Libraries	hydra.uwo.ca	libsoft/internet_libraries.txt
Internet Libraries	zebra.acs.udel.edu	pub/library/
Internet Libraries	ftp.unt.edu	library/catalist/
Internet Maps (Europe)	eunet.fi	nic/pub/netinfo/maps/
Internet Maps (Many)	ftp.uu.net	inet/maps/
Internet Maps (NSFNET)	nic.merit.edu	maps/
Internet Maps (SuraNet)	ftp.sura.net	pub/maps/
Internet Mining	ucdavis.ed	ucd.netdocs/mining/
Internet Monthly Report	nic.merit.net	internet/newsletters/
Internet Navigating	ubvm.cc.buffalo.edu	navigate/
Internet Policy	nic.merit.edu	pub/documents/rfc/rfc1527.t
Internet RFC	nic.merit.edu	documents/rfc/index.rfc
Internet Resource Guide	ds.internic.net	/resource-guide/wholeguide.txt
Internet Resource Guide	ftp.sura.net	pub/nic/wholeguide.txt
Internet Root Domains	ftp.rs.internic.net	domain/
Internet Safari	nic.cerf.net	cerfnet/safari/safari-guide.txt
Internet Security	nic.merit.edu	cise/gao8957.txt
Internet Services FAQ	rtfm.mit.edu	pub/usenet/news.answers/internet-services/faq
Internet Services list	csd4.csd.uwm.edu	pub/inet.services.txt
Internet Sites	ftp.usask.ca	pub/hytelnet/README
Internet Size	ftp.nisc.sri.com	pub/zone/
Internet Statistics	nic.merit.edu	nsfnet/statistics/

Internet Standards	nic.merit.edu	documents/std/index.std
Internet Talk Radio	sunsite.unc.edu	pub/talk-radio/ITRintro.readme
Internet Training	s850.mwc.edu	nettrain/nettrain.ooreadme
Internet Tools Summary	ftp.rpi.edu	pub/communications/internet-tools
Internet Tools/Systems	mailbase.ac.uk	pub/lists/unite/files/systems-list.txt
Internet Tour -Macintosh	nnsc.nsf.net	internet-tour/Internet-Tour-README
Internet Usage	theseus.itc.gu.edu.	
	au uploads/paradis1.txt	
Internet Wiretap	wiretap.spies.com	about/FEATURES/
Navigating the Internet	ftp.sura.net	pub/nic/training
New User's Questions	nic.merit.edu	documents/fyi/fyi_04.txt
NSF Resource Guide	ds.internic.net	resource-guide/
NWNet Internet Guide	ftphost.nwnet.net	nic/nwnet/user-guide/
NYSERNet Internet Guide	nysernet.org	pub/guides/Guide.*.text
SURANet Internet Guide	ftp.sura.net	pub/nic/infoguide.*.txt
Surfing the Internet	nysernet.org	pub/guides/surfing.2.0.2.txt
TCP/IP Tutorial	nic.ddn.mil	rfc
What is the Internet	nic.merit.edu	documents/fyi/fyi_20.txt
Zen & Art of Internet	csn.org	pub/net/zen/

Database: Internet Mailing Lists
Access method: ftp: ads.com

Database: Internet public access providers
Access method: ftp: ftp.netcom.com:/pub/info-deli/public-access/pdial

Database: Internet Relay Chat (IRC) information
Access method: ftp: cs.bu.edu:/irc/support/tutorial*

Database: Internet tools (Archie, Gopher, Whois, etc.)
Access method: ftp: ftp.rpi.edu:/pub/communications/internet-tools

Database: Internetworking Mail Guide
Access method: ftp: ariel.unm.edu:/library/network.guide
                 ftp: csd4.csd.uwm.edu:/pub/internetwork-mail-guide

Database: Internetworking Guide
Access method: ftp: ra.msstate.edu:/pub/docs/internetwork-mail-guide

Database: InterNIC Directory and Database Services update
Access method: ftp: ds.internic.net:/pub/InterNIC-info get dirofdir-request.template

Database: InterNIC FTP Archives
Access method: ftp: ds.internic.net:/pub/InterNIC-info/internic.info

Database: InterNIC Information Services
Access method: ftp: is.internic.net:/netinfo/

Database:	InterNIC Registration Services
Access method:	ftp: rs.internic.net:/netinfo/
Database:	InterNIC public files
Access method:	ftp: rs.internic.host login as: anonymous, using password GUEST
Database:	Iowa State University Department of Computer Science Technical Reports
Access method:	ftp: elroy.cs.iastate.edu:/pub/techreports/
Database:	ISODE Distribution for Pacific Rim
Access method:	ftp: shark.mel.dit.csiro.au
Database:	Israel and Jewish Archives
Access method:	ftp: israel.nysernet.org ftp: shark.mel.dit.csiro.au:/pub/jewish/
Database:	NASA Jet Propulsion Laboratory (JPL)
Access method:	ftp: elroy.jpl.nasa.gov ftp: jpl-devvax.jpl.nasa.gov
Database:	James Cook University (Australia) Anonymous FTP Server
Access method:	ftp: marlin.jcu.edu.au
Database:	JANET Host Computer List
Access method:	ftp: muwaya.ucs.unimelb.edu.au:/pub/janet
Database:	Japanese Anonymous FTP Servers
Access method:	ftp: azabu.tkl.iis.u-tokyo.ac.jp ftp: bash.cc.keio.ac.jp ftp: etlport.etl.go.jp ftp: ftp.ae.keio.ac.jp ftp: ftp.ascii.co.jp ftp: ftp.c.u-tokyo.ac.jp ftp: ftp.cc.saga-u.ac.jp ftp: ftp.cs.keio.ac.jp ftp: ftp.cs.titech.ac.jp ftp: ftp.cs.uec.ac.jp ftp: ftp.csce.kyushu-u.ac.jp ftp: ftp.csrl.aoyama.ac.jp ftp: ftp.dcl.co.jp ftp: ftp.dit.co.jp ftp: ftp.ecei.tohoku.ac.jp ftp: ftp.elcom.nitech.ac.jp

ftp: ftp.foretune.co.jp
ftp: ftp.fujita3.iis.u-tokyo.ac.jp
ftp: ftp.fujixerox.co.jp
ftp: ftp.ics.osaka-u.ac.jp
ftp: ftp.is.titech.ac.jp
ftp: ftp.kuis.kyoto-u.ac.jp
ftp: ftp.kyushu-id.ac.jp
ftp: ftp.mei.co.jp
ftp: ftp.meiji.ac.jp
ftp: ftp.nig.ac.jp
ftp: ftp.phys.keio.ac.jp
ftp: ftp.richo.co.jp
ftp: ftp.sigmath.osaka-u.ac.jp
ftp: ftp.tohoku.ac.jp
ftp: ftp.u-tokyo.ac.jp
ftp: ftp.waseda.ac.jp
ftp: ftp.wg.omron.co.jp
ftp: icpcs41.icpc.fukui-u.ac.jp
ftp: nuis.nuie.nagoya-u.ac.jp
ftp: onlnews.kek.ac.jp
ftp: scslwide.sony.co.jp
ftp: sh.wide.ad.jp
ftp: solaris.ims.ac.jp
ftp: srawgw.sra.co.jp
ftp: theta.iis.u-tokyo.ac.jp
ftp: tutserver.tut.ac.jp
ftp: utsun.s.u-tokyu.ac.jp
ftp: wnoc-fuk.wide.ad.jp

Database:	Jokes
Access method:	ftp: shape.mps.ohio-state.edu:/pub/jokes/
Database:	Jughead Information
Access method:	ftp:boombox.micro.umn.edu:/pub/gopher/Unix/ GopherTools/jughead/jughead.ReadMe
Database:	Kanji Driver
Access method:	ftp: mindseye.berkeley.edu
Database:	Kansas State University Department of Computer and Information Science FTP Archive
Access method:	ftp: procyon.cis.ksu.edu

Database: Kermit Information at Columbia University
Access method: ftp: watsun.cc.columbia.edu:/kermit/read.me

Database: K12 Network Access
Access method: ftp: ftp.cc.berkeley.edu:/k12/README

Database: K-12 On-line Resources Guides
Access method: ftp: ftp.virginia.edu:/pub/IRD/
                   files: IRD-FTP-sites.txt
                            IRD-Telnet-sites.txt
                            IRD-infusion-ideas.txt
                            IRD-listservs.txt

Database: Language Word Lists and Access to 26 dictionaries
Access method: ftp: ftp.cs.vu.nl:/dictionaries/

Database: Lawrence Livermore National Laboratory
Access method: ftp: rogue.llnl.gov

Directories:

DIALER   Assorted code for dialing a modem attached to a
              VMS system
DTSS   An NTP time provider for DECdts (nee DTSS).
              Works with MultiNet
EDWG   Files relevant to the ESnet DECnet Working Group.
              These may also have some general interest for
              those involved in network management
FLIGHT   X windows based flight simulator. Allows multiple
              planes which may engage in dog-fights. Written by
              Digital.
IMAGE   Assorted image manipulation, included are
              XLOADIMAGE and XV, both X-windows programs
              for displaying and, in the case of XV, manipulating
              images in several formats including PBM and GIF
PH   A CSO Ph client for VMS MultiNet. Based on the
              UIUC code by dorner/sandrock

Database: Legal Internet Resources List - University of Maine
Access method: ftp: ftp.midnight.com:/pub/LegalList/legallist.txt

Database: Access method:	The Bulletin Board for Libraries ftp: bubl.bath.ac.ak
Database: Access method:	Library Catalogues ftp: ariel.unm.edu :/library/internet.library ftp: ftp.unt.edu:/library/libraries.txt ftp: dla.ucop.edu:/pub/internet/libcat-guide ftp: umd5.umd.edu:/info-lib/
Database: Access method:	Library-Oriented Computer Conferences ftp: noc.sura.net:/nic/info-servers ftp: hydra.uwo.ca:/libsoft/libconfers.txt
Database: Access method:	Library of Congress document and graphics images ftp: seql.loc.gov:/pub ftp: seql.loc.gov:/pub/1492.exhibit (Quincentenary exhibition 1492: An Ongoing Voyage) ftp: seqlloc.gov:/pub/deadsea.scrolls.exhibit (Scrolls from the Dead Sea)
Database: Access method:	Library Resources on the Internet ftp: dla.ucop.edu:/pub/internet/libcat-guide ftp: ftp.unt.edu:/library/libraries.instructions ftp: sunsite.unc.edu:/pub/docs/about-the-net/libsoft/guide2.txt ftp: nic.cerf.net:/internet/resources/library_catalog/
Database: Access method:	Library Related Application Software Catalog ftp: seq1.loc.gov:/pub/FLICC/cmbls30.txt
Database: Access method:	Library Software Archive ftp: ftp.ncsa.uiuc.edu
Database: Access method:	Linguistics ftp: csli.stanford.edu
Database: Access method:	Linkoping University (Sweden) Vision Laboratory ftp: isy.liu.se
Database: Access method:	Austin Kyoto Common Lisp (AKCL) ftp: rascal.ics.utexas.edu
Database: Access method:	Common Lisp Object System Knowledge Engineering Environment ftp: zaphod.lanl.gov:/pub/clos-on-kee/

Database:	List of Lists (Interest Groups, E-mail)
Access method:	ftp: ftp.nisc.sri.com:/netinfo/interest-groups
Database:	Lyrics/Music Server
Access method:	ftp: ftp.uwp.edu
	ftp: ftp.iastate.edu:/pub/lyrics/
Database:	MaasInfo Indexes
Access method:	niord.shsu.edu:/maasinfo/maasinfo.files
Database:	Mathematica Database
Access method:	ftp: eedsp.gatech.edu:/mathematica/
Database:	MERIT Network Information Center Service Operator of State of Michigan Network
Access method:	ftp: nic.merit.edu
	ftp: ftp.merit.edu
	ftp: ftp.michnet.net
	ftp: nis.nsf.net

Directory overview:

Most of the directories listed below have topical subdirectories below them. Index files using the naming convention INDEX.directory are available at each level of the hierarchy describing that part of the hierarchy in more detail.

acceptable.use .policies/	A directory of policy statements for the acceptable use of the NSFNET backbone and regional networks listed.
cise/	Directory owned by the National Science Foundation's Directorate for Computer and Information Science and Engineering for the placement of NSFNET Backbone Network policy statements and related documents, as well as GAO (Government Accounting Office) reports of interest.
conference proceedings/	Directory containing the proceedings from network related conferences.
documents/	Directory archive for NSFNET, regional, and Internet documents, including RFCs and Internet-Drafts.
internet/	Directory devoted to Internet activities: legislative work to promote the NREN, publications on research, experiments and use of the Internet, and available resources.

introducing.the internet/	A directory providing recent information resources which will help the network novice become familiar with the Internet, including its associated networks, resources, and protocols.
maps/	PostScript maps of NSFNET and MichNet.
michnet/	A directory of information related to MichNet, the regional network in Michigan.
newsletters/	NSFNET, regional, and Internet newsletters.
nren/	Governmental activity pertaining to the National Research and Education Network (NREN).
nsfnet/	Archive for administrative, policy and statistical information relevant to the NSFNET Backbone networks.
omb/	Directory of documents from the Information Policy Branch, Office of Information and Regulatory Affairs, Office of Management and Budget of the U.S. government.
resources/	Information on using the Internet and its available resources, including Merit's Internet Cruise.
statistics/	Statistical reports pertaining to the networks for which Merit provides backbone operation services.
working.groups/	Directory of documents from technical working groups.

Database: MSEN information
Access method: ftp: msen.com.com:/pub/vendor/msen/

Database: List of public access UNIX sites
Access method: ftp: gvl.unisys.com:/pub/nixpub/long

Database: Listserver Lists
Access method: ftp: utarlvm1.uta.edu:/bitnet/listserv.lists
ftp: bitnic.educom.edu:/ANONYMOU/listlist.lists
ftp: dartcms1.dartmouth.edu:/siglists/listserv.lists

Database: MaasInfo Indexes : An index of Internet online file indexes by Robert Mass
Access method: ftp: ftp.unt.edu:/pub/articles/maas/maasinfo.files

Database: Mathematica
Access method: ftp: vax.eedsp.gatech.edu

Database: McMaster University
Hamilton, Ontario, Canada
Access method: ftp: maccs.dcss.mcmaster.ca

Database: Medical Resources on the Internet
Access method: ftp: ftp.sura.net:/pub/nic/medical.resources

Database: Merit Network Information Center
Access method: ftp: nic.merit.edu

Database: Meteorological Information Source List
Access method: ftp: vmd.cso.uiuc.edu:/wx/sources.doc

Database: Mirror University of Michigan Software Archive FTP Sites
                       "Mirrors" are sites that copy files from other archives, typically
                       every day or two. You may get better service by using one of
                       the mirror sites closest to your location. "G" means Gopher,
                       "F" means FTP, and "T" means Telnet access.

Access method:

Country	Access	Address	Directory	Software
Australia	FG	archie.au	/micros/mac/umich	Macintosh
France	F	anl.anl.fr	/pub/mac/umich	Macintosh
Germany	F	athene.uni-paderborn.de	/pcsoft3/mac	Macintosh
Israel	F	ftp.technion.ac.il	/pub/unsupported/mac/umich	Macintosh
Japan	F	ftp.inter.spin.ad.jp	/pub//Mac/Merit.mirror	Macintosh
England	FG	src.doc.ic.ac.uk	/packages/mac/umich	Macintosh, Atari
Switz.	FG	nic.switch.ch	/mirror/umich-mac	(mac, atari, apple2)
Sweden	F	ftp.sunet.se	/pub/mac/mirror-umich	(mac)
Taiwan	F	nctucccca.edu.tw	/Macintosh/umich-mac	(mac)
USA	FG	wuarchive.wustl.edu	/mirrors/archive.umich.edu	
USA	FT	grind.isca.uiowa.edu	/mac/umich	(mac, apple2)
USA	FG	sunsite.unc.edu	/pub/academic/medicine/mac-medical	(mac medical)
USA	FG	archive.orst.edu	/pub/mirrors/archive.umich.edu	(mac, msdos, atari, apple2)

Some sites mirror the mirrors! One of these is:
| USA | F | deja-vu.aiss.uiuc.edu | /wuarchive/systems/mac/umich.edu | |

Database: Micromechanics Information Clearing House
Access method: ftp: gum.isi.edu:/mems/

Database:	MIT
Access method:	ftp: hal.gnu.ai.mit.edu
	ftp: lcs.mit.edu (Telecommunications archive)
	ftp: pion.lcs.mit.edu
	ftp: pit-manager.mit.edu
Database:	MIT Media Laboratory
Access method:	ftp: media-lab.media.mit.edu
Database:	MIT Project Athena papers and source code
Access method:	ftp: athena-dist.mit.edu
Database:	MIT TechInfo (for Macintosh access)
Access method:	ftp: net-dist.mit.edu:/pub/techinfo/
Database:	Modula3
Access method:	ftp: wpi.wpi.edu:/modula3/
Database:	Mosaic Internet Hypermedia Browser
Access method:	ftp: ftp.ncsa.uiuc.edu:/Mosaic
Database:	Multipurpose Internet Mail Extensions (MIME)
Access method	ftp: thumper.bellcore.com:/Interoperability (overview)
	ftp: nic.merit.edu:/documents/rfc/rfc1341.txt (document)
Database:	Murdoch University (Australia)
Access method:	ftp: csuvax1.csu.murdoch.edu.au
	ftp: infolib.murdoch.edu.au
Database:	Name Lookup Service Software
Access method:	ftp: csus.edu:/pub/nls/nls-1.21.tar.Z
Database:	Nanny (VMS)
Access method:	ftp: hamlet.caltech.edu
Database:	NASA Ames Space Center Archives
Access method:	ftp: ames.arc.nasa.gov:pub/space
Database:	NASA Climate Server
Access method:	ftp: iris613.gsfc.nasa.gov
Database:	NASA Langley Technical Report FTP Site
Access method:	ftp: techreports.larc.nasa.gov:/pub/techreports
Database:	NASA Space Physics
Access method:	ftp: nssdca.gsfc.nasa.gov
Database:	National Center for Atmospheric Research

Access method: ftp: ftp.ucar.edu

Database: National Center for Biotechnology Information GenBank,
                    Medline and Repository Databases
Access method: ftp: ncbi.nlm.nih.gov

The following directories are presently in the NCBI repository:

AAtDB - An Arabidopsis thaliana Database, the genomic database for the plant Arabidopsis thaliana. This database was built using software developed for the ACeDB. Maintained by Mike Cherry (cherry@frodo.mgh.harvard.edu).

ACeDB - A Caenorhabditis elegans Database, the genomic database for the nematode Caenorhabditis elegans. This directory includes software and an installation script for running the system on several hardware platforms. Maintained by Richard Durbin (rd@cele.mrc-lmb.cam.ac.uk) and Jean Thierry-Mieg (mieg@frmop11.bitnet).

aids-db - A collection of sequences from HIV and related viruses. Gerald Myers, LANL. (glm@life.lanl.gov) Kersti MacInnes, LANL. (kam@life.lanl.gov)

blocks - A database of protein sequence homology blocks, constructed from SwissProt and PROSITE. Includes Unix and DOS software packages used to make the database. Maintained by Steven and Jorja Henikoff (henikoff@sparky.fhcrc.org)

carbbank - PC-based database and software system that contains information about the structure of complex carbohydrates. Includes the Complex Carbohydrate Structure Database (CCSD) and the CarbBank software system. Maintained by Dana Smith, Scott Doubet and Peter Albersheim. (carbbank@uga.bitnet) or (76424.1122@compuserve.com).

chrominfo - A Macintosh-based database system and associated software containing human chromosome map information. Maintained by Prakash Nadkarni (nadkarni-prakash@cs.yale.edu)

ECO2DBASE - The E. coli gene-protein database, which links information about E. coli genes and their protein spots on 2-D gels. Maintained by Frederick C. Neidhart (frederick_c._neidhardt@um.cc.umich.edu)

enzyme - The Enzyme Data Bank, a database of information about enzymes, including names, catalytic activity, cofactors, and pointers to relevant entries in sequence databases. This directory also includes an ASN.1 encoding of the database. Maintained by Amos Bairoch (bairoch@cmu.unige.ch)

EPD - Eukaryotic Promoter Database. A collection of biologically functional, experimentally defined RNA POL-II promoters active in higher eukaryotes. Maintained by Philipp Bucher (philipp.bucher@isrec.arcom.ch)

FlyBase - The Drosophila Genetic Database, the genomic database for the fruit fly Drosophila melanogaster. Maintained by Michael Ashburner, (ma11@phx.cam.ac.uk)

journals_toc - A collection of journal tables of contents. Maintained by Amos Bairoch (bairoch@cmu.unige.ch)

kabat - A collection of sequences of immunological importance, including aligned protein and nucleic acid sequences in various formats. Compiled by Elvin Kabat (kabat@ncbi.nlm.nih.gov). Maintained by George Johnson (tt@immuno.esam.nwu.edu)

LiMB - Listing of Molecular Biology databases. A collection of information about the content and maintenance of a large number of databases of interest to the molecular biology community. Maintained by Graham Redgrave (gwr@-life.lanl.gov).

metabolism - A collection of notes and datasets relating to intermediate metabolism. Maintained by Peter Karp (pkarp@ai.sri.com).

metproto - A database of metabolic reactions. Maintained by Ray Ochs (rso2@po.cwru.edu)

NFRES - Non-Redundant Functionally Equivalent Sequences. A collection of non-redundant nucleic acid sequences from GenBank, separated into different functional classes (coding regions, exons, introns, etc.). Maintained by Andrzej Konopka (konopka@fcrfv2.ncifcrf.gov).

NGDD - Normalized Gene Designation Database. Normalized gene maps for Escherichia coli, Salmonella, Bacillus subtilus, Pseudomonas aeruginosa, and Caulobacter crescentus. Assembled by Yvon Abel and Robert Cedergren (cedergren@bch.umontreal.ca).

pkinases - A non-redundant annotated collection of protein kinase sequences. Maintained by Anne Marie Quinn (quinn@salk-sc2.sdsc.edu).

prosite - An annotated database of protein sequence motifs. Maintained by Amos Bairoch (bairoch@cmu.unige.ch).

REBASE - Restriction Enzyme Database. A collection of information about restriction enzymes, their cutting sites and commercial sources. Maintained by Richard Roberts (roberts@neb.com)

repbase - A collection of datasets of human repetitive DNA sequences. Maintained by Jerzy Jurka (jurek@jmullins.stanford.edu).

RLDB - The Reference Library DataBase, a collection of information about the chromosomal locations of a set of publicly available DNA probes. Maintained by Guenther Zehetner (G_Zehetner@icrf.ac.uk).

seqanalref - The Sequence Analysis Bibliographic Reference Data Bank, a formatted database of bibliographic references to the literature of sequence analysis, indexed by keywords. Maintained by Amos Bairoch (bairoch@cmu.unige.ch).

t4phage - A genomic database for the T4 phage. Maintained by David Batts, Shane Peterson and Dr. Elizabeth Kutter. (t4phage@milton.u.washington.edu).

TFD - Transcription Factor Database. A relational database of transcription factors and related information. Maintained by David Ghosh (ghosh@ncbi.nlm.nih.gov).

yeast - A collection of files of interest to yeast biologists. Maintained by Francis Ouellette (francis@ncbi.nlm.nih).

Database:	Navy Public Affairs Libary
	1995 Navy Budget Information
Access method:	ftp: ftp.ncts.nvay.mil
Database:	NCEER Directory GeoBase Program for Sun Workstations
Access method:	ftp: lamont.ldgo.columbia.edu
Database:	National Center of Supercomputer Applications (NCSA) FTP Server
Access method:	ftp: ftp.ncsa.uiuc.edu

DIRECTORY STRUCTURE

/Mac	Macintosh software
/PC	IBM PC software
/UNIX	Software for machines running UNIX or equivalent OS
/SGI	Software that primarily runs on Silicon Graphics machines only
/HDF	Hierarchical Data Format applications and tools
/Collab	Collaborative software tools
/Samples	Samples that can be used with most of NCSA software tools

/Documentation	directory for documentation
/ncsapubs	Information produced by the Publications group, including Metacenter announcements, data link & access, a software listing, start-up guides, and other reference documents.
/misc	Miscellaneous documentation and software
/incoming	directory for contributions
/outgoing	swap directory

Database: NCSA Software Archive - PC DOS and Macintosh
Access method: ftp: ftp.ncsa-uiuc.edu:/NCSA-Telnet/PC/

Database: NCSA Telnet
Access method: ftp: uahcs2.cs.uah.edu

Database: Netlib FTP Site
Access method: ftp: netlib.att.com

Database: Network Software FTP Site Listing
Access method: ftp: ux1.cso.uiuc.edu:/doc/pcnet/software

Database: NIH FTP Server
Access method: ftp: lhc.nlm.nih.gov

Database: NIST Anonymous FTP Server
Access method: ftp: enh.nist.gov
ftp: osi.ncsl.nist.gov

Database: Net Etiquette Guide
Access method: ftp: ftp.sura.net:/pub/nic/internet.literature/
netiquette.txt

Database: Netfind Information
Access method: ftp: ftp.cs.colorado.edu:/pub/cs/distribs/netfind/README
pub/cs/techreports/schwartz/ASCII/White.Pages.txt

Database: Network Manager's Reading List of Books and Resources Oriented to TCP/IP and Ethernet
Access method: ftp: ftp.utexas.edu:/pub/netinfo/docs/net-read.txt

Database: Network Time Protocol Patches

Access method: ftp: louie.udel.edu:/pub/ntp/

Database: New England Electronic Economic Data Center BBS
Access method: ftp: neeedc.umesbs.maine.edu

Database: New England Academic and Research Network
Access method: ftp: nic.near.net:/docs/

Database: New York University Anonymous FTP Server
Access method: ftp: cs.nyu.edu
                    ftp: goober.phri.nyu.edu
                    ftp: karron.med.nyu.edu
                    ftp: mcclb0.med.nyu.edu
                    ftp: nyu.edu

Database: NeXT Computer Software and Information
Access method: ftp: sonata.cc.purdue.edu
                    ftp: nova.cc.perdue.edu
                    ftp: cs.orst.edu:/pub/next/
                    ftp: potemkin.cs.pdx.edu:/pub/NeXT/sounds/

Database: North America satellite weather images
Access method: ftp: vmd.cso.uiuc.edu:/wx

Database: North Western University
Access method: ftp: ils.nwu.edu

Database: Northern Arizona University
Access method: ftp.nau.edu

Database: NorthWestNet's (NWNet) User Service Internet Resource
                    Guide
Access method: ftp: ftphost.nwnet.net:/user-docs/nusirg/README.nusirg

Database: Novell Netware
Access method: ftp: ee.umr.edu:/pub/novell/
                    ftp: marlin.jcu.edu.au:/pub/novell/

Database: NREN Information
Access method: ftp: nic.merit.edu:/nren/
                    ftp: nic.merit.edu:/cise/recompete (NREN Interim NSF Plan)
                    ftp: nic.merit.edu:/nren/nrencongr.* (NREN Program Reports)

Database: NSFnet Acceptable User Policy Statement
Access method: ftp: ftp.sura.net:/pub/nic/NSFNET.acceptable.use

Database: NSF Resource Guide to Internet Resources

Access method:	ftp: ds.internic.net:/resource-guide/overview
Database:	NSI File Cabinet Archive (130mb+)
Access method:	ftp: nic.nsi.nasa.gov
Database:	Nucleic Acid Sequence Databank
Access method:	ftp: net.bio.net:/pub/BIOSCI/BIO-JOURNALS/ select appropriate subdirectory by topic
Database:	NYSERnet Information
Access method:	ftp: nysernet.org:/pub/resources/ guide to Internet: pub/guide/Guide.V.2.2.text
Database:	Oakland University Software Archive
Access method:	ftp: oak.oakland.edu
Database:	Ohio-State Education Archives
Access method:	ftp: archive.cis.ohio-state.edu
Database:	Ohio State University
Access method:	ftp: cis.ohio-state.edu ftp: giza.cis.ohio-state.edu ftp: nisca.ircc.ohio-state.edu ftp: shape.mps.ohio-state.edu
Database:	Ohio Supercomputer Center
Access method:	ftp: suna.osc.edu
Database:	On-Line Bibliographic information
Access method:	ftp: vaxb.acs.unt.edu:/library/libraries.txt ftp: ftp.unt.edu:/libraries/libraries.contacts
Database:	On-Line Book Initiative
Access method:	ftp: world.std.com:/obi/README
Database:	On-Line Public Access Library Catalogs (OPACs) Contact Info
Access method:	ftp: ftp.utdallas.edu:/pub/staff/billy/libguide/ Files: libraries.intro libraries.americas libraries.asia libraries.australia libraries.europe libraries.instructions
Database:	Passau University (Germany) Software Archive
Access method:	ftp: forwiss.uni-passau.de

Database: Philosophy Bibliography
Access method: ftp: cogsci.indiana.edu

Database: Ping Information
Access method: ftp: uxc.cso.uiuc.edu:/utils/ping/README

Database: Planetary Data Systems Geosciences Node
Access method: ftp: wuarchive.wustl.edu:/graphics/magellan/

Database: Princeton University
Access method: ftp: pulsar.princeton.edu

Database: Programming Systems Research Group FTP Server
Access method: ftp: psrg.lcs.mit.edu

Database: Prospero Information
Access method: ftp: eddie.mit.edu:/README.prospero

Database: Prospero Software
Access method: ftp: cs.washington.edu:/pub/prospero.tar.z
                   ftp: prospero.isi.edu:/pub/prospero/doc/

Database: Dictionary of Sites and Patterns of Proteins
Access method: ftp: fly.bio.indiana.edu:/molbio/data/prosite/
                   file: prosite.txt (User manual)
                   file: prosite.doc (Handbook)

Database: Proteon's Anonymous FTP Server
Access method: ftp: monk.proteon.com

Database: PSI information and press releases
Access method: ftp: psi.com:/press.rel

Database: PSI White Pages Administrator Guide/User's Manual
Access method: ftp: ftp.psi.com:/wp/src/pilot-ps.tar.Z

Database: PSI White Pages Access
Access method: ftp: wp.psi.net
                   login as: fred

Database: Pulsar Information Programs and Catalog
Access method: ftp: pulsar.princeton.edu

Database: Purdue University
Access method: ftp: harbor.ecn.purdue.edu
                   ftp: gwen.cs.purdue.edu
                   ftp: mace.cc.purdue.edu

	ftp: mordred.cs.purdue.edu ftp: nova.cc.purdue.edu
Database:	Radar Map of the United States Generated at the University of Illinois and updated every few hours
Access method:	ftp: vmd.cso.uiuc.edu:/wx
Database: Access method:	Recipe Archive ftp: gatekeeper.dec.com:/pub/recipes/ ftp: cs.ubc.ca:/pub/local/RECIPES/ ftp: mthvax.cs.miami.edu:/pub/recipes/ ftp: ftp.neosoft.com:/pub/rec.food/recipes/
Database: Access method:	Regional Network Policies (Documents) ftp: ftp.nsic.sri.com:/netinfo/???.policy where ??? is the name of the regional network.
Database: Access method:	Religious Studies Publication Journal ftp: panda1.uottawa.ca:/pub/religion/electric-mystics-guide-v3.txt
Database: Access method:	Restriction Enzyme Database (REBASE) ftp: ncbi.nlm.nih.gov:/repository/ ftp: vent.neb.com:/pub/rebase/
Database: Access method:	RFC documents ftp: nic.ddn.mil:/rfc/rfc-xxxx.txt where xxxx is the number of the RFC

ftp: ds.internic.net:/rfc/rfcnnnn.xxx where nnnn is the RFC document number and xxx indicates the document form,txt for ASCII and ps for Postscript.

ftp: ftp.concert.net:/rfc/rfcnnnn.txt or /rfc/nnnn.ps where nnnn references RFC number.

ftp: nis.nsf.net (login with username anonymous, password guest). cd/internet/documents/rfc

ftp: nisc.jvnc.net:/rfc/RFCnnnn.txt.v where nnnn is the number of the RFC and v references its version number

ftp: ftp.sesqui.net:/pub/rfc/rfcnnnn.xxx where nnnn is the number of the RFC and xxxx indicates the document form, txt for ASCII and ps for Postscript.

ftp: venera.isi.edu:/in-notes/rfcnnnn.txt where nnnn references RFC number. Login with username anonymous, password guest

ftp: wuarchive.wustl.edu:/info/rfc/rfcnnnn.txt.z where nnnn references RFC number and z indicates the document is in compressed form.

ftp: src.doc.ic.ac.uk:/rfc/rfcnnnn.txt.z where nnnn references RFC number and z indicates document is in compressed form

Secondary Repositories:

DENMARK

Site:	University of Copenhagen
Host:	ftp.diku.dk (freja.diku.dk)
Directory:	rfc

FINLAND

Site:	FUNET
Host:	funet.fi
Directory:	rfc
Notes:	RFCs in compressed format. Also provides email access by sending mail to archive-server@funet.fi.

FRANCE

Site:	Institut National de la Recherche en Informatique et Automatique (INRIA)
Address:	info-server@inria.fr
Notes:	RFCs are available via email to the above address. Info Server manager is Mireille Yamajako (yamajako@inria.fr).

GERMANY

Site:	University of Dortmund
Host:	walhalla.informatik.uni-dortmund.de
Directory:	pub/documentation/rfc
Notes:	RFCs in compressed format

NETHERLANDS

Site:	EUnet

Host: mcsun.eu.net
Directory: rfc
Notes: RFCs in compressed format.

NORWAY

Host: ugle.unit.no
Directory: pub/rfc

SWEDEN

Host: sunic.sunet.se
Directory: rfc

Host: chalmers.se

Directory: rfc

Database: Ribosomal Database Project at University of Illinois
Access method: ftp: info.mcs.anl.gov:/pub/RDP/

Database: Rice University Software Archive
Access method: ftp: titan.rice.edu
                    ftp: cs.rice.edu

Database: Royal Institute of Technology (KTH)
                    Stockholm, Sweden
Access method: ftp: kth.se

Directories:

pub/   some local and common software packages

doc/   misc documentation

kthlan/   local info for the KTH local area network

macintosh/   distribution of mac files

tex/   TeX files

CJK/   China/Japan/Korea stuff

NADA/   Nada local stuff

rfc/   most of the current rfcs

unsupported/   mostly old stuff

Database:	RSA Inc.
	Clipper Chip Proposal and Cryptology Information
Access method:	ftp: rsa.com
Database:	Russian Dictionary and Language Information
Access method:	ftp: kekule.osc.edu
Database:	Rutgers University Network Documentation
Access method:	ftp: athos.rutgers.edu:/runet/

acceptable-use .doc	Policies defining who may use the Internet and Bitnet, and for what.
attachment-policy .doc	rules for attaching networks and devices to the Rutgers network [DRAFT]
internet-access.doc	Guidelines for setting up controls on host and routers to conform with Internet accesspolicies [DRAFT]
runet.doc	General description of the Rutgers network Final section gives specific advice on various TCP/IP configuration options appropriate for use at Rutgers [DRAFT]
tcp-ip-intro.doc	General introduction to TCP/IP networking technology
tcp-ip-intro.ps	Postscript version
tcp-ip-admin.doc	How to set up a TCP/IP based network
tcp-ip-admin.ps	Postscript version
ru-cisco-M.N.doc	Rutgers additions to cisco software for cisco release M.N

Other documents of possible interest:

pub/hosts.txt	host table for hosts that do not support named. This host table is kept up to date automatically.
pub/hosts.rutgers	host table with just Rutgers hosts in it
pub/hosts.added	non-Rutgers hosts that we add to the host table

ietf	working papers of the Internet Engineering Taskforce
internet-drafts	drafts of proposed new Internet (TCP/IP) standards
rfc	complete set of Internet (TCP/IP) standards
cisco	files from ftp.cisco.com's public area, including cisco documentation and Unix software that works with cisco equipment

ftp: dimacs.rutgers.edu
ftp: paul.rutgers.edu
ftp: pyrite.rutgers.edu

Top level directory contents

Directory:	*Contents:*
baseball:	QuartzLeague baseball files
books:	About books, bookstores, and authors (see etext)
citadel:	Citadel BBS sources
computer:	Computer-related text files and src
cyberculture:	Cyberspac and cyberculture (future-culture)
disney:	Items about Disney World/Movies/Etc
economic:	Items about economics/policy
etext:	Electronic texts
folklore:	Urban folklore/alt.folklore.urban
food:	Recipies, nutrition, food
fortune:	Datafiles for fortune programs
history:	History-related files
humor:	Humor files
images:	GIF/JPG files of quartz users
internet:	Internet related files
journals:	Electronic journals/magazines/digests/mlists

law:	U.S. Law/Government
misc:	Misc stuff
music:	Some music-related files, no lyrics
nyc:	Files pertaining to New York City
origworks:	QuartzBBS original works archive
pets:	Files pertaining to various pets
purity:	Purity tests
puzzles:	rec.puzzles archive
quartz:	Quartz BBS-related files
railfan:	Files of interest to railroading fans
scitech:	Science & Technology
sex:	Sex-related items
subgenius:	Church of the SubGenius items
theater:	Broadway theater info and show lyrics
tv+movies:	Television and movie items
wired:	Articles from Wired Magazine
ftp:	rutgers.edu

Database: St. Olaf College
Access method: ftp: stolaf.edu

Database: Saint Mary's Anonymous FTP Service (Internet, FAQs, Macintosh, DOS)
Access method: ftp: husky.stmarys.ca

Database: San Diego Supercomputer Center Applied Network Research Group Network Activity Information
Access method: ftp: ftp.sdsc.edu:/pub/sdsc/anr/README

Database: Directory of Scholarly Electronic Conferences
Access method: ftp: ksuvxa.kent.edu:/library/

Database: SELF Programming Language
Access method: ftp: otis.stanford.edu
                  ftp: mushroom.cs.ac.uk:/pub/SELF/3.0

Database: SF-lovers archive
Access method: ftp: gandalf.rutgers.edu:/sfl/

Database: SGI IRIS 4D System
Access method: ftp: godzilla.cgl.rmit.oz.au:/sgi-source/

Database: Shakespeare Publications
Access method: ftp:slopoke.mlb.semi.harris.com:/pub/doc/Shakespeare/

Database: Silicon Graphics Programs, Articles and Posters
Access method: ftp: sgi.com

Directories:

ftp/sg	IRIX and bug fixes
ftp/sgi/fax	FlexFax software. Includes source.
ftp/sgi/src	various source, including ttcp, whois, and fax
ftp/graphics	GL graphics programs/source from Paul Haeberli, et al
ftp/comp.sys .sgi	articles and compressed groups of articles from comp.sys.sgi/info-iris
ftp/comp.sys mips	articles and compressed groups of articles from comp.sys.mips
ftp/support	various goodies and bug fixes, unsupported but from the support organization
ftp/other	other things from elsewhere graphics/images - a bunch of interesting image files

The "Helping Build a Better Dinosaur" poster produced to highlight Silicon Graphics' participation in "Jurassic Park":

jp_poster.rgb.Z - 1363 × 2016 SGI format RGB image file
jp_poster.sm.rgb.Z - 682 × 1008 version
jp_poster.tiny.rgb - 136 × 202 version
jp_poster.tiff.Z - 1363 × 2016 TIFF format RGB image file
jp_poster.sm.tiff.Z - 682 × 1008 version
jp_poster.tiny.tiff - 136 × 202 version

Database: Simple Network Management Protocol (SNMP) Information
Access method: ftp: allspice.lcs.mit.edu:/pub/snmp/

Database: Smithsonian Institution Anonymous FTP System
                  Digitized Reproductions of Art, Artifacts and other holdings
Access method: ftp: photo1.si.edu

Database: Software Archives
Access method: ftp: rusmv1.rus.uni-stuttgart.de (Germany - Macintosh, DOS,
                  SUN, AIX, VAX, UNIX)
                  ftp: ftp.cs.ruu.nl (Netherlands - Atari, HP, TeX, UNIX
                  ftp: pitt.edu:/software/mac/ (Macintosh)

Database: Solar Physics Database
Access method: ftp: solar.stanford.edu

Database: Sound/Rhythm
Access method: ftp: cecelia.media.mit.edu
                  ftp: cujo.curtin.edu.au:/pc/sound/
                  ftp: joker.optics.rochester.edu:/mac/sounds/

Database: Space Telescope Electronic Information System (STEIS)
Access method: ftp: stsci.edu

Database: Sprintlink Networking Activities
Access method: ftp: ftp.sprintlink.net

Database: SRI Network Information
Access method: ftp: ftp.nisc.sri.com:/netinfo/
                  ftp: phoebus.nisc.sri.com

Database: Stanford University
Access method: ftp: fresnel.stanford.edu
                  ftp: gang-of-four.stanford.edu
                  ftp: gregorio.stanford.edu
                  ftp: labrea.stanford.edu
                  ftp: lurch.stanford.edu
                  ftp: sail.stanford.edu
                  ftp: sierra.stanford.edu
                  ftp: solar.stanford.edu

Database: State Department travel advisories for foreign countries
Access method: ftp: ftp.stolaf.edu:/pub/travel-advisories/advisories

Database: State University of NY at Oswego
Access method: ftp: oswego.oswego.edu

Database: State University of New York (SUNY) at Buffalo
Access method: ftp: urth.acsu.buffalo.edu

Database: State University of NY (SUNY)/Buffalo FTP Archive
Access method: ftp: talos.cs.buffalo.edu

Database: State University of New York at Stoney Brook
Access method: ftp: max.physics.sunysb.edu

Database: STN Database Summary Sheets
                   Maintained by Chemical Abstract Service
Access method: ftp: info.cas.org

Database: Stuttgart Faculty of Informatics
Access method: ftp: inf.informatik.uni-stuttgart.de

Database: Stuttgart Informatics
Access method: ftp: ifi.informatik.uni-stuttgart.de

Database: SUMEX-AIM
Access method: ftp: sumex-aim.stanford.edu

Database: SURAnet Information
Access method: ftp: ftp.sura.net:/pub/nic/network.services.guides/
                   how.to.email.guide
                   how.to.ftp.guide
                   how.to.telnet.guide
                   how.to.use.vi.guide
                   ftp: noc.sura.net

Directories found under pub:

archie   Information on the Archie service as well as client software to
                    use Archie

articles   Text versions of articles in the SURAnet newsletter

databases   The databases in raw format that are also offered through WAIS
                    server

dns   Software and documentation to help setup the Domain Name
                    Server software on Unix machines (BIND)

jobs   Positions openings at SURAnet

loads   Subdirectory containing the latest loads for Proteon gateways

maps   Subdirectory containing postscript maps

meetings	Information on meetings SURAnet is planning
mbone	Information regarding the Multicast Backbone
networking	Subdirectory containing papers on networking
new.sites. info	Templates and information to help get new sites up and running quickly
news	Software and documentation to get USENET news running on your host
nic	Subdirectory containing informational files provided by the NIC to help you to better use the network
security	Configuration information and programs to help make your hosts and network more secure
sendmail	Software and documentation to setup sendmail
SURAnet	Subdirectory containing information about SURAnet

SURAnet directories found under NIC:

NREN	Documents of interest related to the National Research and Education Network legislation
directory.services	Information on services which allow for users to locate fellow users on the Internet
internet.literature	A potpourri of documents which enable you to better understand the workings of the Internet
network.service. guides	Services guides which enable the user to better navigate the Internet. Guides are available on the following topics: telnet, FTP, e-mail, and vi.
training	An archive of chapters for an introductory class on the Internet and informational resources available through the Internet

Database:	SUN OS Bugs
Access method:	ftp: elsie.nci.nih.gov:/pub/
Database:	SWITCH (Swiss Metwork) Information
Access method:	ftp: nic.switch.ch:/info_service/

Database:	Sydney University Law School FTP Archive
Access method:	ftp: sulaw.law.su.oz.au
Database:	Talk-Radio in Sparc Audio Format
Access method:	ftp: urth.acsu.buffalo.edu:/talk-radio/
Database:	Taxacom (Systemic Biology) FTP Server
Access method:	ftp: huh.harvard.edu:/pub/README.TAX
Database:	TCP/IP Introduction
Access method:	ftp: topaz.rutgers.edu:/tcp-ip-docs/tcp-ip-intro.doc
	ftp: arthur.cs.purdue.edu:/pub/comer/tcpbook
	ftp: rutgers.edu
Database:	TCP/IP Diagnostic and Monitoring Tools
Access method:	ftp: godzilla.cgl.rmit.oz.au:/nettools/
Database:	Telecommunications Archives
Access method:	ftp: lcs.mid.edu:/telecom-archives/
	ftp: relay.cs.toronto.edu:/doc/telecom-archives/
Database:	Telnet utilization information
Access method:	ftp: ftp.sura.net:/pub/nic/network.service.guides
	ftp: ftp.sura.net:/pub/nic/how.to.telnet.guide
Database:	Telnet Sites and Services List
Access method:	ftp: aug3.augsburg.edu:/files/bbs_lists/na006.txt
Database:	Temple University Information Server
Access method:	ftp: ftp.temple.edu
Database:	TeX
Access method:	ftp: iesd.auc.de
	ftp: pit-manager.mit.edu
	ftp: vax.eedsp.gatech.edu:/pub/TeX/
Database:	Trainpack Repository of Training and Training Related Materials
Access method:	ftp: tuda.ncl.ac.uk:/pub/network-training/README
Database:	Travel Information Library
Access method:	ftp: ftp.cc.umanitoba.ca:/rec-travel/
Database:	TRW Corporation
Access method:	ftp: gumby.dsd.trw.com
	ftp: trwind.trw.com
Database:	Tufts University

Access method:	ftp: pearl.tufts.edu
Database:	Typing Injury Information
Access method:	ftp: soda.berkeley.edu:/typing-injury/
Database:	UIUC Smalltalk Archive
Access method:	ftp: st.cs.uiuc.edu
Database:	Ulam Quarterly (Mathematical Research)
Access method:	ftp: math.ufl.edu:/pub/ulam
Database:	Unidata Scientific Data Management Software
Access method:	ftp: unidata.ucar.edu
Database:	UNIX Book List
Access method:	ftp: ftp.sura.net:/pub/nic/internet.literature/unix.books.4-7
Database:	UNIX Public Access
Access method:	ftp: nnsc.nsf.net:/nsfnet/nixpub
Database:	University of Alabama
Access method:	ftp: risc.ua.edu
Database:	University of Auckland (New Zealand) Anonymous FTP Archive 3D modeling, MaCINTOSH, MSDOS)
Access method:	ftp: ccu1.aukui.ac.nz
Database:	University of British Columbia
Access method:	ftp: mtsg.ubc.ca
Database:	University of California at Berkeley
Access method:	ftp: okeeffe.cs.berkeley.edu
	ftp: peoplesparc.berkeley.edu
	ftp: scam.berkeley.edu
	ftp: soda.berkeley.edu
	ftp: ucbvax.berkeley.edu
	ftp: xcf.berkeley.edu
Database:	University of California at Berkeley Data Communications and Network Services
Access method:	ftp: lilac.berkeley.edu
	ftp: mailhost.berkeley.edu

Directories:

netinfo	Network information files
pub	Public software files

Berkeley Campus Distribution:

etc   "/etc" files for systems on the Berkeley campus data network.

Internal and Special Purpose:

bin   Commands used by anonymous FTP

k12   California Education Network (CENet) Technical Planning Committee

maint   DCNS network/hardware maintance files

Database: University of California at Berkeley
Department of Mathematics
Access method: ftp: math.berkeley.edu

Database: University of California at Berkeley
Open Computing Forum
Access method: ftp: ocf.berkeley.edu

Database: University of California at Irvine
Access method: ftp: ics.uci.edu

Database: University of California at Los Angeles
Department of Mathematics
Access method: ftp: math.ucla.edu

Database: University of California at San Diego
Access method: ftp: ucsd.edu

Database: University of Cincinnati
College of Engineering
Access method: ftp: uceng.uc.edu

Database: University of Chicago
Department of Computer Science
Access method: ftp: gargoyle.uchicago.edu

Database: University of Chicago
Access method: ftp: midway.uchicago.edu
ftp: oddjob.uchicago.edu

Database: University Claude Bernard (France)
Laboratorie de Biometrie

ACNUC Nucleic Acid Sequences Database
Access method: ftp: biom3.univ-lyon1.fr

Database: University of Colorado Annonymous FTP Server
Access method: ftp: boulder.colorado.edu
                 ftp: foobar.cs.colorado.edu
                 ftp: spot.colorado.edu

Database: University of Delaware FTP Server
Access method: ftp: louie.udel.edu
                 ftp: perelandra.cms.udel.edu

Database: University of Georgia Artificial Intelligence Archive
Access method: ftp: aisun1.ai.uga.edu

Files are grouped in the following directories:
ai.natural.language -- Natural language processing programs
ai.nlp.book   -- Programs from the book _NLP for Prolog Programmers
ai.pc.utilities   -- IBM PC utilities and editors
ai.phonetic.fonts   -- Timothy Montler's phonetic fonts for Laserjet II
ai.prolog   -- Prolog programs and Prolog interpreters
ai.prolog.book   -- Programs from the book _Prolog Programming in Depth
ai.prolog.standard   -- Draft proposed ISO Prolog standard, March 1993
ai.reports   -- Research reports from the University of Georgia
ai.misc   -- Other programs (mostly for UNIX)
ai.unix.utilities   -- Useful utilities and shell scripts for UNIX

Database: University of Iowa
                 Department of Mathematics
Access method: ftp: herky.cs.uiowa.edu

Database: University of Iowa Software Archive
Access method: ftp: grind.isca.uiowa.edu

Database: University of Kentucky
Access method: ftp: f.ms.uky.edu

Database: University of Kansas
Access method: ftp: kuhub.cc.ukans.edu

Database: University of Maine
                 Department of Computer Science Anonymous FTP Server

Access method: ftp: gandalf.umcs.maine.edu

/pub/ham-radio	Ham radio, ARES and NTS files
/pub/hazmat	Hazardous Materials chemical spill emergency response information
/pub/WISR	WISR software repository
/pub/gopher	Gopher software
/pub/siggraph	Siggraph
/pub/msdos	MSDOS files
/pub/msdos /compilers	compilers and interpretters for MSDOS

Database: University of Maryland
Access method: ftp: mimsy.umd.edu
ftp: umd5.umd.edu

Database: University of Massachusetts VISIONS Anonymous FTP Server (Motion sequence, color, outdoor, indoor)
Access method: ftp: cicero.cs.umass.edu
other sites: ftp: vax1.cs.umass.edu
                 ftp: vax2.cs.umass.edu

Database: University of Miami
Access method: ftp: mango.rsmas.miami.edu

Database: University of Michigan Software Archives
Access method: ftp: archive.umich.edu
Alternative access: Connect to gopher.archive.merit.edu and select "Software Archives".

Server name	Directory	Description
mac.archive.umich.edu	/mac	Mac software
msdos.archive.umich.edu	/msdos	IBM PC and compatible software
atari.archive.umich.edu	/atari	Atari software
apple2.archive.umich.edu	/apple2	Apple 2 software
linguistics.archive. umich.edu	/linguistics	linguistics software
archive.umich.edu	/apollo	Apollo software
archive.umich.edu	/physics	physics software
archive.umich.edu	/economics	economics software/data

There is also an FTP server (directly from AFS files) in Germany: info2.rus.uni-stuttgart.de /afs/umich.edu/group/itd/archive.

for technical reports ftp: citi.umich.edu
other site: ftp: freebie.engin.umich.edu
      ftp: um.cc.umich.edu

Database:	University of Mississippi
Access method:	ftp: tacky.cs.olemiss.edu

Database:	University of Nevada
Access method:	ftp: unsvax.nevada.edu

Database:	University of North Texas
Access method:	ftp: vaxb.acs.unt.edu

Database:	University of North Carolina Sunsite Network Information
Access method:	ftp: sunsite.unc.edu:/pub/docs/about-the-net/

Database:	University of Oslo Institute for Informatics
Access method:	ftp: ifi.uio.no

Database:	University of Pennsylvania CIS Department FTP Server
Access method:	ftp: linc.cis.upenn.edu

Database:	University of Pittsburgh
Access method:	ftp: ftp.pitt.edu ftp: pitt.edu

Database:	University of Pittsburgh
Access method:	ftp: unixd1.cis.pitt.edu

Database:	University of Rochester Anonymous FTP Server
Access method:	ftp: cc.rochester.edu ftp: cayuga.cs.rochester.edu

Database:	University of Tasmania Hobart, Tasmania, Australia
Access method:	ftp: tasman.cc.utas.edu.au

Database:	University of Texas Anonymous FTP Server
Access method:	ftp: bongo.cc.utexas.edu ftp: emx.utexas.edu (password: guest) ftp: rascal.ics.utexas.edu

Database:	University of Texas at Arlington Department of Mechanical Engineering
Access method:	ftp: me.uta.edu

Database: University of Texas at Dallas
Access method: ftp: vm.utdallas.edu

Database: University of Tokyo Japanese Software Distribution
                   Anonymous FTP
Access method: ftp: utsun.s.u-tokyo.ac.jp

Database: University of Tokyo International Science Network (TISN)
Access method: The following institutes and organizations are currently
                   participating in the network:

s.u-tokyo.ac.jp	Faculty of Science, Univ. of Tokyo
ins.u-tokyo.ac.jp	Institute for Nuclear Study, Univ. of Tokyo
icrr.u-tokyo.ac.jp	Institute for Cosmic Ray Research, Univ. of Tokyo
stelab.nagoya-u.ac.jp	Solar-Terrestrial Environment Lab., Nagoya Univ.
ims.ac.jp	Institute for Molecular Science
isas.ac.jp	The Institute of Space and Astronautical Science
ism.ac.jp	The Institute of Statistical Mathematics
nao.ac.jp	National Astronomical Observatory
nig.ac.jp	National Institute of Genetics
nipr.ac.jp	National Institute of Polar Research
nips.ac.jp	National Institute for Physiological Sciences
aist.go.jp	Agency of Industrial Science and Technology
fri.go.jp	Fermentation Research Institute
giric.go.jp	Government Industrial Research Institute, Chugoku
girik.go.jp	Government Industrial Research Institute, Kyushu
girin.go.jp	Government Industrial Research Institute, Nagoya
girio.go.jp	Government Industrial Research Institute, Osaka
girit.go.jp	Government Industrial Research Institute, Tohoku
gsj.go.jp	Geological Survey of Japan
ipri.go.jp	Industrial Products Research Institute
mel.go.jp	Mechanical Engineering Laboratory
nair.go.jp	National Inst. for Advanced Interdisciplinary Res.
ncl.go.jp	National Chemical Laboratory for Industry
nibh.go.jp	National Inst. of Bioscience and Human-technology
nimc.go.jp	National Inst. of Materials and Chemical Research
nire.go.jp	National Institute for Resources and Environment
nrlm.go.jp	National Research Laboratory of Metrology
ript.go.jp	Research Institute for Polymers and Textiles

affrc.go.jp	Agriculture,Forestry and Fisheries Research Council
bosai.go.jp	National Research Institute for Earth Science and Disaster Prevention
crl.go.jp	Communications Research Laboratory
gsi-mc.go.jp	Geographical Survey Institute
jaeri.go.jp	Japan Atomic Energy Research Institute
jamstec.go.jp	Japan Marine Science and Technology Center
jwa.go.jp	Japan Weather Association
mri-jma.go.jp	Meteorological Research Institute
nasda.go.jp	National Space Development Agency of Japan (NASDA)
ncc.go.jp	National Cancer Center
nies.go.jp	National Institute for Environmental Studies
nirs.go.jp	National Institute of Radiological Sciences
riken.go.jp	Institute of Physical and Chemical Research (RIKEN)
kazusa.or.jp	Kazusa DNA Research Institute
rtri.or.jp	Railway Technical Research Institute
genome.ad.jp	Genome Research Network
kuicr.kyoto-u.ac.jp	Institute for Chemical Research, Kyoto University
imcb.osaka-u.ac.jp	Osaka University
ims.u-tokyo.ac.jp	Institute of Medical Science, Univ. of Tokyo
kyushu-u.ac.jp	Kyushu Univ.
nibb.ac.jp	National Institute for Basic Biology
jfcr.or.jp	Japanese Foundation for Cancer Research
prf.or.jp	Protein Research Foundation

Database:	University of Toronto (Canada) Software Archive (TeX, SLIP for SunOS, S/SL table walker for syntax/semantic language
Access method:	ftp: ftp.cs.toronto.edu
Database:	University of Utah FTP Server
Access method:	ftp: cc.utah.edu
	ftp: science.utah.edu
	ftp: snake.utah.edu
Database:	University of Washington
Access method:	ftp: shrimp.cs.washington.edu
	ftp: sperm.ocean.washington.edu

Database: University of Waterloo
Access method: ftp: watmath.waterloo.edu
                      Ontario, Canada
                      Electrical Engineering Department

Directories:

pub/Amiga	files related to the Commodore "Amiga" computer
pub/bicycle	information about bicycling
pub/enorgy	files of interest to U of Waterloo E&CE alumni
pub/emr	files of interest to U of Waterloo E&CE alumni
pub/fractint	the "fractint" fractal pattern generator
pub/glove	files related to the PowerGlove
pub/jpeg	Eric Praetzel's JPEG viewer
pub/mfs	files relating to Maryknoll Father's School, Hong Kong
pub/misc	anything that doesn't fit into any other category
pub/netgame	ideas related to networked games and shared VR's
pub/nntp	files related to the NNTP client for NOS
pub/polyblit	fast polygon code for 386's
pub/radio	files related to amateur radio
pub/raytracers	a selection of raytracing graphics packages
pub/rend386	fast screen renderer
pub/shadows	files related to the tv series "Dark Shadows"
pub/sound	C source for playing soundfiles on a PC
pub/vgif a	GIF viewer
pub/vr	miscellaneous files related to Virtual Reality
pub/wattcp	implementation of a TCP/IP library
pub/waves	files related to the WAVES virtual reality protocol

Database: University of Wisconsin
Access method: ftp: pgd.adp.wisc.edu

Database: University of Wisconsin
                      Milwaukee Computing Services Division
Access method: ftp: csd4.csd.uwm.edu

Database: University of Wisconsin
                      Waisman Center
Access method: ftp: harry.waisman.wisc.edu

Database: US Geological Service
Access method: ftp: isdres.er.usgs.gov

Database: US Government 1993 Budget On-Line Copy
Access method: ftp: sunsite.unc.edu:/pub/academic/political-science/
                  US-Budget-1993

Database: US Government Information Archive Contact Information for
                  Members of Congress and the Senate
Access method: ftp: nifty.andrew.cmu.edu:/pub/QRD/qrd/info/GOVT/

Database: US Senate Bibliographies from 99th Congress to date
                  maintained at North Carolina State University
Access method: ftp: ncsuvm.cc.ncsu.edu:/SENATE
                  file: README.DOS9111 for explanation of information transfer

Database: US Supreme Court decisions
Access method: ftp: info.umd.edu:/info/Government/US/SupremeCt

Database: USENET Data Repository
Access method: ftp: pit-manager.mit.edu:/pub/usenet/

Database: USENET Information
Access method: ftp: wuarchive.wustl.edu:/doc/misc/acn/acn4-5.txt.z
                  ftp: rtfm.mit.edu:/pub/usenet/news.answers/what-is-
                  usenet/part1

Database: USENET Maps
Access method: ftp: gatekeeper.dec.com:/pub/maps/

Database: USENET Newsgroups
Access method: ftp: pit-manager.mit.edu:/pub/usenet/news.announce.newusers/
                  List_of_Active_Newsgroups
                  ftp: ftp.cs.toronto.edu:/pub/emv/news-archives/list-of-news-
                  groups

Database: USENET Public Access Site List
Access method: ftp: uop.uop.edu:/pub/nixpub.long
                  ftp: uop.uop.edu:/pub/nixpub.short (single line entries)

Database: UUNET Archive
Access method: ftp: ftp.uu.net:/uunet-info/

Database: UUNET Networking Information
Access method: ftp: uu.net:/inet/doc

Database: uwho program
Access method ftp: punisher.caltech.edu:/pub/danl/uwho/uwho218b.tar.Z

Database: University of Western Ontario (UWO) Network Information
Centre
Access method: ftp: julian.uwo.ca:/nic/

Database: VAX Archive
Access method: crvax.sri.com

Database: VAX Networking Guide
Access method: ftp: decoy.uoregon.edu:/pub/vaxbook/
file: vms.ps (postscript format)
file: vms.mem (lineprinter format)

Database: VAX/VMS Networking Beginner's Guide
Access method: ftp: ftp.temple.edu:/pub/info/help-net/vms-mail.guide

Database: Veronica Data Set
Access method: ftp: veronica.scs.unr.edu:/veronica/

Database: Veronica FAQ
Access method: ftp: veronica.scs.unr.edu:/veronica/veronica-faq

Database: Veronica Utilization
Access method: ftp: ftp.cso.uiuc.edu:/doc/net/uiucnet/vol16no1.txt
ftp: cs.dal.ca:/pub/comp.archives/bionet.software/veronica

Database: Vi Full Screen Text Editor Information
Access method: ftp: hubcap.clemson.edu:/pub/info
files: vi-intro
vi_doc

Database: Virus Scanners and Information
Access method: ftp: gondwana.ecr.mu.oz.au:/pub/security/virus/scanner/
ftp: kuhub.cc.ukans.edu:/virus/
ftp: p6xje.ldc.lu.se:/arc/pub/virus/
ftp: risc.ua.edu:/pub/ibm-antivirus/
ftp: vaxb.acs.unt.edu:/pub/antivirus/mac/

Database: VMS Utilities
Access method: ftp: hydra.uwo.ca:/vms_utilities/

Database: WAIS Information
Access method: ftp: think.com:/wais/README (sources and documents)
ftp: hydra.uwo.ca:/libsoft/wais.txt

ftp: julian.uwo.ca:/doc/wais/
ftp: ftp.cnidr.org (UNIX based information server)
ftp: sunsite.unc.edu:/pub/docs/about-the-net/libsoft/wais.txt
ftp: kirk.bond.edu.au:/pub/BOND_Uni/doc/wais/readme
(content of sources)
ftp: life.anu.edu:/pub/wais/sources/
ftp: fits.cx.nrao.edu:/fits/wais-sources/

Database: Washington University Software Archives
Access method: ftp: wuarchive.wustl.edu

Database: Weather Maps
Access method: ftp: vmd.cso.uiuc.edu:/wx/

Database: Weather Maps of Europe and the World in GIF format
Access method: ftp: liasun3.epfl.ch:/pub/weather/

Database: Westnet Information
Access method: ftp: spot.colorado.edu:/westnet/

Database: Wireless LANs
Access method: ftp: tandem.com

Database: White House Frequently Asked Question List
Access method: ftp: ftp.sura.net:/pub/nic/whitehouse.FAQ

Database: WHOIS registration
Access method: ftp: nic.ddn.mil:/netinfo/user-template.txt
mail completed form to: registrar@nic.ddn.mil
ftp: nic.merit.edu:/documents/rfc/rfc0954 (registered net
work names)

Database: WHOIS Server List
Access method: ftp:sipb.mit.edu:/pub/whois/whois-servers.list
ftp: ftp.sura.net:/pub/nic/directory.services/WHOIS.info/
WHOIS.servers

Database: WHOIS Server Software for UNIX and VMS/Multinet TCP/IP
Implementations
Access method: ftp: hamlet.caltech.edu:
/ANON_ROOT:[OOOOOO.WHOIS_UNIX]
ftp: hamlet.caltech.edu:
/ANON_ROOT:[OOOOOO.WHOIS_VMS]

Database: WHOIS Specifications

Access method: ftp: gopher.ucdavis.edu:/pub/IETF/WNILS/Discussion.Paper

Database: World Wide Web Database Browser Information
Access method: ftp: info.cern.ch:/pub/www/doc/
                  ftp: unix.secs.oakland.edu:/pub/www/

Database: World Wide Web Project Description
Access method: ftp: emx.cc.utexas.edu:/pub/mnt/source/services/www/doc
                  /the_www_book.txt

Database: xvgr, xmgr
Access method: ftp:ese3.ese.ogi.edu

Database: X.500 Implementation Availability Information
Access method: ftp: nic.ddn.mil:/rfc/
                  ftp: nic.merit.edu:/documents/rfc/rfc1308.txt
                  ftp: nic.merit.edu:/documents/fyi/fyi_11.txt

Database: Yanoff's Internet Connects List
Access method: ftp: csd4.csd.uwm.edu:/pub/inet.services.txt
                  hypertext version in file: inet.services.html

Database: Yale University
Access method: ftp: cs.yale.edu
                  ftp: ftp.cs.yale.edu
                  ftp: yalevm.ycc.yale.edu

Database: York University (Canada)
Access method: ftp: deadtech.ccs.yorku.ca
                  ftp: ns.nic.yorku.ca

Database: York University
Access method: ftp: dvaco.ccs.york.ca

Database: Zamfield's Internet BBS List
Access method: ftp: sunsite.unc.edu:/pub/docs/about-the-
                  net/libsoft/internet_bbs.txt

Database: Zen and the Internet (book)
Access method: ftp: ashley.cs.widener.edu:/pub/zen

FTP Sites Tracked by Archie Servers

The following list of FTP sites were tracked by the University of Nebraska Archie Server during February, 1994. Since some Archie systems track archive sites globally, while other systems track the archive sites in their country, region or continent to reduce traffic on trans-oceanic circuits, readers may wish to access a specific Archie system to obtain a list of FTP servers in their immediate geographic location. To do so use the Archie addresses listed in Chapter 6 and Telnet to an Archie server. Once connected use the list command to obtain a list of FTP sites tracked by that Archie server. The following example illustrates the use of the list command upon connection to the Archie server at the University of Nebraska.

8 Feb 1994

unl-archie> list

Your queue position: 1

Estimated time for completion: 00:08

working...

a.cs.uiuc.edu	128.174.252.1	12:09	13 Feb 1994
acsc.com	143.127.0.2	22:33	8 Feb 1994
addvax.llnl.gov	128.115.19.32	21:13	8 Feb 1994
aeneas.mit.edu	18.71.0.38	10:17	13 Feb 1994
agate.berkeley.edu	128.32.136.1	10:23	13 Feb 1994
aisun1.ai.uga.edu	128.192.12.9	02:24	4 Dec 1993
aix.rpi.edu	128.113.26.11	12:17	11 Feb 1994
ajpo.sei.cmu.edu	128.237.2.253	12:23	13 Feb 1994
allspice.berkeley.edu	128.32.150.27	12:14	13 Feb 1994
ftp.chpc.utexas.edu	129.116.3.15	14:00	12 Feb 1994
alw.nih.gov	128.231.128.7	10:00	13 Feb 1994
ftp.ccalmr.ogi.edu	129.95.72.34	10:03	14 Feb 1994
ames.arc.nasa.gov	128.102.18.3	22:06	8 Feb 1994
anagram.mcs.anl.gov	140.221.10.1	22:16	8 Feb 1994
andy.bgsu.edu	129.1.1.2	11:53	13 Feb 1994
ftp.nevada.edu	131.216.1.11	10:13	14 Feb 1994
anna.stanford.edu	36.14.0.13	13:28	12 Feb 1994
anthro.anthro.utah.edu	128.110.190.1	12:40	13 Feb 1994
anubis.ac.hmc.edu	134.173.32.18	14:07	12 Feb 1994
ftp.engr.ucf.edu	132.170.200.67	11:37	13 Feb 1994
archive.afit.af.mil	129.92.1.66	21:31	8 Feb 1994
ftp.cis.ohio-state.edu	128.146.8.52	12:26	14 Feb 1994
ftp.egr.msu.edu	35.8.8.177	13:27	12 Feb 1994
archone.tamu.edu	128.194.53.42	12:18	11 Feb 1994
ftp.unm.edu	129.24.8.1	13:29	12 Feb 1994

aristotle.ils.nwu.edu	129.105.100.1	12:12	13 Feb 1994
ftp.cs.purdue.edu	128.10.2.1	15:26	12 Feb 1994
ftp.cs.widener.edu	147.31.254.132	11:40	12 Feb 1994
asuvax.eas.asu.edu	129.219.30.5	12:07	13 Feb 1994
athena.cs.uga.edu	128.192.4.49	15:02	12 Feb 1994
athena.erc.msstate.edu	192.208.145.68	12:19	13 Feb 1994
athos.rutgers.edu	128.6.4.4	12:20	13 Feb 1994
att.att.com	192.20.239.129	10:19	12 Feb 1994
azure.acsu.buffalo.edu	128.205.7.6	11:13	11 Feb 1994
bach.cs.columbia.edu	128.59.28.19	13:49	12 Feb 1994
banjo.concert.net	192.101.21.6	10:08	23 Jan 1994
bbn.com	128.89.0.122	09:57	13 Feb 1994
bcm.tmc.edu	128.249.2.1	12:30	13 Feb 1994
beagle.ee.washington.edu	128.95.31.156	13:43	12 Feb 1994
bears.ece.ucsb.edu	128.111.56.56	12:31	13 Feb 1994
ftp.cic.net	192.131.22.5	14:30	22 Jan 1994
beethoven.cs.colostate.edu	129.82.102.183	11:53	13 Feb 1994
bert.cs.byu.edu	128.187.2.20	12:21	13 Feb 1994
ftp.pyramid.com	129.214.1.100	22:51	8 Feb 1994
beta.xerox.com	13.1.64.94	21:12	8 Feb 1994
bitsy.mit.edu	18.72.0.3	14:28	12 Feb 1994
boole.stanford.edu	36.8.0.65	13:36	12 Feb 1994
boombox.micro.umn.edu	134.84.132.2	10:01	14 Feb 1994
boulder.colorado.edu	128.138.240.1	12:31	13 Feb 1994
ftp.bradley.edu	136.176.5.10	15:07	14 Feb 1994
brazil.cambridge.apple.com	198.112.73.3	09:57	13 Feb 1994
ftp.apple.com	130.43.2.3	22:05	8 Feb 1994
ftp.cs.colorado.edu	128.138.243.150	12:31	13 Feb 1994
bugs.nosc.mil	128.49.4.117	22:42	8 Feb 1994
bull.cs.williams.edu	137.165.8.2	10:02	14 Feb 1994
bulldog.cs.yale.edu	128.36.0.3	13:50	12 Feb 1994
cac.washington.edu	140.142.100.1	11:22	13 Feb 1994
caesar.pica.army.mil	129.139.160.133	10:31	27 Jan 1994
caip.rutgers.edu	128.6.19.83	11:35	13 Feb 1994
caisr2.caisr.cwru.edu	129.22.24.22	23:20	3 Dec 1993
caldwr.water.ca.gov	136.200.32.1	22:33	8 Feb 1994
calpe.psc.edu	128.182.62.148	12:18	11 Feb 1994
calvin.stanford.edu	36.14.0.43	12:10	13 Feb 1994
camel.scubed.com	192.31.63.74	11:43	19 Jan 1994
casbah.acns.nwu.edu	129.105.16.52	11:45	14 Feb 1994
casper.na.cs.yale.edu	128.36.12.1	10:16	14 Feb 1994

castlab.engr.wisc.edu	144.92.60.140	11:08	13 Feb 1994
caticsuf.cati.csufresno.edu	129.8.100.15	12:40	13 Feb 1994
cattell.psych.upenn.edu	130.91.68.31	11:17	13 Feb 1994
ftp.cs.rochester.edu	192.5.53.209	14:17	12 Feb 1994
cb-iris.stanford.edu	36.45.0.14	12:17	14 Feb 1994
cdiac.esd.ornl.gov	128.219.24.36	22:26	8 Feb 1994
cecelia.media.mit.edu	18.85.0.104	10:20	13 Feb 1994
cert.sei.cmu.edu	192.88.209.5	11:39	13 Feb 1994
chem.bu.edu	128.197.30.18	14:20	12 Feb 1994
cicero.cs.umass.edu	128.119.40.189	12:05	13 Feb 1994
cl-next2.cl.msu.edu	35.8.4.22	14:05	12 Feb 1994
ftp.cs.umb.edu	158.121.104.33	10:23	14 Feb 1994
climate.gsfc.nasa.gov	128.183.46.16	21:28	8 Feb 1994
cml.rice.edu	128.42.62.23	11:41	13 Feb 1994
cmns.think.com	131.239.2.100	22:40	8 Feb 1994
cnri.reston.va.us	132.151.1.1	10:02	13 Feb 1994
convex.convex.com	130.168.1.1	23:04	8 Feb 1994
coos.dartmouth.edu	129.170.16.50	11:54	13 Feb 1994
ftp.bucknell.edu	134.82.7.253	10:36	14 Feb 1994
corona.med.utah.edu	128.110.231.1	13:51	12 Feb 1994
cougar.csc.wsu.edu	134.121.1.2	10:04	14 Feb 1994
coyote.cs.wmich.edu	141.218.40.40	12:58	13 Feb 1994
crl.dec.com	192.58.206.2	21:24	8 Feb 1994
cronos.metaphor.com	143.241.0.5	10:00	13 Feb 1994
crs.cl.msu.edu	35.8.1.10	14:17	12 Feb 1994
crvax.sri.com	128.18.30.65	22:50	8 Feb 1994
cs.bu.edu	128.197.2.2	11:30	13 Feb 1994
cs.columbia.edu	128.59.16.20	10:42	13 Feb 1994
cs.ep.utexas.edu	129.108.1.41	10:36	14 Feb 1994
cs.nyu.edu	128.122.140.24	14:00	12 Feb 1994
cs.orst.edu	128.193.32.1	14:32	12 Feb 1994
cs.oswego.edu	129.3.20.253	10:44	14 Feb 1994
cs.rice.edu	128.42.1.30	12:40	13 Feb 1994
cs.utah.edu	128.110.4.21	10:30	13 Feb 1994
cs.utexas.edu	128.83.139.9	11:08	13 Feb 1994
ftp.uwp.edu	131.210.1.4	15:26	10 Feb 1994
cs.wm.edu	128.239.1.30	14:14	12 Feb 1994
csab.larc.nasa.gov	128.155.26.10	22:51	8 Feb 1994
ftp.math.utah.edu	128.110.198.2	14:24	12 Feb 1994
csd4.csd.uwm.edu	129.89.7.4	11:43	14 Feb 1994
cse.ogi.edu	129.95.20.2	11:58	13 Feb 1994

cse.unl.edu	129.93.33.1	12:30	13 Feb 1994
csli.stanford.edu	36.9.0.46	10:35	14 Feb 1994
csus.edu	130.86.90.1	11:02	13 Feb 1994
csustan.csustan.edu	130.17.1.70	11:34	13 Feb 1994
csvax.cs.caltech.edu	131.215.131.131	12:29	13 Feb 1994
ctron.com	134.141.197.25	09:51	13 Feb 1994
daisy.waterloo.edu	129.97.140.58	11:12	12 Feb 1994
ftp.ucdavis.edu	128.120.8.149	11:51	13 Feb 1994
ftp.wang.com	150.124.8.99	09:50	12 Feb 1994
decoy.uoregon.edu	128.223.32.19	11:52	14 Feb 1994
decuac.dec.com	192.5.214.1	22:29	8 Feb 1994
delbruck.pharm.sunysb.edu	129.49.110.3	14:51	12 Feb 1994
ftp.cs.yale.edu	128.36.0.36	11:50	14 Feb 1994
dftnic.gsfc.nasa.gov	128.183.10.3	23:02	8 Feb 1994
ftp.gsfc.nasa.gov	128.183.10.134	22:51	8 Feb 1994
dimacs.rutgers.edu	128.6.75.16	10:54	14 Feb 1994
dime.cs.umass.edu	128.119.40.244	11:09	13 Feb 1994
dix.gps.caltech.edu	131.215.65.13	22:04	8 Feb 1994
ftp.nwnet.net	192.220.251.1	09:46	23 Jan 1994
dorm.rutgers.edu	128.6.18.15	11:31	13 Feb 1994
dra.com	192.65.218.43	10:15	13 Feb 1994
draco.acs.uci.edu	128.200.34.12	10:03	14 Feb 1994
dsinc.dsi.com	192.65.202.1	22:15	8 Feb 1994
duke.cs.duke.edu	152.3.140.1	14:15	12 Feb 1994
durer.cme.nist.gov	129.6.32.4	21:58	8 Feb 1994
dynamo.ecn.purdue.edu	128.46.128.1	09:53	12 Feb 1994
e-math.ams.com	130.44.1.100	22:10	8 Feb 1994
ea.ecn.purdue.edu	128.46.128.2	12:31	13 Feb 1994
ftp.tc.cornell.edu	132.236.201.10	12:39	13 Feb 1994
eceserv0.ece.wisc.edu	144.92.76.2	09:59	14 Feb 1994
ee.lbl.gov	128.3.112.20	22:23	8 Feb 1994
ee.umr.edu	131.151.4.11	11:02	13 Feb 1994
ee.utah.edu	128.110.8.42	12:35	13 Feb 1994
ef.ecn.purdue.edu	128.46.154.18	10:03	14 Feb 1994
ftp.cs.iastate.edu	129.186.3.15	11:07	13 Feb 1994
elsie.nci.nih.gov	128.231.16.1	22:41	8 Feb 1994
elvis.seas.gwu.edu	128.164.16.16	12:10	13 Feb 1994
ftp.emba.uvm.edu	132.198.1.7	13:36	12 Feb 1994
emory.mathcs.emory.edu	128.140.110.1	11:33	14 Feb 1994
emr.cs.uiuc.edu	128.174.246.26	12:57	13 Feb 1994
emx.cc.utexas.edu	128.83.186.11	12:45	13 Feb 1994

en.ecn.purdue.edu	128.46.149.59	11:43 14 Feb 1994
enh.nist.gov	129.6.16.1	22:34 8 Feb 1994
enterprise.berkeley.edu	128.32.149.24	11:02 13 Feb 1994
ftp.ugcs.caltech.edu	131.215.134.135	11:38 13 Feb 1994
ernst.mach.cs.cmu.edu	128.2.209.192	10:30 14 Feb 1994
erratic.bradley.edu	136.176.5.253	11:17 13 Feb 1994
ese.ogi.edu	129.95.74.30	13:55 12 Feb 1994
lassp-ftp.msc.cornell.edu	128.84.241.39	12:58 13 Feb 1994
euclid.colorado.edu	128.138.150.15	10:37 14 Feb 1994
euler.math.usma.edu	129.29.79.198	01:11 4 Dec 1993
ftp.bchs.uh.edu	129.7.2.43	14:05 12 Feb 1994
evolution.genetics.washington.edu	128.95.12.41	14:12 12 Feb 1994
ftp.law.cornell.edu	132.236.108.5	11:46 14 Feb 1994
fcs280s.ncifcrf.gov	129.43.1.11	22:54 8 Feb 1994
ferkel.ucsb.edu	128.111.72.60	11:20 13 Feb 1994
fidelio.rutgers.edu	128.6.126.2	13:52 12 Feb 1994
fido.econlab.arizona.edu	128.196.196.20	14:09 12 Feb 1994
etext.archive.umich.edu	192.131.22.7	14:20 22 Jan 1994
fits.cv.nrao.edu	192.33.115.8	11:21 13 Feb 1994
flash.bellcore.com	192.4.13.90	22:07 8 Feb 1994
fletcher.cs.unca.edu	152.18.52.3	13:33 12 Feb 1994
flubber.cs.umd.edu	128.8.128.99	10:28 13 Feb 1994
ftp.bio.indiana.edu	129.79.224.25	12:25 13 Feb 1994
foxtrot.ccmrc.ucsb.edu	128.111.92.30	10:35 14 Feb 1994
fringe.cis.brown.edu	128.148.176.5	14:48 12 Feb 1994
ftp.cayman.com	143.137.137.4	22:32 8 Feb 1994
ftp.cs.umn.edu	128.101.230.9	10:39 14 Feb 1994
ftp.cse.ucsc.edu	128.114.134.19	11:07 13 Feb 1994
ftp.eos.ncsu.edu	152.1.9.25	09:53 12 Feb 1994
ftp.halcyon.com	192.135.191.2	10:08 13 Feb 1994
ftp.lantronix.com	192.73.220.81	22:34 8 Feb 1994
ftp.mathworks.com	144.212.100.10	21:28 8 Feb 1994
ftp.nau.edu	134.114.64.70	12:17 13 Feb 1994
ftp.uu.net	192.48.96.9	10:01 23 Jan 1994
fuzzy.ucsc.edu	128.114.133.9	13:55 12 Feb 1994
ftp.cc.rochester.edu	128.151.224.6	12:07 13 Feb 1994
ftp.umcs.maine.edu	130.111.112.21	13:37 12 Feb 1994
garfield.catt.ncsu.edu	152.1.43.23	12:55 13 Feb 1994
gargoyle.uchicago.edu	128.135.20.100	14:14 12 Feb 1994
gate.ready.com	138.121.1.2	22:44 8 Feb 1994
ftp.3com.com	129.213.128.5	21:30 8 Feb 1994

gatekeeper.dec.com	16.1.0.2	10:05	12 Feb 1994
gateway.control.com	140.186.37.1	14:16	21 Jan 1994
gazette.bcm.tmc.edu	128.249.2.2	11:33	14 Feb 1994
genome.wi.mit.edu	18.157.0.135	12:17	14 Feb 1994
george.lbl.gov	128.3.196.93	22:38	8 Feb 1994
geosim.cs.vt.edu	128.173.40.85	12:55	13 Feb 1994
gis.mit.edu	18.80.1.118	13:55	12 Feb 1994
golgi.harvard.edu	128.103.161.65	12:08	13 Feb 1994
goober.phri.nyu.edu	128.122.136.10	12:19	13 Feb 1994
gregorio.stanford.edu	36.8.0.11	10:12	14 Feb 1994
gum.isi.edu	128.9.32.31	10:33	13 Feb 1994
gumby.cc.wmich.edu	141.218.20.114	12:31	13 Feb 1994
gumby.dsd.trw.com	129.193.72.50	22:33	8 Feb 1994
gwen.cs.purdue.edu	128.10.3.8	10:32	13 Feb 1994
hallc1.cebaf.gov	129.57.32.62	22:25	8 Feb 1994
hamlet.caltech.edu	131.215.139.3	11:19	13 Feb 1994
hanauma.stanford.edu	36.51.0.16	10:16	22 Dec 1993
harbor.ecn.purdue.edu	128.46.154.76	13:31	12 Feb 1994
hardees.rutgers.edu	128.6.18.2	14:13	12 Feb 1994
harpo.seas.ucla.edu	128.97.2.211	12:32	13 Feb 1994
harvard.harvard.edu	128.103.1.1	11:21	13 Feb 1994
hayes.ims.alaska.edu	137.229.40.200	11:13	13 Feb 1994
helios.cc.gatech.edu	130.207.5.20	10:46	14 Feb 1994
helios.tn.cornell.edu	128.84.241.2	12:40	13 Feb 1994
helmholtz.sdsc.edu	192.31.153.101	11:40	12 Feb 1994
herky.cs.uiowa.edu	128.255.28.100	23:05	3 Dec 1993
ftp.math.ksu.edu	129.130.6.1	12:57	13 Feb 1994
hobbes.ksu.ksu.edu	129.130.8.1	11:08	13 Feb 1994
hobiecat.pcmp.caltech.edu	131.215.131.167	09:58	14 Feb 1994
hope.caltech.edu	131.215.4.231	10:12	14 Feb 1994
hoshi.colorado.edu	128.138.201.31	13:55	12 Feb 1994
hpcsos.col.hp.com	15.255.240.16	22:47	8 Feb 1994
hpcvaaz.cv.hp.com	15.255.72.15	22:32	8 Feb 1994
hplsci.hpl.hp.com	15.255.176.57	22:52	8 Feb 1994
hsdndev.harvard.edu	128.103.202.40	13:55	12 Feb 1994
hub.ucsb.edu	128.111.24.40	12:28	13 Feb 1994
hubcap.clemson.edu	130.127.8.1	13:50	12 Feb 1994
huron.scd.ucar.edu	128.117.8.111	13:45	12 Feb 1994
icaen.llnl.gov	128.115.2.99	22:51	8 Feb 1994
icarus.riacs.edu	134.12.1.1	10:56	14 Feb 1994
iceberg.cs.wwu.edu	140.160.140.160	12:12	13 Feb 1994

ics.uci.edu	128.195.1.1	14:18	12 Feb 1994
idlastro.gsfc.nasa.gov	128.183.57.82	22:41	8 Feb 1994
iear.arts.rpi.edu	128.113.6.10	10:02	14 Feb 1994
iggy.gw.vitalink.com	132.240.4.11	11:09	21 Jan 1994
ftp.primate.wisc.edu	144.92.43.11	12:17	13 Feb 1994
info.cren.net	192.52.179.20	14:37	22 Jan 1994
ftp.psi.com	38.145.211.6	09:51	12 Feb 1994
interviews.stanford.edu	36.22.0.175	13:34	12 Feb 1994
ipac.caltech.edu	131.215.139.35	14:26	12 Feb 1994
ipl.rpi.edu	128.113.14.50	10:45	14 Feb 1994
ftp.er.usgs.gov	130.11.48.2	22:35	8 Feb 1994
isye.gatech.edu	130.207.92.15	13:28	12 Feb 1994
jade.tufts.edu	130.64.1.42	10:33	11 Feb 1994
jaguar.cs.utah.edu	155.99.212.101	12:33	13 Feb 1994
janus.library.cmu.edu	128.2.21.7	11:09	14 Feb 1994
jhunix.hcf.jhu.edu	128.220.2.5	10:58	14 Feb 1994
joker.optics.rochester.edu	128.151.240.1	12:58	13 Feb 1994
josquin.media.mit.edu	18.85.0.38	13:49	12 Feb 1994
jpl-devvax.jpl.nasa.gov	137.79.113.100	10:00	13 Feb 1994
ftp.cs.washington.edu	128.95.1.4	12:13	13 Feb 1994
jupiter.ee.pitt.edu	136.142.87.2	12:10	13 Feb 1994
kaese.cs.wisc.edu	128.105.9.46	13:30	12 Feb 1994
kailua.hls.com	129.47.20.106	09:48	31 Jan 1994
karazm.math.uh.edu	129.7.128.1	13:37	12 Feb 1994
karp.albany.edu	128.204.2.32	14:23	12 Feb 1994
kekule.osc.edu	128.146.36.48	11:29	13 Feb 1994
kiawe.soest.hawaii.edu	128.171.151.16	13:36	12 Feb 1994
killington.dartmouth.edu	129.170.28.17	11:40	13 Feb 1994
labrea.stanford.edu	36.8.0.112	13:40	12 Feb 1994
lancaster.andrew.cmu.edu	128.2.13.21	12:16	13 Feb 1994
larry.sal.wisc.edu	128.104.39.51	12:17	14 Feb 1994
latour.cs.colorado.edu	128.138.204.19	10:35	21 Jan 1994
leland.stanford.edu	36.21.0.69	11:03	13 Feb 1994
lhc.nlm.nih.gov	130.14.1.128	22:31	8 Feb 1994
lib.tmc.edu	129.106.5.1	09:57	14 Feb 1994
life.slhs.udel.edu	128.175.41.33	11:05	13 Feb 1994
lilac.berkeley.edu	128.32.136.21	02:14	4 Dec 1993
ftp.cis.upenn.edu	130.91.6.8	12:39	13 Feb 1994
lisp-rt2.slisp.cs.cmu.edu	128.2.217.10	13:26	12 Feb 1994
lll-crg.llnl.gov	128.115.1.1	22:09	8 Feb 1994
logos.ucs.indiana.edu	129.79.17.29	13:49	12 Feb 1994

ftp.udel.edu	128.175.1.3	11:46	14 Feb 1994
lurch.stanford.edu	36.22.0.14	13:42	12 Feb 1994
lyman.pppl.gov	198.35.4.70	10:11	23 Jan 1994
lynx.ps.uci.edu	128.200.29.14	12:33	13 Feb 1994
ftp.psg.com	147.28.0.33	22:55	8 Feb 1994
mace.cc.purdue.edu	128.210.9.3	13:53	12 Feb 1994
mace.lcs.mit.edu	18.26.0.46	14:27	12 Feb 1994
maggie.telcom.arizona.edu	128.196.128.233	12:41	13 Feb 1994
mail.unet.umn.edu	128.101.101.103	12:06	13 Feb 1994
mammoth.cs.unr.edu	134.197.40.241	12:15	13 Feb 1994
mango.rsmas.miami.edu	129.171.98.18	15:25	12 Feb 1994
math.berkeley.edu	128.32.183.94	11:58	14 Feb 1994
math.mps.ohio-state.edu	128.146.110.30	11:24	13 Feb 1994
math.orst.edu	128.193.80.160	11:22	13 Feb 1994
math.sunysb.edu	129.49.18.1	12:18	11 Feb 1994
math.ucla.edu	128.97.4.254	10:15	13 Feb 1994
ftp.cecer.army.mil	129.229.20.254	22:36	8 Feb 1994
max.stanford.edu	36.22.0.19	14:06	12 Feb 1994
mbcrr.harvard.edu	134.174.79.60	12:13	14 Feb 1994
mbio.med.upenn.edu	128.91.18.14	11:19	13 Feb 1994
mc.lcs.mit.edu	18.111.0.179	10:05	14 Feb 1994
mcs213k.cs.umr.edu	131.151.6.11	12:41	13 Feb 1994
me.uta.edu	129.107.2.20	13:13	12 Feb 1994
me10.lbl.gov	128.3.128.110	22:38	8 Feb 1994
meadow.stanford.edu	36.22.0.202	10:26	14 Feb 1994
media-lab.media.mit.edu	18.85.0.2	11:53	14 Feb 1994
ftp.stat.wisc.edu	128.105.5.39	10:35	14 Feb 1994
ftp.unt.edu	129.120.1.1	11:52	9 Feb 1994
merit.edu	35.42.1.42	09:55	14 Feb 1994
merlin.cs.purdue.edu	128.10.2.3	13:52	12 Feb 1994
mhs-relay.cs.wisc.edu	128.105.8.53	12:23	14 Feb 1994
ftp.msc.cornell.edu	128.84.231.195	14:23	12 Feb 1994
midway.uchicago.edu	128.135.12.73	11:12	13 Feb 1994
milton.u.washington.edu	0.0.0.0	20:17	3 Dec 1993
ftp.cs.unm.edu	198.59.151.2	11:42	14 Feb 1994
ftp.cs.umd.edu	128.8.128.8	11:29	14 Feb 1994
mindseye.berkeley.edu	128.32.232.19	13:26	12 Feb 1994
ftp.lcs.mit.edu	18.26.0.36	14:21	12 Feb 1994
mipgsun.mipg.upenn.edu	130.91.180.111	10:25	14 Feb 1994
mojave.stanford.edu	36.22.0.120	10:25	14 Feb 1994
ftp.eng.umd.edu	129.2.90.15	12:18	13 Feb 1994

mojo.ots.utexas.edu	128.83.185.16	12:16	14 Feb 1994
monk.proteon.com	128.185.123.16	22:09	8 Feb 1994
moose.cccs.umn.edu	128.101.133.53	10:38	14 Feb 1994
moose.cs.indiana.edu	129.79.254.191	13:44	12 Feb 1994
mordred.cs.purdue.edu	128.10.2.2	11:18	13 Feb 1994
morticia.cnns.unt.edu	129.120.4.5	11:53	9 Feb 1994
mthvax.cs.miami.edu	129.171.32.5	11:49	14 Feb 1994
mvax.sonoma.edu	130.157.2.5	12:10	13 Feb 1994
mvb.saic.com	139.121.19.1	22:42	8 Feb 1994
myself.stanford.edu	36.22.0.41	00:23	9 Feb 1994
ftp.ucar.edu	192.52.106.6	14:26	12 Feb 1994
ncbi.nlm.nih.gov	130.14.25.1	10:03	13 Feb 1994
ftp.concert.net	192.101.21.1	12:35	24 Jan 1994
nebula.systemsz.cs.yale.edu	128.36.13.1	12:11	13 Feb 1994
nervous.cis.ohio-state.edu	128.146.61.200	10:20	13 Feb 1994
ftp.iastate.edu	129.186.150.150	11:15	14 Feb 1994
net.bio.net	134.172.2.69	09:55	23 Jan 1994
netix.com	192.88.8.100	22:11	8 Feb 1994
netserv1.its.rpi.edu	128.113.1.5	14:16	12 Feb 1994
ftp.cerf.net	192.102.249.3	09:50	23 Jan 1994
nic.cic.net	192.131.22.2	09:53	23 Jan 1994
nic.ddn.mil	192.112.36.5	10:16	12 Feb 1994
ftp.mr.net	137.192.240.5	14:40	22 Jan 1994
ftp.nordu.net	192.36.148.17	14:38	22 Jan 1994
nic.stolaf.edu	130.71.128.8	11:55	13 Feb 1994
ftp.sura.net	128.167.254.179	09:46	23 Jan 1994
nic.wisc.edu	128.104.30.38	14:50	12 Feb 1994
nigel.msen.com	148.59.1.8	22:40	8 Feb 1994
niord.shsu.edu	192.92.115.8	02:02	4 Dec 1993
ftp.ans.net	147.225.1.2	14:16	22 Jan 1994
nis.nsf.net	35.1.1.48	09:51	23 Jan 1994
nisc.jvnc.net	128.121.50.7	09:59	23 Jan 1994
nisca.acs.ohio-state.edu	128.146.1.7	10:17	14 Feb 1994
noc.sura.net	192.80.214.100	09:48	23 Jan 1994
nog.calstate.edu	130.150.102.100	12:14	13 Feb 1994
nova.cc.purdue.edu	128.210.7.22	13:53	12 Feb 1994
novell.com	137.65.4.1	21:58	8 Feb 1994
ns-mx.uiowa.edu	128.255.1.3	11:06	13 Feb 1994
ftp.network.com	129.191.1.1	22:37	8 Feb 1994
nssdca.gsfc.nasa.gov	128.183.36.23	22:34	8 Feb 1994
nyu.edu	128.122.128.2	10:16	14 Feb 1994

oddjob.uchicago.edu	128.135.4.2	11:27	13 Feb 1994
odin.mda.uth.tmc.edu	129.106.3.17	14:27	12 Feb 1994
oes.orst.edu	128.193.124.2	11:37	14 Feb 1994
ftp.cs.unc.edu	152.2.128.159	10:32	14 Feb 1994
ftp.clarkson.edu	128.153.4.2	14:54	12 Feb 1994
onion.rain.com	147.28.0.161	22:27	8 Feb 1994
ftp.cs.arizona.edu	192.12.69.5	14:59	12 Feb 1994
oregon.uoregon.edu	128.223.32.18	12:16	13 Feb 1994
orion.oac.uci.edu	128.200.80.20	11:27	13 Feb 1994
osceola.cs.ucf.edu	132.170.108.35	14:03	12 Feb 1994
osi.ncsl.nist.gov	129.6.48.100	22:32	8 Feb 1994
ftp.csc.ncsu.edu	152.1.58.11	14:02	12 Feb 1994
osprey.telcom.arizona.edu	128.196.128.232	12:13	11 Feb 1994
oswego.oswego.edu	129.3.1.1	11:46	12 Feb 1994
otis.stanford.edu	36.22.0.201	10:02	14 Feb 1994
otter.stanford.edu	36.190.0.87	12:31	13 Feb 1994
ouchem.chem.oakland.edu	141.210.108.5	12:05	13 Feb 1994
pacific.mps.ohio-state.edu	128.146.37.18	13:43	12 Feb 1994
par.cc.gatech.edu	130.207.119.254	13:49	12 Feb 1994
park.bu.edu	128.197.61.100	11:18	13 Feb 1994
pascal.math.yale.edu	128.36.23.1	10:03	14 Feb 1994
paul.rutgers.edu	128.6.5.53	12:38	13 Feb 1994
pc.usl.edu	130.70.40.3	10:16	13 Feb 1994
pdq.coe.montana.edu	192.31.215.240	01:32	4 Dec 1993
pemrac.space.swri.edu	129.162.155.101	14:16	12 Feb 1994
pencil.cs.missouri.edu	128.206.100.207	12:19	13 Feb 1994
peoplesparc.berkeley.edu	128.32.131.14	12:30	13 Feb 1994
ftp.nisc.sri.com	192.33.33.22	22:54	8 Feb 1994
picard.cc.uakron.edu	130.101.181.50	10:04	14 Feb 1994
pilot.njin.net	128.6.7.38	14:28	22 Jan 1994
pineapple.bbn.com	128.11.0.16	22:31	8 Feb 1994
pion.lcs.mit.edu	18.26.0.64	11:04	13 Feb 1994
plains.nodak.edu	134.129.111.64	10:47	14 Feb 1994
ftp.njit.edu	128.235.1.10	15:28	12 Feb 1994
planchet.rutgers.edu	128.6.60.2	10:40	13 Feb 1994
ftp.cs.clemson.edu	130.127.48.2	14:51	12 Feb 1994
pokey.cs.wisc.edu	128.105.2.7	10:32	11 Feb 1994
polaris.llnl.gov	128.115.14.19	21:29	8 Feb 1994
polyslo.csc.calpoly.edu	129.65.17.1	15:02	12 Feb 1994
pomona.claremont.edu	134.173.4.160	12:29	13 Feb 1994
pop.lbl.gov	131.243.64.10	10:15	13 Feb 1994

primost.cs.wisc.edu	128.105.36.61	12:13	13 Feb 1994
princeton.edu	128.112.128.1	10:51	14 Feb 1994
ftp.cis.ksu.edu	129.130.10.80	15:05	12 Feb 1994
ftp.cco.caltech.edu	131.215.48.151	12:00	13 Feb 1994
puppsr12.princeton.edu	128.112.84.73	10:05	14 Feb 1994
pyrite.rutgers.edu	128.6.4.15	10:31	13 Feb 1994
qiclab.scn.rain.com	147.28.0.97	22:56	8 Feb 1994
quake.think.com	192.31.181.1	10:14	13 Feb 1994
quartz.rutgers.edu	128.6.60.6	12:20	11 Feb 1994
ftp.css.cdc.com	129.179.110.9	10:14	12 Feb 1994
ra.astro.lsa.umich.edu	141.211.104.2	10:32	13 Feb 1994
ra.msstate.edu	130.18.80.10	12:55	13 Feb 1994
ra.nrl.navy.mil	128.60.0.21	22:53	8 Feb 1994
ftp.cs.cornell.edu	128.84.218.75	11:22	13 Feb 1994
rani.chem.yale.edu	130.132.25.65	11:33	13 Feb 1994
relay.cs.toronto.edu	128.100.3.6	12:18	14 Feb 1994
remus.rutgers.edu	128.6.13.3	13:58	12 Feb 1994
research.att.com	192.20.225.2	10:00	13 Feb 1994
retina.chem.psu.edu	128.118.30.113	11:22	13 Feb 1994
ftp.cs.tulane.edu	129.81.132.1	10:31	13 Feb 1994
risc.ua.edu	130.160.4.7	14:11	12 Feb 1994
rml2.sri.com	128.18.22.20	22:30	8 Feb 1994
romulus.rutgers.edu	128.6.13.2	12:32	13 Feb 1994
rsa.com	192.80.211.33	22:35	8 Feb 1994
rutgers.edu	128.6.21.9	10:19	13 Feb 1994
ftp.msi.umn.edu	128.101.24.1	10:00	14 Feb 1994
sbcs.sunysb.edu	130.245.1.15	13:30	12 Feb 1994
scss3.cl.msu.edu	35.8.1.178	13:29	12 Feb 1994
seq1.loc.gov	140.147.3.12	10:45	28 Jan 1994
serv1.cl.msu.edu	35.8.2.41	14:14	12 Feb 1994
ftp.uga.edu	128.192.1.9	11:41	13 Feb 1994
ftp.wag.caltech.edu	131.215.33.4	10:16	14 Feb 1994
shark.cse.fau.edu	131.91.80.13	12:17	13 Feb 1994
shiva.com	192.80.57.1	09:53	13 Feb 1994
shorty.cs.wisc.edu	128.105.10.66	11:53	13 Feb 1994
shrimp.cs.washington.edu	128.95.1.99	13:49	12 Feb 1994
sierra.stanford.edu	36.2.0.98	13:32	12 Feb 1994
sioux.stanford.edu	36.190.0.100	13:52	12 Feb 1994
sirius.llnl.gov	128.115.14.27	22:33	8 Feb 1994
ski.utah.edu	128.110.124.10	09:58	14 Feb 1994
ftp.umiacs.umd.edu	128.8.120.23	11:52	14 Feb 1994

ftp.mines.colorado.edu	138.67.1.3	10:20	13 Feb 1994
slc2.ins.cwru.edu	129.22.8.104	10:32	13 Feb 1994
slopoke.mlb.semi.harris.com	132.158.82.36	22:25	8 Feb 1994
smaug.cs.hope.edu	198.110.97.100	11:37	13 Feb 1994
snake.cs.utah.edu	155.99.212.33	11:27	13 Feb 1994
ftp.cis.ufl.edu	128.227.100.252	12:56	13 Feb 1994
soda.berkeley.edu	128.32.149.19	11:09	13 Feb 1994
software.watson.ibm.com	129.34.139.5	22:31	8 Feb 1994
sol.cs.bucknell.edu	134.82.1.8	10:35	14 Feb 1994
ftp.ctr.columbia.edu	128.59.64.40	10:20	14 Feb 1994
solar.stanford.edu	36.10.0.4	10:29	13 Feb 1994
ftp.cc.gatech.edu	130.207.7.245	13:47	12 Feb 1994
ftp.solbourne.com	141.138.2.2	22:50	8 Feb 1994
sonata.cc.purdue.edu	128.210.15.30	13:50	12 Feb 1994
sony.com	192.65.137.2	09:50	12 Feb 1994
sp2.csrd.uiuc.edu	128.174.153.4	13:52	12 Feb 1994
space.mit.edu	18.75.0.10	14:27	12 Feb 1994
sparky.fammed.wisc.edu	144.92.41.11	12:13	14 Feb 1994
ftp.erg.sri.com	128.18.100.39	21:58	8 Feb 1994
spectrum.xerox.com	192.70.225.78	09:50	13 Feb 1994
sperm.ocean.washington.edu	128.95.119.14	13:28	12 Feb 1994
ftp.gac.edu	138.236.1.3	10:18	13 Feb 1994
ftp.cccd.edu	159.115.1.5	12:13	14 Feb 1994
spot.colorado.edu	128.138.129.2	12:07	14 Feb 1994
src.honeywell.com	129.235.16.32	09:59	13 Feb 1994
ssyx.ucsc.edu	128.114.133.1	10:25	14 Feb 1994
stardent.arc.nasa.gov	128.102.21.44	22:34	8 Feb 1994
stasi.bradley.edu	136.176.5.121	10:26	14 Feb 1994
ftp.u.washington.edu	140.142.56.2	11:30	14 Feb 1994
stis.nsf.gov	128.150.195.40	10:33	30 Jan 1994
stout.atd.ucar.edu	128.117.120.30	14:20	12 Feb 1994
ftp.acs.ncsu.edu	152.1.15.67	12:30	13 Feb 1994
stsci.edu	130.167.1.2	11:44	13 Feb 1994
stubbs.ucop.edu	128.48.108.25	13:27	12 Feb 1994
sumex-aim.stanford.edu	36.44.0.6	12:59	13 Feb 1994
sun.soe.clarkson.edu	128.153.12.3	12:00	14 Feb 1994
sunapee.dartmouth.edu	129.170.28.9	11:06	13 Feb 1994
sunsite.unc.edu	152.2.22.81	09:54	9 Feb 1994
suntan.tandem.com	192.216.220.8	22:12	8 Feb 1994
sutro.sfsu.edu	130.212.15.230	13:39	12 Feb 1994
swedishchef.lerc.nasa.gov	139.88.54.33	21:27	8 Feb 1994

symcom.math.uiuc.edu	128.174.111.3	11:09	13 Feb 1994
syr.edu	128.230.1.49	10:37	14 Feb 1994
syrinx.umd.edu	129.2.8.114	11:06	13 Feb 1994
tacky.cs.olemiss.edu	130.74.96.13	15:02	12 Feb 1994
ftp.tcp.com	128.95.10.106	22:37	8 Feb 1994
ted.cs.uidaho.edu	129.101.100.20	11:39	13 Feb 1994
tehran.stanford.edu	36.28.0.189	11:19	13 Feb 1994
terminator.rs.itd.umich.edu	141.211.164.2	11:27	13 Feb 1994
tesla.ee.cornell.edu	128.84.253.11	13:38	12 Feb 1994
tetra.gsfc.nasa.gov	128.183.8.77	22:31	8 Feb 1994
tgv.com	161.44.128.70	21:32	8 Feb 1994
ftp.cac.psu.edu	128.118.2.23	11:49	13 Feb 1994
theory.lcs.mit.edu	18.52.0.92	11:04	13 Feb 1994
theory.tc.cornell.edu	128.84.181.1	12:11	13 Feb 1994
think.com	131.239.2.1	23:37	8 Feb 1994
thor.atd.ucar.edu	128.117.78.139	13:31	12 Feb 1994
thumper.bellcore.com	128.96.41.1	22:11	8 Feb 1994
thyme.lcs.mit.edu	18.26.0.115	13:30	12 Feb 1994
ti.com	192.94.94.5	21:12	8 Feb 1994
tmc.edu	128.249.1.1	12:13	13 Feb 1994
transit.ai.mit.edu	128.52.38.26	11:19	13 Feb 1994
trwind.trw.com	129.193.120.1	09:59	13 Feb 1994
tucana.tuc.noao.edu	140.252.1.1	12:22	13 Feb 1994
ualret.ualr.edu	144.167.10.48	23:16	3 Dec 1993
ftp.msc.edu	137.66.1.3	10:29	13 Feb 1994
ucbvax.berkeley.edu	128.32.130.12	14:10	12 Feb 1994
uceng.uc.edu	129.137.189.1	12:16	11 Feb 1994
ucrmath.ucr.edu	138.23.203.100	12:39	13 Feb 1994
ucsd.edu	128.54.16.1	09:50	14 Feb 1994
ucselx.sdsu.edu	130.191.1.10	10:37	13 Feb 1994
umaxc.weeg.uiowa.edu	128.255.56.80	12:22	13 Feb 1994
umigw.miami.edu	129.171.97.1	15:02	12 Feb 1994
umnstat.stat.umn.edu	128.101.51.1	12:33	13 Feb 1994
unicorn.cerl.uiuc.edu	128.174.180.9	10:14	13 Feb 1994
unidata.ucar.edu	128.117.140.3	12:04	14 Feb 1994
unix.secs.oakland.edu	141.210.180.2	11:05	13 Feb 1994
unix1.andrew.cmu.edu	128.2.35.66	10:02	14 Feb 1994
unix1.cc.ysu.edu	150.134.10.33	13:57	12 Feb 1994
unr.edu	134.197.1.2	12:06	13 Feb 1994
unx.ucc.okstate.edu	0.0.0.0	20:30	3 Dec 1993
uop.cs.uop.edu	138.9.200.1	12:10	13 Feb 1994

ursa-major.spdcc.com	140.186.80.3	22:30	8 Feb 1994
ftp.acsu.buffalo.edu	128.205.7.9	10:08	9 Feb 1994
usc.edu	128.125.253.136	12:35	14 Feb 1994
ftp.mcs.kent.edu	131.123.2.137	11:39	13 Feb 1994
utadnx.cc.utexas.edu	128.241.0.251	11:13	13 Feb 1994
utkux1.utk.edu	128.169.200.67	12:29	13 Feb 1994
ftp.virginia.edu	128.143.2.7	12:14	14 Feb 1994
ftp.cfht.hawaii.edu	128.171.80.50	12:16	13 Feb 1994
uxa.ecn.bgu.edu	143.43.33.11	11:34	13 Feb 1994
uxc.cso.uiuc.edu	128.174.5.50	10:39	13 Feb 1994
vab02.larc.nasa.gov	128.155.23.47	22:31	8 Feb 1994
ftp.ee.rochester.edu	128.151.160.11	10:21	14 Feb 1994
vangogh.cs.berkeley.edu	128.32.130.2	11:58	14 Feb 1994
vax.cs.pitt.edu	136.142.79.5	13:59	12 Feb 1994
vax.ftp.com	128.127.2.100	22:06	8 Feb 1994
vax1.umkc.edu	134.193.1.1	12:31	13 Feb 1994
ftp.cstp.umkc.edu	134.193.2.1	10:28	11 Feb 1994
vaxb.isi.edu	128.9.2.132	10:26	14 Feb 1994
vela.acs.oakland.edu	141.210.10.2	14:28	12 Feb 1994
ftp.isi.edu	128.9.0.32	11:14	13 Feb 1994
veronica.cs.wisc.edu	128.105.11.87	11:06	13 Feb 1994
vesta.sunquest.com	149.138.1.42	22:41	8 Feb 1994
vgr.brl.mil	128.63.16.6	22:30	8 Feb 1994
volitans.morningstar.com	137.175.2.11	21:26	8 Feb 1994
vxw.ee.lbl.gov	128.3.112.16	22:41	8 Feb 1994
wais.com	192.216.46.98	22:15	8 Feb 1994
ftp.eng.ufl.edu	128.227.116.1	11:20	13 Feb 1994
watserv1.waterloo.edu	129.97.129.140	12:04	13 Feb 1994
ftp.cc.columbia.edu	128.59.39.2	11:55	14 Feb 1994
freebsd.cdrom.com	192.153.46.2	21:46	8 Feb 1994
weedeater.math.yale.edu	128.36.23.17	14:23	12 Feb 1994
whitechapel.media.mit.edu	18.85.0.125	11:08	13 Feb 1994
ftp.eng.auburn.edu	131.204.110.10	12:03	14 Feb 1994
willow.cs.wwu.edu	140.160.140.153	12:54	13 Feb 1994
ftp.spies.com	130.43.43.43	22:52	8 Feb 1994
wolf.brl.mil	128.63.32.158	22:44	8 Feb 1994
ftp.std.com	192.74.137.5	22:59	8 Feb 1994
ftp.wustl.edu	128.252.135.4	10:08	25 Dec 1993
ftp.cs.odu.edu	128.82.4.1	15:14	12 Feb 1994
xcf.berkeley.edu	128.32.138.1	11:35	13 Feb 1994
xylogics.com	132.245.33.7	22:38	8 Feb 1994

yuma.acns.colostate.edu	129.82.100.64	12:18	13 Feb 1994
zaphod.lanl.gov	128.165.44.202	22:33	8 Feb 1994
ftp.ncsa.uiuc.edu	141.142.20.50	10:26	14 Feb 1994
zariski.harvard.edu	128.103.28.10	15:02	12 Feb 1994
zebra.cns.udel.edu	128.175.8.11	12:24	14 Feb 1994
zippy.nimh.nih.gov	128.231.98.32	22:39	8 Feb 1994

CHAPTER *6*

Telnet and Related Services and Database Addresses

In this chapter we turn our attention to the use of the Internet Telnet facility which provides you with the ability to access a remote computer as if you were locally connected. The use of the Internet Telnet facility requires a Telnet client software program operating on your computer, a connection from your computer to the Internet, Telnet software operating on the distant computer and either an account on the distant computer or knowledge of a public access account identifier. Thus, we will first focus our attention upon Telnet and host operations required to establish a Telnet session. This will be followed by a comprehensive table of Telnet database addresses and information concerning the use of related Telnet facilities, such as Gopher, Veronica, and Jughead.

TELNET CLIENT COMMANDS

Telnet is an Internet application which provides you with the ability to log onto another computer connected to the Internet. A Telnet client is a program which operates on your local computer and provides you with a mechanism to access and use a distant computer connected to the Internet.

Assuming you are using a command-based Telnet client communications program, to invoke the Telnet client you enter the command Telnet at your system prompt. If the command is entered without an Internet address, host name or alias the following prompt will be displayed by the Telnet client on your host computer: telnet>

The following client commands can be entered after the Telnet prompt which is the greater than character (>).

Command	*Operational Effect*
close	Close a current connection.
display	Display operating parameters at the site accessed for use with Telnet.
mode	Indicate if entry can occur line by line or one character at a time.
open	Establish a session with a target host if no target host name or a valid Internet address was previously entered.
quit	Terminate the Telnet client session.
send	Enable the transmission of special characters.
set	Set certain parameters to be used during a Telnet session.
status	Obtain information concerning the connection and operating parameters used for the Telnet session.
toggle	Change (toggle) the operating parameters used by a session.
Z	Suspend the Telnet prompt (>).
?	Display valid Telnet commands supported by the site that can be entered after the Telnet prompt (>).

An example of a sample Telnet interactive session is shown below. In this example it was assumed that you were establishing a session with the computer whose Internet address is ghost.buster.com.

```
$ telnet
telnet> open ghost.buster.com
Trying...
Connected to ghost.buster.com
Escape character is '^]'.

login: gxheld

Password: ********

Welcome to ghost

$
```

In the above example you would enter either a login account and password obtained from previously establishing an account on the host computer or a predefined login account and password provided for public access to the Telnet address.

To illustrate the operation of a graphic user interface (GUI) communications program that provides a Telnet capability we will again return to the use of NetManage's Chameleon. Figure 6.1 illustrates Chameleon's Telnet window after the Connect menu was selected and the host name entry, port assignment, and terminal emulation fields were completed. Readers should note that Chameleon automatically fills the Port and Emulate fields with defaults of 23 and VT100, respectively. Most sites which provide Telnet access use the standard Telnet port 23; however, some sites require access to a different port as indicated in the entries in the table included later in this chapter. Terminal emulations supported by Chameleon include ANSI, VT52, VT100 and VT220. For access to IBM host computers you must use a tn3270 terminal emulation program which provides terminal support for the specified terminal control codes used by IBM's 3270 commu-

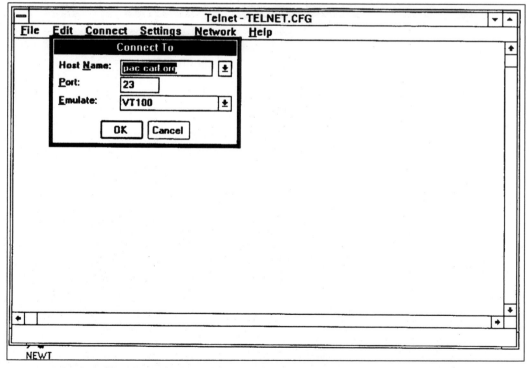

Figure 6.1 Chameleon Telnet Window

nications protocol. Chameleon provides a separate tn3270 terminal emulation program you can use to telnet to IBM hosts.

Once you enter the host address, port and type of terminal emulation you are ready to invoke a telnet session. When using Chameleon or another GUI based communications program all this requires is for you to click the OK button. Figure 6.2 illustrates the resulting connection to PAC.CARL.ORG, which represents the Public Access Catalog developed by the Colorado Alliance of Research Libraries (CARL). This site offers access to library catalogs, current article indexes and access, information databases to include encyclopedias and access to other library systems. CARL provides direct access to 21 libraries and the address PAC.CARL.ORG also provides access to almost a hundred public, academic and school libraries located throughout the United States. Thus, one call to PAC.CARL.ORG can be a researcher's dream fulfilled, as from that address you can explore a large number of libraries to locate a particular document of interest.

In the following table of Internet Telnet addresses and access methods, each

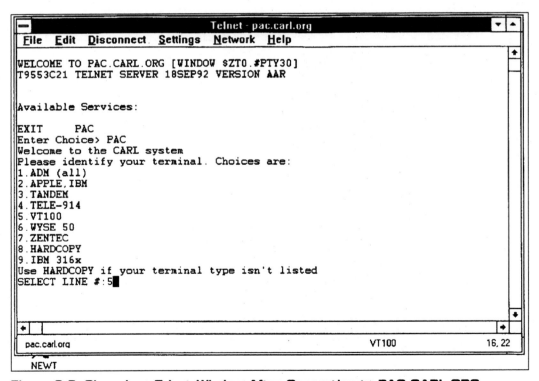

Figure 6.2 Chameleon Telnet Window After Connecting to PAC.CARL.ORG.

Telnet address can be considered as a public access account. That is, each address includes a login identifier you can use for public access. In the following table readers should note that a reference to tn3270 in the access method refers to the use of a full-screen emulation program designed for operation with a computer that supports full-screen IBM 3270 type terminal operating characteristics.

Tn3270 is similar to Telnet, except for its emulation of a 3270-type terminal device. Telnet will not work with many remote IBM host computers, requiring you to use tn3270. For most tn3270 programs the clear screen function is invoked by the CTRL-Z key combination. That key combination should be used when the message "HOLDING" or "MORE" appears at the lower right corner of your screen when using tn3270 to access an IBM host.

INTERNET TELNET DATABASE ADDRESSES AND ACCESS METHODS

Database: Aberdeen University (UK) Library
Access method: telnet to: sun.nsf.ac.uk
login as: janet, password: guest
at hostname prompt enter: uk.ac.aberdeen.library
If another login prompt appears enter: library

Database: Aberystwyth University (UK) Library
Access method: telnet to: sun.nsf.ac.uk
login as: janet, password: guest
at host name prompt enter: uk.ac.aberystwyth.library
At the username prompt enter: library

Database: Agricultural Bibliographic Information
Access method: telnet to: isn.rdns.iastate.edu
login as: querri

Database: AIDS information
Access method: telnet to: debra.doc.ca
login as: chat

Database: Air polution (Environmental Protection Agency) BBS
Access method: telnet to: ttnbbs.rtpnc.epa.gov

Database: American Bibliography of Slavic and East European Studies (ABSEES) maintained at University of Illinois Urbana-Champaign

Access method: telnet to: alexia.lis.uiuc.edu
    login as: absees use password: slavibib

Database: American Institute of Physics advanced abstracts
Access method: telnet to: pinet.aip.org
    login as: new

Database: American Mathematical Society e=MATH Database
Access method: telnet to: e-math.ams.com
    login as: e-math, password: e-math

Database: American Mathematical Society SWAIS Preprints Demo
Access method: telnet to: e-math.ams.com
    login as: waisdemo, password: waisdemo

Database: American Philosophers Association
Access method: telnet to: eis.calstate.edu
    login as: apa

Database: Appalachian State University Campus Wide Information System
Access method: telnet to: conrad.appstate.edu
    login as: info

Database: Archeologicial information
Access method: telnet to: cast.uark.edu
    login as: nadb

Database: Archie Access
Access method: telnet to any of the following locations, preferably
    the closest to your location and logon as archie:
    archie.mcgill.ca (McGill University, Canada)
    archie.ac.il (Israel)
    archie.ans.net (New York, United States)
    archie.au (Australia)
    archie.cs.huji.ac.il (Israel)
    archie.doc.ic.ac.uk (United Kingdom)
    archie.edvz.uni-linz.ac (Austria)
    archie.foretune.co.jp (Japan)
    archie.funet.fi (Finland)
    archie.kr (Korea)
    archie.kuis.kyoto-u.ac.jp (Japan)
    archie.kyoto-u.ac.jp (Japan)
    archie.luth.se (Sweden)
    archie.ncu.edu.tw (Taiwan)

archie.nz (New Zealand)
archie.rediris.es (Spain)
archie.rutgers.edu (Rutgers University, NJ, US)
archie.sogang.ac.kr (Korea)
archie.sura.net (Maryland, United States)
archie.switch.ch (Switzerland)
archie.th-darmstadt.de (Germany)
archie.univie.ac.at (Austria)
archie.unl.edu (Nebraska, United States)
archie.wide.ad.jp (Japan)
login as: archie
type: help for instructions, quit to exit.

Common HELP topics invoked by typing HELP TOPIC include:

about - information about archie

bugs - known bugs and problems

bye - exit archie

email - how to contact the archie e-mail interface

exit - same as bye

help - list of help topics

list - list the sites in the archie database

mail - mail output to a user

prog - search database for a file. Eg, prog filename. You can use
this to locate hosts that have a particular file and then browse
those hosts to see what else of a similar nature is available.

quit - same as bye

set - set a variable
　　use: set search searchtype - to tell archie how to look for in-
　　formation, where searchtype can be:

exact - for an exact match

maxhits - limit search to the specified number. Use to pre-
vent search from running a long time and generating hundreds or thousands of matches. E.g.: set maxhits 30.

regex - treat the search string as a UNIX regular expression
for matching.

sub - cause a search to be case-insensitive. When not used the default is case-sensitive.

subcase - same as sub, but case sensitive.

show - display the value of a variable

site - list the files at an archive site

unset - unset a variable

whatis - search for keyword in the software description database. E.g., whatis <TopicSubstring>

? - to list available subtopics

Archie Client Commands - use to modify the output from the use of Archie.

Format is: archie [options] searchterm, where options include:

case - to search with case-sensitive filter enabled

nocase - enable case-insensitive search

exact - return hit only when exact match occurs

reg - search string is a regular UNIX expression

m # - sets the maximum number of hits for a search

server hostname - enables an alternate archie server for the search

format string - generates output based upon format string file filename - uses the format in the specified file for your output

sort [date|host] - sorts output by date or host

domain string - use when sorting by host, uses order in string to sort the hosts.

version - prints the version number of the program

Readers should note that many times access to an Archie server will provide you with a list of other Archie servers you can consider accessing. In addition, when you initiate an Archie search, its results may provide you with a list of other FTP sites you may wish to consider exploring, even though this was not the intention behind the development of Archie.

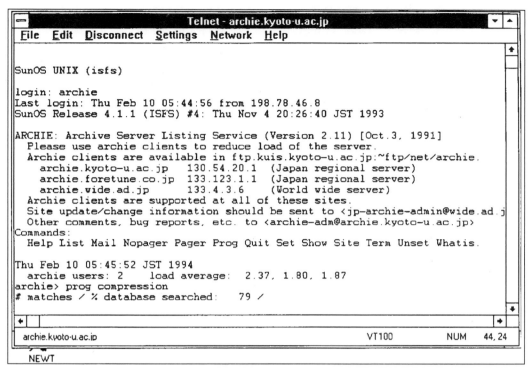

Figure 6.3 Using Chameleon to Access Archie

Figure 6.3 illustrates the use of Chameleon to access Archie at archie.kyoto-u.ac.jp. Note that the initial portion of the screen provides you with information about where you can obtain Archie client software as well as the address of two Japanese regional and one world-wide Archie server. The lower portion of Figure 6.3 illustrates the initiation of a search of the Archie database for files that have the string "compression" in their name. At the time the screen was captured 79 matches had occurred with less than one percent of the database being searched. The search of an Archie database for a common file name will generate a very large number of matches. Those matches will be displayed or mailed to you and will include the host name where the file is located, its' directory location and its' permissions.

Database: Arizona State University Library
Access method: telnet to: carl.lib.asu.edu
                 at destination prompt enter: CARL

Database: Arizona State University University Staff Directory
Access method: tn3270 to: asuvm.inre.asu.edu (login as: helloasu)

Database: Aston University (UK) Library
Access method: telnet to: sun.nsf.ac.uk
                   at login prompt enter: janet, password: guest
                   at hostname prompt enter: uk.ac.aston.geac
                   press RETURN twice

Database: Auburn University Library
Access method: tn3270 to: auducacd.duc.auburn.edu
                   enter: luis

Database: Auggie BBS
Access method: telnet to: nic.augsburg.edu
                   login as: bbs password: Eagles

Database: Australian National University Library
                   Canberra, Australia
Access method: telnet to: library.anu.edu.au
                   at login prompt enter: library

Database: Aviation information, flight planning, weather data
Access method: telnet to: duat.gtefsd.com (for certified pilots)
                   telnet to: duats.gtefsd.com (for uncertified pilots)

Database: Badboy's Inn BBS
Access method: telnet to: nameserver.aue.com (login as: bbs)
                   telnet to: badboy.aue.com (login as: bbs)

Database: Bangor University (UK) Library
Access method: telnet to: sun.nsf.ac.uk
                   at login prompt enter: janet, password: guest
                   at hostname prompt enter: uk.ac.bangor.library

Database: Bar-Ilan University (Israel) Library
Access method: telnet to: aleph.biu.ac.il
                   at username prompt enter: aleph

Database: Bates College Library
                   Lewiston, Maine
Access method: telnet to: ladd.bates.edu

Database: Bath University (UK) Library
Access method: telnet to: sun.nsf.ac.uk
                   at login prompt enter: janet, password: guest

at hostname prompt enter: uk.ac.bath.library
at login prompt enter: opac

Database: Birmingham University (UK) Library
Access method: telnet to: sun.nsf.ac.uk
at login prompt enter: janet, password: guest
at hostname prompt enter: uk.ac.birmingham.library

Database: BIRON Archive System
Social and Economic Life in the United Kingdom
Access method: telnet to: dasun.essex.ac.uk
login as: biron, password: biron

Database: Boise State University Library
Access method: telnet to: catalyst.idbsu.edu
at login prompt enter: catalyst

Database: Boston University Library
Access method: telnet to: library.bu.edu

Database: Bowdoin College Library
Access method telnet to: ladd.bates.edu

Database: Brandon University (Canada) Library
Access method: telnet to: library.brandonu.ca
at username prompt enter: libcat

Database: Bringham Young University Library
Access method: tn3270 to: lib.byu.edu
login as: library

Database: British Online Yellow Pages
Access method: telnet to: sun.nsf.ac.uk
login as:janet, password: janet
hostname: uk.ac.niss
Select U on the NISS Gateway menu
Select B on the Information Services in the UK menu

Database: British Open University International Centre for Distance
Learning
Access method: telnet to: acsvax.open.ac.uk
user name: ICDL

Database: Brookes University Library
Access method: telnet to: sun.nsf.ac.uk
at login prompt enter: janet, password: guest
at hostname prompt enter: uk.ac.oxpoly.lib

Database: Brown University Library
Access method: tn3270 to: brownvm.brown.edu
                   tab to command field and enter: dial josiah
                   tab to : josiah, press RETURN

Database: Buckyball Database of Fullerenes and Related Chemical
                   Structures (University of Arizona)
Access method: telnet to: sabio.arizona.edu
                   select: other databases and remote libraries, then
                   select: Buckyballs database

Database: Buffalo Free-Net
Access method: telnet to: freenet.buffalo.edu
                   login as: freeport

Database: California Polytechnic State University
                   Robert E. Kennedy Library
Access method: telnet to: library.calpoly.edu

Database: California State University at Fresno Library
Access method: telnet to: caticsuf.csufresno.edu
                   at login prompt enter: public

Database: Cambridge University (UK) Library
Access method: telnet to: sun.nsf.ac.uk
                   at login prompt enter: janet, password: guest
                   at hostname prompt enter:
                   uk.ac.cambridge.university.library

Database: CERN Information
                   Newsgroups, E-mail addresses and WAIS Servers
Access method: telnet to: info.cern.ch

Database: Chat Service
Access method: telnet to: ns.speedway.net 5010

Database: CIA World Factbook (Rutgers University)
Access method: telnet to: info.rutgers.edu
                   from main menu select LIBRARY
                   telnet to: hangout.rutgers.edu 98
                   from menu select: Library/Reference

Database: City University of New York Library
Access method: tn3270 to: cunyvm.cuny.edu
                   at login screen press: RETURN, enter: dial vtam

                        tab to: cunyplus, press: RETURN
                        press ctrl-z, enter: lucu

Database: Clemson University Campus Wide Information System
Access method: telnet to: eureka.clemson.edu
                        logoin as: public

Database: Clemson University Forestry and Agriculture Network
Access method: telnet to: eureka.clemson.edu
                        username: public

Database: Cleveland Free-Net BBS
Access method: telnet to: freenet-in-a.cwru.edu
                        telnet to: freenet-in-b.cwru.edu
                        telnet to: freenet-in-c.cwru.edu

Database: Colby College Library
                        Waterville, Maine
Access method: telnet to: ladd.bates.edu

Database: Colorado Alliance of Research Libraries (CARL)
Access method: telnet to: pac.carl.org
                        provides access to:
                            Auraria Library
                            Bemis Public Library (Littletton)
                            CCLINK - Community Colleges
                            Colorado School of Mines
                            Colorado State Publications
                            Colorado State University
                            Denver Public Library
                            Denver University
                            Denver University Law School
                            Government Publications
                            High Plains Regional Libraries
                            Luther College Network
                            Med Connect - Medical Libraries
                            Northwest College
                            Regis University
                            State Department of Education
                            Teikyo Loretto Hts
                            University of Colorado at Bolder
                            University of Colorado Health Sciences Center
                            University of Colorado Film/Video - Stadium

University of Colorado Law Library
University of Northern Colorado
University of Wyoming

Database: Columbia Online Information Network
Access Method: telnet to: bigcat.missouri.edu
                     login as: guest

Database: Columbia University Campus Wide Information System
Access method: telnet to: cal.cc.columbia.edu
                     login as: calendar

Database: Columbia University Library
Access method: telnet to: clio.cul.columbia.edu
                     at port n prompt enter: RETURN

Database: Consumer Access Server to search for/buy
                     CDs, software and video tapes
Access method: telnet to: columbia.ilc.com (login as: cas)
                     telnet to: holonet.net (login as:cdc)
                     telnet to: books.com

Database: Conversational Hypertext Access Technology (CHAT)
                     Government of Canada database access to AIDS
                     UNIX C Shell and Department of Communications Databases
Access method: telnet to: debra.doc.ca
                     login as: chat

Database: Cornell University Campus/Regional Information
Access method: tn3270 to: cuinfo.cornell.edu 300

Database: Cornell University Library
Access method: tn3270 to: cornellc.cit.cornell.edu
                     at userid/password enter: RETURN
                     at cp read enter: library

Database: Cranfield Institute of Technology (UK) Library
Access method: telnet to: sun.nsf.ac.uk
                     at login prompt enter: janet, password: guest
                     at hostname prompt enter: uk.ac.cranfield.library
                     at username prompt enter: janet

Database: CREN/CSNET User Name Server
Access method: telnet to: sh.cs.net
                     login as: ns

Database:	CueCosy BBS for teachers and educators
Access method:	telnet to: cue.bc.ca

Database:	Curtin University of Technology Library
	Bentley, Australia
Access method:	telnet to: cc.curtin.edu.au
	at username prompt enter: guest

Database:	Dartmouth University Library
Access method:	telnet to: lib.dartmouth.edu
	or telnet to: library. dartmouth.edu
	to access Dante Project enter: dante

Database:	Data Research Associates
	Library of Congress Records
Access method:	telnet to: dra.com

Database:	Deakin University Library
	Geelong, Victoria, Australia
Access method:	telnet to: library.deakin.oz.au
	at login prompt enter: alice

| Database: | Defense Data Network Information Center |
| Access method: | telnet to: nic.ddn.mil |

Database:	Delft University BBS (Netherlands)
Access method:	telnet to: tudrwa.tudelft.nl
	login as: bbs

Database:	Denver Free-Net
Access Method:	telnet to: freenet.hsc.colorado.edu
	login as: guest

Database	Department of Commerce Electronic
	Bulletin Board
Access method:	telnet to: ebb.stat-usa

Database:	Dundee Institute of Technology (UK) Library
Access method:	telnet to: sun.nsf.ac.uk
	at login prompt enter: janet, password: guest
	at hostname prompt enter: uk.ac.dundee-tech.library

Database:	Dundee University (UK) Library
Access method:	telnet to: sun.nsf.ac.uk
	at login prompt enter: janet, password: guest

at hostname prompt enter: uk.ac.dund.libb at
next login prompt enter: library

Database: Durham University (UK) Library
Access method: telnet to: sun.nsf.ac.uk
at login prompt enter: janet, password: guest
at hostname prompt enter: uk.ac.durham.libary

Database: E-mail address information from NIC WHOIS database
Access method: telnet to: nri.reston.va.us 185

Database: Eagle's Nest (University of Southern Mississippi) BBS
Access method: telnet to: seabass.st.usm.edu
login as: bbs, password: bbs

Database: Eastern Michigan University Library
Access method: telnet to: ccb9.merit.edu
at which host prompt enter: emu-vax
at username prompt enter: notis

Database: Economic Bulletin Board System
Access method: telnet to: ebb.stat-usa.gov
login as: trial

Database: Edinburgh University (UK) Library
Access method: telnet to: sun.nsf.ac.uk
at login prompt enter: janet, password: guest
at hostname prompt enter: uk.ac.edinburgh.geac
then press RETURN twice

Database: Educational forums/discussion groups covering
medical technology topics
Access method: telnet to: etnet.nlm.nih.gov
login as: etnet

Database: Educational Resources Information Center Documents
Access method: telnet to: acsnet.syr.edu
at > prompt enter: suvm
at userid prompt enter: suinfo
when asked to continue enter: y, then select: eric

Database: Einstein On-Line Service of the Smithsonian Astrophysical
Observatory
Access method: telnet to: einline.harvard.edu
login as: einline

Database: Emory University Library
Access method: tn3270 to: emuvml.cc.emory.edu
                       press RETURN
                       at cp read prompt enter: dial vtam
                       at cics screen enter: ESC and then 1

Database: Empire Schoolhouse (K–12 information)
Access method: telnet to: nysernet.org
                       login as: empire

Database: Endless Forest BBS
Access method: telnet to: forest.unomaha.edu 2001
                       login as: ef

Database: Environmental Protection Agency hazardous waste and
                       cleanup information
Access method: telnet to: epaibm.rtpnc.epa.gov
                       at main menu enter PUBLIC

Database: Epilepsy information
Access method: telnet to: debra.doc.ca
                       login as: CHAT

Database: Essex University (UK) Library
Access method: telnet to: sun.nsf.ac.uk at
                       login prompt enter: janet, password: guest
                       at hostname prompt enter: uk.ac.sersun1
                       at next login prompt enter: library

Database: Exeter University (UK) Library
Access method: telnet to: sun.nsf.ac.uk
                       at login prompt enter: janet, password: guest
                       at hostname prompt enter: uk.ac.ex.lib
                       at username prompt enter: library

Database: European Commission Host Organization
Access method: telnet to: echo.lu
                       login as: echo

Database: European Space Agency
Access method: telnet to: esrin.esa.it

Database: Euston, UK Monochrome Service
Access method: telnet to: euston.city.ac.uk
                       login as: mono, password is: mono

Database: FAQs about Internet

Access method: telnet to: rtfm.mit.edu
    login as: anonymous

Database: FEDIX Minority On-Line Information Service
Access method: telnet to: fedix.fie.com
    login as: fedix

Database: Federal Information Exchange research, scholarship and service information for government agencies
Access method: telnet to: fedix.fie.com
    login as: fedix

Database: FedWorld Gateway (Access to Gov't databases)
Access method: telnet to: fedworld.doc.gov

Database: Flood and Hurricane Information
Access method: telnet to: idea.ag.uiuc.edu (login as: flood)
    telnet to: exnet.iastate.edu (login as: flood)

Database: Food and Drug Administration (FDA) BBS
Access method: telnet to: fdabbs.fda.gov
    login as: bbs

Database: Food Recipes
Access method: telnet to: gatekeeper.dec.com (cd pub/recipes)
    telnet to: mthvax.cs.miami.edu (cd pub/recipes)

Database: Florida State University Library
Access method: tn3270 to: nervm.nerdc.ufl.edu
    enter: RETURN, then enter: dial vtam
    on nerdc vtam is active screen enter: nerluis

Database: Freenet (USA Today, Headline News)
Access method: telnet to: freenet-in-[a,b,c].cwru.edu
    telnet to: yfn.ysu.edu (login as: visitor)

Database: Geographic server (University of Michigan)
Access method: telnet to: martini.eecs.umich.edu 3000
    enter city name or zip code

Database: Georgia State University Library
Access method: telnet to: library.gsu.edu

Database: Glasgow University (UK) Library
Access method: telnet to: sun.nsf.ac.uk
    at login prompt enter: janet, password: guest
    at hostname prompt enter: uk.ac.glasgow.library

Database: Global Land Information System
Access method: telnet to: glis.cr.usgs.gov
                     login as: guest

Database: Gopher Demonstration
Access method: telnet to: consultant.micro.umn.edu
                     (login as: gopher) gopher.micro.umn.edu

Database: Gopher and Veronica Servers
Access method: telnet to: cat.ohiolink.edu   (login as: gopher)
                         consultant.micro.umn.edu   (login as: gopher)
                         ecosys.drdr.virginia.edu   (login as: gopher)
                         envirolink.hss.cmu.edu   (password: envirolink)
                         grits.valdosta.peachnet.edu   (login as: gopher)
                         gopher.internet.com   (login as: enews)
                         gopher.msu.edu   (login as: gopher)
                         gopher.ora.com   (login as: gopher)
                         gopher.uiuc.edu   (login as: gopher)
                         gopher.virginia.edu   (login as: gwis)
                         hermes.merit.edu   (login as: um-gopherblue)
                         infopath.ucsd.edu   (login as: infopath)
                         inform.umd.edu   (login as: gopher)
                         nicol.jvnc.net   (login as: NICOL)
                         panda.uiowa.edu   (login as: gopher)
                         scilibx.ucsc.edu   (login as: INFOSLUG)
                         seymour.md.gov   (login as: gopher)
                         sunsite.unc.edu   (login as gopher)
                         telnet.wiscinfo.wisc.edu   (login as: wiscinfo)
                         twosocks.ces.ncsu.edu   (login as: gopher)
                         ux1.cso.uiuc.edu   (login as: gopher)
                         wsuaix.csc.wsu.edu   (login as: wsuinfo)
                         info.anu.edu.au   (Australia login as: info)
                         nstn.ns.ca   (Canada, login as: fred)
                         camsrv.camosun.bc.ca   (Canada, login as: gopher)
                         tolten.puc.cl   (Chile, login as: gopher)
                         gopher.denet.dk   (Denmark, login as:
                         ecnet.ec   (Ecuador, login as: gopher)
                         gopher.isnet.is   (Iceland, login as: gopher)
                         siam.mi.cnr.it   (Italy, login as: gopher)
                         gopher.torun.edu.pl   (Poland, login as: gopher)
                         gopher.uv.es   (Spain, login as: gopher)
                         gopher.chalmers.se   (Sweden, login as: gopher)

> hugin.ub2.lu.se   (Sweden, login as: gopher)
> sunic.sunet.se   (Sweden, login as: gopher)
> info.brad.ac.uk   (United Kingdom login as: info)

Database: Griffith University Library
                 Nathan, Australia
Access method: telnet to: library.gu.edu.au

Database: Ham Radio call-signs
Access method: telnet to: callsign.cs.buffalo.edu 2000
                 telnet to: ham.njit.edu 2000
                 telnet to: ns.risc.net
                 login as: hamradio

Database: Harris polling information (University of North Carolina)
Access method: tn3270 to: uncvm1.oit.unc.edu
                 login with id of IRSS1, password IRSS1

Database: Harvard University Online Library Information System
Access method: telnet to: hollis.harvard.edu
                 press RETURN, enter: hollis

Database: Hawaii State Government Information
Access method: telnet to: access.uhcc.hawaii.edu
                 login as: visitor, password: visitor
                 select GUEST BOOK to register

Database: Heartland Peoria Illinois Free-Net
Access Method: telnet to: heartland.bradley.edu
                 login as: bbsguest

Database: Health Sciences Information Network
                 Shared Library System of Six Health Science Institutions
Access method: telnet to: hslc.org
                 login as: SAL

Database: Hebrew University (Israel) Library
Access method: telnet to: aleph.huji.ac.il
                 at username prompt enter: aleph

Database: Helsinki University Library
                 Helsinki Finland
Access method: telnet to: hyk.helsinki.fi
                 at login prompt enter: hello yourname,user.clas01
                 select terminal type, at location prompt (Anna

kokelma) enter 100
enter /LANG 1 for English , /LANG 2 for Swedish

Database: Heriot-Watt University Library
Access method: telnet to: sun.nsf.ac.uk
                   login as: janet, password: guest
                   at hostname prompt enter: uk.ac.heriot-watt.library

Database: High-Performance Computing News and Information Service
Access method: telnet to: hpcwire.ans.net
                   login as: hpcwire

Database: Holy Cross Campus and School Information
Access method: telnet to: hcacad.holycross.edu
                   login as: view, password: view

Database: HP Calculator BBS
Access method: telnet to: hpcvbbs.cv.hp.com
                   login as: new

Database: Historian Gopher (HNSOURSE) maintained by the Academic
                   Computer Service and Department of History of the
                   University of Kansas
Access method: telnet to: hnsourse.cc.ukan.edu
                   login as: history

Database: Historical information
Access method: telnet to: ukanaix.cc.ukans.edu
                   login as: history
                   telnet to: clus1.ulcc.ac.uk

Database: Hytelnet Server Access to University and Library
                   Catalogues World Wide
Access method: telnet to: access.usask.ca   (login as: hytelnet)
                      info.anu.edu.au   (login as: library)
                      info.ccit.arizona.edu   (login as: hytelnet)
                      info.mcc.ac.uk   (login as: hytelnet)
                      laguna.epcc.edu   (login as: library)
                      library.adelaide.edu.au   (login as: access)
                      nctuccca.edu.tw   (login as: hytelnet)
                      rsl.ox.ac.uk   (login as : hytelnet)

Database: IDS World Network Public Access System
Access method: telnet to: ids.net (login as: guest)

Database: Indiana University Library
Access method: telnet to: iuis.ucs.indiana.edu
                at userid prompt enter: guest
                or tn3270 to: iuis3270.ucs.indiana.edu
                at userid prompt enter: guest

Database: Information System for Advanced Academic Computing
Access method: telnet to: isaac.engr.washington.edu

Database: Iowa State University Library
Access method: telnet to: isn.iastate.edu
                at dial prompt enter: lib
                after entering terminal type, at MVS welcome screen
                enter: scholar

Database: Instant Math Preprints (Yale University)
Access method: tn3270 to: yalevm.ycc.yale.edu
                use userid, password and operator id Math1,
                Math2, Math3, Math4 or Math5

Database: Internet Relay Chat
Access method: telnet to: irc.demon.co.uk (login as: irc)
                telnet to: sci.dixie.edu (login as: irc)
                telnet to: wbrt.wb.psu.edu (login as: irc)
                telnet to: bradenville.andrew.cmu.edu

Database: Internet WHOIS list of users and sites
Access method: telnet to: nic.ddn.mil
                type: whois [name |site]

Database: InterNIC Directory and Database Services Telnet Interface
Access method: telnet to: ds.internic.net
                login as: guest

Database: InterNIC white pages
Access method: telnet to: rs.internic.net
                type whois |gopher |wais and press return

Database: Iowa Political Stock Market Research Project
Access method: telnet to: ipsm.biz.uiowa.edu

Database: Iowa State Computer Association BBS
Access method: telnet to: bbs.isca.uiowa.edu (login as: guest)
                telnet to: whip.isca.uiowa.edu (login as: guest)
                telnet to: pulse.isca.uiowa.edu (login as: guest)

Database: ITU Telecom Information Exchange Services
                       Interactive Gopher Client
Access method: telnet to: into.itu.ch
                       login as: gopher

Database: JANET Public Access Directory Service
Access method: telnet to: sun.nsf.ac.uk
                       login as: janet, use password: janet
                       hostname: uk.ac.jnt.dir

Database: Jewish interest information
Access method: telnet to: vms.huji.ac.il
                       login as: jewishnet

Database: Johns Hopkins University Library
Access method: telnet to: jhuvm.hcf.jhu.edu
                       enter: logon msel

Database: Johns Hopkins University Applied Physics Laborator Library
Access method: telnet to: library.jhuapl.edu
                       press RETURN, at ID prompt enter: lib

Database: Kalamazoo College Library
Access method: telnet to: ccb9.merit.edu
                       at which host prompt enter: kzoo-lib

Database: Kansas State University Library
Access method: tn3270 to: ksuvm.ksu.edu
                       at logon prompt enter: lynx
                       at cics screen press RETURN

Database: Kent State University Library
Access method: telnet to: catalyst.kent.edu
                       press RETURN, enter terminal type
                       at select application prompt enter: a
                       at CICS screen enter: luks
                       or tn3270 to: kentvm.kent.edu
                       tab to command and enter: dial vtam
                       at select application prompt enter: A
                       at CICS screen enter: luks

Database: Knowbot search using netaddress program
Access method: telnet to: nri.reston.va.us 185   or
                       telnet to: sol.bucknell.edu 185
                       at > prompt enter appropriate Knowbot command

org name - list persons by their organization

query username - search for specified username

quit - quit use of netaddress program

services - list services available from netaddress

service - add a directory service for searching
    qualify with directory e.g.: service attmail
    qualify with country e.g.: service attmail us

username - search for specified username

Database:	Lafayette University Integrated Networked Campus
Access method:	telnet to: lafibm.lafayette.edu When LINC logo apprears press Enter, on next screen type DIAL MUSIC and use GUEST as ID and as password
Database:	Lancaster University Library
Access method:	telnet to: sun.nsf.ac.uk at login prompt enter: janet, password: guest at hostname prompt enter: uk.ac.lancaster.library
Database:	Law Library
Access method:	telnet to: fatty.law.cornell.edu gopher.law.csuohio.edu lawnet.law.columbia.edu (login as: lawnet) liberty.uc.wlu.edu www.law.indiana.edu (World Wide Web Law Server)
Database:	Leeds University Library
Access method:	telnet to: sun.nsf.ac.uk at login prompt enter: janet, password: guest at hostname prompt enter: uk.ac.leeds.libcat
Database:	Legal Information Institute - Cornell Law School (Information on US Copyright Act, US Patent Act, US Lanham Act)
Access method:	telnet to: fatty.law.cornell.edu login as: www
Database:	Leicester University Library and access to other UK libraries
Access method:	telnet to: sun.nsf.ac.uk at login prompt enter: janet, password: guest

at hostname prompt enter: uk.ac.leicester.library
at username prompt enter: library

Database: Lehigh University Campus Wide Information System
Access method: tn3270 to: ibm1.cc.lehigh.edu
                   at VM prompt type DIAL MUSIC and at the ID prompt
                   type LUNA

Database: Lehigh University Library
Access method: telnet to: asa.lib.lehigh.edu

Database: Librarian Yellow Pages
Access method: telnet to: database.carl.org

Database: Library Catalogues
Access method: telnet to: access.usask.ca (login as: hytelnet)
                   telnet to: info.anu.edu.au (login as: library)
                   telnet to: info.ccit.arizona.edu (login as: hytelnet)
                   telnet to: laguna.epcc.edu (login as: library)
                   telnet to: library.adelaide.edu.au (login as: access)
                   telnet to: rsl.ox.ac.uk (login as: hytelnet)

Database: Library of Congress bibliograph information
Access method: telnet to: locis.loc.gov
                   Searching hours (Eastern Standard Time) are:
                       Monday–Friday: 06:30 to 21:30
                       Saturday: 08:00 to 17:00
                       Sunday: 13:00 to 17:00
                   during off-hours telnet to: dra.com

Database: Library of Congress MARVEL information system
                   telnet to: marvel.loc.gov 70
                   login as: MARVEL

Database: Liverpool University Library
Access method: telnet to: sun.nsf.ac.uk
                   at login prompt enter: janet, password: guest
                   at hostname prompt enter: uk.ac.liverpool.library
                   enter terminal type, when screen clears press RETURN

Database: London University British Library of Political and
                   Economic Science
Access method: telnet to: sun.nsf.ac.uk
                   at login prompt enter: janet, password: guest
                   at hostname prompt enter: uk.ac.lse.blpes
                   at username prompt enter: library

Database: London University Central Library Consortium
Access method: telnet to: sun.nsf.ac.uk
                at login prompt enter: janet, password: guest
                at hostname prompt enter: uk.ac.lon.consull
                at username prompt enter: library

Database: London Guidhall University (UK) Library
Access method: telnet to: sun.nsf.ac.uk
                at login prompt enter: janet, password: guest
                at hostname prompt enter: uk.ac.city-poly.tower-vax
                at username prompt enter: library
                at next username prompt enter: library

Database: London University, Imperial College Library
Access method: telnet to: sun.nsf.ac.uk
                at login prompt enter: janet, password: guest
                at hostname prompt enter: uk.ac.imperial.lib
                at username prompt enter: library

Database: London University, Kings College Library
Access method: telnet to: sun.nsf.ac.uk
                at login prompt enter: janet, password: guest
                at hostname prompt enter: uk.ac.kcl.lib
                at username prompt enter: library

Database: London University, Royal Holloway and Bedford New College Library
Access method: telnet to: sun.nsf.ac.uk
                at login prompt enter: janet, password: guest
                at hostname prompt enter: uk.ac.rhbnc.lib
                at username prompt enter: library

Database: London University, University College Library
Access method: telnet to: sun.nsf.ac.uk
                at login prompt enter: janet, password: guest
                at hostname prompt enter: uk.ac.ucl.lib
                at username prompt enter: library

Database: Lorain County (Elyria, OH) Free-Net
Access Method: telnet to: freenet.lorain.oberlin.edu
                login as: guest

Database: Loughborough University Library
Access method: telnet to: sun.nsf.ac.uk

at login prompt enter: janet, password: guest
at hostname prompt enter: uk.ac.loughborough.library

Database: Louis Harris Data Center
Institute for Research in Social Science
Access method: th3270 to: uncvm1.oit.unc.edu
login as: irss1 or irss2, password: irss

Database: Lunar and Planetary Institute
(Astronomy, Geology, Geophysics Information)
Access method: telnet to: lpi.jsc.nasa.gov
login as: lpi

Database: Lund University Library
Access method: telnet to: lolita.lu.se
at login prompt enter: hello telnet.lolita
for English enter: /lang 1

Database: Macintosh Usergroup (Austria)
Access method: telnet to: amdalinz.edvz.uni-linz.ac.at
at UserId/Password prompt press return

Database: Manchester University Library
Access method: telnet to: sun.nsf.ac.uk
at login prompt enter: janet, password: guest
at hostname prompt enter: uk.ac.man.cn.xb
at class prompt enter: library

Database: Maricopa Community Colleges Library System
Access method: telnet to: lib.maricopa.edu
at username prompt enter: lib

Database: Marquette University Library
Access method: telnet to: libus.csd.mu.edu

Database: Martin Luther King, Jr. Bibliographic References
Access method: telnet to: forsythetn.stanford.edu
account: socrates, SELECT MLK

Database: Massachusetts Institute of Technology Library
Access method: telnet to: library.mit.edu

Database: Math Algorithm Bibliographies
Access method: telnet to: research.att.com
login as: walk

Database: Maryland State Government Information
Access method: telnet to: seymour.md.gov

Database: McGill University Library
Access method: tn3270 to: mvs.mcgill.ca

Database: McMaster University Library
Access method: tn3270 to: mcmvm1.cis.mcmaster.ca
                           press the F9 key, tab to morrisp, select entering: s

Database: MELVYL (University of California) online library
                           catalog and periodical listings
Access method: telnet to: melvyl.ucop.edu

Database: Meckler Publishing's Electronic Information Service
Access method: telnet to: nicol.jvnc.net (login as: nicol)

Database: Michigan State University Library
Access method: tn3270 to: magic.lib.msu.edu
                           at vm screen tab to command line, enter: dial magic
                           or telnet to: merit.msu.edu
                           at which host prompt enter: magic
                           tab to command line, enter: dial magic

Database: MichNet - Merit Computer Network
Access method: telnet to: hermes.merit.edu

Database: MindVOX Public Access BBS
Access method: telnet to: phantom.com
                           login as: mindvox +'guest' at ID prompt

Database: Minority Online Information Service
Access method: telnet to: fedix.fie.com
                           login as: molis

Database: Mississippi State University Campus Wide
                           Information System
Access method: telnet to: isis.msstate.edu
                           login as: msuinfo

Database: MIT TechInfo
Access method: telnet to: techinfo.mit.edu

Database: Mount Allison University Library
Access method: telnet to: bigmac.mta.ca
                           at username prompt enter: catalog

Database: Murdoch University Library
Access method: telnet to: library.murdoch.edu.au

Database: NASA Ames Research Center Electronic Phone Book
Access method: use whois to: orion.arc.nasa.gov
                     example:
                         to locate held: whois -h orion.arc.nasa.gov held

Database: NASA Mid-Continent Regional Technology Transfer
                     Center Bulletin Board System
Access method: telnet to: technology.com
                     login as: guest

Database: NASA Network Information Center Online Aid System
Access method: telnet to: dftnic.gsfc.nasa.gov
                     Username: DFTNIC

Database: NASA Spacelink satellite/spacecraft information
Access method: telnet to: spacelink.msfc.nasa.gov

Database: NASE Extragalactic Database
Access method: telnet to: ipac.caltech.edu
                     login as: ned

Database: National Capital (Ottawa, Canada) Free-Net
Access Method: telnet to: freenet.carleton.ca
                     login as: guest

Database: National Education BBS
Access method: telnet to: nebbs.nersc.gov
                     login as: guest

Database: National Gallery of Art Database
Access method: telnet to: ursus.maine.edu
                     logon as: ursus
                     at main menu press B, then 4 to access
                     the database

Database: National Ham Radio Call-Sign Callbook
Access method: telnet to: callsign.cs.buffalo.edu 2000

Database: National Information Services & Systems (NISSPAC)
                     Library
Access method: telnet to: sun.nsf.ac.uk
                     at hostname prompt enter: janet, password: guest
                     at next hostname prompt enter: uk.ac.niss.pac
                     at dot (.) prompt enter: logon nisscat

Database: National Library of Wales
Access method: telnet to: sun.nsf.ac.uk
                 at login prompt enter: janet, password: guest
                 at hostname prompt enter: uk.ac.nat-lib-wales
                 at logon prompt enter: enguiry

Database: National Nuclear Data Center
                 Brookhaven National Laboratory
Access method: telnet to: bnlnd2.dne.bnl.gov
                 username: nndc

Database: National Oceanic and Atmospheric Admin (NOAA)
Access method: telnet to: esdiml.nodc.noaa.gov
                 login as: noaadir

Database: National Radio Astronomy Observatory
Access method: telnet to: zia.aoc.nrao.edu
                 login as: vlais

Database: National Science Foundation Science & Technology
Access method: telnet to: stis.nsf.gov
                 login as: public

Database: National Space Development Agency of Japan
Access method: telnet to: nsaeoc.eoc.nasda.go.jp
                 login as: nasdadir

Database: National Space Science Data Center
Access method: telnet to: nssdc.gsfc.nasa.gov
                 login as: nodis

Database: Netcom Internet Service Provider BBS
Access method: telnet to: netcom.netcom.com
                 login as: guest, enter CR at password prompt

Database: NetFind Prototype Internet White Pages Directory
Access method: telnet to any of the following locations,logon as: netfind
                 archie.au   (AARNet, Melbourne, Australia)
                 bruno.cs.colorado.edu   (University of Colorado,Boulder)
                 ds.internic.net   (InterNIC Directory and Database
                     Services, S. Plainfield, NJ)
                 lincoln.technet.sg   (Technet Unit, Singapore)
                 macs.ee.mcgill.ca   (McGill University, Canada)
                 malloco.ing.puc.cl   (Catholic University of Chile,
                     Santiago, Chile)

monolith.cc.ic.ac.uk   (Imperial College, London, England)

mudhoney.micro.umn.edu   (University of Minnesota)

netfind.oc.com   (OpenConnect Systems, Dallas, TX)

netfind.vslib.cz   (Liberec University of Technology, Czech Republic)

nic.nm.kr   (Korea Network Information Center, Taejon, Korea)

nic.uakom.sk   (Academy of Sciences, Banska Bystrica, Slovakia)

redmont.cis.uab.edu   (University of Alabama, Birmingham, Alabama)

Database: Net Happenings Archive
Access method: telnet to: gopher.cni.org
                 login as: brsuser

Database: Net Mail Hosts Database for Bitnet/UUCP addresses
Access method: telnet to: merit-telnet-gw.msu.edu
                 at WHICH HOST? prompt enter: netmailsites

Database: Net Mail Site Service
                 (Enter site name obtain node name and vice versa)
Access method: telnet to: hermes.merit.edu
                 at WHICH HOST? prompt enter: netmailsites

Database: Newton (computer science, science, math) BBS
Access method: telnet to: newton.dep.anl.gov
                 login as: cocotext

Database: New Mexico State University Campus Wide Information
Access method: telnet to: info.nmsu.edu
                 login as: info

Database: New Mexico State University Library
Access method: telnet to: library.nmsu.edu

Database: New York Public Library
Access method: telnet to: nyplgate.nypl.org

Database: New York University Information System
Access method: telnet to: info.nyu.edu

Database: New York University Library
Access method: telnet to: bobcat.nyu.edu
                     press RETURN

Database: NIX-Hensa/Micros Information Exchange
                     (Software Clearinghouse in the UK)
Access method: telnet to: micros.hensa.uk
                     login as: hensa, password: hensa

Database: NNTP News Service
Access method: telnet to: vaxc.cc.monash.edu.au (Australia)
                     telnet to: munnari.oz.au (Australia)
                     telnet to: news.fu-berlin.de (Germany)
                     telnet to: etl.go.jp (Japan)

Database: North Carolina State University Campus/School Info
Access method: telnet to: ccvax1.cc.ncsu.edu
                     telnet to: happenings.ncsu.edu
                     login as: info

Database: Northeastern Ohio Universities College of Medicine
                     Library and Campus Information
Access method: telnet to: scotty.neoucom.edu
                     at login prompt enter: neocat
                     for command list enter: help

Database: Northwestern University Library
Access method: tn3270 to: nuacvm.acns.nwu.edu
                     tab to command line and enter: dial vtam
                     at application id prompt enter: library
                     or telnet to: nvacvm.acns.nwu.edu

Database: Nottingham University Library
Access method: telnet to: sun.nsf.ac.uk
                     at login prompt enter: janet, password: guest
                     at hostname prompt enter: uk.ac.nottingham.library
                     at username prompt enter: library

Database: Novanet Libraries in Nova Scotia, Canada
                     provides access to libraries at:
                         Atlantic School of Technology
                         Dalhousie University
                         Mount Saint Vincent University
                         Nova Scotia College of Art and Design
                         Saint Mary's University

                         Technical University of Nova Scotia
                         University College of Cape Breton
                         University of Kings College
Access method: telnet to: novanet.dal.ca

Database: Nuclear Data Center
Access method: telnet to: bnlnd2.dne.bnl.gov
                         login as: nndc

Database: Nyx (University of Denver) BBS
Access method: telnet to: nyx.cs.du.edu
                         login as: new

Database: Oberlin College Library
Access method: telnet to: obis.lib.oberlin.edu

Database: Occidental College
Access method: telnet to: oasys.lib.oxy.edu

Database: Oceanic Information Center - University of Delaware
Access method: telnet to: delocn.udel.edu
                         login as: info

Database: Ohio State University Library
Access method: telnet to: lcs.us.ohio-state.edu

Database: Olajier (Imperial College, London) BBS
Access method: telnet to: castor.ee.ic.ac.uk
                         login as: Olajier, password: Olajier

Database: Old Dominion University Library
Access method: telnet to: geac.lib.odu.edu

Database: Open University Library Service
Access method: telnet to: sun.nsf.ac.uk
                         at login prompt enter: janet, password: guest
                         at hostname prompt enter: uk.ac.open.library
                         at username prompt enter: oulibrary

Database: Oregon State University William Jasper Keer Library
Access method: telnet to: oasis.kerr.orst.edu
                         at login prompt enter: oasis

Database: O'Reilly and Associates
                         Book Publishers
Access method: telnet to: ora.com
                         login as: gopher

Database: OuluBox (Finish) BBS
Access method: telnet to: tolsun.oulu.fi
                    login as: box

Database: Oxford University Library
Access method: telnet to: sun.nsf.ac.uk
                    at login prompt enter: janet, password: guest
                    at hostname prompt enter: uk.ac.ox.pacx
                    at service prompt enter: library

Database: Paddington, UK Monochrome Service
Access method: telnet to: paddington.city.ac.uk
                    login as: mono, password is: mono

Database: Paradise X.500 Directory Services Pilot
Access method: telnet to: paradise.ulcc.ac.uk
                    login as: dua

Database: Pennsylvania State University Campus and
                    School Information
Access method: tn3270 to: psuvm.psu.edu
                    login as: EBB on command line

Database: Pennsylvania State University Library
Access method: telnet to: lias.psu.edu

Database: PENpages agriculturally oriented database
Access method: telnet to: psupen.psu.edu
                    login as: PNOTPA

Database: Periodic Tables
Access method: telnet to: camms2.caos.kunl.nl

Database: Physics Information Network Bibliographical
                    Databases
Access method: telnet to: pinet.aip.org
                    login as: new, password: new

Database: Planetary Data Systems
Access method: telnet to: jpl-pds.nasa.gov
                    Username: pds_guest, no password required

Database: Pima Community College Campus Information
Access method: telnet to: pimacc.pima.edu
                    login as: pimainfo

Database: Portland State University Library
Access method: telnet to: psulib.cc.pdx.edu
                      at login prompt enter: dialin

Database: Princeton University Library
Access method: telnet to: catalog.princeton.edu

Database: Princeton University Manuscripts Catalog
Access method: tn3270 to: pucc.rrinceton.edu
                      at vm screen press: ENTER
                      to access online research resources enter: folio

Database: Princeton University News Network
Access method: telnet or tn3270 to: pucc.princeton.edu
                      When VM 370 logo appears clear it. Instead of logging
                      on, enter pnn.

Database: Privacy Rights Clearinghouse Bulletin Board Service
Access method: telnet to: teetot.acusd.edu
                      login as: privacy

Database: PSI White Pages list of Internet users
Access method: telnet to: wp.psi.com
                      login as: FRED

Database: Public access to Unix
Access method: telnet to: nyx.cs.du.edu
                      login as: new
                      telnet to: hermes.merit.edu
                      telnet to: m-net.ann-arbor.mi.us
                      login as: newuser

Database: Purdue University Library
                      also provides access to libraries at:
                          Ball State University
                          Indiana State University
                          Indiana University
                          University of Southern Indiana
                          Vincennes University
Access method: tn3270 to: lib.cc.purdue.edu

Database: Queen's University Library Network
Access method: tn3270 to: qucdnadm.queensu.ca

Database: Queens University Library Belfast
Access method: telnet to: sun.nsf.ac.uk

at login prompt enter: janet, password: guest
at hostname prompt enter: uk.ac.queens-belfast.library

Database: Reading University Library
Access method: telnet to: sun.nsf.ac.uk
at login prompt enter: janet, password: guest
at hostname prompt enter: uk.ac.rdg.linnet

Database: Rensselaer Polytechnic Institute Library and Campus Information
Access method: telnet to: infotrac.rpi.edu

Database: Research Activity and Products Information Database (RAPID) maintained at University of Edinburgh, UK
Access method: telnet to: ercvax.ed.ac.uk
Username: RAPID, password: RAPID

Database: Rice University Fondren Library
Access method: tn3270 to: library.rice.edu
at connect press RETURN

Database: Rochester Institute of Technology Library
Access method: telnet to: ritvax.isc.rit.edu

Database: Royal Melbourne Institute of Technology Library
Access method: telnet to: ccannex02.rmit.oz.au
at connect press RETURN
at menu select vicnet2400 or vicnet9600
at which system prompt enter: matlas
or telnet to: vicnet.xx.rmit.oz.au
at which system prompt enter: matlas

Database: Rutgers University Campus and School Info
Access method: telnet to: info.rutgers.edu 98

Database: Rutgers University Bulletin Board Service
Access method: telnet to: quartz.rutgers.edu
login as: bbs

Database: Rutgers University Libraries
Access method: telnet to: library.rutgers.edu

Database: Rutherford Appleton Laboratory Library
Access method: telnet to: sun.nsf.ac.uk
at login prompt enter: janet, password: guest

at hostname prompt enter: uk.ac.rutherford.ibm-b
enter page size (usually 24)
at login prompt enter: lib4, or lib5, or lib7 or lib8
at password prompt enter password based upon season,
e.g.: dec–feb 94 is winter93
     mar–may 94 is spring94
     jun–aug 94 is summer94
     sept–nov 94 is autumn94

Database: St. Andrews University Library
Access method: telnet to: sun.nsf.ac.uk
at login prompt enter: janet, password: guest
at hostname prompt enter: uk.ac.st-andrews.lib
for circulation system at hostname prompt enter:
   uk.ac.st-andrews.circon

Database: St. Johns University (Tiny) BBS
Access method: telnet to: tiny.computing.csbsju.edu
login as: bbs

Database: San Diego State University Campus Information
Access method: telnet to: wintermute.sdsu.edu

Database: Science and Technology Information System
Access method: telnet to: stis.nsf.gov
login as: public

Database: Scrabble board game
Access method: telnet to: phoenix.aps.muohio.edu

Database: SENDIT bbs (North Dakota K—12 Educational Network)
Access method: telnet to: sendit.nodak.edu
login as: bbs using password: sendit2me

Database: SFI BBS
Access method: telnet to: bbs.santafe.edu
login as: bbs

Database: Shakespeare on the Internet
Access method: telnet to: lib.dartmouth.edu
type: SELECT FILE, no password required

Database: Sheffield University Library
Access method: telnet to: sun.nsf.ac.uk
at login prompt enter: janet, password: guest
at hostname prompt enter: uk.ac.sheffield.library

Database: Smithsonian Institute Bibliographic Information System
Access method: telnet to: gandalf.si.edu
                   at service prompt enter: SIBIS

Database: Software Information Server
Access method: telnet to: rusinfo.rus.uni-stuttgart.de
                   login as: info
                   telnet to: askhp.ask.uni-karlsruhe.de
                   login as: ask, password: ask

Database: Southeast Florida AIDS Information Network Database
Access method: telnet to: 129.171.78.1
                   login as: library, select L on main menu,
                   select 1 on next menu

Database: Southern Methodist University Library
Access method: tn3270 to: vm.cis.smu.edu
                   tab to command line, enter: dial vtam
                   press RETURN, at sign-on scree enter: poni
                   at cics screen press ctrl-z to clear, enter:lusm

Database: Southampton University Library
Access method: telnet to: sun.nsf.ac.uk
                   at login prompt enter: janet, password: guest
                   at hostname prompt enter: uk.ac.southampton.using
                   at the dot (.) prompt enter: login using

Database: South West Research Data Display and Analysis Center
Access method: telnet to: espsun.space.swri.edu

Database: Space environment resource information
Access method: telnet to: envnet.gsfc.nasa,gov
                   login as: envnet, password: henniker

Database: SpaceMet BBS
                   (Science and Space Exploration Information)
Access method: telnet to: spacemet.phast.umass.edu

Database: Sports Schedules
Access method: telnet to: culine.colorado.edu 859 (NBA)
                   telnet to: culine.colorado.edu 860 (NHL)
                   telnet to: culine.colorado.edu 862 (MLB)
                   telnet to: culine.colorado.edu 863 (NFL)

Database: Stock market information
Access method: telnet to: rahul.net
                         login as: GUEST

Database: Staffordshire Polytechnic Library
Access method: telnet to: sun.nsf.ac.uk
                         at login prompt enter: janet, password: guest
                         at hostname prompt enter: uk.ac.stafpol.lib

Database: STInfo (Hubble Telescope information)
Access method: telnet to: stinfo.hq.eso.org
                         login as: stinfo

Database: Strathclyde University Andersonian Library
Access method: telnet to: sun.nsf.ac.uk
                         at login prompt enter: janet, password: guest
                         at hostname prompt enter: uk.ac.strathclyde.library

Database: Sussex University/ University of Brighton Library
Access method: telnet to: sun.nsf.ac.uk
                         at login prompt enter: janet, password: guest
                         at hostname prompt enter: uk.ac.sussex.library

Database: Swansea University Library
Access method: telnet to: sun.nsf.ac.uk
                         at login prompt enter: janet, password: guest
                         at hostname prompt enter: uk.ac.swansea.library
                         at username prompt enter: library

Database: Syracuse University Campus and School Information
Access method: telnet to: acsnet.syr.edu
                         login as: suinfo on command line

Database: Tallahassee Free-Net
Access Method: telnet to: freenet.fsu.edu
                         login as: visitor

Database: TC Forum - University of Nebraska, Lincoln host
                         system dedicated to education
Access method: telnet to: tcforum.unl.edu

Database: Technology Resources in Education, California
                         Technology Project(for educators to communicate with
                         other educators)
Access method: telnet to: eis.calstate.edu
                         login as: ctp and request an account from main menu

Database: Tel Aviv University (Israel) Library
Access method: telnet to: tauvax.tau.ac.il
                     at username prompt enter: aleph

Database: Texas A&M Library
Access method: tn3270 to: tammvs1.tamu.edu
                     for applications enter: notis

Database: Texas Cancer Data Center
Access method: telnet to: txcancer.mda.uth.tmc.edu
                     login as: TCDC

Database: Thames Polytechnic Library
Access method: telnet to: sun.nsf.ac.uk
                     at login prompt enter: janet, password: guest
                     at hostname prompt enter: uk.ac.thames.lib

Database: The Picayune (North Dakota Higher Education) BBS
Access method: telnet to: milo.ndsu.nodak.edu (login as: new)
                     telnet to: star96.nodak.edu (login as: new)
                     telnet to: star24.nodak.edu (login as: new)
                     telnet to: star12.nodak.edu (login as: new)

Database: Tilburg University Library Access
Access method: telnet to: kublib.kub.nl
                     login as: kubgids

Database: Tri-State Online Free-Net
Access method: telnet to: cbos.uc.edu
                     login as: cbos,visitor,9999
                     telnet to: tso.uc.edu (login as: visitor)

Database: Tufts University Library
Access method: telnet to: library.tufts.edu
                     at username prompt enter: tulips

Database: Universidad de las Americas, Pueblas Library
Access method: telnet to: bibes.pue.udlap.ma
                     at username prompt enter: library

Database: Universitaet des Saarlandes Library
Access method: telnet to: unisb.rz.uni-sb.de
                     at slash (/) prompt enter: .a logon ub, ub

Database: University of Adelaide Barr Smith Library
Access method: telnet to: library.adelaide.edu.au
                     at login prompt enter: bslnet

Database: University of Akron Library
Access method: telnet to: library.uakron.edu

Database: University of Arizona Library
Access method: telnet to: idx.telcom.arizona.edu
                       at connect press RETURN
                       AT > PROMPT ENTER: GEAC

Database: University of Arkansas Campus Information
Access method: telnet to: uafsysb.uark.edu
                       login as: info

Database: University of Bristol (UK) Library
Access method: telnet to: sun.nsf.ac.uk
                       at login prompt enter: janet, password: guest
                       at hostname prompt enter: uk.ac.bristol.lib
                       at username prompt enter: library

Database: University of Buffalo Library
Access method: telnet to: bison.cc.buffalo.edu

Database: University of Calgary Library
Access method: telnet to: develnet.ucalgary.ca
                       at request prompt enter: library

Database: University of California Berkeley
                       Network Infomation
Access method: telnet to: netinfo.berkeley.edu 117

Database: University of California at Berkeley Library
Access method: telnet to: gopac.berkeley.edu

Database: University of Canberra Library
Access method: telnet to: library.canberra.edu.au
                       at login prompt enter: uclid

Database: University of Chicago Library
Access method: telnet to: olorin.uchicago.edu
                       at class prompt enter: lib48
                       at connected prompt press RETURN

Database: University of Cincinnati Library
Access method: telnet to: uc7171.uc.edu
                       after entering terminal type enter: uclid

Database: University of Colorado at Boulder Campus Information
Access method: telnet to: culine.colorado.edu 852
                    login as: CULINE

Database: University of Colorado at Colorado Springs Library
Access method: telnet to: arlo.colorado.edu
                    at login prompt enter: arlo

Database: University of Dayton Roesch Library
Access method: telnet to: udaprl.oca.udayton.edu
                    at blank screen enter: login pub02, password:public

Database: University of Delaware College of Marine Studies
Access method: telnet to: delocn.udel.edu
                    login as: info

Database: University of Delaware Library
Access method: telnet to: delcat.udel.edu

Database: University of Denver Campus Information
Access method: telnet to: du.edu
                    login as: atdu

Database: University of Georgia EduNET Bulletin Board System
                    for educators in the state of Georgia
Access method: telnet to: gcedunet.peachnet.edu

Database: University of Hawaii Library System
                    provides access to other libraries throughout the US
Access method: telnet to: starmaster.uhcc.hawaii.edu
                    at class prompt enter: lib

Database: University of Illinois at Chicago Library
Access method: tn3270 to: uicvm.uic.edu
                    at signon screen press: RETURN
                    enter: luis
                    tab to first s of notis and press: RETURN

Database: University of Illinois at Urbana/Champaign Library
Access method: tn3270 to: uicmvsa.aiss.uic.edu
                    tn3270 to: illinet.aiss.uiuc.edu

Database: University of Iowa Library
Access method: tn3270 to: uidpjes2.adp.uiowa.edu
                    select terminal id, then enter: oasis

or telnet to: oasis.uiowa.edu
select terminal id, select oasis from menu

Database: University of Kansas Campus Wide Information
Access method: telnet to: ukanaix.cc.ukans.edu

Database: University of Kansas Library
Access method: telnet to: kuhub.cc.ukans.edu
                      at username prompt enter: relay
                      at system prompt enter: ocat

Database: University of Konstanz (Germany) Library
Access method: telnet to: polydos.uni-konstanz.de 775

Database: University of Maine
Access method: telnet to: ursus.maine.edu
                      at login prompt enter: ursus

Database: University of Maryland
Access method: telnet to: info.umd.edu
                      login as: info

Database: University of Maryland Library System
                      provides access to libraries at:
                           University of Maryland
                           University of Maryland Law Library
                           University of Maryland Baltimore County
                           University of Maryland College Park
                           University of Maryland Eastern Shore
                           University of Maryland University College
Access method: telnet to: victor.umd.edu

Database: University of Massachusetts
                      Image Description
Access method: telnet to: cicero.cs.umass.edu

Database: University of Massachusetts, Boston Library
Access method: telnet to: libra.cc.umb.edu
                      at username prompt enter: catalog

Database: University of Melbourne Library
Access method: telnet to: library.unimelb.edu.au

Database: University of Michigan Library
Access method: telnet to: hermes.merit.edu
                      at host prompt enter: mirlyn

Database: University of Minnesota Campus and Computer
                 Info
Access method: telnet to: consultant.micro.umn.edu
                 login as: gopher

Database: University of Minnesota at Duluth Campus Information
Access method: telnet to: ub.d.umn.edu
                 login as: info

Database: University of Minnesota Public Access Information Service
Access method: telnet to: lumina.lib.umn.edu

Database: University of Missouri at Columbia Library
Access method: tn3270 to: umcvmb.missouri.edu
                 tab to command line, enter: dial vtam
                 at vtam logon prompt enter: libcics

Database: University of Missouri at Rolla Library
Access method: tn3270 to: umrvmb.umr.edu
                 at vm screen tab to command line, enter: dial vtam
                 at next screen enter: lumin

Database: University of Missouri at St. Louis Library
Access method: tn3270 to: umslvma.umsl.edu
                 tab to command line, enter: dial vtam
                 at vtam logon enter: libcics

Database: University of Nebraska Library
Access method: telnet to: iris.unl.edu
                 at login prompt enter: library

Database: University of Nebraska Press On-Line Catalog
Access method: telnet to: crcvms.unl.edu
                 username: info, goto University Press option

Database: University of Nevada Las Vegas Library
Access method: telnet to: library.lv-lib.nevada.edu

Database: University of Nevada, Reno Library
Access method: telnet to: wolfpac.unr.edu

Database: University of New Brunswick (Canada) Campus Information
Access method: tn3270 to: unbmvs1.csd.unb.ca
                 login with application id: INFO

Database: University of New Brunswick Library

Access method:	tn3270 to: unbmvs1.csd.unb.ca select option 8, Internet library search
Database: Access method:	University of New Hampshire Campus Information telnet to: unhvtx.unh.edu respond to USERNAME: student
Database: Access method:	University of New Mexico Library telnet to: libros.unm.edu at login prompt enter: library
Database: Access method:	University of New South Wales telnet to: libprime.libsys.unsw.oz.au at ok prompt enter: libcat
Database: Access method:	University of North Carolina BBS (Usenet News, Library of Congress) telnet to: launchpad.unc.edu (login as: launch) telnet to: bbs.oit.unc.edu (login as: bbs) telnet to: lambada.oit.unc.edu (login as: bbs)
Database: Access method:	University of North Carolina Campus and School Info telnet to: info.acs.unc.edu
Database: Access method:	University of North Carolina at Chapel Hill Campus Information telnet to: info.oit.unc.edu
Database: Access method:	University of North Carolina at Greensboro Campus Information telnet to: steffi.acc.uncg.edu login as: info or MINERVA
Database: Access method:	University of North Carolina Libraries telnet to: librot1.lib.unc.edu
Database: Access method:	University of North Carolina at Wilmington Campus Information telnet to: vxc.uncwil.edu login as: info
Database: Access method:	University of North Texas Library telnet to: library.unt.edu enter: hello user.lib
Database:	University of Northern Iowa Campus Information

Access method: telnet to: infosys.uni.edu
                   login as: public

Database: University of Notre Dame Library
                   also provides access to libraries at:
                         Bethel College
                         Holy Cross College
                         Saint Mary's College
                   telnet to: irishmvs.cc.nd.edu
                   at enter command prompt enter: library

Database: University of Oregon Library
Access method: telnet to: janus.uoregon.edu
                   at login prompt enter: janus

Database: University of Pennsylvania Campus and School Information
Access method: telnet to: penninfo.upenn.edu

Database: University of Pennsylvania Library
Access method: telnet to: pennlib.upenn.edu

Database: University of Pittsburgh Library
Access method: telnet to: gate.cis.pitt.edu
                   at service prompt enter: pittcat

Database: University of Plymouth Library Computer System
Access method: telnet to: sun.nsf.ac.uk
                   at login prompt enter: janet, password: guest
                   at hostname prompt enter: uk.ac.poly-south-
                   west.library
                   at username prompt enter: library

Database: University of Prince Edward Island Library
Access method: telnet to: lib.cs.upei.ca
                   at username prompt enter: bobcat
                   or tn3270 to: lib.cs.upei.ca
                   at username prompt enter: bobcat

Database: University of Queensland Library
Access method: telnet to: libsys.campus.uq.oz.au
                   enter: be

Database: University of Saskatchewan Library
Access method: telnet to: skdevel.usask.ca
                   or telnet to: skdevel2.usask.ca

at request prompt enter: lib
or telnet to: sklib.usask.ca
at username prompt enter: sonia

Database: University of South Australia Library
Access method: telnet to: lv.levels.unisa.edu.au
                   at username prompt enter: opac

Database: University of Tennessee at Memphis Health Science Library
Access method: telnet to: utmem1.utmem.edu
                   at username prompt enter: harvey

Database: University of Texas at Arlington Library
Access method: telnet to: admin.uta.edu
                   at connect press RETURN
                   enter terminal type, at vtam menu enter: notis
                   at cics logo screen press RETURN
                   on next screen enter: luut

Database: University of Texas at Austin Library
Access method: telnet to: utcat.utexas.edu
                   at connect press RETURN
                   at go prompt press RETURN
                   enter terminal type, then enter: utcat

Database: University of Texas at Dallas Library
Access method: tn3270 to: vm.utdallas.edu
                   press RETURN to clear screen
                   enter: library
                   or
                   telnet to: ibm.utdallas.edu
                   enter terminal type, press RETURN
                   enter: library

Database: University of Toledo Library
Access method: tn3270 to: uoft01.utoledo.edu
                   at UT screen press RETURN
                   at enter commands.. prompt enter: dial mvs
                   at enter application prompt enter: utmost

Database: University of Ulster
Access method: telnet to: sun.nsf.ac.uk
                   at login prompt enter: janet, password: guest
                   at hostname prompt enter: uk.ac.ulster.library

Database: University of Utah Library
Access method: tn3270 to: lib.utah.edu
                tab to command line, enter: dial unis

Database: University of Vermont Library
Access method: telnet to: luis.uvm.edu

Database: University of Virginia Library
Access method: telnet to: ublan.acc.virginia.edu
                press RETURN. at >> prompt enter: c virgo
                for law library at >> prompt enter: connect law

Database: University of Wales College of Cardiff Library
Access method: telnet to: sun.nsf.ac.uk
                at login prompt enter: janet, password: guest
                at hostname prompt enter: uk.ac.cardiff.library

Database: University of Wales College of Medicine Library
Access method: telnet to: sun.nsf.ac.uk
                at login prompt enter: janet, password: guest
                at hostname prompt enter: uk.ac.uwcm.library

Database: University of Warwick Library
Access method: telnet to: sun.nsf.ac.uk
                at login prompt enter: janet, password: guest
                at hostname prompt enter: uk.ac.warwick.opac
                at connect press RETURN

Database: University of Western Australia Library
Access method: telnet to: fennel.cc.uwa.oz.au
                at username prompt enter: library

Database: University of Western Ontario Library
Access method: telnet to: geac.lib.uwo.ca
                at connect press RETURN

Database: University of Westminster
Access method: telnet to: sun.nsf.ac.uk
                at login prompt enter: janet, password: guest
                at hostname prompt enter: uk.ac.pcl.yak
                at user prompt enter: library

Database: University of Wisconsin Library
Access method: tn3270 to: blue.adp.wisc.edu
                tab to left of nls1 and press F1
                at next prompt press RETURN to select Madison

or telnet to: nls.adp.wisc.edu
select terminal type, tab to left of nls1
press RETURN, at next prompt press RETURN to
select Madison

Database: University of Wisconsin, Green Bay Library
Access method: telnet to: gbls2k.uwgb.edu

Database: University of Wisconsin, Superior Library
Access method: telnet to: sail.uwsuper.edu
                 at connect press RETURN

Database: University of York Library
Access method: telnet to: sun.nsf.ac.uk
                 at login prompt enter: janet, password: guest
                 at hostname prompt enter: uk.ac.york.library

Database: US Department of Commerce
                 Economic Bulletin Board System
Access method: telnet to: ebb.stat-usa.gov
                 login as: trial

Database: US Food and Drug Administration reports,
                 regulations and press release information
Access method: telnet to: fdabbs.fda.gov
                 login as: bbs

Database: US General Accounting Office Reports
Access method: telnet to: cap.gwu.edu
                 login as: guest, password: visitor
                 type GO GAO at main menu

Database: US Naval Observatory
Access method: telenet to: tycho.usno.navy.mil
                 login as: ads

Database: US Supreme Court decisions
Access method: telnet to: info.umd.edu
                 login as: info

Database: Vanderbilt University
                 Jean and Alexander Heard Library
Access method: telnet to: ctrvax.vanderbilt.edu
                 at username prompt enter: acorn

Database: Victoria (British Columbia) Free-Net

Access method: telnet to: freenet.victoria.bc.ca
login as: guest

Database: Victoria University of Wellington
Access method: telnet to: library.vuw.ac.nz
at connect press RETURN
at service prompt enter: lib

Database: Victoria, UK Monochrome Service
Access method: telnet to: victoria.city.ac.uk
login as: mono, password is: mono

Database: Vienna Stock Exchange
Access method: telnet to: fiivs01.tu-graz.au
login as: BOERSE

Database: Virginia Commonwealth University Library
Access method: tn3270 to: vcuvm1.ucc.vcu.edu
tab to command line, enter: dial vtam
select: library

Database: Virginia Institute of Technology CBX Data Network
Access method: telnet to: vtcbx.vt.edu
at call, display, or modify prompt enter: call vtls
to access library

Database: Virginia Institute of Technology Branching Exchange
Access method: telnet to: vtcbx.cc.vt.edu

Database: Virginia Institute of Technology Conferencing BBS
Access method: telnet to: vtcosby.cns.vt.edu
login as: bbs

Database: Virtual Work Bulletin Board System
Access method: telnet to: ctp.org
login as: lewisnts

Database: Washington University Library Services
Access method: telnet to: wugate.wustl.edu
login as: luis

Database: Wayne State University Library
Access method: tn3270 to: cms.cc.wayne.edu
tab to command line, enter: dial vtam
at wsunet menu enter: luis
or telnet to: ccb9.merit.edu

at which host prompt enter: wsunet
at wsunet menu enter: luis

Database:	Weather information maintained by University of Michigan
Access method:	telnet to: downwind.sprl.wmich.edu 3000
	enter three-letter city code for forecast
	telnet to: measun.nrrc.ncsu.edu 3000
	telnet to: wind.atmos.uah.edu 3000

Database:	Weather Information for US and Canada
Access method:	telnet to: madlab.sprl.umich.edu 3000

Database:	Webster dictionary and spelling service
Access method:	telnet to: cs.indiana.edu
	telnet to: chem.ucsd.edu
	login as: webster, type HELP for information.

Database:	Weitzmann Institute of Science (Israel) Library
Access method:	telnet to: wislib.weizmann.ac.il
	at username prompt enter: aleph

Database:	Western Michigan University Library
Access method:	telnet to: ccb9.merit.edu
	at which host prompt enter: wmu-finder
	to access Western Michigan Information Network enter: w

Database:	Wide Area Information Server (WAIS) text file search
Access method:	telnet to: ds.internic.net (login as: wais)
	telnet to: info.funet.fi (login as: info)
	telnet to: swais.cwis.uci.edu (login as: swais)
	telnet to: wais.nis.garr.it (login as: wais)
	telnet to: hub.nnsc.nsf.net (login as: wais)
	telnet to: quake.think.com (login as: wais)
	telnet to: nnsc.nsf.net (login as wais)

Database:	The World Public Access Unix BBS
Access method:	telnet to: world.std.com
	login as: new

Database:	X.500 Directory Search
Access method:	telnet to:
	archie.au (login as: de)
	wp.adelaide.edu.au (login as: de or fred)
	wp.monash.edu.au (login as: fred)

                    jethro.ucc.su.oz.au (login as: fred)
                    paradise.ulcc.ac.uk (login as: dua)

Database: Yale University Library
Access method: tn3270 to: orbis.yale.edu
                    at connect press RETURN

Database: Yale University On-line Directory and Campus Information
Access method: telnet to: yalevm.ycc.yale.edu 300

Database: York University
Access method: telnet to: yorkline.yorku.ca
                    at enter term prompt enter terminal prompt
                    at Yorkline screen enter: yorkline

Database: Youngstown Ohio Free-Net (Youngstown State University)
Access Method: telnet to: yfn.ysu.edu
                    login as: visitor

Database: ZIB Electronic Library
                    (Software and connections to other libraries)
Access method: telnet to: elib.zib-berlin.de
                    login as: elib

Database: 1992 Presidential Campaign Resources
Access method: telnet to: info.umd.edu

GOPHER AND VERONICA ACCESS

If you have a gopher client:

Access method: gopher to: gopher.micro.umn.edu
features: change to directory "8. Other Gopher and Information
                    Servers/"
                    to use Veronica go to item named: "2. Search titles
                    in Gopherspace using veronica/"

                    for a gopher menu of veronica items
                    gopher to: veronica.scs.unr.edu 70
                      wisteria.cnidr.org 70
                      nysernet.org 70

If you do not have a gopher client you can telnet to one of the following sites and access gopher and veronica :

    consultant.micro.umn.edu
    gopher.uiuc.edu
    panda.uiowa.edu
    info.anu.edu.au (Australia)
    gopher.chalmers.se (Sweden)

JUGHEAD: A DATABASE OF GOPHER LINKS

[From the Washington & Lee gopher: liberty.uc.wlu.edu]

Jughead is a database of Gopher links. It accepts word searches and the search result can be used to access menus on either the W&L Gopher or on many remote Gophers. There are two Jughead databases on the W&L Gopher, one (on the main Gopher menu) indexes all menus at the W&L Gopher, and the other (on the "Other Gopher Resources" menu) indexes all Gopher sites but is selective in only including high-level menu items, and does not include any file-name menus.

   Searches may use AND, OR, NOT connectors (a space between search-words = AND) Multiple ANDs, ORs and NOTs are evaluated left to right and Upper and lower case are ignored. Words may be truncated with an '*' as the last character of the root-word.

Search examples follow:

    SUPREME COURT   = both supreme and court
    SUPREME AND COURT   = both supreme and court
    LAW OR LEGAL   = either law or legal
    CONSTIT*   = any word beginning with 'constit'
    COURT NOT SUPREME   = all entries with 'court' but excluding any with
                             'supreme'

Jughead supports some special commands, where each special command must be preceeded by a question mark '?', and are listed below:

    ?all what
    ?help [what]

```
?limit  =n what
?range =n1-n2 what
?version [what]
```

Where 'what' is a standard search string, anything enclosed in square brackets is optional, and all special commands must be preceded with '?'.

Each command is described below:

?all what	Returns all the hits on 'what'.
?help [what]	Gives you this document and any optional hits on 'what'.
?limit=n what	Returns the 'n' items on 'what'.
?range=n1-n2	Returns items from 'n1' through 'n2'
?version [what]	Returns the version of jughead and any optional hits on 'what'.

Only 1 special command is supported per query, and if any syntax error is encountered it is reported.

Currently there is no way to search on the words "AND", "OR",or "NOT"; nor is there a way to break an expression into a group of smaller expressions.

All words are broken into smaller words if any word contains a whitespace character or one of the following characters:

```
!"#$%&'()+,-./:;<=>?@[\]^_`{|}~
```

For example, if a menu item has the name "A sample.file", this is broken into the three words "A", "sample", and "file". So if your search statement is: "sample.file some_thing-else", your query gets broken into the statement: "sample AND file AND some AND thing AND else", which will only return those items with all these words in the menu.

FINGER RETRIEVAL

for:	Andrew Toolkit Demonstration
Access method:	finger help@atk.itc.cmu.edu
for:	Auroral and Solar activity information
Access method:	finger aurora@xi.uleth.ca
	finger daily@xi.uleth.ca
	finger solar@xi.uleth.ca

| for: | Billboard (Top Pop Music) Charts |
| Access method: | finger buckmr@rpi.edu |

for:	Candy and drink machine information
Access method:	finger coke@cmu.edu
	finger drink@drink.csh.rit.edu
	finger info@drink.csh.rit.edu
	finger graph@drink.csh.rit.edu

| for: | Earthquake Information |
| Access method: | finger quake@geophys.washington.edu |

| for: | FAQs listings |
| Access method: | finger nichol@stavanger.sgp.slb.com |

| for: | NASA Headline News |
| Access method: | finger nasanews@space.mit.edu |

| for: | Nielsen TV Ratings |
| Access method: | finger normg@halcyon.halcyon.com |

| for: | Star Trek Quotes |
| Access method: | finger franklin@ug.cs.dal.ca |

CHAPTER 7

Bitnet Communications and Mailing Lists

Bitnet, an acronym for "because it's time network," represents a network that interconnects approximately 3000 mainly large mainframe computer systems located at academic institutions throughout the world. In this chapter we turn our attention to BITNET, examining its key features to include inter- and intra-network addressing and its network servers and services. Once we have an appreciation for BITNET addressing and its servers and services, a table of BITNET mailing lists will be presented. That table contains the network-wide identification for the mailing list, its full address and list title. By using the information in the table in conjunction with previously presented information readers can become subscribers to mailing lists or obtain additional information about those mailing lists.

Addressing

BITNET is an independent network which is interconnected to the Internet. BITNET has its own addressing format, such as user%hostsite, which is only applicable for use on BITNET. Other Internet users that desire to communicate with a BITNET user must direct their message via a BITNET/Internet gateway or try appending .bitnet to the BITNET address. For example, to communicate with the

BITNET user gxheld at hostsite msu you could address your message to gx-held%msu and then add the address of one of the three BITNET/Internet gateways listed in chapter 3. Doing so, you could send your message using one of the three addresses indicated below:

> gxheld%msu@cunyvm.cuny.edu
> gxheld%msu@pucc.princeton.edu
> gxheld%wuvmd.wustl.edu

As a fourth and more popular option, you could address your message as gx-held%msu.bitnet. Concerning the fourth option, its use presumes that your Internet service provider has sufficient updated information to route the address to an appropriate gateway.

You can communicate with a Bitnet user or system in one of three ways: via a single line message, via file transfer or via E-mail.

Intra Network Message communications:

Use the TELL (VM/CMS systems) command or the SEND (VAX/VMS systems) to send a one-line message to another Bitnet user. That user must be logged on to receive the message.

Format: VM/CMS   TELL userid AT node message
              VAX/VMS   SEND userid@node "message"

Example: VM/CMS   TELL HELD AT MSU watch channel six at five
              VAX/VMS   SEND HELD@MSU "watch channel six at five"

File communications:

You can transmit a file to another Bitnet user and the file will be stored in their mailbox until they logon to their system.

Format:
  for VM/CMS: SENDFILE filename filetype filemode userid AT node
  for VAX/VMS: SEND/FILE filename.extension userid@node

To receive the transmitted file, the recipient must use the command RECEIVE or RDRLIST (VM/CMS) or RECEIVE (VAX/VMS)

NAMESERV UTILIZATION

The directory server which functions as a "white pages" is appropriately named NAMESERV. To search the NAMESERV for a specific name use the following format:

for VM/CMS: TELL NAMESERV AT node SEARCH/NAME firstname last-name

for VAX/VMS: SEND NAMESERV@node "SEARCH/NAME firstname last-name"

To register your name at a name server use the following format:

for VM/CMS: TELL NAMESERV AT node REGISTER firstname lastname keyword

for VAX/VMS: SEND NAMESERV@node "REGISTER firstname lastname keywords"

where you can specify up to five keywords you wish associated with your name. For example, jogging, tv, beer, corvette, pets.

BITNET MAILING LISTS

Bitnet mailing lists are maintained on computers known as list servers, which are appropriately referred to as LISTSERVS. The mailing list functions as an electronic distribution list which is used for a discussion concerning a particular topic. Once you subscribe to a mailing list you become a member of the list. Thereafter, when anyone has a question related to the list topic or wishes to express an opinion concerning the list topic, that person sends a message to the mailing list address which forwards the message to all subscribers to the mailing list.

The frequency of activity of a particular mailing list depends upon the topic as well as the electronic verbosity of members of the mailing list. Some lists may generate one or a few messages per day or week, whereas other mailing lists may generate several hundred messages per week and may swamp your electronic in-basket. Thus, it is suggested that you make sure you really want to subscribe to a mailing list prior to doing so.

To subscribe to a mailing list use the TELL command if you are using a VM/CMS computer, the SEND command if you are using a VAX/VMS computer, or an electronic mail message to the appropriate LISTSERV using one of the following formats:

TELL listserv at bitnic.bitnet SUB list-name your-name
SEND listserv@bitnic.bitnet "SUB list-name your-name"

where SUB is the abbreviated SUBscribe command.

When sending an E-mail message to subscribe to a BITNET mailing list send the message to: listserv@bitnic.bitnet. Place the following in the body of the message: SUB list-name your-name.

Examples:

> TELL LISTSERV AT bitnic.bitnet SUB PETS-R-FUN Gilbert Held
> SEND LISTSERV@bitnic.bitnet "SUB TRUMAN Gilbert Held"

or E-mail to listserv@bitnic.bitnet and place SUB list-name your-name in the body of the message.

To remove yourself from a mailing list use the UNSUBscribe command with a TELL, or SEND command or in an E-mail message as indicated in the following examples.

> TELL LISTSERV AT bitnic.bitnet UNSUB PETS-R-FUN
> SEND LISTSERV@bitnic.bitnet "UNSUB TRUMAN"

When sending an E-mail message to remove yourself from a BITNET mailing list send the message to: listserv@bitnic.bitnet. Place the following in the body of the message: UNSUB listname.

Other Bitnet Mailing List Requests:

To obtain a list of groups use the message: SEND LISTSERV GROUPS in a request to: listserv@bitnic.bitnet.

To obtain a List of Lists use the message: SENDME INTEREST PACKAGE in a request to: listserv@ndsum1.bitnet.

To obtain a list of new mailing lists as they appear use the message: SUB NEW-LIST your-name in a request to: listserv@ndsuvm1.

BITNET MAILING LISTS

Note that in the "Full address" column the word before the @ sign references the name of the list, while the information following the @ is the name of the computer where the list resides.

Network-wide ID	Full address	List title
I-AMIGA-UIUC...	I-AMIGA@UIUCVMD	Archive of I-AMIGA list elsewhere on net (Do+
NEW-SUPERCOM...	S-COMPUT@UGA	(Peered) SuperComputers List (UGA)
UPDATE-ELECT...	UPNEWS@MARIST	Update Electronic Music Newsletter - renamed t+
ECONLIST	CORRYFEE@HASARA11	List of the Faculty of Economics, University+
A-GROUP	A-GROUP@UMSLVMA	The A-Group (Kind of like the A-Team)
AAASHRAN	AAASHRAN@GWUVM	AAAS Human Rights Action Network
AAASMSP	AAASMSP@GWUVM	AAAS Minority Perspectives on Ethics in Scie+
AAHESGIT	AAHESGIT@GWUVM	AAHE Info. Tech. Activities & Projects Steve+
AARPUB-L	AARPUB-L@JPNIMRTU	AAR Electronic Publication list
AASCU-L	AASCU-L@UBVM	American Association of State Colleges and U+
AASIG-L	AASIG-L@GSUVM1	GSU Academic Administrators
AASNET-L	AASNET-L@UHUPVM1	African American Student Network
AATG	AATG@INDYCMS	American Association of Teachers of German
AAUA-L	AAUA-L@UBVM	American Association of University Administr+
AAUFD-L	AAUFD-L@UNBVM1	AAU Faculty Development Committee List
AAVLD-L	AAVLD-L@UCDCVDLS	American Assoc of Vet Lab Diagnosticians
ABE-L	ABE-L@BRLNCC	Forum da Associacao Brasileira de Estatistica
ABEP-L	ABEP-L@BRUFSC	Associacao de Brasileiros Estudantes e Pesqu+
ABILITY	ABILITY@ASUACAD	Journal for the study and advancement of the+
ABLE-L	ABLE-L@ASUACAD	ABILITY Journal - Discussion & submission
ABOG-L	ABOG-L@UCSBVM	UCSB Academic Business Officers Group (ABOG)
	ABOG-L@UCSFVM	UCSF Academic Business Officers Group
ABSJRN-L	ABSJRN-L@CMUVM	ABS Journal Committee
ABSLST-L	ABSLST-L@CMUVM	Association of Black Sociologists
ABSTRACT	ABSTRACT@TAMVM1	LINGUIST-ABSTRACTS
ACADDR-L	ACADDR-L@MCGILL1	Academic Computing Centre Directors Forum
ACADEMIC	ACADEMIC@BRUFMG	Forum de Ciencia Computacional
ACADV	ACADV@NDSUVM1	ACADV Academic Advising Forum
ACC-L	ACC-L@GITVM1	ACC-L: "Advanced Computer Controls Discussio+
ACCES-L	ACCES-L@UNBVM1	Associated Competitions for Can. Eng. Studen+
ACCESS-L	ACCESS-L@BRUFPB	List for MS ACCESS

Network-wide ID	Full address	List title
	ACCESS-L@INDYCMS	Microsoft Access Database Discussion List
ACCY-L	ACCY-L@UHUPVM1	ACCY-L Accounting Distribution List
ACDGIS-L	ACDGIS-L@AWIIMC12	Geographische Informationssysteme
ACE-COM	ACE-COM@WSUVM1	ACE Communication Management SIG
ACES-L	ACES-L@UNBVM1	Atlantic Congress of Engineering Students (F+
ACEWEST	ACEWEST@WSUVM1	Ag Communicators in Education
ACH-EC-L	ACH-EC-L@BROWNVM	ACH Executive Council Discussion List
ACHNEWS	ACHNEWS@UCSBVM	Newsletter of the Association for Computers +
ACLA-L	ACLA-L@WSUVM1	Association of Collegiate Licensing Administ+
ACM-L	ACM-L@KENTVM	ACM-L List for discussing ACM; gatewayed to +
	ACM-L@UCF1VM	Florida ACM Student Chapter Discussion List
ACMMEX-L	ACMMEX-L@ITESMVF1	ACM MEXICO
ACMR-L	ACMR-L@UHCCVM	Association for Chinese Music Research Netwo+
ACMSTCHP	ACMSTCHP@SUVM	ACM Student Chapters
ACORN-L	ACORN-L@GREARN	ACORN computers Discussion List
ACRA-L	ACRA-L@BINGVMB	Advisory Committee on Regional Automation
ACRL	ACRL@UICVM	Association of College and Research Librarie+
ACSOFT-L	ACSOFT-L@WUVMD	Academic Software Development
ACTIV-L	ACTIV-L@MIZZOU1	Activists Mailing List
ACTNOW-L	ACTNOW-L@BROWNVM	College Activism/Information List
ACTOR-L	ACTOR-L@HEARN	ACTOR-L: The OOP language Actor user list
ACUA-L	ACUA-L@UVMVM	acua-l
ACUHOI-L	ACUHOI-L@PSUVM	Coll. & Univ. Housing Officers Int.
ACW-L	ACW-L@TTUVM1	Alliance For Computers and Writing
AC603-L	AC603-L@CLVM	Student Info List for AC603
ADA-LAW	ADA-LAW@NDSUVM1	ADA Law
ADACC-L	ADACC-L@UCSBVM	ADA Campus Coordinators
ADAMO	ADAMO@UKACRL	"The ADAMO Data System"
ADAP-ORG	ADAP-ORG@JPNYITP	Preprint server Adaptation/Self-organizing s+
ADAPT-L	ADAPT-L@AUVM	Library Adaptive Technology
ADDICT-L	ADDICT-L@KENTVM	Academic & Scholarly discussion of addiction+
ADLTED-L	ADLTED-L@UREGINA1	Canadian Adult Education Network
ADMIN-L	ADMIN-L@ALBNYDH2	NYS DEPARTMENT OF HEALTH ADMINISTRATIVE INFO+
	ADMIN-L@BRUFSC	(Peered) Forum ADMIN-L - Discussao de assunt+

Network-wide ID	Full address	List title
	ADMIN-L@UCSFVM	UCSF Network Administrators List
ADMINSEC	ADMINSEC@UTORONTO	Netnorth Administrative Secretary
ADMRA-L	ADMRA-L@ALBNYDH2	ADIRONDACK MEDICAL RECORDS ASSOCIATION LIST
ADND-L	ADND-L@GITVM1	(Peered) Advanced Dungeons and Dragons discu+
	ADND-L@PUCC	(Peered) Advanced Dungeons and Dragons discu+
	ADND-L@UTARLVM1	(Peered) Advanced Dungeons and Dragons discu+
ADR-L	ADR-L@ALBNYVM1	ADR Database Products Discussion List
ADS-L	ADS-L@UGA	American Dialect Society
ADSM-L	ADSM-L@MARIST	Dist. Stor. Manager(ADSM) List
ADV-ELO	ADV-ELO@UTFSM	Latest Electronic Advances
ADV-INFO	ADV-INFO@UTFSM	Latest Computing Advances
ADV-PAS	ADV-PAS@BRUFPB	List for Advanced Pascal Users
ADVANC-L	ADVANC-L@IDBSU	ADVANC-L - USERS OF THE GEAC ADVANCE LIBRARY+
ADVANCED	ADVANCED@JPNIMRTU	ADVANCED COURSE USER
ADVICE-L	ADVICE-L@JPNTUVM0	Technical Assistance for Users at JPNTOHOK
ADVISE-L	ADVISE-L@EBCESCA1	(Peered) User Services List
	ADVISE-L@NDSUVM1	(Peered) User Services List
	ADVISE-L@UBVM	(Peered) User Services List
	ADVISE-L@UGA	(Peered) User Services List
ADVISERS	ADVISERS@UWAVM	ADVISERS
ADVISORS	ADVISORS@TECHNION	ADVISORS - TECHNION CC user support discussi+
ADV93-L	ADV93-L@JPNTUVM0	ECIP 1993 Advanced Course Students List
AE	AE@SJSUVM1	Alternative Energy Discussion List
AEELIST	AEELIST@PUCC	Association for Experiential Education
AEICNR	AEICNR@UWAVM	AEICNR (Acadamic Exchange Information Center+
AEJMC93D	AEJMC93D@CMUVM	Discussion list for 1993 AEJMC Papers
AEJMC93L	AEJMC93L@CMUVM	1993 AEJMC Papers
AERA	AERA-K@ASUACAD	AERA-K Division K: Teaching and Teacher Educ+
AERAMC-L	AERAMC-L@UAFSYSB	American Education Research Association - Me+
AESRG-L	AESRG-L@MIZZOU1	Applied Expert Systems Research Group List
AFAM-L	AFAM-L@MIZZOU1	African-American Research
AFAS-L	AFAS-L@KENTVM	African American Studies and Librarianship
AFRICA-L	AFRICA-L@BROWNVM	(Peered) FORUM PAN-AFRICA (Peer Distribution+
	AFRICA-L@BRUFPB	(Peered) FORUM PAN-AFRICA

Network-wide ID	Full address	List title
	AFRICA-L@VTVM1	Pan-Africa Discussion List
AFRICA-N	AFRICA-N@UTORONTO	AFRICA-N Africa News & Information Service
AFRICANA	AFRICANA@WMVM1	Information Techonlogy and Africa
AFROAM-L	AFROAM-L@HARVARDA	CRITICAL ISSUES IN AFRICAN AMERICAN LIFE AND+
AF4H-L	AF4H-L@VTVM1	Airfield 4H Center
AG-EXP-L	AG-EXP-L@NDSUVM1	AG-EXP-L Ag Expert Systems
AGEN-KS	AGEN-KS@RUTVM1	ASAE Knowledge Systems Discussion List
AGENET-L	AGENET-L@UTORONTO	CARNET Discussion
AGENG-L	AGENG-L@DGOGWDG1	Agricultural Engineering and Intelligent Con+
AGFTECH	AGFTECH@DEARN	AGF-Subnetz-Koordinatoren
AGING-L	AGING-L@BROWNVM	Researchers In Population Aging Computer Con+
AGRIC-L	AGRIC-L@UGA	Agriculture Discussion
AGRIS-L	AGRIS-L@IRMFAO01	The Food and Agriculture Organization Libra+
AGR6	AGR6@ICNUCEVM	CNR - Comitato 6, Agricoltura (AGR6)
AHC-L	AHC-L@DGOGWDG1	Association for History & Computing
AIAA	AIAA@ARIZVM1	AIAA Listserv
AIB-CUR	AIB-CUR@ICINECA	Discussione Associazione Italiana Biblioteche
AIBI-L	AIBI-L@UOTTAWA	The Computerised Analysis of Biblical Texts +
AIBIBL	AIBIBL@PLEARN	ACADEMIC INITIATIVE IBM , PROJECT "LIBRARY S+
AICS-L	AICS-L@UBVM	Architectures for Intelligent Control System+
AIDE	AIDE@UDESVM	Liste d'aide et de suggestions pour l'U. de +
AIDS	AIDS@EBCESCA1	(Peered) Sci.Med.AIDS Newsgroup
	AIDS@RUTVM1	Sci.Med.AIDS Newsgroup
AIDS_INTL	ICECA@RUTVM1	Intl Committee for Elec Comm on AIDS
AIDSBKRV	AIDSBKRV@UICVM	AIDSBKRV - AIDS Book Review Journal
AIESEC-L	AIESEC-L@KENTVM	List for national membership of AIESEC
AIKIDO-L	AIKIDO-L@PSUVM	Aikido List
AIR-L	AIR-L@VTVM1	Institutional Researchers/University Planners
AIRCRAFT	AIRCRAFT@GREARN	The Aircraft Discussion List
	AIRCRAFT@IUBVM	The Aircraft Discussion List
AIRLINE	AIRLINE@CUNYVM	The Airline List
AISDIRS	AISDIRS@CUVMC	AIS Directors
AISTFDM	AISTFDM@CUVMC	AIS Task Force Data Management
AISTFLAN	AISTFLAN@CUVMC	AIS Task Force LAN Management

Network-wide ID	Full address	List title
AISTFLDR	AISTFLDR@CUVMC	AIS Task Force Leaders
AISTFMFD	AISTFMFD@CUVMC	AIS Task Force Mainframe Direction
AISTFNI	AISTFNI@CUVMC	AIS Task Force Network Integration
AISTFP	AISTFP@CUVMC	AIS Task Force Program Global List For Every+
AISTFPUI	AISTFPUI@CUVMC	AIS Task Force Presentation / User Interface
AISTFTBM	AISTFTBM@CUVMC	AIS Task Force Technology Business Management
AIX-L	AIX-L@PUCC	IBM AIX Discussion List
	AIX-L@SAKAAU03	Advanced Instruction eXecutive Operating Sys+
AIXESA-L	AIXESA-L@RPITSVM	AIXESA Discussion List
AIXL	AIXL@ICNUCEVM	AIX Working Group Discussion List
AIXNEWS	AIXNEWS@PUCC	IBM AIX News to Mail Distribution
AIX370-L	AIX370-L@UWAVM	AIX370 Discussion List
AJCUASD	AJCUASD@GUVM	AJCU Arts and Sciences Deans
AJCUAVP	AJCUAVP@GUVM	AJCU Academic Vice Presidents
AJCUCOMP	AJCUCOMP@GUVM	AJCU Computer Center Directors
AJCUEDU	AJCUEDU@GUVM	AJCU Conference on Teacher Education
AJCUFAID	AJCUFAID@GUVM	AJCU Financial Aid Directors
AJCUILL	AJCUILL@GUVM	AJCU Law Librarians/Interlibrary Loan Contac+
AJCULIB	AJCULIB@GUVM	AJCU Librarians
AJCUNEWS	AJCUNEWS@GUVM	AJCU News for those not on other AJCU lists
AJCUPRES	AJCUPRES@GUVM	AJCU Presidents
AJCURES	AJCURES@GUVM	AJCU Conference on Research
ALA	ALA@UICVM	ALA Filelist
ALA-SERV	ALA-SERV@UA1VM	ALA-SERV Discussion List
ALA-WO	ALA-WO@UICVM	ALA Washington Office Update
ALACRO-L	ALACRO-L@UICVM	ALACRO-L List Discussion list ALA -+
ALAMEMB	ALAMEMB@UICVM	ALA Membership Committee
ALANEWS	ALANEWS@UICVM	ALANEWS - ALA news releases
ALATREAS	ALATREAS@UICVM	ALA Treasurer-COPES Chair-ALA Finiancial Sta+
ALC-L	ALC-L@TCUBVM	ALC-L Abilene Library Consortium Internet C+
ALCOHOL	ALCOHOL@LMUACAD	ALCOHOL & DRUG STUDIES
ALCTS	ALCTS@UICVM	ALCTS List
ALEPHINT	ALEPHINT@TAUNIVM	International ALEPH Users List
ALERTSYS	ALERTSYS@MIAMIU	MCIS System Alert
ALF-L	ALF-L@YORKVM1	Academic Librarian's Forum
ALG-GEOL	ALG-GEOM@JPNYITP	Preprint server for Algebraic Geometry
ALGCOMP	ALGCOMP@BRLNCC	Forum de Computacao Algebrica
ALGNEWS	ALGNEWS@GWUVM	Algeria News List

Network-wide ID	Full address	List title
ALIAS-L	ALIAS-L@UGA	Alias software discussion
ALICETEC	ALICETEC@ICNUCEVM	ALICE Discussioni Tecniche
ALLIANCE	ALLIANCE@HARVARDA	Alliance for International Educational and C+
ALLIN1-L	ALLIN1-L@SBCCVM	ALL-IN-1 Managers and Users mailing list.
ALLMUSIC	ALLMUSIC@AUVM	Discussions on all forms of Music
	ALLMUSIC@UFRJ	ALLMUSIC PEERED LIST
ALMS-NN	ALMS-NN@UA1VM	AL-MS Neural Network Discussion List
ALPHA-L	ALPHA-L@LEPICS	L3 Alpha physics block analysis diagram group
ALPHAFT	ALPHAFT@UKACRL	"Discussion on Alpha Cobra Field Test at RAL"
ALPHAPT	ALPHAPT@UKACRL	"Discussion on the RAL Alpha Project"
ALPHASUP@IBM-...	ALPHASUP@UKACRL	Alpha Support Mailing Listing
ALTLEARN	ALTLEARN@SJUVM	Alternative Approaches to Learning Discussio+
ALTUFO-L	ALTUFO-L@PSUVM	Gateway to alt.paranet.ufo
ALUMNET	ALUMNET@TRINITY	ALUMNET (Trinity University Alumni) discussi+
ALUMNI-L	ALUMNI-L@UCSBVM	UCSB GSE Alumni Announcement List
AMALGAM	AMALGAM@DEARN	Dental AMALGAM and MERCURY Poisoning
AMATH-IL	AMATH-IL@TAUNIVM	Applied Mathematics in Israel List
AMB13	AMB13@ICNUCEVM	CNR - Comitato 13, Ambiente e Habita (AMB1+
AMCA-L	AMCA-L@MCGILL1	Alumni and Friends of Croatian Universities
AMERCATH	AMERCATH@UKCC	AMERCATH - A DISCUSSION LIST ON THE HISTORY +
AMERSTDY	AMERSTDY@MIAMIU	American Studies
AMFCH-L	AMFCH-L@UCHCECVM	Noticias Acerca de la Cooperacion Franco-Chi+
AMIA-L	AMIA-L@UKCC	Association for Moving Image Archivists
AMIA-37	AMIA-37@UMAB	AMIA Anesthesiology, Critical Care Medicine +
AMIED-L	AMIED-L@MCGILL1	American Medical Informatics Association Edu+
AMIEDC-L	AMIEDC-L@UBVM	AMIA Education PSG Administrative Committee +
AMIGA-TR	AMIGA-TR@TREARN	Turk Amiga'cilar listesi...
AMIGAHAR	AMIGAHAR@DEARN	AMIGAGHAR COMP.SYS.AMIGA.HARD-WARE redist.
AMINT-L	AMINT-L@PSUVM	Academy of Management International
AMLG-L	AMLG-L@IUBVM	AMLG Mail Distribution List
AMLIT-L	AMLIT-L@MIZZOU1	American Literature Discussion Group
AMSSIS-L	AMSSIS-L@UAFSYSB	AMS/SIS Discussion

Network-wide ID	Full address	List title
AMSSIS-T	AMSSIS-T@UAFSYSB	AMS/SIS Technical Issues
AMUSIC-D	AMUSIC-D@AUVM	ALLMUSIC Digest
AMWEST-H	AMWEST-L@DOSUNI1	(Peered) AmWest-H - American West History Fo+
	AMWEST-H@UMRVMB	(Peered) AmWest-H - American West History Fo+
ANCANACH	ANCANACH@UABDPO	Clan Henderson Society of US/Canada
ANCIEN-L	ANCIEN-L@ULKYVM	History of the Ancient Mediterranean
ANDESIS	ANDESIS@ANDESCOL	Renovacion Curricular en Sistemas y Computac+
ANEST-L	ANEST-L@UBVM	Anesthesiology Discussion List
ANET-L	ANET-L@OSUVM1	ANET Discussion List
ANGLICAN	ANGLICAN@AUVM	Episcopal Mailing List
ANIME-L	ANIME-L@VTVM1	Japanese animedia and other animation news.
ANKIETA	ANKIETA@PLEARN	A SPECIAL LIST ANKIETA
ANN-LOTS	ANN-LOTS@NDSUVM1	Indexing Forum for Annotated Lists-of-Things
ANNONSTD	ANNONSTD@BITNIC	Announcements of new ANSI and OSI draft stan+
ANNOUNCE	ANNOUNCE@UMRVMB	UMR Campus Computing Services Announcements
ANONYM-L	ANONYM-L@UCSFVM	For anonymous mail - use only an anonymous m+
ANSADM	ANSADM@MSU	ANSADM
ANSAX-L	ANSAX-L@WVNVM	ANSAXNET Discussion Forum
ANSIREXX	ANSIREXX@PSUVM	Documents from X3J18 - ANSIREXX standards co+
ANSP-L	ANSP-L@BRUSPVM	Rede ANSP
ANSSTDS	ANSSTDS@MSU	ANSST-L
ANSWER-L	ANSWER-L@EMUVM1	Emory Computing Questions and Answers
ANTAC-L	ANTAC-L@BRUFSC	(Peered) FORUM ANTAC-L - Associacao Nacional+
ANTHRO-L	ANTHRO-L@UBVM	General Anthropology Bulletin Board
	ANTHRO-L@UCSBVM	Anthropology Graduate Students' List Server
ANU-NEWS	ANU-NEWS@NDSUVM1	ANU-NEWS Discussion
ANYSUG-L	ANYSUG-L@ALBNYDH2	Albany New York SAS User's Group
AOBULL-L	AOBULL-L@ALBNYDH2	NEW YORK STATE DEPARTMENT OF HEALTH AREA OFF+
AOSVS-L	AOSVS-L@TRMETU	AOS/VS Operating System Discussion List AOSV+
AOUNET-L	AOUNET-L@UMDD	AOU Legislative Alert System
APASD-L	APASD-L@VTVM1	APA Research Psychology Network
APASLN	APASLN@GWUVM	APA Science Leaders Network
APC	APC@FRMOP11	Amicale du personnel du CNUSC (bureau)

Network-wide ID	Full address	List title
APDA	APDA@PUCC	American Parlimentary Debate Association
APG-L	APG-L@BRUFSC	Forum Eletronico de Debate e Troca de Inform+
APICS	APICS@UBVM	UB A. P. I. C. S. Discussion List
APIII-L	APIII-L@BRUSPVM	Associacao de Programas de Integracao e Info+
APL-ERS	APL-ERS@IRLEARN	UCD APL Interest Group
APL-L	APL-L@UNBVM1	APL Language Discussion
APLEDU-L	APLEDU-L@UNBVM1	APL in Education
APLIEM-L	APLIEM-L@BRUFU	Assoc. of English Language Teachers of the S+
APO-L	APO-L@PURCCVM	Alpha Phi Omega
APOSEC52	APOSEC52@INDYCMS	Alpha Phi Omega Region 6 (Sections 48/52/54)
APOSOC-L	APOSOC-L@PSUVM	Alpha Phi Omega Social topics
APO90-L	APO90-L@PSUVM	Alpha Phi Omega Section 90
APPAM-L	APPAM-L@QUCDN	Queen's University: Assoc. for Public Policy+
APPC-L	APPC-L@AUVM	APPC Discussion List
APPL-L	APPL-L@PLTUMK11	Computer applications in science and educati+
APPLENET	APPLENET@TECMTYVM	Lista de Discusion sobre la red AppleTalk en+
APPLE2-L	APPLE2-L@BROWNVM	Apple II List
APPLE3-L	APPLE3-L@WVNVM	Apple III Discussion Group
APPLICAT	APPLICAT@BITNIC	(Peered) Applications under BITNET
	APPLICAT@DEARN	(Peered) Applications under BITNET
	APPLICAT@HEARN	(Peered) Applications under BITNET
	APPLICAT@MARIST	(Peered) Applications under BITNET
	APPLICAT@UGA	(Peered) Applications under BITNET
APRX-NET	APRX-NET@TECHNION	APRX-NET -
APSSCNET	APSSCNET@MCGILL1	American Psychological Society Student Caucus
AQUA-L	AQUA-L@UOGUELPH	Aquaculture Discussion List
AQUARIUM	AQUARIUM@EMUVM1	Fish and Aquaria
AQUAWEST	AQUAWEST@ARIZVM1	Info Link/Univ & Professional Aquaculturists
AQUIFER	AQUIFER@IBACSATA	Pollution and groundwater recharge
ARACHNET	ARACHNET@KENTVM	An Association of Electronic Discussion Grou+
	ARACHNET@UOTTAWA	An Association of Electronic Discussion Grou+
ARCANA	ARCANA@UNCCVM	ARCANA Discussion List for the Study of the +
ARCH-L	ARCH-L@DGOGWDG1	

Network-wide ID	Full address	List title
	ARCH-L@TAMVM1	Archaeology List
ARCHIVES	ARCHIVES@ARIZVM1	Archives & Archivists
ARCITRON	ARCITRON@KENTVM	Architronic: The Electronic Journal of Archi+
ARCLIB-L	ARCLIB-L@IRLEARN	Mailing List for Irish and UK Architectural +
AREE	AREE@ICNUCEVM	CNR - Aree di Ricerca (AREE)
AREV-L	AREV-L@UCDCVDLS	Advanced Revelation Discussion Group
AREXX-L	AREXX-L@UCF1VM	Amiga REXX Discussion List
ARGUS-L	ARGUS-L@YALEVM	ARGUS Collections Management List
ARICA-L	ARICA-L@BRUFSC	ARICA-L - Lista de discussao sobre a ESCOLA +
ARIE-L	ARIE-L@IDBSU	ARIE-L - DISCUSSION OF THE RLG ARIEL DOCUMEN+
ARIEL	ARIEL@USACHVM1	"Software Estadistico Ariel"
ARIZSLS	ARIZSLS@ARIZVM1	Library Science Conference
ARKNET-L	ARKNET-L@UAFSYSB	Arkansas State Network Discussions
ARLIS-L	ARLIS-L@UKCC	ART LIBRARIES SOCIETY DISCUSSION LIST
ARMS-L	ARMS-L@BUACCA	Arms-L Mailing List
ARNOMAN	ARNOMAN@ICNUCEVM	Configurazioni cisco su MAN Toscana
ARPABBS	ARPABBS@UBVM	Arpanet Bulletin-Boards
ARRTECH	ARRTECH@TECHNION	Technion's architecture faculty general list
ARTCRIT	ARTCRIT@YORKVM1	Art Criticism Discussion Forum
ARTIST-L	ARTIST-L@UAFSYSB	Student Artist Discussions
ARTMGT-L	ARTMGT-L@BINGVMB	Arts Management Discussion Group
ARTSMIN	ARTSMIN@MCGILL1	Minutes and discussion for Faculty of Arts
AS-ACADE	AS-ACADE@UCHCECVM	Asociacion de Academicos Fac. de Cs. Fis. y+
ASA-L	ASA-L@TAMVM1	African(-American) Students Association
ASAT-DIS	ASAT-DIS@UNLVM	AG-SAT Special Bulletins
ASAT-EVA	ASAT-EVA@UNLVM	AG-SAT Distance Education Evaluation Group
ASAT-POC	ASAT-POC@UNLVM	AG-SAT Production Operations Council
ASAT-REC	ASAT-REC@UNLVM	AG-SAT Research Council
ASAT-TEC	ASAT-TEC@UNLVM	AG-SAT Technical Group
ASCD-SCI	ASCD-SCI@PSUVM	Alliance for Teaching of Science
ASEE-IED	ASEE-IED@ETSUADMN	Industrial Engineering Division of ASEE
ASEH-L	ASEH-L@TTUVM1	AMERICAN SOCIETY OF ENVIRONMENTAL HISTORIANS
ASHE-L	ASHE-L@MIZZOU1	Association for the Study of Higher Educatio+
ASIANAD	ASIANAD@JPNSUT00	Asia (JP,KR,TW) Node Administrator
ASIMOV-L	ASIMOV-L@UTDALLAS	Discussion of Isaac Asimov's works
ASIPP-L	ASIPP-L@ULKYVM	Chinese Plasma Physics Forum

Network-wide ID	Full address	List title
ASISMI	ASISMI@WAYNEST1	ASIS Michigan Chapter Discussion List
ASKSAM-L	ASKSAM-L@VTVM1	For users of askSam: A Free-form Information+
ASPIRE-L	ASPIRE-L@IUBVM	ASPIRE-L: Linkages for Students from Asean +
ASSEMBLER-LIST	ASM370@DEARN	(Peered) IBM 370 Assembly Programming Discus+
	ASM370@EBCESCA1	(Peered) IBM 370 Assembly Programming Discus+
	ASM370@UCF1VM	(Peered) IBM 370 Assembly Programming Discus+
	ASM370@UGA	(Peered) IBM 370 Assembly Programming Discus+
ASSESS	ASSESS@UKCC	ASSESS - Assessment in Higher Education
ASSMPC	ASSMPC@USACHVM1	"Assembly for the IBM-PC"
ASTR-L	ASTR-L@UIUCVMD	Theatre History Discussion List - Amer. Soc.+
ASTRA-UG	ASTRA-UG@ICNUCEVM	ASTRA Users Group Discussion List
ASTRO	ASTRO@GITVM1	Astronomy Discussion List
ASTRO-PL	ASTRO-PH@JPNYITP	Preprint server for Astrophysics
ASTROL-L	ASTROL-L@BRUFPB	FORUM FOR ASTROLOGICAL DISCUSSION
ASUNOVEL	ASUNOVEL@ASUACAD	ASUNOVEL
ASYSM-L	ASYSM-L@UA1VM	Associate Members of the ASM (Association of+
AS400-L	AS400-L@PCCVM	Discussion forum on the use of AS400 systems
AT-NET	AT-NET@TECHNION	AT-NET - Approximation theory network
ATALK-L	ATALK-L@WUVMD	Campuswide Appletalk Discussion List
ATATS	ATATS@NRCVM01	Automated Training Activity Tracking System
ATHENA	ATHENA@ITOCSIVM	ATHENA Progetto polo UNIX
ATHTRN-L	ATHTRN-L@IUBVM	Discussion list for athletic trainers
ATLANT-L	ATLANT-L@UNBVM1	Atlantic Canada Region Computing Centre Staff
ATLANTIS	ATLANTIS@HARVARDA	ATLANTIS - American Theological Library Disc+
ATLAS-L	ATLAS-L@TCUBVM	ATLAS-L DRA Library systems interest list
ATLAS-TI	ATLAS-TI@DB0TUI11	Discussion about ATLAS-TI
ATLAS-UK@IBM-...	ATLAS-UK@UKACRL	Discussion List for ATLAS-UK
ATLCALOC	ATLCALOC@CERNVM	ATLAS Collaboration sub-list: Software (Repr+
ATLCALOR	ATLCALOR@CERNVM	ATLAS Collaboration sub-list: Calorimeter (+
ATLCALOX	ATLCALOX@CERNVM	ATLAS Collaboration sub-list: Calorimeter
ATLDAQC	ATLDAQC@CERNVM	ATLAS Collaboration sub-list: Software (Repr+

Network-wide ID	Full address	List title
ATLDAQR	ATLDAQR@CERNVM	ATLAS Collaboration sub-list: Software (Repr+
ATLDAQX	ATLDAQX@CERNVM	ATLAS Collaboration sub-list: DAQ/Trigger
ATLGENC	ATLGENC@CERNVM	ATLAS Collaboration sub-list: Software (Repr+
ATLGENR	ATLGENR@CERNVM	ATLAS Collaboration sub-list: General (Repr+
ATLGENX	ATLGENX@CERNVM	ATLAS Collaboration sub-list: General
ATLIDSGC	ATLIDSGC@CERNVM	ATLAS Collaboration sub-list: Inner Detector+
ATLIDSGR	ATLIDSGR@CERNVM	ATLAS Collaboration sub-list: Inner Detector+
ATLIDSGX	ATLIDSGX@CERNVM	ATLAS Collaboration sub-list: Inner Detector+
ATLINFRC	ATLINFRC@CERNVM	ATLAS Collaboration sub-list: Software (Repr+
ATLINFRR	ATLINFRR@CERNVM	ATLAS Collaboration sub-list: Software (Repr+
ATLINFRX	ATLINFRX@CERNVM	ATLAS Collaboration sub-list: Infrastructure
ATLINKC	ATLINKC@CERNVM	ATLAS Collaboration sub-list: Software (Repr+
ATLINKR	ATLINKR@CERNVM	ATLAS Collaboration sub-list: Software (Repr+
ATLINTKR	ATLINTKR@CERNVM	ATLAS Collaboration sub-list: Inner Tracking+
ATLINTKX	ATLINTKX@CERNVM	ATLAS Collaboration sub-list: Inner Tracking
ATLLIOBC	ATLLIOBC@CERNVM	ATLAS Collaboration sub-list: Software (Repr+
ATLLIOBR	ATLLIOBR@CERNVM	ATLAS Collaboration sub-list: Letter of Inte+
ATLLIOBX	ATLLIOBX@CERNVM	ATLAS Collaboration sub-list: Letter of Inte+
ATLMUONC	ATLMUONC@CERNVM	ATLAS Collaboration sub-list: Software (Repr+
ATLMUONR	ATLMUONR@CERNVM	ATLAS Collaboration sub-list: Muon (Represe+
ATLMUONX	ATLMUONX@CERNVM	ATLAS Collaboration sub-list: Muon
ATLPHYSC	ATLPHYSC@CERNVM	ATLAS Collaboration sub-list: Software (Repr+
ATLPHYSR	ATLPHYSR@CERNVM	ATLAS Collaboration sub-list: Software (Repr+
ATLPHYSX	ATLPHYSX@CERNVM	ATLAS Collaboration sub-list: Physics
ATLRD1C	ATLRD1C@CERNVM	ATLAS Collaboration sub-list: Software (Repr+

Network-wide ID	Full address	List title
ATLRD1R	ATLRD1R@CERNVM	ATLAS Collaboration sub-list: Software (Repr+
ATLRD1X	ATLRD1X@CERNVM	ATLAS Collaboration sub-list: RD1
ATLRD11C	ATLRD11C@CERNVM	ATLAS Collaboration sub-list: Software (Repr+
ATLRD11R	ATLRD11R@CERNVM	ATLAS Collaboration sub-list: Software (Repr+
ATLRD11X	ATLRD11X@CERNVM	ATLAS Collaboration sub-list: RD11
ATLRD12C	ATLRD12C@CERNVM	ATLAS Collaboration sub-list: Software (Repr+
ATLRD12R	ATLRD12R@CERNVM	ATLAS Collaboration sub-list: Software (Repr+
ATLRD12X	ATLRD12X@CERNVM	ATLAS Collaboration sub-list: RD12
ATLRD13C	ATLRD13C@CERNVM	ATLAS Collaboration sub-list: Software (Repr+
ATLRD13R	ATLRD13R@CERNVM	ATLAS Collaboration sub-list: Software (Repr+
ATLRD13X	ATLRD13X@CERNVM	ATLAS Collaboration sub-list: RD13
ATLRD16C	ATLRD16C@CERNVM	ATLAS Collaboration sub-list: Software (Repr+
ATLRD16R	ATLRD16R@CERNVM	ATLAS Collaboration sub-list: Software (Repr+
ATLRD16X	ATLRD16X@CERNVM	ATLAS Collaboration sub-list: RD16
ATLRD19C	ATLRD19C@CERNVM	ATLAS Collaboration sub-list: RD19 (Chiefs +
ATLRD19R	ATLRD19R@CERNVM	ATLAS Collaboration sub-list: RD19 Represe+
ATLRD19X	ATLRD19X@CERNVM	ATLAS Collaboration sub-list: RD19
ATLRD2C	ATLRD2C@CERNVM	ATLAS Collaboration sub-list: RD2 (Chiefs o+
ATLRD2R	ATLRD2R@CERNVM	ATLAS Collaboration sub-list: RD2 (Represen+
ATLRD2X	ATLRD2X@CERNVM	ATLAS Collaboration sub-list: RD2
ATLRD20C	ATLRD20C@CERNVM	ATLAS Collaboration sub-list: RD20 (Chiefs +
ATLRD20R	ATLRD20R@CERNVM	ATLAS Collaboration sub-list: RD20 (Represe+
ATLRD20X	ATLRD20X@CERNVM	ATLAS Collaboration sub-list: RD20
ATLRD23C	ATLRD23C@CERNVM	ATLAS Collaboration sub-list: Software (Repr+
ATLRD23R	ATLRD23R@CERNVM	ATLAS Collaboration sub-list: Software (Repr+
ATLRD23X	ATLRD23X@CERNVM	ATLAS Collaboration sub-list: RD23
ATLRD27C	ATLRD27C@CERNVM	ATLAS Collaboration sub-list: Software (Repr+

Network-wide ID	Full address	List title
ATLRD27R	ATLRD27R@CERNVM	ATLAS Collaboration sub-list: Software (Repr+
ATLRD27X	ATLRD27X@CERNVM	ATLAS Collaboration sub-list: RD27
ATLRD28C	ATLRD28C@CERNVM	ATLAS Collaboration sub-list: RD28 chiefs
ATLRD28R	ATLRD28R@CERNVM	ATLAS Collaboration sub-list: RD28 represent+
ATLRD28X	ATLRD28X@CERNVM	ATLAS Collaboration sub-list: RD28
ATLRD3C	ATLRD3C@CERNVM	ATLAS Collaboration sub-list: Software (Repr+
ATLRD3R	ATLRD3R@CERNVM	ATLAS Collaboration sub-list: RD3 (Represen+
ATLRD3X	ATLRD3X@CERNVM	ATLAS Collaboration sub-list: RD3
ATLRD34C	ATLRD34C@CERNVM	ATLAS Collaboration sub-list: RD34 (Chiefs +
ATLRD34R	ATLRD34R@CERNVM	ATLAS Collaboration sub-list: RD34 Represe+
ATLRD34X	ATLRD34X@CERNVM	ATLAS Collaboration sub-list: RD34
ATLRD4C	ATLRD4C@CERNVM	ATLAS Collaboration sub-list: Software (Repr+
ATLRD4R	ATLRD4R@CERNVM	ATLAS Collaboration sub-list: Software (Repr+
ATLRD4X	ATLRD4X@CERNVM	ATLAS Collaboration sub-list: RD4
ATLRD5C	ATLRD5C@CERNVM	ATLAS Collaboration sub-list: Software (Repr+
ATLRD5R	ATLRD5R@CERNVM	ATLAS Collaboration sub-list: Software (Repr+
ATLRD5X	ATLRD5X@CERNVM	ATLAS Collaboration sub-list: RD5
ATLRD6C	ATLRD6C@CERNVM	ATLAS Collaboration sub-list: Software (Repr+
ATLRD6R	ATLRD6R@CERNVM	ATLAS Collaboration sub-list: RD6 (Represen+
ATLRD6X	ATLRD6X@CERNVM	ATLAS Collaboration sub-list: RD6
ATLRD8C	ATLRD8C@CERNVM	ATLAS Collaboration sub-list: Software (Repr+
ATLRD8R	ATLRD8R@CERNVM	ATLAS Collaboration sub-list: Software (Repr+
ATLRD8X	ATLRD8X@CERNVM	ATLAS Collaboration sub-list: RD8
ATLSWC	ATLSWC@CERNVM	ATLAS Collaboration sub-list: Software (Repr+
ATLSWR	ATLSWR@CERNVM	ATLAS Collaboration sub-list: Software (Rep+
ATLSWX	ATLSWX@CERNVM	ATLAS Collaboration sub-list: Software
ATLTRIGC	ATLTRIGC@CERNVM	ATLAS Collaboration sub-list: Software (Repr+
ATLTRIGR	ATLTRIGR@CERNVM	ATLAS Collaboration sub-list: Software (Repr+

Network-wide ID	*Full address*	*List title*
ATLTRIGX	ATLTRIGX@CERNVM	ATLAS Collaboration sub-list: Trigger
ATLWS	ATLWS@MSU	WA Global Village
ATMTUG-L	ATMTUG-L@TAMVM1	"ATMTUG-L (TAMU TeX Users Group Discussion l+
ATP-EMTP	ATP-EMTP@NDSUVM1	ATP-EMTP Electromagnetic Transients Program
ATTEND	ATTEND@BITNIC	BITNET Technical Meeting Attendees
ATTENDBF	ATTENDBF@BITNIC	BITNET BOF Registration only
AUBER-L	AUBER-L@WVNVM	Association of University Business and Econo+
AUDIO-L	AUDIO-L@ITESMVF1	Audio discussion list
AUDITORY	AUDITORY@MCGILL1	Research in auditory perception
AUGLBC-L	AUGLBC-L@AUVM	TAU: Gay, Lesbian and Bisexual Community
AULCCD	AULCCD@ASUACAD	AULC-CD List
AUSTEN-L	AUSTEN-L@MCGILL1	Jane Austen discussion list
AUTISM	AUTISM@SJUVM	SJU Autism and Developmental Disablities List
AUTOCAD	AUTOCAD@JHUVM	AUTOCAD Discussion List
AUTOCAT	AUTOCAT@UBVM	AUTOCAT: Library cataloging and authorities +
AUTORACE	AUTORACE@VTVM1	AUTORACE - A Discussion of Auto Racing
AUTOS-L	AUTOS-L@TRITU	The List For Classic And Sports Cars
AUXTEN-L	AUXTEN-L@MCGILL1	Jane Austen discussion list
AVHIMA-L	AVHIMA-L@UIUCVMD	American Veterinary Health Information Manag+
AVIATION	AVIATION@BRUFPB	General Aviation List
AWARDS-B	AWARDS-B@OSUVM1	Commerce Business Daily - Awards
AWARE-L	AWARE-L@UKANVM	Discussion of the dual platform authoring pr+
AWR-L	AWR-L@TTUVM1	A WRITER'S REPERTOIRE
AXE-LIST	AXE-LIST@MCGILL1	Quebec Litterature Studies
AXE-TALK	AXE-TALK@MCGILL1	AXE-Talk (Quebec Literature Studies Discu+
AXIOM	AXIOM@NDSUVM1	AXIOM Computer Algebra System
AXSLIB-L	AXSLIB-L@SJUVM	AXSLIB-L list
AYN-EDUC	AYN-EDUC@IUBVM	Moderated Introduction of Objectivist Philos+
AYN-RAND	AYN-RAND@IUBVM	Moderated Discussion of Objectivist Philosop+
AYUDA1	AYUDA1@USACHVM1	"Consultas y Soluciones"
AYUDA2	AYUDA2@USACHVM1	"Lista interna para la Unidad de Soporte Tec+
AYUDA4	AYUDA4@USACHVM1	"Lista para PRUEBAS de la Unidad de Soporte +
AZCENTER	AZCENTER@ARIZVM1	Arizona East Asia Events List

Network-wide ID	Full address	List title
BABL-L	BABL-L@MITVMA	Boston Area Business Librarians Discussion L+
BABSON	BABSON@HARVARDA	Discussions on Organizational Design of Acad+
BACIS-L	BACIS-L@UKANVM	KU BACIS Staff
BACW-L	BACW-L@TTUVM1	Alliance For Computers and Writing
BALT-L	BALT-L@UBVM	(Peered) Baltic Republics Discussion List
	BALT-L@UKACRL	(Peered) Baltic Republics Discussion List
BALTUVA	BALTUVA@MCGILL1	BALTUVA: Issues & questions of concern to ob+
BANNER-L	BANNER-L@WVNVM	Student Information System Discussions
BANYAN	BANYAN-L@AKRONVM	Banyan Networks Discussion List
BAPTIST	BAPTIST@UKCC	BAPTIST—Open Baptist Mailing List
BATCH-L	BATCH-L@PURCCVM	Purdue BATCH discussion list
	BATCH-L@VTVM1	Virginia Tech Batch Facility Users List
BATCHX-L	BATCHX-L@UFRJ	BATCHX - Discussoes e Informacoes
BATLINE	BATLINE@UNMVMA	BATLINE: Bat Research Information Exchange N+
BAYOUDOC	BAYOUDOC@LATECH	Bayou Area Government Documents Discussion G+
BAYSGI-L	BAYSGI-L@SJSUVM1	Bay Area Silicon Graphics Users Group
BA275A	BA275A@UMSLVMA	UNIVERSITY OF MISSOURI - Bill Meade - BA275A
BA275B	BA275B@UMSLVMA	UNIVERSITY OF MISSOURI - Bill Meade - BA275B
BA315	BA315@UMSLVMA	BA315-MARKETING MANAGEMENT
BA329	BA329@UMSLVMA	BA329-BUSINESS FORECASTING
BA471	BA471@UMSLVMA	BA471-MKTG PLANNING & STRATEGY
BBS-L	BBS-L@SAUPM00	Discussion forum about BBSs, creation, usage+
BCLASS	BCLASS@UMSLVMA	UNIVERSITY OF MISSOURI - BITNET SHORT COURSE
BCS-L	BCS-L@NMSUVM1	Business Computer Systems Class List
BCS110-L	BCS110-L@NMSUVM1	Wayne Headrick
BCS271-L	BCS271-L@NMSUVM1	Wayne Headrick
BCS33802	BCS33802@NMSUVM1	BCS class list (D.B.O.)
BCS33804	BCS33804@NMSUVM1	BCS class list (J.W.)
BCS371-L	BCS371-L@NMSUVM1	Wayne Headrick
BCVICOUT	BCVICOUT@UVVM	BCNet Outages and Operations - Victoria
BEACON-L	BEACON-L@MAINE	Beacon-L mailing list
BEE-L	BEE-L@ALBNYVM1	Discussion of Bee Biology
BEEF-L	BEEF-L@WSUVM1	Beef Specialists
BEER-L	BEER-L@UA1VM	Homebrew Digest Redistribution List
BEHAVIOR	BEHAVIOR@ASUACAD	Behavioral and Emotional Disorders in Childr+
BEL-HD	BEL-HD@DHDURZ1	BEL-HD BelWue/HD-Net maintenance

Network-wide ID	Full address	List title
BELFERON	BELFERON@PLEARN	BELFERON DISCUSSION LIST FOR TEACHERS. SOC-R+
BELIEF-L	BELIEF-L@BROWNVM	Personal Ideologies Discussion List
	BELIEF-L@UCF1VM	(Peered) Personal Ideologies Discussion List
BERITA-L	BERITA-L@UIUCVMD	M'sia, S'pore & related SEA news [no discuss+
BERWRO-L	BERWRO-L@UBVM	Discussion of Berkely/Wroclaw Activities List
BEST-L	BEST-L@UTORONTO	Best North America Discussion group
BETA-L	BETA-L@LEPICS	L3 Analysis Group Beta
BETTAS	BETTAS@ARIZVM1	Keeping and Breeding Bettas
BEVPUB-L	BEVPUB-L@VTVM1	Blacksburg Electronic Village Open Discussio+
BFS-PERS	BFS-PERS@UCSFVM	B&FS Personnel Team List
BFS-TASK	BFS-TASK@UCSFVM	B&FS Personnel Task Force List
BGEDU-L	BGEDU-L@UKCC	BGEDU-L is a forum for persons concerned wit+
BGRASS-L	BGRASS-L@UKCC	Bluegrass music discussion
BGSA	BGSA@SUVM	African American Graduate Students at Syracu+
BGU-TALK	BGU-TALK@BGUVM	BGU-TALK - BGU general discussion forum
BHRD-L	BHRD-L@ALBNYDH2	BHRD-L Bureau of Health Resources Developme+
BI-L	BI-L@BINGVMB	Bibliographic Instruction Discussion Group
BIACT-L	BIACT-L@BROWNVM	Bisexual Activists' Discussion List
BIAL	BIAL@PLEARN	DISCUSSION LIST OF THE PLBIAL11 BIAL
BIBLIST	BIBLIST@SEARN	Topics in Nordic research library user servi+
BIBSOCAN	BIBSOCAN@UTORONTO	Bibliographical Society of Canada
BIBSOFT	BIBSOFT@INDYCMS	Discussion of software for citations and bib+
BICOMPAL	BICOMPAL@SJUVM	The Big Computer Pals Discussion List
BICYCLE	BICYCLE@BITNIC	The Cycling Discussion List
BIFEM-L	BIFEM-L@BROWNVM	Bisexual Women's Discussion List
BIG-LAN	BIG-LAN@EBCESCA1	Campus-Size LAN Discussion Group
	BIG-LAN@IRLEARN	UCD Distribution of BIG-LAN
	BIG-LAN@SUVM	Campus-Size LAN Discussion Group
	BIG-LAN@TECMTYVM	Selected archives of the BIG-LAN discussion +
BIKEVT	BIKEVT@UVMVM	BikeVT: Vermont Biking and Weather Reports
BILDIL	BILDIL@TRMETU	Turkish Natural Language Processing Discussi+

Network-wide ID	Full address	List title
BILFEL	BILFEL@TRITU	Bilim ve Felsefe Uzerine Tartisma Listesi
BILLING	BILLING@HEARN	Chargeback of (computer) resources
BIO-DOST	BIO-DOST@TREARN	Biyolojik Bilimlerde Calisan Turk Bilim Adam+
BIOCIS-L	BIOCIS-L@SIVM	Biology Curriculum Innovation Study
BIODIDAC	BIODIDAC@UOTTAWA	Electronic Discussion Group for Biology teac+
BIOMAT-L	BIOMAT-L@HEARN	Biomaterials Mailing List
BIOMCH-L	BIOMCH-L@HEARN	Biomechanics and Movement Science listserver
BIOMED-L	BIOMED-L@MCGILL1	Assoc. of Biomedical Communications Directors
	BIOMED-L@NDSUVM1	BIOMED-L Biomedical Ethics
BIOMED4	BIOMED4@ICNUCEVM	CNR - Comitato 04, Biologia e Medicina (BIO+
BIOMET-L	BIOMET-L@ALBNYDH2	BUREAU OF BIOMETRICS AT ALBNYDH2
BIOPI-L	BIOPI-L@KSUVM	Secondary Biology Teacher Enhancement PI
BIOSPH-L	BIOSPH-L@UBVM	Biosphere, ecology, Discussion List
BIOTECH	BIOTECH@UMDD	Biotechnology Discussion List
BIOVOTE	BIOVOTE@IRLEARN	BIOSCI Ballot Box
BIPM-L	BIPM-L@FRORS12	Bureau International des Poids et Mesures
BIRD_RBA	BIRD_RBA@ARIZVM1	National Birding Hotline Cooperative
BIRDBAND	BIRDBAND@ARIZVM1	Bird Bander's Forum
BIRDCHAT	BIRDCHAT@ARIZVM1	National Birding Hotline Cooperative (Chat L+
BIRDCNTR	BIRDCNTR@ARIZVM1	National Birding Hotline Cooperative (Centra+
BIRDEAST	BIRDEAST@ARIZVM1	National Birding Hotline Cooperative (East)
BIRDTRIP	BIRDTRIP@ARIZVM1	A Special BIRDCHAT LOGO Project
BIRDWEST	BIRDWEST@ARIZVM1	National Birding Hotline Cooperative (West)
BISEXU-L	BISEXU-L@BROWNVM	Bisexuality Discussion List
BITFTP-L	BITFTP-L@EARNCC	Discussion list for BITFTP Server
BITHRY-L	BITHRY-L@BROWNVM	BITHRY-L: Bisexual Theory Discussion List
BITLIB-D	BITLIB-D@UTCVM	BITLIB Distribution List
BITLIB-L	BITLIB-L@UTCVM	BITLIB Discussion List
BITNET-L	BITNET-L@BRLNCC	USUARIOS DE BITNET NO LNCC
	BITNET-L@BRUFPB	LISTA PARA OS USUARIOS DA BITNET
BITNET-2	BITNET-2@PUCC	Discussion of BITNET II
BITNEWS	BITNEWS@BITNIC	(Peered) BITNET Network News List
	BITNEWS@DEARN	(Peered) BITNET News List
	BITNEWS@HEARN	(Peered) BITNET News List
	BITNEWS@MARIST	(Peered) BITNET News List
	BITNEWS@UGA	(Peered) BITNET News

Network-wide ID	Full address	List title
BITTECH	BITTECH@BITNIC	BITNET Technical Meeting announcements and d+
BITUSE-L	BITUSE-L@UMAB	Bitnet User's Group
BIXANET	BIXANET@JHUVM	Brainwave Systems users group
BIZLAW-L	BIZLAW-L@UMAB	Law Regarding Business Associations and Secu+
BKGAMMON	BKGAMMON@INDYCMS	Backgammon strategy
BKKBN	BKKBN@SUVM	Indonesian Pop/Family Planning Discussion
BLACKLIB	BLACKLIB@GUVM	Conference of Black Librarians
BLIND-L	BLIND-L@UAFSYSB	Computer Use by and for the Blind
BLINDNWS	BLINDNWS@NDSUVM1	Blind News Digest
BLISS-L	BLISS-L@BROWNVM	Barus Lab Interactive Speech System List
BLUES-L	BLUES-L@BROWNVM	Blues Music List
BMDP-L	BMDP-L@MCGILL1	BMDP discussion list
BMMR	BMMR@UWAVM	BMMR
BNOVEL-L	BNOVEL-L@AUVM	Rise of the British Novel
BOARD-F	BOARD-F@FRMOP11	Bureau de l'association EARN-France
BOARD-L	BOARD-L@UOTTAWA	Board of Directors of Canadian Association o+
BODY-L	BODY-L@LSUVM	The Body Electric: E-Journal of Poetry & Fic+
BOGEN-L	BOGEN-L@UALTAVM	Discussion on the Industrial Engineering dep+
BONSAI	BONSAI@WAYNEST1	Bonsai Discussion List
BOREAL-L	BOREAL-L@UTFSM	Lista de Informacion para el BOletin REdes A+
BORIKEN	BORIKEN@ENLACE	BORIKEN: Cultura y sociedad de Puerto Rico
BORSA-L	BORSA-L@TREARN	Turkiye Ekonomisi ve Borsa Listesi (in Turki+
BOXES	BOXES@FRMOP11	Personnel CNUSC de box
BPI	BPI@UTXVM	Business Process Improvement: Issues, op-port+
BPWSP-L	BPWSP-L@ALBNYDH2	BPWSP-L Bureau of Public Water Supply Prote+
BRAILLE	BRAILLE@CSEARN	Discussion club for blinds, in Czech and Eng+
BRAIN-L	BRAIN-L@MCGILL1	Mind-Brain Discussion Group
BRAINTMR	BRAINTMR@MITVMA	Brain Tumor Research/Support
BRANCH-D	BRANCH-D@IRLEARN	Solitary Pagan Practitioner Digest
BRAS-CON	BRAS-CON@FRORS12	Brasnet na Europa Continental
BRAS-NET	BRAS-NET@BRUFMG	Brasileiros no Exterior
	BRAS-NET@BRUFPB	Brasileiros no Exterior
	BRAS-NET@PCCVM	Brazilian Students Comn-net
BRASLNCC	BRASLNCC@BRLNCC	Usuarios BRASNET no LNCC

Network-wide ID	Full address	List title
BRC-L	BRC-L@UMAB	BRC-L
BRCTR	BRCTR@ULKYVM	Braille Research Center forum
BRFC-L	BRFC-L@PUCC	BITNET RFC Discussion List
BRIDGE-L	BRIDGE-L@UCSBVM	The Bridge Across Consciousness
BRINE-L	BRINE-L@UGA	Brine Shrimp Discussion List
BRIT-L	BRIT-L@KSUVM	Behavioral Research In Transplantation
BRS-L	BRS-L@USCVM	BRS/Search Full Text Retrieval Software Disc+
BRTHPRNT	BRTHPRNT@INDYCMS	List for Birthparents of Adoptees
BRU-L	BRU-L@HEARN	BRU-L: Lijst voor Bibliotheek Rijksuniversit+
BRUCE-L	BRUCE-L@NIHLIST	Bruce's own test list
BRUNONIA	BRUNONIA@BROWNVM	Brown Alumni Discussion List
BRUNSWIK	BRUNSWIK@ALBNYVM1	Brunswikian psychology and Social Judgment T+
BRUPROJ	BRUPROJ@BROWNVM	Brown Projects Discussion List
BRW1EXP	BRW1EXP@PLEARN	Discussion list for testing. BRW1EXP
BSCS-L	BSCS-L@EMUVM1	Business School Computing Support
BSRUSERS	BSRUSERS@PUCC	BSR Software discussion list
BUBIRDENEMELI...	DENEME@TRITU	(Peered) ListEARN Testing
BUCKS-L	BUCKS-L@TAMVM1	Gigabucks Discussion List
BUDANEWS	BUDANEWS@PLEARN	BUDANEWS LIST FOR SCHOOL NEWS EXCHANGE. BUDA+
BUDDHA-L	BUDDHA-L@ULKYVM	Buddhist Academic Discussion Forum
BUDDHIST	BUDDHIST@JPNTUVM0	Forum on Indian and Buddhist Studies
BUDPRI-L	BUDPRI-L@UBVM	UB Faculty Senate Budget Priorities Committe+
BURC	BURC@TREARN	Bogazici University Graduates Communication +
BURG-CEN	BURG-CEN@HEARN	List issued for the J.M. Burgers Centre for +
BUSETH-L	BUSETH-L@UBVM	Business Ethics Computer Network
BUSFAC-L	BUSFAC-L@CMUVM	International Business Faculty Discussion
BUSH	BUSH@MARIST	Discussion of campaigning for President by G+
BUSLIB-L	BUSLIB-L@IDBSU	BUSLIB-L - BUSINESS LIBRARIES DISCUSSION LIST
BUSMGT-L	BUSMGT-L@YALEVM	Business Management Board List
BUSTALK	BUSTALK@TEMPLEVM	Cochran Research Center Discussion
C++USERS	C++USERS@MITVMA	Discussion list for MIT C++ Language Develop+
C+HEALTH	C+HEALTH@IUBVM	Health effects of computer use
C-ALERTL	C-ALERT@JPNYITP	CONTENTS-Alert by Elsevier Science Publishers
C-BOARD	C-BOARD@UOTTAWA	Board of Advisors for CONTENTS Projects
C-L	C-L@INDYCMS	Discussion of C Programming

Network-wide ID	Full address	List title
C_C++	C_C++@TRITU	C ve C++ Programlama Dilleri Tartisma Listesi
CA-CR-L	CA-CR-L@NMSUVM1	Classroom assessment and classroom research +
CA-L	CA-L@MITVMA	BITNET part of CA@Think.COM (Cellular Automa+
CA-VMNET	CA-VMNET@UTORONTO	Canadian VMNET Backbone Group
CAAH	CAAH@PUCC	CONSORTIUM OF ART AND ARCHITECTURAL HISTORIA+
CACCS-L	CACCS-L@UOTTAWA	Canadian Association of Campus Computer Stor+
CACI-L	CACI-L@UALTAVM	Research and Advanced Study: Canada and Italy
CADAM-L	CADAM-L@SUVM	Computer Aided Design and Manufacturing (CAD+
CADLIST	CADLIST@SUVM	CAD General Discussion Group
CAEDS-L	CAEDS-L@SUVM	Computer Aided Engineering Design (CAEDS) In+
CAEJ-L	CAEJ-L@UOTTAWA	Canadian Association of Electronic Journal P+
CAFSS-L	CAFSS-L@VTVM1	CAFSS-L is a list for members of the CAFSS T+
CAHECUG	CAHECUG@WSUVM1	CAHE Computer User Group
CAL-SE	CAL-SE@SEARN	Newsletter for CAL in higher education in Sw+
CALCSYMB	CALCSYMB@BLIULG11	CALCSYMB General Discussion list
CALCUL	CALCUL@FRMOP11	Equipe Assistance Scientifique CNUSC
CALIBACA	CALIBACA@SJSUVM1	California Academic Librarians
CALIBALL	CALIBALL@SJSUVM1	All California Librarians
CALIBK12	CALIBK12@SJSUVM1	California K–12 Librarians
CALIBPUB	CALIBPUB@SJSUVM1	California Public Librarians
CALL-L	CALL-L@UNBVM1	Canadian Academic Law Libraries List
CALLCD	CALLCD@SIUCVMB	CALLCD List
CALPAR	CALPAR@ICNUCEVM	CNUCE Reparto Calcolo Vettoriale e Parallelo
CAMEL-L	CAMEL-L@SAKFU00	Discussion Forum on Camels Researches
CAMPCLIM	CAMPCLIM@UAFSYSB	Campus Climate
CAMPINAS	CAMPINAS@PCCVM	Campinas forum - (Portuguese language)
CAN-TEST	CAN-TEST@UBVM	SUNY Canton Test List
CANADA-L	CANADA-L@MCGILL1	Canadian Issues Forum
CANALC	CANALC@YORKVM1	Canadian Association for Latin American and +
CANALC-D	CANALC-D@YORKVM1	A DIGEST of CANALC@vm1.yorku.ca Postings
CANARIE	CANARIE@UNBVM1	CANARIE open discussion
CANCER-L	CANCER-L@WVNVM	WVNET CANCER discussion list
CANCHID	CANCHID@YORKVM1	Canadian Network on Health in International +

Network-wide ID	Full address	List title
CANCHIDD	CANCHIDD@YORKVM1	An Occasional Digest of CANCHID@vm1.yorku.ca+
CANDG-L	CANDG-L@UCSFVM	Contract and Grant Representatives List
CANDI-L	CANDI-L@MIZZOU1	Curriculum and Instruction Department Discus+
CANDLE-L	CANDLE-L@UA1VM	Candle Products Discussion List
CANDRAMA	CANDRAMA@UNBVM1	Canadian Theatre Research
CANEWS	CANEWS@UVVM	CA*net Newsletter
CANINE-L	CANINE-L@PCCVM	(Peered) Discussion forum for Dog fanciers
	CANINE-L@PSUVM	(Peered) Discussion forum for Dog fanciers
CANSPACE	CANSPACE@UNBVM1	Canadian Space Geodesy Forum
CAPES-L	CAPES-L@BRUFMG	Grupo de discussao da CAPES
CAPNOTE	CAPNOTE@GWUVM	Capital Notebook Advisory Committee List
CAR-CS	CAR-CS@CSEARN	CAROLINA - Elektronicky tydennik FSVUK
CAR-ENG	CAR-ENG@CSEARN	CAROLINA - E-mail news weekly
CARA-D	CARA-D@ICNUCEVM	CARA Donna del CNUCE
CARECON	CARECON@YORKVM1	Caribbean Economy
CAREER-L	CAREER-L@BINGVMB	SUNY-wide Career Development Organization li+
CARET	CARET@GWUVM	Capital Area Researchers in Educational Tech+
CARIB-L	CARIB-L@FRCPN11	Liste MTP Spring School of the Caribbean
CARL-L	CARL-L@UHCCVM	CARL User's Information List
CARO-DIR	CARO-DIR@ICNUCEVM	CNUCE Comunicazioni dei dipendenti col Diret+
CARR-L	CARR-L@ULKYVM	Computer-assisted Reporting & Research
CARS-L	CARS-L@SAUPM00	Discussion forum about cars
CART-L	CART-L@UICVM	CART Discussion Group
CARWAR-L	CARWAR-L@UBVM	Car Wars Discussion List
CASE-L	CASE-L@UCCVMA	Computer Aided Software Engineering
CASID-L	CASID-L@MCGILL1	Canadian Assoc. for the Study of Internation+
CASLL	CASLL@UNBVM1	CASLL/Inkshed
CASTOR	CASTOR@YORKVM1	American Schools of Oriental Research in Can+
CATALA	CATALA@EBCESCA1	Forum de discussio per a catalanoparlants
CATALYST	CATALYST@VTVM1	The Community Services CATALYST electronic j+
CATHAR-M	CATHAR-M@SJUVM	CATHARSIS creative newsmagazine CFS/CFIDS/ME
CATHOLIC	CATHOLIC@AUVM	Free Catholic Mailing List
CATIA-L	CATIA-L@SUVM	Computer Aided Three Dimensional Interactive+

Network-wide ID	Full address	List title
CAUCE-L	CAUCE-L@UREGINA1	Canadian Association for University Continui+
CAUCE-PP	CAUCE-PP@UREGINA1	Canadian University Continuing Education Pol+
CAUSEASM	CAUSEASM@VTVM1	Constituent Group for Administrative Systems+
CAVITY	CAVITY@UWAVM	CAVITY
CAVMEN	CAVMEN@UICVM	Chicago Area VM ENthusiasts Forum
CBA-LAB	CBA-LAB@UICVM	CBA PC Lab Faculty Support
CBDS-L	CBDS-L@SUVM	Circuit Board Design System (CBDS) Interest +
CBEHIGH	CBEHIGH@BLEKUL11	CBEHIGH list : Computer Based Education in h+
CC	CC@MCGILL1	Computing Centre Staff Names
CCANET	CCANET@RPITSVM	Canadian Communication Association Network
CCCCC-L	CCCCC-L@TTUVM1	INTERCLASS COMPUTERS & WRITING
CCCECS	CCCECS@ICNUCEVM	Commiss. per il Coord. dei Centri Erogatori +
CCCRN	CCCRN@NRCVM01	Canadian Coordinating Committee for Research+
CCD-L	CCD-L@HUMBER	Computer Centre Directors' List
CCDIC-L	CCDIC-L@UALTAVM	Canadian Centre for the Development of Instr+
CCDOC	CCDOC@ICNUCEVM	Commissione Consuntiva CNUCE -Database
CCES-L	CCES-L@UNBVM1	Congress of Canadian Engineering Students (F+
CCID-L	CCID-L@UCF1VM	Community College International Development +
CCIJLEX	CCIJLEX@UCHCECVM	Foro de Informatica Juridica.
CCMAIL-L	CCMAIL-L@OSUVM1	cc:Mail Interest Group
CCMAN-L	CCMAN-L@UGA	CND Chinese Magazine Network
CCN	CCN@MSU	Campus Computing News
CCNET-L	CCNET-L@UGA	Chinese Computing Network
CCNEWS	CCNEWS@BITNIC	Campus Computing Newsletter Editors
CCNL	CCNL@UTARLVM1	Newsletter on Chinese Community
CCUMC-L	CCUMC-L@UHCCVM	CCUMC Membership Discussion List
CDC-L	CDC-L@UALTAVM	Collections Development Committee
CDCNAD-F	CDCNAD-F@FRMOP11	Liste des 'Node ADministators' CDC francais
CDMAJOR	CDMAJOR@KENTVM	Communication Disorder Discussion List
CDOBRD-L	CDOBRD-L@BINGVMB	CDO Board of Directors
CDPLUS-L	CDPLUS-L@UTORONTO	CDPLUS User Group
CDROM-L	CDROM-L@UCCVMA	CD-ROM
CDROMLAN	CDROMLAN@IDBSU	CDROMLAN - USE OF CDROM PRODUCTS IN LAN ENVI+

Network-wide ID	Full address	List title
CDS-ISIS	CDS-ISIS@HEARN	Electronic user-group for Unesco's CDS/ISIS +
CDSBC-L	CDSBC-L@UFRJ	CDSBC-L - Conselho da Sociedade Brasileira d+
CEC	CEC@QUCDN	Canadian Electro-Acoustics Community (CEC)
CELTIC-L	CELTIC-L@IRLEARN	CELTIC-L - The Celtic Culture List.
CENASIA	CENASIA@MCGILL1	Former Soviet Republic - Central Asia Politi+
CENTAM-L	CENTAM-L@UBVM	Central America Discussion List
CENTER-L	CENTER-L@JPNTUVM0	Suggestion and Complaints to JPNTOHOK
CENTINFO	CENTINFO@INDYCMS	Center Availability Information
CENTRG-L	CENTRG-L@UTORONTO	Central Region Directors
CEPES-L	CEPES-L@HEARN	CEPES UNESCO (European Centre for Higher Edu+
CERES-L	CERES-L@WVNVM	Collaborative Environments for Conserving Ea+
CERN	CERN@PLEARN	The CERN discussion list. CERN
CERRO-L	CERRO-L@AEARN	Central European Regional Research Organizat+
CESNEWS	CESNEWS@BROWNVM	Coalition of Essential Schools News
CETH	CETH@PUCC	Center for Electronic Texts in the Humanities
CEVRE-L	CEVRE-L@TRITU	Cevre ve Cevre Sorunlari Uzerine Tartisma Li+
CFD	CFD@UKCC	Computational Fluid Dynamics Group
CFS-D	CFS-D@ALBNYDH2	Chronic Fatigue Syndrome File Storage
CFS-FILE	CFS-FILE@SJUVM	Chronic Fatigue Syndrome files CFIDS/ME
CFS-L	CFS-L@NIHLIST	Chronic Fatigue Syndrome discussion CFIDS/ME
CFS-MED	CFS-MED@NIHLIST	Chronic Fatigue Syndrome/CFIDS medical list
CFS-NEWS	CFS-NEWS@NIHLIST	Chronic Fatigue Syndrome Newsletter CFIDS/ME
CFS-WIRE	CFS-WIRE@SJUVM	Chronic Fatigue Syndrome NEWSWIRE CFIDS/ME
CGE	CGE@MARIST	Computer Graphics Education Newsletter
CGSA-L	CGSA-L@UBVM	Chinese Graduate Student Association List
CH-LADB	CH-LADB@UNMVMA	Latin America Data Base
CHAIRLNK	CHAIRLNK@GWUVM	ASA Communication with Sociology Department +
CHANGE-L	CHANGE-L@UCSFVM	AIS Change Production Notices
CHANN-L	CHANN-L@BROWNVM	GRA Microscope List

Network-wide ID	Full address	List title
CHAO-DYN	CHAO-DYN@JPNYITP	Preprint server for Dynamical systems/Chaos/+
CHATBACK	CHATBACK@SJUVM	SJU Chatback Planning Group
CHEAT	CHEAT@TTUVM1	Procedures Database
CHEMCOMP	CHEMCOMP@HUEARN	Magyar Kemikusok Egyesuletenek Kibernetika l+
CHEMCONF	CHEMCONF@UMDD	Conferences on Chemistry Research and Educat+
CHEMCORD	CHEMCORD@UMDD	Gen. Chem. Coordinators Discussion Group
CHEMDISC	CHEMDISC@UMDD	ChemConf Discussion
CHEME-L	CHEME-L@PSUVM	Chemical Engineering List
CHEMED-L	CHEMED-L@UWF	Chemistry Education Discussion List
CHEMIC-L	CHEMIC-L@TAUNIVM	Chemistry in Israel List
CHESS-L	CHESS-L@GREARN	The Chess Discussion List
CHEST-L	CHEST-L@IRLEARN	CHEST-L
CHICLE	CHICLE@UNMVMA	Chicano literature discussion list
CHILDLIT	CHILDLIT@RUTVM1	Children's Literature: Criticism and Theory
CHILDMUS	CHILDMUS@RICEVM1	CHILDMUS - A Forum for Children's Museum Pro+
CHILE-L	CHILE-L@UCHCECVM	(Peered) Discussion Regaring Chile (Peer Lis+
	CHILE-L@USACHVM1	Discussion regarding Chile
	CHILE-L@UTARLVM1	(Peered) Discussion Regarding Chile
CHILEHOY	CHILEHOY@USACHVM1	"Diario del acontecer en Chile"
CHILENET	CHILENET@UCHCECVM	(Peered) Lista de Informaciones para la Red +
	CHILENET@UTFSM	(Peered) Lista de Informaciones para la Red +
CHIM3	CHIM3@ICNUCEVM	CNR - Comitato 03, Chimica (CHIM3)
CHINA	CHINA@PUCC	Chinese Studies list
CHINA-L	CHINA-L@UCF1VM	Florida - China Linkage Institute Discussion+
CHINA-ND	CHINA-ND@KENTVM	China News Digest (US News)
CHINA-NN	CHINA-NN@ASUACAD	(Peered) China News Digest (Global News)
	CHINA-NN@UTARLVM1	(Peered) China News Digest (Global News)
CHINA-NT	CHINA-NT@UGA	China-Net
CHINANET	CHINANET@TAMVM1	CHINANET: Networking In China
CHIP-L	CHIP-L@BRUFPB	Lista do Laboratorio Chip (CCHLA)
CHMINF-L	CHMINF-L@IUBVM	CHEMICAL INFORMATION SOURCES DISCUSSION LIST
CHOP-L	CHOP-L@UAFSYSB	Lambda Chi Alpha Fraternity

Network-wide ID	Full address	List title
CHPOEM-L	CHPOEM-L@UBVM	Chinese Poem Exchange and Discussion List
CHRISTIA	CHRISTIA@ASUACAD	Practical Christian Life
CHUG-L	CHUG-L@BROWNVM	Brown University Computing in the Humanities+
CIBER-L	CIBER-L@UMDD	Dept. of Ed. Center for International Bus. E+
CICS-L	CICS-L@AKRONVM	(Peered) CICS Discussion List
	CICS-L@AWIIMC12	(Peered) CICS List
	CICS-L@MARIST	(Peered) CICS List
	CICS-L@UALTAVM	(Peered) CICS List
	CICS-L@UGA	(Peered) CICS List
	CICS-L@UTARLVM1	(Peered) CICS List
CIENCIA	CIENCIA@PTEARN	Discussao da Implementacao do Programa CIENC+
CIESIN	CIESIN@POLYVM	Polytechnic CIESIN Distribution
CINBENGL	CINBENGL@MIAMIU	Cincinnati Bengals
CINEMA-L	CINEMA-L@AUVM	Discussions on all forms of Cinema
CINS-L	CINS-L@UALTAVM	Canadian-Scandinavianist info-sharing networ+
CINTIRED	CINTIRED@MIAMIU	Cincinnati Reds
CIO-L	CIO-L@WVNVM	Higher Education Chief Information Officers
CIPE-L	CIPE-L@UWF	Computers in Physics Education
CIPE-PUB	CIPE-PUB@UWF	"Read-only circulation of CIPE'S deliberatio+
CIRCPLUS	CIRCPLUS@IDBSU	CIRCPLUS - LIBRARY CIRCULATION ISSUES
CIRLNET	CIRLNET@RUTVM1	Community of Industrial Relations Librarians+
CISCO-L	CISCO-L@BLIULG11	CISCO-L Redistribution List
	CISCO-L@DEARN	CISCO Anwendergruppe
CIT$P	CIT$P@PLEARN	The Cracow Institute of Technology private d+
CIT$W	CIT$W@PLEARN	The Cracow Institute of Technology open disc+
CITAS-L	CITAS-L@UWAVM	CITAS-L
CITERG	CITERG@FRMOP11	Centro de Intercambios Telematizados aplicad+
CITYNET	CITYNET@UNCCVM	Charlotte Freenet Discussion
CIUW	CIUW@PLEARN	Lista dyskusyjna dla pracownikow CIUW
CIUW-L	CIUW-L@PLEARN	CIUW and PLEARN users discussion list CIUW-L
CIVIL-L	CIVIL-L@UNBVM1	Civil Engineering Reasearch & Education
CJ-L	CJ-L@ALBNYVM1	Discussion of beliefs and practices of Conse+

Network-wide ID	Full address	List title
CJKLIB-L	CJKLIB-L@DHDURZ1	CJKLIB-L Distribution List
CJMOVIES	CJMOVIES@ALBNYVM1	Journal of Criminal Justice and Popular Cult+
CJUST-L	CJUST-L@CUNYVM	CJUST-L: Criminal Justice Discussion List
CL_NEWS	CL_NEWS@IUBVM	News on teaching with collaborative learning+
CLAN	CLAN@FRMOP11	Cancer Liaison and Action Network
CLARION	CLARION@VMTECSLP	Clarion Language and related tools Discussio+
CLASS-L	CLASS-L@SBCCVM	Classification, clustering, and phylogeny es+
CLASSICS	CLASSICS@UWAVM	Classical Greek and Latin Discussion Group
CLASSLST	CLASSLST@UMAB	LISTSERV LIST FOR CLASS EXERCISES
CLASSM-L	CLASSM-L@BROWNVM	Classical Music List
CLASTALK	CLASTALK@WCU	Class Talk
CLAYART	CLAYART@UKCC	Ceramic Arts Discussion List
CLEAN-L	CLEAN-L@HEARN	Discussions on the functional language Clean
CLEIP94	CLEIP94@ITESMVF1	Informacion Panel CLEI '94
CLGSG-L	CLGSG-L@RICEVM1	Coalition of Lesbian and Gay Student Groups +
	CLGSG-L@TAMVM1	Coalition of Lesbian and Gay Student Groups +
CLIMLIST	CLIMLIST@PSUVM	CLIMLIST Climatology Distribution List
CLINALRT	CLINALRT@UMAB	Clinical Alerts from NIH
CLINTON	CLINTON@MARIST	Discussion of campaigning for President by B+
CLIOBIT	CLIOBIT@BRUFSC	Forum eletronico de debate e troca de inform+
CLIOLOGY	CLIOLOGY@MSU	Theories of History
CLIPPER	CLIPPER@BRUFPB	List for Clipper and DBMS systems for IBM PC
CLOCKS	CLOCKS@SUVM	Clock/Watch Repair, Collecting, and Construc+
CLUB-USM	CLUB-USM@UTFSM	Lista de Informacion de la U.T.F.S.M.
CLUBP-L	CLUBP-L@YALEVM	Club Presidents List
CLUSTER	CLUSTER@BLIULG11	Parallel RS/6000 CLUSTER General Discussion +
CMA-L	CMA-L@LATECH	Discussion List for members of College Media+
CMC	CMC@RPITSVM	Computer Mediated Communication
CMDNET-L	CMDNET-L@KSUVM	Conflict Management Division List
CMIS-L	CMIS-L@UMAB	CMIS Project
CMPENET	CMPENET@PSUVM	Computer Enginerring List
CMPHENGL	CMPHENGL@TECHNION	CMPHENGL - Inter-Faculty Seminar on Scienti+

Network-wide ID	Full address	List title
CMPSU-L	CMPSU-L@PSUVM	CND Chinese Magazine Network (Service II)
CMS-PIPELINES	CMSPIP-L@AWIIMC12	(Peered) VM/SP CMS Pipelines Discussion List
	CMSPIP-L@MARIST	(Peered) VM/SP CMS Pipelines Discussion List
CMSAPPL	CMSAPPL@UKACRL	CMSAPPL LIST
CMSC411	CMSC411@UMDD	On-line study section for Prof. Ricart's Int+
CMSR4-L	CMSR4-L@UIUCVMD	CMS release 4 discussions
CMSR5-L	CMSR5-L@UIUCVMD	CMS release 5 discussions
CMSUG-L	CMSUG-L@NDSUVM1	(Peered) CMSUG-L CMS List
	CMSUG-L@UTARLVM1	(Peered) CMS User Guide List
CMUWA-L	CMUWA-L@UWAVM	(CND-CM/HXWZ Hz Service)
CNC-L	CNC-L@UVVM	China News (Canada)
CND-EP	CND-EP@IUBVM	China News Digest - Europe/Pacific
CNDPSU-L	CNDPSU-L@PSUVM	China News Digest (Global Service) IV
CNDUB-L	CNDUB-L@UBVM	China News Digest (Global Service) III
CNDUWA-L	CNDUWA-L@UWAVM	(CND-US Service II)
CNDVT-L	CNDVT-L@VTVM1	China News Digest - US Regional News (CND-US+
CNEDUC-L	CNEDUC-L@TAMVM1	Computer Networking Education Discussion List
CNETIE-L	CNETIE-L@UALTAVM	International Centre Communication Network (+
CNFINFO	CNFINFO@CERNVM	List CNFINFO
CNG	CNG@ASUACAD	China News Group (ASU Local)
CNI-ARCH	CNI-ARCH@UCCVMA	CNI-Architecture and Standards WG
CNIDR-L	CNIDR-L@UNCCVM	Networked Information Discovery and Retrieval
CNIS	CNIS@HARVARDA	Coordination of Network Information Services
CNPQ-L	CNPQ-L@BRUFMG	Grupo de discussao do CNPQ
CNR	CNR@ICNUCEVM	CNR Electronic Mail of C.N.R. people
CNRE	CNRE@NERVM	College of Natural Resources and the Environ+
CNRE-EB	CNRE-EB@DEARN	CNRE Editorial Board
CNSF-L	CNSF-L@UBVM	Cornell National Supercomputer Facility Anno+
CNUCE-CC	CNUCE-CC@ICNUCEVM	CNUCE Commissione Consuntiva
COAACAD	COAACAD@UBVM	SUNY COA Academic Subcommittee Discussion Li+
COASTGIS	COASTGIS@IRLEARN	Coastal GIS Distribution List
COASTNET	COASTNET@URIACC	Coastal Management Conference
COCAMED	COCAMED@UTORONTO	Computers in Canadian Medical Education
COCHCOSH	COCHCOSH@UTORONTO	COCHCOSH Discussion
COCO	COCO@PUCC	COCO - Tandy Color Computer List
COCTA-L	COCTA-L@UHCCVM	INTERCOCTA network forum

Network-wide ID	Full address	List title
COGS	COGS@UICVM	Computing on a Grand Scale List
COGSCI-L	COGSCI-L@MCGILL1	COGNITIVE SCIENCE CENTRE
COHERENT	COHERENT@IRISHVMA	Coherent operating system
COHO-L	COHO-L@VTVM1	Consumer Horticulture Discussion List
COINF-L	COINF-L@BRUFSC	FORUM COINF-L - Comite de Informatica da UFSC
COLA-L	COLA-L@UALTAVM	College on Location Analysis
COLDEV-L	COLDEV-L@UNBVM1	CLA Collections Development Interest Group
COLEXT	COLEXT@ANDESCOL	(Peered) Los Colombianos en el Exterior
	COLEXT@CUVMB	(Peered) Los Colombianos en el Exterior
COLLDV-L	COLLDV-L@USCVM	Library Collection Development List
COLORCAT	COLORCAT@BROWNVM	COLORCAT: Color Categorization List
COLT-L	COLT-L@HUMBER	Committee on Learning Technologies Discussio+
COM-ALG	COM-ALG@NDSUVM1	COM-ALG - Commutative Algebra
COMCIV-L	COMCIV-L@IUBVM	CompCiv-L:
COMCOM-L	COMCOM-L@NMSUVM1	Stephen Bernhardt's English Class
COMDEV	COMDEV@RPITSVM	Communication & international development
COMEDIA	COMEDIA@ARIZVM1	A discussion of Hispanic Classic Theater
COMENIUS	COMENIUS@CSEARN	Discussion and forum for news on the develop+
COMHIST	COMHIST@RPITSVM	History of human communication
COMICS-L	COMICS-L@UNLVM	COMICS Discussion List
COMICW-L	COMICW-L@UNLVM	COMIC Writers Workshop
COMLAW-L	COMLAW-L@UALTAVM	Computers and Legal Education
COMMCOLL	COMMCOLL@UKCC	COMMCOLL - a discussion list for community a+
COMMDIS	COMMDIS@RPITSVM	Speech disorders
COMMED	COMMED@RPITSVM	Communication education
COMMERCE	COMMERCE@IRLEARN	UCD Faculty of Commerce Staff
COMMJOBS	COMMJOBS@RPITSVM	Position announcements in Communication Stud+
COMMODOR	COMMODOR@UBVM	COMMODORE COMPUTERS DISCUSSION
COMNET-L	COMNET-L@UALTAVM	Communicators Network for U of A
COMP-CEN	COMP-CEN@UCCVMA	Computer Center Managers' Issues
COMP-GAS	COMP-GAS@JPNYITP	Preprint server for Computational methods/Ti+
COMP-SCI	COMP-SCI@TAUNIVM	Comp-Sci Distribution List
COMPACT	COMPACT@INDYCMS	IUPUI Campus Compact
COMPIL-L	COMPIL-L@AUVM	Redistribution of comp.compilers
COMPMED	COMPMED@WUVMD	Comparative Medicine List
COMPSY-L	COMPSY-L@UIUCVMD	Midwest Forum for community/ecological psych+

Network-wide ID	Full address	List title
COMPTECH	COMPTECH@TTUVM1	Computing issues at Texas Tech
COMPUMED	COMPUMED@SJUVM	St. John's University Computers in Medicine +
COMSOC-L	COMSOC-L@AUVM	Computers and Society ARPA Digest
COMTEC-L	COMTEC-L@NMSUVM1	NCTE Scitech committee list
COMTEN-L	COMTEN-L@UCSBVM	COMTEN FEP and Related Products
COM470-L	COM470-L@NMSUVM1	Ken Hacker's Class
CONCHR-L	CONCHR-L@TEMPLEVM	Conservative Christian Discussion List
COND-MAL	COND-MAT@JPNYITP	Preprint server for Condensed Matter
CONFLIST	CONFLIST@UCSFVM	School of Medicine Conference List
CONFOCAL	CONFOCAL@UBVM	Confocal Microscopy List
CONFSERV	CONFSERV@PSUVM	University Conference Services
CONNECT	CONNECT@UNMVMA	IETF ISN WG Subcommittee on Connectivity Mod+
CONS-L	CONS-L@MCGILL1	Consultant's discussion list
CONSALD	CONSALD@UTXVM	Comm. on South Asian Libraries and Documenta+
CONSBIO	CONSBIO@UWAVM	CONSBIO
CONSBIO-	CONSBIO-@UWAVM	CONSBIO-L
CONSGIS	CONSGIS@URIACC	Biological Conservation and GIS
CONSIM-L	CONSIM-L@UALTAVM	Conflict simulation Games
CONSLINK	CONSLINK@SIVM	CONSLINK - The Conservation Network
CONSLT-L	CONSLT-L@IUBVM	Consultation and discussion of research and +
CONSULT	CONSULT@UMSLVMA	UM-St.Louis Computer Lab Consultants - CONSU+
	CONSULT@WAYNEST1	C&IT/PaSS CONSULTING LIST
CONTENTS	CONTENTS@UOTTAWA	Religious Studies Publications Journal
CONYERS	CONYERS@UBVM	Conyers, GA Apparition List
COOPCAT	COOPCAT@NERVM	Cooperative Cataloging Discussion Group
COOPRARE	COOPRARE@FRORS12	RARE and EARN Cooperation
COORDCOM	COORDCOM@MSU	Coordinating Committee for USTIMSS
COPRSMTH	COPRSMTH@ASUACAD	U.S. Rep. Sam Coppersmith Information and Ne+
CORDEL-L	CORDEL-L@BRUFMG	Coordenadores de graduacao em Eng.Eletrica
CORE-NET	CORE-NET@TRINITY	Core Knowledge Views and News
CORECURR	CORECURR@MSU	Core Curricula
CORRIM-L	CORRIM-L@UWAVM	CORRIM-L COMMITTEE ON RENEWABLE RESOURCES FO+
CORROS-L	CORROS-L@UKACRL	"Corrosion Special Interest List"
COSNDISC	COSNDISC@BITNIC	Consortium for School Networking Discussion +
COSW-L	COSW-L@ASUACAD	COSW-L
COUNCIL	COUNCIL@SJSUVM1	Global Council Forum - Moving Beyond the Nat+

Network-wide ID	Full address	List title
COUNTY-L	COUNTY-L@VTVM1	All Virginia Counties on LGNET
COURTSHP	COURTSHP@TAMVM1	For discussion of research and ideas relatin+
CO065	CO065@UMSLVMA	CO065-INTRO TO INFO TECH
CPAC-L	CPAC-L@MARIST	ConnectPac(tm) Discussion list
CPGIS-L	CPGIS-L@UBVM	Chinese Professionals Geographic Information+
CPI-L	CPI-L@CUNYVM	CPI-L: College Preparatory Initiative List (+
CPM-L	CPM-L@RPITSVM	CPM-L Mailing List
CPRI-COD	CPRI-COD@UMAB	CPRI: Subgroup - "codes" of Work Group 3 on +
	CPRI-COD@UWAVM	CPRI: Subgroup - "codes" of Work Group 3 on +
CPRI-WG3	CPRI-WG3@UMAB	CPRI: Work Group 3 on Codes and Structures.
	CPRI-WG3@UWAVM	CPRI: Work Group 3 on Codes and Structures.
CPRIDEMO	CPRIDEMO@WUVMD	Demonstration Projects Work Group of the Com+
CPR4-L	CPR4-L@UIUCVMD	CP release 4 discussions
CPR5-L	CPR5-L@UIUCVMD	CP release 5 discussions
CPS-L	CPS-L@HEARN	CPS-L: Centre for Pacific Studies Discussion+
CPSR	CPSR@GWUVM	Computer Professionals for Social Responsibi+
CPT-L	CPT-L@PURCCVM	Mailing list for all CPT students
CPTCOOP	CPTCOOP@PURCCVM	CPT Co-op discussion list
CPTFAC-L	CPTFAC-L@PURCCVM	All CPT Faculty
CPTLAB-L	CPTLAB-L@PURCCVM	CPT Lab discussion list
CPTSCHED	CPTSCHED@PURCCVM	CPT Course Scheduling Committee
CPTSTAFF	CPTSTAFF@PURCCVM	All CPT Faculty/Clerical/Admin Staff & PSTECH
CPT155-L	CPT155-L@PURCCVM	CPT 155 discussion List
CPT305-L	CPT305-L@PURCCVM	CPT 305 discussion list
CPT365-L	CPT365-L@PURCCVM	CPT 365 discussion list
CPT487D	CPT487D@PURCCVM	CPT 487D discussion list
CRALO-L	CRALO-L@HUMBER	College Registrars and Liaison Officers Disc+
CRAP	CRAP@CERNVM	ATLAS Collaboration sub-list: Software (Repr+
CREA-CPS	CREA-CPS@HEARN	CREA-CPS Creativity and Creative Problem Sol+
CREAD	CREAD@YORKVM1	Latin American and Caribbean Electronic Dist+
CREATE-L	CREATE-L@ASUACAD	CREATE-L
CRENBDST	CRENBDST@BITNIC	CREN Board and Staff Principals

Network-wide ID	Full address	List title
CRENDOC	CRENDOC@BITNIC	CREN Documentation Review list
CRENLIST	CRENLIST@BITNIC	CREN RFP list
CRENONLY	CRENONLY@BITNIC	CRENONLY Board of Trustees Mailing List
CRENTECH	CRENTECH@BITNIC	CREN Technical Committee
CREWRT-L	CREWRT-L@MIZZOU1	Creative Writing in Education for Teachers a+
CRE8TV-L	CRE8TV-L@PSUVM	Teaching Creative Problem Solving to Enginee+
CRIC-L	CRIC-L@UALTAVM	Discussion on semiotics of culture
CRICKET	CRICKET@NDSUVM1	Cricket Redistribution
CROMED-L	CROMED-L@AEARN	CROatian MEDical List
CROSS-L	CROSS-L@UMINN1	CROSS-L Cross Cultural Research in Informat+
CRP510	CRP510@UNMVMA	Planning and Communications Studio
CRTNET	CRTNET@PSUVM	Communication Research and Theory Network
CRUST-L	CRUST-L@SIVM	Crustacean systematics, distribution, ecology
CRYPTO-L	CRYPTO-L@JPNTUVM0	Forum on Cryptology and Related Mathematics
CSAC	CSAC@UVMVM	CSAC: CSAC Conference Administation
CSACM-L	CSACM-L@MIZZOU1	Mizzou Student ACM Chapter Discussion
CSAMIGA	CSAMIGA@DEARN	CSAMIGA COMP.SYS.AMIGA.TECH redist.
CSANR-L	CSANR-L@WSUVM1	Center for Sustainable Agriculture and Natur+
CSCI207	CSCI207@INDYCMS	Learning List for CSCI207
CSEA-L	CSEA-L@UNBVM1	Canadian Society for Education Through Art
CSEMLIST	CSEMLIST@HASARA11	List of the Society of Computational Economi+
CSERV-L	CSERV-L@UCSFVM	Client Server Conference
CSG-L	CSG-L@UIUCVMD	Control Systems Group Network (CSGnet)
CSI-L	CSI-L@MAINE	CSI Management
CSIMIDAS	CSIMIDAS@ITOCSIVM	MIDAS Progetto ESPRIT
CSISU-L	CSISU-L@UNCCVM	Carolina SIS User Discussion
CSLESL	CSLESL@PSUVM	Regional DEC CSLG/ESL Discussions
CSMS94-L	CSMS94-L@UMSLVMA	Computer Services Management Symposium - XXI+
CSP-L	CSP-L@TREARN	Cross System Product Discussion List
CSR-L	CSR-L@UALTAVM	University of Alberta Center for Systems Res+
CSS-L	CSS-L@UBVM	Univ of Buffalo Chinese Students and Scholar+
CSSA-L	CSSA-L@AUVM	Chinese Student and Scholar List
CSSE-L	CSSE-L@UALTAVM	CSSE Discussion List
CSSWU-L	CSSWU-L@WUVMD	Chinese Students List

Network-wide ID	Full address	List title
CSTG-L	CSTG-L@VTVM1	CSTG-L DISCUSSION LIST
CSTORE	CSTORE@MSU	MSU Computer Store
CSYS-L	CSYS-L@UALTAVM	COPPUL Systems Group
CS1OBJ-L	CS1OBJ-L@PSUVM	Object Oriented Programming in the First Year
CS256	CS256@IPFWVM	CS256 COURSE DISCUSSION LIST
CTC-L	CTC-L@BRUFSC	Divulgacao de eventos do Centro Tecnologico +
CTHEORY	CTHEORY@MCGILL1	CTHEORY is an international, electronic revi+
CTURTLE	CTURTLE@NERVM	Sea Turtle Biology and Conservation
CTYTWN-L	CTYTWN-L@VTVM1	All Virginia Cities and Towns On LGNET
CUBA-L	CUBA-L@UNMVMA	Cuba today Spanish/English
CUC-L	CUC-L@FRORS12	Comite des Utilisateurs du CIRCE
CUFMA-L	CUFMA-L@SUVM	College and University Facilities Management+
CUFS-L	CUFS-L@MIAMIU	College & University Financial System (CUFS)
CUFSTECH	CUFSTECH@CUVMC	CUFSTECH
CULTU7-L	CULTU7-L@NMSUVM1	Communication Class Project
CUMREC-L	CUMREC-L@NDSUVM1	CUMREC-L Administrative computer use
CUPLE-L	CUPLE-L@UBVM	CUPLE (Physics Learning Environment) Softwar+
CURDEV-L	CURDEV-L@PSUORVM	CURDEV-L Science Curriculum Development List
CURRENTS	CURRENTS@PCCVM	South Asian News and Culture Electronic Maga+
CURRICUL	CURRICUL@PURCCVM	CPT Curriculum Mailing List
CVUTNET	CVUTNET@CSEARN	Diskusni klub o provozu site CVUT
CW-EMAIL	CW-EMAIL@TECMTYVM	Campus-Wide Electronic Mail Systems discussi+
CWC94-L	CWC94-L@MIZZOU1	MU's 94 Computers and Writing Conference
CWIS-L	CWIS-L@WUVMD	Campus-Wide Information Systems
CYAN-TOX	CYAN-TOX@GREARN	The Cyanobacterial Toxins Discussion List
CYBCOM	CYBCOM@GWUVM	Cybernetics Discussion Group
CYBER-L	CYBER-L@BITNIC	(Peered) CYBER List
	CYBER-L@DEARN	(Peered) CYBER List
	CYBER-L@HEARN	(Peered) CYBER List
	CYBER-L@MARIST	(Peered) CYBER List
	CYBER-L@UGA	(Peered) CDC Computer Discussion
CYBERLAW	CYBERLAW@WMVM1	The Law and Policy of Computer Networks
CYBSYS-L	CYBSYS-L@BINGVMB	Cybernetics and Systems
CYCOOP-L	CYCOOP-L@BRUSPVM	Rede Ibero-Americana da Gestao de Cooperacao+

Network-wide ID	Full address	List title
CYPRUS-L	CYPRUS-L@TRITU	Discussion List on CYPRUS
CZE-ITP	CZE-ITP@CSBRMU11	CZE-ITP Discussion on Problems of Capillary +
C18-L	C18-L@PSUVM	18th Century Interdisciplinary Discussion
C2SN-L	C2SN-L@FRCPN11	C2SN: Comite Consultatif pour la Structure N+
C2SNDI-L	C2SNDI-L@FRCPN11	Liste de diffusion du C2SN
C3NI-L	C3NI-L@FRMOP11	Utilisateurs C3NI
C370-L	C370-L@CMUVM	C/370 Discussion List
D-ORAL-L	D-ORAL-L@NIHLIST	Oral Microbiology/Immunology Interest Group
D-PERIO	D-PERIO@NIHLIST	NIDR, Periodontal Diseases Program Discussio+
DAHC-L	DAHC-L@DGOGWDG1	Deutsches Apple Hochschul Consortium
DAIRY-L	DAIRY-L@UMDD	Dairy Discussion List.
DAL-L	DAL-L@MITVMA	DAL (Data Access Language) List
DALNET	DALNET@WAYNEST1	Detroit Area Library Network Discussion List
DANCE-HC	DANCE-HC@CUNYVM	DANCE-HC: Dance Heritage Coalition Listserv +
DANCE-L	DANCE-L@HEARN	International folkdance and traditional danc+
DANISMAN	DANISMAN@TRITU	TUVAKA Servisleri Danisma Listesi
DANNY	DANNY@UWAVM	LISTNAME Short Oneline Description
DARGON-L	DARGON-L@BROWNVM	Dargon Project Writers Forum
DARS-L	DARS-L@MIAMIU	Degree Audit Reporting System (DARS)
DAS-L	DAS-L@UBVM	UB Distributed Application Support Discussio+
DASP-L	DASP-L@CSEARN	Digital Acoustic Signal Processing
DATABASE	DATABASE@MCGILL1	"DATABASE" is a forum to pose questions, sup+
DATAEASE	DEASE-L@AKRONVM	DataEase Discussion List
DATAPERF	DATAPERF@WSUVM1	DataPerfect User Group
DATPERS	DATPERS@YORKVM1	DATPERS - Dalit and Tribal Peoples Electroni+
DATUS-L	DATUS-L@DEARN	DATUS Anwendergruppe
DBASE-L	DBASE-L@HEARN	Info-uitwisseling Ashton.Tate en contact-pers+
	DBASE-L@NMSUVM1	(Peered) Discussion on the use of the dBase +
	DBASE-L@TECMTYVM	(Peered) Discussion on the use of the dBase +
DBCLASS	DBCLASS@PURCCVM	CPT 382/482 discussion list
DBLIST	DBLIST@UMAB	Databases for Dentistry
DBTOOL-L	DBTOOL-L@NERVM	NERDC DB2 User Group Tools Committee

Network-wide ID	Full address	List title
DB2-L	DB2-L@AUVM	DB2 Data Base Discussion List
DCCFUA-L	DCCFUA-L@BRLNCC	Forum do Depto. de Ciencia da Computacao da +
DCEAK-L	DCEAK-L@DGOGWDG1	Probleme der verteilten Datenverarbeitung
DCRAVES	DCRAVES@AUVM	Washington D.C. Rave List
DCRLY-L	DCRLY-L@AUVM	Wash_DC Relay Mailing List
DDFIND-L	DDFIND-L@GITVM1	"Forum for Information Networking on Disabil+
DDMS-L	DDMS-L@UCSBVM	Display Device Management System (DDMS) Disc+
DDS-L	DDS-L@EMUVM1	Document Delivery Services
DEAF-L	DEAF-L@SIUCVMB	DEAF LIST
DEAFBLND	DEAFBLND@UKCC	DEAFBLND—Deaf-Blind Mailing List
DEAR-BOD	DEAR-BOD@IRLEARN	EARN Directors - open submission
DEARNADM	DEARNADM@DEARN	Node administrators/contacts of German EARN +
DEARNDIR	DEARNDIR@DEARN	Directors of German EARN nodes/sites
DEARNOWN	DEARNOWN@DEARN	DEARNOWN (list of listserv owner at DEAR+
DEBATE	DEBATE@LMUACAD	DEBATE
DEC-WIND	DEC-WIND@UKACRL	"UK open discussion list for DEC WINDOWS"
DECAD-L	DECAD-L@SEARN	DECAD - pilot course
DECMCC-L	DECMCC-L@AUVM	DEC DECmcc and Related Software
DECNEWS	DECNEWS@UBVM	Digital Equipment Corporation EDU News List
DECRDB-L	DECRDB-L@SBCCVM	Digital Equipment Corporation Relational Dat+
DECTEI-L	DECTEI-L@UBVM	DEC's The Education Initiative Discussion Li+
DECUS_H	DECUS_H@GREARN	Decus Hellas
DECUS_M	DECUS_M@GREARN	Decus Hellas Members List
DED-L	DED-L@UALTAVM	Distance Education
DEELT-L	DEELT-L@BRUFMG	Professores/pesquisadores ligados aos Deptos+
DEEPSEA	DEEPSEA@UVVM	Deep Sea and Vent News
DEF-PBX	DEF-PBX@UMDD	DEFINITY PBX Group
DEF-SEC	DEF-SEC@UMDD	DEFINITY Security Issues Group
DEF-SYSM	DEF-SYSM@UMDD	DEFINITY System Management Products Group
DEF-VP	DEF-VP@UMDD	DEFINITY Voice Processing Products Group
DEFINITY	DEFINITY@UMDD	DEFINITY User Group
DELINKF	DELINKF@DEARN	German LINKFAIL list
DELTACHI	DELTACHI@UBVM	Delta Chi Fraternity Discussion List
DEMING-L	DEMING-L@UHCCVM	The W. Edwards Deming Forum

Network-wide ID	Full address	List title
DEMO-L	DEMO-L@CSEARN	Konference pro praktickou vyuku studentu
	DEMO-L@JPNSUT10	demonstration for JPNSUT20
DEMOLIST	DEMOLIST@BITNIC	Demonstration List
DENIZ-L	DENIZ-L@TRITU	Gemi Insaati/Makinalari ve Deniz Bilimleri
DENTAL	MEMBERS@UMAB	DENTAL TEST LIST
DENTAL-L	DENTAL-L@IRLEARN	Cosine Project - Dental Research unit, UCC
DENTALMA	DENTALMA@UCF1VM	For Dentistry related articles reports and t+
DEOS-L	DEOS-L@PSUVM	DEOS-L - The Distance Education Online Sympo+
DEOSNEWS	DEOSNEWS@PSUVM	DEOSNEWS - The Distance Education Online Sym+
DEPORTES	DEPORTES@ANDESCOL	Actividad Deportiva Mundial
DERRIDA	DERRIDA@CFRVM	A discussion of Jacques Derrida and Deconstr+
DESIGN-L	DESIGN-L@PSUVM	Basic and applied design (Art and Architectu+
	DESIGN-L@UKANVM	KU Computer Center Local Area Networking Des+
DESQVIEW	DESQVIEW@BRUFPB	List for Desqview and Qemm users
DEVEL-L	DEVEL-L@AUVM	Technology Transfer in International Develop+
DFNMVS	DFNMVS@DEARN	(Peered) DFN-Software Diskussionsforum MVS
DFNVM	DFNVM@DEARN	DFN-Software Diskussionsforum VM
DGTLCLAS	DGTLCLAS@MCGILL1	Discussion on Digital Media and Multi Media +
DIABETES	DIABETES@IRLEARN	International Research Project on Diabetes
DIABETIC	DIABETIC@PCCVM	Open Discussion forum for DIABETIC patient c+
DIAL-L	DIAL-L@BRLNCC	USUARIOS REMOTOS VIA LINHA DISCADA
DIATOM-L	DIATOM-L@IUBVM	Research on the diatom algae
DICKNS-L	DICKNS-L@UCSBVM	Charles Dickens Forum
DIET	DIET@UBVM	Support and Discussion of Weight Loss
DIGIT-L	DIGIT-L@CFRVM	DIGIT
DINI-L	DINI-L@DEARN	DINI-L Mailliste fuer die Diplomanden- und Do+
DIPL-L	DIPL-L@MITVMA	Discussion Group for the Game Diplomacy
DIRECT-L	DIRECT-L@UAFSYSB	MacroMind Director for the Macintosh
DIS-L	DIS-L@IUBVM	Drosophila workers to receive DIS Newsletter
DISARM-D	DISARM-D@ALBNYVM1	Disarmament Discussion Monthly Digest
DISARM-L	DISARM-L@ALBNYVM1	Disarmament Discussion List
DISASTER	DISASTER@UTXVM	Disaster Plans and Recovery Resources
DISPRAC	DISPRAC@RPITSVM	Disciplinary Practices in Comm. Studies
DISSPLA	DISSPLA@TAUNIVM	DISSPLA List

Network-wide ID	Full address	List title
DISTDIR	DISTDIR@VTVM1	VCES District Director Userids
DISTED	DISTED@UWAVM	Online Journal of Distance Ed. and Communica+
DISTLABS	DISTLABS@INDYCMS	Teaching Science Labs Via Distance
DISTPROF	DISTPROF@UWAVM	DISTPROF
DITTO-LIST	DITTO-L@AWIIMC12	Data Interfile Transfer, Testing and Operati+
DIVERS-L	DIVERS-L@PSUVM	Diversity List
DIVERSE	DIVERSE@MSU	Diversity In Development
DIVRSITY	DIVRSITY@UICVM	Diversity Issues at UIC Discussion List
DIVULGAR	DIVULGAR@PTEARN	PEDIDO DE DIVULGACAO
DIV28	DIV28@GWUVM	APA's Division 28 Discussion List
DIV34	DIV34@POLYVM	Rich Wener DIV34 Distribution List
DJ-L	DJ-L@NDSUVM1	DJ-L Campus Radio Disk Jockey Discussion List
DKB-L	DKB-L@TREARN	DKB/POV Ray Tracer Development List
DLDG-L	DLDG-L@IUBVM	DLDG-L Dance Librarians Discussion Group
DMA-LIST	DMA-LIST@HEARN	DMANET
DNA-L	DNA-L@UCSFVM	Departmental Network Administrators List
DNN-L	DNN-L@AUVM	DevelopNet News distribution
DOC-COOR	DOC-COOR@IRISHVMA	Documentation Coordinators
DOC-L	DOC-L@SAKAAU03	K.A.A.U Computer Center Documentation List
DOCDIS	DOCDIS@UA1VM	DOCDIS Discussion List
DOCSM	DOCSM@ICNUCEVM	DOCSM Data Database Documentazione Sala Mac+
DOHMEM-L	DOHMEM-L@ALBNYDH2	NEW YORK STATE DEPARMENT OF HEALTH MEMORANDA
DOLLH-L	DOLLH-L@FERRIS	DOLLH-L Doll's House Construction and Enjoym+
DOMAIN	DOMAIN@ICNUCEVM	NIS Gestione Domini Posta Elettronica
DOMAIN-L	DOMAIN-L@BITNIC	(Peered) Domains Discussion Group
	DOMAIN-L@DEARN	(Peered) Domain discussion group
	DOMAIN-L@HEARN	(Peered) Domain discussion group
	DOMAIN-L@MARIST	(Peered) Domain discussion group
	DOMAIN-L@UGA	(Peered) Domains Discussion Group
DOMAINIT	DOMAINIT@IBACSATA	Responsabili dei domini Italiani di Posta el+
DOMAINS	DOMAINS@UKACRL	
DORMS-L	DORMS-L@TECMTYVM	Residence Halls: Something more than a place+
DOROTHYL	DOROTHYL@KENTVM	Mystery Literature E-conference
DOSRZ-L	DOSRZ-L@DOSUNI1	MS-DOS-Probleme, (lokale Liste, Uni Osnabrue+
DOST	DOST@TREARN	Turkish Scientists' Discussion Group
DOWN-SYN	DOWN-SYN@NDSUVM1	Down Syndrome

Network-wide ID	Full address	List title
DOXNJ	DOXNJ@RUTVM1	Government Documents in New Jersey Forum
DPASYM-L	DPASYM-L@FRCPN11	bb DELPHI inclusive Sub-Groups
DPC-L	DPC-L@YALEVM	Digital Preservation Consortium List
DPCDIR-L	DPCDIR-L@YALEVM	Digital Preservation Consortium Director's L+
DPMA-L	DPMA-L@PURCCVM	Discussion list for Purdue chapter of DPMA
DPMAST-L	DPMAST-L@CMSUVMB	Data Processing Management Association
DPRB-L	DPRB-L@ALBNYDH2	Data Protection Review Board Correspondence
DQS-L	DQS-L@RPITSVM	DQS Discussion List
DRIV-L	DRIV-L@TAMVM1	The TUG DVI driver standards discussion list
DRP-L	DRP-L@MARIST	Disaster Recovery Plan for Computing Services
DRS	DRS@DARTCMS1	Dead Runners Society
DRT	DRT@DARTCMS1	Dead Runners Texas
	DRT@TAMVM1	Dead Runners Texas
	DRT@UTXVM	Dead Runners Texas
DRUGABUS	DRUGABUS@UMAB	Drug Abuse Education Information and Research
DRUGHIED	DRUGHIED@TAMVM1	Drug Abatement Research Discussion
DSI	DSI@MAINE	DSI - Employer/Employee cross reference list
DSP-L	DSP-L@NMSUVM1	Delta Sigma Pi Professional Fraternity
DSSHE-L	DSSHE-L@UBVM	Disabled Student Services in Higher Education
DTEAM-L	DTEAM-L@VTVM1	Diversity Team Discussion List
DTS-L	DTS-L@IUBVM	Dead Teachers Society Discussion List
DUB-MAN	DUB-MAN@IRLEARN	Dublin Metropolitan Area Network Project
DUMBLIST	DUMBLIST@UWAVM	DUMBLIST
DUMMY	DUMMY@UWAVM	DUMMY
DUVAR-L	DUVAR-L@TRITU	Genel Amacli Duyuru ve Tartisma Listesi
DVL	DVL@MCGILL1	Economic Development 154-313D
DW	DW@UCSBVM	UCSB Data Warehouse Project Discussion List +
D20A-L	D20A-L@MITVMA	10 Player Diplomacy Game List (Sam Huntsman +
E-EUROPE	E-EUROPE@PUCC	Eastern Europe Business Network
E-HUG	E-HUG@DARTCMS1	Electronic Hebrew Users Newsletter
E-POETRY	E-POETRY@UBVM	Electronic Poetry Distribution List
EAESPNET	EAESPNET@BLEKUL11	EAESP Forum
EARAM-L	EARAM-L@KENTVM	Society of Early Americanists
EARLI-AE	EARLI-AE@HEARN	European Association for Research on Learnin+
EARLYM-L	EARLYM-L@AEARN	Early Music List

Network-wide ID	Full address	List title
EARN-BOD	EARN-BOD@IRLEARN	EARN Board of Directors
EARN-IXI	EARN-IXI@FRMOP11	EARN-IXI Testing
EARN-MC	EARN-MC@IRLEARN	EARN Membership Committee
EARN-NOG	EARN-NOG@FRMOP11	Network Operations Group
EARN-RTC	EARN-RTC@IRLEARN	EARN RTC Users Group
EARN-SNA	EARN-SNA@FRMOP11	EARN-SNA Coordination
EARN-UG	EARN-UG@IRLEARN	EARN Users Group Discussion List
EARNBRUK	EARNBRUK@NOBIVM	List for EARN users i Norway.
EARNDOC	EARNDOC@EARNCC	EARN Documentation List
EARNEST	EARNEST@FRORS12	EARN Newsletter Broadcasting
EARNEWS	EARNEWS@FRMOP11	EARN News
EARNEXEC	EARNEXEC@FRORS12	EARN Executive
	EARNEXEC@IRLEARN	EARN Executive
EARNINFO	EARNINFO@EARNCC	EARN Group on Information Services
EARNSITE	EARNSITE@EBCESCA1	Lista de miembros Espanyoles de EARN (cerrad+
EARNSTAT	EARNSTAT@DEARN	EARN Statistics Group
	EARNSTAT@EARNCC	EARN Statistics Group
EARNTECH	EARNTECH@BITNIC	(Peered) EARN Technical Group
	EARNTECH@CEARN	(Peered) EARN Technical Group
	EARNTECH@DEARN	(Peered) EARN Technical Group
EARNUS	EARNUS@UKACRL	"UK EARN Users Mailing List"
EASI	EASI@SJUVM	EASI Project List
EASI-EPC	EASI-EPC@DEARN	EASInet Project Committee
EASIM-L	EASIM-L@DEARN	EASI-Verbund Management
EASIWG-L	EASIWG-L@RITVM	EASI On-line Working Group
EAT-L	EAT-L@VTVM1	Foodlore/Recipe Exchange
EAWOP-L	EAWOP-L@HEARN	The European Association of Work and Organiz+
EBSS-ALA	EBSS-ALA@MAINE	University of Maine Library Distribution List
EC	EC@TRMETU	European Community EC
ECA-L	ECA-L@GSUVM1	European Center-Atlanta of the Institute for+
ECAPS	ECAPS@GWUVM	ECAPS Research Projects Discussion List
ECC-L	ECC-L@MCGILL1	Engineering Committee on Computing
ECCIRN-O	ECCIRN-O@HEARN	EuroCCIRN Open Distribution List
ECENET-L	ECENET-L@UIUCVMD	Early childhood education/young children (0-+
ECEOL-L	ECEOL-L@MAINE	Early Childhood Education On-Line mailing li+
ECGRAD-L	ECGRAD-L@MIZZOU1	Grad Students in Dept. or Ed. & Counseling P+
ECID-L	ECID-L@PURCCVM	Educational Computing and Instructional Deve+
ECIDGRAD	ECIDGRAD@PURCCVM	ECID graduate students
ECIDNEWS	ECIDNEWS@PURCCVM	ECID news, conferences, seminars

Network-wide ID	Full address	List title
ECIDSTAF	ECIDSTAF@PURCCVM	ECID staff
ECIDTA	ECIDTA@PURCCVM	ECID teaching assistants
ECKNET	ECKNET@ASUACAD	ECKNET
ECL3-L	ECL3-L@LEPICS	Open forum on the ECL3 program
ECMA-L	ECMA-L@KSUVM	Engineering College Magazines Associated
ECOLOG-L	ECOLOG-L@UMDD	Ecological Society of America: grants, jobs,+
ECOLOGY	ECOLOGY@EMUVM1	Politics and the Environment
ECONED-L	ECONED-L@UTDALLAS	Research in Economic Education
ECONHIST	ECONHIST@MIAMIU	Teaching and Research in Economic History
ECONOM-L	ECONOM-L@BRUFSC	(Peered) FORUM ECONOM-L - Discussao sobre ec+
ECONOMY	ECONOMY@TECMTYVM	Economic Problems in Less Developed Countries
ECON10	ECON10@ICNUCEVM	CNR - Comitato 10, Economia, Sociologia e St+
ECOSYS-L	ECOSYS-L@DEARN	ECOSYS-L Liste fuer 'ecosystem theory and mo+
ECOVIS-L	ECOVIS-L@YALEVM	Trends in Ecology of Vision
ECU-L	ECU-L@ECUVM1	East Carolina University User and Alumni List
EDAD-L	EDAD-L@WVNVM	Educational Administration Discussion List
EDD-L	EDD-L@KENTVM	The EDD Data Editor List
EDFA-L	EDFA-L@PURCCVM	Purdue Educational Foundations and Administr+
EDI-L	EDI-L@UCCVMA	Electronic Data Interchange Issues
EDISTA	EDISTA@USACHVM1	"Educacion a Distancia"
EDLAW	EDLAW@UKCC	Law and Education
EDNETNY	EDNETNY@SUVM	Educational Development Network of New York
EDPGRADS	EDPGRADS@ARIZVM1	Forum for U of Arizona EdPsych Grad Students
EDPOLYAN	EDPOLYAN@ASUACAD	Education Policy Analysis Forum
EDPOLYAR	EDPOLYAR@ASUACAD	EDUC POLICY ANALYSIS ARCHIVES: An Electronic+
EDST-L	EDST-L@PURCCVM	Educational Studies Faculty and Staff - List
EDSTYLE	EDSTYLE@SJUVM	The Learning Styles Theory and Research List
EDTECH	EDTECH@MSU	EDTECH - Educational Technology
EDTECPOL	EDTECPOL@UMDD	Conference on Educational Technology Policy
EDTOAX-L	EDTOAX-L@BINGVMB	EdTOA Executive Committee Communications
EDU-EXEC	EDU-EXEC@UBVM	DECUS EDUSIG Executive & Steering Committees+
EDUCATIONAL-R...	ERL-L@ASUACAD	Educational Research List (ASUACAD)

Network-wide ID	Full address	List title
EDUCOM-W	EDUCOM-W@BITNIC	EDUCOM-W - EDUCOM Women and Information Tech+
EDUMATE	EDUMATE@USACHVM1	"Educacion Matematica en Chile"
EDUPAGE	EDUPAGE@BITNIC	EDUCOM EDUPAGE List
EDUSIG-L	EDUSIG-L@UBVM	DECUS EDUSIG Discussion List
EDUTEL	EDUTEL@RPITSVM	Education and information technologies
EEC-L	EEC-L@AUVM	European Training and Technology List
EEL-L	EEL-L@BRUFSC	FORUM EEL-L - Coordenadores dos Grupos de Pe+
EF-L	EF-L@NOBIVM	Diskusjon om Norge, EF og EOES (Norwegian).
EGRET-L	EGRET-L@DARTCMS1	Discussion of EGRET epidemiological software
EGR180A	EGR180A@MIAMIU	Culture & Technology (Miami Univ EGR 180 A)
EHS-L	EHS-L@ALBNYDH2	EHS-L Environmental Health System
EISSIG	EISSIG@ASUACAD	Executive Information Systems Special Intere+
EJCREC	EJCREC@RPITSVM	Electronic Journal of Communication
EJVC-L	EJVC-L@KENTVM	Electronic Journal on Virtual Culture
EL-VALLE	EL-VALLE@ANDESCOL	Hablemos del Valle del Cauca
ELAG-L	ELAG-L@HEARN	ELAG-L: Library Automation in Europe
ELDERS	ELDERS@SJUVM	The Elders List of St. John's University
ELDNET-L	ELDNET-L@UIUCVMD	(ASEE) Engineering Libraries Division Network
ELEASAI	ELEASAI@ARIZVM1	Open Lib/Info Sci Research Forum
ELECTECH	ELECTECH@UOTTAWA	Group for Electronic Technologies in the Hum+
ELENCHUS	ELENCHUS@UOTTAWA	Christianity in Late Antiquity Discussion Gr+
ELLASBIB	ELLASBIB@GREARN	List for the Greek Library Automation System.
ELLHNIKA	ELLHNIKA@DHDURZ1	ELLHNIKA Distribution List for TeX+
EMAIL-L	EMAIL-L@ALBNYDH2	List about EMAIL at NYDoH
	EMAIL-L@EMUVM1	Electronic Mail at Emory
EMAILMAN	EMAILMAN@VTVM1	Learning about accessing electronic informat+
EMAILSIG	EMAILSIG@GSUVM1	GSU Electronic Mail Special Interest Group
EMBINFO	EMBINFO@IBACSATA	EMBNet (European Molecular Biology Network) +
EMBLGR	EMBLGR@GREARN	Greek EMBL Managment List
EMD569-L	EMD569-L@NMSUVM1	Educational Management and Development
EMEDCH-L	EMEDCH-L@USCVM	The Early Medieval China Mailing List
EMERG-L	EMERG-L@MARIST	Emergency Services Discussion List

Network-wide ID	Full address	List title
EMFLDS-L	EMFLDS-L@UBVM	Electromagnetics in Medicine, Science & Comu+
EMHIST-L	EMHIST-L@RUTVM1	EMHIST-L Early Modern History Forum
EMPACT	EMPACT@UCSFVM	EMPACT! News
EMRG-L	EMRG-L@UCSBVM	Emergency Information List Server for UCSB
EMSNY-L	EMSNY-L@ALBNYDH2	EMS Issues for NYS Providers
EMUFOC-L	EMUFOC-L@EMUVM1	Emory FOCUS Discussion Group
EMULPC	EMULPC@USACHVM1	"Emulation SW & HW on the IBM-PC"
EMUNIM	EMUNIM@MSU	Jewish Campus Network in Michigan
EMUSIC-D	EMUSIC-D@AUVM	Electronic Music Digest
EMUSIC-L	EMUSIC-L@AUVM	Electronic Music Discussion List
ENDIF-L	ENDIF-L@WVNVM	Enterprise Network Data Interconnectivity Fa+
ENDNOTE	ENDNOTE@UCSBVM	EndNote/EndLink Users Forum
ENERGY-L	ENERGY-L@TAUNIVM	Energy List
ENET-EX	ENET-EX@UNBVM1	Electronic Networking SIG (AERA) Executive
ENGLISH	ENGLISH@UTARLVM1	Dept. of English Discussion
ENGLMU-L	ENGLMU-L@MIZZOU1	ENGLMU-L
ENGL219	ENGL219@GWUVM	List for English 219 Class
ENGRNEWS	ENGRNEWS@UICVM	Engineering Undergraduate News
ENG111HG	ENG111HG@MIAMIU	College Composition (Miami Univ ENG 111 HG)
ENG111JG	ENG111JG@MIAMIU	College Composition (Miami Univ ENG 111 JG)
ENG111KE	ENG111KE@MIAMIU	College Composition (Miami Univ ENG 111 KE)
ENG339-L	ENG339-L@UBVM	English 339 Class List
ENG501-L	ENG501-L@UBVM	English 501 Class List
ENTRENAR	ENTRENAR@HARVARDA	Mellon-LASPAU training participants support +
ENTREP-L	ENTREP-L@KSUVM	Entrepreneurs Division List
ENVBEH-L	ENVBEH-L@POLYVM	Forum on Environment and Human Behavior
ENVST-L	ENVST-L@BROWNVM	Environmental Studies Discussion List
EN212	EN212@UMSLVMA	EN212-BUSINESS WRITING
EN213	EN213@UMSLVMA	EN213-TECHNICAL WRITING
EOCHR-L	EOCHR-L@QUCDN	Eastern Orthodox Christianity discussion
EPISTEMO	EPISTEMO@UFRJ	Forum de Debates da Mulher na C&T
EPP-L	EPP-L@BUACCA	Albert Einstein Papers Project and Discussio+
EPPD-L	EPPD-L@UNBVM1	Engineering and Public Policy Discussion List
EPUBS-L	EPUBS-L@UBVM	Ad-Hoc UB Electronic Publications Task Force+
EQUEST-L	EQUEST-L@PSUVM	ELFQUEST Comic Book

Network-wide ID	Full address	List title
EQUINE-D	EQUINE-D@PCCVM	Rec.Equestrian Digest
EQUINE-L	EQUINE-L@PCCVM	(Peered) Discussion forum for Horse fanciers
	EQUINE-L@PSUVM	(Peered) Discussion forum for Horse fanciers
EQUITE-L	EQUITE-L@UOTTAWA	Salary and Job Equity Discussion Group
ERAPPA-L	ERAPPA-L@PSUVM	Association of Physical Plant Administrators
ERC	ERC@FRMOP11	Equipe Reseau du CNUSC + Pupitre
ERECS-L	ERECS-L@ALBNYVM1	Management & Preservation of Electronic Reco+
ERIC-L	ERIC-L@IUBVM	Experimental list for teaching and study of +
ERM-L	ERM-L@EMUVM1	Electronic Research Methods
ERSC	ERSC@FRMOP11	Equipe Reseau-Systeme du CNUSC
ERUDITIO	ERUDITIO@ASUACAD	ERUDITIO: KNOWLEDGE THROUGH ELECTRONIC COMMU+
ESBDC-L	ESBDC-L@FERRIS	ESBDC-L Small Business Development Centers L+
ESE-L	ESE-L@SBCCVM	Expert Systems Environment mailing list
ESIABUDG	ESIABUDG@GWUVM	ESIA Budgeted Faculty Discussion List
ESIAFAC	ESIAFAC@GWUVM	ESIA Faculty Discussion List
ESPANA-L	ESPANA-L@ALBNYVM1	Discussion Spain and its people
ESPER-L	ESPER-L@TREARN	Esperanto List
ESPORA-L	ESPORA-L@UKANVM	History of the Iberian Peninsula
ESSCO-L	ESSCO-L@UOTTAWA	Engineering Student Societies Council of Ont+
ET-ANN	ET-ANN@SEARN	Announcements: Ecotechnology conference 1994
ET-PARTI	ET-PARTI@SEARN	Participants: Intl. Conf. on Ecotechnology f+
ET-PLAN	ET-PLAN@SEARN	Planning: Ecotechnology conference 1994
ETCC-L	ETCC-L@HUMBER	Educational Technology Co-Ordinating Committ+
ETECESP	ETECESP@ETSUADMN	Educational Computing at East Texas State Un+
ETEXTCTR	ETEXTCTR@RUTVM1	Discussion Group on Electronic Text Centers
ETH-NET	ETH-NET@WAYNEST1	Ethnic Conflict
ETHCSE-L	ETHCSE-L@UTKVM1	Ethical Issues in Software Engineering
ETHICRND	ETHICRND@UICVM	CAUSE - Electronic Rountable Discussion on E+
ETHICS-L	ETHICS-L@DEARN	(Peered) Discussion of Ethics in Computing
	ETHICS-L@MARIST	(Peered) Discussion of Ethics in Computing
	ETHICS-L@POLYVM	(Peered) Discussion of Ethics in Computing

Network-wide ID	Full address	List title
	ETHICS-L@UGA	(Peered) Discussion of Ethics in Computing
ETHIQUE	ETHIQUE@UDESVM	RESEAU QUEBECOIS DES ETHICIENNES ET ETHICIENS
ETHMUS-L	ETHMUS-L@UMDD	EthnoFORUM, a global ethnomusicology forum.
ETHNET-L	ETHNET-L@YSUB	Irish and British Ethnographic Research List
ETHNO	ETHNO@RPITSVM	Ethnomethodology/conversation analysis
ETHNOHIS	ETHNOHIS@HEARN	ETHNOHIS: General Ethnology and History Disc+
ETHOLOGY	ETHOLOGY@SEARN	Ethology
EU-ROUTE	EU-ROUTE@HEARN	Routers in Europe : discussion on interworki+
EU-SOAR	EU-SOAR@HEARN	EU-SOAR European SOAR research communications
EUDKRB-L	EUDKRB-L@BROWNVM	Kerberized Eudora List
EUDORA	EUDORA@UIUCVMD	Eudora mailing list
EUEARN-L	EUEARN-L@UBVM	Discussion of Eastern Europe Telecommunicati+
EUITLIST	EUITLIST@BITNIC	Educational Uses of Information Technology (+
EUNBUG-L	EUNBUG-L@EMUVM1	Emory University Nota Bene Users Group
EURO-LEX	EURO-LEX@DEARN	EURO-LEX (All EUROpean Legal Information EXc+
EUSDEMO	EUSDEMO@WSUVM1	Extended University Services Demonstration
EV	EV@SJSUVM1	Electric Vehicle Discussion List
EWM	EWM@ICNUCEVM	EWM European Women in Mathematics
EXECOMM	EXECOMM@MSU	Executive Committee of NAFSA
EXECSEC	EXECSEC@UTORONTO	Netnorth Executive Secretary
EXEC28	EXEC28@GWUVM	APA's Division 28 Executive Board Discussion+
EXLIBRIS	EXLIBRIS@RUTVM1	Rare Books and Special Collections Forum
	EXLIBRIS@UMRVMB	UMR Library Users
EXTVET-L	EXTVET-L@UNLVM	EXTVET Discussion List (Extension Veterinari+
EZTRV-L	EZTRV-L@ULKYVM	EZTrieve Discussion Group
FACAFF	FACAFF@PURCCVM	CPT Faculty Affairs Committee
FACES-L	FACES-L@UTEPA	Interdisciplinary study of faces
FACILITY	FACILITY@PURCCVM	CPT Facilities Committee
FACINTL	FACINTL@PSUVM	International Funding oppor. & related info
FACOUNCL	FACOUNCL@INDYCMS	IUPUI Faculty Council Mail LIst
FACSEN-L	FACSEN-L@UBVM	UB Faculty Senate Discussion List
FACSER-L	FACSER-L@WVNVM	Facilities and Services Discussion List

Network-wide ID	Full address	List title
FACT-L	FACT-L@UBVM	SUNY Faculty Access to Computing Technology +
FACTCOM	FACTCOM@UBVM	SUNY Faculty Access to Computing Technology +
FACULT-L	FACULT-L@KENTVM	Kent State University Faculty discussion of +
FACULTY	FACULTY@UCSFVM	UCSF Faculty Scholarship and Related Academi+
FACXCH-L	FACXCH-L@PSUVM	Exchange list for Department of Architecture+
FALBTI-L	FALBTI-L@TAMVM1	BTI/K200/NECU driver distribution list
FAMCOMM	FAMCOMM@RPITSVM	Marital/family & relational communication
FAMILY-L	FAMILY-L@MIZZOU1	Academic Family Medicine Discussion.
FAMLYSCI	FAMLYSCI@UKCC	Family Science Network
FAMSTECH	FAMSTECH@ASUACAD	Financial Aid Systems - Technical Discussion+
FAO-BULL	FAO-BULL@IRMFAO01	Food and Agriculture Organization,AFCO Tec+
FAO-DOC	FAO-DOC@IRMFAO01	Food and Agriculture Organization - Computer+
FAO-INFO	FAO-INFO@IRMFAO01	The Food and Agriculture Organization INFO L+
FAOLIST	FAOLIST@IRMFAO01	Food and Agriculture Organization Open Discu+
FAPERJ-L	FAPERJ-L@BRLNCC	BOLETIM INFORMATIVO DA FAPERJ
FAQ	FAQ@UNMVMA	Sub-committee of ISN/IETF WG
FASTBS-L	FASTBS-L@UALTAVM	FASTBUS Discussion
FASTLN-L	FASTLN-L@VTVM1	Virginia Tech Computing Center News — FASTL+
FBS-L	FBS-L@FREIA11	Discussion on French Business Schools
FC-NEXUS	FC-NEXUS@UWAVM	FC-NEXUS
FCCCMIN	FCCCMIN@UGA	Franklin College Minutes
FCR-B	FCR-B@EBCESCA1	Servei d'Informacio d'Ajuts i Beques
FCR-FQ	FCR-FQ@EBCESCA1	Servei d'Informacio d'Ajuts i Beques
FCR-H	FCR-H@EBCESCA1	Servei d'Informacio d'Ajuts i Beques
FCR-INT	FCR-INT@EBCESCA1	Servicio de Informacion de Ayudas y Becas (I+
FCR-MIE	FCR-MIE@EBCESCA1	Servei d'Informacio d'Ajuts i Beques
FCSSCD	FCSSCD-L@UALTAVM	FCSSCD-L is a list for the open discussion a+
FCSSCN	FCSSCN-L@UALTAVM	FCSSCN-L stands for FCSSC News Release
FDR	FDR@MARIST	Discussion of FDR
FEDJOBS	FEDJOBS@DARTCMS1	Federal Job Bulletin Board
FEDSIG-L	FEDSIG-L@WVNVM	Federal Electronic Data Special Interest Gro+

Network-wide ID	Full address	List title
FELINE-L	FELINE-L@PCCVM	(Peered) Discussion forum for cat fanciers
	FELINE-L@PSUVM	(Peered) Discussion forum for cat fanciers
FELLOWS	FELLOWS@IUBVM	Big 10 Committee On Institutional Cooperatio+
FEMINIST	FEMINIST@MITVMA	ALA Feminist Task Force Discussion List
FEMJUR	FEMJUR@SUVM	Discussions and Information About Feminist L+
FEMREL-L	FEMREL-L@MIZZOU1	Open discussion of women, religion, and femi+
FEMSEM	FEMSEM@SBCCVM	Stony Brook Feminist Philosophy Mailing list
FET-NET	FET-NET@HEARN	Topics concerning research in fetal and peri+
FIBROM-L	FIBROM-L@UIUCVMD	FIBROM-L Fibromyalgia / Fibrositis Discussio+
FICTION	FICTION@PSUVM	Fiction Writers Workshop
FIGI-L	FIGI-L@BRUSPVM	Forth Interest Group International List (FIG+
FIGLET-L	FIGLET-L@UIUCVMD	Discussions about the multi-font large-lette+
FILM-L	FILM-L@ITESMVF1	Film making and reviews list
FILMUS-L	FILMUS-L@IUBVM	Film Music Discussion List
FINADMIN	FINADMIN@UBVM	UB Financial Administrators List
FINAID-L	FINAID-L@PSUVM	Administration of Student Financial Aid
FINAN-HC	FINAN-HC@WUVMD	Health Care Financial Matters Discussion List
FINANCE	FINANCE@TEMPLEVM	The Electronic Journal of Finance
FINE-ART	FINE-ART@RUTVM1	(Peered) Fine-Art Forum
FINISP-L	FINISP-L@UKANVM	Financial ISP Announcements/Discussion
FINVOL-L	FINVOL-L@VTVM1	VCES Satellite Training for Financial Volunt+
FIPEFS-L	FIPEFS-L@UICVM	Fiscal Issues, Policy and Education Finance
FIREARMS	FIREARMS@UTARLVM1	FIREARMS Discussion List
FISC-L	FISC-L@NDSUVM1	FISC-L Fee-Based Info Serv Centers in Academ+
FISHNET	FISHNET@SBCCVM	Fiber-based Island-wide Super High-speed NET+
FISICA-L	FISICA-L@BRUFMG	(Peered) Forum FISICA-L
	FISICA-L@UFRJ	(Peered) Forum FISICA-L
	FISICA-L@UKACRL	Forum FISICA-L
FIS2	FIS2@ICNUCEVM	CNR - Comitato 02, Fisica (FIS2)
FIT-L	FIT-L@ETSUADMN	Exercise, diet, and wellness discussion list
FITNESS	FITNESS@INDYCMS	Fitness and the IUPUI campus
FKFIC-L	FKFIC-L@PSUVM	Forever Knight TV show stories
FLAC-L	FLAC-L@BROWNVM	Foreign Language Across Curriculum List

Network-wide ID	Full address	List title
FLADOCS	FLADOCS@NERVM	Southeast Document Librarians
FLAIRS	FLAIRS@UCF1VM	FLorida Artificial Intelligence Research Sym+
FLAX-L	FLAX-L@HARVARDA	Fulbright-LASPAU Academic eXchange
FLEXWORK	FLEXWORK@PSUHMC	Flexible Work Environment List
FLINN	FLINN@ARIZVM1	Network of Flinn Scholars and Mentors
FLIPPER	FLIPPER@NERVM	"Fla. Libr. Interested in Preserv. Pgms., Ed+
FLITSERV	FLITSERV@SIUCVMB	FLITSERV LIST
FLN	FLN@ICINECA	Figurative Language Network
FLTALK	FLTALK@WSUVM1	CE Family Living Conversations at WSU
FLYFISH	FLYFISH@UMAB	Fly Fishing Digest
FNORD-L	FNORD-L@UBVM	New Ways of Thinking List
FOCUS-L	FOCUS-L@ASUACAD	FOCUS-L
FOLKLORE	FOLKLORE@TAMVM1	Folklore Discussion List
FOLKTALK	FOLKTALK@WMVM1	Folk Music Discussion
FOODWINE	FOODWINE@CMUVM	Discussion List for Food and Wine
FORAGE-L	FORAGE-L@UNLVM	FORAGE Discussion List
FORBEQ	FORBEQ@UFRJ	Forum de Engenharia Quimica
FORENSIC	FORENSIC@UNMVMA	FORENSIC MED., ANTHRO., DEATH INVEST., MORTA+
FORKNI-L	FORKNI-L@PSUVM	Forever Knight TV show
FORMS-L	FORMS-L@UCSFVM	Online form templates discussion list
FORO-L	FORO-L@ARIZVM1	FORO-L (Transborder Libraries Forum/Foro int+
FORSUM-L	FORSUM-L@BROWNVM	Forest Summit Online Project
FOXPRO-L	FOXPRO-L@UKANVM	KU FOXPRO List
FRAC-L	FRAC-L@GITVM1	"FRACTAL" discussion list
FRANCEHS	FRANCEHS@UWAVM	FRANCEHS List for French history scholars
FREE-L	FREE-L@INDYCMS	Fathers' Rights and Equality Exchange
FREENET	FREENET@WAYNEST1	Greater Detroit Free-Net
FREETALK	FREETALK@BROWNVM	(Peered) A list for free-talking
	FREETALK@KRSNUCC1	(Peered) A list for free-talking
FRIEND-L	FRIEND-L@TREARN	FRIEND Server Discussions
FROGJOBS	FROGJOBS@BITNIC	FROGJOBS
FROGPROF	FROGPROF@BITNIC	AATFREN American Association of Teachers of +
FROGTALK	FROGTALK@BITNIC	FROGTALK
FRONTIER	FRONTIER@DARTCMS1	Discussion of Userland Frontier for Macintosh
FSEC-L	FSEC-L@UBVM	UB Faculty Senate Executive Committee Discus+
FSIG	FSIG@RPITSVM	Feminist studies special interest group
FSSC-L	FSSC-L@GSUVM1	Field Service Steering Comm., NAFSA
FSVS-L	FSVS-L@CSEARN	Free software na VS - zdroje, instalace, pou+
FTPGROUP	FTPGROUP@ICNUCEVM	CNUCE Anonymous FTP Server Group
FTPSEGI	FTPSEGI@BLIULG11	FTPSEGI Program Information List

Network-wide ID	Full address	List title
FULBNEWS	FULBNEWS@BRLNCC	FULBRIGHT Educational Advising Newsletter
FUNCT-AL	FUNCT-AN@JPNYITP	Preprint server for Functional Analysis
FUNDACJA	FUNDACJA@PLEARN	The Foundation of the Search and Academic Co+
FUNDERES	FUNDERES@FRMOP11	FUNDERES
FUNDLIST	FUNDLIST@JHUVM	List for the discussion of university fund r+
FUR-L	FUR-L@PCCVM	Feline Underground Railroad (FUR) Stationmas+
FUSION	FUSION@NDSUVM1	Fusion - Redistribution of sci.physics.fusion
FUTURE-L	FUTURE-L@BITNIC	(Peered) The Future of BITNET
	FUTURE-L@DEARN	(Peered) Discussion about the future of BITN+
	FUTURE-L@HEARN	(Peered) Discussion about the future of BITN+
	FUTURE-L@MARIST	(Peered) The future of BITNET
	FUTURE-L@UGA	(Peered) The Future of BITNET
FUTUREC	FUTUREC@UAFSYSB	Future Culture
FWAKE-L	FWAKE-L@IRLEARN	Finnegans Wake (by James Joyce) Discussion L+
FWAKEN-L	FWAKEN-L@IRLEARN	Finnegans Wake - Textual Notes
GAELIC-L	GAELIC-L@IRLEARN	GAELIC Language Bulletin Board
GALACTIC	GALACTIC@UGA	GALACTIC Industries Discussion
GAMES-L	GAMES-L@BROWNVM	(Peered) Computer Games List
	GAMES-L@GREARN	(Peered) Computer Games List
	GAMES-L@KRSNUCC1	(Peered) Computer Games List
	GAMES-L@UTARLVM1	(Peered) Computer Games List
GAMS-L	GAMS-L@DEARN	GAMS user list
GARDENS	GARDENS@UKCC	Gardens & Gardening
GARR-BA	GARR-BA@IBACSATA	GARR-BA Bari GARR Working Group
GARR-IP	GARR-IP@ICNUCEVM	GARR-IP Gruppo di Lavoro reti IP
GARR-PE	GARR-PE@ICNUCEVM	GARR Italian WG on Electronic Mail
GARR-PMN	GARR-PMN@ITOCSIVM	GARR Piemonte
GARR-USR	GARR-USR@ITOCSIVM	GARR Piemonte
GARUDA	GARUDA@SUVM	Indonesian Students at Syracuse
GAY-LIBN	GAY-LIBN@USCVM	The Gay/Lesbian/Bisexual Librarians Network
GBRC-L	GBRC-L@LEPICS	L3 Analysis Group Beta Resource Commitment
GC-L	GC-L@URIACC	GC-L, Global Classroom: International Studen+
GCS-L	GCS-L@UIUCVMD	GCS discussions
GDDM-L	GDDM-L@POLYVM	The GDDM Discussion list
GDON	GDON@FRMOP11	Equipe Gestion de donn{es CNUSC
GEACMUS	GEACMUS@RUTVM1	GEAC Music Users List
GEGSTAFF	GEGSTAFF@UKCC	Discussion list for the G/L/B Caucus of the +

Network-wide ID	Full address	List title
GEMINI	GEMINI@NRCVM01	Gemini Project
GENDER	GENDER@RPITSVM	Study of communication and gender
GENRED-L	GENRED-L@MIZZOU1	Discussion list for English 370, Section 2
GENSTAT	GENSTAT@UKACRL	"Open discussion list for the statistical sy+
GENSYS-L	GENSYS-L@ULKYVM	Genesys software users forum
GEODESIC	GEODESIC@UBVM	List for the discussion of Buckminster Fulle+
GEOGED	GEOGED@UKCC	Geography Education List
GEOGFEM	GEOGFEM@UKCC	Discussion list for Feminism in Geography
GEOGRAPH	GEOGRAPH@SEARN	Geography
GEOLOGY	GEOLOGY@PTEARN	Geology Discussion List
GEOL5	GEOL5@ICNUCEVM	CNR - Comitati
GEONET-L	GEONET-L@IUBVM	GEONET-L Geoscience Librarians & Informati+
GEOREF	GEOREF@UNALCOL	SISTEMAS DE INFORMACION GEO-REFERENCIAL
GER-RUS	GER-RUS@NDSUVM1	GER-RUS Germans from Russia
GERINET	GERINET@UBVM	Geriatric Health Care Discussion Group
GERLINGL	GERLINGL@UIUCVMD	Older Germanic languages (to 1500), their li+
GERMAN-L	GERMAN-L@UALTAVM	German Teaching Materials
GFULMED	GFULMED@NDSUVM1	GFULMED Grateful Med via BITNET
GGUIDE	GGUIDE@BITNIC	(Peered) BITNET User's Guide List
	GGUIDE@DEARN	(Peered) Users Guide list
	GGUIDE@HEARN	(Peered) Users Guide list
	GGUIDE@MARIST	(Peered) Users Guide list
	GGUIDE@UGA	(Peered) BITNIC GGUIDE List
GIF-L	GIF-L@ITESMVF1	GIF Graphics and applications list
GIGA	GIGA@DEARN	Leserforum des Informationsdienstes 'GIGA'
GIGA-L	GIGA-L@DEARN	GIGA - GeNeRIC Informationen GMD Ankuendigun+
GIGGLES	GIGGLES@VTVM1	House of Laughter; Jokes, Stories, and Anecd+
GIK2-L	GIK2-L@AWIIMC12	Graphics Interface Kit/2 Discussion
GIS-L	GIS-L@UBVM	Geographic Information Systems Discussion Li+
GISBUS-L	GISBUS-L@ECUVM1	Geographic Information Systems for Business +
GIUPOL9	GIUPOL9@ICNUCEVM	CNR - Comitato 09, Scienze Giuridiche e Poli+
GI3ABS-L	GI3ABS-L@DHDURZ1	GI-ABS Mailing list
GLB-NEWS	GLB-NEWS@BROWNVM	Information Repository for News of Interest +
GLED	GLED@UICVM	Great Lakes Economic Development Research Gr+
GLFTRAIN	GLFTRAIN@SAKAAU03	The GULF Network discussion group

Network-wide ID	Full address	List title
GLIM-L	GLIM-L@UKACRL	"GLIM and Generalised Linear Modelling of Da+
GLOBALMC	GLOBALMC@TAMVM1	Global Marketing Consortium Discussion List
GLOBLX-L	GLOBLX-L@QUCDN	Global Christianity discussion
GLOBMKT	GLOBMKT@UKCC	Applied Global Marketing
GLOMOD-L	GLOMOD-L@UHCCVM	The Global Modeling Forum
GLRC	GLRC@SUVM	Great Lakes Research Consortium Information +
GMAST-L	GMAST-L@UTCVM	Gamemasters Interest Group
GMIS-L	GMIS-L@UMSLVMA	Graduate MIS Discusion List
GMRLIST	GMRLIST@UICVM	GMRLIST List Greater Midwest Region Heal+
GNI-L	GNI-L@BROWNVM	Global Nomads List
GN9AM-O	GN9AM-O@SAUPM00	9th Annual Gulfnet Meeting Discussion List
GOHCS7L	GOHCS7-L@MSU	GOH Productions/Seven Loaves
GOLF-L	GOLF-L@UBVM	The Golf Discussion List
GOMED-L	GOMED-L@QUCDN	Ontario Medical Education Group
GONE-L	GONE-L@TAUNIVM	GONE Rexx EXEC discussion list
GOP-L	GOP-L@PCCVM	A discussion of all things Republican and Co+
GOPH-L	GOPH-L@TECHNION	GOPH-L - Local List
GOPHER-L	GOPHER-L@UMSLVMA	The UM-St.Louis Gopher discussion group
GOPHERN	GOPHERN@UBVM	Let's Go Gopherin'
GOPUB-L	GOPUB-L@BROWNVM	Translating Formatted Text to ASCII Discussi+
GOULDBUG	GOULDBUG@CLVM	Gould CSD User's List
GOVDOC-L	GOVDOC-L@PSUVM	(Peered) Discussion of Government Document I+
	GOVDOC-L@UALTAVM	(Peered) Discussion of Government Document I+
GO4LIB-L	GO4LIB-L@UCSBVM	Library Gopher List
GPNDG	GPNDG@WSUVM1	Great Pacific Northwest Gather
GPTEAM	GPTEAM@POLYVM	The Green Pages Team Discussion
GR-QC-L	GR-QC@JPNYITP	Preprint server for General Relativity & Qua+
GRAD-L	GRAD-L@UALTAVM	German Graduate Student Discussion Forum
GRADNRSE	GRADNRSE@KENTVM	Questions and Answers About Nursing Practice+
GRADREF	GRADREF@TEMPLEVM	CAS GRADREF INFORMATION
GRAFIK-L	GRAFIK-L@DEARN	GRAFIK-L
GRAFOS-L	GRAFOS-L@UFRJ	GRAFOS-L Aspectos matematicos e computaciona+
GRAMIC-L	GRAMIC-L@BROWNVM	GRAMICIDIN LIST

Network-wide ID	Full address	List title
GRANT	GRANT@GWUVM	Fulbright Awards and Grants for Faculty and +
GRANT-L	GRANT-L@UA1VM	OSP Funding Alert List
GRAPH-L	GRAPH-L@BRUFPB	Mathematical aspects of Computer Graphics, C+
	GRAPH-L@YALEVM	Yale University Graphics Users
GRAPH-UG	GRAPH-UG@SAUPM00	KFUPM Graphics Users Group.
GRAPHIX	GRAPHIX@UTFSM	Graphics Formats List IDX GIF FLI ETC.
GRAPHNET	GRAPHNET@NDSUVM1	GRAPHNET - Graph Theory
GRDEMP-L	GRDEMP-L@UBVM	Graduate employment issues discussion list
GRFTP-L	GRFTP-L@GREARN	TESTFTP server discussion list
GRIPE-L	GRIPE-L@UMSLVMA	The UM-St.Louis Complaint discussion group
GRLINKFL	GRLINKFL@GREARN	Greek EARN Linkfail List
GRMNHIST	GRMNHIST@DGOGWDG1	GRMNHIST - German History Forum
GRNSCH-L	GRNSCH-L@BROWNVM	Green School List
GRNSD-MF	GRNSD-MF@HEARN	GRNSD Member Forum
GRNSD-SC	GRNSD-SC@HEARN	Discussion Forum for the GRNSD Steering Comm+
GRNSD-SD	GRNSD-SD@HEARN	Discussion Forum for the GRNSD Information S+
GRTECH	GRTECH@GREARN	Greek EARN Technical Group List
GRUDES-L	GRUDES-L@BRUFSC	(Peered) FORUM GRUDES-L - Assuntos pertinent+
GRUFO-L	GRUFO-L@DGOGWDG1	Gruppenforschung / Forum
GRUNGE-L	GRUNGE-L@UBVM	Grunge Rock Discussion List
GRUPIN-L	GRUPIN-L@DGOGWDG1	Group Research / International
GSA	GSA@IUBVM	GSA - Genetic Stock Administrator's Discussi+
GSA-L	GSA-L@VTVM1	Graduate Student Assembly of Va Tech
GSEAA-L	GSEAA-L@UCSBVM	UCSB GSE Alumni Discussion List
GSLIS-L	GSLIS-L@UTKVM1	UTK Graduate School of Library and Informati+
GSS-L	GSS-L@UGA	Group Support Systems
GSUACM-L	GSUACM-L@GSUVM1	GSU Chapter of ACM Discussion List
GSUCUG-L	GSUCUG-L@GSUVM1	GSU Computer Users Group Discussion
GTAP-L	GTAP-L@PURCCVM	Users of GTAP GE model and data
GTGUN	GTGUN@GITVM1	GTGUN- Discussion List for the GT Marksman+
GTRTI-L	GTRTI-L@GSUVM1	Research & Teaching in Global Info Tech
GUIDO-L	GUIDO-L@UALTAVM	Guiding Users to Icpsr Data On-Line
GULFNAD	GULFNAD@SAUPM00	GulfNet Node ADministrators (NADs) Discussio+
GUM	GUM@BRUFMG	Grupo de Usuarios MUSIC do Brasil (GUM)
GUN-NEWS	GUN-NEWS@PCCVM	News and information related to Firearms and+

Network-wide ID	Full address	List title
GUST-L	GUST-L@PLTUMK11	Polish TeX users group disscusion list
GUTNBERG	GUTNBERG@UIUCVMD	Project Gutenberg Email List
GWCOMM	GWCOMM@GWUVM	GWU's GWCOMM Discussion List
GWDG-NEU	GWDG-NEU@DGOGWDG1	Mitteilungen der GWDG
GWDTCP-L	GWDTCP-L@DGOGWDG1	TCP/IP-Liste der GWDG
GWHONORS	GWHONORS@GWUVM	GWU's Honors Program Discussion List
GWPC	GWPC@GWUVM	GWPC Discussion List
GWTESTL	GWTESTL@GWUVM	Test list for LISTSERV at GWU
H-ALBION	H-ALBION@UICVM	H-Net British and Irish History discussion l+
H-AMSTDY	H-AMSTDY@UICVM	American Studies discussion list
H-CIVWAR	H-CIVWAR@UICVM	Civil War History discussion list
H-DIPLO	H-DIPLO@UICVM	H-DIPLO Diplomatic History discussion list
H-DURKHM	H-DURKHM@UICVM	Durkheim History discussion list
H-EDIT	H-EDIT@UICVM	Information on editing lists & Hnet business
H-ETHNIC	H-ETHNIC@UICVM	Ethnic History discussion list
H-FILM	H-FILM@UICVM	History of film discussion list
H-GRAD	H-GRAD@UICVM	H-Net History Graduate Students discussion l+
H-JUDAIC	H-JUDAIC@UICVM	Jewish Studies discussion list
H-LABOR	H-LABOR@UICVM	H-Net Labor History discussion list
H-LATAM	H-LATAM@UICVM	Latin American History discussion list
H-LAW	H-LAW@UICVM	Legal History discussion list
H-NET	H-NET@HUEARN	Discussion on Hungarian Academic & Research +
	H-NET@UICVM	H-NET Incoming Mail Only
H-POL	H-POL@UICVM	H-Net Political History discussion list
H-POST	H-POST@UICVM	Items which may be worth posting
H-RHETOR	H-RHETOR@UICVM	H-NET HISTORY OF RHETORIC DISCUSSION LIST
H-RURAL	H-RURAL@UICVM	H-Rural Rural & Agricultural History discuss+
H-SOUTH	H-SOUTH@UICVM	H-South U.S. Southern History discussion list
H-TEACH	H-TEACH@UICVM	H-Net Teaching History discussion list
H-URBAN	H-URBAN@UICVM	H-URBAN Urban History discussion list
H-WOMEN	H-WOMEN@UICVM	H-WOMEN Women's History discussion list
HABSBURG	HABSBURG@PURCCVM	Austrian History since 1500
HARLIC-L	HARLIC-L@RICEVM1	HARLIC Libraries Discussion Group
HARNTECH	HARNTECH@HKUVM1	HARNET Technical Group
HASTRO-L	HASTRO-L@WVNVM	History of Astronomy Discussion Group
HBONE-L	HBONE-L@HUEARN	Hungarian IP Backbone
HC-L	HC-L@ALBNYDH2	HC-L HEALTHCOM/VM Discussion
HCDB-L	HCDB-L@LEPICS	Open forum on the Hadron Calorimeter Data Ba+

Network-wide ID	Full address	List title
HCFNET	HCFNET@UCSBVM	Humanities Computing Facilities Network
HCISTN-L	HCISTN-L@VTVM1	HCISTN-L Discussion List
HCSCEPD	HCSCEPD@GWUVM	Clinical Education Program Directors Group
HDESK-L	HDESK-L@WVNVM	Help Desk Discussions
HDR-PPL	HDR-PPL@MARIST	Header-People Discussion
	HDR-PPL@UIUCVMD	Hdr-Ppl (log files only)
HEAFAULT	HEAFAULT@IRLEARN	HEAnet Faults database
HEALTH-L	HEALTH-L@IRLEARN	International Discussion on Health Research
HEALTHCO	HEALTHCO@RPITSVM	Communication in health/medical context
HEALTHRE	HEALTHRE@UKCC	Health Care Reform Discussion List
HEAVY-L	HEAVY-L@LEPICS	Heavy Monte-Carlo Flavours Subgroup
HEBREW-L	HEBREW-L@UMINN1	HEBREW-L Jewish & Near Eastern Studies (Subs+
HEDSDIRS	HEDSDIRS@BITNIC	HEDSDIRS - HEDS Board of Directors and Staff+
HEDTEC-L	HEDTEC-L@ALBNYVM1	Technology Impacts on Higher Education
HELLAS	HELLAS@AUVM	(Peered) The Hellenic Discussion List
	HELLAS@PSUVM	(Peered) The Hellenic Discussion List
	HELLAS@UGA	(Peered) The Hellenic Discussion List
HELP-L	HELP-L@SAKAAU03	KAAU Computer center Info + Help List
HELP-NET	HELP-NET@TEMPLEVM	Bitnet/Internet Help Resource
HELPDESK	HELPDESK@IBACSATA	Info DIR-ITA Heldesk
	HELPDESK@INDYCMS	IUPUI Help Desk Staff List
HELPNET	HELPNET@NDSUVM1	HELPNET Network Emergency Response Planning
HELWA-L	HELWA-L@PSUVM	Malaysian Women in U.S. and Canada
HEP-LATL	HEP-LAT@JPNYITP	Preprint server for Computational and Lattic+
HEP-PH-L	HEP-PH@JPNYITP	Preprint server for Particle Phenomenology
HEP-TH-L	HEP-TH@JPNYITP	Preprint server for String/Conformal/Field T+
HEPDB	HEPDB@CERNVM	HEPDB Distribution List
HEPHIN	HEPHIN@ICNUCEVM	HEPHIN Discussion List
HEPIX-F	HEPIX-F@FRCPN11	HEP Unix France
HEPROC-L	HEPROC-L@AUVM	Higher Education Processes Conference Hall
HERB	HERB@TREARN	Medicinal and Aromatic Plants discussion lis+
HESSE-L	HESSE-L@UCSBVM	The Works of Hermann Hesse
HFS-L	HFS-L@VTVM1	Human Factors and Ergonomics Society Va Tech+
HHI-RES	HHI-RES@UTARLVM1	HHI Research Findings
HHS-L	HHS-L@UBVM	Huntington High School Discussion List

Network-wide ID	Full address	List title
HIGGL3-L	HIGGL3-L@LEPICS	Higgs Analysis Group in L3
HIGHLA-L	HIGHLA-L@PSUVM	Highlander movies and TV series
HIH-L	HIH-L@VTVM1	Human Issues in Horticulture Discussion List
HILAT-L	HILAT-L@BRUSPVM	Research on Higher Education in Latin Americ+
HINDU-D	HINDU-D@ARIZVM1	Hindu Digest
HINTS-L	HINTS-L@ALBNYDH2	HINTS-L HINTS using the NYS Dept of Health +
HIRIS-L	HIRIS-L@ICINECA	HIgh Resolution Infrared Spectroscopy - List
HIS-WG20	HIS-WG20@UCDCVDLS	AMIA Hospital Information Systems - Working +
HISLAW-L	HISLAW-L@ULKYVM	History of Law (Feudal, Common, Canon)
HIST-L	HIST-L@UKANVM	(Peered) History - Peer Distribution List
HISTEC-L	HISTEC-L@UKANVM	History of evangelical Christianity
HISTNEWS	HISTNEWS@UKANVM	Historians' Newsletter
HISTORY	HISTORY@CSEARN	(Peered) History
	HISTORY@DGOGWDG1	(Peered) History
	HISTORY@IRLEARN	(Peered) History
	HISTORY@MCGILL1	(Peered) History - History Discussion Forum
	HISTORY@PSUVM	(Peered) History Discussion Forum
	HISTORY@RUTVM1	(Peered) History Discussion Forum
	HISTORY@UBVM	(Peered) History Discussion Forum
	HISTORY@UMRVMB	(Peered) History Discussion List
HISTORYA	HISTORYA@UWAVM	HISTORYA History Department
HISTORYF	HISTORYF@UWAVM	LISTNAME History Faculty
HISTOWNR	HISTOWNR@UBVM	HistOwnr - Discussion list for owners of his+
HIS393	HIS393@SBCCVM	Stony Brook HIS393 Discussion List
HIT	HIT@UFRJ	Highly Imaginative Tech and Science Fiction
HKN-L	HKN-L@ASUACAD	Eta Kappa Nu Discussion List
HLPCMD-L	HLPCMD-L@BROWNVM	HELP Commands for VM/CMS
HL4H-L	HL4H-L@VTVM1	Holiday Lake 4H Center
HN-ASK-L	HN-ASK-L@UKANVM	History Network Forum
HN-ORG-L	HN-ORG-L@UKANVM	THE HISTORY NETWORK
HOCKEY-D	HOCKEY-D@MAINE	A digest of HOCKEY-L - The College Hockey Di+
HOCKEY-L	HOCKEY-L@MAINE	College Hockey discussion list
HOLISTIC	HOLISTIC@SIUCVMB	Holistic Discussion Group
HOLMESGP	HOLMESGP@MSU	HOLMES ED School Reform
HOLOCAUS	HOLOCAUS@UICVM	Holocaust List
HOMESAT	HOMESAT@NDSUVM1	HOMESAT - Home Satellite Technology
HONDA-L	HONDA-L@BROWNVM	Honda Digest
HONORS	HONORS@ARIZVM1	Info about Honors Center Classes, Activities

Network-wide ID	Full address	List title
	HONORS@GWUVM	National Collegiate Honors Council Discussio+
	HONORS@UICVM	Honor College discussion list
HONRDS	HONRDS@GWUVM	HONR 71.13, Western Civilization Course Disc+
HOPOS-L	HOPOS-L@UKCC	A Forum for Discussion of the History of the+
HORROR	HORROR@PACEVM	Horror Films and Fiction
HORT-L	HORT-L@VTVM1	Va Tech Horticulture Dept. - Monthly Releases
HORTPGM	HORTPGM@VTVM1	Va Tech Horticulture Dept. - Programs in Con+
HOSPEX	HOSPEX@PLEARN	HOSPitality EXchange database (homestays) HO+
HOSPEX$P	HOSPEX$P@PLEARN	Discussion of HOSPEX policies: HOSPEX$P
HOSPEX-L	HOSPEX-L@PLEARN	HOSPitality EXchange (homestays) discussion +
HOTEL-L	HOTEL-L@MIZZOU1	Hotel and Restaurant Educators Discussion
HOTTOPIC	HOTTOPIC@ETSUADMN	HOT TOPICS: RECRUITMENT/SCHOOL RELATIONS
HOUINFO	HOUINFO@RICEVM1	Houston Information Access Discussion List
HP-28	HP-28@NDSUVM1	HP-28 - HP-28C and HP-28S Calculators
HP-48	HP-48@NDSUVM1	HP-48 - HP-48sx Hand Held System
HPMINI-L	HPMINI-L@UAFSYSB	Hewlett-Packard 9000 Series MiniComputer Dis+
HPSST-L	HPSST-L@QUCDN	History and Philosophy of Science and Scienc+
HP3000-L	HP3000-L@UTCVM	HP-3000 Systems Discussion
HQ-L	HQ-L@PSUHMC	HealthQuest Products Discussion List
HRD-L	HRD-L@MIZZOU1	Human Resource Development Group List
HRIS-L	HRIS-L@UALTAVM	Human Resources Information (Canada)
HRM-L	HRM-L@NMSUVM1	Management 332 Class Discussion
HRMS-L	HRMS-L@UKANVM	KU Human Resource Management System User Dis+
HRS-IDMS	HRS-IDMS@UNMVMA	IA HRS IDMS discussion list
HRS-L	HRS-L@BINGVMB	Systematic Studies of Human Rights
HSJOURN	HSJOURN@LATECH	High School Scholastic Journalism
HSNETM-L	HSNETM-L@MIZZOU1	Health Sciences LAN Management Discussion Li+
HSPASCAL	HSPASCAL@ITESMVF1	Amiga High-Speed Pascal Language Discussion
HSPBED-L	HSPBED-L@ALBNYDH2	HSPBED-L Hospital Bed Availability in NY S+
HSPNET-D	HSPNET-D@ALBNYDH2	Hospital Computer Network Discussion Group a+

Network-wide ID	Full address	List title
HSPNET-L	HSPNET-L@ALBNYDH2	Hospital Computer Network Discussion Group a+
HST-L	HST-L@WVNVM	NASA Classroom of the Future Software/Curric+
HTECH-L	HTECH-L@SIVM	History of Technology Discussion
HTUG-L	HTUG-L@HUEARN	Hungarian Transputer User's Group
HUCFF-L	HUCFF-L@BRLNCC	Staff computacional do Hospital Universitari+
HUEARN-L	HUEARN-L@HUEARN	Discussion on the Hungarian EARN
HUEARN-X	HUEARN-X@HUEARN	Hungarian EARN executive board discussion
HULINFO	HULINFO@HARVARDA	Harvard University Library Information Discu+
HULINTRO	HULINTRO@HARVARDA	HULINTRO - Harvard University Library Introd+
HUMA-L	HUMA-L@HUMBER	Humber College Human Studies Humanities Disc+
HUMAGE-L	HUMAGE-L@ASUACAD	HUMANISTIC ASPECTS OF AGING
HUMANETS	HUMANETS@RUTVM1	Human Nets Digest
HUMANIST	HUMANIST@BROWNVM	HUMANIST: Humanities Computing
HUMANS-L	HUMANS-L@HUMBER	Humber College Human Studies Division discus+
HUMBUL	HUMBUL@UKACRL	HUMBUL
HUME-L	HUME-L@WMVM1	Hume Discussion List
HUMEVO	HUMEVO@GWUVM	Human Evolutionary Research Discussion List
HUMOR	HUMOR@UGA	UGA Humor List
HUMSPC-L	HUMSPC-L@BROWNVM	Humanist Special List
HUM3301	HUM3301@UTEPA	Modern European / Atlantic Culture - at UTEP
HUNGARY	HUNGARY@GWUVM	Hungarian Discussion List
HUNTING	HUNTING@TAMVM1	Rec.hunting discussion list
HYDROGEN	HYDROGEN@URIACC	Hydrogen as an alternative fuel
HYPBAR-L	HYPBAR-L@TECHNION	HyperBaric & Diving Medicine List
HYPERCRD	HYPERCRD@MSU	Hypercard Discussion List
HYPERMED	HYPERMED@UMAB	Biomedical Hypermedia Instructional Design
HYPER93	HYPER93@INDYCMS	Integrated Technologies' Hypermedia Conferen+
HYTEL-L	HYTEL-L@KENTVM	HYTELNET Updates Distribution
I-AMIGA	I-AMIGA@RUTVM1	(Peered) Info-Amiga List
	AMIGA-L@UALTAVM	(Peered) Info-Amiga List
	I-AMIGA@UBVM	(Peered) Info-Amiga List
	I-AMIGA@UTARLVM1	(Peered) Info-Amiga List
I-IBMPC	I-IBMPC@UIUCVMD	IBM PC discussions
I-PASCAL	I-PASCAL@UTFSM	Info-Pascal List Peer of Internet.

Network-wide ID	Full address	List title
I-REDES	I-REDES@UTFSM	Lista sobre acceso a redes WAN (INTERNET, UU+
I-TECH	I-TECH@BITNIC	I-TECH
I-UNIX	I-UNIX@BITNIC	Info-Unix distribution list
I-VIDTEK	I-VIDTEK@UIUCVMD	VideoTech
IA-ADS	IA-ADS@MARIST	IA's ADS Discussion
IA-FRS	IA-FRS@MARIST	IA's FRS Discussion
IA-HRS	IA-HRS@MARIST	IA's HRS Discussion
IA-SCT	IA-SCT@MARIST	Discussion of SCT's acquisition of IA
IA-SIS	IA-SIS@MARIST	IA's SIS Discussion
IAC-L	IAC-L@IRLEARN	Irish Academic Computing
IACM-L	IACM-L@TTUVM1	INTERNATIONAL ASSOCIATION FOR CONFLICT MANAG+
IACRL	IACRL@UICVM	IACRL List Illinois Association of College &+
IAFA-L	IAFA-L@VTVM1	Scholarly discussion of Fantastic Literature
IAIMU-L	IAIMU-L@ULKYVM	IDMS-based I/A software discussion list
IAMCRNET	IAMCRNET@RPITSVM	A service of IAMCR/AIERI
IAMEX-L	IAMEX-L@TECMTYVM	Artificial Intelligence list of ITESM.
IANETW-L	IANETW-L@BRUSPVM	Forum de discussao sobre Inteligencia Artifi+
IAP-PLAN	IAP-PLAN@NDSUVM1	International Arctic Project Planning
IAPABOVE	IAPABOVE@IUBVM	International Arctic Project POISON FROM ABO+
IAPADV	IAPADV@IUBVM	International Arctic Project Adventure - Rea+
IAPCIRC	IAPCIRC@IUBVM	International Arctic Project CIRCLES AND CYC+
	IAPCIRC@NDSUVM1	International Arctic Project Student Projects
IAPEXPED	IAPEXPED@IUBVM	International Arctic Project Expedition
	IAPEXPED@NDSUVM1	International Arctic Project Expeditions
IAPHS	IAPHS@IUBVM	International Arctic Project HIGH SCHOOL
IAPLAND	IAPLAND@IUBVM	International Arctic Project LAND
IAPLIFE	IAPLIFE@IUBVM	International Arctic Project LIFE
IAPPLAN	IAPPLAN@IUBVM	International Arctic Project Planning
IAPSY-L	IAPSY-L@ALBNYVM1	Interamerican Psychologists List (SIPNET)
IAPWILD	IAPWILD@IUBVM	International Arctic Project Wildlife
	IAPWILD@NDSUVM1	International Arctic Project Wildlife
IAPWIRE	IAPWIRE@IUBVM	International Arctic Project WIRE SERVICE
IASEE-L	IASEE-L@DEARN	xxx Beschreibung der Liste xxx
IATEX-L	IATEX-L@TAMVM1	INFORMATION ASSOCIATES OF TEXAS USERS GROUP
IAUG-L	IAUG-L@PSUVM	International AIX Users Group

Network-wide ID	Full address	List title
IAUP-UN	IAUP-UN@BITNIC	IAUP-UN Int'l Assoc of Univ Presidents, UN C+
IBIS-L	IBIS-L@UICVM	IBIS-L LIST
IBM-HESC	IBM-HESC@PSUORVM	IBM Higher Education Consortium
IBM-KERM	IBM$KERM@CUVMB	IBM mainframe KERMIT developers
IBM-MAIL	IBM-MAIL@EARNCC	Discussion list about IBM-MAIL facilities
IBM-MAIN	IBM-MAIN@AKRONVM	(Peered) IBM Mainframe Discussion List
	IBM-MAIN@DEARN	(Peered) IBM Mainframe Discussion List
	IBM-MAIN@RUTVM1	(Peered) IBM Mainframe Discussion List
	IBM-MAIN@UA1VM	(Peered) IBM Mainframe Discussion List
IBM-NETS	IBM-NETS@BITNIC	(Peered) BITNIC IBM-NETS List
	IBM-NETS@UGA	(Peered) IBM Networking
IBM-SRD	IBM-SRD@NDSUVM1	IBM-SRD Screen Reader
IBMAS-L	IBMAS-L@IRISHVMA	IBM's Application System
IBMSND-L	IBMSND-L@BROWNVM	MSDOS Sound Card Forum and Discussion List
IBMTCP-L	IBMTCP-L@PUCC	IBM TCP/IP List
IBM7171	IBM7171@IRLEARN	Protocol Converter List
	IBM7171@UIUCVMD	Log files only
IBSCG	IBSCG@MIAMIU	Intl Business School Computer User's Group (+
IBYCUS-L	IBYCUS-L@IUBVM	The Ibycus Scholarly Computer discussion list
ICACBR-L	ICACBR-L@QUCDN	Community Rehabilitation Programs for Person+
ICAD	ICAD-L@UALTAVM	ICAD-L Discussion List
ICADD	ICADD@ASUACAD	International Committee for Accessible Docum+
ICADDB	ICADDB@ASUACAD	International Committee for Accessible Docum+
ICAM-L	ICAM-L@IRMFAO01	ICAM - Integrated Coastal Area Management IC+
ICEBERG	ICEBERG@BRLNCC	Forum de Ciencia da Informacao
ICEE94-L	ICEE94-L@UGA	International Conference on Environmental Et+
ICEN-L	ICEN-L@IUBVM	ICEN-L International Career and Employment +
ICIS-L	ICIS-L@UGA	International Conference on Information Syst+
ICOMALL	ICOMALL@JPNIMRTU	ICOM USER
ICONEWS	ICONEWS@FRMOP11	International Commission for Optics NEWSlett+
ICONOL-L	ICONOL-L@UBVM	Iconology Discussion List
ICPSR-NL	ICPSR-NL@HEARN	Discussielijst voor Nederlandse deelnemers a+
ICRC-L	ICRC-L@IRLEARN	22nd Int'l Cosmic Ray Conference List

Network-wide ID	Full address	List title
ICS-L	ICS-L@UMDD	International Chemometrics Society
ICU-C	ICU-C@WVNVM	WVNET Instructional Computing Users Committee
ID-LINE	ID-LINE@URIACC	Idea Exchange For Chinese Communication Scho+
IDAHONET	IDAHONET@IDBSU	IDAHONET - ACADEMIC AND ADMINISTRATIVE NETWO+
IDFORUM	IDFORUM@YORKVM1	Industrial Design Forum
IDMS-L	IDMS-L@UGA	CA-IDMS Discussion
IDS	IDS@MCGILL1	International Development Studies at McGill
	IDS@SUVM	Indonesian Development Studies - Network
IDS-CLUB	IDS-CLUB@UICVM	IDS Club
IEAHCNET	IEAHCNET@UICVM	American Colonial History Discussion List
IEDC-L	IEDC-L@UTKVM1	International Education Data Collection Comm+
IEDUCOM	IEDUCOM@USACHVM1	"Informatica y Computacion en Educacion"
IEEE	IEEE@USACHVM1	"Eventos en Ingenieria Electrica e Informati+
IEEE-EGE	IEEE-EGE@TREARN	IEEE Ege Student Branch Discussion and Annou+
IEEE-L	IEEE-L@BINGVMB	List for all EE students
IEEE-TR	IEEE-TR@TRITU	IEEE Turkey Section Communication List
IERGNRL	IERGNRL@TECHNION	I.E.& M. - General User Group
IERLIST	IERLIST@TECHNION	I.E.& M. - Faculty
IES-L	IES-L@PSUVM	Illuminating Engineering Society (IES)
IFCSS-NL	IFCSS-NL@PSUORVM	IFCSS Newsletter Mailing List
IFDO-L	IFDO-L@HEARN	Discussion list of the International Federat+
IFER-L	IFER-L@MIAMIU	Institute for Educational Renewal (IFER)
IFIP-MMM	IFIP-MMM@IBACSATA	IFIP Multimedia Multimode Messaging
IFIP82-L	IFIP82-L@BINGVMB	International Federation for Information Pro+
IFIP84	IFIP84@UKACRL	IFIP84
IFPHEN-L	IFPHEN-L@WSUVM1	Interfacial Phenomena Interest List
IFPS-L	IFPS-L@VTVM1	Interactive Financial Planning System
IG-GIS-L	IG-GIS-L@UKCC	IG-GIS-L
IHOUSE-L	IHOUSE-L@WUVMD	International House Newsletter Prototype List
IIESCNET	IIESCNET@ASUACAD	IIE Student Communications Network
IIF-FELH	IIF-FELH@HUEARN	IIF felhasznalok levelezese
IIF-KOOR	IIF-KOOR@HUEARN	IIF koordinator lista
IIRG	IIRG@UICVM	IIRG List Illinois Internet Resources Group
IIRS	IIRS@TAUNIVM	Israeli Information Retrieval Specialists Li+

Network-wide ID	Full address	List title
IL-ADS	IL-ADS@TAUNIVM	IL-ADS — Israel Bulletin Board for Advertis+
IL-BOARD	IL-BOARD@TAUNIVM	IL-BOARD — Israel Bulletin Board Service
IL-FAIL	IL-FAIL@TAUNIVM	Israeli System and Network Failure List
IL-TALK	IL-TALK@TAUNIVM	IL-TALK — Israel General Discussion Forum
ILAN-H	ILAN-H@TAUNIVM	ILAN-H Discussion in and about Hebrew in th+
ILAS-NET	ILAS-NET@TECHNION	ILAS-NET - The International Linear Algebra +
ILASTEST	ILASTEST@TECHNION	ILASTEST - The International Linear Algebra +
ILDOS-L	ILDOS-L@TECHNION	ILDOS-L Israeli Anonymous FTP update infor+
ILFTP-L	ILFTP-L@TECHNION	ILFTP-L Israeli Anonymous FTP update infor+
ILMAC-L	ILMAC-L@TECHNION	ILMAC-L Israeli Anonymous FTP update infor+
ILSPEEDE	ILSPEEDE@UIUCVMD	ILLLINOIS ACRAO SPEEDE DISCUSSION LIST
ILWIN-L	ILWIN-L@TECHNION	ILWIN-L Israeli Anonymous FTP update infor+
IMAGE-L	IMAGE-L@HEARN	SURFdoc Images project
	IMAGE-L@TREARN	Image Processing And Applications
IMAGRS-L	IMAGRS-L@CSEARN	Digital Image Processing of Remotely Sensed +
IMAMEDIA	IMAMEDIA@UMDD	Compatability of Multimedia Applications
IMIA-L	IMIA-L@UMAB	International Medical Informatics Assn. Boar+
IMMNET-L	IMMNET-L@DARTCMS1	Medical Immunization Tracking systems
IMSE-L	IMSE-L@UICVM	Institute for Math and Science Education
IN-NOTIS	IN-NOTIS@IRISHVMA	Indiana NOTIS Sites and Users
INAIR	INAIR@INDYCMS	Indiana Assoc for Institutional Research
INBRIEF	INBRIEF@MARIST	Marist's "FoxNet - In Brief"
INCENTER	INCENTER@UNMVMA	International Center
INCONT-L	INCONT-L@MAINE	Incontinence Support List
INDEX-L	INDEX-L@BINGVMB	Indexer's Discussion Group
INDIA	INDIA@PCCVM	The India List
INDIA-D	INDIA-D@TEMPLEVM	(Peered) The India Interest Group at TEMPLEVM
	INDIA-D@UKCC	(Peered) The India Interest Group at UKCC
	INDIA-D@UTARLVM1	(Peered) The India Interest Group at UTARLVM1
INDIA-L	INDIA-L@TEMPLEVM	(Peered) The India News Network (at TEMPLEVM)

Network-wide ID	Full address	List title
	INDIA-L@UKCC	(Peered) The India News Network (at UKCC)
	INDIA-L@UTARLVM1	(Peered) The India News Network (at UTARLVM1)
INDIANWS	INDIANWS@PCCVM	The India List (NeWS)
INDKNOW	INDKNOW@UWAVM	INDKNOW
INDNOTIS	INDNOTIS@INDYCMS	NOTIS Implementation in Indiana
INDVIRUS	INDVIRUS@PURCCVM	Virus Info for Universities in Indiana (Indi+
INDYMAIN	INDYMAIN@INDYCMS	IUPUI Mainframe Discussion List
INDYSAS	INDYSAS@INDYCMS	SAS at IUPUI
INDYSPSS	INDYSPSS@INDYCMS	SPSSx at IUPUI
INET-TR	INET-TR@TRMETU	Turkiye-Internet Tartisma Listesi INET-TR
INF-Z100	INF-Z100@CLVM	Heath/Zenith Z100 Information Mailing List
INFO-ADA	INFO-ADA@NDSUVM1	Ada programming language
INFO-APP	INFO-APP@NDSUVM1	INFO-APP Info-Apple List
INFO-ATARI16	INFO-A16@MARIST	INFO-ATARI16 Discussion
INFO-ATARI8	INFO-A8@MARIST	(Peered) INFO-ATARI8 Discussion
INFO-AUX	INFO-AUX@PUCC	LISTSERV list for A/UX discussion and softwa+
INFO-C	INFO-C@NDSUVM1	Info-C List
	INFO-C@UIUCVMD	INFO-C (log files only)
INFO-CLS	INFO-CLS@DEARN	SmallTalk programming language discussion
INFO-IBMPC	IBMPC-L@CEARN	(Peered) Info-IBMPC Digest
	IBMPC-L@DEARN	(Peered) IBMPC-L
	IBMPC-L@HEARN	(Peered) IBMPC-L
	IBMPC-L@POLYVM	(Peered) INFO-IBMPC Digest
	$$INFOPC@RICEVM1	(Peered) Info-IBMPC redistribution list
	IBMPC-L@TAMVM1	(Peered) INFO-IBMPC Digest
	IBMPC-L@TAUNIVM	(Peered) Info-IBMPC Digest
	IBMPC-L@UBVM	(Peered) INFO-IBMPC Digest
	IBMPC-L@UGA	(Peered) INFO-IBMPC Digest
	IBMPC-L@UTORONTO	(Peered) IBMPC Digest
	IBMPC-L@VTVM1	(Peered) INFO-IBMPC Digest
INFO-KERMIT	I-KERMIT@CLVM	(Peered) INFO-KERMIT Digest
	I$KERMIT@CUVMB	(Peered) INFO-KERMIT Digest
	I-KERMIT@DEARN	(Peered) INFO-KERMIT Digest
	I-KERMIT@EBCESCA1	(Peered) INFO-KERMIT Digest
	I-KERMIT@HEARN	(Peered) INFO-KERMIT Digest
	I-KERMIT@MARIST	(Peered) INFO-KERMIT Digest
	I-KERMIT@RUTVM1	(Peered) INFO-KERMIT Digest
	I-KERMIT@UBVM	(Peered) INFO-KERMIT Digest
	I-KERMIT@UGA	(Peered) INFO-KERMIT Digest
	I-KERMIT@UTORONTO	(Peered) INFO-KERMIT Digest

Network-wide ID	Full address	List title
	I-KERMIT@VTVM1	(Peered) INFO-KERMIT Digest
INFO-MAC	INFO-MAC@CEARN	(Peered) INFO-MAC Digest
	INFO-MAC@DEARN	(Peered) INFO-MAC Digest
	INFO-MAC@EBCESCA1	(Peered) INFO-MAC Digest
	INFO-MAC@HEARN	(Peered) INFO-MAC Digest
	INFO-MAC@ICNUCEVM	INFO-MAC Digest
	INFO-MAC@IRLEARN	INFO-MAC list
	INFO-MAC@RICEVM1	(Peered) INFO-MAC Digest
	INFO-MAC@UIUCVMD	(Peered) INFO-MAC Digest
	INFO-MAC@UTORONTO	(Peered) INFO-MAC Digest
INFO-M2	INFO-M2@UCF1VM	Modula2 List
INFO-NETS	INFONETS@BITNIC	(Peered) Info-Nets List
	INFONETS@DEARN	(Peered) Info-Nets List
	INFONETS@HEARN	(Peered) Info-Nets List
	INFONETS@MARIST	(Peered) Info-Nets List
	INFONETS@UGA	(Peered) Info-Nets List
INFO-PC	INFO-PC@IRLEARN	Distribution of Info-IBMPC
INFO-VAX	INFO-VAX@DEARN	(Peered) Info Vax
	INFO-VAX@HEARN	(Peered) Info Vax
	INFO-VAX@IRLEARN	(Peered) VAX Information Distribution List
	INFO-VAX@MARIST	(Peered) INFO-VAX Discussion
	INFO-VAX@TAMVM1	(Peered) INFO-VAX Discussion
	INFO-VAX@UBVM	(Peered) INFO-VAX Discussion
	INFO-VAX@UGA	(Peered) INFO-VAX Discussion
INFOCESC	INFOCESC@EBCESCA1	Llista d'Informacio del CESCA
INFOCHIM	INFOCHIM@ICINECA	INFOCHIM - Chimica Computazionale e Informat+
INFODEPT	INFODEPT@WSUVM1	Information Department List
INFOEARN	INFOEARN@EBCESCA1	Grupo de interes en la red earn espanyola.
INFOHAMS	INFOHAMS@TAUNIVM	INFOHAMS redistribution list
INFORM-L	INFORM-L@VMTECSLP	Cultura Informatica en Mexico y America Lati+
INFORMA	INFORMA@LSUVM	Informa List
INGARC7	INGARC7@ICNUCEVM	CNR - Comitato 07, Ingegneria e Architettura+
INGEST	INGEST@CUVMB	Ingestive Disorders Mailing list.
INGRAFX	INGRAFX@PSUVM	Information Graphics
INHEALTH	INHEALTH@RPITSVM	International Health Communication
INHIB	INHIB@MCGILL1	Growth inhibitory molecule theme research gr+
INIC	INIC@PTEARN	Discussao da Situacao Criada pela sua Extinc+
INJURY-L	INJURY-L@WVNVM	Injury Surveillance Controland Intervention
INNOPAC	INNOPAC@MAINE	III Online Public Access Catalog Discussion +

Network-wide ID	Full address	List title
INNS-L	INNS-L@UMDD	International Neural Network Society
INSC-L	INSC-L@RPITSVM	International Narrative Society Conference D+
INSEA-L	INSEA-L@UNBVM1	International Society for Education Through +
INSERM-L	INSERM-L@FRORS13	Conference electronique a l'INSERM
INSIDE	INSIDE@ICNUCEVM	INSIDE Progetto TIDE
INSTOOLS	INSTOOLS@MCGILL1	Discussion on Technical Tools Used for Instr+
INT-ED	INT-ED@MSU	Education, International Students
INT-LAW	INT-LAW@UMINN1	INT-LAW Foreign and International Law Libra+
INTAUD-L	INTAUD-L@UALTAVM	University Internal Audit (Canada)
INTCOM-L	INTCOM-L@UICVM	ILCSO Interfaces Committee
INTDEV-L	INTDEV-L@URIACC	International Development and Global Educati+
INTER-CH	INTER-CH@USACHVM1	(Peered) Internet - Chile
INTER-L	INTER-L@VTVM1	A list for members of NAFSA operated by VPI&+
INTERCOM	INTERCOM@ARIZVM1	NCBES Inter-Member Communication Network
INTERCUL	INTERCUL@RPITSVM	Study of intercultural communication
INTERDIS	INTERDIS@MIAMIU	Interdisciplinary Studies
INTERDOC	INTERDOC@UWAVM	INTERDOC
INTERF-L	INTERF-L@TAUNIVM	Israeli Group on Interfacial Phenomena
INTERNET	INTERNET@ICNUCEVM	ARPA-Internet News
INTERPER	INTERPER@RPITSVM	Interpersonal/small group communication
INTERQ-L	INTERQ-L@MCGILL1	INTERNET QUEBEC
INTGROUP	INTGROUP@NDSUVM1	INTGROUP - DATABASE Searchable Copy of INTER+
	INTGROUP@TECMTYVM	DATABASE Searchable Copy of INTEREST GROUPS +
INTLNEWS	INTLNEWS@INDYCMS	News from the IUPUI International Affairs of+
INTRGULF	INTRGULF@SAKFU00	Discussion about Gulfnet connection to Inter+
INTUDM-L	INTUDM-L@UTEPA	Using Intuition in Decision Making
INVEST-L	INVEST-L@TCUBVM	INVEST-L Student-Managed Portfolios Discussi+
IOOB-L	IOOB-L@UGA	Industrial Psychology
IOOBF-L	IOOBF-L@UGA	Industrial Psychology Forum
IOUDAIOS	IOUDAIOS@YORKVM1	First Century Judaism Discussion Forum
IPCT-J	IPCT-J@GUVM	Interpersonal Computing and Technology EJour+
IPCT-L	IPCT-L@GUVM	Interpersonal Computing and Technology
IPNIBM-L	IPNIBM-L@FRCPN11	IPN Information

Network-wide ID	Full address	List title
IPNUNI-L	IPNUNI-L@FRCPN11	IPN Information
IPNVAX-L	IPNVAX-L@FRCPN11	IPN Information
IQSA-L	IQSA-L@GITVM1	IQSA-L Discussion List for the International+
IR-L	IR-L@UCCVMA	Information Retrieval List
IR-LIST	IR-LIST@IRLEARN	Information Retrieval Distribution List
IRCRETE	IRCRETE@IBACSATA	IRC Rete Interregionale IATINET
IRL-NET	IRL-NET@IRLEARN	Research Network
IRL-POL	IRL-POL@IRLEARN	IRL-POL - Discussion of Irish Politics
IROQUOIS	IROQUOIS@UTORONTO	Iroquois Language Discussion
IRSC-L	IRSC-L@HUMBER	Inter-Institutional Resource Sharing(Curricu+
IRTRAD-D	IRTRAD-D@IRLEARN	Periodical digest of postings to IRTRAD-L
IRTRAD-L	IRTRAD-L@IRLEARN	Irish Traditional Music List
ISAFPAS	ISAFPAS@ASUACAD	International Studies Association FPAS
ISAGA-L	ISAGA-L@UHCCVM	Int'l Simulation and Gaming Association Foru+
ISAPL-L	ISAPL-L@BRUFSC	(Peered) FORUM ISAPL-L - International Socie+
ISC	ISC@NRCVM01	Informatics Steering Committee
ISCAMI	ISCAMI@GREARN	Computer Assist. Management & Manipulation o+
ISDN-ITA	ISDN-ITA@ICNUCEVM	Mailing List sulla diffusione di ISDN in Ita+
ISDS	ISDS@UIUCVMD	ISDS Illini Space Development Society List
ISE-L	ISE-L@NMSUVM1	ISE LIST
ISETL-L	ISETL-L@CLVM	ISETL (Interpretive SETL) Discussion List
ISIS-L	ISIS-L@UTDALLAS	SCT ISIS product discussion list excluding B+
ISLAM-L	ISLAM-L@ULKYVM	History of Islam
ISLAMIAT	ISLAMIAT@SAKAAU03	ISLAMIC Information and Issues Discussion Gr+
ISN	ISN@RITVM	ISN Data Switch Technical Discussion Group
ISN-WG	ISN-WG@UNMVMA	IETF WG on internet school networking (ISN)
ISODE	ISODE@IRLEARN	ISO/OSI Protocol Development Environment Dis+
ISOS-L	ISOS-L@NKI	ISoS Support List
ISO10646	ISO10646@JHUVM	Multi-byte Code Issues
ISO8859	ISO8859@JHUVM	ASCII/EBCDIC character set related issues
ISO9000	ISO9000@NDSUVM1	ISO9000 Standards Discussion
ISPF-L	ISPF-L@IRISHVMA	ISPF discussion list
ISPS	ISPS@BLEKUL11	teachers Int. Study Program in Statistics
ISRG	ISRG@ARIZVM1	Information Studies Research Group
ISSC	ISSC@CUVMC	Information Systems Security Committee

Network-wide ID	Full address	List title
ISSS	ISSS@JHUVM	International Student Space Simulations
ISSS-L	ISSS-L@UIUCVMD	Illinois Summer Software Skool
ISSTFL	ISSTFL@CUVMC	Information System Security Task Force Leade+
ITALIA-L	ITALIA-L@IRLEARN	ITALIA-L - Discussion list for Italianists
ITALIC-L	ITALIC-L@IRLEARN	ITALIC-L - The Irish Tex And Latex Interest +
ITC-LIB	ITC-LIB@UTXVM	U.T. System ITC Library Work Group
ITC-NET	ITC-NET@UTXVM	U.T. System ITC Network Work Group
ITC-SEC	ITC-SEC@UTXVM	U.T. System ITC Security Work Group
ITCOLLAB	ITCOLLAB@HARVARDA	Collaborative Study on Academic Information +
ITDHELP	ITDHELP@PURCCVM	Purdue Libraries
ITDSTAFF	ITDSTAFF@PURCCVM	Purdue Libraries
ITEACH-L	ITEACH-L@UNLVM	University of Nebraska Interactive Project
ITEC1-L	ITEC1-L@ECUVM1	Industrial Technologist information and issu+
ITEX-L	ITEX-L@TAUNIVM	ITEX Discussion List
ITIG-L	ITIG-L@UNBVM1	CLA Information Technology Interest Group
ITISALAT	ITISALAT@GUVM	ITISALAT: IT IS Arabic Language And Techno+
ITP-L	ITP-L@TECHNION	ITP-L - Institute of Theoretical Physics,+
ITPT-CCL	ITPT-CCL@UMINN1	InfoTech Planning Team Liaison Group
ITRDBFOR	ITRDBFOR@ASUACAD	Dendrochronology Forum for the International+
ITS-L	ITS-L@VMTECSLP	Intelligent Tutoring Systems Discussion List
ITSMGMT	ITSMGMT@UCSFVM	ITS Management
ITSNEWS	ITSNEWS@UCSFVM	Information Technology Services Newsletter
ITSSTAFF	ITSSTAFF@UCSFVM	ITS Staff List
ITU-L	ITU-L@TRITU	I.T.U. Mezunlari Listesi
IUFIS-L	IUFIS-L@IUBVM	Indiana University Financial Information Sys+
IULRES-L	IULRES-L@IUBVM	Research Support for Indiana University Libr+
IUMMEDIA	IUMMEDIA@IUBVM	MultiMedia Discussion List - Indiana Univers+
IUTINFO	IUTINFO@FRORS13	Messagerie des Departements Informatique des+
IVCF-L	IVCF-L@UBVM	InterVarsity Christian Fellowship List
IVRITEX	IVRITEX@TAUNIVM	Hebrew TeX list
IVY+	IVY+@MITVMA	Ivy+ Administrative Computing Group
IXI-APM	IXI-APM@HEARN	Distribution list for IXI Access Point Manag+
J-FOOD-L	J-FOOD-L@JPNKNU01	Japanese food & culture discussion list

Network-wide ID	Full address	List title
JANITORS	JANITORS@UKANVM	College and University Housekeeping Informat+
JAPAN	JAPAN@PUCC	Japanese Business and Economics Network
JAZZ-L	JAZZ-L@TEMPLEVM	Jazz Lovers' List
JCGLIST	JCGLIST@UKACRL	
JCGTEST	JCGTEST@UKACRL	JCGTEST
JCMST-L	JCMST-L@PURCCVM	JOURNAL OF COMPUTERS IN MATHEMATICS AND SCIE+
JCMT-L	JCMT-L@UALTAVM	James Clerk Maxwell Telescope
JEI-L	JEI-L@UMDD	Technology in Education Mailing List
JERICHO	JERICHO@BITNIC	The Jericho Project
JESSE	JESSE@ARIZVM1	Open Lib/Info Sci Education Forum
JES2-L	JES2-L@CEARN	(Peered) JES2 discussion group
	JES2-L@NDSUVM1	(Peered) JES2 discussion group
	JES2-L@VTVM1	(Peered) JES2 discussion group
JES3-L	JES3-L@UGA	JES3 Systems Programmers List
JEWISHGT	JEWISHGT@GITVM1	JEWISHGT: Discussion List for the Jewish Com+
JHU-CSA	JHU-CSA@JHUVM	Hopkins Chinese Students Association
JMCLASS	JMCLASS@MSU	ISP201 Information
JMEDCLUB	JMEDCLUB@BROWNVM	Medical Journal Discussion Club
JNET-L	JNET-L@BITNIC	(Peered) JNET Discussion Group
	JNET-L@DEARN	(Peered) JNET Discussion Group
	JNET-L@HEARN	(Peered) JNET Discussion Group
	JNET-L@MARIST	(Peered) JNET Discussion Group
	JNET-L@UGA	(Peered) BITNIC JNET-L List
	JNET-L@UIUCVMD	JNET-L (log files only)
JOB-LIST	JOB-LIST@FRORS12	Job offers from EARN Institute members
JOBPLACE	JOBPLACE@UKCC	JobPlace (Self Directed Job Search Technique+
JOURN-L	JOURN-L@JHUVM	JOURN-L
JOURNET	JOURNET@QUCDN	Discussion List for Journalism Education
JPBIT-L	JPBIT-L@JPNSUT00	discussion about Japan BITNET
JPBOARD	JPBOARD@JPNSUT00	Japan BITNET Board meeting
JPINFO-L	JPINFO-L@JPNSUT00	Information list about Japan
JPNAD-L	JPNAD-L@JPNSUT00	Japan Node Administrator's discussion list
JPSI-L	JPSI-L@FRCPN11	Production de JPSI
JPSOFT	JPSOFT@IRISHVMA	JP Software products (4DOS/4OS2 et al)
JRNTUT-A	JRNTUT-A@CMUVM	Online Journalism Seminar - Admin
JRNTUT-L	JRNTUT-L@CMUVM	Online Journalism Seminar
JSD-L	JSD-L@UCSFVM	Discussion of Jackson System Development
JTE-L	JTE-L@VTVM1	Journal of Technology Education electronic j+
JTEM-L	JTEM-L@UGA	Japanese Through Electronic Media
JTIT-L	JTIT-L@PSUVM	Japanese Teachers and Instructional Technolo+

Network-wide ID	Full address	List title
JT4H-L	JT4H-L@VTVM1	Jamestown 4H Center
JU-DA	JU-DA@BARILVM	Discussion on Judaism and Databases
JUDAFF-L	JUDAFF-L@BINGVMB	JUDAFF-L Judicial Affairs Discussion List
JUDAICA	JUDAICA@TAUNIVM	(Peered) Judaic Studies Newsletter
	JUDAICA@UMINN1	(Peered) JUDAICA Jewish & Near Eastern Studi+
JURIST-L	JURIST-L@HEARN	Juristen informeren juristen over netwerkgeb+
JURIX-L	JURIX-L@HEARN	Discussielijst van stichting juridische kenn+
KAIROS	KAIROS@UTCVM	KAIROS E-Mail Distribution Service
KATALIST	KATALIST@HUEARN	Discussion on librarian systems and database+
KAWAALL	KAWAALL@JPNIMRTU	KAWAZOE LAB. USER
KENTUCKY	KENTUCKY@UKCC	KENTUCKY—KY Civic and Political Discussion
KERMIT-L	KERMIT-L@JPNSUT30	Kermit discussion list
KIDCAFE	KIDCAFE@NDSUVM1	KIDCAFE Youth Dialog
KIDCAFEJ	KIDCAFEJ@NDSUVM1	Japanese Youth Dialog
KIDCAFEP	KIDCAFEP@NDSUVM1	Portuguese Youth Dialog
KIDFORUM	KIDFORUM@NDSUVM1	KIDFORUM KIDLink Coordination
KIDINTRO	KIDINTRO@SJUVM	Project Introducing for Children in Project +
KIDLEADJ	KIDLEADJ@NDSUVM1	Japanese KIDLink Coordination
KIDLEADN	KIDLEADN@NDSUVM1	Scandinavian KIDLink Coordination
KIDLEADP	KIDLEADP@NDSUVM1	Portuguese KIDLink Coordination
KIDLEADR	KIDLEADR@NDSUVM1	KIDLEADR KIDLink Coordination
KIDLEADS	KIDLEADS@NDSUVM1	Spanish KIDLink Coordination
KIDLINK	KIDLINK@NDSUVM1	KIDLINK Project List
KIDLIT-L	KIDLIT-L@BINGVMB	Children and Youth Literature List
KIDNEWS	KIDNEWS@NDSUVM1	KIDLink Newsletter Distribution
KIDPLAN	KIDPLAN@NDSUVM1	KIDPLAN KIDLink Planning
KIDPLAN2	KIDPLAN2@NDSUVM1	KIDPLAN2 Kidlink Work Group
KIDPROJ	KIDPROJ@NDSUVM1	Special KIDLink Projects
KIDS-ACT	KIDS-ACT@NDSUVM1	KIDS-ACT What can I do now?
KIDS-ITA	KIDS-ITA@ICNUCEVM	KIDS-ITA Mailing list
KIDZMAIL	KIDZMAIL@ASUACAD	KIDZMAIL: KIDS EXPLORING ISSUES AND INTERES+
KIMYA-L	KIMYA-L@TRITU	Kimya ve Kimya Muhendisligi Grubu
KITAP-L	KITAP-L@TRITU	Kitaplar Uzerine Tartisma Listesi
KKYTBS-L	KKYTBS-L@MIAMIU	Kappa Kappa Psi / Tau Beta Sigma
KLARINET	KLARINET@VCCSCENT	Klarinet - Clarinettist's Network
KLEIO-L	KLEIO-L@DGOGWDG1	List for Users of Kleio-Software
KNIHOVNA	KNIHOVNA@CSEARN	Diskusni skupina knihoven a automazice kniho+
KNUG	KNUG@KENTVM	The Kent Network Users Group
KOKIKAI	KOKIKAI@PSUVM	Kokikai Aikido List

Network-wide ID	Full address	List title
KONFER-L	KONFER-L@TREARN	Conference Announcements lists
	KONFER-L@UBVM	Conference Announcements lists
KONTROL	KONTROL@TRITU	Otomatik Kontrol Uzerine Tartisma Listesi
KRB-L	KRB-L@MSU	Kenneth R. Beittel Research Seminar Series
KRBGRD-L	KRBGRD-L@MSU	Ken R. Beittel Graduate Student List
KSGOV-L	KSGOV-L@UKANVM	KANSAS GOVERMENT FORUM
KSUOWN-L	KSUOWN-L@KENTVM	Kent State List-Owners Discussion List
KTH-STIFTELSE	KTH-ST@SEARN	Diskussion om KTH som stiftelse
KUAAA-L	KUAAA-L@UKANVM	KU Acadamic Advising Assoc.
KUFUSE-L	KUFUSE-L@UKANVM	KU Focus Users Group
KUHIST-L	KUHIST-L@UKANVM	History at KU
KULHUM-L	KULHUM-L@UKANVM	KU Library Humanities Bibliographers
KUL6000	KUL6000@BLEKUL11	K.U.Leuven RISC/6000 users
KUSEARCH	KUSEARCH@UKANVM	KUSEARCH
KUTUP-L	KUTUP-L@TRMETU	Turkish Libraries Discussion List KUTUP-L
KUVS-L	KUVS-L@DHDURZ1	Mailing List der GI FG 3.3.1 "Kommunikation +
KYACAD-L	KYACAD-L@ULKYVM	Kentucky Academic Computing Discussion
KYCCS	KYCCS@UKCC	Center for Computational Sciences
KYHONORS	KYHONORS@UKCC	Kentucky Honors Students
KYUGIS-L	KYUGIS-L@UKCC	Kentucky Universities Geographic Information+
K12ADMIN	K12ADMIN@SUVM	K–12 Educators Interested in Educational Adm+
K12NAV-L	K12NAV-L@KENTVM	Internet navigation course for K–12 educator+
K12NAV-N	K12NAV-N@KENTVM	Internet navigation course for K–12 educator+
K12STCTE	K12STCTE@BITNIC	Consortium for School Networking (CoSN) Offi+
L-EDUC	L-EDUC@PSUVM	College of Education List
L-HCAP	L-HCAP@NDSUVM1	L-HCAP List
L-OHACAD	L-OHACAD@AKRONVM	OHECC Academic Discussion List
L-VIRUS	L-VIRUS@PSUVM	Virus List
LABMGR	LABMGR@UKCC	Computer Lab Managers
LABOR-L	LABOR-L@YORKVM1	Forum on Labor in the Western Hemisphere
LACTACID	LACTACID@SEARN	Lactic Acid Bacteria Forum
LADIG-L	LADIG-L@UNMVMA	Latin American Database Interest Group
LAFFAC	LAFFAC@PURCCVM	Lafayette CPT Faculty
LAFSTAFF	LAFSTAFF@PURCCVM	All Lafayette CPT Faculty/Clerical/Admin Sta+
LAI571	LAI571@UBVM	LAI571 Class List
LAI672	LAI672@UBVM	LAI672 Class List
LALA-L	LALA-L@UGA	Latin Americanist Librarians' Announcements +

Network-wide ID	Full address	List title
LALINC-L	LALINC-L@LSUVM	LALINC Discussion List
LANGIT	LANGIT@ICINECA	Discussione Centri Linguistici Italiani
LANMAN-L	LANMAN-L@NIHLIST	Microsoft Windows NT Advanced Server and LAN+
LANTRA-L	LANTRA-L@SEARN	Interpreting (and) translation
LANWORKS	LANWORKS@MIAMIU	Digital's PCSA product
LARC-L	LARC-L@UFRJ	Laboratorio Nacional de Redes de Computadores
LARCH-L	LARCH-L@SUVM	Landscape Architecture Electronic Forum
LASER-L	LASER-L@IRLEARN	Laser Printer Information Distribution List
LASMED-L	LASMED-L@TAUNIVM	Laser Medicine
LASPAU-L	LASPAU-L@HARVARDA	"LATIN AMERICAN SCHOLARSHIP PROGRAM OF AMERI+
LASUP-L	LASUP-L@MSU	Latin American Studies Undergraduate Programs
LATAMMUS	LATAMMUS@ASUACAD	Discussion of all aspects and styles of musi+
LATEX-L	LATEX-L@BRUFSC	FORUM LATEX-L - Discussao de assuntos pertin+
	LATEX-L@DHDURZ1	Mailing list for the LaTeX3 project
LATEX-UG	LATEX-UG@SAUPM00	LaTeX Users Group.
LATIN-L	LATIN-L@PSUVM	Latin and NeoLatin discussions
LATIN-TE	LATIN-TE@FRMOP11	Union Latine (Programme avec Terminometre-Re+
LATIN-TF	LATIN-TF@FRMOP11	Terminometro eletronique en francais
LATIN-TP	LATIN-TP@FRMOP11	Terminometro eletronico em portugues
LAWAID	LAWAID@RUTVM1	Law School Finanacial Aid Discussion
LAWSCH-L	LAWSCH-L@AUVM	Law School Discussion List
LCC-L	LCC-L@BRUFMG	Lista para intercambio de informacoes entre +
LCLTEST	LCLTEST@TECHNION	LCLTEST - Local Test List
LCOORD-L	LCOORD-L@CEARN	Listserv Coordination Board
LDBASE-L	LDBASE-L@UKANVM	A Discussion of Listserv Database Search Cap+
LDSSA-L	LDSSA-L@UIUCVMD	LDS Student Association at U. of IL. Newslet+
LEADTCHR	LEADTCHR@PSUVM	Networking lead teachers
LECTU-L	LECTU-L@BRUFSC	(Peered) FORUM LECTU-L - International Semin+
LEPICSP3	LEPICSP3@LEPICS	LEPICS Parallel Processing Project Group
LEXCHAT	LEXCHAT@UKCC	Lexington Kentucky Discussion List
LEXX-L	LEXX-L@IRISHVMA	LEXX editor discussions
LGA-L	LGA-L@UREGINA1	Local Government Administration List
LHU-L	LHU-L@ALBNYDH2	LHU-L Local Health Unit Discussion Forum
LIAISON	LIAISON@BITNIC	(Peered) Network Site Liaisons
	LIAISON@DEARN	(Peered) Network Sites Liaison

Network-wide ID	Full address	List title
	LIAISON@HEARN	(Peered) Network Sites Liaison
	LIAISON@MARIST	(Peered) Network Sites Liaison
	LIAISON@UGA	(Peered) BITNIC LIAISON
LIB-LUIS	LIB-LUIS@UICVM	UIC Library - LUIS
LIBADMIN	LIBADMIN@UMAB	Library Administration and Management
LIBALL	LIBALL@PURCCVM	Purdue Libraries
LIBENV-L	LIBENV-L@YALEVM	Yale Librarian Environmental LIST (LIBENV-L)
LIBERP-L	LIBERP-L@BRUFSC	FORUM - Pedagogia Libertaria
LIBEVENT	LIBEVENT@USCVM	Library Events in Southern California
LIBEX-L	LIBEX-L@MAINE	Exhibits and Academic Libraries Discussion L+
LIBFAC-L	LIBFAC-L@UBVM	UB Libraries Faculty Distribution List
LIBFAP	LIBFAP@PURCCVM	Purdue Libraries
LIBGENL	LIBGENL@PURCCVM	Purdue Libraries
LIBINFO	LIBINFO@HARVARDA	LIBINFO - Harvard Library Information Discus+
LIBMASTR	LIBMASTR@UOTTAWA	Library Master Bibliographic Database
LIBPER-L	LIBPER-L@KSUVM	Library Personnel Issues
LIBPLN-L	LIBPLN-L@UKANVM	University Library Planning Discussion
LIBRARY	LIBRARY@ARIZVM1	Libraries & Librarians
	LIBRARY@UCSFVM	UCSF Library and Center for Knowledge Manage+
LIBREF-L	LIBREF-L@KENTVM	Discussion of Library Reference Issues
LIBRES	LIBRES@KENTVM	Library and Information Science Research Ele+
LIBSCRN	LIBSCRN@PURCCVM	Purdue Libraries
LIBSUP-L	LIBSUP-L@UWAVM	LIBSUP-L UW Cataloging
LIBTECH	LIBTECH@PURCCVM	Purdue Libraries
	LIBTECH@UMSLVMA	Library Technical Support
LICENSE	LICENSE@BITNIC	(Peered) Software Licensing List
	LICENSE@DEARN	(Peered) Software Licensing List
	LICENSE@HEARN	(Peered) Software Licensing List
	LICENSE@MARIST	(Peered) Software Licensing List
	LICENSE@UGA	(Peered) Software Licensing List
LINES-L	LINES-L@NDSUVM1	LifeLines Genealogical System
LINGFAC	LINGFAC@ARIZVM1	Linguistics Faculty, University of Arizona
LINGUA	LINGUA@ARIZVM1	Linguistics at the University of Arizona
LINGUIST	LINGUIST@TAMVM1	The LINGUIST Discussion List
LINHA	LINHA@PTEARN	Extincao da linha EARN
LINK-L	LINK-L@GSUVM1	GSU Wells Computer Center newsletter discuss+
LINKFAIL	LINKFAIL@BITNIC	(Peered) Link failure announcements
	LINKFAIL@CEARN	(Peered) Link failure announcements
	LINKFAIL@DEARN	(Peered) Link failure announcements
	LINKFAIL@HEARN	(Peered) Link failure announcements

Network-wide ID	Full address	List title
	LINKFAIL@MARIST	(Peered) Link failure announcements
	LINKFAIL@TAUNIVM	(Peered) Link failure announcements
	LINKFAIL@UGA	(Peered) Link failure announcements
LIS-L	LIS-L@UIUCVMD	Library and Information Science Student Disc+
LISR-ALL	LISR-ALL@NMSUVM1	ACRL RESEARCH - LIBRARY discussion list
LISRBC1L	LISRBC1L@NMSUVM1	ACRL RESEARH - BIBL. CONTROL LIST1
LISRBC2L	LISRBC2L@NMSUVM1	ACRL RESEARH - BIBL. CONTROL LIST2
LISRCM-L	LISRCM-L@NMSUVM1	ACRL RESEACH - COLLECTION MANAGEMENT
LISRES-L	LISRES-L@NMSUVM1	ACRL RESEARCH - EXPERT SYSTEMS
LISRLE-L	LISRLE-L@NMSUVM1	ACRL RESEARCH - LIBRARY EFFECTIVENESS
LISRLE1L	LISRLE1L@NMSUVM1	ACRL RESEARCH - LIBRARY EFFECTIVENESS 1
LISRLE2L	LISRLE2L@NMSUVM1	ACRL RESEARCH - LIBRARY EFFECTIVENESS 2
LISRSC-L	LISRSC-L@NMSUVM1	ACRL RESEARCH - SCHOLARLY COMMUNICATION
LISRUU-L	LISRUU-L@NMSUVM1	ACRL RESEARCH - UNDERSTANDING THE USER
LISTOLD	LISTOLD@ICNUCEVM	TEST Lista di TEST
LIS566-L	LIS566-L@UBVM	LIS566 Class Discussion List
LIS571A	LIS571A@UBVM	LIS 571A Class List
LIS571B	LIS571B@UBVM	LIS 571B Discussion List
LITAEDU	LITAEDU@WAYNEST1	LITA Education Committee
LITANEWS	LITANEWS@DARTCMS1	Library & Information Technology Assn Newsle+
LITCOL	LITCOL@MSU	LITCOL Mailing List
LITERA-L	LITERA-L@TECMTYVM	Literatura en Ingles y Espa~ol//Literature i+
LITERARY	LITERARY@UCF1VM	Discussions about Literature
LITSCI-L	LITSCI-L@UIUCVMD	Society for Literature and Science - philos.+
LIVE-EYE	LIVE-EYE@YORKVM1	Color and Vision Discussion Forum
LL-L	LL-L@UGA	IBM LoadLeveler Discussion
LLTI	LLTI@DARTCMS1	Language Learning and Technology Internation+
LLU-ALUM	LLU-ALUM@LLUVM	Banner Alumni System Implementation
LM_NET	LM_NET@SUVM	School Library Media & Network Communications
LMAIL-L	LMAIL-L@SEARN	LMail give-and-take forum
LMAIL-M	LMAIL-M@SEARN	LMail maintainers
LMAN-L	LMAN-L@GREARN	Discussion of the LMAN interface of LIST-MAN

Network-wide ID	Full address	List title
LN	LN@FRMOP11	Langage Naturel
LN-FR	LN-FR@FRMOP11	Langage Naturel France
LNGTEACH	LNGTEACH@ARIZVM1	Linguistics Instructors, University of Arizo+
LOCGOV-L	LOCGOV-L@VTVM1	Local Govn Adv Ctee to Virginia's Council on+
LODZ$L	LODZ$L@PLEARN	DISTRIBUTION LIST OF THE USERS LODZ$L
LOG	LOG@UIUCVMD	LOG (log files only)
LOGBANK	LOGBANK@PLEARN	DISTRIBUTION LIST OF LOGIC BANK MEMBERS LOGB+
LOJBAN	LOJBAN@CUVMB	Lojban list
LOLA-L	LOLA-L@LSUVM	LOLA Users
LORE	LORE@NDSUVM1	LORE - Folklore List
LOWNR-TR	LOWNR-TR@TREARN	Turk liste sahipleri listesi (in Turkish)
LPN-L	LPN-L@BROWNVM	Laboratory Primate Newsletter List
LREVSYMP	LREVSYMP@VILLVM	Villanova Law Review Symposium
LSTERN-L	LSTERN-L@FRMOP11	LISTEARN Discussion List
LSTEST2	LSTEST2@NRCVM01	NRC-TRAINING SAMPLE LSTEST2
LSTEST5	LSTEST5@NRCVM01	NRC SAMPLE LSTEST5 - demo05
LSTOWN-L	LSTOWN-L@SEARN	LISTSERV list owners' forum
LSTREV-L	LSTREV-L@UMSLVMA	Listserv Review
LSTSRV-L	LSTSRV-L@SEARN	(Peered) LISTSERV give-and-take forum
	LSTSRV-L@UGA	(Peered) LISTSERV give-and-take forum
LSTSRV-M	LSTSRV-M@SEARN	Revised LISTSERV Maintainers
LWUSERS	LWUSERS@NDSUVM1	LWUsers LANWatch User List
LYH-L	LYH-L@QUCDN	Queen's Chinese Friendship Association
LYOBIB-L	LYOBIB-L@FRCPN11	Information bibliotheque IPN Lyon
L3ANA-L	L3ANA-L@LEPICS	L3 Analysis Group A
L3GRAF-L	L3GRAF-L@LEPICS	L3 Graphics/Interactivity Group
L3OFFS-L	L3OFFS-L@LEPICS	L3 OFFSite Analysis Forum
MAALL	MAALL@WUVMD	Mid-America Association of Law Libraries
MAC-CONF	MAC-CONF@UVMVM	Mac-Conf : Discontinued list, see CSAC-L in+
MAC-L	MAC-L@YALEVM	Macintosh News and Information
MAC-TEL	MAC-TEL@IRLEARN	EARN Macintosh Users List - Extension for Ma+
MAC-USER	MAC-USER@IRLEARN	EARN Macintosh Users List
MACAPPLI	MACAPPLI@DARTCMS1	Usage tips about Macintosh applications
MACASSOC	MACASSOC@UA1VM	Macintosh Association of the Capstone Discus+
MACGIL-L	MACGIL-L@MCGILL1	McGill Macintosh Users Group
MACHRDWR	MACHRDWR@DARTCMS1	Macintosh hardware and related perpherials
MACIRC-L	MACIRC-L@BROWNVM	Macintosh IRC Client Design List
MACLANAD	MACLANAD@UWAVM	MACLANAD FOR MACINTOSH LAN ADMINISTRATORS

Network-wide ID	Full address	List title
MACMAIL	MACMAIL@UTORONTO	MAC Mail Discussion List
MACMULTI	MACMULTI@FCCJ	Macintosh Multimedia Discussion List
MACNET-L	MACNET-L@YALEVM	Macintosh Networking Issues
MACPB-L	MACPB-L@YALEVM	Macintosh Powerbook Issues
MACPROG	MACPROG@WUVMD	Macintosh Programming Discussion List
MACRAO	MACRAO@UMVMA	MACRAO List
MACSYSTM	MACSYSTM@DARTCMS1	Macintosh system software
MACTURK	MACTURK@TREARN	Turkish Macintosh Users Group
MACUO-L	MACUO-L@UOTTAWA	University of Ottawa's Mac Users Discussion +
MAES-L	MAES-L@TAMVM1	Society of Mexican American Engineers and Sc+
MAESTX-L	MAESTX-L@TAMVM1	Society of Mexican American Engineers and Sc+
MAGAZINE	MAGAZINE@RPITSVM	Magazines
MAGIC-L	MAGIC-L@AUVM	Tom Robbins Discussion Group
MAIL-ITA	MAIL-ITA@ICNUCEVM	Electronic Mail in Italy
MAIL-L	MAIL-L@BITNIC	(Peered) Mail Transfer/User Agents
	MAIL-L@DEARN	(Peered) Mail Discussion List
	MAIL-L@HEARN	(Peered) Mail Discussion List
	MAIL-L@IRLEARN	Network Mail Discussion
	MAIL-L@MARIST	(Peered) Mail Discussion List
	MAIL-L@UGA	(Peered) BITNIC MAIL-L List
MAILBOOK	MAILBOOK@DEARN	(Peered) RiceMail discussion list
	MAILBOOK@RICEVM1	RiceMail discussion list
MAKE-L	MAKE-L@UREGINA1	MAKE-L LIST
MALACHI	MALACHI@UMDD	Metro Area Liaison for Academics in Computer+
MALSLC	MALSLC@WUVMD	Mid-America Law School Library Consortium Re+
MAPLE-L	MAPLE-L@IRLEARN	MAPLE-L Discussion on MAPLE software Local +
MAPS-L	MAPS-L@UGA	Maps and Air Photo Systems Forum
MARCHA-L	MARCHA-L@YALEVM	Marcha-L Distribution List
MARINE-L	MARINE-L@UOGUELPH	MARINE STUDIES/SHIPBOARD EDUCATION DISCUSSIO+
MARITGR	MARITGR@UNBVM1	The Maritime Group
MARKET-L	MARKET-L@UCF1VM	For marketing academics and practitioners.
MARKUP-L	MARKUP-L@DGOGWDG1	GLDV-AK fuer TEI-Guideline-Anpassung
MARMAM	MARMAM@UVVM	Marine Mammals Research and Conservation Dis+
MASSCOMM	MASSCOMM@RPITSVM	Mass comm. and new technologies
MAT-DSGN	MAT-DSGN@JPNTUVM0	Forum on Materials Design by Computer
MATCHELP	MATCHELP@HARVARDA	K–12 Matchmaker's Help Discussion List
MATDB-L	MATDB-L@JPNIMRTU	Forum on Materials Database System
MATERI-L	MATERI-L@TAUNIVM	Material List

Network-wide ID	Full address	List title
MATH-L	MATH-L@TECHNION	MATH-L - Mathematica & Matlab administrato+
MATHDEP	MATHDEP@IRLEARN	UCD Maths Department Distribution List
MATHDEPT	MATHDEPT@TECHNION	MATHDEPT - Technion Mathematics Net - Intern+
MATLS-L	MATLS-L@PSUVM	Materials Synthesis
MBA-L	MBA-L@MARIST	MBA Student curriculum discussion
MBU-L	MBU-L@TTUVM1	Megabyte University (Computers & Writing)
MBUS-L	MBUS-L@ALBNYDH2	OGS Mailbus Project
MCCF	MCCF@MCGILL1	McGill Chinese Christian Fellowship Discussi+
MCGLPWR	MCGLPWR@MCGILL1	McGill University Power Outages Distribution+
MCIS	MCIS@MIAMIU	Miami Computing & Information Services
MCISNEWS	MCISNEWS@MIAMIU	MCIS News
MCJRNL	MCJRNL@UBVM	Media Journal Distribution List
MCLIS-L	MCLIS-L@MCGILL1	McGill Library and Information Studies List
MCLR-L	MCLR-L@MSU	MIDWEST CONSORTIUM FOR LATINO RESEARCH
MCLUSTER	MCLUSTER@JPNIMRTU	Forum on Micro Cluster
MCMA-L	MCMA-L@HUMBER	Metro Colleges Math Association List
MCRIT-L	MCRIT-L@HEARN	Multicriteria Discussion List
MCSINFO	MCSINFO@MCGILL1	McGill Computer Store Information.....
MCUG-L	MCUG-L@MIAMIU	Alternative Colorful Postings
MDCETP	MDCETP@UMDD	Maryland Collaborative for Excellence in Tea+
MDE-L	MDE-L@MIZZOU1	Discussion list for Midwest Differential Equ+
MDK-12	MDK-12@UMDD	Discussions with State of Maryland K–12 Comm+
MDPHD-L	MDPHD-L@UBVM	Dual Degree Programs Discussion List
MDS32-L	MDS32-L@INDYCMS	MDS32 Menu Definition System for Vax/VMS by +
MEANING	MEANING@ASUACAD	The meaning of life and other weighty contem+
MEASURES	MEASURES@VTVM1	Reallocation Measures
MECH-L	MECH-L@UTARLVM1	Mechanical Engineering Discussion List
MEDEVLIT	MEDEVLIT@SIUCVMB	MEDEVLIT MEDIEVAL ENGLISH LITERATURE DISCU+
MEDFEM-L	MEDFEM-L@UWAVM	An open discussion forum for medievalist fem+
MEDFORUM	MEDFORUM@ARIZVM1	Med Student Organization/Policy Forum
MEDGAY-L	MEDGAY-L@KSUVM	Gay-Lesbian Medieval Studies Discussion Group
MEDIA-L	MEDIA-L@BINGVMB	Media in Education

Network-wide ID	Full address	List title
MEDIEV-L	MEDIEV-L@UKANVM	Medieval History
MEDIMAGE	MEDIMAGE@POLYVM	Medical Imaging Discussion List
MEDINF-L	MEDINF-L@DEARN	MEDINF-L
MEDLIB-L	MEDLIB-L@UBVM	Medical Libraries Discussion List
MEDNETS	MEDNETS@NDSUVM1	MEDNETS Medical Telecommunications Networks
MEDNEWS	MEDNEWS@ASUACAD	MEDNEWS - Health Info-Com Network Newsletter
MEDPHY-L	MEDPHY-L@AWIIMC12	EFOMP Medical Physics Information Services
MEDSCI-L	MEDSCI-L@BROWNVM	Medieval Science Discussion List
MEDSEA-L	MEDSEA-L@AEARN	Marine Biology of the Adriatic Sea
MEDSTU-L	MEDSTU-L@UNMVMA	Medical student discussion list
MEDSUP-L	MEDSUP-L@YALEVM	Medical Support List
MEDTEXTL	MEDTEXTL@UIUCVMD	Medieval Texts - Philology Codicology and Te+
MEH2O-L	MEH2O-L@TAUNIVM	Middle East Water List
MELLON-L	MELLON-L@YORKVM1	MELLON Fellows Discussion Forum
MEMCOM-L	MEMCOM-L@UKANVM	MEMCOM-L
MEMOIR-L	MEMOIR-L@LATECH	First-Hand Accounts
MEMORIES	MEMORIES@SJUVM	Project Memories for Children in Project Cha+
MEMSNET	MEMSNET@UABDPO	Mineral Economics and Mgmt Society
MENDELE	MENDELE@YALEVM	Mendele: Yiddish Literature and Language
MENOPAUS	MENOPAUS@PSUHMC	Menopause Discussion List
MEREBA-L	MEREBA-L@NERVM	Florida Scholars 500-1750
MERIT	MERIT@ARIZVM1	Network of National Merit Scholars
METALIB	METALIB@JPNTUVM0	Metallibrary
METHODS	METHODS@RPITSVM	Research methodology
	METHODS@UNMVMA	Social Science Research Methods Instructors
METRONET	METRONET@NDSUVM1	Twin Cities Area Libraries and Information C+
METU-L	METU-L@TRMETU	METU-Middle East Technical University Gradua+
MEXICO	MEXICO@ITESMVF1	Noticias de Mexico, en espanol.
MEXICO-L	MEXICO-L@TECMTYVM	Knowing Mexico: people, places, culture.
MEXNEXT	MEXNEXT@TECMTYVM	Lista para Mexico y Am. Latina: NeXT, Aplica+
MFJ-L	MFJ-L@IPFWVM	MFJ International Products Discussion List
MGARDEN	MGARDEN@WSUVM1	Master Gardeners
MGSA-L	MGSA-L@UCBCMSA	MGSA-L - Modern Greek Studies List
MGSFAC	MGSFAC@UBVM	UB Management Science Faculty List
MGSGRAD	MGSGRAD@UBVM	UB Management Science Graduate Students List
MGSNEWS	MGSNEWS@UBVM	UB Management Science Discussion List

Network-wide ID	Full address	List title
MGT-L	MGT-L@NMSUVM1	Management Dept Listserv
MGTCOM-L	MGTCOM-L@NMSUVM1	Listserv for NMSU MGT336 Class
MGT460	MGT460@UNMVMA	MGT460 Class Discussions
MGT510	MGT510@UNMVMA	MGT510 Class Discussions
MHCARE-L	MHCARE-L@MIZZOU1	Managed Health Care
MHSADMIN	MHSADMIN@DEARN	MHS-ADMINS NOTEBOOK
MHSNEWS	MHSNEWS@IBACSATA	MHS News
MI-DEV	MI-DEV@FERRIS	MI-DEV Michigan Economic Development Practio+
MI-EDUC	MI-EDUC@UMAB	Education in Medical Informatics
MIA-L	MIA-L@MCGILL1	McGill Information Access
MIAST-L	MIAST-L@UIUCVMD	Maghrebian Scientific Institute
MIBSRV-L	MIBSRV-L@UA1VM	IBM Antiviral Update List
MICRO-EL	MICRO-EL@TAUNIVM	MICROELECTRONICS IN ISRAEL List
MICRO-L	MICRO-L@RPITSVM	MICRO-L Mailing List (formerly DIST-MDM)
MICS-L	MICS-L@HEARN	MVS Information Control System from Legent C+
MIDAS	MIDAS@ITOCSIVM	MIDAS Progetto ESPRIT
MIDDLE-L	MIDDLE-L@UIUCVMD	Middle level education/early adolescence (10+
MIDEUR-L	MIDEUR-L@UBVM	Discussion of Middle Europe topics
MIDNET-L	MIDNET-L@KSUVM	MIDnet Discussion Group
MIDNET-T	MIDNET-T@KSUVM	MIDnet Technical Discussion
MIDNET-U	MIDNET-U@KSUVM	MIDnet User Services Discussion Group
MIDWPDE	MIDWPDE@UICVM	MIDWest Partial Differential Equations
MILES	MILES@HEARN	Discussion of Jazz trumpeter Miles Davis & h+
MILHST-L	MILHST-L@UKANVM	Military History
MILLEN-L	MILLEN-L@AUVM	Future Projects List
MIMUW-L	MIMUW-L@PLEARN	Affairs of Warsaw U. Fac. of Math., Informat+
MINCON	MINCON@UKCC	Conference on Minority Recruitment and Reten+
MINI-JIR	MINI-JIR@MITVMA	The Mini-Journal of Irreproducible Results
MINITEL	MINITEL@STLAWU	MINITEL is
MINIX-L	MINIX-L@DEARN	(Peered) Minix operating system
	MINIX-L@NDSUVM1	(Peered) Minix operating system
MIS-L	MIS-L@ALBNYDH2	NYS DEPARTMENT OF HEALTH MANAGEMENT INFORMAT+
	MIS-L@SAUPM00	Discussion forum about Management Informatio+
MISC	MISC@TREARN	Miscellaneous Questions, Requests
MISCONF	MISCONF@NDSUVM1	Mid-America Informational Conference
MISG-L	MISG-L@PSUVM	Malaysian Islamic Study Group
MIT-TV-L	MIT-TV-L@MITVMA	MIT Cable Television Schedule
MITAUS	MITAUS@MITVMA	MIT Club of Austin Texas

Network-wide ID	Full address	List title
MITBAY	MITBAY@MITVMA	MIT Bay Area Club E-Mail Network
MITIRLIB	MITIRLIB@MITVMA	MIT Industrial Relations Library
MITSECT	MITSECT@MITVMA	MIT Class Secretaries E-Mail Network
MIT1962	MIT1962@MITVMA	MIT Class of 1962 E-Mail network
MIT1966	MIT1966@MITVMA	MIT Class of 1966 E-Mail network
MIT1972	MIT1972@MITVMA	MIT Class of 1972 E-Mail network
MIT1987	MIT1987@MITVMA	MIT Class of 1987 E-Mail Network
MIT1988	MIT1988@MITVMA	MIT Class of 1988 E-Mail Network
MIT1992	MIT1992@MITVMA	MIT Class of 1992 E-Mail Network
MIZAR	MIZAR@PLEARN	MIZAR USERS FORUM MIZAR
MLA-L	MLA-L@IUBVM	Music Library Association Mailing List
MLABD-L	MLABD-L@IUBVM	MLA Board of Directors Correspondence
MLAETC-L	MLAETC-L@BROWNVM	MLA Emerging Technologies Committee Discussi+
MMARCAMC	MMARCAMC@MSU	MicroMARC:amc Users
MMDNEWS	MMDNEWS@UCSFVM	Material Management Department newsletter
MMEDIA	MMEDIA@ICNUCEVM	MMEDIA Multi Media List
MMEDIA-L	MMEDIA-L@ITESMVF1	Multimedia discussion list
	MMEDIA-L@UOTTAWA	University of Ottawa's Multimedia Discussion+
MMNUG-L	MMNUG-L@MIZZOU1	Mid-Missouri Network Users Group
MMT-L	MMT-L@HEARN	Distribution and mailing list for MMT-member+
MOBILITY	MOBILITY@SJUVM	SJU Mobility Disablties List
MOCAVES	MOCAVES@UMSLVMA	Missouri Caving Discussion
MODAL	MODAL@VTVM1	Modal Analysis
MODBRITS	MODBRITS@KENTVM	Modern British and Irish Literature: 1895-19+
MODELUN	MODELUN@INDYCMS	Model UN Bulletin
MODEMS-L	MODEMS-L@RPITSVM	MODEMS-L Mailing List (formerly DIST-MDM)
MODULA-L	MODULA-L@UALTAVM	Modula-2 (language) discussions
	MODULA-L@UIUCVMD	Modula-2 (language) discussions
MOLBIO-L	MOLBIO-L@MIZZOU1	Molecular Biology Discussion
MON-L	MON-L@BITNIC	(Peered) BITNET Monitoring List
	MON-L@DEARN	(Peered) BITNET Monitoring List
	MON-L@HEARN	(Peered) BITNET Monitoring List
	MON-L@MARIST	(Peered) BITNET Monitoring List
	MON-L@UGA	(Peered) BITNIC MON-L List
MOPOLY-L	MOPOLY-L@MIZZOU1	Discussion of Missouri political issues
MORPHMET	MORPHMET@CUNYVM	Biological Morphometrics Mailing List
MORRIS	MORRIS@SUVM	Morris Dancing Discussion List
MORTAR-L	MORTAR-L@MIZZOU1	Mortar Board, Inc. Discussion Group
MOSSBA	MOSSBA@USACHVM1	"Mossbauer Spectroscopy, Software & Forum"

Network-wide ID	Full address	List title
MOTORDEV	MOTORDEV@UMDD	Human Motor Skill Development List
MOUNT-L	MOUNT-L@TRMETU	Mountaineering Discussion List MOUNT-L
MOUSER-L	MOUSER-L@MIZZOU1	MOREnet User's Discussion List
MPB-L	MPB-L@BRUFPB	Lista para Musica Popular Brasileira
MPG-L	MPG-L@YALEVM	Yale MultiProtocol Gateway Discussion Group
MPSYCH-L	MPSYCH-L@BROWNVM	Society for Mathematical Psychology
MSA-L	MSA-L@PSUVM	Muslim Student Association List
MSLIST-L	MSLIST-L@TECHNION	Multiple Sclerosis Discussion/Support
MSMAIL-L	MSMAIL-L@YALEVM	Microsoft Mail Discussion List
MSP-L	MSP-L@ALBNYVM1	Msg Send Protocol (RFC1312) Discussion
MSPROJ	MSPROJ@MSU	Annenberg/CPB Math & Science Project
MSSC-L	MSSC-L@UBVM	Middle States Steering Committee Discussion +
MSSQL-L	MSSQL-L@DUKEFSB	Microsoft SQL Server Discussion List
MSTREET	MSTREET@UNBVM1	Main$treet - small business simulator LIST
MSUPBND	MSUPBND@UBVM	Math Science Upward Bound Discussion List
MS480	MS480@UMSLVMA	MS480-MNGMNT INFORM SYSTEMS
MTLNET	MTLNET@MCGILL1	"MTLNET" is a forum to discuss freenet issue+
MTN	MTN@IUBVM	MAPPA Trainers Network
MTN-IA	MTN-IA@IUBVM	MAPPA Trainers Network - Iowa
MTN-IL	MTN-IL@IUBVM	MAPPA Trainers Network - Illinois
MTN-IN	MTN-IN@IUBVM	MAPPA Trainers Network - Indiana
MTN-MI	MTN-MI@IUBVM	MAPPA Trainers Network - Michigan
MTN-MN	MTN-MN@IUBVM	MAPPA Trainers Network - Minnesota
MTN-OH	MTN-OH@IUBVM	MAPPA Trainers Network - Ohio
MTN-WI	MTN-WI@IUBVM	MAPPA Trainers Network - Wisconsin
MT3270-L	MT3270-L@BROWNVM	Macintosh TN3270 Beta-test List
MU-SAS	MU-SAS@MIAMIU	Miami University SAS News
MU-UNIX	MU-UNIX@MIAMIU	Miami University UNIX News
MU-VM	MU-VM@MIAMIU	Miami University VM News
MU-VMS	MU-VMS@MIAMIU	Miami University VMS News
MUALERTS	MUALERTS@MIAMIU	Miami University Alerts
MUCO-FR	MUCO-FR@FRMOP11	Cystic Fibrosis list - France (MucoViscidose)
MUDA-L	MUDA-L@GREARN	The MUDA list
MUG	MUG@MARIST	(Peered) MUSIC/SP discussion list
	MUG@UGA	(Peered) Marist MUG List
MULBRI	MULBRI@FRMOP11	MULBRI
MULTI	MULTI@UNMVMA	Multimedia talk group to discuss current mul+
MULTI-L	MULTI-L@BARILVM	Language and Education in Multi-Lingual Sett+
MULTILIS	MULTILIS@ALBNYVM1	MULTILIS users discussion list
MUL3-L	MUL3-L@LEPICS	L3 Muon Reconstruction Software Forum

Network-wide ID	Full address	List title
MUMPS-L	MUMPS-L@UGA	MUMPS List
MUNEWS	MUNEWS@MIAMIU	Miami University News
MUNUG-L	MUNUG-L@MIZZOU1	Missouri University NeXT User's Group
MUS-L	MUS-L@MARIST	(Peered) MUSIC/SP User discussion list
	MUS-L@UGA	(Peered) MUSIC/SP User discussion list
MUSE-L	MUSE-L@HARVARDA	MUSE Software Discussion List
MUSEUM-L	MUSEUM-L@UNMVMA	Museum discussion list
MUSIC-ED	MUSIC-ED@UMINN1	MUSIC-ED Music Education
MUSLIMS	MUSLIMS@ASUACAD	(Peered) The Islamic Information & News Netw+
	MUSLIMS@PSUVM	(Peered) The Islamic Information & News Netw+
MUSPRF-L	MUSPRF-L@CMSUVMB	Music Performance and Pedagogy
MUTEX	MUTEX@CSBRMU11	MUTEX - Masaryk University TEX discussion li+
MVMUA-L	MVMUA-L@MARIST	Metropolitan VM Users Association
MVS-UTIL	MVS-UTIL@MARIST	MVS-UTIL MVS Utilities
MVSCON-L	MVSCON-L@YALEVM	MVS Dataset Conversion List
MVSESA-L	MVSESA-L@NMSUVM1	MVS/ESA List
MVSLPD-L	MVSLPD-L@UNBVM1	MVS LPD and MVS NJE-over-IP Discussion
MVSNAD-F	MVSNAD-F@FRMOP11	Liste des 'Node ADministators' MVS francais
MWL-L	MWL-L@WMVM1	Discussion Group for Marshall-Wythe Law Scho+
MWSUG-L	MWSUG-L@CMSUVMB	Midwest SAS user Group
MWTOPSEM	MWTOPSEM@IRISHVMA	Midwestern Topology Seminar Discussions
MYTHUS-L	MYTHUS-L@BROWNVM	Mythus Fantasy Roleplaying Game List
M204	M204-L@AKRONVM	Model 204 Database Discussion List
NA-L	NA-L@UOTTAWA	National Social Sciences and Humanities FTP +
NABOKV-L	NABOKV-L@UCSBVM	Vladimir Nabokov Forum
NAC	NAC@NDSUVM1	NAC - News Announce Conferences
NACB	NACB@GWUVM	NACB Discussion List
NACC	NACC@INDYCMS	Non-profit Academic Centers Council discussi+
NACUBO	NACUBO@BITNIC	NACUBO College and University Business Offic+
NAD-F	NAD-F@FRMOP11	Liste des 'Node ADministators' francais
NAD-IE	NAD-IE@IRLEARN	EARN Node Administrators - Ireland
NAD-IST	NAD-IST@TRITU	TUVAKA ISTANBUL NAD-lari
NAD-SE	NAD-SE@SEARN	Swedish EARN Node ADministrators - all opera+
NADBR-L	NADBR-L@BRUFMG	Forum de discussao da BITNET no Brasil
NADJES-D	NADJES-D@DEARN	German Node Administrators (NAD) JES2/JES3
NADJ2-D	NADJ2-D@DEARN	German Node Administrators (NAD) JES2

Network-wide ID	Full address	List title
NADJ3-D	NADJ3-D@DEARN	German Node Administrators (NAD) JES3
NADUNX-D	NADUNX-D@DEARN	German Node Administrators (NAD) UNIX
NADVAR-D	NADVAR-D@DEARN	German Node Administrators (NAD) for VARious+
NADVM-D	NADVM-D@DEARN	German Node Administrators (NAD) VM
NADVMS-D	NADVMS-D@DEARN	German Node Administrators (NAD) VMS
NAEB-L	NAEB-L@RITVM	National Association of Educational Buyers
NAF	NAF@NRCVM01	Network Architecture Focus Group
NAFIPS-L	NAFIPS-L@GSUVM1	North American Fuzzy Information Processing +
NAFTA-L	NAFTA-L@VMTECSLP	Impacto del Tratado Trilateral de Libre Come+
NAHIA-L	NAHIA-L@MSU	North American Historians of Islamic Art
NARA-L	NARA-L@NIHLIST	Internal NARA Staff Listserv
NARFE-L	NARFE-L@PCCVM	National Assoc of Retired Federal Employees
NASIRN-L	NASIRN-L@UBVM	North American Service Industries Research N+
NASK	NASK@PLEARN	Discussion list NASK
NASPA1-L	NASPA1-L@MAINE	NASPA Region 1 Distribution List
NASSR-L	NASSR-L@WVNVM	North American Society for the Study of Roma+
NASU-L	NASU-L@MSU	National Association of Sigma Users Conferen+
NAT-EDU	NAT-EDU@INDYCMS	NAT-EDU Educational Issues Pertaining to Ab+
NAT-HLTH	NAT-HLTH@TAMVM1	NAT-HLTH Health Issues of Native Peoples
NAT-LANG	NAT-LANG@TAMVM1	NAT-LANG Languages of Aboriginal Peoples
NAT-1492	NAT-1492@TAMVM1	NATIVE-L Columbus Quincentenary Mailing List
NATCHAT	NATCHAT@TAMVM1	NATCHAT Issues Pertaining to Aboriginal Pe+
NATIVE-L	NATIVE-L@TAMVM1	NATIVE-L Issues Pertaining to Aboriginal Pe+
NATODATA	NATODATA@BLEKUL11	North Atlantic Treaty Organisation (NATO) pu+
NATOSCI	NATOSCI@BLEKUL11	Information on the NATO Science and Environm+
NATURA-L	NATURA-L@UCHCECVM	Ecologia y Proteccion de la Naturaleza en Ch+
NATUSR-L	NATUSR-L@MAINE	NATURAL NEWS Distribution List
NAUSICAA	NAUSICAA@BROWNVM	Hayao Miyazaki Discussion Group
NAVIG-L	NAVIG-L@EMUVM1	Emory hosted Internet Class over the Inter+

Network-wide ID	Full address	List title
NAVIGATE	NAVIGATE@UBVM	Navigating The Internet Workshop List
NB-L	NB-L@DGOGWDG1	Deutsche Nota Bene-Benutzer
NBEA	NBEA-L@AKRONVM	National Business Education Association Disc+
NBS-AEP	NBS-AEP@CUNYVM	NBS-AEP: National Broadcasting Society - Alp+
NCC-L	NCC-L@TAMVM1	National Communication Chairs Discussion List
NCE-AD	NCE-AD@UFRJ	NCE/AD - Forum dos Pesquisadores da Area de +
NCE-RESP	NCE-RESP@MCGILL1	Respiratory Health Network of Centres of Exc+
NCEOA-L	NCEOA-L@NDSUVM1	National Council of Educational Opportunity +
NCIW-L	NCIW-L@YALEVM	Nutrient Cycling Issues - Worldwide at Yale +
NCPRSE-L	NCPRSE-L@ECUVM1	Reform discussion list for Science Education
NCS-L	NCS-L@UMDD	National Crime Survey Discussion
NCURA-L	NCURA-L@UMAB	NCURA
NDCFA-L	NDCFA-L@IRISHVMA	ND Chinese Friends Assoc.
NDDESIGN	NDDESIGN@IRISHVMA	Graphic and Industrial Design Educators
NDINFO-L	NDINFO-L@IRISHVMA	NDInfo Information Topics
NDRG-L	NDRG-L@WVNVM	Nonlinear Dynamics Research Group
NDS-KONT	NDS-KONT@DGOGWDG1	Niedersaechsisches Kontingentierungssystem
NEDBIB-L	NEDBIB-L@HEARN	Op SURFnet aangesloten bibliotheken
NEDER-L	NEDER-L@HEARN	Elektronisch tijdschrift voor de neerlandist+
NENCO-L	NENCO-L@WVNVM	Network of the Northern West Virginia Math &+
NENUG-L	NENUG-L@YALEVM	Northeast Notis Users Group
NEOM-ATC	NEOM-ATC@KENTVM	NE Ohio Major Academic And Research Librarie+
NERA-L	NERA-L@PSUVM	Forum for Northeastern Educational Research +
NERPS	NERPS@HEARN	Net Enhancements for Role Playing Shadowrn
NESUG-L	NESUG-L@UMAB	NorthEast SAS Users Group
NET-L	NET-L@PLTUMK11	STUDENT'S INTERNET/EARN DISCUSSION LIST
NET-ED	NET-ED@UBVM	Internet/BITNET Network Trainers
NET-NATL	NET-NATL@IRISHVMA	Notre Dame rebroadcast of National Networkin+
NET-ND	NET-ND@IRISHVMA	Notre Dame Campus Networking News
NET-TEAM	NET-TEAM@GREARN	Network Team Discussion LIst

Network-wide ID	Full address	List title
NET_LIC	NET_LIC@SUVM	Network Licensing List
NETADV-L	NETADV-L@MCGILL1	Network Advisory Committee
NETCOM-L	NETCOM-L@DEARN	Diskussionsforum fuer Nutzer von Netcomm Swi+
NETCON-L	NETCON-L@UTORONTO	Netnorth Transport Service Technical Contacts
	NETCON-L@VTVM1	NetCon 93 Info list
NETD-FIX	NETD-FIX@MONROE	North Ridge Software Fix/PTF List
NETDIR-L	NETDIR-L@UTORONTO	Netnorth Directors
NETLIB-L	NETLIB-L@YALEVM	Internet Library Connections List
NETMGR-L	NETMGR-L@WUVMD	Net Managers' Discussion List
NETMON-L	NETMON-L@BITNIC	(Peered) Discussion of NETMON
	NETMON-L@DEARN	(Peered) Discussion of NETMON
	NETMON-L@HEARN	(Peered) Discussion of NETMON
	NETMON-L@MARIST	(Peered) Discussion of NETMON
	NETMON-L@UGA	(Peered) Discussion of NETMON
NETMONTH	NETMONTH@MARIST	NetMonth Magazine
NETNWS-L	NETNWS-L@NDSUVM1	NETNWS-L Netnews List
NETNYS-L	NETNYS-L@ALBNYDH2	NETNYS-L NYS Inter-Agency Networking Group
NETONE	NETONE@UKCC	U-B Net_One Discussion Group
NETOP-L	NETOP-L@CSEARN	Informace o selhani pevnych linek v sitich CR
NETPST-L	NETPST-L@UTORONTO	Netnorth Mail Application Technical Contacts
NETREP-L	NETREP-L@UTORONTO	Netnorth Representatives
NETSCOUT	NETSCOUT@ITESMVF1	The BITnet/Internet scouts.
NETSRV-L	NETSRV-L@CEARN	NETSRV-L LIST
NETTRAIN	NETTRAIN@UBVM	Internet/BITNET Network Trainers
NETV-L	NETV-L@MARIST	IBM's NETView discussion list
NETWORKS	NETWORKS@ARIZVM1	UofA Networking Discussion
	NETWORKS@WAYNEST1	WSU Network Managers Discussion List
NET3270	NET3270@MCGILL1	Net3270 Forum
NET93	NET93@MCGILL1	Net93 Conference - General Discussion List
NET93PC	NET93PC@MCGILL1	Net93 Conference - Program Committee
NEUCHILE	NEUCHILE@UCHCECVM	(Peered) CHILE NEUROCIENCIAS
	NEUCHILE@YALEVM	(Peered) CHILE NEUROCIENCIAS
NEURAL-N	NEURAL-N@ANDESCOL	Artificial Neural Networks Discussion
NEURL	NEURL@UICVM	Neuroscience Strategic Planning
NEURO1-L	NEURO1-L@UICVM	Neuroscience Information Forum
NEW-LIST	NEW-LIST@IRLEARN	(Peered) NEW-LIST - New List Announcements
	NEW-LIST@NDSUVM1	(Peered) NEW-LIST - New List Announcements
NEWBOOKS	NEWBOOKS@RPITSVM	New Books in Communication
NEWCROPS	NEWCROPS@PURCCVM	Discussion list for New Crops

Network-wide ID	Full address	List title
NEWEDU-L	NEWEDU-L@USCVM	New Paradigms in Education List
NEWLMS-L	NEWLMS-L@JHUVM	NEWLMS-L New Library System
NEWNAD-X	NEWNAD-X@HARPERVM	New BITNET Node Admins discussions
NEWNIR-L	NEWNIR-L@ITOCSIVM	NEWNIR-L : New NIR services and OPAC Announc+
NEWS-L	NEWS-L@TAIVM1	Texas A&I University Computer News Letter
NEWSLINE	NEWSLINE@RPITSVM	Comserve News Service
NEWS92-L	NEWS92-L@BRUFMG	Grupo da grande midia da ECO 92
NEWTON-L	NEWTON-L@DARTCMS1	Discussion of Apple Newton Family of Equipme+
NEXT-L	NEXT-L@BROWNVM	NeXT Computer List
	NEXT-L@MITVMA	NeXT Computer Info Exchange List
NEXTDE-L	NEXTDE-L@TECMTYVM	Development for NeXT computers. Shareware, Bu+
NEXTSTEP	NEXTSTEP@IRISHVMA	NeXTSTEP 3.0 & NeXTSTEP 486 for Intel
NFDL-L	NFDL-L@SEARN	Nordisk Forum for Datast|ttet L{ring
NHILLEL	NHILLEL@GWUVM	National List for Jewish Students
NIATRN-L	NIATRN-L@BROWNVM	Researchers In Population Aging Computer Con+
NIH-L	NIH-L@WSUVM1	WSU OGRD NIH Redistribution List
NIHDIS-L	NIHDIS-L@JHUVM	NIH Guide Discussion List
NIHGDE-L	NIHGDE-L@JHUVM	NIH Guide Primary Distribution
NIHGUIDE	NIHGUIDE@UWAVM	NIH Guide U of Washington Distribution
NIHONGO	NIHONGO@MITVMA	Japanese Language Discussion List
NIR-IT-L	NIR-IT-L@ITOCSIVM	NIR-IT-L : NIR activities in Italy.
NIR-PMN	NIR-PMN@ITOCSIVM	NIR-PMN : NIR activities in Piemonte (Italy)
NIRI	NIRI@GWUVM	The National Indian Policy Research Institut+
NIS-REP	NIS-REP@ICNUCEVM	GARR-NIS News
NISO-L	NISO-L@NERVM	National Information Standards Organization
NISS	NISS@PLEARN	Discussion list NISS
NKI-BBS	NKI-BBS@NKI	NKI Electronic Bulletin Board
NL-KR	NL-KR@DB0TUI11	Local redistribution of NL-KR@CS.ROCHESTER.E+
NL-KR-L	NL-KR-L@TAUNIVM	Natural Language & Knowledge Representation +
NMBRTHRY	NMBRTHRY@NDSUVM1	Number Theory List
NMG	NMG@NRCVM01	Novell Netware Master's Group
NMP-L	NMP-L@IUBVM	NACO Music Project
NMSUBCS	NMSUBCS@NMSUVM1	LIST FOR BCS MAJORS AT NMSU (rheadric)
NN-TEST	NN-TEST@PURCCVM	Test list for VMNETNEWS postings
NNDIRONT	NNDIRONT@UTORONTO	Netnorth Directors in Ontario (NNDIRONT)
NNEWS	NNEWS@NDSUVM1	Network-News

Network-wide ID	Full address	List title
NNLM-SEA	NNLM-SEA@UMAB	National Network of Libraries of Medicine, S+
NNMVS-L	NNMVS-L@IRISHVMA	MVS/TSO NNTP News Reader (NNMVS) Discussion
NNRP-L	NNRP-L@BROWNVM	Network News Reader Protocol List
NNRVM-L	NNRVM-L@VMTECQRO	Discussion of NNR/VM (News Client Software f+
NNWESTDOWN	DOWN-L@UALTAVM	NetNorth West System Down Announcements.
NNWESTVIP	NNWEST-L@UALTAVM	NetNorth West VIP's
NO-ARG-B	NO-ARG-B@UKACRL	NO-ARG-B (not yet operational)
NO-L-ARG	NO-L-ARG@UKACRL	NO-L-ARG : Nitric Oxide/L-Arginine discussio+
NODAK-L	NODAK-L@NDSUVM1	NODAK-L North Dakota Issues
NODAPPLS	NODAPPLS@JPNSUT30	student's discussion list at Noda campus
NODEINFO	NODEINFO@CUNYVM	Discussion of Node Mail Delivery Problems
NODMGT-L	NODMGT-L@BITNIC	(Peered) Node Management Discussion
	NODMGT-L@DEARN	(Peered) Node Management Discussion
	NODMGT-L@HEARN	(Peered) Node Management Discussion
	NODMGT-L@MARIST	(Peered) Node Management Discussion
	NODMGT-L@UGA	(Peered) Node Management
NOEARN-L	NOEARN-L@NOBIVM	Drift og planlegging av EARN i Norge
NOKOBIT	NOKOBIT@NOBIVM	Norsk konferanse for organisasjoners bruk av+
NOMAD2-L	NOMAD2-L@TAMVM1	The NOMAD2 Discussion List
NOMINATE	NOMINATE@BITNIC	NOMINATE - CREN Nominating Committe
NONLIN-L	NONLIN-L@NIHLIST	Economic Nonlinear Dynamics List
NONLINSS	NONLINSS@EMUVM1	Nonlinear Dynamical Social Systems
NONMEM-L	NONMEM-L@UBVM	NONMEM AND THE USE OF POPULATION PHARACOKINE+
NORDBALT	NORDBALT@SEARN	Networking between Nordic and Baltic countri+
NORDREN	NORDREN@SEARN	Nordic Initiative for a Research and Educati+
NORMAN-L	NORMAN-L@UCSFVM	Discuss Donald Norman's Books and Ideas - De+
NORML-L	NORML-L@TAMVM1	National Organization for the Reform of Mari+
NORTH-FX	NORTH-FX@MONROE	North Ridge Software Fix/PTF List
NORTHBAY	NORTHBAY@UCSFVM	North Bay ITS Commuter Info. Exchange
NOTABENE	NOTABENE@TAUNIVM	Nota Bene List
NOTICIA	NOTICIA@BRLNCC	REVISTA ELETRONICA DO CENTRO LATINO-AMERICAN+
NOTICOL	NOTICOL@ANDESCOL	Noticias de Colombia
NOTIS-AR	NOTIS-AR@UMINN1	NOTIS-AR Archives & Manuscripts Discussion G+

Network-wide ID	Full address	List title
NOTIS-L	NOTIS-L@UICVM	NOTIS discussion group list
NOTISACQ	NOTISACQ@CUVMB	NOTIS Acquisitions Discussion Group
NOTISCJK	NOTISCJK@PUCC	NOTIS CJK Dicussion List
NOTISSER	NOTISSER@UKCC	Notis Serials Discussion List
NOTMUS-L	NOTMUS-L@UBVM	NOTIS MUSIC LIBRARY LIST
NOVELL	NOVELL@SUVM	Novell LAN Interest Group
	NOVELL@UIUCVMD	NOVELL from SUVM (log files only)
NOVOPS	NOVOPS@SUVM	Novell Technology Operations List
NOVTTP	NOVTTP@SUVM	Novell Technology Transfer Partners List
NPY-L	NPY-L@SBCCVM	NPY Discussion list
NRCLAN	NRCLAN@NRCVM01	NRC Novell LAN Administrators Group
NRSOCSCI	NRSOCSCI@UWAVM	NRSOCSCI
NSC92	NSC92@FRORS12	The Networking Services Conference '92
NSC93-L	NSC93-L@FRORS12	The Networking Services Conference '93
NSC94-OC	NSC94-OC@EARNCC	Organizing Committee for NSC'94
NSC94-PC	NSC94-PC@EARNCC	Program Committee for NSC'94
NSNNEWS	NSNNEWS@FINHUTC	Nsn/News
NSP-L	NSP-L@RPITSVM	Noble Savage Philosophers mailing list
NTJ-ISH	NTJ-ISH@JPNYITP	Kakuriron Kondankai Bulletin Board for ISHed+
NTJ-L	NTJ-L@JPNYITP	Kakuriron Kondankai Bulletin Board
NTRNET-L	NTRNET-L@UTKVM1	LIS 590: Electronic Communications & Inform+
NTS-L	NTS-L@DHDURZ1	NTS-L Distribution list
NUCL-THL	NUCL-TH@JPNYITP	Preprint server for Nuclear Theory
NUPES-L	NUPES-L@BRUSPVM	Nucleo de Pesquisa sobre Ensino Superior da +
NURSENET	NURSENET@UTORONTO	NURSENET - A Global Forum for Nursing Issues
NUSLIST	NUSLIST@NUSVM	NUSVM General Discussion Group
NUTCHAIR	NUTCHAIR@OSUVM1	Chairpersons of NUTN's Resource Groups
NUTEPI	NUTEPI@DB0TUI11	Nutritional epidemiology
NUTN-L	NUTN-L@OSUVM1	NUTN Member List
NUTNEXEC	NUTNEXEC@OSUVM1	List for the NUTN Executive Committee
NVAS-L	NVAS-L@CUVMC	NetView Access Services session manager disc+
NV6000-L	NV6000-L@DHDURZ1	NetView/6000-Betreiber Erfahrungsaustausch
NYGDEC-L	NYGDEC-L@ALBNYDH2	NYS Government DEC Users Group
NYJMATH	NYJMATH@ALBNYVM1	New York Journal of Mathematics
NYJMTH-A	NYJMTH-A@ALBNYVM1	Abstracts from the New York Journal of Mathe+
NYSERTEC	NYSERTEC@POLYVM	NYSERNet Technical List
NYSLUX-L	NYSLUX-L@UBVM	NY Consortium for Model European Community S+
NYSO-L	NYSO-L@UBVM	MLA New York State/Ontario Chapter Discussio+

Network-wide ID	Full address	List title
N4H-L	N4H-L@VTVM1	Northern 4H Center
OBJ-REL	OBJ-REL@EMUVM1	Objective Discussion of Religion
OBSERVER	OBSERVER@RPITSVM	COMCONF Observers
OCAS-L	OCAS-L@HUMBER	(Peered) OCAS Users Discussion List
OCASYS-L	OCASYS-L@HUMBER	(Peered) OCAS Systems People's Discussion Li+
OCCSA	OCCSA@MIAMIU	Ohio Collegiate Service Association (OCCSA)
OCULINU	OCULINU@QUCDN	Ontario College and University Libraries — +
ODCNET-L	ODCNET-L@PSUVM	Academy of Management - ODC Section
ODP-L	ODP-L@TAMVM1	Ocean Drilling Program Open Discussion List
OFFCAMP	OFFCAMP@WAYNEST1	Off-Campus Library Services List
OFFICE-L	OFFICE-L@UKANVM	KU OFFICE Users
OH-ADMN	OH-ADMN@AKRONVM	OHECC Administrative Discussion List
OH-DIR	OH-DIR@AKRONVM	OHECC Directors Discussion List
OHA-L	OHA-L@UKCC	Oral History Association Discussion List
OHCOS-L	OHCOS-L@WVNVM	Ohio County (West Virginia) School System Di+
OICISNET	OICISNET@SAIRTI00	NETWORK PROJECT OF OIC MEMBER COUNTRIES
OIS-KUMC	OIS-KUMC@UKANVM	KU Medical Center Computing Services
OISMT-L	OISMT-L@UKANVM	OIS Microcomputer and LAN Team
OISNEWS	OISNEWS@IUBVM	OISNEWS: News For IU International Students +
OLADE-L	OLADE-L@UNALCOL	Organizacion Latinoamericana de Energia
OLONG	OLONG@MIAMIU	Long Term Plan for Anthropology Majors
OLYMPUCK	OLYMPUCK@MAINE	Olympic Ice Hockey discussion list
OMERACT	OMERACT@HEARN	Focused on Outcome Measures in Rheumatoid Ar+
ONACLABS	ONACLABS@HUMBER	Ontario Academic Computer Lab Administrators
ONE-L	ONE-L@CLVM	Organization and the Natural Environment
OOO-L	OOO-L@PLTUMK11	UMK Computer Centre discussion list
OPERATIONS	OPERS-L@AKRONVM	(Peered) Mainframe Operations Discussion List
	OPERS-L@PCCVM	(Peered) Mainframe Operations Discussion List
OPGRP-L	OPGRP-L@VTVM1	Virginia Tech Vax Operations Group/LUG
OPT-PROC	OPT-PROC@TAUNIVM	Optical Computing and Holography List
OPTICS-L	OPTICS-L@TAUNIVM	Optics Newsletter
OR-L	OR-L@UALTAVM	An Informal List for Official Representative+
ORACL-UT	ORACL-UT@UTORONTO	ORACL-UT - University of Toronto ORACLE Issu+
ORACLE-L	ORACLE-L@SBCCVM	ORACLE database mailing list

Network-wide ID	Full address	List title
ORCS-L	ORCS-L@OSUVM1	Operations Research/Computer Science Interfa+
OREBAN-L	OREBAN-L@PSUORVM	Oregon Banner List
ORGCOMM	ORGCOMM@RPITSVM	Communication in organizations
ORTHODOX	ORTHODOX@ARIZVM1	Orthodox Christianity
ORTRAD-L	ORTRAD-L@MIZZOU1	Comparative Oral Traditions Discussion List
OSC	L-OSC@AKRONVM	Ohio SuperComputing Discussion List
OSDSC-L	OSDSC-L@ALBNYVM1	OSDSC-L Discussion of the Organizational Stu+
OSF-BUS	OSF-BUS@UKACRL	"Open Software Foundation, Business and Mark+
OSF-EDUC	OSF-EDUC@UKACRL	"Open Software Foundation, Educational Maili+
OSF-L@IBM-B.R...	OSF-L@UKACRL	Open Systems Foundation Discussion List
OSF-PR	OSF-PR@UKACRL	"Open Software Foundation, Public Relations +
OSF-PRIM	OSF-PRIM@UKACRL	"Open Software Foundation, Primary Contact M+
OSF-TECH	OSF-TECH@UKACRL	"Open Software Foundation, Technical Mailing+
OSFMAN-L@IBM-...	OSFMAN-L@UKACRL	RAL/CCD OSF/1 Project Team
OSTF	OSTF@CUVMC	Operations Security Task Force
OS2-L	OS2-L@HEARN	IBM OS/2 Unedited Discussion List
OS2RZ-L	OS2RZ-L@DOSUNI1	Fragen zu OS2, (lokale Liste, Uni Osnabrueck+
OS2USERS	OS2USERS@MCGILL1	OS/2 Users Discussion List
OT_NATL	OT_NATL@ARIZVM1	Theta Tau National Fraternity
OTS-L	OTS-L@YALEVM	Organization for Tropical Studies at Yale Un+
OUSSS-L	OUSSS-L@UTORONTO	Ontario University Systems Software Support +
OUTAGES	OUTAGES@ASUACAD	ASU Network Outage Notification
OUTDOR-L	OUTDOR-L@ULKYVM	Outdoor Discussion Group
OVERLEG	ONS-L@HEARN	Discussielijst over Nijmeegse Universitaire +
OXD	OXD@MIAMIU	Oxford area conversation
OXDNET	OXDNET@MIAMIU	Oxford area network
OXYGEN-L	OXYGEN-L@MIZZOU1	Oxygen Free Radical Biology and Medicine Dis+
PA_NET	PA_NET@SUVM	Public Administration Network
PACARC-L	PACARC-L@WSUVM1	Pacific Rim Archaeology Interest List
PACE-L	PACE-L@GSUVM1	PACE-L — PACE degree audit system discussio+
PACES-L	PACES-L@UNBVM1	Publications Assoc. of Canadian Engineering +

Network-wide ID	Full address	List title
PACIFIC	PACIFIC@BRUFPB	FORUM FOR AND ABOUT PACIFIC OCEAN AND ISLANDS
PACS-L	PACS-L@UHUPVM1	Public-Access Computer Systems Forum
PACS-P	PACS-P@UHUPVM1	Public-Access Computer Systems Publications
PACV-L	PACV-L@DEARN	PACV-L Discussions list
PAGE-L	PAGE-L@UCF1VM	IBM 3812/3820 Tips and Problems Discussion L+
PAGEIN-L	PAGEIN-L@HEARN	Discussion List for the CEC RARE II PAGEIN p+
PAGEMAKR	PAGEMAKR@INDYCMS	PageMaker for Desktop Publishers
PAIG-L	PAIG-L@MIZZOU1	Discussions of Programmer/Analyst is the Ame+
PAKISTAN	PAKISTAN@ASUACAD	(Peered) The Pakistan News Service
	PAKISTAN@PSUVM	(Peered) The Pakistan News Service
PAN	PAN@GWUVM	Physical Anthropology News List
PANET-L	PANET-L@YALEVM	Medical Education and Health Information Dis+
PANIC	PANIC@UCHCECVM	Avisos de Condiciones de Error en los Server+
PAOK-L	PAOK-L@GREARN	The P.A.O.K. fans discussion List
PARA-DAP	PARA-DAP@IRLEARN	"Parallel Computing / AMT DAP mailing list"
PARADOX	PARADOX@BRUFPB	List for Borland Paradox users
PARAGN-L	PARAGN-L@IUBVM	Intel Paragon List for System Administrators+
PARAGUAY	PARAGUAY@USCVM	Paraguay Discussion List
PARKINSN	PARKINSN@UTORONTO	Parkinson's Disease - Information Exchange N+
PAROUTE	PAROUTE@BITNIC	Pathalias Routing Mailing List
PASCAL-L	PASCAL-L@TREARN	Pascal Language Discussion List
	PASCAL-L@UIUCVMD	Pascal (language) discussions
PATT-SOL	PATT-SOL@JPNYITP	Preprint server for Pattern formation/Cohere+
PAYHR-L	PAYHR-L@OSUVM1	Payroll Benefits and HR in Higher Ed
PBATCH-L	PBATCH-L@RPITSVM	Posix Batch Working Group (P1003.15) Discuss+
PBP-L	PBP-L@ETSUADMN	Play-by-Play Sportscasters list
PC-EVAL	PC-EVAL@IRLEARN	Personal Computer Evaluation
PC-FORUM	PC-FORUM@TAUNIVM	Tel Aviv University PC Forum
PC-L	PC-L@UFRJ	(Peered) Forum IBM PC
PC-REXX	PC-REXX@UCF1VM	Personal REXX Discussion List
PCARAB-L	PCARAB-L@SAKFU00	Discussion Forum on Personal Computers Arabi+
PCBR-L	PCBR-L@UHCCVM	Pacific Business Researchers Forum (PCBR-L)

Network-wide ID	Full address	List title
PCBUILD	PCBUILD@TSCVM	Building PCs
PCDOS-L	PCDOS-L@ALBNYDH2	PCDOS-L HINTS using DOS on the NYS Dept of +
PCIP	PCIP@IRLEARN	TCP/IP Protocol Implementations for PC Discu+
	PCIP@NIHLIST	TCP/IP for PCs Discussion
PCIP-L	PCIP-L@TAMVM1	PCIP
PCORPS-L	PCORPS-L@CMUVM	Discussion List for Intl Volunteers
PCPURDUE	PCPURDUE@PURCCVM	Personal Computers at Purdue
PCSERV-L	PCSERV-L@UALTAVM	Public domain software servers
PCSUPT-L	PCSUPT-L@YALEVM	Forum for the discussion of PC user support +
PCTECH-L	PCTECH-L@TREARN	(Peered) MS-DOS Compatibles Support Group
PCTRAN-L	PCTRAN-L@YALEVM	PCTrans Issues
PC9801	PC9801@JPNSUT30	NEC PC-9800 series discussion list
PDC-L	PDC-L@HEARN	PDC-L: A discussion list for PDC Prolog user+
PDOXWIN	PDOXWIN@DB0TUI11	Paradox fuer Windows
PDPPL	PDPPL@PLWRTU11	Parallel and distributed processing list.
PEIRCE-L	PEIRCE-L@TTUVM1	PEIRCE-L The Philosophy of Charles S. Pei+
PEN	PEN@GWUVM	PEN Discussion List
PEN-L	PEN-L@USCVM	Progressive Economists Network
PENPAL-L	PENPAL-L@UNCCVM	UNCC PENPAL-L Discussion
PER	PER@PLEARN	PROJECT ON ETHNIC RELATIONS PER
PERBAZ	PERBAZ@PLEARN	DATABASE PERBAZ PERBAZ
PERBIB	PERBIB@PLEARN	DATABASE PERBIB PERBIB
PERDB	PERDB@PLEARN	DATABASE PERDB PERDB
PERDIR-L	PERDIR-L@UBVM	Personnel Directors, Associates, Managers - +
PERFORM	PERFORM@IUBVM	PERFORM - Medieval Performing Arts
PERMIAS	PERMIAS@SUVM	Indonesian Student Association
PERMIKA	PERMIKA@MCGILL1	Indonesian Group - Montreal
PEROT	PEROT@MARIST	Discussion of campaigning for President by H+
PERSEUS	PERSEUS@BROWNVM	Perseus Discussion List
PERSIA-L	PERSIA-L@EMUVM1	Jewish Literature and History in the Persian+
PERSON-L	PERSON-L@IRLEARN	Personal and Micro Computer Users Distributi+
PESQ-L	PESQ-L@BRUFSC	Forum Eletronico de Debate e Troca de Inform+
PETS-L	PETS-L@ITESMVF1	Domestic animal care and education list.
PFCOOR	PFCOOR@ICNUCEVM	Progetto Finalizzato Sistemi Informatici e C+
PFERDE	PFERDE@DLRVM	Pferde Diskussionsliste (German Language)

Network-wide ID	Full address	List title
PFSICP-1	PFSICP-1@ICNUCEVM	1 - CALCOLO SCIENTIFICO PER GRANDI SISTEMI
PFSICP-2	PFSICP-2@ICNUCEVM	2 - Processori Dedicati
PFSICP-3	PFSICP-3@ICNUCEVM	3 - Architetture Parallele
PFSICP-4	PFSICP-4@ICNUCEVM	4 - Linguaggi di nuova concezione
PFSICP-5	PFSICP-5@ICNUCEVM	5 - Sistemi evoluti per basi di dati
PFSICP-6	PFSICP-6@ICNUCEVM	6 - Metodi e strumenti per la progettazione +
PFSICP-7	PFSICP-7@ICNUCEVM	7 - Sistemi di supporto al lavoro intellettu+
PFSICP-8	PFSICP-8@ICNUCEVM	8 - Iniziative di supporto per il calc. para+
PFUG-L	PFUG-L@JHUVM	Parallel FORTRAN Users' Group newsletter
PG-BLN	PG-BLN@DB0TUI11	Ankuendigungen der Physikalischen Gesellscha+
PH-BSG	PH-BSG@SEARN	Biological Sciences Group, STACnet-Philippin+
PH-PSG	PH-PSG@SEARN	Physical Sciences Group, STACnet-Philippines
PH-SSG	PH-SSG@SEARN	Social Sciences Group, STACnet-Philippines
PHASE-L	PHASE-L@BROWNVM	Geology 246 (Phase Equilibria)
PHIGS-L	PHIGS-L@SUVM	GRAFIGS Interest Group
PHIKAP-L	PHIKAP-L@PSUVM	Phi Kappa Theta
PHIL-L	PHIL-L@UALTAVM	Dedicated to the Philosophical/Technical Asp+
PHILCOMM	PHILCOMM@RPITSVM	Philosophy of communication
PHILOSED	PHILOSED@SUVM	Students and Teachers Discussing Philosophy +
PHILOSOP	PHILOSOP@YORKVM1	Philosophy Discussion Forum
PHONEDIR	PHONEDIR@NRCVM01	NRC Phone Directory
PHOTO-L	PHOTO-L@BUACCA	Photography Phorum
PHOTOSYN	PHOTOSYN@TAUNIVM	Photosynthesis Researchers' List
PHOTREAC	PHOTREAC@JPNTUVM0	Electro- and Photo-Nuclear Reaction Discussi+
PHYS-L	PHYS-L@UWF	Forum for Physics Teachers
PHYS-STU	PHYS-STU@UWF	Physics Student Discussion List
PHYSHARE	PHYSHARE@PSUVM	Sharing resources for high school physics
PHYSIC-L	PHYSIC-L@TAUNIVM	Physics List
PHYSICS	PHYSICS@MARIST	(Peered) Physics Discussion
	PHYSICS@UBVM	(Peered) Physics Discussion
PHYSJOB	PHYSJOB@WAYNEST1	Physics Jobs Discussion List
PHYSL-TR	PHYSL-TR@TRITU	Physiology Discussion List
PIADAS	PIADAS@PCCVM	Humor Distribution forum - (Portuguese langu+
PILOT5-L	PILOT5-L@FRCPN11	DECnet Phase V Pilot Group
PIPORG-L	PIPORG-L@ALBNYVM1	Pipe Organs and Related Topics

Network-wide ID	Full address	List title
PITSREG2	PITSREG2@UBVM	BITNET2 Mid-Eastern U.S. List
PJAL	PJAL@UTXVM	PJAL - The Progressive Jewish Activism List
PJD-L	PJD-L@TEMPLEVM	Philadelphia Jewish Discussion Group
PJML	PJML@UTXVM	The Progressive Jewish Mailing List
PLA-L	PLA-L@HUMBER	Prior Learning Assesment PLA-L
PLAN-C	PLAN-C@WVNVM	WVNET Planning Committee
PLEARN-L	PLEARN-L@UBVM	Discussion of Polish EARN topics
PLOT-D	PLOT-D@HEARN	Administrative and Plot Discussions for SHAD+
PL1-L	PL1-L@UIUCVMD	PL1 (language) discussions
PM-NEWS	PM-NEWS@UA1VM	Pegasus Mail Announcments
PMAC-L	PMAC-L@PURCCVM	Information exchange for Macintosh administr+
PMAIL	PMAIL@UA1VM	Pegasus Mail Discussion List
PMDF-L	PMDF-L@IRLEARN	PMDF Distribution List
PMN-MGR	PMN-MGR@ITOCSIVM	GARR-PMN NET MANAGEMENT
PNN-L	PNN-L@PUCC	PNN discussion list
PNS-L	PNS-L@PSUVM	Pakistan News Service Discussion
PNWCSC	PNWCSC@UWAVM	PNWCSC Pacific Northwest Canadian Studies Co+
PNWMARKT	PNWMARKT@WSUVM1	Agricultural Market News for WA and OR
PNWMLA-L	PNWMLA-L@UWAVM	PNWMLA-L
POD-L	POD-L@TAMVM1	Professional Organizational Developement dis+
PODIUM-L	PODIUM-L@UKCC	PODIUM-L LIST
POESIA	POESIA@UNALCOL	Poesia Latinoamericana
POET-L	POET-L@GSUVM1	Workshop for Poetry
	POET-L@UNCCVM	POET-L Listserv Discussion
POFP-J	POFP-J@UGA	Public Opinion and Foreign Policy Journal
POFP-L	POFP-L@UGA	Public Opinion and Foreign Policy
POL$CRYS	POL$CRYS@PLEARN	Discussion list for the Polish Crystallograp+
POLAND-L	POLAND-L@UBVM	Discussion of Polish Culture list
POLCAN	POLCAN@YORKVM1	POLCAN Canadian Political Science Discussion+
POLCOMM	POLCOMM@RPITSVM	Study of political communication
POLI-SCI	POLI-SCI@RUTVM1	Political Science Digest
POLICY-L	POLICY-L@BITNIC	(Peered) Discussion about BITNET policies
	POLICY-L@DEARN	(Peered) Discussion about BITNET policies
	POLICY-L@HEARN	(Peered) Discussion about BITNET policies
	POLICY-L@MARIST	(Peered) Discussion about BITNET policies
	POLICY-L@UGA	(Peered) Discussion about BITNET policies

Network-wide ID	Full address	List title
	POLICY-L@UIUCVMD	POLICY-L (log files only)
POLITICA	POLITICA@UFRJ	Discussoes sobre a Politica Brasileira
POLITICS	POLITICS@UCF1VM	Forum for the Discussion of Politics
POLITIKA	POLITIKA@TRITU	Turk Siyaseti Uzerine Tartisma Listesi
POLYMERP	POLYMERP@HEARN	(Peered) Polymer Physics discussions
	POLYMERP@RUTVM1	(Peered) Polymer Physics discussions
PONG-ANN	PONG-ANN@BROWNVM	PONG-ANN Brown Multimedia List
POSAB-L	POSAB-L@VTVM1	Professional Office Staff Advisory Board
POSCIM	POSCIM@DEARN	POSCIM POlitical SCIences Mailinglist
POST-STD	POST-STD@BITNIC	POSTMAST STANDARD List
POSTCARD	POSTCARD@IDBSU	POSTCARD - FOR THOSE INTERESTED IN EXCHANGIN+
POSTMAST	POSTMAST@UICVM	UICVM Postmaster
	POSTMAST@UREGINA1	POSTMASTER INFOMATION.
POTATO-L	POTATO-L@WSUVM1	Potato Research Topics at WSU
POWER-L	POWER-L@NDSUVM1	POWER-L IBM RS/6000 POWER Family
POWER-PC	POWER-PC@UGA	IBM Power PC Discussion
POWERH-L	POWERH-L@UNBVM1	Discussion list for the PowerHouse Software
PPAGES-L	PPAGES-L@PSUVM	PENPAGES project between Penn State and Wisc+
PPEINFO	PPEINFO@CERNVM	No title defined
PPSINF-L	PPSINF-L@UCSFVM	Payroll Technical Information Exchange
PRACTICE	PRACTICE@ARIZVM1	UofA Practice List for Testing LISTSERV
	PRACTICE@ASUACAD	Get your practice in here!
	PRACTICE@UCF1VM	UCF Practice List - junk mail only
PRASAD-L	PRASAD-L@MSU	The Prasad Network
PRECALC	PRECALC@IPFWVM	Precalc/Development Math Curriculum Teaching+
PRENAT-L	PRENAT-L@ALBNYDH2	Perinatal Outcomes
PRETELD	PRETELD@INDYCMS	Learning Disabilities Minors Receiving Grant+
PREVIEW	PREVIEW@RPITSVM	Current research in human communication
PRIE-L	PRIE-L@UCSFVM	Packet Radio Internet Extension List.
PRIMENJI	PRIMENJI@UKCC	UK's Prime-NJI Emulator
PRIPROM	PRIPROM@PURCCVM	CPT Primary Promotions Sub-Comm
PRISON-L	PRISON-L@DARTCMS1	Prison Teacher's Discussion List
PRNCYB-L	PRNCYB-L@BINGVMB	Principia Cybernetica Project
PRO-CITE	PRO-CITE@IUBVM	PRO-CITE The Personal Bibliographic Soft+
PROCUR-B	PROCUR-B@OSUVM1	Commerce Business Daily - Procure
PROFNET	PROFNET@SBCCVM	PROFNET mailing list
PROFS-L	PROFS-L@DEARN	(Peered) PROFS discussion
	PROFS-L@MARIST	(Peered) PROFS discussion
	PROFS-L@RUTVM1	(Peered) PROFS discussion

Network-wide ID	Full address	List title
	PROFS-L@UGA	(Peered) PROFS discussion
	PROFS-L@VTVM1	(Peered) PROFS discussion
PROFSALT	PROFSALT@PCCVM	PROFS Alternatives
PROGDIL	PROGDIL@TREARN	Programlama dillerini tartisma listesi (in T+
PROINFO	PROINFO@IBACSATA	LISTA SERVIZI DI INFORMAZIONI DI PROMOZIONE
PROP-L	PROP-L@UTARLVM1	Programmable Operator List
PROSEN-L	PROSEN-L@UBVM	UB Professional Staff Senate Discussion List
PROSODY	PROSODY@MSU	Prosody Discussion List
PROSTAFF	PROSTAFF@UWAVM	PROSTAFF PROFESSIONAL STAFF
PROTEON	PROTEON@NUSVM	Proteon Mailing List
PROTOCOL	PROTOCOL@UIUCVMD	Computer Protocol Discussion
PROVPL-L	PROVPL-L@BROWNVM	Providence Plan List
PSATC-L	PSATC-L@UBVM	Problem Solving Across the Curriculum Confer+
PSEALAC	PSEALAC@MCGILL1	McGill Phys. Sci. & Eng. Area Library Adviso+
PSI-L	PSI-L@RPITSVM	Parapsychology Discussion Forum
PSIKOLOG	PSIKOLOG@TRITU	Insan Psikolojisini irdeleyen Arastirma ve T+
PSRT-L	PSRT-L@MIZZOU1	Political Science Research and Teaching List
PSTAT-L	PSTAT-L@IRLEARN	Discussion of Stats and Programming relating+
PSUPER-L	PSUPER-L@RPITSVM	Posix Supercomputing (P1003.10) Discussion L+
PSUTOOLS	PSUTOOLS@PSUVM	Discussion of the programs in the PSU-TOOLS F+
PSYART	PSYART@NERVM	Institute for Psychological Study of the Arts
PSYC	PSYC@PUCC	PSYCOLOQUY: Refereed Electronic Journal of P+
PSYCGRAD	PSYCGRAD@UOTTAWA	Psychology Graduate Students Discussion Grou+
PSYCH-L	PSYCH-L@UOTTAWA	UOTTAWA School of Psychology Discussion List
PSYCHE-D	PSYCHE-D@NKI	PSYCHE Discussion Forum
PSYCHE-E	PSYCHE-E@NKI	"Forum for Psyche editors"
PSYCHE-L	PSYCHE-L@NKI	PSYCHE: a journal of research on consciousn+
PSYGRD-J	PSYGRD-J@UOTTAWA	The Psychology Graduate-Student Journal: The+
PSYLAW-L	PSYLAW-L@UTEPA	Psychology and Law, international discussion
PSYSTS-L	PSYSTS-L@MIZZOU1	Psychology Statistics Discussion
PS319-L	PS319-L@MIZZOU1	Discussion of Heath Policy Students

Network-wide ID	Full address	List title
PTAPE-L	PTAPE-L@RPITSVM	Posix Removable Media Study Group
PTFAIL	PTFAIL@PTEARN	National Network (.pt) Link Failures Annouce+
PTM-L	PTM-L@ASUACAD	PTM-L
PTNET	PTNET@PTEARN	Cultura Iberica
PTT-L	PTT-L@TREARN	List for discussion of Turkish issues
PUBMAX-L	PUBMAX-L@QUCDN	Public Management Research Exchange
PUBPOL-L	PUBPOL-L@UMINN1	PUBPOL-L Public Policy Graduate Studies Netw+
PUBRADIO	PUBRADIO@IDBSU	PUBRADIO - PUBLIC RADIO DISCUSSION GROUP
PUBS-L	PUBS-L@UTKVM1	PUBS-L
PUMP-L	PUMP-L@UVVM	PUMP Discussion List
PURSPAN	PURSPAN@PURCCVM	Spanish at Purdue
PURTOPOI	PURTOPOI@PURCCVM	Rhetoric, Language, Prof Writing
PURXTEAM	PURXTEAM@UWAVM	PURXTEAM UW Purchasing Team
PVM-L	PVM-L@JHUVM	Pass-Through Virtual Machines discussion list
PWRUSR-L	PWRUSR-L@MCGILL1	Power Users Group
Q-METHOD	Q-METHOD@KENTVM	Q Methodology Network
Q-XCHG	Q-XCHG@EMUVM1	Quilt and Fabric Exchange
QADATA-L	QADATA-L@ALBNYDH2	New York State Department of Health: Data Q+
QAPA-L	QAPA-L@BROWNVM	Queer Asian Pacific Americans Discussion List
QIFORVM	QIFORVM@UABDPO	qi for VM Discussion Group
QLIB-L	QLIB-L@QUCDN	Queen's University Libraries Information
QM-L	QM-L@YALEVM	QuickMail (CE Software) Users
QNTEVA-L	QNTEVA-L@PSUVM	Quantitative Methods: Theory and Design. A +
QTEST-L	QTEST-L@QUCDN	Sample List
QUAKE-L	QUAKE-L@NDSUVM1	QUAKE-L Discussion List
QUAKER-L	QUAKER-L@UIUCVMD	Quaker concerns re community, consensus proc+
QUAKER-P	QUAKER-P@UIUCVMD	Quaker concerns related to peace and social +
QUALITY	QUALITY@PUCC	TQM in Manufacturing and Service Industries +
QUALNET	QUALNET@SUVM	Wordcrunchers - Microcomputer Analysis of Qu+
QUALRS-L	QUALRS-L@UGA	Qualitative Research for the Human Sciences
QUALRSED	QUALRSED@UNMVMA	Qualitative Research in Education
QUARKXPR	QUARKXPR@IUBVM	The Quark Express List
QUASI-L	QUASI-L@DEARN	QUASI-L Quasiperiodicity — Theory and Appli+
QUEENS-L	QUEENS-L@DEARN	QUEENS-L LIST

Network-wide ID	Full address	List title
QUESTION	QUESTION@IPFWVM	IPFW User Question and Answer List
QUIDNOVI	QUIDNOVI@ASUACAD	QUIDNOVI: WHAT'S NEW— COMPUTER APPLICATIONS+
QUILTNET	QUILTNET@EMUVM1	Quilting
R-CALDAS	R-CALDAS@ANDESCOL	Hablemos sobre la Red Caldas
RAC-L	RAC-L@BRUFSC	RAC-L - Rede de Apoio Computacional - CTC-CFM
RACF-L	RACF-L@UGA	RACF Discussion List
RADCH-L	RADCH-L@FRCPN11	liste de distribution pour les RADIOCHIMISTEs
RADIS-L	RADIS-L@UWAVM	RADIS-L
RADSIG	RADSIG@UWAVM	Radiology Special Interest Group
RAILROAD	RAILROAD@CUNYVM	The Railroad List
RAL-YMP	RAL-YMP@UKACRL	"Discussion list for the RAL-YMP."
RALLY-L	RALLY-L@GUVM	The Road Rallyists' Worldwide Discussion/New+
RAMIS-L	RAMIS-L@CFRVM	RAMIS - 4GL Discussion List
RANDOM	RANDOM@IBACSATA	RANDOM meeting group
RARE-MME	RARE-MME@IBACSATA	RARE Working Group 1 Multi Media Environment
RARE-WG1	RARE-WG1@IBACSATA	RARE Working Group 1
RARE-WG8	RARE-WG8@HEARN	RARE Working Group 8
RATION-L	RATION-L@TAUNIVM	Hebrew University Center for Rationality
RBM-L	RBM-L@YALEVM	RBM test list
RBMI	RBMI@FRORS13	Groupe de Recherche en Biologie Moleculaire +
RC-LIST	RC-LIST@UCF1VM	Reevaluation Co-counseling discussion list
RCLIB-L	RCLIB-L@KENTVM	Kent State University Regional Campus Librar+
RCP-L	RCP-L@BRUFSC	(Peered) FORUM RCP-L - Rede Catarinense de P+
RCUG	RCUG@IRLEARN	Real COKE Users Group
RDBMS-L	RDBMS-L@YALEVM	Relational Database Management System Resear+
RDM-L	RDM-L@UVVM	RDM Discussion List
RE-FORUM	RE-FORUM@UTARLVM1	Real Estate Forum
REACH	REACH@UCSBVM	Research and Educational Applications of Com+
REACTIVE	REACTIVE@MCGILL1	List: Short-lived reactive air pollutants
RECYCLE	RECYCLE@UMAB	Recycling in Practice
RED-BUG	RED-BUG@TREARN	Red (TRICKLE) File Server Bug Report Line
RED-DIG	RED-DIG@ANDESCOL	Red Tematica en Disenio Digital
RED-INFO	RED-INFO@UCHCECVM	LIsta de Informaciones y Consultas con respe+
RED-NET	RED-NET@ICINECA	Discussione Research in Education and Didact+

Network-wide ID	Full address	List title
RED-SYS	RED-SYS@TREARN	Red File Server System Performance Discussio+
RED-UG	RED-UG@HEARN	(Peered) Red File Server Users Group on Prov+
	RED-UG@PTEARN	Red Users Group on Provided Software
	RED-UG@TREARN	(Peered) Red Users Group on Provided Software
REDADMIN	REDADMIN@UCHCECVM	Administracion Red
REDAIERI	REDAIERI@RPITSVM	A service of IAMCR/AIERI
REDALC	REDALC@FRMOP11	Reseau Amerique Latine et Caraibes
REDEMG-L	REDEMG-L@BRUFMG	Forum de discussao da Rede Minas
REDINT	REDINT@FRMOP11	Coordination interne projet REDALC
REDSKINS	REDSKINS@MIAMIU	Miami's Redskins debate
REDTEC	REDTEC@UCHCECVM	Administracion Tecnica de la red REUNA.
REDUCE-L	REDUCE-L@DEARN	reduce-forum
REDUL	REDUL@FRMOP11	COORDINACION DEL PROYECTO REDALC
REDULC	REDULC@FRMOP11	Reunion Electronica de Educadores para Usuar+
REED-L	REED-L@UTORONTO	REED-L: Records of Early English Drama Discu+
REGIST-L	REGIST-L@GSUVM1	Registrar Discussion
REGS-L	REGS-L@ALBNYDH2	Title 10 Rules and Regulations
REGSC-L	REGSC-L@WVNVM	Regional Science Information Exchange
REHRED	REHRED@FRMOP11	Reseau telematique Haitien pour la Recherche+
RELATIV1	RELATIV1@UWF	Group 1 - Special Relativity
RELATIV2	RELATIV2@UWF	Group 2 - Special Relativity
RELAY-L	RELAY-L@UCHCECVM	Lista de ayuda del Relay U_Chile
RELAY-TR	RELAY-TR@TREARN	RELAY ile ilgili tartisma...
RELIGCOM	RELIGCOM@UKCC	RELIGCOM —A Discussion forum re: RELigious +
RELUSR-L	RELUSR-L@UALTAVM	(Peered) Relay Users Forum
	RELUSR-L@VTVM1	Relay Users Forum
REL3-L	REL3-L@LEPICS	L3 reconstruction software forum
REMOTE-L	REMOTE-L@SUVM	Discussion of Remote Control Hobbies
RENAIS-L	RENAIS-L@ULKYVM	Early Modern History - Renaissance
RENPAC-L	RENPAC-L@BRLNCC	USUARIOS REMOTOS VIA RENPAC
REPARCHI	REPARCHI@ICNUCEVM	CNUCE Reparto Architetture Hardware e Softwa+
REPRENDO	REPRENDO@UMAB	Reproductive Endocrinology
REPUB-L	REPUB-L@MARIST	Discussion of Republican Politics
REPUBLIC	REPUBLIC@GITVM1	College Republicans
RES-COMP	RES-COMP@NKI	Research Computing Forum
RESADM-L	RESADM-L@ALBNYDH2	Research Administration Discussion Group
RESEARCH	RESEARCH@TEMPLEVM	Research news from Temple University

Network-wide ID	Full address	List title
RESMON-L	RESMON-L@UAFSYSB	VMRESMON Maintainers List
RESPONSE	RESPONSE@NDSUVM1	RESPONSE to KIDLink Questions
REVIEW-L	REVIEW-L@UOTTAWA	The CONTENTS Project Full Text Review List
REVIEWS	REVIEWS@VTVM1	Forum for Hardware & Software Reviews
REXX-L	REXX-L@UIUCVMD	Rexx (language) discussions
REXXCOMP	REXXCOMP@UCF1VM	Rexx Compiler Discussion List
REXXLIST	REXXLIST@DEARN	(Peered) General REXX Discussion List
	REXXLIST@HEARN	(Peered) VM/SP REXX Language Discussion List
	REXX-L@UALTAVM	(Peered) The Rexx Language Discussion List
	REXXLIST@UCF1VM	(Peered) General REXX Language Discussion Li+
	REXXLIST@UGA	(Peered) REXX Programming discussion list
RFERL-L	RFERL-L@UBVM	RFE/RL Research Institute Daily Report
RFMH-BBS	RFMH-BBS@NKI	RFMH Electronic Bulletin Board
RGAUQ-L	RGAUQ-L@MCGILL1	Regroupement de Gestionnaires en Approvision+
RGC-L	RGC-L@GSUVM1	GA Regents' Global Center Info
RHA-L	RHA-L@TAMVM1	Resident Hall Association Discussion List
RHCFRP-L	RHCFRP-L@ALBNYDH2	RHCFRP-L Residential Health Care Facilitie+
RHETAREA	RHETAREA@UMDD	Rhetoric and Composition Discussion
RHETORIC	RHETORIC@RPITSVM	Rhetoric, social movements, persuasion
RIAD	RIAD@USACHVM1	"Red Interamericana De Agricultura y Democr+
RIAD-CA	RIAD-CA@USACHVM1	"RIAD Subregion America Central, Mexico y E+
RIAD-CC	RIAD-CC@USACHVM1	"RIAD Comite de Coodinacion"
RIAD-CS	RIAD-CS@USACHVM1	"RIAD Subregion Cono Sur"
RIAD-PA	RIAD-PA@USACHVM1	"RIAD Subregion Paises Andinos"
RIBO-L	RIBO-L@URIACC	Title German/English discussion group
RICECWIS	RICECWIS@RICEVM1	Rice CWIS Discussion List
RIGHTS-L	RIGHTS-L@AUVM	Rights and Responsibilities List
RINAF-L	RINAF-L@ICNUCEVM	RINAF News
RINAF-PI	RINAF-PI@ICNUCEVM	RINAF-PI RINAF Staff Pisa
RINAF-T	RINAF-T@ICNUCEVM	RINAF Technical News
RIP-EXP	RIP-EXP@BROWNVM	RI.K12.Experiences
RIP-FUND	RIP-FUND@BROWNVM	RI.K12.Providers.Funding
RIP-SS	RIP-SS@BROWNVM	RI.K12.SocialStudies
RIP-STAF	RIP-STAF@BROWNVM	RI.K12.Providers.Staff
RIP-TECH	RIP-TECH@BROWNVM	RI.K12.Providers.Tech
RIRR	RIRR@ICNUCEVM	CNUCE Reparto Infrastrutture di Rete per la +

Network-wide ID	Full address	List title
RIRRPRIV	RIRRPRIV@ICNUCEVM	CNUCE Reparto Infrastrutture di Rete per la +
RISK	RISK@UTXVM	Risk and Insurance Issues
RISKS	RISKS@MARIST	(Peered) Risks List
	RISKS@UBVM	(Peered) Risks List
	RISKS@UGA	(Peered) Risks List
RITIM-L	RITIM-L@URIACC	Telecommunications and Information Marketing
RLGAMSC	RLGAMSC@RUTVM1	RLG Archives, Manuscripts and Special Collec+
RLGART-L	RLGART-L@YALEVM	RLG Art and Architecture
RLGLAW-L	RLGLAW-L@UMINN1	RLGLAW-L RLG Law Library List
RLGPRE-L	RLGPRE-L@YALEVM	RLG PRESERVATION LIST
RLGPSCD	RLGPSCD@BROWNVM	RLG Public Service and Collection Developmen+
RLIN-L	RLIN-L@RUTVM1	RLIN-L, a forum devoted to RLIN issues
RMBL-L	RMBL-L@UMDD	Rocky Mountain Biological Lab's List
RMCLAS	RMCLAS@UNMVMA	Rocky Mountain Council for Latin American St+
RMUSIC-L	RMUSIC-L@GITVM1	"Music Discussion List"
RNA	RNA@UTFSM	Lista de Informacion sobre Redes de Neuronas+
RNPTEC-L	RNPTEC-L@BRLNCC	Forum Tecnico da Rede Nacional de Pesquisa
ROB-L	ROB-L@UMAB	TEST LIST
ROCK	ROCK@TRITU	Rock&Roll Music Discussion List
ROOTS-L	ROOTS-L@NDSUVM1	ROOTS-L Genealogy List
ROUTTAB	ROUTTAB@BITNIC	ROUTTAB Test Sites List
RPCENTER	RPCENTER@PUCC	Rutgers-Princeton Center
RPI-ASME	RPI-ASME@UBVM	RPI's local chapter of American Society of M+
RPIFDM-L	RPIFDM-L@WUVMD	Regional Planetary Image Facility Data Manag+
RPTCRD	RPTCRD@GWUVM	Daily Report Card News Service
RRA-L	RRA-L@KENTVM	Romance Readers Anonymous
RSCS-L	RSCS-L@PUCC	RSCS Discussion List
RSCSMODS	RSCSMODS@POLYVM	The RSCS Modifications List
	RSCSMODS@UGA	The RSCS modifications list
RSI-EAST	RSI-EAST@SJUVM	St. John's University Repetitive Strain Inju+
RSTRAN-L	RSTRAN-L@YALEVM	RSCS Transparent Line Drivers for IBM 7171
RS1-L	RS1-L@NDSUVM1	RS1-L RS/1 List
RUC-C	RUC-C@WVNVM	WVNET Research Users Committee
RUNCOL	RUNCOL@ANDESCOL	Red Universitaria Nacional de Colombia
RUNCOL-D	RUNCOL-D@UNALCOL	Directorio de RunCol (Red Universitaria Colo+

Network-wide ID	Full address	List title
RURALAM	RURALAM@MSU	Rural America Cluster Evaluation
RURALDEV	RURALDEV@KSUVM	Community and Rural Economic Development Int+
RURALUSA	RURALUSA@ERS	Rural US Trends & Conditions Electronic Jour+
RUSAG-L	RUSAG-L@UMDD	Russian Agriculture
RUSHIST	RUSHIST@CSEARN	(Peered) RusHist - Russian History Forum
	RUSHIST@DOSUNI1	(Peered) RusHist - Russian History Forum
	RUSHIST@UMRVMB	(Peered) RusHist - Russian History Forum
RUSSIA	RUSSIA@ARIZVM1	Russia & her neighbors
RUSTEX-L	RUSTEX-L@UBVM	Russian TeX and Cyrillic text processing list
RUUNET-L	RUUNET-L@HEARN	RUUNET-L: Lijst over netwerkgebruik aan de R+
RXIRC-L	RXIRC-L@VMTECQRO	Discussion of rxIRC (Internet Relay Chat cli+
R2B2	R2B2@UBVM	BITNET II REGION 2 INFORMATION LIST
SAB2-L	SAB2-L@BRUFSC	Forum Eletronico para Troca de Informacoes s+
SAC-L	SAC-L@UCSFVM	Staff Advisory Committee List
SAEDUCOM	SAEDUCOM@TRINITY	SAEDUCOM (Trinity University S.A. EDUCOM) di+
SAFETY	SAFETY@UVMVM	Safety
SAG-L	SAG-L@UAFSYSB	Software AG Discussion List
SAGU-L	SAGU-L@UOTTAWA	Student Affairs Groupe d'Usagers
SAIS-L	SAIS-L@UNBVM1	Science Awareness and Promotion Discussion
SAM-L	SAM-L@TEMPLEVM	Sigma Alpha Mu Discussion List
SAMATH	SAMATH@SAKSU00	Discussion forum on Saudi Association for Ma+
SAME	SAME@FRORS13	SAME : Symbolic and Algebraic Manipulation i+
SAMORZ-L	SAMORZ-L@PLTUMK11	List for all Polish student governments
SAMPLE	SAMPLE@BGEARN	LISTEARN Sample List. This is the list's hea+
	SAMPLE@ESOC	LISTEARN Sample List. This is the list's hea+
	SAMPLE@TREARN	LISTEARN Sample List. This is the list's hea+
SANAT-L	SANAT-L@TRITU	Sanat Uzerine Tartisma Listesi
SAO-L	SAO-L@UHCCVM	Student Affairs Officers — Discussion List +
SAPHYSIA	SAPHYSIA@SAKSU00	Discussion forum on Saudi Physics Discussion+
SAS-L	SAS-L@AWIIMC12	(Peered) SAS(r) Discussion
	SAS-L@MARIST	(Peered) SAS(r) Discussion
	SAS-L@SAKAAU03	SAS Package Information and Help disccussion+

Network-wide ID	Full address	List title
	SAS-L@UALTAVM	(Peered) SAS(r) Discussion
	SAS-L@UGA	(Peered) SAS(r) Discussion
	SAS-L@VTVM1	(Peered) SAS(r) Discussion
SASADMIN	SASADMIN@BLEKUL11	SAS gebruikers binnen de administratie van d+
SASJOB-L	SASJOB-L@ALBNYDH2	SAS JOBS-SAS CLASSES/SEMINARS
SASKERN	SASKERN@BLEKUL11	K.U.Leuven SAS kerngroep users mailing list
SASKUL	SASKUL@BLEKUL11	K.U.Leuven SAS users mailing list
SASPAC-L	SASPAC-L@UMSLVMA	SAS Public Access Consortium - SASPAC-L
SASUG	SASUG@MARIST	Marist SAS Users Group
SATEDU-L	SATEDU-L@WCU	Satellite Education List
SATURN	SATURN@HEARN	Sun Ra and his Arkestra
SAVEIT-L	SAVEIT-L@USCVM	'SAVEIT' software discussion list.
SAW-L	SAW-L@UBVM	SAW Discussion List
SBC-EP	SBC-EP@UFRJ	SBC-EP - Forum de ensino e pesquisa da SBC
SBC-GRAF	SBC-GRAF@UFRJ	Comissao Especial de Computacao Grafica da S+
SBC-L	SBC-L@UFRJ	SBC - Forum de Debates dos Socios da SBC
SBDC-L	SBDC-L@VTVM1	Virginia's Small Business Development Centers
SBIEEE-L	SBIEEE-L@SBCCVM	SUNY/Stony Brook IEEE Local Chapter
SBM-L	SBM-L@UFRJ	SBM-L - FORUM DOS ASSOCIADOS DA SOCIEDADE BR+
SBMICR-L	SBMICR-L@UFRJ	SBMICRO - Forum de Debates em micro eletroni+
SBMICRO	SBMICRO@UFRJ	SBMICRO - Forum de Debates em micro eletroni+
SBN	SBN@IRISHVMA	South Bend area conversation
SBNC-L	SBNC-L@BRUSPVM	Sociedade Brasileira de Neurociencias e Comp+
SBNWX	SBNWX@IRISHVMA	South Bend area weather
SBPC-L	SBPC-L@SBCCVM	SUNY/Stony Brook PC Interest Group
SBPCHOJE	SBPCHOJE@BRLNCC	REVISTA ELETRONICA DA SBPC
SBRHYM-L	SBRHYM-L@SBCCVM	SUNY/Stony Brook Literary Underground
SBSTAT-L	SBSTAT-L@SBCCVM	SUNY/Stony Brook Statistical Software Intere+
SBSUPER	SBSUPER@SBCCVM	Stony Brook Supercomputer Mailing list
SBSWE-L	SBSWE-L@SBCCVM	Society of Women Engineers - Student Section+
SCAHRLDS	SCAHRLDS@PUCC	Discussions of SCA Heraldry
SCAI-L	SCAI-L@UICVM	SCAI Lab Instructor Discussion List
SCAP-L	SCAP-L@UBVM	SUNY Student Computing Access Program List
SCAPCOM	SCAPCOM@UBVM	SUNY Student Access to Computing Technology

Network-wide ID	Full address	List title
SCCE-L	SCCE-L@PLTUMK11	Supercomputing in Central Europe.
SCCIM	SCCIM@SIVM	Scientific Computing & Collections Informati+
SCD333-L	SCD333-L@ICINECA	Students of Prof. Becchi (Venice) and Prof. +
SCERP-L	SCERP-L@NMSUVM1	Max Scott Southwest Center for En+
SCGREEK	SCGREEK@GREARN	Social Culture Greek list.
SCHOLAR	SCHOLAR@CUNYVM	SCHOLAR: Natural Language Processing
SCHOOL-L	SCHOOL-L@IRLEARN	
SCIFAQ-L	SCIFAQ-L@YALEVM	Science FAQ List (SCIFAQ-L)
SCIFRAUD	SCIFRAUD@ALBNYVM1	Discussion of Fraud in Science
SCIMAT-L	SCIMAT-L@UAFSYSB	Arkansas Science and Math Education
SCIMIN	SCIMIN@MCGILL1	Minutes for Faculty of Science
SCIT-BIB	SCIT-BIB@QUCDN	Studies in Communication and Information Tec+
SCIT-L	SCIT-L@QUCDN	Studies in Communication and Information Tec+
SCOBA	SCOBA@UMSLVMA	School of Business Test List
SCODAE	SCODAE@UMAB	Communications Network for Pharmacy-School-B+
SCOUTS-L	SCOUTS-L@TCUBVM	SCOUTS-L Youth Groups Discussion List
SCR-L	SCR-L@MIZZOU1	Study of Cognitive Rehabilitation
SCREEN-L	SCREEN-L@UA1VM	Film and TV Studies Discussion List
SCRIB-L	SCRIB-L@HEARN	SCRIB-L Handwriting Production, Recognition,+
SCRIPT-L	SCRIPT-L@DEARN	(Peered) IBM vs Waterloo SCRIPT discussion g+
	SCRIPT-L@IRLEARN	SCRIPT-L Bulletin Board
	SCRIPT-L@UGA	(Peered) IBM vs Waterloo SCRIPT discussion g+
SCRNWRIT	SCRNWRIT@TAMVM1	Screen Writing Discussion List
SCR97-D	SCR97-D@TAMVM1	The SCRIPT/9700 Distribution List
SCR97-L	SCR97-L@TAMVM1	The SCRIPT/9700 Information List
SCT-INFO	SCT-INFO@POLYVM	The SCT-INFO distribution list
SCT-L	SCT-L@LLUVM	Banner System Implementation
SCTEAC-L	SCTEAC-L@BRUSPVM	Forum de discussao sobre Ensino de Ciencias
SCUBA-D	SCUBA-D@BROWNVM	Scuba Digest Redistribution
SCUBA-L	SCUBA-L@BROWNVM	Scuba diving discussion list
SCUG-G	SCUG-G@DGOGWDG1	Systems Center User Group - German
SCUPNEWS	SCUPNEWS@UCBCMSA	SCUPNEWS - Society for College & University +
SDA-L	SDA-L@LLUVM	Seventh-Day Adventists
SDOMINGO	SDOMINGO@ENLACE	SDOMINGO: Cultura y sociedad de la Republica+
SDS-L	SDS-L@AUVM	SDS List

Network-wide ID	Full address	List title
SDSFORUM	SDSFORUM@TAMVM1	SOFTWARE DEVELOPMENT SYSTEMS FORUM
SEANET-L	SEANET-L@NUSVM	Southeast Asian Studies List
SEARCH-L	SEARCH-L@PURCCVM	CPT Faculty Search & Screen Committee
SEASIA-L	SEASIA-L@MSU	Southeast Asia Discussion List
SEATLA-L	SEATLA-L@EMUVM1	Theological Libraries in the SE US
SEBSEL	SEBSEL@ARIZVM1	NCBES Science, Eng, Business & Science Ed
SECURITY	SECURITY@MARIST	(Peered) SECURITY Digest
	SECURITY@UBVM	(Peered) SECURITY Digest
	SECURITY@UGA	(Peered) SECURITY Digest
SECUSS-L	SECUSS-L@UBVM	SECUSSA Discussion List
SEC82-L	SEC82-L@VTVM1	Alpha Phi Omega Section 82 Discussion List
SEDIT-L	SEDIT-L@UMDD	Scholarly Editing Forum
SEDS-L	SEDS-L@TAMVM1	Interchapter Communications for SEDS
SEDSNEWS	SEDSNEWS@TAMVM1	News about Space from SEDS
SEELANGS	SEELANGS@CUNYVM	SEELangs: Slavic & E. European Languages & l+
SEISM-L	SEISM-L@BINGVMB	Seismological Data Distribution
SEISMD-L	SEISMD-L@BINGVMB	Seismological Discussion
SEMIOS-L	SEMIOS-L@ULKYVM	Visual and Verbal Semiotics
SEMLA-L	SEMLA-L@UGA	Southeast Music Library Association Mailing +
SEMNET	SEMNET@UA1VM	SEMNET Discussion List
SENAT	SENAT@PLEARN	The Senate of Warsaw University discussion l+
SENFONI	SENFONI@TREARN	SENFONI - Haftalik guncel yorum dergisi (i+
SENS@IBM-B.RU...	SENS@UKACRL	Relating Sensory, Instrumental and Consumer +
SERAVES	SERAVES@AUVM	South East Rave List
SERCITES	SERCITES@MITVMA	Citations for Serial Literature
SERCUC	SERCUC@UKACRL	"South-East Region Computer Users' Committee"
SEREXP94	SEREXP94@TECHNION	SEREXP94 - Worshop on SERies EXPansions +
SERIALST	SERIALST@UVMVM	SERIALST: Serials in Libraries Discussion Fo+
SERSO	SERSO@UDESVM	Forum electronique en service social
SERVER-L	SERVER-L@IRLEARN	EARNTECH Servers Discussion
SERVNET	SERVNET@ASUACAD	SERVNET, A SERVICES RESEARCH NETWORK.
SERVRFP	SERVRFP@BITNIC	CREN Server RFP List
SFER-L	SFER-L@UCF1VM	South Florida Environmental Reader
SFLOVERS	SFLOVERS@RUTVM1	SF-Lovers List

Network-wide ID	Full address	List title
	SFLOVERS@UGA	(Peered) SF-Lovers List
SFS-L	SFS-L@SEARN	VM Shared File System (SFS) forum
SG-L	SG-L@JPNYITP	Soryuushiron Group Bulletin Board
SG-L-ISH	SG-L-ISH@JPNYITP	Soryuushiron Group Bulletin Board for ISHed +
SGAN-GA	SGAN-GA@UGA	Univ System of Georgia Student Government As+
SGAN-SAV	SGAN-SAV@VTVM1	SGANet - Student Association of Virginia (SA+
SGANET	SGANET@VTVM1	STUDENT GOVERNMENT GLOBAL MAIL NETWORK
SGANET-A	SGANET-A@VTVM1	Student Government Asian/Australian Mail Net+
SGANET-E	SGANET-E@VTVM1	Student Government European Mail Network
SGANET-N	SGANET-N@VTVM1	Student Government North American Mail Netwo+
SGANET-S	SGANET-S@VTVM1	STUDENT GOVERNMENT LATIN AMERICAN MAIL NETWO+
SGANET-T	SGANET-T@VTVM1	SGANet Technical Discussion Group
SGML-L	SGML-L@DHDURZ1	SGML-L Mailing list
SHADOWRN	SHADOWRN@HEARN	Discussion of the Fantasy game ShadowRun
SHADOWTK	SHADOWTK@HEARN	BBS for ShadowRun. Interactive Fiction for S+
SHAKER	SHAKER@UKCC	Shaker - A forum on the United Society of Be+
SHAKSPER	SHAKSPER@UTORONTO	Shakespeare Electronic Conference
SHAPE-L	SHAPE-L@DB0TUI11	Shape discussion list
SHARE-L	SHARE-L@FRORS12	Spectroscopic Happenings on Actinides and Ra+
SHARP-L	SHARP-L@IUBVM	SHARP-L Society for the History of Authorshi+
SHED	SHED@ETSUADMN	Secondary and Higher Ed discussion from East+
SHOGI-L	SHOGI-L@TECHNION	The Shogi Discussion List
SHOTHC-L	SHOTHC-L@SIVM	History of Computing Issues
SHPEASU	SHPEASU@ASUACAD	Society of Hispanic Professional Engineers
SHS	SHS@UTKVM1	Student Health Services
SI-GROUP	SI-GROUP@HARVARDA	Systems Integration Group Discussion List
SIBERIA	SIBERIA@JPNIMRTU	Discussion list on Siberia
SICHAT-L	SICHAT-L@SIVM	Smithsonian Internal Discussion Group
SIG-TEA	SIG-TEA@UKCC	Special Interest Group- Teaching in Educatio+
SIGMA-NU	SIGMA-NU@HEARN	Sigma Nu fraternity discussion list
SIGMA-XI	SIGMA-XI@NIHLIST	Multidisciplinary, DC area scientists

Network-wide ID	Full address	List title
SIGTEL-L	SIGTEL-L@UNMVMA	SIG/Tel (Special Interest Group/Telecommunic+
SIGTELBD	SIGTELBD@UNMVMA	ISTE Sig/Tel Board of Directors
SIGUCCS	SIGUCCS@UMDD	SIGUCCS Discussion List
SIGUCCSB	SIGUCCSB@UMDD	SIGUCCS Board of Directors Discussion List
SIIN-L	SIIN-L@UNBVM1	UPEI Inst. of Island Studies-Small Islands I+
SIIR-L	SIIR-L@TRITU	Siir Listesi
SILS-L	SILS-L@UBVM	UB School of Information & Library Studies L+
SIMEDU-L	SIMEDU-L@NMSUVM1	Simulation Applications in Business/Education
SIMLIST	SIMLIST@NMSUVM1	Wayne Headrick List for Distribution o+
SIMULA	SIMULA@BITNIC	(Peered) The SIMULA Language List
	SIMULA@DEARN	(Peered) The SIMULA Language List
	SIMULA@HEARN	(Peered) The SIMULA Language List
	SIMULA@MARIST	(Peered) The SIMULA Language List
	SIMULA@UGA	(Peered) The SIMULA Language List
SINAPE-L	SINAPE-L@BRLNCC	SIMPOSIO NACIONAL DE PROBABILIDADE E ESTATIS+
	SINAPE-L@BRUFMG	Forum dos participantes do XI SINAPE
SINEMA-L	SINEMA-L@TRITU	Sinema Uzerine Tartisma Listesi
SINFONIA	SINFONIA@ASUACAD	Phi Mu Alpha Sinfonia discussion group
SIR-L	SIR-L@UREGINA1	SIR/DBMS(r) Software Discussion List
SIREN	SIREN@SEARN	Swedish Initiative for a Research and Educat+
SIRIAC-L	SIRIAC-L@ENLACE	Red del Caribe y Latinoamerica
SITE-LIC	SITE-LIC@UCSFVM	Site Licensing at UC Discussion List.
SJ-CENT	SJ-CENT@UKACRL	"SJ-CENT SuperJanet Central Facilities Maili+
SKATING	SKATING@UMAB	Figure Skating Fans
SKEPTIC	SKEPTIC@JHUVM	SKEPTIC Discussion Group
SLA-PAM	SLA-PAM@UKCC	SLA-PAM Special Libraries Association-Physic+
SLA-TECH	SLA-TECH@UKCC	Discussion group for Technical Services in
SLAJOB	SLAJOB@IUBVM	Special Libraries Association Employment Opp+
SLART-L	SLART-L@CUNYVM	SLA Research and Teaching
SLAVCOOP	SLAVCOOP@CUVMB	SLAVCOOP
SLFHLP-L	SLFHLP-L@UIUCVMD	Discussion of issues related to research int+
SLIS-L	SLIS-L@IUBVM	Indiana University School of Library and Inf+
	SLIS-L@UA1VM	University of Alabama SLIS Discussion List
SLLING-L	SLLING-L@YALEVM	Sign Language Linguistics List
SLOVAK-L	SLOVAK-L@UBVM	Discussion of Slovak issues
SLUISO-L	SLUISO-L@STLAWU	SLU International Students Organization

Network-wide ID	Full address	List title
SM-LADB	SM-LADB@UNMVMA	Latin America Data Base
SMCDCME	SMCDCME@WAYNEST1	Continuing Medical Education Discussion List
SMDL3-L	SMDL3-L@LEPICS	L3 SMD Software discussion list
SMDM-L	SMDM-L@DARTCMS1	Medical Decision Making List
SMKCC-L	SMKCC-L@QUCDN	Subject Matter, Knowledge, Conceptual Change
SMT4H-L	SMT4H-L@VTVM1	Smith Mountain Lake 4H Center
SNAMGT-L	SNAMGT-L@UMRVMB	SNA Network Management Discussion
SNET-L	SNET-L@ARIZVM1	Strategic Network System User Group
SNIFF-L	SNIFF-L@DEARN	SNIFFER-Diskussionsforum
SNPLAN-L	SNPLAN-L@UKANVM	Systems and Programming Microcomputer and LA+
SNSTCP-L	SNSTCP-L@NIHLIST	Users of Interlink SNS/TCPaccess for MVS
SNURSE-L	SNURSE-L@UBVM	Student Nurses's List
SOAP-L	SOAP-L@UHCCVM	Student Opportunities for Academic Publishin+
SOC-REH	SOC-REH@PLEARN	SOC-REH DISCUSSION LIST ON SOCIAL REHABILITA+
SOCCER-L	SOCCER-L@UKCC	Soccer Boosters List
SOCETH-L	SOCETH-L@USCVM	The Social Ethics Discussion List
SOCHIFI	SOCHIFI@USACHVM1	(Peered) Sociedad Chilena de Fisica
SOCHIST	SOCHIST@USCVM	SocHist - Social History List.
SOCINSCT	SOCINSCT@ALBNYVM1	Social Insect Biology Research
SOCNETW2	SOCNETW2@FRORS12	2nd European Conference on Social Networks
SOCO-L	SOCO-L@UBVM	Southern Rock Music List
SOCORG-K	SOCORG-K@UTORONTO	Social Organization of Knowledge Discussion +
SOCWET-L	SOCWET-L@HEARN	SOCWET-L: Discussielijst over netwerkgebruik+
SOCWORK	SOCWORK@UMAB	Social Work Discussion List
SOFT-L	SOFT-L@UCHCECVM	Lista de Software para Microcomputadores y o+
SOFTRB-L	SOFTRB-L@YALEVM	Yale Project Eli Software Review Board
SOFTREVU	SOFTREVU@BROWNVM	Small Computing Systems Software Review and +
SOLARIS	SOLARIS@IRISHVMA	Solaris 2.0 & Solaris for Intel
SOLV-INT	SOLV-INT@JPNYITP	Preprint server for Exactly solvable systems+
SOMACHI	SOMACHI@USACHVM1	(Peered) Sociedad Matematica de Chile
SONIC-VERSE	SONIC-L@MARIST	Sonic Verse Music Magazine
SONNEWS	SONNEWS@MSU	Student Outreach Network
SOREHAND	SOREHAND@UCSFVM	Discussion of Carpal Tunnel Syndrome, Tendon+
SOVHIST	SOVHIST@CSEARN	(Peered) SovHist - Soviet History Forum

Network-wide ID	Full address	List title
	SOVHIST@DOSUNI1	(Peered) SovHist - Soviet History Forum
	SOVHIST@UMRVMB	(Peered) SovHist - Soviet History Forum
SPA-L	SPA-L@TEMPLEVM	Sponsored Projects Admin Discussion
SPACE	SPACE@UBVM	(Peered) SPACE Digest
	SPACE@UGA	(Peered) SPACE Digest
SPACE-IL	SPACE-IL@TAUNIVM	Israeli Space & Remote Sensing List
SPAD	SPAD@FRORS13	SPAD : GROUPE DE DISCUSSION AUTOUR DE SCRATC+
SPC	SPC-L@UMAB	Scientific Program Committee - Med Info 95
SPC-L	SPC-L@GSUVM1	Strategic Planning Committee, Professional D+
SPCPD-L	SPCPD-L@GSUVM1	Strategic Planning Committee, Professional D+
SPEEDE-L	SPEEDE-L@VTVM1	AACRAO electronic transcript discussion
SPHALB-L	SPHALB-L@ALBNYDH2	SUNYA/DOH/AMC SCHOOL OF PUBLIC HEALTH
SPILIB-L	SPILIB-L@SUVM	SPIRES Library Discussion Group
SPIRES-L	SPIRES-L@MARIST	SPIRES Conference List
	SPIRES-L@PUCC	SPIRES Conference List
SPIROC-L	SPIROC-L@WVNVM	Spirochete Research Discussion Group
SPISIS-L	SPISIS-L@BRUSPVM	UNESCO MICROISIS Users Group
SPORTMGT	SPORTMGT@UNBVM1	Sport Management
SPORTPC	SPORTPC@UNBVM1	Use of computers in sport
SPORTPSY	SPORTPSY@TEMPLEVM	Exercise and Sports Psychology
SPRDSHET	SPRDSHET@MCGILL1	"SPRDSHET" is a forum to pose questions, sup+
SPRINT-L	SPRINT-L@NDSUVM1	SPRINT-L Borland Sprint Word Processor Discu+
SPSS-L	SPSS-L@SAKAAU03	KAAU SPSS Package Info + Help List
SPSSX-L	SPSSX-L@MARIST	(Peered) SPSSX(r) Discussion
	SPSSX-L@UALTAVM	(Peered) SPSSX(r) Discussion
	SPSSX-L@UGA	(Peered) SPSSX(r) Discussion
SPUD	SPUD@WSUVM1	Potato Research
SP1-L	SP1-L@UGA	IBM SP1 Discussion
SQL-L	SQL-L@MITVMA	SQL Info Exchange
SQLINFO	SQLINFO@UICVM	Forum for SQL/DS and Related Topics
SRIS-L	SRIS-L@UKANVM	KU Student Records Information System Staff
SRSA-L	SRSA-L@WVNVM	Southern Regional Science Association
SRVREQ-L	SRVREQ-L@INDYCMS	Server-Requester Discussion List
SSCLD0	SSCLD0@UTDALLAS	Discussion of SSC Issues
SSCNEWS	SSCNEWS@UTARLVM1	News from the Superconducting Super Collider
SSREL-L	SSREL-L@UTKVM1	Scientific Study of Religion
SSSSINFO	SSSSINFO@TAMVM1	For dissemination of information between mem+

Network-wide ID	Full address	List title
SSSSTALK	SSSSTALK@TAMVM1	For discussion of issues relating to sexuali+
SSW-L	SSW-L@NIHLIST	Soft-Switch products discussion list
STACNET	STACNET@SEARN	Philippines S&T Advisory Council's Electroni+
STAFF	STAFF@JPNIMRTU	Kawazoe Lab. staffs
STAFF-L	STAFF-L@BRUFMG	Lista para troca de informacoes entre os fun+
	STAFF-L@BRUFU	Lista dos coordenadores BITNET na UFU
STAFFGOV	STAFFGOV@NDSUVM1	Staff Governance in Higher Education
STAMPS	STAMPS@CUNYVM	The Stamps List
STARDATA	STARDATA@HASARA11	Sociaal Wetenschappelijke Databestanden
STARGAME	STARGAME@PCCVM	STARTREK Role Playing game list
STAT-GEO	STAT-GEO@UFRJ	Forum of Quantitative Methods in Geosciences
STAT-L	STAT-L@MCGILL1	Stat-l Discussion List
STATEFAC	STATEFAC@PURCCVM	Statewide Technology Faculty
STATEPOL	STATEPOL@UMAB	Politics in the American States
STATINFO	STATINFO@BLEKUL11	Informatie statistici & data-analysten K.U.L+
STATKERN	STATKERN@BLEKUL11	K.U.Leuven UCS stuurgroep
STATLG-L	STATLG-L@BROWNVM	Baseball (and Lesser Sports) Discussion List
STATNEWS	STATNEWS@SNYCENVM	SUNY OCLC Electronic News
STATSIG	STATSIG@UBVM	UB Statistical Applications Users Special In+
STD-L	STD-L@BITNIC	(Peered) BITNET Standards List
	STD-L@DEARN	(Peered) BITNET Standards List
	STD-L@HEARN	(Peered) BITNET Standards List
	STD-L@MARIST	(Peered) BITNET Standards List
	STD-L@UGA	(Peered) BITNIC STD-L List
STINGCRN	STINGCRN@CERNVM	List STINGCRN
STLHE-L	STLHE-L@UNBVM1	Forum for Teaching & Learning in Higher Educ.
STOPRAPE	STOPRAPE@BROWNVM	Sexual Assault Activist List
STPAUL-L	STPAUL-L@UOTTAWA	St-Paul's User Discussion Group
STLHE-L	STLHE-L@UNBVM1	Forum for Teaching & Learning in Higher
STRATEGY	STRATEGY@BITNIC	CREN Board list for strategy discussion
STREK-D	STREK-D@PCCVM	Star Trek Fan Club (Digests)
STREK-L	STREK-L@PCCVM	Star Trek Fan Club list
STRFLEET	STRFLEET@PCCVM	STARFLEET forum
STROKE-L	STROKE-L@UKCC	Stroke Discussion List
STU-DEV	STU-DEV@WAYNEST1	Student Development Discussion List
STUD-VM	STUD-VM@HUEARN	Student discussion on VM and EARN (Hungarian+
STUDEMP	STUDEMP@ARIZVM1	Issues related to student employment
STUDENTS	STUDENTS@JPNTUVM0	Tohoku Univ Students Forum
STUDIUM	STUDIUM@BLEKUL11	University history discussion list

Network-wide ID	Full address	List title
STUDSRVC	STUDSRVC@PURCCVM	CPT Student Services Commmittee
STUDYUSA	STUDYUSA@TWNMOE10	USA Study Discussion Group (For Chinese Stud+
STUNET-L	STUNET-L@HEARN	Prikbord voor alle studenten op het Nederlan+
STUNT	STUNT@HEARN	STUNT (Samenwerkingsverband Thuiswerkende Un+
STUTT-L	STUTT-L@TEMPLEVM	Stuttering: Research and Clinical Practice
STUXCH-L	STUXCH-L@PSUVM	Exchange list for Department of Architecture+
SU-OCLC	SU-OCLC@SNYCENVM	SUNY OCLC Electronic News
SUEARN-L	SUEARN-L@UBVM	Connecting the USSR to Internet digest
SUGGEST	SUGGEST@TEMPLEVM	Temple's mainframe discussion
SUMINFO	SUMINFO@UNBVM1	Information Summit Discussion
SUN-ITU	SUN-ITU@TRITU	ITU SUN Kullanici Grubu Tartisma Listesi
SUNIBI-L	SUNIBI-L@YALEVM	Focus/Sun Discussion Group
SUNSPOTS	SUNSPOTS@RICEVM1	(Peered) Sun Microsystems Hardware and Softw+
	SUNSPOTS@UBVM	(Peered) Sun Spots Discussion
SUNYCSSC	SUNYCSSC@UBVM	Common SUNY Support Center Discussion list
SUNYEC-L	SUNYEC-L@BINGVMB	SUNY Educational Communications Centers
SUNYGOPH	SUNYGOPH@UBVM	SUNY-Wide Gopher Information System List
SUNYHA-L	SUNYHA-L@BINGVMB	SUNY Housing Affairs Discussion List
SUNYHC-L	SUNYHC-L@BINGVMB	SUNY Health Council Discussion List
SUNYLA-L	SUNYLA-L@BINGVMB	SUNY Library Association Listserv
SUNYSA-L	SUNYSA-L@BINGVMB	SUNY Student Affairs Discussion List
SUNYSPHL	SUNYSPHL@ALBNYDH2	State University of New York School of Publi+
SUP-COND	SUP-COND@TAUNIVM	SuperConductivity List
SUPER	SUPER@BLEKUL11	Super list
SUPER-L	SUPER-L@BRUSPVM	Supercomputadores
	SUPER-L@MCGILL1	Super Computer Users Forum
SUPERESP	SUPERESP@EBCESCA1	Supercomputacion en Espanya
SUPERGUY	SUPERGUY@UCF1VM	UCF SUPERGUY List
SUPERIBM	SUPERIBM@UKCC	Super Computing Issues Forum
SUPEUR	SUPEUR@FRMOP11	Supercomputing in Europe (user's group)
SUPSTEER	SUPSTEER@FRMOP11	Supeur Steering Committee
SUSCON-L	SUSCON-L@CFRVM	SUS SOFTWARE CONSORTIUM
SUSIG	SUSIG@MIAMIU	Teaching in the Mathematical Sciences with S+
SUTPPLS	SUTPPLS@JPNSUT10	student's discussion list
SUTTOOLS	SUTTOOLS@JPNSUT00	SUT tool's discussion list
SWIM-L	SWIM-L@UAFSYSB	Discussion of all aspects of swimming

Network-wide ID	*Full address*	*List title*
SWIP-L	SWIP-L@CFRVM	Society for Women in Philosophy Information +
SWL-L	SWL$L@CUVMB	Short Wave Listener's List
SWL-TR	SWL-TR@TRITU	Short Wave Listening in Turkiye
SWVW	SWVW@CERNVM	No title defined
SW4H-L	SW4H-L@VTVM1	Southwest 4H Center
SYBASE-L	SYBASE-L@UCSBVM	Discussion of SYBASE Products, Platforms & U+
SYNTAX	SYNTAX@UNCCVM	SYNTAX Listserv Discussion
SYNTH-L	SYNTH-L@AUVM	Electronic music "gearhead" list
SYSCI-L	SYSCI-L@UOTTAWA	System Science Discussion List
SYSCOMM	SYSCOMM@UMAB	UMAB Systems and Communications
SYSINFO	SYSINFO@INDYCMS	System Availability Information
SYSPRG-L	SYSPRG-L@TRITU	System Programmers List
SYSTAT-L	SYSTAT-L@UICVM	SYSTAT Discussion List
SYS7-L	SYS7-L@UAFSYSB	Macintosh System 7.0-Specific Discussions
T-ASSIST	T-ASSIST@UNMVMA	University Teaching Assistant Discussion list
T_LEVAL	T_LEVAL@ARIZVM1	CNI Teaching & Learning Working Group.
TACT-L	TACT-L@UTORONTO	TACT-L Discussion - Electronic Forum for TAC+
TAG-L	TAG-L@NDSUVM1	TAG-L Talented and Gifted Education
TAINS-L	TAINS-L@JPNTUVM0	Forum on Tohoku Univ OSI Network
TAIR-L	TAIR-L@UTDALLAS	Texas Association for Institutional Research
TALKBACK	TALKBACK@SJUVM	Talkback: Discussion Group for Children in P+
TAMCHINA	TAMCHINA@TAMVM1	TAMU China Club Discussion List
TAMCNSF	TAMCNSF@TAMVM1	Cornell National Supercomputing Facility Dis+
TAMIL-L	TAMIL-L@DHDURZ1	TAMIL-L Tamil Studies
TAMU-CCN	TAMU-CCN@TAMVM1	TAMU China Club Discussion List
TAPLIST	TAPLIST@UTXVM	The Austin Project
TASM-L	TASM-L@BRUFPB	Borland Turbo Assembler and Debugger List
TAXACOM	TAXACOM@HARVARDA	Biological Systematics Discussion List
TBI-SPRT	TBI-SPRT@SJUVM	St. John's University Traumatic Brain Injury+
TBIRDS	TBIRDS@ARIZVM1	Discussion of Internation Business
TCHED-L	TCHED-L@UREGINA1	WestCan List
TCL-DGST	TCL-DGST@BROWNVM	THINK Class Library Digest List
TCLTK	TCLTK@CERNVM	Tcl/Tk mail mirror of comp.lang.tcl
TCP-IP	TCP-IP@BLIULG11	TCP-IP Redistribution List
	TCP-IP@PUCC	ARPA TCP-IP Discussion Redistribution
TCP-ITA	TCP-ITA@ICNUCEVM	TCP-ITA Utenti Internet italiani
TCPIP-L	TCPIP-L@IRLEARN	TCPIP Information Distribution List
	TCPIP-L@UIUCVMD	TCP-IP Bitnet discussions

Network-wide ID	Full address	List title
TCPLUS-L	TCPLUS-L@UCF1VM	TURBO C++ Discussion group
TCUIS-L	TCUIS-L@TCUBVM	TCUIS-L TCU Information Services Department +
TCUMICRO	TCUMICRO@TCUBVM	TCUMICRO-L TCU Info Service Microcomputer In+
TCUMVS-L	TCUMVS-L@TCUBVM	TCUMVS-L TCU VM/ESA 1.1 and MVS Conversion
TCUSER-L	TCUSER-L@TCUBVM	TCUSER-L TCU User Services Discussion List
TC11-I	TC11-I@HEARN	TC11-I IFIP TC11 Global information
TEACH-L	TEACH-L@UALTAVM	TEACH-L allows teachers to exchange ideas ab+
	TEACH-L@UICVM	Classroom Dynamics
TEACHDAT	TEACHDAT@KENTVM	Description of the list
TEACHEFT	TEACHEFT@WCU	Teaching Effectiveness
TEACHER	TEACHER@UTORONTO	Seminar for Teachers of Computing in the Hum+
TEACHING	TEACHING@MCGILL1	Teaching discussion group
TEACHNET	TEACHNET@KENTVM	Teachers and Student Discussions
TEAM-L	TEAM-L@NMSUVM1	NMSU/Sandia Team learning center
TEC-L	TEC-L@ICNUCEVM	TEC-L News
TECGRP-L	TECGRP-L@PSUVM	Technology and Social Behavior Group
TECH-L	TECH-L@BITNIC	(Peered) TECH-L List
	TECH-L@DEARN	(Peered) TECH-L List
	TECH-L@HEARN	(Peered) TECH-L List
	TECH-L@MARIST	(Peered) TECH-L List
	TECH-L@UGA	(Peered) BITNIC TECH-L List
TECH-LAN	TECH-LAN@TECHNION	TECH-LAN - Technion Technic user group
TECHMATH	TECHMATH@TECHNION	TECHMATH - Technion Mathematics Net
TECHNET	TECHNET@UOTTAWA	Technical Support for Education and Research
TECHNEWS	TECHNEWS@BITNIC	BITNET Technical News List
TECHNO-L	TECHNO-L@MITVMA	Issues In Technology Licensing
TECHTR	TECHTR@ARIZVM1	Technology Transfer
TECHWR-L	TECHWR-L@OSUVM1	Technical Writers List; for all Technical Co+
TECLAC-L	TECLAC-L@TECMTYVM	Comite Tecnico de la Red Latinoamericana y d+
TECMAT-L	TECMAT-L@UBVM	Special Interest Group for Technology in Sec+
TECNOMED	TECNOMED@ICNUCEVM	TECNOMED Database list
TECN11	TECN11@ICNUCEVM	CNR - Comitato 11, Tecnologia e Innovazione +
TECSUN-L	TECSUN-L@MITVMA	SUN Computer Technical Users List
TEI-L	TEI-L@UICVM	TEI-L: Text Encoding Initiative public disc+

Network-wide ID	Full address	List title
TELEX	TELEX@CEARN	TELEX Users List
TELE290	TELE290@GWUVM	Telecom, Competitiveness, and Org. Change (M+
TELUGU	TELUGU@NDSUVM1	World Telugu People Network
TELXCH-L	TELXCH-L@ALBNYDH2	Telecomunications Exchange, NY State
TEMPUS	TEMPUS@HUEARN	Discussion on the TEMPUS
TESL-L	TESL-L@CUNYVM	TESL-L: Teachers of English as a Second Lang+
TESLA	TESLA@NERVM	Technical Standards for Library Automation
TESLCA-L	TESLCA-L@CUNYVM	TESLCA-L: Computer Assisted Language Learnin+
TESLFF-L	TESLFF-L@CUNYVM	TESLFF-L: Fluency First and Whole Language (+
TESLIE-L	TESLIE-L@CUNYVM	TESLIE-L: Intensive English Program (TESL-L +
TESLIT-L	TESLIT-L@CUNYVM	TESLIT-L: Adult Education and Literacy TESL+
TESLJB-L	TESLJB-L@CUNYVM	TESLJB-L: Jobs and Employment Issues (TESL-L+
TESLMW-L	TESLMW-L@CUNYVM	TESLMW-L: Materials Writers Sub-list of TESL+
TEST	TEST@EARNCC	xxx test list xxx
	TEST@FRORS12	Test
	TEST@ICNUCEVM	test lista di test
	TEST@TRITU	(Peered) ListEARN Testing
TEST-L	TEST-L@DB0TUI11	Test
	TEST-L@GREARN	Error test List
	TEST-L@IRISHVMA	Notre Dame's Test List
	TEST-L@IRLEARN	TEST LIST
	TEST1-L@JPNYITP	Just for testing LIST functions
	TEST-L@NIHLIST	Test Listserv List
	TEST-L@NMSUVM1	Test list
	TEST-L@PLTUMK11	This is the list for tests
	TEST-L@UCSFVM	TESTING STUFF...
	TEST-L@UHUPVM1	Public-Access Computer Systems Review Editor+
	TEST-L@UIUCVMD	(Peered) Test list
	TEST-L@UNMVMA	Testing list (UNM use only. Created for inte+
	TEST-L@UOTTAWA	Test List
	TEST-L@WUVMD	For folks learning how to use Listserv
TESTE-L	TESTE-L@BRUFSC	(Peered) FORUM TESTE-L - Lista utilizada par+
	TESTE-L@BRUSPSCE	Exemplo de definicao de lista
	TESTE-L@BRUSPVM	Teste1

Network-wide ID	Full address	List title
TESTER	TESTER@UCBCMSA	Title of sample list
TESTES-L	TESTES-L@BRUSPVM	Rede para testes internos da Consultoria
TESTL	TESTL@PUCC	TEST Listserv list
TESTLIST	TESTLIST@UTXVM	A test list
TESTMAIL	TESTMAIL@INDYCMS	Test network mail
TEST1-L	TEST1-L@GSUVM1	TEST1-L: Wells Computer Center local test li+
TEST2	TEST2@TREARN	Test
TEST2-L	TEST2-L@UCSFVM	TESTING STUFF...
	TEST2-L@UNCCVM	Test LISTSERV List 2
TEUTH-L	TEUTH-L@ITOCSIVM	TEUTH-L:Italian list of topics relevant for +
TEX-D-L	TEX-D-L@DEARN	German TeX Users Communication List
TEX-ED	TEX-ED@UICVM	TeX Education Forum List
TEX-EURO	TEX-EURO@DHDURZ1	TeX-Euro Distribution List for European TeX+
TEX-IBM	TEX-IBM@DHDURZ1	TEX-IBM Distribution list
TEX-L	TEX-L@CLVM	(Peered) The TeXnical topics list
	TEX-L@DEARN	(Peered) The TeXnical topics list
	TEX-L@FRORS13	TeX-L : TeXhax redistribution from ASTON
	TEX-L@HEARN	(Peered) The TeXnical topics list
	TEX-L@MARIST	(Peered) The TeXnical topics list
	TEX-L@UBVM	(Peered) The TeXnical topics list
	TEXHAX@UWAVM	(Peered) TeXhax Distribution List
TEX-NL	TEX-NL@HEARN	TEX-NL
TEXHAX-L	TEXHAX-L@IRLEARN	TeX Information Distribution List
TEXIS-L	TEXIS-L@UTDALLAS	A Texas IS Faculty Research Forum
TEXMAG-L	TEXMAG-L@DEARN	(Peered) TeXMaG list
	TEXMAG-L@HEARN	(Peered) (TeXMaG)
	TEXMAG-L@IRLEARN	(Peered) TeXMaG - Magazine for TeX Enthusias+
	TEXMAG-L@PUCC	(Peered) (TeXMaG)
	TEXMAG-L@UICVM	(Peered) (TeXMaG)
	TEXMAG-L@UTORONTO	(Peered) (TeXMaG)
TEXROX-L	TEXROX-L@TAMVM1	The TeXrox Information List
TEXTILES	TEXTILES@TREARN	Textiles & Clothing Studies Discussion List
TFTD-L	TFTD-L@TAMVM1	THOUGHT FOR THE DAY
TGIS-L	TGIS-L@UBVM	Temporal Topics on GIS List
THEATRE	THEATRE@GREARN	The Theatre Discussion List
THEO-L	THEO-L@FRCPN11	Journal des theoriciens des particules
THEORIST	THEORIST@UTKVM1	Theorist Math Forum
THEORY-A	THEORY-A@NDSUVM1	Theory-A - TheoryNet World-Wide Events
THEORY-B	THEORY-B@NDSUVM1	Theory-B - TheoryNet Ongoing Seminars and Le+
THEORY-C	THEORY-C@NDSUVM1	Theory-C - TheoryNet General Discussions
THEORYNT	THEORYNT@NDSUVM1	TheoryNet List
	THEORYNT@UICVM	Computer Science Theory Net

Network-wide ID	Full address	List title
THETAXI	THETAXI@GITVM1	Discussion list for Theta Xi Fraternity
THINKTNK	THINKTNK@ARIZVM1	NCBES Inter-Organization Communication Net
THPHYSIO	THPHYSIO@FRMOP11	Thermal Physiology
THR10101	THR10101@SBCCVM	Stony Brook THR101-01 Discussion List
THR10102	THR10102@SBCCVM	Stony Brook THR101-02 Discussion List
THYST-L	THYST-L@BROWNVM	Thistle Discussion List
TIBET-L	TIBET-L@IUBVM	Tibet Interest List
TIDBITS	TIDBITS@RICEVM1	TidBITS - a newsletter for Mac users
TIKSUVON	TIKSUVON@TECHNION	Tikshuvon - Technion Computer Center NewsLe+
TIME-L	TIME-L@UFRJ	Forum para debates do Grupo de Eng. Software+
TIMECAP	TIMECAP@SJUVM	Project Time Capsule for Children in Project+
TINCAN-L	TINCAN-L@YALEVM	Macintosh Terminal Emulator Issues
TIP	TIP@PLEARN	LIST OF THEORETICAL COMPUTER SCIENCE TIP
	TIP@TAMVM1	Texas Academy of Mathematics and Science Ema+
TIPSHEET	TIPSHEET@WSUVM1	Computer Help and Tip Exchange
TJLREF-L	TJLREF-L@UMSLVMA	Thomas Jefferson Library Reference List
TLA-L	TLA-L@UTKVM1	Tennessee Library Association and other Tenn+
TLC-OPS	TLC-OPS@ICNUCEVM	CNUCE TLC-OPS Network Control Operators Group
TLCPRV	TLCPRV@ITOCSIVM	Lista di Prova x Uff. Telecom.
TMA-L	TMA-L@PSUVM	The Maintenance Authority user group
TML-L	TML-L@IUBVM	Thesaurus Musicarum Latinarum Database for L+
TN-WP4	TN-WP4@IRLEARN	TN-WP4
TNC	TNC@GITVM1	TECHNOCULTURE discussion list
TNT-L	TNT-L@UMAB	TNT Discussion Group
TN3270-L	TN3270-L@RUTVM1	tn3270 protocol discussion list
TN3270E	TN3270E@NIHLIST	IETF TN3270E Working Group List
TOLKIEN	TOLKIEN@JHUVM	J.R.R. Tolkien's readers
TOM-GILB	TOM-GILB@UCSFVM	Discuss Principles of Software Engineering M+
TOOLB-L	TOOLB-L@UAFSYSB	Asymetrix "Toolbook" product discussions
TOUCHE	TOUCHE@RICEVM1	Rice Fencing Club
TOUCHTON	TOUCHTON@SJSUVM1	Touch-Tone/Voice Response Systems Discussion+
TOUS	TOUS@FRMOP11	Liste du personnel du CNUSC
TOW	TOW@NDSUVM1	The Online World book info
TPRINT-L	TPRINT-L@YALEVM	TPrint Issues
TQM-L	TQM-L@UKANVM	Total Quality Management In Higher Education

Network-wide ID	Full address	List title
TQMEDU-L	TQMEDU-L@HUMBER	TQMEDU - Total Quality Management in Educati+
TQMLIB	TQMLIB@WAYNEST1	Total Quality Management for Libraries
TRACK-D	TRACK-D@AWIIMC12	(Peered) "TRACK Distribution List"
	TRACK-D@MARIST	(Peered) "TRACK Distribution List"
	TRACK-D@PUCC	(Peered) "TRACK Distribution List"
TRACK-L	TRACK-L@AWIIMC12	(Peered) "TRACKers forum"
	TRACK-L@MARIST	(Peered) "TRACKers forum"
	TRACK-L@PUCC	(Peered) "TRACKers forum"
TRAFIC-L	TRAFIC-L@BITNIC	(Peered) Traffic Monitoring List
	TRAFIC-L@DEARN	(Peered) Traffic Monitoring List
	TRAFIC-L@HEARN	(Peered) Traffic Monitoring List
	TRAFIC-L@MARIST	(Peered) Traffic Monitoring List
	TRAFIC-L@UGA	(Peered) Traffic Monitoring List
TRAIN-L	TRAIN-L@BROWNVM	College and University Computer Trainer's Li+
	TRAIN-L@UTMARTNV	UTM Training List
TRAINSCH	TRAINSCH@MIAMIU	MCIS Training
TRAN-AMB	TRAN-AMB@UNALCOL	Transporte y Medio Ambiente en el Contexto L+
TRANS-L	TRANS-L@BITNIC	(Peered) File transfer list
	TRANS-L@DEARN	(Peered) File transfer list
	TRANS-L@HEARN	(Peered) File transfer list
	TRANS-L@MARIST	(Peered) File transfer list
	TRANS-L@UGA	(Peered) BITNIC TRANS-L List
TRANSGEN	TRANSGEN@BROWNVM	TS/TV/TG List
TRANSIT	TRANSIT@GITVM1	Transit Issues Discussion List
TRANSLAT	TRANSLAT@WUVMD	Discussion of theory and practice of transla+
TRANSP-L	TRANSP-L@ASUACAD	Transportation & Traffic Engineering Discuss+
TRANSY-L	TRANSY-L@UKCC	Transylvania University Alumni
TRAOM-L	TRAOM-L@AEARN	TRends in Angular Overlap Model
TRASHCAN	TRASHCAN@UICVM	The Music of the Trash Can Sinatras
TRAVEL-L	TRAVEL-L@TREARN	Tourism Discussions
TRDEV-L	TRDEV-L@PSUVM	Training and Development List
TRECO	TRECO@UFRJ	TREinamento COoperativo
TREPAN-D	TREPAN-D@BROWNVM	Weird News Discussion List
TREPAN-L	TREPAN-L@BROWNVM	Weird News List
TRIO	TRIO@NDSUVM1	TRIO Program Educators
TRKDAY-L	TRKDAY-L@NMSUVM1	NMSU CC — Daily Problem Reporting List
TRKMAC-L	TRKMAC-L@CMUVM	Track results & discussion list of the MAC
TRKMTH-L	TRKMTH-L@NMSUVM1	NMSU CC — Monthly Problem Reporting List
TRKNWS-L	TRKNWS-L@USCVM	Turkish Cultural Program List
TRKWK-L	TRKWK-L@NMSUVM1	NMSU CC — Weekly Problem Reporting List

Network-wide ID	Full address	List title
TRNSPLNT	TRNSPLNT@WUVMD	Organ transplant recipients and anyone else +
TSA-L	TSA-L@MSU	Turkish Studies Association
TSAA-L	TSAA-L@PURCCVM	Turkish Students Assistance Association
TSO-REXX	TSO-REXX@UCF1VM	TSO REXX Discussion List
TSSACT-L	TSSACT-L@UTKVM1	Tunisian Scientific Society Scientific Activ+
TSSNEWS	TSSNEWS@PSUVM	Tunisian Information Office, Washington D.C.
TSTA-L	TSTA-L@UTORONTO	TSTA-l - Toronto School of Theology: Academi+
TSTEVL-L	TSTEVL-L@EMUVM1	Testing and Evaluation Discussion
TSTS-L	TSTS-L@UTORONTO	TSTS-l - Toronto School of Theology - Studen+
TSTU-L	TSTU-L@UTORONTO	TSTU-l - Toronto School of Theology - Comput+
TUBA-L	TUBA-L@VTVM1	Tupa Players Mailing List
TUDOR-L	TUDOR-L@TEMPLEVM	Temple University Dept. of Religion Discussi+
TUG-Q	TUG-Q@TAMVM1	TUG Conference question list
TUGBD-L	TUGBD-L@IRLEARN	TEX User Group Board of Directors
TUGBGT-L	TUGBGT-L@IRLEARN	TeX Users Group Budget Committee
TUGBY-L	TUGBY-L@IRLEARN	TeX User Group Bylaws Committee
TUGCPC-L	TUGCPC-L@IRLEARN	TEX User Group Conference Planning Committee
TUGEL-L	TUGEL-L@IRLEARN	TeX User Group Election Procedures Committee
TUGEX-L	TUGEX-L@IRLEARN	TEX User Group Executive Committee
TUGPRO-L	TUGPRO-L@IRLEARN	TeX Users Group Promotions Committee
TUGSD-L	TUGSD-L@IRLEARN	TeX Users Group Special Directors
TUITREIM	TUITREIM@MITVMA	Industry-Wide Tuition Reimbursement Policies
TUNA	TUNA@UTDALLAS	Texas University Netware Administrator's List
TUNINFO	TUNINFO@PSUVM	Tunisian Information Office, Washington D.C.
TUNISNET	TUNISNET@PSUVM	The Tunisia Network
TURBOC-L	TURBOC-L@TREARN	(Peered) TURBO C Discussion group
	TURBOC-L@UCF1VM	(Peered) TURBO C Discussion group
	TURBOC-L@UTFSM	TURBO C Discussion group, Peer in UTFSM
TURBVIS	TURBVIS@VTVM1	TURBVIS DISCUSSION LIST
TURKCE-L	TURKCE-L@TRITU	Bilim Dili Olarak TURKCE
TURKMATH	TURKMATH@TRMETU	(Peered) Turkish Mathematician's Discussion +
TV-L	TV-L@DB0TUI11	Diskussion zum Thema "Wandel im Umgang mit T+
	TV-L@TREARN	TV Discussions.. ..

Network-wide ID	Full address	List title
TWAIN-L	TWAIN-L@YORKVM1	Mark Twain Forum
TWGMLC-L	TWGMLC-L@IRLEARN	TWGMLC-L TeX Users Group TeXnical Working Gr+
TWGTFD-L	TWGTFD-L@IRLEARN	TeX Users Group TeXnical Working Group on Te+
TWNAD-L	TWNAD-L@TWNMOE10	TWNAD-L Taiwan BITNET NODE administration di+
TWSGIS-L	TWSGIS-L@NDSUVM1	TWSGIS-L TWS GIS Working Group
TWUNIV-L	TWUNIV-L@TWNMOE10	Chinese Scholars and students discussion list
TW2002-L	TW2002-L@FERRIS	TW2002-L Trade Wars 2002 Discussion List
TXBITNET	TXBITNET@UTDALLAS	Texas BITNET issues list
TXCENSUS	TXCENSUS@UTDALLAS	Texas 1990 Census Issues
TXDXN-L	TXDXN-L@UHUPVM1	Texas Documents Information Network
TYPO-L	TYPO-L@IRLEARN	TYPO-L Discussion of Typography, Type and Ty+
T271-L	T271-L@MIZZOU1	Discussion List for T271
T321-L	T321-L@MIZZOU1	Teaching Science in Elementary Schools
T40-L	T40-L@MIZZOU1	Advisory Seminar in Curriculum & Instruction
UACSR-L	CAPDU-L@UALTAVM	Canadian Association of Public Data Users
UADEANS	UADEANS@ARIZVM1	University of Arizona Deans
UAEXT-L	UAEXT-L@UALTAVM	An Informal List for Discussion at UOFA Exte+
UA2PRIME	UA2PRIME@CERNVM	UA2 Collaboration
UB-ADAPT	UB-ADAPT@UBVM	UB Adaptive Computing Discussion List
UBGSEU-L	UBGSEU-L@UBVM	GSEU Updates List
UBLIB-L	UBLIB-L@UBVM	UB Libraries Distribution List
UBMUT-L	UBMUT-L@UBVM	UB Music Theory List
UBNACUBO	UBNACUBO@UBVM	UB N. A. C. U. B. O. List
UBNMA-L	UBNMA-L@DEARN	UBNMA-L (Uni Bonn Mathematik - Liste)
UBOWN-L	UBOWN-L@UBVM	UB Lists Owners List
UCEA-L	UCEA-L@PSUVM	University Council for Educational Administr+
UCF-ED-L	UCF-ED-L@UCF1VM	University of Central Florida Educator's List
UCGIA-L	UCGIA-L@UBVM	Univ Consort for Geo Info & Analysis List
UCONF-L	UCONF-L@WVNVM	WVNET User Conference List
UCP-L	UCP-L@UBVM	University Computing Project Mailing List
UCRC-L	UCRC-L@VTVM1	University Communications Resources Committee
UCSFANGR	UCSFANGR@UCSFVM	UCSF Department of Anesthesia Grand Rounds C+
UCSFNEWS	UCSFNEWS@UCSFVM	Information from the UCSF News and Public In+

Network-wide ID	Full address	List title
UCSGCORR	UCSGCORR@UKACRL	Univ. S/W Group Committee Correspondents
UCSGMEMB	UCSGMEMB@UKACRL	University Software Group Committee - Members
UCSMON	UCSMON@IUBVM	UCS MONITOR - Computing News From Indiana Un+
UD-L	UD-L@URIACC	Ultimate Dungeon List
UDD-L	UDD-L@CEARN	LISTSERV User Directory Database discussion
UDRAG	UDRAG@ULKYVM	University Disaster Recovery Analysis forum
UDS-L	UDS-L@ALBNYDH2	UDS Documentation Materials
UFIT-L	UFIT-L@TRMETU	Applied Physics Group List UFIT-L
UFO-L	UFO-L@BRUFPB	FORUM FOR UFOLOGY
	UFO-L@PSUVM	UFO related phenomenon
UFRJNCEN	UFRJNCEN@UFRJ	Jornal Eletronico UFRJ-NCE Noticias
UFSC	UFSC@BRUFSC	(Peered) FORUM UFSC
UFT-L	UFT-L@EARNCC	Discussion list for User-initiated File Tran+
UG-L	UG-L@BITNIC	(Peered) Usage Guidelines List
	UG-L@DEARN	(Peered) Usage Guidelines List
	UG-L@HEARN	(Peered) Usage Guidelines List
	UG-L@MARIST	(Peered) Usage Guidelines List
	UG-L@UGA	(Peered) Usage Guidelines
UGCOLL-L	UGCOLL-L@UBVM	SUNY/Buffalo Undergraduate College Discussio+
UICMAPLE	UICMAPLE@UICVM	UIC Maple Discussion List
UICMATH	UICMATH@UICVM	UIC Mathematics
UICNETP	UICNETP@UICVM	UIC Campus Network Discussions
UIGIS-L	UIGIS-L@UBVM	User Interfaces for Geographic Information S+
UIRS6000	UIRS6000@UICVM	UIC RS/6000 Discussion List
UKARC	UKARC@UKCC	University of Kentucky Amateur Radio Club
UKERA-L	UKERA-L@UKCC	Dialogue on Educational Reform
UKGEG	UKGEG@UKCC	Discussion list for anyone in Geography Depa+
UKPILOT5	UKPILOT5@UKACRL	"Discussion on UK HEP/SPAN DECnet Phase V Pi+
UKRAINE	UKRAINE@ARIZVM1	Ukraine
UKRHEEO	UKRHEEO@UKACRL	"UKRHEEO Bulletin list"
UKRHEEO1	UKRHEEO1@UKACRL	TITLE "UKRHEEO Bulletin list"
UKTEX	UKTEX@FRORS13	UKTeX : UKTeX redistribution from ASTON
UKTEX-L	UKTEX-L@DHDURZ1	UKTeX-L Distribution List for German TeX Use+
ULGNET	ULGNET@BLIULG11	ULGNET General Discussion list

Network-wide ID	Full address	List title
ULGNETAD	ULGNETAD@BLIULG11	ULGNET Administrators List
ULTIMATE	ULTIMATE@PUCC	Princeton Ultimate Frisbee List
ULTRA-L	ULTRA-L@HASARA11	List for discussion of Ultranet LAN's
ULTRA-M	ULTRA-M@HASARA11	ULTRA-Mailing list
UMCLIS-L	UMCLIS-L@UMDD	CLIS Discussion List
UMIS-L	UMIS-L@UMSLVMA	Undergraduate MIS Discusion List
UMSFAC-L	UMSFAC-L@MAINE	University of Maine System Facilities Manage+
UN-LIB	UN-LIB@IRMFAO01	UN-LIB Electronic Bulletin Board of United+
UNC-L	UNC-L@YALEVM	University Network Committee
UNCC-L	UNCC-L@UNCCVM	UNCC LISTSERV Discussion
UNCEDGEN	UNCEDGEN@UFRJ	UNCEDGEN - Public discussion List about Envi+
UNCJIN-L	UNCJIN-L@ALBNYVM1	United Nations Criminal Justice Information +
UNCLETEX	UNCLETEX@TRINITY	UNCLETEX (Trinity University EDUCOM follow-u+
UNDLAN-L	UNDLAN-L@NDSUVM1	UND LAN Administrators
UNIANDES	UNIANDES@ANDESCOL	Espacio Abierto para UniAndinos
UNICHAT	UNICHAT@SJUVM	The Unichat Steering Committee List
UNICRN-L	UNICRN-L@PSUORVM	SIRSI/UNICORN Automated Library Systems
UNINFSEC	UNINFSEC@CUVMC	University Administrative Information Securi+
UNIRAS	UNIRAS@HEARN	UNIRAS Discussion List
UNISYS	UNISYS@UBVM	SUNY Unisys Sites Discussion List
UNISYS-L	UNISYS-L@UFRJ	Forum dos Usuarios UNISYS - Brasil
UNIV-SUN	UNIV-SUN@ANDESCOL	Comite de Trabajo UniverSUN
UNIVOC	UNIVOC@UCBCMSA	UNIVOC - NCRVE UC Berkeley Voc Ed Universi+
UNIX-L	UNIX-L@ALBNYDH2	UNIX-L HINTS using UNIX on the NYS Dept of+
UNIX-SRC	UNIX-SRC@NDSUVM1	Unix-Sources Mailing List
UNIX-TR	UNIX-TR@TRITU	UNIX Tartisma ve Yardimlasma Listesi
UNIX-WIZ	UNIX-WIZ@NDSUVM1	Unix-Wizards Mailing List
UNIXAK-L	UNIXAK-L@DOSUNI1	UNIX-Arbeitskreis der Uni Osnabrueck (lokal+
UNIXPRGS	UNIXPRGS@TECHNION	UNIXPRGS - TECHNION CC Unix programmers list
UNIXRZ-L	UNIXRZ-L@DOSUNI1	Fragen zu UNIX-Problemen, (lokale Liste, Uni+
UNMETHOD	UNMETHOD@GWUVM	UN University Millennium Project Discussion +
UNXNAD-F	UNXNAD-F@FRMOP11	Liste des 'Node ADministators' UNIX francais

Network-wide ID	Full address	List title
UP-LADB	UP-LADB@UNMVMA	Latin America Data Base
UPCDATA	UPCDATA@UMSLVMA	Scanner Data Modeling Discussion List
UPGRADE	UPGRADE@IPFWVM	IBM UPGRADE DISCUSSIONS
UPSA-L	UPSA-L@UKANVM	KU Unclassified Professional Staff Associati+
UPSAC	UPSAC@GWUVM	UPSAC Discussion List
URANTIAL	URANTIAL@UAFSYSB	Discussion of _The_Urantia_Book_
URBAN-L	URBAN-L@TREARN	Urban Planning Discussion List
URBANET	URBANET@MSU	Urban Planning Student Network
UREP-L	UREP-L@IRLEARN	(Peered) Discussion of UREP software
	UREP-L@PSUVM	(Peered) UREP-L Mailing list
USCINT-L	USCINT-L@USCVM	USC Office of International Student Services+
USERSERV	USERSERV@UVMVM	USERSERV: Vt. User Services Support Group
USG-L	USG-L@TECHNION	USG-L - User Support Groups discussion li+
USGA-L	USGA-L@SIUCVMB	Student Government Net
USPID	USPID@ICNUCEVM	USPID mailing list
USRDIR-L	USRDIR-L@BITNIC	(Peered) User Directory List
	USRDIR-L@DEARN	(Peered) User Directory List
	USRDIR-L@HEARN	(Peered) User Directory List
	USRDIR-L@MARIST	(Peered) User Directory List
	USRDIR-L@UGA	(Peered) User Directory List
USTC85-L	USTC85-L@RICEVM1	Discussion for Univ of Science & Technology +
USTIMSS	USTIMSS@MSU	TIMSS Info List
USUMTS-L	USUMTS-L@BRLNCC	Usuarios do sistema MTS no LNCC
USUVM-L	USUVM-L@BRLNCC	Usuarios do Sistema VM/XA (no Bitnet: BRLNC+
UTCRB-L	UTCRB-L@UTORONTO	UofT Subcommittee on Computing of the Reasea+
UTIL-L	UTIL-L@ALBNYDH2	PLATFORM UTILITIES LIST AT ALBNYDH2
UTINET-L	UTINET-L@BRLNCC	UTI Eletronica do Hospital Universitario da +
UTOS2-L	UTOS2-L@UTKVM1	Discussion of OS/2 Operating System at UTK
UTS-ITC	UTS-ITC@UTXVM	UT System Information Technology Council List
UTS-L	UTS-L@DEARN	Amdahl UTS discussion list
UUS-L	UUS-L@UBVM	Unitarian Universalists
UVCOUS-A	UVCOUS-A@UVVM	Computing User Services Announcements
UVHINF-L	UVHINF-L@UVVM	UVic Health Info Science Bulletins
UVICBIO2	UVICBIO2@UVVM	UVICBIO2 - UVic Biology Department Announcem+
UVNETS-L	UVNETS-L@UVVM	UVic Network Contacts

Network-wide ID	Full address	List title
UVOUTAGE	UVOUTAGE@UVVM	UVic Scheduled Outages Bulletins
UVP-A	UVP-A@BITNIC	BITNIC Update Program Administration list
UVP-D	UVP-D@BITNIC	BITNIC Update Program development list
UVTERM-L	UVTERM-L@UVVM	UVic UVTERM users
UWDECUS	UWDECUS@UWAVM	Mailing list for UW DECUS group
UWINGRES	UWINGRES@UWAVM	UW Ingres List
UWNSF-L	UWNSF-L@UWAVM	NSF Doc U of Washington Distribution
UWSA	UWSA@MIAMIU	United We Stand America (UWSA)
UZAY-L	UZAY-L@TRITU	Hava-Uzay Bilimleri ve Teknolojileri Tartism+
VAL-L	VAL-L@UCF1VM	Valentine Michael Smith's commentary
VAL-X400	VAL-X400@IRLEARN	Value X.400 Implementation Contract (closed)
VAMPYRES	VAMPYRES@GUVM	Vampiric lore, fact and fiction
VAPDC-L	VAPDC-L@VTVM1	Virginia's Planning District Commissions
VAXVMS	VAXVMS@UKACRL	VMS discussion
VECSRV-L	VECSRV-L@TREARN	Ege University Remote Vector Processor Users+
VECTOR-L	VECTOR-L@UNBVM1	IBM 3090 Vector Facility
VEGAN-L	VEGAN-L@TEMPLEVM	Vegan Discussion Group
VEGCMTE	VEGCMTE@VTVM1	Vegetarian Resource Committee
VEGLIFE	VEGLIFE@VTVM1	Vegetarian Lifestyle Discussion List
VERN-USR	VERN-USR@VTVM1	VERnet Users
VETADM-L	VETADM-L@TAMVM1	VETERINARY HOSPITAL ADMINISTRATION ISSUES
VETCAI-L	VETCAI-L@KSUVM	VETERINARY MEDICINE COMPUTER ASSISTED INSTRU+
VETE-ULG	VETE-ULG@BLIULG11	VETE-ULG General Discussion list
VETHIS-L	VETHIS-L@UIUCVMD	Veterinary Hospital Information Systems - VE+
VETIMM-L	VETIMM-L@UCDCVDLS	Veterinary Immunology Discussion Group
VETINFO	VETINFO@UCDCVDLS	Veterinary Informatics Discussion Group
VETLIB-L	VETLIB-L@VTVM1	Veterinary Medicine Library issues and infor+
VETMED-L	VETMED-L@UGA	Veterinary Medicine
VETMICRO	VETMICRO@UCDCVDLS	Veterinary Microbiology Discussion Group
VETMYCOP	VETMYCOP@UCDCVDLS	Veterinary Mycoplasma Discussion Group
VETTE-L	VETTE-L@EMUVM1	Corvette Discussion - Service Info, Shows, e+
VEVA-L	VEVA-L@VTVM1	Virginia Educational Vax Association List
VFORT-L	VFORT-L@EBCESCA1	(Peered) VS-Fortran discussion list
	VFORT-L@JHUVM	(Peered) VS-Fortran discussion list
VIACON-L	VIACON-L@ALBNYVM1	Discussion of Issues Related to Viability of+
VICTORIA	VICTORIA@IUBVM	VICTORIA All Aspects of 19th-Century British+

Network-wide ID	Full address	List title
VIDEOCON	VIDEOCON@ASUACAD	VIDEOCON: Video Conferencing list
VIDEOTEC	VIDEOTEC@VTVM1	ARPA Videotech relay
VIDNET-L	VIDNET-L@UGA	Video Network Discussion List
VIETNET	VIETNET@USCVM	The Bitnet feed for the soc.cuture.viet-names+
VIFLIS	VIFLIS@ARIZVM1	Virtual Int'l Faculty in Library & Info Scie+
VIGIS-L	VIGIS-L@UWAVM	VIGIS-L
VINTAGVW	VINTAGVW@SJSUVM1	Air-Cooled Volkswagen Discussion List
VIOLEN-L	VIOLEN-L@BRUSPVM	Violence Discussion Forum
VIRTU-L	VIRTU-L@UIUCVMD	VR / sci.virtual-worlds
VIRUS-L	VIRUS-L@TRITU	Open Discussion List About PC Viruses
VIRUS-TR	VIRUS-TR@TRITU	Bilgisayar Virusleri Uzerine Tartisma Listes+
VISBAS-L	VISBAS-L@TAMVM1	Discussion for Microsoft Visual Basic and Re+
VISION-L	VISION-L@PSUVM	Vision Research Group
VISIONS	VISIONS@UBVM	Christian Visions Discussion List
VISUAL-L	VISUAL-L@VTVM1	VISUAL-L DISCUSSION LIST
VIZGRP-L	VIZGRP-L@UGA	Visual Computing Users Group
VM-MIG-L	VM-MIG-L@SUVM	VM/CMS Migration Discussion List
VM-REXX	VM-REXX@MARIST	(Peered) VM/SP REXX Language Discussion List
	VM-REXX@UCF1VM	(Peered) VM/SP REXX Language Discussion List
VM-SHOW	VM-SHOW@TREARN	VM-Show - Comics Magazine in Turkish
VM-UTIL	VM-UTIL@DEARN	(Peered) VM Utilities Discussion List
	VM-UTIL@MARIST	(Peered) VM Utilities Discussion List
	VM-UTIL@PCCVM	(Peered) VM Utilities Discussion List
	VM-UTIL@TECMTYVM	(Peered) VM Utilities Discussion List
	VM-UTIL@TREARN	(Peered) VM Utilities Discussion List
	VM-UTIL@UBVM	(Peered) VM Utilities Discussion List
	VM-UTIL@UCF1VM	(Peered) VM Utilities Discussion List
	VM-UTIL@UTARLVM1	(Peered) VM Utilities Discussion List
VMAINT-L	VMAINT-L@UIUCVMD	VM Maintenance discussions
VMCENTER	L-VMCTR@AKRONVM	VMCENTER Components Discussion List
VMCMS	VMCMS@UKACRL	TITLE "VM at RAL discussion list"
VMCOMMS	VMCOMMS@UKACRL	TEST LIST
VMEDIA-L	VMEDIA-L@UOTTAWA	VIP Media Discussion Group
VMESA-L	VMESA-L@UAFSYSB	VM/ESA Discussions
	VMESA-L@UCSFVM	VM ESA Conversion List
VMGOPHER	VMGOPHER@PUCC	VM GOPHER discussion list
VMKIDS-L	VMKIDS-L@DEARN	(Peered) VM low-key Tech-staff discussion
	VMKIDS-L@IRISHVM	(Peered) VM low-key Tech-staff discussion
	VMKIDS-L@MARIST	(Peered) VM low-key Tech-staff discussion
	VMKIDS-L@UBVM	(Peered) VM low-key Tech-staff discussion
VMNAD-F	VMNAD-F@FRMOP11	Liste des 'Node ADministators' VM francais
VMPR-L	VMPR-L@MCGILL1	VM PERFORMANCE

Network-wide ID	Full address	List title
VMPROB-D	VMPROB-D@UTCVM	VMPROBE Distribution List
VMPROB-L	VMPROB-L@UTCVM	VMPROBE List
VMREL6-L	VMREL6-L@UAFSYSB	VM Release 6 (SP and HPO) Discussions
VMS-L	VMS-L@SEARN	VMS give-and-take forum
VMS-SE	VMS-SE@SEARN	Swedish EARN Node ADministrators - VMS syste+
VMS-STORE	VMS-STOR@SEARN	VMS Store administrators
VMSLSV-L	VMSLSV-L@UBVM	VAX/VMS LISTSERV Discussion List
VMSNAD-F	VMSNAD-F@FRMOP11	Liste des 'Node ADministators' VMS francais
VMSTEX-L	VMSTEX-L@UICVM	VMSTEX-L
VMSYS-L	VMSYS-L@UGA	VM Systems Programmers List
VMTOOL-L	VMTOOL-L@UIUCVMD	VM Tools discussions
VMUSER-L	VMUSER-L@JPNSUT00	IBM soft & hard discussion list
VMUTIL-A	VMUTIL-A@UIUCVMD	VMUTIL-A (archive files only)
VMVIRUS	VMVIRUS@PCCVM	Open Discussion forum on VM viruses and worms
VMVTAM-L	VMVTAM-L@UIUCVMD	VM VTAM discussions
VMWKSHOP	VMWKSHOP@MARIST	1994 VM Workshop - June 7-10
VMWK93-L	VMWK93-L@MSU	VM Workshop '93 Administrivia List
VMWK94-L	VMWK94-L@IRISHVMA	1994 VM workshop discussions
VMXA-L	VMXA-L@DEARN	(Peered) VM/XA Discussion List
	VMXA-L@UGA	(Peered) VM/XA Discussion List
VM3800-L	VM3800-L@UIUCVMD	VM 3800 printer discussions
VNEWS-L	VNEWS-L@UBVM	VNEWS Discussion List
VNIX-L	VNIX-L@RICEVM1	(Peered) Personal UNIX on VM discussion
	VNIX-L@TAMVM1	(Peered) Personal UNIX on VM discussion
VOCEVAL	VOCEVAL@SJUVM	Vocational Evaluation for Rehabilitation List
VOCNET	VOCNET@UCBCMSA	VOCNET - NCRVE UC Berkeley Voc Ed Practiti+
VOLCANO	VOLCANO@ASUACAD	VOLCANO
VOXHUM-L	VOXHUM-L@EMUVM1	VOX Humanities
VPIEJ-L	VPIEJ-L@VTVM1	Publishing E-Journals : Publishing, Archivin+
VRA-L	VRA-L@UAFSYSB	Visual Resources Association
VRAPP-L	VRAPP-L@UIUCVMD	VR Apps/sci.virtual-worlds.apps
VRTP	VRTP@UMDD	Virtual Reality, Telepresence and Beyond Cou+
VSAM-L	VSAM-L@TREARN	Virtual Storage Access Method Discussion List
VSNU-L	VSNU-L@HEARN	Vereniging van Samenwerkende Nederlandse Uni+
VSTAT-L	VSTAT-L@ALBNYDH2	Vital Statistics at NYS DOH
VT-HSNET	VT-HSNET@VTVM1	VT K-12 School Network
VTCAD-L	VTCAD-L@VTVM1	Virginia Tech Computer Aided Design Discussi+
VTLOG	VTLOG@VTVM1	Virginia Tech Computing Center LOG

Network-wide ID	Full address	List title
VTLSLIST	VTLSLIST@VTVM1	VTLS users list
VTNOVELL	VTNOVELL@VTVM1	Virginia Tech NOVELL users
VTWOMEN	VTWOMEN@VTVM1	Virginia Tech Women
VUG	VUG@UKACRL	VUG
VUGMAIL	VUGMAIL@UKACRL	VUGMAIL LIST
VUGMEMB	VUGMEMB@UKACRL	VUGMEMB
VWAR-L	VWAR-L@UBVM	Viet Nam War Discussion List
WAACC-L	WAACC-L@UMDD	Washington Area Academic Computing Centers d+
WAC-L	WAC-L@UIUCVMD	WAC-L Writing Across the Curriculum (Center +
WAKONS-L	WAKONS-L@MIZZOU1	WAKONS-L Wakonse Fellows College Teaching El+
WATER-L	WATER-L@WSUVM1	Water Quality Discussion List
WAVEFR-L	WAVEFR-L@PSUVM	WaveFront Software
WBBALL-L	WBBALL-L@PSUVM	Women's Basketball at Penn State
WBFO-L	WBFO-L@UBVM	WBFO Program Highlights & Local Events List
WCDRT-L	WCDRT-L@UALTAVM	Western Canadian Dairy Research and Technolo+
WCENTER	WCENTER@TTUVM1	Center List
WCETALL	WCETALL@UNMVMA	WICHE Western cooperative for educational te+
WCETINFO	WCETINFO@UNMVMA	Western Cooperative Information Clearinghous+
WEIRD-L	WEIRD-L@BROWNVM	Mmytacist Mmanufacture
WELSH-L	WELSH-L@IRLEARN	WELSH Language Bulletin Board
WEPAN-L	WEPAN-L@PURCCVM	Women in Engineering Program Advocates Netwo+
WESTAM-L	WESTAM-L@YALEVM	Western Americana List WESTAM-L
WESTDIR	WESTDIR@UREGINA1	Western Canadian Computer Center Directors
WFFT-L	WFFT-L@UBVM	WFFT Member Distribution List
WFW-L	WFW-L@UMDD	Microsoft Windows for Workgroups
WH-NEWS	WH-NEWS@UWAVM	WH-NEWS
WHIM	WHIM@TAMVM1	WHIM - a discussion list for "Humour Studies"
WHIRL	WHIRL@PSUVM	Women's History in Rhetoric and Language
WHITE-PG	WHITE-PG@BITNIC	CREN White Pages List
WHR-L	WHR-L@PSUVM	Women's History in Rhetoric
WHSCL-L	WHSCL-L@EMUVM1	Health Sciences Library Discussion
WIG-L	WIG-L@UCBMSA	WIG-L - Women in German
WILDORNT	WILDORNT@PUCC	WILDORNT
WILEY-L	WILEY-L@UBVM	Wiley groups discussion list
WIML-L	WIML-L@IUBVM	WIML-L (Women's issues in music librarianshi+

Network-wide ID	Full address	List title
WIN-L	WIN-L@DEARN	X.25 - Wissenschaftsnetz (techn. Koord.)
WIN-VAX	WIN-VAX@UMDD	MS-Windows interfaces to VAX-Rdb
WINDOWS	WINDOWS@MCGILL1	"WINDOWS" is a forum to pose questions, supp+
WINGS-IP	WINGS-IP@UBVM	UB Wings Information Providers List
WINGS-L	WINGS-L@UBVM	Wings Information Providers List
WINTCP-L	WINTCP-L@UBVM	Wollongong TCP/IP Discussion List
WIN3-L	WIN3-L@UICVM	Microsoft Windows Version 3 Forum
WIOLE-L	WIOLE-L@MIZZOU1	Writing Intensive Online Learning Environmen+
WISE	WISE@UICVM	Workshop on Information Systems Economics
WISENET	WISENET@UICVM	Women In Science and Engineering NETwork
WISP-L	WISP-L@IUBVM	Women in Scholarly Publishing Discussion List
WITSENDO	WITSENDO@DARTCMS1	ENDOmetriosis Treatment and Support
WKSH-L	WKSH-L@UCSFVM	Windowing Korn Shell Discussion List.
WKSPHYS	WKSPHYS@IDBSU	WKSPHYS - WORKSHOP PHYSICS LIST
WMN-HLTH	WMN-HLTH@UWAVM	WMN-HLTH
WMST-L	WMST-L@UMDD	Women's Studies List
WMSYS-L	WMSYS-L@WMVM1	William and Mary Systems Engineering Staff D+
WMTS-L	WMTS-L@WMVM1	William and Mary Technology Support Staff Di+
WMUN-L	WMUN-L@CSEARN	WMUN-L World Model United Nations 1993
	WMUN-L@DEARN	WMUN-L World Model United Nations 1993
WNS699	WNS699@SBCCVM	Stony Brook WNS699 Discussion List
WONCAR-L	WONCAR-L@BROWNVM	Woncar-l List
WOODWEEK	WOODWEEK@IPFWVM	WOODWORKING DISCUSSIONS WEEKLY DIGEST
WOODWORK	WOODWORK@IPFWVM	Woodworking Discussions
WOPEC	WOPEC@UKACRL	"Current Awareness Service for Working Paper+
WORDPRO	WORDPRO@MCGILL1	"WORDPRO" is a forum to pose questions, supp+
WORDS-L	WORDS-L@TWNMOE10	English Languaged Discussion Group
	WORDS-L@UGA	English Language Discussion Group
WORKS	WORKS@RUTVM1	WorkS List
WORKS-L	WORKS-L@NDSUVM1	WORKS-L Writers List Works
WORLD-L	WORLD-L@UBVM	World-L - Forum on non-Eurocentric world his+
WPCORP-L	WPCORP-L@UBVM	WordPerfect Corporation Products Discussion +

Network-wide ID	Full address	List title
WPWIN-L	WPWIN-L@UBVM	WordPerfect For Windows Discussion List
WP51-L	WP51-L@UOTTAWA	WordPerfect 5.1 Discussion Group List
WRITERS	WRITERS@NDSUVM1	WRITERS
WS_T4_AU	WS_T4_AU@ICNUCEVM	WS_T4_AU INET92 DEV. COUNTRIES WORKSHOP AND +
WSFIBL-L	WSFIBL-L@HEARN	Vergadermedium van de WSF IBL medewerkers
WU-AIDS	AIDS@WUVMD	Sci.Med.AIDS Newsgroup
WUNET-L	WUNET-L@WUVMD	General list for Campuswide Network Users
WUNIHG-L	WUNIHG-L@WUVMD	Washington University NIH Guide Distribution
WUNOVELL	WUNOVELL@WUVMD	Campuswide Novell Network Discussion List
WUSCT-L	WUSCT-L@WUVMD	Washington University Sentence Completion Te+
WVGIS-L	WVGIS-L@WVNVM	WVa GIS Discussion List
WVNCSF-L	WVNCSF-L@WVNVM	WVNET Computer Science Faculty List
WVNK12-L	WVNK12-L@WVNVM	Internet Access for K–12 Discussions
WVRK12-L	WVRK12-L@WVNVM	RuralNet Discussion Group
WVUBBN-L	WVUBBN-L@WVNVM	Campus Backbone Network Information Exchange
WVUBOT-L	WVUBOT-L@WVNVM	Board of Trusties Initiatives on Instruction+
WVUEGS-L	WVUEGS-L@WVNVM	English Graduate Students
WVUENG-L	WVUENG-L@WVNVM	English Faculty and Staff
WVURFP-L	WVURFP-L@WVNVM	RFP for Voice, Video and Data Facility
WVUSAB-L	WVUSAB-L@WVNVM	Electrical & Computer Engineering Student Ad+
WVUSEN-L	WVUSEN-L@WVNVM	Mailing List Faculty Senate
WVUVTC-L	WVUVTC-L@WVNVM	WVU Video Technology Coordinating Council
WWII-L	WWII-L@UBVM	World War II Discussion List
WWP-L	WWP-L@BROWNVM	Brown University Women Writers Project
WX-LSR	WX-LSR@UIUCVMD	WX-LSR Local Storm Reports and other local WX
WX-MISC	WX-MISC@UIUCVMD	WX-MISC Miscellaneous WX products
WX-NATNL	WX-NATNL@UIUCVMD	National Wx Summary and Selected City Fcsts
WX-PCPN	WX-PCPN@UIUCVMD	WX-PCPN Precipitation WX products
WX-STLT	WX-STLT@UIUCVMD	WX-STLT Satellite interpretive messages
WX-SUM	WX-SUM@UIUCVMD	WX-SUM Summary Weather Products
WX-SWO	WX-SWO@UIUCVMD	WX-SWO Severe Weather Outlooks
WX-TALK	WX-TALK@UIUCVMD	WX-TALK General weather discussions and talk
WX-TOR	WX-TOR@UIUCVMD	Tornado Warning dissemination
WX-TROPL	WX-TROPL@UIUCVMD	WX-TROPL Tropical Storm and Hurricane WX pro+

Network-wide ID	Full address	List title
WX-WATCH	WX-WATCH@UIUCVMD	WX-WATCH WX Watches and cancellations
WX-WSTAT	WX-WSTAT@UIUCVMD	WX-WSTAT WX Watch status and storm reports
WYLBUR-L	WYLBUR-L@CUNYVM	WYLBUR System Maintainers Mailing List
W5AC	W5AC@TAMVM1	TAMU Amateur Radio Club
XCULT-L	XCULT-L@PSUVM	International Intercultural Newsletter
XCULTINS	XCULTINS@UNMVMA	Effects of Culture on Instruction Design
XEDIT-L	XEDIT-L@MARIST	(Peered) VM System Editor List
	XEDIT-L@RUTVM1	(Peered) VM System Editor List
	XEDIT-L@UGA	(Peered) VM System Editor List
XEROX-L	XEROX-L@TAMVM1	The Xerox Discussion List
XF-L	XF-L@DB0TUI11	Tcl/Tk based interface builder XF
XF-PATCH	XF-PATCH@DB0TUI11	Patches for XF-L list
XMAILBUG	XMAILBUG@PUCC	Mailer release 2.0 bug list
XMAILER	XMAILER@BITNIC	(Peered) The Columbia Mailer List
	XMAILER@DEARN	(Peered) The Crosswell Mailer List
	XMAILER@HEARN	(Peered) The Crosswell Mailer List
	XMAILER@MARIST	(Peered) The Crosswell Mailer List
	XMAILER@UGA	(Peered) Crosswell Mailer
XTMS-L	XTMS-L@UKACRL	"Discussion list for TMS X user interface"
XTROPY-L	XTROPY-L@UBVM	Extropians - discussion/development of Extro+
XWIN-L	XWIN-L@TREARN	X Window discussion list
XXI	XXI@UCHCECVM	XXI Ciencia & Tecnologia. (Science & Techno+
X25-L	X25-L@UFRJ	Acesso X.25 - Discussoes e Informacoes
X400-L	X400-L@BITNIC	(Peered) BITNET X.400 Discussion
	X400-L@DEARN	(Peered) BITNET X400 List
	X400-L@HEARN	(Peered) BITNET X400 List
	X400-L@MARIST	(Peered) BITNET X400 List
	X400-L@UGA	(Peered) x.400 Protocol List
Y-RIGHTS	Y-RIGHTS@SJUVM	Y-Rights: Kid/Teen Rights Discussion Group
YACHT-L	YACHT-L@GREARN	The Sailing and amateur BoatBuilding List
YARDIMCI	YARDIMCI@TREARN	Sistem ile ilgili tartisma
YCIAS-L	YCIAS-L@YALEVM	YCIAS Student Discussion List
YESCAMP	YESCAMP@UNBVM1	Youth Engineering and Science Camps of Canada
YMP-TEST	YMP-TEST@UKACRL	"Discussion on the RAL YMP Acceptance Tests"
YONEYLEM	YONEYLEM@TRITU	Yoneylem Arastirmasi Tartisma Listesi
YOUTHNET	YOUTHNET@INDYCMS	Youth Net
YP_TECH	YP_TECH@YALEVM	Technical Issues Relating to the Yale People+
YP_USER	YP_USER@YALEVM	Yale People Project User Discussion
YTERM-L	YTERM-L@YALEVM	Yale Terminal Emulator Issues
YUNUS	YUNUS@TRMETU	(Peered) Turkish TeX Users Group YUNUS

Network-wide ID	Full address	List title
Z-SENATU	Z-SENATU@PLTUMK11	Reports from sessions of Nicolaus Copernicus+
ZAPP	ZAPP@UCSFVM	Zapp! The Lightning of Empowerment
ZIKBN	ZIKBN@PLEARN	DISCUSSION LIST FOR NASK-KBN RELATIONS. ZIKBN
ZINES-L	ZINES-L@URIACC	The Scent of a ZINE
ZWSUG	ZWSUG@MARIST	Marist Zwriter Users Group
ZZZ-L	ZZZ-L@UCSFVM	Zeke/Zebb/Zack Project group
Z3950IW	Z3950IW@NERVM	Z39.50 Implementors Workshop
12SLAFES	12SLAFES@USACHVM1	(Peered) XII Simposio Latinoamericano de Fis+
2BNFCC	2BNFCC@SEARN	2nd BNFNET Annual Computer Conference
21ST-C-L	21ST-C-L@BRUFPB	Forum about the 21ST century discussions
3COM-L	3COM-L@NUSVM	3Com Discussion List
3D-L	3D-L@ARIZVM1	A discussion of 3D-Graphics
4AD-L	4AD-L@JHUVM	4ad recording artists list
4351	4351@GITVM1	"4351 Group" discussion list
9NOV89-L	9NOV89-L@DB0TUI11	Events around the Berlin Wall
9370-L	9370-L@HEARN	IBM 9370 and VM/IS specific topics list
94PGM-L	94PGM-L@EMUVM1	SRA/NCURA Regional Program 1994 in Puerto Ri+

8

E-mail with X.400 Addressing

The purpose of this chapter is to provide readers with information concerning the Consultative Committee for International Telephone and Telegraph (CCITT) X.400 recommendation. That recommendation defines how messages should be addressed so that electronic mail providers can interconnect with one another and provide message interoperability between commercial services offering X.400 gateways as well as the Internet, which now supports X.400 message addressing. To provide readers with an understanding of X.400 we will examine the CCITT X.400 electronic address to include its address elements and the International Standards Organization (ISO) country codes whose inclusion within an electronic address is mandatory for the delivery of inter-country communications.

X.400 ADDRESS ELEMENTS

Under the CCITT X.400 addressing scheme there are nine unique identifiers that can be included in an electronic message to identify the recipient. Two of those identifiers can be further distinguished as up to four subidentifiers can be denoted for one identifier and three subidentifiers for the second identifier. The following table lists the X.400 address elements to include their identifier which is used in the electronic mail address as an abbreviated acronym to identify the address element, and an example of the use of the identifier in an electronic message.

X.400 ADDRESS ELEMENTS

Element Name	Identifier	Example
Country	C=	C=US
Administrative Mgt Domain	A=	A=CompuServe
Private Mgt Domain	P=	P=CSMAIL
Surname	S=	S=HELD
Given Name	G=	G=GILBERT
Initial	I=	I=X
Domain Defined Attribute	DDA=Type=Value	DDA=ID:40102.7776
	(up to 4 DDAs can be specified)	
Organization Name	O=	O=4DEGREECONSULTING
Organization Unit	OU=	OU=ENGIN

(up to three levels can be specified in ascending order appearing as
OU1=value1;OU2=Value2;OU3=Value3)

where: Administrative Management Domain (ADMD) represents the public messaging service, such as CompuServe and MCI.

Private Management Domain (PRMD) represents a private electronic messaging system connected to an ADMD, such as a corporate E-mail system.

Country represents the country in which the PRMD or ADMD is registered.

Organization Name represents the name of the organization the recipient belongs to.

Domain Defined Attribute (DDA) represents a special field that may be required to enable the receiving system to understand how to deliver a message to the recipient. A DDA address consists of two parts, a Type and a Value. In the above example the Type is "ID" while the Value is "40102.7776".

Note: Some elements, such as the Initial are optional. You should determine the elements required to reach an intended recipient.

COUNTRY CODES

The following list of country codes is based upon the International Standards Organization 3166 standard which provides country codes in both English and French based upon six different orders. The table which follows is based upon the alphabetical order of countries and includes their two (A2) and three (A3) letter abbreviation as well as their numeric (Number) identifier. Under X.400 addressing you can use either two or three character country codes.

Country	A 2	A 3	Number
AFGHANISTAN	AF	AFG	004
ALBANIA	AL	ALB	008
ALGERIA	DZ	DZA	012
AMERICAN SAMOA	AS	ASM	016
ANDORRA	AD	AND	020
ANGOLA	AO	AGO	024
ANGUILLA	AI	AIA	660
ANTARCTICA	AQ	ATA	010
ANTIGUA AND BARBUDA	AG	ATG	028
ARGENTINA	AR	ARG	032
ARUBA	AW	ABW	533
AUSTRALIA	AU	AUS	036
AUSTRIA	AT	AUT	040
BAHAMAS	BS	BHS	044
BAHRAIN	BH	BHR	048
BANGLADESH	BD	BGD	050
BARBADOS	BB	BRB	052
BELGIUM	BE	BEL	056
BELIZE	BZ	BLZ	084
BENIN	BJ	BEN	204
BERMUDA	BM	BMU	060
BHUTAN	BT	BTN	064
BOLIVIA	BO	BOL	068
BOTSWANA	BW	BWA	072
BOUVET ISLAND	BV	BVT	074
BRAZIL	BR	BRA	076
BRITISH INDIAN OCEAN TERRITORY	IO	IOT	086
BRUNEI DARUSSALAM	BN	BRN	096
BULGARIA	BG	BGR	100
BURKINA FASO	BF	BFA	854
BURUNDI	BI	BDI	108

Country	A 2	A 3	Number
BYELORUSSIAN SSR	BY	BYS	112
CAMBODIA	KH	KHM	116
CAMEROON	CM	CMR	120
CANADA	CA	CAN	124
CAPE VERDE	CV	CPV	132
CAYMAN ISLANDS	KY	CYM	136
CENTRAL AFRICAN REPUBLIC	CF	CAF	140
CHAD	TD	TCD	148
CHILE	CL	CHL	152
CHINA	CN	CHN	156
CHRISTMAS ISLAND	CX	CXR	162
COCOS (KEELING) ISLANDS	CC	CCK	166
COLOMBIA	CO	COL	170
COMOROS	KM	COM	174
CONGO	CG	COG	178
COOK ISLANDS	CK	COK	184
COSTA RICA	CR	CRI	188
COTE D'IVOIRE	CI	CIV	384
CUBA	CU	CUB	192
CYPRUS	CY	CYP	196
CZECHOSLOVAKIA	CS	CSK	200
DENMARK	DK	DNK	208
DJIBOUTI	DJ	DJI	262
DOMINICA	DM	DMA	212
DOMINICAN REPUBLIC	DO	DOM	214
EAST TIMOR	TP	TMP	626
ECUADOR	EC	ECU	218
EGYPT	EG	EGY	818
EL SALVADOR	SV	SLV	222
EQUATORIAL GUINEA	GQ	GNQ	226
ETHIOPIA	ET	ETH	230
FALKLAND ISLANDS (MALVINAS)	FK	FLK	238
FAROE ISLANDS	FO	FRO	234
FIJI	FJ	FJI	242
FINLAND	FI	FIN	246
FRANCE	FR	FRA	250
FRENCH GUIANA	GF	GUF	254
FRENCH POLYNESIA	PF	PYF	258
FRENCH SOUTHERN TERRITORIES	TF	ATF	260
GABON	GA	GAB	266
GAMBIA	GM	GMB	270
GERMANY	DE	DEU	276
GHANA	GH	GHA	288
GIBRALTAR	GI	GIB	292
GREECE	GR	GRC	300
GREENLAND	GL	GRL	304

Country	A 2	A 3	Number
GRENADA	GD	GRD	308
GUADELOUPE	GP	GLP	312
GUAM	GU	GUM	316
GUATEMALA	GT	GTM	320
GUINEA	GN	GIN	324
GUINEA-BISSAU	GW	GNB	624
GUYANA	GY	GUY	328
HAITI	HT	HTI	332
HEARD AND MC DONALD ISLANDS	HM	HMD	334
HONDURAS	HN	HND	340
HONG KONG	HK	HKG	344
HUNGARY	HU	HUN	348
ICELAND	IS	ISL	352
INDIA	IN	IND	356
INDONESIA	ID	IDN	360
IRAN (ISLAMIC REPUBLIC OF)	IR	IRN	364
IRAQ	IQ	IRQ	368
IRELAND	IE	IRL	372
ISRAEL	IL	ISR	376
ITALY	IT	ITA	380
JAMAICA	JM	JAM	388
JAPAN	JP	JPN	392
JORDAN	JO	JOR	400
KENYA	KE	KEN	404
KIRIBATI	KI	KIR	296
KOREA, DEMOCRATIC PEOPLE'S REPUBLIC OF	KP	PRK	408
KOREA, REPUBLIC OF	KR	KOR	410
KUWAIT	KW	KWT	414
LAO PEOPLE'S DEMOCRATIC REPUBLIC	LA	LAO	418
LEBANON	LB	LBN	422
LESOTHO	LS	LSO	426
LIBERIA	LR	LBR	430
LIBYAN ARAB JAMAHIRIYA	LY	LBY	434
LIECHTENSTEIN	LI	LIE	438
LUXEMBOURG	LU	LUX	442
MACAU	MO	MAC	446
MADAGASCAR	MG	MDG	450
MALAWI	MW	MWI	454
MALAYSIA	MY	MYS	458
MALDIVES	MV	MDV	462
MALI	ML	MLI	466
MALTA	MT	MLT	470
MARSHALL ISLANDS	MH	MHL	584
MARTINIQUE	MQ	MTQ	474
MAURITANIA	R	MRT	478
MAURITIUS	MU	MUS	480

Country	A 2	A 3	Number
MEXICO	MX	MEX	484
MICRONESIA	FM	FSM	583
MONACO	MC	MCO	492
MONGOLIA	MN	MNG	496
MONTSERRAT	MS	MSR	500
MOROCCO	MA	MAR	504
MOZAMBIQUE	MZ	MOZ	508
MYANMAR	MM	MMR	104
NAMIBIA	NA	NAM	516
NAURU	NR	NRU	520
NEPAL	NP	NPL	524
NETHERLANDS	NL	NLD	528
NETHERLANDS ANTILLES	AN	ANT	532
NEUTRAL ZONE	NT	NTZ	536
NEW CALEDONIA	NC	NCL	540
NEW ZEALAND	NZ	NZL	554
NICARAGUA	NI	NIC	558
NIGER	NE	NER	562
NIGERIA	NG	NGA	566
NIUE	NU	NIU	570
NORFOLK ISLAND	NF	NFK	574
NORTHERN MARIANA ISLANDS	MP	MNP	580
NORWAY	NO	NOR	578
OMAN	OM	OMN	512
PAKISTAN	PK	PAK	586
PALAU	PW	PLW	585
PANAMA	PA	PAN	590
PAPUA NEW GUINEA	PG	PNG	598
PARAGUAY	PY	PRY	600
PERU	PE	PER	604
PHILIPPINES	PH	PHL	608
PITCAIRN	PN	PCN	612
POLAND	PL	POL	616
PORTUGAL	PT	PRT	620
PUERTO RICO	PR	PRI	630
QATAR	QA	QAT	634
REUNION	RE	REU	638
ROMANIA	RO	ROM	642
RWANDA	RW	RWA	646
ST. HELENA	SH	SHN	654
SAINT KITTS AND NEVIS	KN	KNA	659
SAINT LUCIA	LC	LCA	662
ST. PIERRE AND MIQUELON	PM	SPM	666
SAINT VINCENT AND THE GRENADINES	VC	VCT	670
SAMOA	WS	WSM	882
SAN MARINO	SM	SMR	674

Country	A 2	A 3	Number
SÃO TOME AND PRINCIPE	ST	STP	678
SAUDI ARABIA	SA	SAU	682
SENEGAL	SN	SEN	686
SEYCHELLES	SC	SYC	690
SIERRA LEONE	SL	SLE	694
SINGAPORE	SG	SGP	702
SOLOMON ISLANDS	SB	SLB	090
SOMALIA	SO	SOM	706
SOUTH AFRICA	ZA	ZAF	710
SPAIN	ES	ESP	724
SRI LANKA	LK	LKA	144
SUDAN	SD	SDN	736
SURINAME	SR	SUR	740
SVALBARD AND JAN MAYEN ISLANDS	SJ	SJM	744
SWAZILAND	SZ	SWZ	748
SWEDEN	SE	SWE	752
SWITZERLAND	CH	CHE	756
SYRIAN ARAB REPUBLIC	SY	SYR	760
TAIWAN, PROVINCE OF CHINA	TW	TWN	158
TANZANIA, UNITED REPUBLIC OF	TZ	TZA	834
THAILAND	TH	THA	764
TOGO	TG	TGO	768
TOKELAU	TK	TKL	772
TONGA	TO	TON	776
TRINIDAD AND TOBAGO	TT	TTO	780
TUNISIA	TN	TUN	788
TURKEY	TR	TUR	792
TURKS AND CAICOS ISLANDS	TC	TCA	796
TUVALU	TV	TUV	798
UGANDA	UG	UGA	800
UKRAINIAN SSR	UA	UKR	804
UNITED ARAB EMIRATES	AE	ARE	784
UNITED KINGDOM	GB	GBR	826
UNITED STATES	US	USA	840
UNITED STATES MINOR OUTLYING ISLANDS	UM	UMI	581
URUGUAY	UY	URY	858
USSR	SU	SUN	810
VANUATU	VU	VUT	548
VATICAN CITY STATE (HOLY SEE)	VA	VAT	336
VENEZUELA	VE	VEN	862
VIET NAM	VN	VNM	704
VIRGIN ISLANDS (BRITISH)	VG	VGB	092
VIRGIN ISLANDS (U.S.)	VI	VIR	850
WALLIS AND FUTUNA ISLANDS	WF	WLF	876
WESTERN SAHARA	EH	ESH	732
YEMEN, REPUBLIC OF	YE	YEM	887

Country			A 2	A 3	Number
YUGOSLAVIA			YU	YUG	890
ZAIRE			ZR	ZAR	180
ZAMBIA			ZM	ZMB	894
ZIMBABWE			ZW	ZWE	716

X.400 ADMD NAMES AND SERVICE PROVIDERS

Country	Country Code	ADMD Name	Service Provider
UNITED STATES	US	ATTMAIL	AT&T Easylink
		BELLSOUTH	Bell South
		COMPUSERVE	CompuServe
		DIALCOM	BT North America
		IBMX400	Advantis
		INFONET	Infonet
		MARK400	GE Information Services
		TELEMAIL	Sprint
		WESTERN UNION	AT&T Easylink Services
AUSTRALIA	AU	OTC	Australian Overseas TC
		TELEMEMO	Australian Overseas TC
AUSTRIA	AT	ADA	Radio Austria Communications
BELGIUM	BE	RTT	Belgacom
BRAZIL	BR	EMBRATEL	Embratel
	BR	EMBRATEL.INTL	Embratel
CANADA	CA	TELECOM.CANADA	Stentor
CHILE	CL	TOMMAIL	VTR Telecomunications
COSTA RICA	CR	RACSAMAIL	Radiografica Costarricense
DENMARK	DK	DK400	Telecom Denmark
	DK	TELDK	Telecom Denmark
FINLAND	FI	ELISA	Helsinki Telephone
	FI	MAILNET	Telecom Finland
FRANCE	FR	ATLAS	Transpac France
	FR	MISSIVE	French Cable et Radio
GERMANY	DE	DBP	Deutsche Bundespost Telekom
	DE	GEONET	GeoNet Mailbox Systems
INDIA	IN	VSNB	VSN
IRELAND	IE	EIRMAIL400	Eirtrade
ITALY	IT	MASTER400	Teleo
	IT	MASTER400T	Teleo
	IT	OMEGA400	Italcable
	IT	PTPOSTEL	PT Italia
JAPAN	JP	ATI	ACE Telemail
	JP	KDD	KDD
KOREA	KR	DACOMMHS	DACOM Korea
NETHERLANDS	NL	400NET	Unisource Business Networks

Country	Country Code	ADMD Name	Service Provider
NEW ZEALAND	NZ	SYNET	Synet Communications
NORWAY	NO	TELEMAX	Telepost
PORTUGAL	PT	MARCONI-SVA	Marconi SVA
RUSSIA	SU	SOVMAIL	Sprint
SINGAPORE	SG	SGMHS	Singapore Telecom
SPAIN	ES	MENSATEX	Telefonica Services
SWEDEN	SE	400NET	Unisource Business Networks
	SE	SIL	Scandinavian Information Link
SWITZERLAND	CH	ARCOM	Swiss PTT
	CH	ITU	ITU Geneva
UNITED KINGDOM	GB	BT	BT plc
	GB	CWMAIL	Mercury Communications
	GB	GOLD 400	BT plc
	GB	TMAILUK	Sprint International

X.400 NON-DELIVERY REPORT CODES

Diagnostic 0 - Unrecodnized ORName - Recipient name is not valid on the receiving mail system.

Diagnostic 1 - Ambiguous ORName - Recipient name is not unique on the receiving mail system.

Diagnostic 2 - MTA Congestion - Message Transfer Agent overloaded and cannot process the message.

Diagnostic 3 - Loop Detected - Message was routed to the same intermediate MTA more than once.

Diagnostic 4 - UA Unavailable - Targeted User Agent mail system is unavailable at this time.

Diagnostic 5 - Maximum Time Expired - Maximum time for the MTA to route and process the message has expired.

Diagnostic 6 - Encoded Information Types Unsupported - Information type in message is not supported by the target mail system.

Diagnostic 7 - Contents Too Long - The length of the contents of the message exceeds the supported limits.

Diagnostic 8 - Conversion Impractical - Requested conversion of message data type is impractical.

Diagnostic 9 - Conversion Prohibited - Requested conversion of message data type is prohibited.

Diagnostic 10 - Implicit Conversion not registered - Requested conversion is not registered with the mail system you are using.

Diagnostic 11 - Invalid Parameters - Invalid parameters were encountered in the message.

X.400 Demonstration/Test and Information Addresses

ACE Telemail (Japan) demonstration/test address for automatic answering of a message.
    X.400: s=autoanswer;a=ati;c=jp

AOTC Telememo (Australia) demonstration/test address for automatic answering of a message.
    X.400:s=autoanswer;o=telecom;p=telecom;a=telememo;c=au

Belgacom DCS.Mail demonstration/test address for automatic answering of a message.
    X.400:s=autoanswer;o=rtt;a=rtt;c=be

EMBRATEL.INT (Brazil) electronic mail demonstration/test address for automatic answering of a message.
    X.400:g=embratel.int;s=autoanswer;o=stm400.intl;a=embratel.intl;c=br

Radio Austria TELEBOX electronic mail directory and information service.
    X.400: s=directory;o=radaus;a=ada;c=at
    place HELP in subject field

Radio Austria TELEBOX demonstration/test address for automatic answering of a message.
    X.400:s=autoanswer;a=ada;c=at

Radio Austria TELEBOX list of PRMDs connected to this service provider.
    X.400:s=directory;o=radaus;a=ada;c=at
    place ADAPRMD in subject field

BT Gold 400 Service test address for automatic answering of a message.
    X.400:g=auto;s=reply;o=btt;a=gold;c=gb

CPRM Marconi demonstration/test address for automatic answering of a message.

    X.400: s=autoanswer;o=m400;p=email1400;a=marconi-sva;c=pt

DACOMMHS (South Korea) demonstration/test address for automatic answering of a message.

    X.400: s=autoanswer; a=dacommhs;c=kr

DBP (Germany) demonstration/test address for automatic answering of a message.

    X.400: s=AUTOANSWER;A=DBP;C=DE

DK400 (Denmark) demonstration/test address for automatic answering of a message.

    X.400: s=autoanswer;a=dk400;c=dk

Interagency (Federal) E-mail Help Desk:

    X.400:g=emailhelp;s=interagency;o=gsa2;p=gov+gsa2;a=telemail;c=us

Interagency (Federal) E-mail Users' Working Group:

    X.400:g=mike;s=stein;o=epa;p=gov+epa;a=attmail;c=us

International Telecommunications Union (ITU) official electronic mail address.

    X.400: s=itumail;p=itu;a=arcom;c=ch

International Telecommunications Union (ITU) help desk address.

    X.400: s=helpdesk;p=itu;a=arcom;c=ch

Mailnet (Finland) demonstration/test address for automatic answering of a message.

    X.400: s=autoanswer;a=mailnet;c=fi

Singapore Telecom demonstration/test address for automatic answering of a message.

    X.400: s=autoanswer;o=svc;a=sgmhs;c=sg

9

CompuServe and MCI Mail

The purpose of this chapter is to provide readers with information concerning the use of two commercial electronic massaging services. First we will examine the use of CompuServe's electronic mail facility. Next, we will turn our attention to MCI Mail. In doing so we will note the telephone access numbers you can dial to connect to each electronic mail service, the commands used to create and transmit different types of messages, and examples of the actual creation and transmission of messages on each service to subscribers of other electronic massaging services. The types of electronic messages that can be transmitted through the use of both systems range in scope from electronic mailbox to electronic mailbox messages to messages delivered via telex and fax.

COMPUSERVE ACCESS TELEPHONE NUMBERS

CANADA

City	St	Phone	Baud				Modem type
Calgary	AB	403/294-9155	300	1200	2400		CPS 224MNP
Calgary	AB	403/294-9120				9600	CPS V.302
Edmonton	AB	403/466-5083	300	1200	2400		CPS 224MNP
Edmonton	AB	403/440-2744				9600	CPS V.32/V.42

UNITED STATES

City	St	Phone	Baud				Modem type
Anchorage	AK	907/563-8425	300	1200	2400		CPS 224MNP
Fairbanks	AK	907/479-4102	300	1200	2400		CPS 224MNP
Birmingham	AL	205/558-4000	300	1200	2400		CPS 224MNP
Birmingham	AL	205/933-6212				9600	CPS V.32/V.42
Dothan	AL	205/671-3917	300	1200	2400		CPS 224MNP
Florence	AL	205/766-9925	300	1200	2400		CPS 224MNP
Huntsville	AL	205/536-1346	300	1200	2400		CPS 224MNP
Mobile	AL	205/660-6920	300	1200	2400		CPS 224MNP
Mobile	AL	205/660-6948				9600	CPS V.32/V.42
Montgomery	AL	205/260-0171	300	1200	2400		CPS 224MNP
Montgomery	AL	205/270-5845				9600	CPS V.32/V.42
Tuscaloosa	AL	205/553-1120	300	1200	2400		CPS 224MNP
Fayetteville	AR	501/521-5386	300	1200	2400		CPS 224MNP
Fayetteville	AR	501/521-3774				9600	CPS V.32/V.42
Little Rock	AR	501/376-8374	300	1200	2400		CPS 224MNP
Little Rock	AR	501/376-8544				9600	CPS V.32/V.42
Phoenix	AZ	602/955-1464	300	1200	2400		CPS 224MNP
Phoenix	AZ	602/468-0285				9600	CPS V.32/V.42
Sierra Vista	AZ	602/459-6390	300	1200	2400		CPS 224MNP
Tucson	AZ	602/745-8745	300	1200	240		CPS 224MNP
Tucson	AZ	602/750-9575				1200	CPS VADIC
Tucson	AZ	602/571-0207				9600	CPS V.32/V.42
Yuma	AZ	602/782-7191	300	1200	2400		CPS 224MNP
Vancouver	BC	604/737-2452	300	1200	2400		CPS 224MNP
Vancouver	BC	604/739-8194				9600	CPS V.32/V.42
Anaheim	CA	714/520-5231	300	1200	2400		CPS 224MNP
Anaheim	CA	714/563-9431				9600	CPS V.32/V.42
Bakersfield	CA	805/324-0971	300	1200	2400		CPS 224MNP
Bakersfield	CA	805/324-4303				9600	CPS V.32/V.42
Castro Valley	CA	510/889-0369	300	1200	2400		CPS 224MNP
Chula Vista	CA	619/498-0099	300	1200	2400		CPS 224MNP
Culver City	CA	310/397-7887	300	1200	2400		CPS 224MNP
Culver City	CA	310/390-4188				9600	CPS V.32/V.42
Davis	CA	916/661-7250	300	1200	2400		CPS 224MNP
Davis	CA	916/661-9296				9600	CPS V.32/V.42
Encinitas	CA	619/753-2728	300	1200	2400		CPS 224MNP
Encinitas	CA	619/753-0235				9600	CPS V.32/V.42
Fresno	CA	209/251-2890	300	1200	2400		CPS 224MNP
Fresno	CA	209/453-1487				9600	CPS V.32/V.42
Lancaster	CA	805/942-3888	300	1200	2400		CPS 224MNP
Long Beach	CA	310/599-5966	300	1200	2400		CPS 224MNP
Long Beach	CA	310/591-5768				9600	CPS V.32/V.42
Los Angeles	CA	213/629-4095	300	1200	2400		CPS 224MNP
Los Angeles	CA	213/689-9019				1200	CPS VADIC
Los Angeles	CA	213/624-3730				9600	CPS V.32/V.42

City	St	Phone	Baud				Modem type
Los Angeles	CA	213/623-7486				14.4	CPS V32/BIS
Modesto	CA	209/521-9970	300	1200	2400		CPS 224MNP
Monterey	CA	408/646-1687	300	200	2400		CPS 224MNP
N. Hollywood	CA	818/506-6734	300	1200	2400		CPS 224MNP
N. Hollywood	CA	818/752-8045				9600	CPS V.32/V.42
Napa	CA	707/257-7710	300	1200	2400		CPS 224MNP
Newport Beach	CA	714/833-9915	300	1200	2400		CPS 224MNP
Newport Beach	CA	714/252-1131				9600	CPS V.32/V.42
Newport Beach	CA	714/263-0244				14.4	CPS V32/BIS
Oakland	CA	510/482-0190	300	1200	2400		CPS 224MNP
Oakland	CA	510/530-3393				9600	CPS V.32/V.42
Oxnard	CA	805/486-3386	300	1200	2400		CPS 224MNP
Palm Springs	CA	619/325-4584	300	200	2400		CPS 224MNP
Pleasant Hill	CA	510/682-0762	300	1200	2400		CPS 224MNP
Pleasant Hill	CA	510/682-2055				9600	CPS V.32/V.42
Pleasanton	CA	510/373-0546	300	1200	2400		CPS 224MNP
Pomona	CA	909/622-5454	300	1200	2400		CPS 224MNP
Pomona	CA	909/865-0553				9600	CPS V.32/V.42
Redding	CA	916/223-1144	300	1200	2400		CPS 224MNP
Riverside	CA	909/358-1300	300	1200	2400		CPS 224MNP
Riverside	CA	909/358-0205				9600	CPS V.32/V.42
Sacramento	CA	916/568-0636	300	1200	2400		CPS 224MNP
Sacramento	CA	916/568-0241				9600	CPS V.32/V.42
Salinas	CA	408/754-2751	300	1200	2400		CPS 224MNP
San Bernardino	CA	909/882-9626	300	1200	2400		CPS 224MNP
San Bernardino	CA	909/882-6646				9600	CPS V.32/V.42
San Diego	CA	619/569-4282	300	1200	2400		CPS 224MNP
San Diego	CA	619/467-9508				9600	CPS V.32/V.42
San Francisco	CA	415/296-8362	300	1200	2400		CPS 224MNP
San Francisco	CA	415/296-8972				1200	CPS VADIC
San Francisco	CA	415/434-1580				9600	CPS V.32/V.42
San Luis Obispo	CA	805/549-8605	300	1200	2400		CPS 224MNP
San Marcos	CA	619/471-0960	300	1200	2400		CPS 224MNP
San Mateo	CA	415/591-5415	300	1200	2400		CPS 224MNP
San Mateo	CA	415/802-0130				9600	CPS V.32/V.42
San Rafael	CA	415/454-9935	300	1200	2400		CPS 224MNP
San Rafael	CA	415/721-7226				9600	CPS V.32/V.42
Santa Barbara	CA	805/968-7079	300	1200	2400		CPS 224MNP
Santa Barbara	CA	805/968-8210				9600	CPS V.32/V.42
Santa Clara	CA	408/988-5366	300	1200	2400		CPS 224MNP
Santa Clara	CA	408/727-8113				9600	CPS V.32/V.42
Santa Clara	CA	408/980-1044				14.4	CPS V32/BIS
Santa Cruz	CA	408/476-0126	300	1200	2400		CPS 224MNP
Santa Cruz	CA	408/462-9666				9600	CPS V.32/V.42
Santa Maria	CA	805/934-5322	300	1200	2400		CPS 224MNP
Santa Maria	CA	805/937-5490				9600	CPS V.32/V.42

City	St	Phone	Baud				Modem type
Santa Rosa	CA	707/579-4611	300	1200	2400		CPS 224MNP
Santa Rosa	CA	707/579-1588				9600	CPS V.32/V.42
Sierra Madre	CA	818/303-5780	300	1200	2400		CPS 224MNP
Sierra Madre	CA	818/303-3869				9600	CPS V.32/V.42
So. Lake Tahoe	CA	916/541-5940	300	1200	2400		CPS 224MNP
Stockton	CA	209/465-7284	300	1200	2400		CPS 224MNP
Thousand Oaks	CA	805/498-3453	300	1200	2400		CPS 224MNP
Thousand Oaks	CA	805/499-6110				9600	CPS V.32/V.42
Torrance	CA	310/214-1442	300	1200	2400		CPS 224MNP
Torrance	CA	310/370-2831				9600	CPS V.32/V.42
Vallejo	CA	707/645-8880	300	1200	2400		CPS 224MNP
Van Nuys	CA	818/786-6382	300	1200	2400		CPS 224MNP
Van Nuys	CA	818/988-9791				9600	CPS V.32/V.42
Ventura	CA	805/648-1906	300	1200	2400		CPS 224MNP
Aspen	CO	303/925-5892	300	1200	2400		CPS 224MNP
Colorado Sprngs	CO	719/596-0910	300	1200	2400		CPS 224MNP
Denver	CO	303/623-4711				1200	CPS VADIC
Denver	CO	303/629-9145	300	1200	2400		CPS 224MNP
Denver	CO	303/595-0123				9600	CPS V.32/V.42
Dillon	CO	303/668-0991	300	1200	2400		CPS 224MNP
Durango	CO	303/259-5880	300	1200	2400		CPS 224MNP
Ft. Collins	CO	303/223-1535	300	1200	2400		CPS 224MNP
Glenwood Spring	CO	303/945-0351	300	1200	2400		CPS 224MNP
Grand Junction	CO	303/241-1885	300	1200	2400		CPS 224MNP
Greeley	CO	303/356-1180	300	1200	2400		CPS 224MNP
Longmont	CO	303/651-3207	300	1200	2400		CPS 224MNP
Loveland	CO	303/663-0992	300	1200	2400		CPS 224MNP
Pueblo	CO	719/546-1891	300	1200	2400		CPS 224MNP
Steamboat Spngs	CO	303/879-4900	300	1200	2400		CPS 224MNP
Vail	CO	303/949-1336	300	1200	2400		CPS 224MNP
Bridgeport	CT	203/926-0316	300	1200	2400		CPS 224MNP
Bridgeport	CT	203/929-4918				9600	CPS V.32/V.42
Danbury	CT	203/794-9169	300	1200	2400		CPS 224MNP
East Haven	CT	203/387-8528	300	1200	2400		CPS 224MNP
East Haven	CT	203/397-0512				9600	CPS V.32/V.42
Hartford	CT	203/548-9369	300	1200	2400		CPS 224MNP
Hartford	CT	203/727-8708				9600	CPS V.32/V.42
New London	CT	203/444-2509	300	1200	2400		CPS 224MNP
Stamford	CT	203/324-8943	300	1200	2400		CPS 224MNP
Stamford	CT	203/324-1115				9600	CPS V.32/V.42
Waterbury	CT	203/756-5022	300	1200	2400		CPS 224MNP
Waterbury	CT	203/756-2832				1200	CPS VADIC
Westport	CT	203/222-8558	300	1200	2400		CPS 224MNP
Washington	DC	202/547-0061	300	1200	2400		CPS 224MNP
Washington	DC	202/547-0103				9600	CPS V.32/V.42
Rehoboth Beach	DE	302/945-5245	300	1200	2400		CPS 224MNP

City	St	Phone	Baud				Modem type
Wilmington	DE	302/452-1370	300	1200	2400		CPS 224MNP
Wilmington	DE	302/452-1448				9600	CPS V.32/V.42
Daytona Beach	FL	904/258-8433	300	1200	2400		CPS 224MNP
Deerfield Beach	FL	305/429-0552	300	1200	2400		CPS 224MNP
Deerfield Beach	FL	305/426-0228				9600	CPS V.32/V.42
Ft. Lauderdale	FL	305/772-1339	300	1200	2400		CPS 224MNP
Ft. Lauderdale	FL	305/772-9264				9600	CPS V.32/V.42
Ft. Myers	FL	813/337-0136	300	1200 2400			CPS 224MNP
Gainesville	FL	904/377-5227	300	1200	2400		CPS 224MNP
Gainesville	FL	904/371-0661				9600	CPS V.32/V.42
Jacksonville	FL	904/448-5624	300	1200	2400		CPS 224MNP
Jacksonville	FL	904/730-0046				9600	CPS V.32/V.42
Kissimmee	FL	407/933-5703	300	1200	2400		CPS 224MNP
Melbourne	FL	407/723-2622	300	1200	2400		CPS 224MNP
Miami	FL	305/262-1643	300	1200	2400		CPS 224MNP
Miami	FL	305/262-9325				9600	CPS V.32/V.42
Naples	FL	813/566-9562	300	1200	2400		CPS 224MNP
Naples	FL	813/566-7015				9600	CPS V.32/V.42
Orlando	FL	407/896-3053	300	1200	2400		CPS 224MNP
Orlando	FL	407/896-6122				9600	CPS V.32/V.42
Orlando	FL	407/894-0199				14.4	CPS V32/BIS
Panama City	FL	904/871-0660	300	1200	2400		CPS 224MNP
Pensacola	FL	904/432-1007	300	1200	2400		CPS 224MNP
Sarasota	FL	813/355-0832	300	1200	2400		CPS 224MNP
St. Petersburg	FL	813/896-1001	300	1200	2400		CPS 224MNP
St. Petersburg	FL	813/896-8007				9600	CPS V.32/V.42
Tallahassee	FL	904/385-8699	300	1200	2400		CPS 224MNP
Tallahassee	FL	904/422-9604				9600	CPS V.32/V.42
Tampa	FL	813/229-7406	300	1200	2400		CPS 224MNP
Tampa	FL	813/229-3200				9600	CPS V.32/V.42
Vero Beach	FL	407/778-0550	300	1200	2400		CPS 224MNP
West Palm Beach	FL	407/863-7031	300	1200	2400		CPS 224MNP
West Palm Beach	FL	407/881-7439			1200		CPS VADIC
West Palm Beach	FL	407/840-1219				9600	CPS V.32/V.42
Winter Haven	FL	813/293-3911	300	1200	2400		CPS 224MNP
Albany	GA	912/435-9420	300	1200	2400		CPS 224MNP
Athens	GA	706/353-6133	300	1200	2400		CPS 224MNP
Athens	GA	706/353-6120				9600	CPS V.32/V.42
Atlanta	GA	404/266-7060	300	1200	2400		CPS 224MNP
Atlanta	GA	404/261-0646			1200		CPS VADIC
Atlanta	GA	404/841-0578				9600	CPS V.32/V.42
Augusta	GA	706/738-3018	300	1200	2400		CPS 224MNP
Brunswick	GA	912/264-0351	300	1200	2400		CPS 224MNP
Brunswick	GA	912/265-0527				9600	CPS V.32/V.42
Columbus	GA	706/596-2700	300	1200	2400		CPS 224MNP
Macon	GA	912/929-0804	300	1200	2400		CPS 224MNP

City	St	Phone	Baud				Modem type
Macon	GA	912/922-2179				9600	CPS V.32/V.42
Savannah	GA	912/355-0222	300	1200	2400		CPS 224MNP
Savannah	GA	912/353-8559				9600	CPS V.32/V.42
Honolulu	HI	808/521-6292	300	1200	2400		CPS 224MNP
Honolulu	HI	808/528-0430				9600	CPS V.32/V.42
Maui	HI	808/871-8328	300	1200	2400		CPS 224MNP
Cedar Rapids	IA	319/364-1437	300	1200	2400		CPS 224MNP
Davenport	IA	319/323-7388	300	1200	2400		CPS 224MNP
Des Moines	IA	515/276-5992	300	1200	2400		CPS 224MNP
Des Moines	IA	515/276-7231				9600	CPS V.32/V.42
Boise	ID	208/344-1845	300	1200	2400		CPS 224MNP
Ketchum	ID	208/788-5060	300	1200	2400		CPS 224MNP
Pocatello	ID	208/232-9452	300	1200	2400		CPS 224MNP
Aurora	IL	708/801-9488	300	1200	2400		CPS 224MNP
Aurora	IL	708/801-9468				9600	CPS V.32/V.42
Bloomington	IL	309/827-3343	300	1200	2400		CPS 224MNP
Champaign	IL	217/352-0041	300	1200	2400		CPS 224MNP
Champaign	IL	217/356-1082				9600	CPS V.32/V.42
Chicago	IL	312/372-1402				1200	CPS VADIC
Chicago	IL	312/263-5636	300	1200	2400		CPS 224MNP
Chicago	IL	312/693-0330	300	1200	2400		CPS 224MNP
Chicago	IL	312/201-0711				9600	CPS V.32/V.42
Chicago	IL	312/693-4100				9600	CPS V.32/V.42
Chicago	IL	312/857-0008				14.4	CPS V32/BIS
Decatur	IL	217/422-2075	300	1200	2400		CPS 224MNP
Dekalb	IL	815/748-5288	300	1200	2400		CPS 224MNP
Kankakee	IL	815/933-3782	300	1200	2400		CPS 224MNP
Lombard	IL	708/261-1400	300	1200	2400		CPS 224MNP
Lombard	IL	708/261-0040				9600	CPS V.32/V.42
Peoria	IL	309/685-1275	300	1200	2400		CPS 224MNP
Rockford	IL	815/226-8211	300	1200	2400		CPS 224MNP
Springfield	IL	217/789-0944	300	1200	2400		CPS 224MNP
Bloomington	IN	812/330-1327	300	1200	2400		CPS 224MNP
Bloomington	IN	812/330-1424				9600	CPS V.32/V.42
Elkhart	IN	219/294-8629	300	1200	2400		CPS 224MNP
Evansville	IN	812/479-0165	300	1200	2400		CPS 224MNP
Ft. Wayne	IN	219/447-0510	300	1200	2400		CPS 224MNP
Gary	IN	219/884-4940	300	1200	2400		CPS 224MNP
Indianapolis	IN	317/638-5785	1200				CPS VADIC
Indianapolis	IN	317/631-6824	300	1200	2400		CPS 224MNP
Indianapolis	IN	317/638-8129				9600	CPS V.32/V.42
Lafayette	IN	317/448-9925	300	1200	2400		CPS 224MNP
Lafayette	IN	317/447-5557				9600	CPS V.32/V.42
Muncie	IN	317/284-3812	300	1200	2400		CPS 224MNP
Richmond	IN	317/935-0061	300	1200	2400		CPS 224MNP
South Bend	IN	219/271-0489	1200				CPS VADIC

City	St	Phone	Baud				Modem type
South Bend	IN	219/271-9197	300	1200	2400		CPS 224MNP
South Bend	IN	219/271-0016				9600	CPS V.32/V.42
Warsaw	IN	219/267-7712	300	1200	2400		CPS 224MNP
Lawrence	KS	913/843-0140	300	1200	2400		CPS 224MNP
Lawrence	KS	913/749-2900				9600	CPS V.32/V.42
Manhattan	KS	913/776-7111	300	1200	2400		CPS 224MNP
Topeka	KS	913/232-9520	300	1200	2400		CPS 224MNP
Topeka	KS	913/232-1317				9600	CPS V.32/V.42
Wichita	KS	316/689-8132	300	1200	2400		CPS 224MNP
Wichita	KS	316/687-0634				9600	CPS V.32/V.42
Lexington	KY	606/254-0585	300	1200	2400		CPS 224MNP
Lexington	KY	606/254-6557				9600	CPS V.32/V.42
Louisville	KY	502/583-1277	300	1200	2400		CPS 224MNP
Louisville	KY	502/568-6250				9600	CPS V.32/V.42
Owensboro	KY	502/683-0777	300	1200	2400		CPS 224MNP
Baton Rouge	LA	504/383-9801	300	1200	2400		CPS 224MNP
Baton Rouge	LA	504/383-9998				9600	CPS V.32/V.42
Lafayette	LA	318/234-9880	300	1200	2400		CPS 224MNP
Lake Charles	LA	318/433-0215	300	1200	2400		CPS 224MNP
Monroe	LA	318/324-9982	300	1200	2400		CPS 224MNP
New Orleans	LA	504/585-1200	300	1200	2400		CPS 224MNP
New Orleans	LA	504/585-1120				9600	CPS V.32/V.42
Shreveport	LA	318/424-5380	300	1200	2400		CPS 224MNP
Amherst	MA	413/549-7431	300	1200	2400		CPS 224MNP
Billerica	MA	508/667-2939	300	1200	2400		CPS 224MNP
Billerica	MA	508/667-1765				9600	CPS V.32/V.42
Boston	MA	617/542-1779		1200			CPS VADIC
Boston	MA	617/482-7061	300	1200	2400		CPS 224MNP
Boston	MA	617/426-9295				9600	CPS V.32/V.42
Brockton	MA	508/588-1837	300	1200	2400		CPS 224MNP
Cambridge	MA	617/661-7071				9600	CPS V.32/V.42
Cambridge	MA	617/868-0524	300	1200	2400		CPS 224MNP
Cambridge	MA	617/576-0013				14.4	CPS V32/BIS
Fall River	MA	508/677-0405	300	1200	2400		CPS 224MNP
Framingham	MA	508/820-9349	300	1200	2400		CPS 224MNP
Framingham	MA	508/371-0354	300	1200	2400		CPS 224MNP
Groton	MA	508/448-3007	300	1200	2400		CPS 224MNP
Hudson	MA	508/568-8019	300	1200	2400		CPS 224MNP
Lawrence	MA	508/975-2040	300	1200	2400		CPS 224MNP
Maynard	MA	508/897-4746	300	1200	2400		CPS 224MNP
Medfield	MA	508/359-7603	300	1200	2400		CPS 224MNP
Medway	MA	508/533-2722	300	1200	2400		CPS 224MNP
Mendon	MA	508/478-0653	300	1200	2400		CPS 224MNP
Springfield	MA	413/747-4400	300	1200	2400		CPS 224MNP
Springfield	MA	413/747-4460				9600	CPS V.32/V.42
Westborough	MA	508/366-2617	300	1200	2400		CPS 224MNP

City	St	Phone	Baud				Modem type
Worcester	MA	508/791-0745	300	1200	2400		CPS 224MNP
Worcester	MA	508/849-1000				9600	CPS V.32/V.42
Winnipeg	MB	204/489-9292	300	1200	2400		CPS 224MNP
Winnipeg	MB	204/489-9747				9600	CPS V.32/V.42
Annapolis	MD	410/266-7530	300	1200	2400		CPS 224MNP
Baltimore	MD	410/832-2702		1200			CPS VADIC
Baltimore	MD	410/832-0160	300	1200	2400		CPS 224MNP
Baltimore	MD	410/494-8403				9600	CPS V.32/V.42
Hyattsville	MD	301/403-1600	300	1200	2400		CPS 224MNP
Hyattsville	MD	301/403-1687				9600	CPS V.32/V.42
Ocean City	MD	410/548-1502	300	1200	2400		CPS 224MNP
Portland	ME	207/871-1276	300	1200	2400		CPS 224MNP
Portland	ME	207/775-6249				9600	CPS V.32/V.42
Ann Arbor	MI	313/769-2012	300	1200	2400		CPS 224MNP
Ann Arbor	MI	313/761-9300				9600	CPS V.32/V.42
Detroit	MI	313/535-1122	300	1200	2400		CPS 224MNP
Detroit	MI	313/535-0084		1200			CPS VADIC
Detroit	MI	313/535-1466				9600	CPS V.32/V.42
Flint	MI	313/238-6202	300	1200	2400		CPS 224MNP
Grand Rapids	MI	616/957-9733	300	1200	2400		CPS 224MNP
Grand Rapids	MI	616/956-0075				9600	CPS V.32/V.42
Kalamazoo	MI	616/373-3700	300	1200	2400		CPS 224MNP
Kalamazoo	MI	616/373-3750				9600	CPS V.32/V.42
Lansing	MI	517/332-6808	300	1200	2400		CPS 224MNP
Lansing	MI	517/332-7141				9600	CPS V.32/V.42
Mt. Clemens	MI	313/463-1945	300	1200	2400		CPS 224MNP
Pontiac	MI	313/334-2900	300	1200	2400		CPS 224MNP
Pontiac	MI	313/335-2680				9600	CPS V.32/V.42
Saginaw	MI	517/754-9177	300	1200	2400		CPS 224MNP
Saginaw	MI	517/753-5100				9600	CPS V.32/V.42
Troy	MI	313/362-3242	300	1200	2400		CPS 224MNP
Troy	MI	313/244-8740				9600	CPS V.32/V.42
Duluth	MN	218/722-0058	300	1200	2400		CPS 224MNP
Mankato	MN	507/388-8723	300	1200	2400		CPS 224MNP
Minneapolis	MN	612/375-0328		1200			CPS VADIC
Minneapolis	MN	612/339-2507	300	1200	2400		CPS 224MNP
Minneapolis	MN	612/339-1805				9600	CPS V.32/V.42
Rochester	MN	507/285-1277	300	1200	2400		CPS 224MNP
Branson	MO	417/336-5786	300	1200	2400		CPS 224MNP
Columbia	MO	314/875-0746	300	1200	2400		CPS 224MNP
Jefferson City	MO	314/635-9170	300	1200	2400		CPS 224MNP
Kansas City	MO	816/472-1283	300	1200	2400		CPS 224MNP
Kansas City	MO	816/221-3817				9600	CPS V.32/V.42
Springfield	MO	417/887-8422	300	1200	2400		CPS 224MNP
St. Louis	MO	314/241-3110		1200			CPS VADIC
St. Louis	MO	314/241-5337	300	1200	2400		CPS 224MNP

City	St	Phone	Baud				Modem type
St. Louis	MO	314/421-5651				9600	CPS V.32/V.42
Jackson	MS	601/948-6411	300	1200	2400		CPS 224MNP
Jackson	MS	601/352-5182				9600	CPS V.32/V.42
Billings	MT	406/245-0863	300	1200	2400		CPS 224MNP
Helena	MT	406/449-3680	300	1200	2400		CPS 224MNP
Asheville	NC	704/274-9491	300	1200	2400		CPS 224MNP
Burlington	NC	919/584-8808	300	1200	2400		CPS 224MNP
Charlotte	NC	704/331-0905	300	1200	2400		CPS 224MNP
Charlotte	NC	704/358-8991				9600	CPS V.32/V.42
Durham	NC	919/687-4300	300	1200	2400		CPS 224MNP
Durham	NC	919/687-4049				9600	CPS V.32/V.42
Greensboro	NC	919/272-4994	300	1200	2400		CPS 224MNP
Raleigh	NC	919/664-5800	300	1200	2400		CPS 224MNP
Raleigh	NC	919/664-5848				9600	CPS V.32/V.42
Wilmington	NC	919/392-4700	300	1200	2400		CPS 224MNP
Winston-Salem	NC	919/723-9471	300	1200	2400		CPS 224MNP
Winston-Salem	NC	919/724-9748				9600	CPS V.32/V.42
Fargo	ND	701/232-0904	300	1200	2400		CPS 224MNP
Lincoln	NE	402/474-9005	300	1200	2400		CPS 224MNP
Lincoln	NE	402/474-2316				9600	CPS V.32/V.42
Omaha	NE	402/345-3602		1200			CPS VADIC
Omaha	NE	402/345-5012	300	1200	2400		CPS 224MNP
Omaha	NE	402/345-9557				9600	CPS V.32/V.42
Concord	NH	603/225-7322				9600	CPS V.32/V.42
Concord	NH	603/225-4277	300	1200	2400		CPS 224MNP
Manchester	NH	603/625-2940	300	1200	2400		CPS 224MNP
Nashua	NH	603/886-6035	300	1200	2400		CPS 224MNP
Nashua	NH	603/886-6080				9600	CPS V.32/V.42
Atlantic City	NJ	609/645-8778	300	1200	2400		CPS 224MNP
Atlantic City	NJ	609/641-1460				9600	CPS V.32/V.42
Bound Brook	NJ	908/356-4747	300	1200	2400		CPS 224MNP
Cherry Hill	NJ	609/482-8770	300	1200	2400		CPS 224MNP
Cherry Hill	NJ	609/667-8865				9600	CPS V.32/V.42
Eatontown	NJ	908/935-0065	300	1200	2400		CPS 224MNP
Eatontown	NJ	908/935-0137				9600	CPS V.32/V.42
Hackettstown	NJ	908/852-8502	300	1200	2400		CPS 224MNP
Montclair	NJ	201/783-5400	300	1200	2400		CPS 224MNP
Montclair	NJ	201/783-0644				9600	CPS V.32/V.42
Morristown	NJ	201/984-7921	300	1200	2400		CPS 224MNP
Morristown	NJ	201/984-7633		1200			CPS VADIC
Morristown	NJ	201/984-5113				9600	CPS V.32/V.42
Newark	NJ	201/643-0404	300	1200	2400		CPS 224MNP
Newark	NJ	201/623-5666				9600	CPS V.32/V.42
Princeton	NJ	609/921-2207		1200			CPS VADIC
Princeton	NJ	609/921-2855	300	1200	2400		CPS 224MNP
Princeton	NJ	609/497-2384				9600	CPS V.32/V.42

City	St	Phone	Baud				Modem type
Ridgewood	NJ	201/444-3913	300	1200	2400		CPS 224MNP
Rochelle Park	NJ	201/368-8300	300	1200	2400		CPS 224MNP
Rochelle Park	NJ	201/368-0912				9600	CPS V.32/V.42
Rochelle Park	NJ	201/712-0479				14.4	CPS V32/BIS
Toms River	NJ	908/914-0405	300	1200	2400		CPS 224MNP
Toms River	NJ	908/914-1954				9600	CPS V.32/V.42
Trenton	NJ	609/530-9521	300	1200	2400		CPS 224MNP
Trenton	NJ	609/530-1517				9600	CPS V.32/V.42
Wayne	NJ	201/696-6104	300	1200	2400		CPS 224MNP
Woodbridge	NJ	908/632-8755	300	1200	2400		CPS 224MNP
Woodbridge	NJ	908/632-9384				9600	CPS V.32/V.42
Albuquerque	NM	505/265-7046		1200			CPS VADIC
Albuquerque	NM	505/255-8626	300	1200	2400		CPS 224MNP
Farmington	NM	505/326-2305	300	1200	2400		CPS 224MNP
Farmington	NM	505/326-5338				9600	CPS V.32/V.42
Los Alamos	NM	505/662-4122	300	1200	2400		CPS 224MNP
Las Vegas	NV	702/737-1292	300	1200	2400		CPS 224MNP
Las Vegas	NV	702/796-4877				9600	CPS V.32/V.42
Reno	NV	702/323-6608	300	1200	2400		CPS 224MNP
Reno	NV	702/322-8968				9600	CPS V.32/V.42
Albany	NY	518/439-8104	300	1200	2400		CPS 224MNP
Binghamton	NY	607/724-1171	300	1200	2400		CPS 224MNP
Buffalo	NY	716/875-3711	300	1200	2400		CPS 224MNP
Buffalo	NY	716/876-7680				9600	CPS V.32/V.42
Ithaca	NY	607/257-0155	300	1200	2400		CPS 224MNP
Ithaca	NY	607/257-4264				9600	CPS V.32/V.42
Lake Grove	NY	516/981-1120	300	1200	2400		CPS 224MNP
Limestone	NY	716/925-7042	300	1200	2400		CPS 224MNP
Long Island	NY	516/932-2088	300	1200	2400		CPS 224MNP
Long Island	NY	516/937-1719				9600	CPS V.32/V.42
Middletown	NY	914/344-3800	300	1200	2400		CPS 224MNP
New York	NY	212/608-9012		1200			CPS VADIC
New York	NY	212/758-0330		1200			CPS VADIC
New York	NY	212/608-6021	300	1200	2400		CPS 224MNP
New York	NY	212/888-1020	300	1200	2400		CPS 224MNP
New York	NY	212/766-2080				9600	CPS V.32/V.42
New York	NY	212/593-3972				9600	CPS V.32/V.42
New York	NY	212/755-9080				14.4	CPS V32/BIS
Niagara Falls	NY	716/284-3570	300	1200	2400		CPS 224MNP
Poughkeepsie	NY	914/473-5991	300	1200	2400		CPS 224MNP
Rochester	NY	716/647-1567	300	1200	2400		CPS 224MNP
Rochester	NY	716/254-1390				9600	CPS V.32/V.42
Syracuse	NY	315/451-0337	300	1200	2400		CPS 224MNP
Syracuse	NY	315/451-8093				9600	CPS V.32/V.42
Tonawanda	NY	716/694-6263	300	1200	2400		CPS 224MNP
Utica	NY	315/737-2101	300	1200	2400		CPS 224MNP

City	St	Phone	Baud				Modem type
White Plains	NY	914/761-3163	300	1200	2400		CPS 224MNP
White Plains	NY	914/761-9780				9600	CPS V.32/V.42
Williston Park	NY	516/222-6850	300	1200	2400		CPS 224MNP
Williston Park	NY	516/222-8050				9600	CPS V.32/V.42
Akron	OH	216/869-5085	300	1200	2400		CPS 224MNP
Akron	OH	216/836-0679				9600	CPS V.32/V.42
Athens	OH	614/592-2109	300	1200	2400		CPS 224MNP
Cambridge	OH	614/439-7360	300	1200	2400		CPS 224MNP
Canton	OH	216/452-3491	300	1200	2400		CPS 224MNP
Cincinnati	OH	513/771-8543	300	1200	2400		CPS 224MNP
Cincinnati	OH	513/771-0592				9600	CPS V.32/V.42
Cleveland	OH	216/781-4135	300	1200	2400		CPS 224MNP
Cleveland	OH	216/781-7598				9600	CPS V.32/V.42
Columbus	OH	614/442-2082		1200			CPS VADIC
Columbus	OH	614/457-2105	300	1200	2400		CPS 224MNP
Columbus	OH	614/761-1133	300	1200	2400		CPS 224MNP
Columbus	OH	614/876-2116	300	1200	2400		CPS 224MNP
Columbus	OH	614/792-0669				9600	CPS V.32/V.42
Columbus	OH	614/764-2957				14.4	CPS V32/BIS
CompuServe 800	OH	800/848-4480	300	1200	2400		CPS 224MNP
CompuServe 800	OH	800/331-7166				9600	CPS V.32/V.42
CompuServe 800	OH	800/544-3095				14.4	CPS V32/BIS
Dayton	OH	513/226-1907	300	1200	2400		CPS 224MNP
Dayton	OH	513/224-4576				9600	CPS V.32/V.42
Granville	OH	614/587-0932	300	1200	2400		CPS 224MNP
Ravenna	OH	216/678-5066	300	1200	2400		CPS 224MNP
Toledo	OH	419/243-2818	300	1200	2400		CPS 224MNP
Toledo	OH	419/242-5706				9600	CPS V.32/V.42
Youngstown	OH	216/757-0084	300	1200	2400		CPS 224MNP
Lawton	OK	405/355-4747	300	1200	2400		CPS 224MNP
Lawton	OK	405/355-8118				9600	CPS V.32/V.42
Oklahoma City	OK	405/945-1018	300	1200	2400		CPS 224MNP
Oklahoma City	OK	405/942-7278				9600	CPS V.32/V.42
Stillwater	OK	405/624-5107	300	1200	2400		CPS 224MNP
Tulsa	OK	918/621-1000		1200			CPS VADIC
Tulsa	OK	918/621-1002	300	1200	2400		CPS 224MNP
Tulsa	OK	918/621-1036				9600	CPS V.32/V.42
Ottawa	ON	613/830-7385	300	1200	2400		CPS 224MNP
Toronto	ON	416/367-8122				9600	CPS V.32/V.42
Toronto	ON	416/367-1743	300	1200	2400		CPS 224MNP
Albany	OR	503/967-2460	300	1200	2400		CPS 224MNP
Eugene	OR	503/689-9800	300	1200	2400		CPS 224MNP
Eugene	OR	503/689-6031				9600	CPS V.32/V.42
Medford	OR	503/779-0504	300	1200	2400		CPS 224MNP
Portland	OR	503/295-6000	300	1200	2400		CPS 224MNP
Portland	OR	503/274-6400				9600	CPS V.32/V.42

City	St	Phone	Baud				Modem type
Salem	OR	503/362-2523	300	1200	2400		CPS 224MNP
Salem	OR	503/362-0358				9600	CPS V.32/V.42
Allentown	PA	215/776-1087	300	1200	2400		CPS 224MNP
Allentown	PA	215/776-0801				9600	CPS V.32/V.42
Butler	PA	412/285-8187	300	1200	2400		CPS 224MNP
Carlisle	PA	717/245-2066	300	1200	2400		CPS 224MNP
Carlisle	PA	717/243-6477				9600	CPS V.32/V.42
Erie	PA	814/864-4018	300	1200	2400		CPS 224MNP
Harrisburg	PA	717/545-7116	300	1200	2400		CPS 224MNP
Harrisburg	PA	717/541-0210				9600	CPS V.32/V.42
Norristown	PA	215/277-3708	300	1200	2400		CPS 224MNP
Norristown	PA	215/277-1301				9600	CPS V.32/V.42
Philadelphia	PA	215/563-1305	300	1200	2400		CPS 224MNP
Philadelphia	PA	215/561-1634				9600	CPS V.32/V.42
Philadelphia	PA	215/665-0360				14.4	CPS V32/BIS
Pittsburgh	PA	412/261-4192	300	1200	2400		CPS 224MNP
Pittsburgh	PA	412/391-8218		1200			CPS VADIC
Pittsburgh	PA	412/471-6417				9600	CPS V.32/V.42
Reading	PA	215/375-0914	300	1200	2400		CPS 224MNP
Scranton	PA	717/941-3239	300	1200	2400		CPS 224MNP
Somerset	PA	814/443-6402	300	1200	2400		CPS 224MNP
State College	PA	814/238-7910	300	1200	2400		CPS 224MNP
Wilkes-Barre	PA	717/822-2964	300	1200	2400		CPS 224MNP
York	PA	717/845-7631	300	1200	2400		CPS 224MNP
Montreal	PQ	514/879-8519	300	1200	2400		CPS 224MNP
Montreal	PQ	514/879-5826				9600	CPS V.32/V.42
San Juan	PR	809/722-2999	300	1200	2400		CPS 224MNP
San Juan	PR	809/722-0995				9600	CPS V.32/V.42
Providence	RI	401/438-7960	300	1200	2400		CPS 224MNP
Charleston	SC	803/556-0422		1200			CPS VADIC
Charleston	SC	803/766-8099	300	1200	2400		CPS 224MNP
Charleston	SC	803/763-3423				9600	CPS V.32/V.42
Columbia	SC	803/776-5355	300	1200	2400		CPS 224MNP
Columbia	SC	803/776-2229				9600	CPS V.32/V.42
Greenville	SC	803/676-9777	300	1200	2400		CPS 224MNP
Greenville	SC	803/676-9228				9600	CPS V.32/V.42
Hilton Head	SC	803/842-6314	300	1200	2400		CPS 224MNP
Myrtle Beach	SC	803/238-8625	300	1200	2400		CPS 224MNP
Spartanburg	SC	803/585-9611	300	1200	2400		CPS 224MNP
Rapid City	SD	605/341-3733	300	1200	2400		CPS 224MNP
Chattanooga	TN	615/892-4311	300	1200	2400		CPS 224MNP
Clarksville	TN	615/647-2005	300	1200	2400		CPS 224MNP
Clarksville	TN	615/647-2859				9600	CPS V.32/V.42
Johnson City	TN	615/928-2644	300	1200	2400		CPS 224MNP
Kingsport	TN	615/239-0051	300	1200	2400		CPS 224MNP
Kingsport	TN	615/239-0052				9600	CPS V.32/V.42
Knoxville	TN	615/558-8808	300	1200	2400		CPS 224MNP

City	St	Phone	Baud				Modem type
Knoxville	TN	615/558-8180				9600	CPS V.32/V.42
Memphis	TN	901/323-0220	300	1200	2400		CPS 224MNP
Memphis	TN	901/452-2470		1200			CPS VADIC
Memphis	TN	901/454-6851				9600	CPS V.32/V.42
Nashville	TN	615/360-7923	300	1200	2400		CPS 224MNP
Nashville	TN	615/367-0014				9600	CPS V.32/V.42
Abilene	TX	915/698-1111	300	1200	2400		CPS 224MNP
Amarillo	TX	806/379-8411	300	1200	2400		CPS 224MNP
Austin	TX	512/444-0566	300	1200	2400		CPS 224MNP
Austin	TX	512/326-1155				9600	CPS V.32/V.42
Beaumont	TX	409/835-0236	300	1200	2400		CPS 224MNP
Brownsville	TX	210/233-6682	300	1200	2400		CPS 224MNP
College Station	TX	409/696-7986	300	1200	2400		CPS 224MNP
Conroe	TX	409/756-8904	300	1200	2400		CPS 224MNP
Corpus Christi	TX	512/882-1465	300	1200	2400		CPS 224MNP
Corpus Christi	TX	512/887-2891				9600	CPS V.32/V.42
Dallas	TX	214/953-1168		1200			CPS VADIC
Dallas	TX	214/953-0436	300	1200	2400		CPS 224MNP
Dallas	TX	214/720-9183				9600	CPS V.32/V.42
Denton	TX	817/387-8900	300	1200	2400		CPS 224MNP
El Paso	TX	915/565-0970	300	1200	2400		CPS 224MNP
El Paso	TX	915/564-0380				9600	CPS V.32/V.42
Ft. Worth	TX	817/685-2700	300	1200	2400		CPS 224MNP
Ft. Worth	TX	817/685-2737				9600	CPS V.32/V.42
Galveston	TX	409/763-5125	300	1200	2400		CPS 224MNP
Houston	TX	713/650-5000	300	1200	2400		CPS 224MNP
Houston	TX	713/650-5143				9600	CPS V.32/V.42
Laredo	TX	210/722-8008	300	1200	2400		CPS 224MNP
Longview	TX	903/753-1479	300	1200	2400		CPS 224MNP
Longview	TX	903/753-0596				9600	CPS V.32/V.42
Lubbock	TX	806/797-0018	300	1200	2400		CPS 224MNP
Lubbock	TX	806/797-0479				9600	CPS V.32/V.42
McAllen	TX	210/318-5750	300	1200	2400		CPS 224MNP
McAllen	TX	210/318-5767				9600	CPS V.32/V.42
Midland	TX	915/561-5811	300	1200	2400		CPS 224MNP
San Angelo	TX	915/942-8787	300	1200	2400		CPS 224MNP
San Antonio	TX	210/736-8600	300	1200	2400		CPS 224MNP
San Antonio	TX	210/736-8645				9600	CPS V.32/V.42
Texarkana	TX	903/832-2077	300	1200	2400		CPS 224MNP
Texarkana	TX	903/832-1066				9600	CPS V.32/V.42
Tyler	TX	903/561-5565	300	1200	2400		CPS 224MNP
Waco	TX	817/776-7090	300	1200	2400		CPS 224MNP
Waco	TX	817/751-9590				9600	CPS V.32/V.42
Kaysville	UT	801/544-0338	300	1200	2400		CPS 224MNP
Kaysville	UT	801/544-3791				9600	CPS V.32/V.42
Park City	UT	801/649-0121	300	1200	2400		CPS 224MNP
Provo	UT	801/377-1120	300	1200	2400		CPS 224MNP

City	St	Phone	Baud				Modem type
Provo	UT	801/375-1748				9600	CPS V.32/V.42
Salt Lake City	UT	801/521-6326	300	1200	2400		CPS 224MNP
Salt Lake City	UT	801/521-9777				9600	CPS V.32/V.42
Charlottesville	VA	804/979-5159	300	1200	2400		CPS 224MNP
Charlottesville	VA	804/295-2846				9600	CPS V.32/V.42
Fairfax	VA	703/352-8750		1200			CPS VADIC
Fairfax	VA	703/591-0506	300	1200	2400		CPS 224MNP
Fairfax	VA	703/591-0461				9600	CPS V.32/V.42
Fredericksburg	VA	703/374-5100	300	1200	2400		CPS 224MNP
Fredericksburg	VA	703/374-5115				9600	CPS V.32/V.42
Manassas	VA	703/368-5707	300	1200	2400		CPS 224MNP
Norfolk	VA	804/855-0241	300	1200	2400		CPS 224MNP
Norfolk	VA	804/855-6499				9600	CPS V.32/V.42
Reston	VA	703/934-2200	300	1200	2400		CPS 224MNP
Reston	VA	703/934-2267				9600	CPS V.32/V.42
Richmond	VA	804/287-8500	300	1200	2400		CPS 224MNP
Richmond	VA	804/287-8566				9600	CPS V.32/V.42
Roanoke	VA	703/265-1013	300	1200	2400		CPS 224MNP
Staunton	VA	703/885-0253	300	1200	2400		CPS 224MNP
Williamsburg	VA	804/888-2556	300	1200	2400		CPS 224MNP
Williamsburg	VA	804/887-5377				9600	CPS V.32/V.42
Burlington	VT	802/862-1575	300	1200	2400		CPS 224MNP
Manchester Ctr	VT	802/362-5580	300	1200	2400		CPS 224MNP
Blaine	WA	206/332-8100	300	1200	2400		CPS 224MNP
Everett	WA	206/252-3550	300	1200	2400		CPS 224MNP
Olympia	WA	206/754-2200	300	1200	2400		CPS 224MNP
Seattle	WA	206/242-5767	300	1200	2400		CPS 224MNP
Seattle	WA	206/242-9992				9600	CPS V.32/V.42
Spokane	WA	509/326-6526	300	1200	2400		CPS 224MNP
Spokane	WA	509/326-0318				9600	CPS V.32/V.42
Tacoma	WA	206/922-7181	300	1200	2400		CPS 224MNP
Tacoma	WA	206/922-1246				9600	CPS V.32/V.42
Appleton	WI	414/731-4345	300	1200	2400		CPS 224MNP
Green Bay	WI	414/494-0917	300	1200	2400		CPS 224MNP
La Crosse	WI	608/785-7530	300	1200	2400		CPS 224MNP
Madison	WI	608/256-5346	300	1200	2400		CPS 224MNP
Madison	WI	608/256-6716				9600	CPS V.32/V.42
Milwaukee	WI	414/453-5132	300	1200	2400		CPS 224MNP
Milwaukee	WI	414/453-3010				9600	CPS V.32/V.42
Sheboygan	WI	414/458-3421	300	1200	2400		CPS 224MNP
Charleston	WV	304/345-9730	300	1200	2400		CPS 224MNP
Huntington	WV	304/733-4010	300	1200	2400		CPS 224MNP
Morgantown	WV	304/291-5884	300	1200	2400		CPS 224MNP
Morgantown	WV	304/291-6783				9600	CPS V.32/V.42
Parkersburg	WV	304/485-4225	300	1200	2400		CPS 224MNP
Wheeling	WV	304/233-9470	300	1200	2400		CPS 224MNP
Casper	WY	307/234-6914	300	1200	2400		CPS 224MNP

City	St	Phone	Baud				Modem type
Cheyenne	WY	307/637-3027	300	1200	2400		CPS 224MNP
Jackson	WY	307/733-1640	300	1200	2400		CPS 224MNP
Laramie	WY	307/742-9641	300	1200	2400		CPS 224MNP
Laramie	WY	307/742-2320				9600	CPS V.32/V.42

COMPUSERVE TOLL FREE TELEPHONE NUMBERS

CompuServe 800	OH	800/848-4480	300	1200	2400			CPS 224MNP
CompuServe 800	OH	800/331-7166				9600		CPS V.32/V.42
CompuServe 800	OH	800/544-3095					14.4	CPS V32/BIS

COMPUSERVE'S CANADIAN ACCESS INSTRUCTIONS

First establish a telephone connection by dialing the CompuServe access number listed below for access from Canada.

City/Province	300-2400B	9600B
Edmonton, AB	403/466-5083	403/440-2744
Vancouver, BC	604/737-2452	604/739-8194
Ottawa, ON	613/830-7385	
Toronto, ON	416/367-1743	416/367-8122
Montreal, PQ	514/879-8519	514/879-5826

Once the connection has been made, enter: RETURN

Once your screen displays CompuServe's network prompt, enter CIS followed by a RETURN after which you will see the User ID prompt. At this point enter your User ID and log on as usual.

To log off from the CompuServe Information Service, enter: OFF

COMPUSERVE INFORMATION

Online Directory Listing of Subscriber names, locations and IDs:

To access the CompuServe directory enter GO DIRECTORY. This action will place you in the member directory from which you can select one of three choices: explanation, member directory search and include/exclude "this" User ID. When performing a member directory search you will be prompted to enter the last name, first name, city, country and state. You may ignore one or more of the previous search criterias, however, if more than 30 members are found you will be prompted to enter or re-enter your search criteria to reduce the number of members located.

COMPUSERVE MAIL COMMANDS

ADDRESS LIST – list the contents of your address book.

ADDRESS BOOK COMMANDS

DELETE – deletes an entry in the address book.

INSERT – adds an entry to the address book.

LIST – displays the names and addresses in the address book.

NAME – enters your name in address book for use in the "FROM:" field for messages you send.

SEARCH name – searches the address book for the specified name.

DELETE – deletes the message just read from your mailbox.

DOWNLOAD – transfers a message from CompuServe mail to your computer.

END – terminates current read cycle and returns to Read Messages Menu.

FILE – files message you just read into a file in your Personal File Area.

FORWARD – forwards a message to another CompuServe subscriber.

NEXT – permits you to process the next message, bypassing the Action Menu.

REPLY – permits you to reply to a message you just read.

REREAD – redisplays the message you just read.

SAVE – saves the message you just read in your mailbox.

SEARCH – searches the address book for the name you specify.

SEND – transmits the message in your workspace.

SEND/RECEIPT – sends a message which generates notification when it is read by the recepient(s).

TYPE – displays the entire message being composed or edited.

COMPUSERVE EDITING COMMANDS

/ABORT – interrupts text being entered and returns you to previous menu.

/ACOPY[n] – copies n lines from the file and appends them to the current contents of the text buffer.

/AMOVE[n] – deletes n lines from the file and appends them to the current contents of the text buffer.

/B – moves the line pointer to the last line in the file.

/C – permits specific changes to be made to a line.

/C[n] [/old-string/new-string/] – changes nth occurrence of old string.

/C[n]/old-string/ – deletes nth occurrence of old string.

/C //new-string/ – inserts new string at the beginning of the line.

/COPY[n] – copies n lines from the file to the empty text buffer.

/D[n] – deletes n lines starting with the current line.

/EXIT – closes files and return to command mode.

/F[/string/] – finds the first occurrence of the specified string at the start of the line.

/GC[string1/string2] – changes string1 to string2 if string1 is in the current line.

/GC[/string1/string2/] – changes every occurrence of string1 to string2.

/GET – inserts the contents of the text buffer into the current file immediately following the current line.

/GET filename – inserts the contents of the specified file at the position of the current line.

/HELP – displays valid EDIT commands.

/I[/string/] – inserts the specified string into the line following the current line.

/L[n][/string/] – locates the first line containing the specified number of occurrences of the indicated string.

/MOVE[n] – deletes the specified number of lines fom the file, relocating them to the empty text buffer.

/N[n] | /[N][-n] – moves the line pointer forward or backward (-) n places.

/P[n] – prints the specified number of lines starting with the current line.

/POS[n] – positions the line pointer to the specified line in the file.

/R[/string/] – replaces the current line with the specified string.

/S[/string/] – searches for the first line that starts with the specified string, ignoring leading nonprintable characters.

/SEND | /SEND/RECEIPT – exits compose mode and generates a prompt for obtaining information required to send the message.

/SET – provides you with the ability to change the method by which messages are displayed (page vs. continuous), the editor being used and other features.

/T – moves the pointer to the top of the file and causes prior changes to the file to become permanent.

/TYPE – displays the contents of the text in your workspace.

/UNC – restores the current line to its state prior to the last change.

/UPLOAD – uploads text into your workspace commencing at the current line.

/W – displays the position of the line pointer.

SENDING AND RECEIVING MAIL VIA COMPUSERVE MAIL

A. Enter GO MAIL to access CompuServe Mail Main Menu. If no messages are pending the first entry is replaced by the message *** No mail waiting *** . Figure 9.1 illustrates the CompuServe Mail lMain Menu when mail is waiting.

B. To read pending mail select 1.

```
CompuServe Mail  Main Menu

1 READ mail, 1 message pending (displayed if mail waiting)

2 COMPOSE a new message
3 UPLOAD a message
4 USE a file from PER area

5 ADDRESS Book
6 SET options

9 Send a CONGRESSgram ($)

Enter choice !
```

Figure 9.1 CompuServe Mail Main Menu

C. To Send mail
1. Select 2, 3 or 4.
2. Enter /EXIT on a line by itself
3. Select entry from CompuServe Mail Send Menu.

CompuServe Mail Send Menu

For current message

1 SEND ($)
2 EDIT
3 TYPE
4 TYPE/POSTAL
5 FILE DRAFT copy
6 SEND with /RECEIPT ($)

Enter choice !1

4. Enter address in response to Send ($) to (Name or User ID): prompt message.

CompuServe Mail Addressing

The method used to address a message on CompuServe is based on the destination electronic mail system.

COMMUNICATING WITH A COMPUSERVE PRIVATE E-MAIL SYSTEM USER

To send a message:

>   Address format: HCC:ADDRESS

where HCC is the host company's code and ADDRESS is the intended recipient's mailbox address.

To receive a message:

Originator enters CompuServe User ID in brackets after a SEND or FORWARD command.

>   example: /SEND [99999,888]
>   /FORWARD [99999,888]

TO SEND A FAX MESSAGE

1. Enter text message, use CTRL-L at locations where you want page breaks to occur.

2. At Send To: prompt enter:

>   FAX:<country code><area code|city code><telephone number>

>   example: FAX:19124770293

To send multiple fax messages separate routing information through the use of semicolons as indicated below:

>   example: FAX: 19124770293;FAX:18036713088

3. You will be prompted to enter recipient's name and subject for use on the fax cover sheet.

COMMUNICATING WITH AN AT&T EASYLINK SUBSCRIBER

To send a message:

>   Address format: X400:(c=us;a=western union;s=surname;g=given-
>   name;d=ELN:ID)

where: ELN=Easylink Number

example: X400:(c=us;a=western
union;s=held;g=gil;d=ELN:87654321)

To receive a message from AT&T Easylink:

X.400 address values:

Country=us
ADMD=CompuServe
PRMD=csmail
DDA Value=id | mailbox

where: DDA Value=User ID for public CompuServe Mail, replacing the comma in your ID with a period.

DDA Value=HCC.ADDRESS for private email system

example: For an AT&T Easylink user to send a message to Gil Held whose CompuServe ID is 40102,7776:

To: mhs/c=us/ad=compuserve/pd=csmail/d.id=40102.7776

COMMUNICATING WITH AN AT&T MAIL SUBSCRIBER

To send a message:

Address format: X400:(c=us;a=attmail;s=surname;g=given-name=initial;d=id:UNIQUE ID)

example: X400:(c=us;a=attmail;s=held;g=gil;d=id:gheld)

To receive a message from AT&T Mail:

X.400 address values:

Country=us
ADMD=CompuServe
PRMD=csmail
DDA Value=id | mailbox

where: DDA Value=User ID for public CompuServe Mail, replacing the comma in your ID with a period.

DDA Value=HCC.ADDRESS for private e-mail system

example: For an AT&T Mail user to send a message to Gil Held whose CompuServe ID is 40102,7776:

To: mhs/c=us/ad=compuserve/pd=csmail/d.id=40102.7776

Note: AT&T Mail has defined the gateway mhs!csmail which replaces the use of X.400 addressing, only requiring the CompuServe Mailbox address as indicated below:

To: mhs!csmail!40102.7776

For a Private CompuServe Mail address an AT&T Mail user would enter:

To: mhs/c=us/ad=compuserve/pd=csmail/d.id=HCC.ADDRESS or if using the mhs!csmail gateway

To: mhs!csmail!HCC.ADDRESS

COMMUNICATING WITH AN INTERNET USER

To send a message:

Address format: INTERNET: recepient-address@domain

example: INTERNET: held@risc1.msu.edu

To receive a message:

Address format: User.ID@compuserve.com

example: 40102.7776@compuserve.com

COMMUNICATING WITH AN MCI MAIL USER

To send a message:

Address formats: MCIMAIL:MCI ID

MCIMAIL:Registered Name

X400:(c=us;a=mci;s=surname;
g=given-name;i=initial;d=id:MCI ID)

examples: MCIMAIL:GHELD
MCIMAIL:
X400:(c=us;a=mci;s=held;g=gilbert;d=id:GHELD)

To send a message to a Private Management Domain (PRDM) mailbox serviced by MCI XChange 400 use the following format:

X400:(c=us;a=mci;p=PRMD;o=organization;s=surname;g=given-name;i=initial)

To receive a message from MCI Mail:

X400 address values:

Country=us
ADMD=CompuServe
PRMD=csmail
DDA Value=id | mailbox

where: DDA Value=User ID for public CompuServe Mail
DDA Value=HCC.ADDRESS for private email system

example: For an MCI Mail user to send a message to Gil Held whose CompuServe ID is 40102,7776:

To: Gil Held (ems)
EMS: CompuServe
MBX: p=csmail
MBX: d=id=40102,7776

COMMUNICATING WITH AN IBMIN PRIVATE MANAGEMENT DOMAIN USER

To send a message:

format: TO: recipient's surname (EMS)

EMS: IBMX400
MBX: PR=private domain name
MBX: GI=recipient's first name

COMMUNICATING WITH AN INFONET USER

To send a message:

    format: TO: recipient's surname (EMS)
               EMS: INFONET
               MBX: CO=country code US (default), CA (Canada), AU (Australia)
               MBX: PR=NOTICE   if user on Infonet Host Mail System
    or   MBX: PR=NOTICE400   if recepient accesses Infonet via a PC
               MBX: OR=organization

COMMUNICATING WITH A SPRINTMAIL SUBSCRIBER

To send a message:

    Address format: X400:(c=us;a=telemail;o=organization;s=surname;
                              g=given-name)

    example: X400:(c=us;a=telemail;o=4Degree;s=held;g=gil)

If an address is within a private domain (PRMD) the PRMD field must be included in the address as indicated below:

    example: X400:(c=us;a=telemail;p=agroup;s=held;g=gil)

To receive a message from SprintMail:

X.400 address values:

Country=us
ADMD=CompuServe
PRMD=csmail

DDA Type=id
DDA Value= mailbox

where: DDA Value=User ID for public CompuServe Mail, replacing the comma in your ID with a period.

DDA Value=EMI.ADDRESS for private email system, where EMI is your E-mail System Identifier.

example: For an SprintMail user to send a message to Gil Held whose CompuServe ID is 40102,7776:

To: mhs/c=us/ad=compuserve/pd=csmail/d.id=40102.7776

Note: A SprintMail user can also send messages to a MHS mailbox via the CompuServe Mail Hub. To do so requires the entry of the following address information:

Country=us
ADMD=CompuServe
PRMD=csmail
DDA Type=id
DDA Value=mhs:username(a)workgroup

Note: The "@" used in a NetWare MHS address must be replaced by a "(a)" in an X.400 address.

COMMUNICATING WITH A TELIX

To send a Telix:

Address format: TLX:<country code><Telex machine #><answerback>

To receive a Telix:

Originator sends message to CompuServe User Id using Telex machine number 3762848 which is answerback of CompuServe.

TO SEND A POSTAL LETTER

1. Enter text message and terminate with /EXIT on separate line.
2. At Send To: prompt enter POSTAL
3. At Recipient's name: prompt enter NANE of Person
4. At Title/Company: prompt enter optional TITLE/COMPANY
5. At Address Line 1: prompt enter ADDRESS
6. At Address Line 2: prompt enter optional 2nd address line
7. At City: prompt enter CITY
8. At State or Province: prompt enter STATE/PPROVINCE
9. At Zip: prompt enter ZIP code

Example:
Send To (Name or User ID): POSTAL
Recipient's name: Gilbert Held
Title/Company: 4-Degree Consulting
Address Line 1: 4736 Oxford Road
Address Line 2:
City: Macon
State: GA
Zip: 31210

Once you complete the recepient's address you will be prompted to enter your return address unless it was previously entered in the CompuServe address book.

MCI MAIL

MCI Mail Global Access Telephone Numbers

In the following list numbers designated with the label "MNP4" support the MNP error-correction protocol while numbers designated with the label "MNP5" support both the MNP error-correction and data compression protocols. Readers should note that there is a charge of (US)$0.50/minute to connect via MCI Mail Global Access which will be applied to your MCI Mail invoice.

Country or city	Speed(s) and modem type	City code	Telephone number
ARGENTINA (IN CITY: DIAL NO.; IN COUNTRY: DIAL 0+CITY CODE+NO.; INTL: DIAL 54+CITY CODE+NO.)			
***BUENOS AIRES	300-2400 MNP5	1	00009530969

***NO SPECIAL LOGON PROCEDURE NEEDED; DIAL NUMBER AND WAIT FOR MCI MAIL'S "PLEASE ENTER YOUR USER NAME:" PROMPT.

AUSTRALIA (IN CITY: DIAL NO.; IN COUNTRY: DIAL TOLLFREE NO. SHOWN; INTL: DIAL 61+CITY CODE+NO.)

BRISBANE	300-2400 MNP4	7	8323088
MELBOURNE	1200-2400 MNP4	3	6391660
	9600 MNP4	3	6391880
SYDNEY	300-2400 MNP4	2	2110034
	9600 MNP4	2	2127873
COUNTRY-WIDE	300-2400		1800-811167
TOLL FREE	9600 MNP4		1800-809439

AUSTRIA (IN CITY: DIAL NO.; IN COUNTRY: DIAL 0+222+NO.; INTL: DIAL 43+CITY CODE+NO.)

VIENNA	300-2400 MNP5	1	50148

BELGIUM (IN CITY: DIAL NO.; IN COUNTRY: DIAL 0+CITY CODE+NO.; INTL: DIAL 32+CITY CODE+NO.)

BRUSSELS	1200-2400	2	6479847
	1200-2400 MNP5	2	6476398
	9600 MNP5	2	6469070

BRAZIL (IN COUNTRY: DIAL TOLLFREE NO.SHOWN; INTL: DIAL TRANSIT NO. SHOWN)

COUNTRY-WIDE TOLL FREE	300-2400 MNP5	000672
FROM OTHER COUNTRIES (TRANSIT TRAFFIC):	300-2400 MNP5	55-11-1081212

CANADA: Access is provided via DATAPAC. Type HELP ACCESS CANADA at the Command prompt for sign-on procedures. Type HELP PHONES <province> for a list of access numbers for a specific province. There is a charge of (US)$0.15/minute to connect via DATAPAC.

DENMARK (IN CITY: DIAL NO.; IN COUNTRY: DIAL NO.; INTL: DIAL 45+NO.)

COPENHAGEN	300-2400 MNP5	38331499
	9600 MNP5	38341449

FINLAND (IN COUNTRY: DIAL NO., CITY CODE NOT NEEDED; INTL: SEE NOTE BELOW.)

HELSINKI	1200-2400	92917
	300-2400 MNP5	92919

(*Note:* Users outside Finland must dial either 358-2917 or 358-2919; no city code needed.)

FRANCE (IN CITY: DIAL NO.; IN COUNTRY: DIAL 16+CITY CODE+NO.; INTL: DIAL 33+CITY CODE+NO.)

PARIS	300-2400 MNP5	1	43441212
***PARIS	300-2400 MNP5	1	43421525

***No special logon procedure needed; dial number and wait for MCI Mail's "Please enter your user name:" prompt.

GERMANY (IN CITY: DIAL NO.; IN COUNTRY: DIAL 0+CITY CODE+NO.; INTL: DIAL 49+CITY CODE+NO.)

BERLIN	1200-2400 MNP5	30	2170662
DUSSELDORF	1200-2400 MNP5	211	132590
FRANKFURT	300-2400	69	6666881
	1200-2400 MNP5	69	6666886
	9600 MNP5	69	6662100
HAMBURG	1200-2400 MNP5	40	443775
MUNICH	1200-2400 MNP5	89	29160706

HONG KONG (IN COUNTRY: JUST DIAL NO.; INTL: DIAL 852+NO.)

HONG KONG	300-2400 MNP5*		8241121
	9600 MNP5		8274559

*Note: This number supports both CCITT & Bell modem standards at all speeds.)

INDONESIA (IN CITY: DIAL NO.; IN COUNTRY: DIAL 0+CITY CODE+NO.; INTL: DIAL 62+CITY CODE+NO.)

JAKARTA	300-2400 MNP5	21	5229252

IRELAND (IN CITY: DIAL NO.; IN COUNTRY: DIAL 0+CITY CODE+NO.; INTL: DIAL 353+CITY CODE+NO.)

DUBLIN	300-2400 MNP5	1	6768800

ITALY (IN CITY: DIAL NO.; IN COUNTRY: DIAL 0+CITY CODE+NO.; INTL: DIAL 39+CITY CODE+NO.)

MILAN	300-2400 MNP5	2	40910853
	300-2400 MNP5	2	40910891
	300-2400 MNP5	2	40910939
	300-2400 MNP5	2	48201828
ROME	300-2400 MNP5	6	2315728

JAPAN (IN CITY: DIAL NO.; IN COUNTRY: DIAL 0+CITY CODE+NO.; INTL: DIAL 81+CITY CODE+NO.)

OSAKA	1200-2400 MNP5	6	9476611
TOKYO	1200-2400 MNP5	3	33431100

KOREA (IN CITY: DIAL NO.; IN COUNTRY: DIAL 0+CITY CODE+NO.; INTL: DIAL 82+CITY CODE+NO.)

SEOUL	1200-2400 MNP4	2	7951002

LUXEMBOURG (IN COUNTRY: JUST DIAL NO.; INTL: DIAL 352+NO.)

LUXEMBOURG	300-2400 MNP5		498822

MALAYSIA - SEE SINGAPORE, BELOW

MEXICO (IN CITY: DIAL NO.; IN COUNTRY: DIAL 91+CITY CODE+NO.; INTL: DIAL 52+CITY CODE+NO.)

CANCUN	300-2400 MNP5	988	30013
	300-2400 MNP5	988	30035
	300-2400 MNP5	988	30124
	300-2400 MNP5	988	30146
	300-2400 MNP5	988	30149
GUADALAJARA	1200	36	260337
	300-2400 MNP5	36	260231
	300-2400 MNP5	36	260236
	300-2400 MNP5	36	260250
	300-2400 MNP5	36	260258
	300-2400 MNP5	36	260259
MEXICO CITY	300-2400 MNP5	5	7267600
MONTERREY	300-2400 MNP5	83	542202
	300-2400 MNP5	83	542291
	300-2400 MNP5	83	542292
	300-2400 MNP5	83	542310

NETHERLANDS (IN CITY: DIAL NO.; IN COUNTRY: DIAL 0+CITY CODE+NO.; INTL: DIAL 31+CITY CODE+NO.)

AMSTELVEEN	300 CCITT	20	6417855
	1200	20	6450952
	1200-2400 MNP5	20	6476171
	9600 MNP5	20	6403331

NEW ZEALAND (IN CITY: DIAL NO.; IN COUNTRY: DIAL 0+CITY CODE+NO.; INTL: DIAL 64+CITY CODE+NO.)

AUCKLAND	1200-2400 MNP4	9	3664520
CHRISTCHURCH	1200-2400 MNP4	3	3651800
HAMILTON	1200-2400 MNP4	7	8466002
WELLINGTON	1200-2400 MNP4	4	4732600

(*Note:* Logon procedure is different - callers get prompt 'Select Host:', at which point they enter 'Infonet' and press <return>, then follow normal logon.)

NORWAY (IN CITY: DIAL NO.; IN COUNTRY: DIAL NO.; INTL: DIAL 47+NO.)

OSLO	300 CCITT		22421217
	300-2400 MNP5		22423590

PHILIPPINES (IN CITY: DIAL NO.; IN COUNTRY: DIAL 0+CITY CODE+NO.; INTL: DIAL 63+CITY CODE+NO.)

MANILA	300-2400 MNP5	2	8171449

PORTUGAL (IN CITY: DIAL NO.; IN COUNTRY: DIAL 0+CITY CODE+NO.; INTL: DIAL 351+CITY CODE+NO.)

LISBON	300-2400 MNP5	1	3956446

PUERTO RICO: Use any of MCI Mail's toll-free access numbers. Type HELP ACCESS at the Command prompt for a list of access numbers. MCI Mail does not charge for this access; however your local phone company may charge for making the call.

RUSSIA (IN CITY: DIAL NO.; IN COUNTRY: DIAL 8+CITY CODE+NO.; INTL: DIAL 7+CITY CODE+NO.)

MOSCOW	300-2400 MNP4	095	9715101

SINGAPORE (IN COUNTRY: DIAL NO.; FROM MALAYSIA: DIAL 2+TRANSIT NO.; INTL: DIAL 65+TRANSIT NO.)

SINGAPORE	1200-2400 MNP5	5351444
	9600 MNP5	5351940
FROM OTHER COUNTRIES (TRANSIT TRAFFIC):	300-2400 MNP5	5356743
	9600 MNP5	5342172

SOUTH AFRICA (IN CITY: DIAL NO.; IN COUNTRY: DIAL 0+CITY CODE+NO.; INTL: DIAL 27+CITY CODE+NO.)

CAPE TOWN	300-2400 MNP4	21	6898242
	9600	21	6898247
	9600 MNP4	21	6898248
DURBAN	300-2400 MNP4	31	836860
JOHANNESBURG	300-2400 MNP4	11	4035730
	300-2400 MNP4	11	4036934
	9600	11	4035101
	9600	1	4032710

SPAIN (IN CITY: DIAL NO.; IN COUNTRY: DIAL 9+CITY CODE+NO.; INTL: DIAL 34+CITY CODE+NO.)

BARCELONA	300-2400 MNP4	3	4300202
	9600 MNP5	3	4108773
	9600 MNP5	3	4109127
MADRID	300-2400 MNP5	1	3581951
	9600 MNP5	1	3581428

SWEDEN (IN CITY: DIAL NO.; IN COUNTRY: DIAL 0+CITY CODE+NO.; INTL: DIAL 46+CITY CODE+NO.)

STOCKHOLM	300-2400 MNP5	8	6531960
	9600 MNP5	8	6531980

SWITZERLAND (IN CITY: DIAL NO.; IN COUNTRY: DIAL 0+CITY CODE+NO.; INTL: DIAL 41+CITY CODE+NO.)

BERN	300 CCITT	31	3820931
	1200-2400	31	3820787
	1200-2400 MNP5	31	3820691
GENEVA	300 CCITT	22	7985756
	1200-2400 MNP5	22	7986364

TAIWAN (IN CITY: DIAL NO.; IN COUNTRY: DIAL 0+CITY CODE+NO.; INTL: DIAL 886+CITY CODE+NO.)

TAIPEI	300-2400	2	3955100
	300-2400 MNP5	2	3955090
	9600 MNP5	2	3955101

UNITED KINGDOM (IN CITY: DIAL NO.; IN COUNTRY: DIAL 0+CITY CODE+NO.; INTL: DIAL 44+CITY CODE+NO.)

LONDON	300-2400 MNP5	71		4374393
	300-2400	71		4394055
	9600 MNP5	71	4	343442

U.S. VIRGIN ISLANDS: Use any of MCI Mail's toll free access numbers. Type HELP ACCESS at the Command prompt for a list of access numbers. MCI Mail does not charge for this access, but your local phone company may charge for making the call.

Access via non-800 access numbers

The following non-800 numbers may be used to to connect to MCI Mail. MCI Mail does not charge for this access but your local phone company or PTT may charge for making the call.

These numbers accept speeds from 300 to 2400 bps and are configured for 8 Data bits, No parity and 1 Stop bit.

Note that one number in each location supports X.PC error-correction (used in Lotus Express and other software) while the other supports MNP5 error-correction; any of the numbers can be used without error-correction.

Arlington, VA (US East Coast):
703-769-0700	X.PC available
703-769-0750	MNP5 available

San Francisco, CA (US West Coast):
415-543-1560	X.PC available
415-543-6364	MNP5 available

MCI Mail also has a non-800 access number operating at 9600 bps:
9600 bps (V.32)   202-467-6667
(MNP4 available)

MCI **MAIL SUBSCRIBER ADDRESSES**

Mail can be addressed to an MCI MIL subscriber in one of three ways

1. Use the unique 7 digit subscriber ID. e.g., 235-8068
2. Use subscriber's username. e.g., GHELD
3. Use subscriber's MCI mail registered name. e.g., Gilbert Held

MCI **MESSAGE CREATION**

1. At Command: prompt enter CREATE
2. At TO: prompt enter:

MCI Mail subscriber name or ID.

EMS in parenthesis after name to send electronic mail to a subscriber on a different E-mail system. (See list of addresses.)

FAX to send your message as a fax.

PAPER to enter a postal delivery address.

TELEX to send your message to a telex machine.

LIST OF MCI MAIL ADDRESSES

Note: To cancel an address, type a slash "/" at any address prompt.

ATTMAIL – To send electronic mail to a US AT&T Mail subscriber or system.

BOARD – To post messages to your Bulletin Board.

COMPUSERVE – To send electronic mail to Compuserve subscribers.

DELETE – To delete an address from your previously created envelope.

EMS – To send a message to a subscriber on another elecronic mail system connected to MCI Mail.

example: To: Gilbert Held (ems)

FAX – To send your message to a Group 3 facsimile device.

example: To: Gilbert Held (fax)

COVER PAGE– Enables the suppression of the cover page on a per address basis when sending fax messages.

HEADER – Permits you to include a one-line header on a per address basis when sending fax messages. The header is printed at the top of each page and includes the recipient's name, your name and the date and time the message was sent.

example: To: Gilbert Held (fax, header)

NO HEADER – Permits the suppression of a header on a per address basis when sending fax messages.

example: To: Gilbert Held (fax, no header)

PAGE – Permits you to include page numbers on fax messages either alone or in conjunction with page headers on a per address basis.

example: To: Gilbert Held (fax, page)

NO PAGE – Enables the suppression of page numbers on a per address basis when sending fax messages.

example: To: Gilbert Held (fax, no page)

HANDLING – Enables Handling options to be specified in the address.

INTERNET – Use to send a messages to someone with an Internet mailbox.

INSTANT – Use to send a message to an MCI Mailbox. This is the default address.

LIST – Use to send a message to people in a Shared List.

OWNER – Use to send a message to a Bulletin Board or Shared List owner.

PAPER – Use to have a message delivered to a postal address.

PRINT – Use to send paper mail to an MCI Mail user's registered address.

TELEMAIL – Use to send a message to a Sprint Telemail subscriber or system.

TELEX – Use to send a message to a telex terminal.

UPLOAD – Use to upload an address file.

VERIFY – Use to verify that an address will post.

X400 – Use to send a message to an X.400 electronic mail system registered with MCI Mail.

1. At CC: prompt enter address or CR to ignore.
2. At Subject: prompt enter subject of message or CR to ignore.
3. At Text: prompt enter text. Enter "/" on a line by itself to terminate text entry.
4. At Handling: prompt enter one of the following:

CHARGE – To assign a project code for reference on your MCI Mail invoices.

DOC – To send an MCI Mail message in document format.

FORM – To specify the use of a letterhead in place of a standard letterhead.

ONITE – To specify Courier delivery for paper mail and priority delivery.

<RETURN> – for electronic mail.

PRINT – Sends paper mail to an MCI Mail subscriber. The letters will be delivered to the recipient's registered postal address.

RECEIPT – To have a notice sent to your INBOX when electronic mail is read or paper mail is prepared for delivery.

NO RECEIPT – To suppress the receipt confirmation notice for fax delivery. This option will not suppress the notification of cancellation of delivery.

SIGN – To specify a signature to use in place of a standard signature.

FORM:FAX132 – To support a fax with up to 132 columns per line which is delivered using a compressed character set.

NO COVER – To suppress the cover page when sending fax messages.

HEADER – Use to include a one-line header when sending fax messages. The header is printed at the top of each page.

NO HEADER – Use to suppress the header on a per message basis when sending fax messages.

PAGE – Use to include page numbers either alone or when using page headers for fax messages.

NO PAGE – Permits the suppression of page numbers on a per message basis when sending fax messages.

MCI MESSAGE CREATION EXAMPLE

TO: Gilbert Held (EMS)

Enter name of mail system.

EMS: CompuServe
     EMS   592-7515 CompuServe   CompuServe Columbus, OH

Enter recipient's mailbox information.

MBX: 40102,7776

If additional mailbox lines are not needed press RETURN.

MBX:

TO: Gilbert Held
     EMS: CompuServe / MCI ID: 592-7515
     MBX: 40102,7776

Is this address correct (Yes or No)? yes

TO: (enter RETURN to bypass additional recepients)

CC: (enter RETURN to bypass carbon copies if desired)

Subject: Test Message

Text: (Enter text or transmit file. Type / on a line by itself to end.)

MCI MAIL X.400 LABELS

MCI Mail Label	Originator/Recipient Component	X.400 Label
not applicable	Country name	c
not applicable	ADMD (Administrative domain)	a
p	PRMD (Private domain)	p
OR=	Organization name	o
u	Organizational unit	ou1,ou2,ou3,ou4
SU=	Surname	s
GI=	Given name	g
IN=	Initials	i
GE=	General qualifier	q
dda=	Domain-defined attribute	dda

Note: There is no MCI Mail label for country name or administrative domain. The ADMD name is entered at the MCI EMS: prompt. The MCI Mail system is programmed to recognize the country associated with the EMS.

MCI MAIL ELECTRONIC MESSAGE EXCHANGE FORMAT AND EXAMPLES

MCI Mail to an AT&T Mail Subscriber:

format:

To: RECIPIENT's LAST NAME (ems)
EMS: ATTMAIL
MBX: GI=RECIPIENT'S FIRST NAME

example:

To: Held (ems)
EMS: ATTMAIL
MBX: GI=Gilbert

format:

MBX: OR=recipient's organization
MBX: DDA=ID=RECIPIENTS
    ATTMAIL USERNAME
MBX: Carriage Return

example:

MBX: OR=4DEGREE

MBX: DDA=ID=GHELD
MBX: Carriage Return

Note: A username in the address with the DDA of type ID is required when the subscriber's name and organization are not unique. If the message is addressed to someone on a private mail system connected to AT&T Mail enter the PRMD=recipient's mail system name.

MCI Mail to a CompuServe Subscriber:

format: *example:*

To: RECIPIENT's LAST NAME (ems)   To: Held (ems)
EMS: CompuServe   EMS: CompuServe
MBX: p=csmail   MBX: p=csmail
MBX: dda=ID=99999,999   MBX: dda=ID=40102,7776

MCI Mail to an Internet Subscriber:

format: *example:*

To: RECIPIENT's LAST NAME   To: Gil Held (ems)
EMS: INTERNET   EMS: Internet
MBX: Internet Address   MBX: gxheld@mail.opm.gov

Note: If the Internet Address exceeds 80 characters you must split it using multiple MBX lines, splitting the address at the character @, !, or !.

MCI Mail to an IBMIN Mail XChange Subscriber:

format:

To: RECIPIENT's LAST NAME (ems)
EMS: IBMX400
MBX: P=IBMMAIL
MBX: c=country code
MBX: g=surname plus first letter of first name and middle initial
MBX: pr=private domain name (optional)
MBX: dda=Domain Defined Attribute (optional)

MCI Mail to an SprintMail Subscriber:

format: *example:*

To: RECIPIENT's LAST NAME   To: Held (ems)
(ems)
EMS: TELEMAIL   EMS: TELEMAIL
MBX: GI=RECIPIENT'S FIRST   MBX: GI=Gilbert
NAME
MBX: OR=recipient's   MBX: OR=4DEGREE
organization

format:	*example:*
MBX: DDA=UA=RECIPIENTS	MBX: DDA=UA=GHELD
SPRINTMail USERNAME	
MBX: Carriage Return	MBX: Carriage Return

Note: A username in the address with the DDA of type UA is required when the subscriber's name and organization are not unique. If the message is addressed to someone on a private mail system connected to SprintMail enter the PRMD=recipient's mail system name.

MCI MAIL MAILBOX COMMANDS

ANSWER – Use to create an MCI Mailbox message in response to one you received from another user. This command will not work when responding to a telex terminal.

ANSWER EACH – Use to reply to the sender and everyone else who received the message (TO's and CC's).

Note: For both ANSWER and ANSWER EACH MCI MAIL automatically constructs the return envelope, completing the TO: and CC: fields and placing the original subject in the Subject: field.

CREATE – Enables you to write an MCI MAIL message. This command generates the TO:, CC:, Subject:, Text: and Handling: prompts whose entries are indicated below:

TO:	Enter name(s) of the recipients
CC:	Enter name(s) of the recipients of copies
Subject:	Enter a brief title for the message
Text:	Enter the body of your message. When the message is completed type a slash (/) on the next blank line
Handling:	Enter any special instructions
Send?	Enter yes or no

Note: To cancel your message, type / (slash) at TO, CC, or Subject prompts.

DELETE – Use to remove messages from any of your mailbox areas (INBOX, OUTBOX, DESK, PENDING).

Scan your mailbox area to identify the message(s) you want deleted and note their scan number(s).

Type DELETE followed by the scan number(s) you would like to delete. For example to delete messages 1 and 3 you would enter: DELETE 1,3

FORWARD – Use to send a copy of one or more messages in your mailbox to other persons. You can use one of two ways to forward a message:

Read the message then type FORWARD at the "Command:"prompt.

Use SCAN to locate the message(s) to be forwarded; then, in response to the "Command:" prompt type FORWARD followed by the scan numbers of the message(s) you wish to forward.

INCLUDE – Use to insert TEXT from other messages into your message. To use creating your message. When inside the TEXT, type /IN-CLUDE/ at the beginning of a line, then skip a space and type the scan number of the text of a message you want to include. For example, to include the text from messages 1 and 4 and 5 enter: /INCLUDE/ 1, 4-5

You can select messages to INCLUDE by mailbox area (folder), SUBJECT, ON, BEFORE or AFTER a date; FROM or TO a name. For example:

/INCLUDE/ DESK SUBJECT "VACATION" AFTER 1-APRIL

Note: INCLUDE operates when using the commands CREATE, ANSWER, ANSWER EACH and FORWARD. It doesn't work while editing.

NEXT – Use this command to continue reading your messages.

PRINT – Use to display a number of messages one after the other without stopping. To use the PRINT command first scan the area of your mailbox that you wish to print and then type PRINT followed by the scan numbers of the messages you want printed or you can type PRINT followed by an area of your mailbox (INBOX, OUTBOX, DESK, PENDING or ALL).

Note: You can identify message(s) to be printed by specifying one of the following:

ON <date>	SUBJECT <"words">	AFTER <date>
TO <lastname>	BEFORE <date>	FROM <lastname>

The date can be entered as per the following formats:

day-month	day/month	month day

You can combine options in a single command line. For example:

Command: PRINT DESK FROM HELD ON 31-DEC SUBJECT "New Year"

READ – Use to display one or more of your messages with page breaks. To identify messages to be displayed:

Type READ followed by the scan numbers of the messages you want.

Type READ followed by an area of your mailbox (INBOX, OUTBOX, DESK, PENDING or ALL) and one or more of the following options:

ON <date>   SUBJECT <"words">   AFTER <date>
TO <lastname>   BEFORE <date>   FROM <lastname>

Note: See PRINT command for date enty format and methods by which you can combine options in a single line, substituting READ for PRINT

SCAN – Use to obtain a summary of the messages in your mailbox. Information listed for each message includes:

NO   Scan number used in referencing the message
POSTED   Date and time the message was posted
FROM   Who sent the message
SUBJECT   The title of the message

Note: One or more of the following options can be used with the SCAN command:

INBOX   ALL   SUBJECT <"words">
OUTBOXON <date>   TO <name>
DESK   AFTER <date> FROM <name>
PENDING   BEFORE <date>

SEND – Use to post a DRAFT message for non-priority delivery if electronic mail or postal delivery of paper mail.

SEND ONITE – Use to add a priority notation to your electronic message or to use courier service for paper mail.

SEND 4HOUR – Use to add priority notification for electronic mail.

UPLOAD – Use UPLOAD ADDRESS to upload an address into the message envelope or UPLOAD MESSAGE to upload ASCII or BINARY files into the body of your message.

MCI COMMAND REFERENCE

For specific information on a command, type HELP COMMAND.

Command	*Utilization*
ACCOUNT	Set your MCI Mailbox to fit your terminal.
ANSWER	Reply to the sender of a message.

CREATE	Write an MCI letter.
DELETE	Delete messages in your MCI Mailbox.
DOWJONES	Access Dow Jones News and Retrieval information.
EDIT	Make changes to PENDING messages.
FILE	Obtain a complete listing of helpfiles available from the Command Prompt.
FIND	Search for an MCI Mail subscriber's name.
FORWARD	Forward a message to another recipient.
INDEX	Obtain a listing of all topics available to MCI Mail users.
INCLUDE	Insert text from other messages into your message.
NEXT	Read the next message in your INBOX.
PENDING	Retrieve a pending message.
PRINT	Display messages nonstop.
READ	Read messages with page breaks.
SCAN	Obtain a summary of your mail.
SEND	Send a message.
UPLOAD	Upload addresses from a PC onto an envelope or into the body of a message.

MCI MAIL TOPIC INFORMATION

For specific information on any listed topic, type HELP TOPIC.

Topic	*Information Contained*
ACCESS	US and international access information plus TYMNET information.
ACCOUNT	How to set your MCI Mailbox to fit your terminal.
ADDRESS	Addressing options availble.

APPENDIX	Prices and information on searching the MCI Mail directory for subscribers.
AUTOFORWARD	Request incoming messages automatically be forwarded to other recipients.
BULLETIN BOARD	Information on owning or viewing bulletin boards.
CREATE	Initiate the message process for different formats for your message.
CUSTOMER SUPPORT	Information on how to contact MCI Mail Customer service.
DELIVER	US and international delivery information.
EDIT	How to make changes to PENDING messages.
FAX	Description of MCI Mail Fax Dispatch.
FILES	Obtain the help file names of all the online help files on MCI Mail.
FIND	To search the on-line MCI Mail Directory to see if a name, list, script, board or EMS (electronic mail system) is in the directory.
GLOSSARY	A reference guide to MCI Mail commands.
GRAPHICS	Information on using letterheads and signatures.
HANDLING	Variety of option commands which specify how your message is to be handled or delivered.
LISTS	Create lists of people and addresses for addressing messages.
MAILBOX	Information on your MCI Mailbox.
PC	Create files off-line and upload them into MCI Mail.
PRICES	Display general rates for sending messages from MCI.
MESSAGES	Mail.
REQUEST	Order reference manuals from MCI Mail.
SPECIAL FEATURES	Additional features of MCI Mail.

TELEX   Information on exchanging messages with telex sub-
                             cribers.

TEXT   Creating the text of a message.

X400   For sending to an X.400 address.

MCI MAIL HELP FILES

To request a listing of the contents of a helpfile, type HELP followed by the name
of the file at the Command. For example:

Command: HELP ADDRESS ATTMAIL

will display the helpfile for addressing mail to a subscriber of AT&T Mail. Note
that the helpfiles in the following list that are shown in all CAPS are not accessible by Basic MCI MAIL users.

A
Access
Access Canada
Access International
Account
Account Change
Account Read
Address
Address Address
Address Attmail
Address Board
Address Compuserve
Address Delete
Address Ems
Address Fax
ADDRESS HANDLING
Address Instant
Address Internet
Address List
Address Missive
Address Owner

Address Paper International
Address Print
Address Telemail
Address Telex
Address Telex International
Address Upload
ADDRESS VERIFY
Address X400
Advanced
Answer
Appendix
Attmail
Autoforward
Autoforward Create

B
Bulletin Board
Bullentin Board Directory
Bullentin Board Prices
Bullentin Board View

C

Compuserve
Compuserve Receive
Contro
<Country>*
Courier Pricing
Create
CREATE DOC
CREATE MEMO
Customer Support
* Enter country of interest

D

DELETE
Deliver
Deliver International
Deliver Onite
Delivery Schedule
Desk
Dow Jones
Download
Download Message

E

Edit
Edit Add
Edit Cancel
Edit Change
EDIT COPY
Edit Delete
Edit Envelop
Edit Format
Edit MOVE
Edit Number
Edit Read
Edit Stop
Edit Text

F

Fax
Fax Address

Fax Cancel
Fax Cover Pag
FAX FORMAT
Fax Header
Fax Landscape
Fax Link
Fax Page Numbers
Fax PC File
Fax Pricing
Fax Send
Fax Upload
Files
File Transfer
Find
Find Name
Format
FORWARD

G

Glossary
Graphics
Graphics Scan

H

HANDLING
HANDLING CHARGE
HANDLING DOC
HANDLING FORM
HANDLING MEMO
HANDLING RECEIPT
HANDLING SIGN
Help*
Holiday
*typed by itself

I

Inbox
INCLUDE
Index
Internet

L
Lists
Lists Create
Lists Edit
Lists Read
Lists Scan

M
Mailbox
MailDirect
Missive
Missive Receive

N
Next

O
Outbox

P
Password
PC
PC Address
PC Download
PC Logon
PC Text
PC Trouble
PC Upload Address
PC Upload Text
PENDING
Phones
Phones 9600
Phones <State>*
Phones <Canadian Province>*
Phones International
Post
Prices
Prices Access
Prices Messages
Prices Scripts
Prices Services

Prices Shared List
Print
PRINT PAPER
*type in name of State or Province

R
Read
READ DRAFT
Read Fax
Read Paper
Request

S
Scan
Scan Select
Script
Send
Shared List
Special Features

T
Telemail
Telex
Telex Cancel
Telex Carrier
Telex Directory
Telex Inbound
Telex Network ID
Telex Pricing
Telex Receive
Telex Send
Text
TEXT INCLUDE
Text Online
Text Upload
Tollfreebox
Tymnet Sign-on

U
Upload
Upload Address

Upload Message
X400
X400 Address
X400 Cancel

X400 Receive
X400 Terms
XPC

CHAPTER *10*

SprintNet and SprintMail

The global communications company Sprint operates a worldwide packet switched network that some readers may have used when it was formerly known as Telenet. Now known as SprintNet, this data communications network provides a communications infrastructure which links thousands of computer systems throughout the world, enabling a user to make a local call and connect to different computer based services he or she wishes to access.

In addition to SprintNet's providing users with the ability to access computer systems operated by a variety of organizations, academic institutions and governments you can also use SprintNet to access SprintMail, a subscription based electronic communications program operated by Sprint. SprintMail provides subscribers with the ability to send electronic messages for delivery to other SprintMail subscribers as well as subscribers of other electronic mail services that support X.400 addressing. In addition, you can use SprintMail to send electronic messages that can be delivered via postal, fax, or telex.

In this chapter we will first briefly discuss how readers can access SprintNet and obtain a list of telephone access numbers without cost. This will be followed by a listing of a few SprintNet access numbers and a table of international SprintNet access numbers to provide readers with a starting point to retrieve additional access numbers to satisfy specific requirements. Next, we will focus our attention

425

upon SprintMail, listing its key commands and how you can obtain online assistance, as well as creating a few simple test messages to illustrate its ease of use.

SprintNet local access telephone numbers.

You can access SprintNet with a local phone call from thousands of cities and towns or by using SprintNet's In-WATS service. The network is also accessible from over 100 international locations.

For SprintNet customer service (voice), call toll-free 1-800/877-5045. From overseas locations with non-WATS access, call 404/859-7700.

You can dial SprintNet In-WATS telephone numbers listed below to obtain a listing of telephone access numbers. Since the use of In-WATS adds a surcharge to your bill, it is more economical to use a local telephone number when one is available. You can dial one of the toll-free numbers listed below to obtain a listing of telephone numbers without charge. To do so you would first dial one of the numbers listed below:

Data rate/Modem type	Telephone number
300-2400bps	1-800/546-1000
9600bps (V.32)	1-800/546-2500
9600bps (V.29)	1-800/546/2000

Once you obtain a connection to a SprintNet access center you will receive the prompt sign "@." In response to that prompt enter the command: MAIL. You will then receive the prompt "User Name?" Respond to that prompt by entering: PHONES. Next, the prompt "Password" will be displayed. Respond to that prompt with: PHONES.

The previously described sequence will display a menu similar to the one listed below, providing you with the ability to retrieve the telephone access number or numbers you may require.

US SPRINT'S ONLINE
LOCAL ACCESS TELEPHONE NUMBERS DIRECTORY

1. Domestic Asynchronous Dial Service
2. International Asynchronous Dial Service
3. Domestic X.25 Dial Service
4. New Access Centers and Recent Changes

5. Product and Service Information
6. Exit the Phones Directory

SPRINTNET INTERNATIONAL ASYNCHRONOUS DIAL SERVICE

Country	City code	City	300/1200 BPS	2400 BPS	9600 BPS
Australia+	8	Adelaide	232-5941	232-5941	232-5941
Australia+	7	Brisbane	236-1082	236-1082	236-1082
Australia+	6	Canberra	257-5055	257-5055	257-5055
Australia+	3	Melbourne	764-0421	764-0421	764-0421
Australia+	9	Perth	481-1122	481-1122	481-1122
Australia+	2	Sydney	281-0800	281-0800	281-0800
Austria	1	Vienna	504-2811	504-2811	504-2811
Belgium	2	Brussels	725-3400	725-3400	725-3400
Bulgaria	2	Sophia	73-361	73-361	73-361
Belarus	0172	Minsk	26-0812	26-0812	None
Canada	514	Montreal	392-0202	392-0202	392-0202
Canada	416	Toronto	594-1121	594-1121	594-1121
Canada	604	Vancouver	684-4696	684-4696	684-4696
Colombia	1	Bogota	320-3811	320-3811	320-3811
Denmark+	1	Copenhagen	32-96-1511	32-96-1511	32-96-1511
Estonia+	3726	Tallinn	31-2286	31-2286	None
Finland	0	Helsinki	146-3022	146-3022	146-3022
France	2	Lille	065-3260	065-3260	065-3260
France	7	Lyon	864-5095	864-5095	864-5095
France	1	Paris	6928-0404	6928-0404	6928-0404
France	9	Sofia Antipolis	296-0049	296-0049	296-0049
Germany	69	Frankfurt	666-9151	666-9151	666-9151
Germany+	40	Hamburg	279-5411	279-5411	279-5411
Germany+	511	Hannover	879-1800	879-1800	879-1800
Germany+	89	Munich	369-031	369-031	369-031
Guam	671	Tumon	649-3282	649-3282	649-3282
Hong Kong	852	Hong Kong	754-8442	754-8442	754-8442
Indonesia	21	Jakarta	386-1044	386-1044	386-1044
Ireland	1	Dublin	661-4466	661-4466	661-4466
Italy	2	Milan	953-01301	953-01301	953-01301
Japan	6	Osaka	910-7111	910-7111	910-7111
Japan	3	Tokyo	3794-6381	3794-6381	3794-6381
Kazakhstan	3272	Alma-Ata	50-7000	50-7000	None
Kuwait+		Kuwait City	484-4155	484-4155	484-4133
Latvia+	3712	Riga	22-3816	22-3816	None

Country	City code	City	300/1200 BPS	2400 BPS	9600 BPS
Luxembourg		Echternach	31-6667	31-6667	31-6667
Netherlands	01719	Noordwijk (Amsterdam)	46370	46370	46370
New Zealand+	9	Auckland	358-4491	358-4491	358-4491
New Zealand+	4	Wellington	499-3617	499-3617	499-3617
Norway	66	Oslo	845-011	845-011	845-011
Peru		Lima	722-692	722-692	None
Portugal	1	Lisbon	395-5445	395-5445	395-5445
Romania	0	Bucharest	1311-2525	1311-2525	1311-2525
Puerto Rico	809	San Juan	273-7400	273-7400	273-7400
Russia+	818	Arkhangelsk	43-5401	43-5401	None
Russia+	218	Angarsk	9-4821	9-4821	None
Russia+	3852	Barnaul	26-1601	26-1601	None
Russia+	38538	Biysk	4-2401	4-2401	None
Russia+	3953	Bratsk	42-0620	42-0620	None
Russia+	30222	Chita	6-4218	6-4218	None
Russia+	3432	Ekaterinburg	51-9949	51-9949	None
Russia+	3952	Irkutsk	33-6116	33-6116	None
Russia+	34794	Ishimbaj	3-3708	3-3708	None
Russia+	4212	Khabarovsk	21-4937	21-4937	None
Russia+	42172	Komsomolsk na Amure	3-6504	3-6504	None
Russia+	3912	Krasnoyarsk	21-0529	21-0529	None
Russia+	34764	Meleuz	4-0008	4-0008	None
Russia+	095	Moscow	928-0985	928-0985	None
Russia+	423	Nakhodka	664-2710	664-2710	None
Russia+	34713	Neftekamsk	5-7301	5-7301	None
Russia+	8312	Nizhniy Novgorod	38-9071	38-9071	None
Russia+	86134	Novorossijsk	9-1800	9-1800	None
Russia+	3832	Novosibirsk	29-8861	29-8861	None
Russia+	34767	Oktyabrskij	4-3831	4-3831	None
Russia+	3812	Omsk	25-4396	25-4396	None
Russia+	3422	Perm	65-9636	65-9636	None
Russia+	814	Petrozavodsk	4-7410	4-7410	None
Russia+	8632	Rostov	69-6911	69-6911	None
Russia+	3472	Ufa	52-9410	52-9410	None
Russia+	34763	Salavat	2-4322	2-4322	None
Russia+	8462	Samara	33-0021	33-0021	None
Russia+	4240	So. Sakhalinsk	0-29091	0-29091	None
Russia+	812	St Petersburg	110-7792	110-7792	None
Russia+	34711	Sterlitamak	5-5161	5-5161	None
Russia+	8480	Toljatti	28-7196	28-7196	None
Russia+	3822	Tomsk	21-1556	21-1556	None
Russia+	3452	Tumen	25-1910	25-1910	None
Russia+	30122	Ulan-Ude	6-2277	6-2277	None

Country	City code	City	300/1200 BPS	2400 BPS	9600 BPS
Russia+	39543	Usolje-Sibirskoe	4-5110	4-5110	None
Russia+	39535	Ust-Ilimsk	5-7365	5-7365	None
Russia+	4232	Vladivostok	22-3310	22-3310	None
Russia+	8442	Volgograd	32-9965	32-9965	None
Russia+	41122	Yakutsk	6-2801	6-2801	None
Singapore	65	Singapore	738-0566	738-0566	738-0566
Spain	3	Barcelona	335-9000	335-9000	335-9000
Spain	1	Madrid	766-2122	766-2122	766-2122
Sweden+	8	Stockholm	751-15-15	751-15-15	751-15-15
Switzerland	31	Bern	382-1049	382-1049	382-1049
Switzerland	13	Zurich	02-8868	02-8868	02-8868
Taiwan+	5	Chiayi	232-4430	232-4430	None
Taiwan+	35	Hsinchu	718-946	718-946	None
Taiwan+	7	Kaohsiung	315-1365	315-1365	None
Taiwan+	4	Taichung	381-4064	381-4064	None
Taiwan+	6	Tainan	220-4166	220-4166	None
Taiwan	2	Taipei	651-6119	651-6119	651-6119
Taiwan+	3	Touyan	335-1633	335-1633	None
Ukraine+	044	Kiev	245-0379	245-0379	None
Ukraine+	0642	Lugansk	53-9010	53-9010	None
Ukraine+	0482	Odessa	26-2801	26-2801	None
U.K.	25	Basingstoke	660-0061	660-0061	660-0061
U.K.	31	Edinburg, Scotland	459-1290	459-1290	459-1290
U.K.	71	London	973-1030	973-1030	973-1030
U.K.	061	Manchester	747-5000	747-5000	747-5000
Uzbekistan	3712	Tashkent	49-0356	49-0356	None
Venezuela	2	Caracas	993-0364	993-0364	993-0364

+ Please note dial-in access procedures are slightly different than standard SprintNet procedures. If you need assistance, please contact SprintNet Customer Service in Reston, VA at 703-318-7740.

INTERNATIONAL VALUE ADDED CARRIER INFORMATION AND TEST MESSAGING

If you would like to try the facilities of SprintNet the following list of electronic address should be considered as they provide access to the indicated facilities.

for: *Australia information and assistance*
access method: c 0505321000x,name,password
        where x is
          1 for test echo

2 for online terminal assistance
3 continuous test message

for: **British Telecom modem tour and online directory**
access method: c 023421920100515,name,password

for: **British Telecom master clock**
access method: c 02342190100605,name,password

for: **Hong Kong Telephone Company data network tour**
access method: c 04545500104,name,password

for: **Hong Kong Telephone Company manual assistance during Hong Kong business hours**
access method: c 05252115039,name,password

for: **Hong Kong Telephone Company test line**
access method: c 04545030002,name,password
c 04540500002,name,password
c 04545090002,name,password

for: **Mexico customer service**
access method: c 03340906007005,name,password

for: **Singapore data network description**
access method: c 05252116688,name,password
login: ID TELEPAC INFO

for: **Singapore test line**
access method c 05252116060,name,password

for: **Sweden customer service**
access method: c 0240200120001,name,password

for: **Switzerland customer service**
access method: c 02284010999,name,password

for: **Telebox (Germany) Mail System information**
access method: c 026245621040000,name,password
login: ID INF300 password DATACOM for network information
ID INF400 password TELEBOX-E for Telebox Mail information

for: *Venus-P (Japan) network*
access method: c 044820060xx,name, password
                          where xx
                                    00 echo mode
                                    01 test message sent to you
                                    02 help message about system
                                    03 test message sent to you
                                    04 master clock

To obtain additional information concerning Sprint's International Value Added Services, once you connect to SprintNet respond to the at sign (@) prompt as indicated below:

    @C MAIL

Sprint will then prompt you to login by entering your user name and password. Do so using INTL/ASSOCIATES for your user name and INTL for your password as indicated below:

    User name? INTL/ASSOCIATES

    Password? INTL

SPRINTMAIL COMMANDS AND TOPICS

Upon being connected to SprintMail the system will issues the Command prompt, indicating it is waiting for instructions from you. The system commands you can enter in response to that prompt are as follows:

ADMINS OF	ALTER	ANSWER	BOARDS OF
BYE	CANCEL	CHECK	COMPOSE
COPY	DELETE	DIRECTORY	DISPLAY
DIVISIONS OF	DOWNLOAD	EDIT	ENCODE
EXIT	FILE	FORWARD	GOTO
INQUIRE	INSERT	LIST	LISTS OF
LOGON	MEMBERS OF	MODIFY	NICKNAMES
NODES OF	NUMBER	PASSKEYS	PASSWORD
PURGE	READ	RECOVER	REGISTER
REMOVE	SAVE	SCAN	SCRIPTS OF
SECTIONS OF	SEND	SET	STATIONS OF
STATUS	SUBDIVISIONS OF	SUBSECTIONS OF	SYSTEMS OF

TALLY	TRANSFER	TRY	UNPURGE
UNREAD	UPLOAD	USERS OF	

SprintMail also provides several features that are described by the following topics:

ADDRESS	EDITING	NEWS
AUTOFORWARD	FAX	OAG (OFFICIAL AIRLINE GUIDE)
BATCH	FILE.TRANSFER	POST
BULLETIN.BOARDS	HOTLINE	SHORT.ADDRESS
DIRECT.DELIVERY	INFORM.SCRIPTS	SITE.NICKNAME
DOCUMENTATION	INTERCONNECTION	TELEX
DJ (DOW JONES)	INTERNET	X.400

You can obtain detailed information on any of the above commands and topics by entering a question mark (?) or the word HELP followed by a space and the command or topic name:

```
    Command?  ? SCAN        Command? HELP SCAN
```

OR

```
    Action?  ? TELEX        Action? HELP TELEX
```

Always press RETURN after typing a system command.

The following are valid control characters in the system. To use them, hold down the CONTROL key, and press the key you need.

CONTROL H - Backspace/deletes characters

CONTROL X - Deletes the current line

CONTROL R - Displays the most recent line

CONTROL S - Stops the display, until you press CONTROL Q

CONTROL Q - Restarts the display after CONTROL S

BREAK KEY - Interrupts the current display and returns you to the Command or Action prompt

To suppress system prompts and messages associated with certain commands, enter the command name followed by an exclamation point (!):

```
Command? READ!
```

You may instruct the system to perform multiple commands in sequence at a single Command prompt by entering each command separated by a semicolon (;):

```
Command? SCAN SINCE JANUARY 15;READ
```

The following example shown in Figure 10.1 illustrates the creation and transmission of a simple message via SprintNet. In this example a RETURN was entered to skip the transmission of a carbon copy (CC) of the message. Note that to terminate a message on SprintMail you must enter a period (.) on a separate line.

The following examples illustrate the use of the SCAN, READ and PURGE commands. SCAN provides a one line summary of each message in your mailbox, while READ provides you with the ability to display the contents of messages. PURGE provides you with the ability to remove a message from your storage area. Each of those commands as well as many other SprintMail commands support the use of optional parameters that further define the resulting command action. You can obtain additional information on the use of command parameters by entering HELP followed by the command name.

```
Command?  compose
To:  g.held/eval.mail
CC:
Subject:  test message
Text:
This is a test message.......
.
Send?  y

  Msg posted  Jan 14, 1994  8:12 AM EST  MSG: GGJE-6050-3803
```

Figure 10.1 Creating and sending a SprintMail Message

```
Command?   scan

No.  Delivered      From           Subject              Lines

1 Jan 14  8:12 G.HELD  test message                      2

Command?   read 1

Posted: Fri, Jan 14, 1994  8:12 AM EST  Msg: GGJE-6050-3803
From: G.HELD
To:   g.held/eval.mail
Subj: test message
This is a test message.......

Action?      purge

Purged.
```

ACCESSING OTHER ELECTRONIC MAIL SYSTEM

SprintMail supports the CCITT X.400 addressing recommendation previously described in Chapter 4. This means you can address messages to subscribers of other electronic messaging services that support the X.400 recommendation. To do so you would use the COMPOSE command and place the X.400 address in parenthesis on the To: line. The following example shown in Figure 10.2 illustrates the creation and transmission of a small test message from SprintMail to the author's MCI Mail account.

The X.400 Messaging Address format is:(<keyword>:<value>,<keyword>: value> ..)

```
Command?   compose
To:   (FN:Gilbert,SN:Held,A:MCI,C:USA)
CC:
Subject:   Test message
Text:
This test message originated on Sprint.
.
Send?   y
```

Figure 10.2 Sending a Message from SprintMail to an MCI Mail Subscriber

where:

    <keyword>   represents the abbreviation for an envelope component

    <value>   specifies information for <keyword>

    ...   indicates repetitions of <keyword>:<value>

Abbreviations and examples of the <keyword> components are:

Component	Keyword	Example
COUNTRY NAME	C	C:USA
DOMAIN NAME:		
Public System	A or ADMD or PUB	A:Telemail
Private System	P or PRMD or PVT	P:COMPANY.PRIVATE
PERSONAL NAME:		
Surname	SN	SN:JONES
First Name	FN	FN:Jane
Initials	I	I:J
ORGANIZATION NAME	O	O:XYZ.CORP
ORGANIZATION UNIT	OU	OU:ABC.DIV

Up to four levels are supported—these must be entered in ascending order when addressing a SprintMail system user and in descending order for other systems.

Domain-defined attributes are keywords defined and utilized by the systems which can vary among X.400 vendors.

Component	Keyword	Example
DOMAIN-DEFINED (DDA) ATTRIBUTES:		
○ MAILBOXES:		
User Name, List, Station,		
Bulletin Board, Admin	UN	UN:RSmith
User Code	UC	UC:*XYQ1234
System Name (used only for	TS	TS:MAIL
communicating within domestic		
systems of Telemail ADMD)–UN		
must be used with TS		

Reading X400 Messages

The X400 option of the READ command displays the X.400 protocol information.
The following examples illustrate the use of the X400 option:

Entering this command:	Displays:
READ	Envelope information and message text
READ TEXT	Message text
READ X400	Envelope information, X400 header, and message text
READ TEXT X400	X400 header and message text

   The following error messages are displayed if you make an error in addressing
an X.400 message.

X.400 ERROR MESSAGES	
Message displayed. . .	Addressing error. . .
The value field contains an invalid character.	Address contains a character that is not an alpha or numeric or accepted special character
A keyword in the above is unrecognized.	Keyword is 0 length, longer than 8 address characters, or needs to be in quotes (if it is not a recognized keyword)
Mail system is ambiguous	Only one value for either C: or PUB: keyword is supplied. This keyword and value pair does not uniquely identify a system.
Conflicting options	Both UC: and UN: keywords supplied

ACCESSING SUBSCRIBERS OF OTHER E-MAIL SERVICES

The following table lists examples of X.400 addressing to send electronic messages to subscribers on several different messaging services.

ATTMAIL - The following are examples of sending an X.400 message to an ATTMAIL user.

> (C:USA,A:ATTMAIL,O:CO.ABC,ID:JJONES)
>   or
> (C:USA,A:ATTMAIL,ID:JJONES,SN:JONES,FN:JOHN)
>   or
> (C:USA,A:ATTMAIL,SN:JONES,FN:JOHN)

MCI - The following are examples of sending an X.400 message to an MCI user:

> (C:USA,A:MCI,SN:SMITH,FN:JOHN)
>   or
> (C:USA,A:MCI,ID:0123456789)

Internet - The following is an example of sending an X.400 message to an Internet user. Note that the actual Internet address is in <> with (a) replacing @.

> TO: (C:USA,A:Telemail,P:Internet,"RFC-822":<JAD(a)XYZ.EDU>)

Western Union - Use the following format to send a message to users on Western Union's service.

> (C:USA,A:WESTERN UNION,"ELN":xxxxxxxx,O:CO.XYZ)

> where: ELN is the person's Easylink ID

SPRINTMAIL DIRECT DELIVERY SERVICES

SprintMail provides subscribers with the ability to transmit messages to many different types of communications equipment, such as telex, fax, or a station connected to the network.

The following table indicates five SprintMail direct delivery services to include a description of each service, the keyword to use to inform SprintMail to use the requested service (shown in parenthesis) and an example of the use of each service in response to the To:or CC: prompts invoked by the use of the COMPOSE command.

TELEX (TLX) - This direct delivery identifier informs SprintMail to transmit the message to any international telex device.

>   To: John Smith(AC:23,TLX:123455567,ANS:abc)

where AC:23 indicates the telex area code, TLX:1234567 represents the telex network address, and ANS:abc represents the SprintMail telex answerback.

DIRECT DISTANCE DIAL(DDD) - This direct delivery identifier results in SprintMail transmitting your message to any indicated telephone number in the United States. That telephone number can be connected to an autoanswer modem serving a computer or printing device.

>   To: Jane Doe(DDD:912-123-4567,SPD:1200)

where SPD:1200 indicates transmission to the indicated modem telephone number is to occur at 1200bps. Currently only 300 and 1200 are supported.

NETWORK (NET) - This direct delivery identifier is used to inform SprintMail to transmit the message to any terminal device to include printer, personal computer, or host computer directly attached to the SprintNet data network.

>   To: Mary Smith(NET:123456789)

where 123456789 represents the SprintNet destination address.

FACSIMILE (FAX) - This direct delivery identifier informs SprintMail to transmit your electronic message to any Group III fax machine anywhere in the world.

>   To: Gilbert Held(Fax:912-477-0293)

where 912-477-0293 represents the telephone number SprintMail will transmit the fax message to.

STATION (STN) - This direct delivery identifier is used to transmit a message to a previously registered device. That registered device can represent any of the above four direct delivery devices or another type of receiving device that is registered as a station on SprintMail.

>   To: Fred Unger(STN:Fred)

where Fred represents the name assigned to a previously registered station.

US POSTAL SERVICE DELIVERY

You can use SprintMail's Post facility to transmit your messages to a SprintMail Post Service Center where they will be printed on a laser printer, placed in an en-

velope and delivered by the United States Postal Service as priority first class mail.
To do so you can either use the COMPOSE command and enter Mail.Post in response to the To: prompt or enter the command COMPOSE POST. The following example illustrates the use of the COMPOSE POST message which results in
a menu system that leads you through the creation of a message for final delivery
by the US Postal Service.

Command?   compose post

WELCOME TO SprintMail POST SERVICE!

```
* * * * * * * * * * * * * * * * * * * * * * * * * * * * * * * * * * * * * * * * * * * * * * * * * * * *
**   1.   Send a POST Message                                    **
**   2.   Create Stored Workspaces or Profiles                   **
**   3.   Added Service Registrations                            **
**   4.   Help and Information                                   **
**   5.   Exit POST Service                                      **
* * * * * * * * * * * * * * * * * * * * * * * * * * * * * * * * * * * * * * * * * * * * * * * * * * * * *
```

        Enter Selection: (1-5 or ?) ===>> 5

```
* * * * * * * * * * * * * * * * * * * * * * * * * * * * * * * * * * * * * * * * * * * * * * * * * * * * *
**   1.   Send a QUICK POST Message                              **
**   2.   Send a POST Message WITHOUT a Profile                  **
**   3.   Send a POST Message WITH a Profile                     **
**   4.   Return to POST Main Menu                               **
* * * * * * * * * * * * * * * * * * * * * * * * * * * * * * * * * * * * * * * * * * * * * * * * * * * * *
```

        Enter Selection (1-4 OR ?) ===>> 1

WELCOME TO SprintMail POST SERVICE

Please enter a 2-4 line RETURN ADDRESS.

```
YOUR NAME:    Gilbert Held
STREET (1):   4736 Oxford Road
STREET (2):
CITY:         Macon
STATE:        GA
ZIP CODE:     31210
```

```
ADDRESSEE(S)
--------------
Please enter a 2-5 line ADDRESSEE.

NAME:         Beverly Held
COMPANY:      4Degree Consulting
STREET (1):   4736 Oxford Road
STREET (2):
CITY:         Macon
STATE:        GA
ZIPCODE:      31210


Do you have another Addressee?

YES or NO?   n

Please enter your TEXT (80 characters max per line).  End with
a PERIOD (.) <CR>.

Text:


This test message delivered by the use of SprintMail.
.

Do you wish to SEND, EDIT or CANCEL this Letter ?

SEND, EDIT or CANCEL ?  send
  Msg posted  Jan 14, 1994  8:23 AM EST  MSG: NGJE-6050-3866
          THANK YOU FOR USING SprintMail POST SERVICE.
  Msg posted  Jan 14, 1994  8:28 AM EST  MSG: BGJE-6050-3896
```

CHAPTER 11

The Relaynet Information and Message Exchange Network

Relaynet™ is one of the oldest international bulletin board system networks. This network consists of more that 1100 bulletin board systems located throughout the United States, Canada, Europe, Japan, Taiwan, New Zealand, South America, Eastern Europe, South Africa, and the Middle East. The network supports more than 450 conferences, with conference topics ranging in scope from product and software support sponsored by authors to current events, political discussions, an on-line AA meeting, hardware support, and the exchange of mail with MetroLink, Fido, UseNet and other bulletin board system networks.

For additional information concerning Relaynet, an updated conference and node list you can contact Dr. Bonnie Anthony at The Running Board whose telephone access number is 301-229-5623/5342. You can also leave a message for Dr. Anthony at: 301-229-7028 (work), 301-229-7244 (home), or 301-229-7574 (fax).

The Relaynet International Message Exchange Bulletin Board System Network is commonly referred to by its acronym RIME, or the RIME network. In this chapter are two comprehensive tables which provide readers with a good indication of the scope of coverage of topics supported by RIME as well as how to access a RIME hub close to your location. The first table consists of a list of conferences carried by the RIME network, while the second table consists of a list of nodes sorted by state and country abbreviation to facilitate reference to a node located close to a readers location.

RIME **MAIL AND CONFERENCE TRANSFER OPERATION**

Electronic messages on RIME flow in a hierarchical manner. Each day the nodes in a region call their Regional Hub and upload all new messages entered during the day. The Regional Hub downloads all public and routed messages from every other node on the network.

The Regional Hub takes messages received from the boards it serves and transmits those messages to a Super-Regional Hub. Each Super-Regional Hub calls the NetHub located in Bethesda, MD and uploads its messages and downloads waiting mail for Hubs they service.

TYPES OF RIME **NETWORK MESSAGES**

Public Message - A message available for reading by all network users.

R/O - Receiver Only - A message directed to a single individual.

Routed Message - A message meant to be delivered to a specific board.

Unrouted Message - A message sent to every board in the network. Also known as plain mail.

ROUTING A MESSAGE

Enter the routing line in the upper left corner on the first line of your message and then skip a line prior to beginning your message.

    RIME Routing symbol: ->

    RIME Routing format: ->IDCODE   or ->SITE NUMBER

    RIME Routing example: ->BIGBOARD   ->121

Multicasting - Routing a message to more than one site by entering multiple site numbers and/or IDCODES on a routing line.

    Multicasting example: ->BIGBOARD 121 RUNNINGA 1234

RIME INTERNATIONAL CONFERENCE LISTING
NAME TO NUMBER CROSS REFERENCE

RIME INTERNATIONAL CONFERENCE LISTING
NAME TO NUMBER CROSS REFERENCE

RIME INTERNATIONAL CONFERENCE LISTING
NAME TO NUMBER CROSS REFERENCE

RIME INTERNATIONAL CONFERENCE LISTING
NAME TO NUMBER CROSS REFERENCE

NODE LIST

1/03/94   BBS Name, Node, Sysop Name, Phone

BBS Name	Nodeid	Site	Sysop Name	BBS Number
Aardvark BBS	AARDVARK	48	David Greenberger	(212) 496-8324
Abaforum	ABAFORUM	1006	David Llamas	34 35 893 888
Abacus BBS	ABIGAIL	872	Loren Marks	(205) 393-6312
The Above Board II	ABOVETWO	1439	Thomas Carlisle	(701) 727-4842
Advanced Computer Concepts	ACC	4	Skip Ross	(914) 654-1981
Alachua County Computer Users	ACCUG	1776	Greg Barton	(904) 335-7289
Ace Online	ACE	5365	Brian Neale	(301 942-2218
A.C.M.E.	ACME	5080	Jeff Hochstetler	(707) 539-4050
ACS BBS	ACSBBS	1631	Tim Rarden	(513) 746-4746
Action-Link Systems	ACTION	56	Jim Davie	(813) 747-9295
Adagio BBS	ADAGIO	1046	Robert Hubert	(404) 508-0431
The Addcition BBS	ADDICTON	139	Michael Scribner	(207) 727-3065
After Five BBS	AFTERFIVE	1044	Bill Clinton	(501) 835-5830
A.I.M.S.	AIMS	5356	Justin Long	(804) 523-7632
Mountain Air BBS	AIR	1402	Edward Wood	(703) 427-0226
Airboat Online	AIRBOAT	1429	Donald Shelton	(713) 855-6724
Airways Online	AIRWAYS	277	Roger Holm	47 29 423 82
CT Dept. of Revenue Services	AJJJR	5011	A.J. Janschewitz	(203) 297-5907
Alex's Place	ALEXS	1063	Alex Pappadakis	(914) 668-1635
Alpha and Omega	ALPHA	1765	Eric Carlson	(510) 247-0297
Alpha Software BBS	ALPHABBS	5403	Steve Wilsson	(617) 229-2915
Alternative Insights	ALTINS	5376	Celia Varga	(516) 676-0741
AmerIServe	AMERISERVE	927	David Shapiro	(212) 876-5885
The Right Angle BBS	ANGLE	5191	Bill Roark	(303) 337-0219
Animal House	ANIMALHOUSE	5386	Dick Wilson	(601) 328-4971
A_P_A_P BBS!	APAP	5024	Adrain Preston	(214) 296-1151
AOF II: The Next Dimension PCB	APOGEE	1674	Joe Siegler	(215) 742-9641
The Apple-Wize BBS	APPLEWIZ	950	Mike Baumann	(914) 779-0388
Aquila BBS	AQUILA	731	Steve Williams	(708) 820-8344

BBS Name	Nodeid	Site	Sysop Name	BBS Number
Arc Light	ARCLIGHT	1392	Jim St. John	(317) 575-8833
Argosy and Wimsey Games	ARGOSY	667	Geoff White	(404) 255-8646
Arbor Ridge BBS	ARIDGE	5468	Dean Cohen	(301) 797-5495
Aries Knowledge Systems BBS	ARIES	5407	Waddell Robey	(410) 625-0426
The Arts Place BBS	ARTS	1680	Ron Fitzherbert	(703) 528-8467
ASA CompuHelp BBS	ASACOMP	5092	Rick Korecki	(614) 476-4058
Asian Connection	ASIAN	1856	Denny Chuang	(909) 781-4066
ASP	ASP	1231	Juan Arias	(708) 259-8549
Asylum	ASYLUM	962	Lewis Schaller	(803) 763-9335
ATIS	ATIS	1278	Bill Downing	(703) 242-3520
Com 1:Atlanta BBS	ATLPCUG	1334	Paul Sponaugle	(404) 808-4696
Atlanta Windows Exchange	ATLWIN	1434	Warren Royal	(404) 516-0048
The Atrium BBS	ATRIUM	5207	Steve Melone	(813) 785-6563
Austech BBS	AUSTECH	5275	Lucas Lozo	61 38 942 155
Avalon BBS	AVALONSP	811	Carlos Barahona	34 3 430 5942
Axios BBS	AXIOS	1686	Daniel Gorham	501 8 23633
The Gover~NET BBS	AYRISTA	1676	Earl Austria	(708) 837-7552
The BackDoor BBS	BACKDOOR	1406	Ed Maroon	(217) 762-2847
The Bad Element BBS	BADELEMENT	5396	Debbie Caudill	(513) 625-0020
The Badger's Byte	BADGERBYTE	5338	Dick Roosa	(402) 376-3120
Balder BBS	BALDER	5172	Aslak Sveen	06 84 428 4
Blood & Guts	BANDG	1447	Steve Strunk	(708) 969-9380
The Complete Sports BBS	BASEBALL	1549	Jonathan Arnold	(617) 335-2238
Base Line BBS	BASELINE	5214	Steve Keith	(508) 535-0446
The Bat Cave	BATCAVE	589	Sidney Moore	(904) 384-2112
Baudeville BBS	BAUDEVILLE	1412	Ian Evans	(416) 283-0114
Baud Horizon's	BAUDHORIZON	668	Mike Adams	(504) 436-9590
Baudville MEGA-ROM!	BAUDMEGAROM	5239	Alan Torres	(503) 343-1483
Bay Cafe BBS	BAYNY	5454	Carmine Prinzo	(718) 769-6787
BlackBoard International	BBI	1559	Warren Salmon	(416) 260-8985
BB's BBS	BBSBBS	1551	Bob Browne	(609) 768-6585
BBS-Ohio	BBSOHIO	5260	Keith Ross	(216) 944-5639
Beacon Studios	BEACONBBS	5368	Conrad Koblack	(201) 863-5253
BEC BBS	BECBBS	282	George Lollar	(217) 585-1279
The Beckett BBS	BECKETT	281	Jerry Liddle	(609) 467-3898
Bedrock Cafe	BEDROCK	1693	Michael Dodge	(803) 899-6940
Beggars Banquet	BEGRSBANQUET	5431	Dan Cooney	(716) 265-3505
Bellevue Downtown Community BB	BELLEVUE	1594	John Haro	(402) 731-9847
Belle Plains BBS	BELLPLAINS	672	Clayton Lawrence	(703) 373-7438
The Berean Connection	BEREAN	5095	John Dibble	(303) 693-9263
Berryessa Central BBS	BERRYESSA	5093	Mark Shapiro	(408) 946-8592
The Beta Connection	BETACON	643	David Reynolds	(219) 293-6465
BFWK	BFWK	1616	Bob Vesey	(201) 941-3302
The Black Hole][	BHII	5404	Scott Gray	(808) 834-1877

BBS Name	Nodeid	Site	Sysop Name	BBS Number
Broadcaster's Information CTR	BIC	1362	Tim Sawyer	(301) 654-6462
Billy's Best BBS	BILLBEST	1467	Bill Wahlstrom	(612) 869-3869
Billboard BBS	BILLBOARD	553	William Robbins	(503) 688-2056
Bill's BBS	BILLSNJ	1224	Bill Williams	(609) 845-9171
Bill's Board	BILLSTOY	5375	Bill Ballenger	(317) 529-4889
Bingo Bango Bongo	BINGO	1093	Steve Gerber	(818) 842-2956
The 32 Bit Bus	BITBUS	711	Bob Bernstein	(215) 741-9893
Bits 'N Bytes BBS	BITBYTES	1201	Bryan Leaman	(717) 757-4141
Bits and Bytes BBS	BITSNBYTES	1154	Barly Redsar	(909) 356-8345
Bizbase	BIZBASE	434	Chris Kalaboukis	(416) 698-7495
Black Gold	BLACKGOLD	1279	John Cline	(918) 272-7779
Black River Systems	BLACKRIVER	776	Clyde Messinger	(313) 679-2408
B-Link BBS	BLINEBBS	5184	Antonio Jorge	35 11 491 0755
Blue Foxx BBS	BLUEFOXX	513	Tim Maloney	(405) 482-3855
The Blue Knights BBS	BLUEKNIGHT	1670	Gil Mitchell	(603) 464-4176
Blue Lake System	BLUELAKE	433	Mark Adkins	(503) 656-9790
The Big Blue Mac	BLUEMAC	1814	Todd Miller	(714) 498-8638
Bell Microcomputer Club BBS	BMCBBS	351	Lyle Giese	(312) 727-5043
BMC West	BMCWEST	1083	Lyle Giese	(815) 337-0191
Bell Muticultureal HS BBS	BMHSBBS	1562	Jwayanza Igwe	(202) 673-2330
The Bone Yard BBS	BONEYARD	5418	Kenneth Jones	(408) 738-6616
Borealis Computer Systems	BOREALIS	914	David Schimmel	(303) 750-7136
The Brass Cannon	BRASS	1126	Blaine Binkerd	(801) 226-8310
Brentwood BBS!	BRENTWOOD	24	Guy Cappello	(914) 381-1600
Brodmann's Place	BRODMANN	1286	Dave Brodmann	(301) 843-5732
Beyond The Event Horizon	BTEH	5199	Mike Flanigan	(317) 644-0006
Buccaneer's Harbor	BUCCANEER	5401	Carl Slawinski	(901) 873-2837
Buffalo Data Systems	BUFDATASYS	1899	Bill Deer	(716) 895-1146
Bufferd's Place A Ham Radio	BUFERD	1437	Andre Shumate	(408) 365-1644
The Byte Barn BBS	BYTEBARN	5268	George Husted	(512) 776-3732
THE BYTELINE! BBS	BYTELINE	365	Ron Rieman	(612) 931-0275
Bytes BBS	BYTES	5427	Bob Delugach	(216) 677-4978
Cabana BBS	CABANA	5113	Margaret Hobbie	(904) 926-5936
The File Cabinet BBS	CABINET	1855	Richard Vonzel	(612) 888-9739
Carolina Forum	CAFORUM	1272	Sam Grier	(704) 563-5857
La Cantina!	CANTINA	173	John Dodson	(915) 532-0332
The Ctrl AR Netware User's Gr	CANUG	1427	Eric Lentz	(501) 682-1722
Capital Connection	CAPCON	12	Bob Shuck	(703) 280-5490
Capricorn Rising BBS	CAPCORN	838	Bob Covington	(503) 370-9777
Cape Cod Salt Air	CAPECOD	153	Robert Baker	(508) 385-3427
CASA West	CASAWEST	5138	Tony Cooper	(304) 264-0280
The Casino PCBoard BBS	CASINO	18	Dave Schubert	(609) 561-3377

BBS Name	Nodeid	Site	Sysop Name	BBS Number
The Castle Aggghhh	CASTLE	5393	Chad Smith	(219) 294-5453
The Castles Gate	CASTLESGATE	5299	Larry Bristow	(301) 206-5323
Wildcat's Den	CATDEN	116	Ken Engler	(703) 491-5726
The Cat Eye	CATEYE	5012	Doug Moore	(304) 592-3390
The Catholic Mailbox	CATHMAIL	5424	Delbert McCord	(313) 631-6870
The Cat House BBS	CATHOUSE	583	Tangee Brusherd	(904) 778-4236
The Black Cauldron	CAULDRON	463	Dave Biggs	(407) 699-6613
ThunderBall Cave	CAVE	334	Jon Orten	47 22 994 41
Ken's Cavern	CAVERN	238	Ken Jessup	(201) 796-0619
Columbia Online - the CBUB BBS	CBUG	5297	Bob Weber	(410) 750-1253
Crimson Cross BBS	CCBBS	1390	Kevin Cummins	(618) 253-3608
Charleston Computer Connection	CCCBBS	1010	Tony Oliver	(803) 767-4190
Computer Corner	CCORNER	1725	Alan Shoemaker	(909) 683-3367
Complete Computer Solutions	CCSBBS	1113	Paul Sink	(513) 424-2495
Computer Enterprises BBS	CEBBS	1642	Jack Blue	(218) 326-4205
Center Point PCBoard	CENTER	80	Kelvin Hyatt	(801) 968-0258
The Computer Forum BBS	CFORUM	109	Jim Rhodes	(804) 471-3360
Channel 1	CHANNEL1	15	Brian Miller	(617) 354-7077
ChatMaster BBS	CHATMSTR	830	Micheal Redman	(417) 886-6639
The Chatterbox Lounge & Hotel	CHATTERBOX	1907	James Lunsford	(412) 795-4454
The Old Fart's BBS	CHEERS	1893	Tom Butler	(804) 526-4422
Chemeeketa Online	CHEMEK	233	Bob Hunter	(503) 393-5580
The Chesapeake BBS	CHESA	1114	Michael Nelson	(301) 929-9122
The Cheshire Cat	CHESHIRE	548	Sally Kosh	(916) 544-1682
The Chess Board BBS	CHESSBOARD	1649	James Reames	(312) 784-3019
Chesapeake PC Users Group	CHESSIE	1262	Wally Babbitt	(410) 266-5939
China-Link	CHINALINK	5217	How-Sun Chow	(301) 990-6362
China Rider	CHINARIDER	5439	Douglas Boustead	(914) 422-2993
ChowdaNet BBS	CHOWDANET	1365	Brad Shipp	(401) 331-0334
Corporate Headquarters BBS	CHQBBS	1255	Robert Neal	(815) 886-3233
UltraBBS HQ & Support	CHWATAL	1040	John Chwatal	(318) 487-0800
The Circus BBS	CIRCUSBBS	5348	Dennis Lotto	(916) 446-0752
The Citadel	CITADEL	5046	Dale Nawrocki	(716) 668-0295
The City Limits BBS	CITYLIMITS	5202	John Jagiello	(803) 821-1634
City Lites	CITYLITES	1045	John Lundell	(701) 775-5399
City People BBS	CITYPEOPLE	43	Barry Weiser	(212) 255-6656
Clavius BBS Educacional	CLAVIUS	1497	Antonio Lopez	34 13 112 371
Clever Endeavor BBS	CLEVER	5097	George Ramos	(707) 263-6612
Cliffside Park BBS	CLIFFSIDPK	5009	Stephen Leon	(201) 886-8041
The River Grove BBS	CLIPHEAVEN2	896	Vince Montana	(708) 453-5589

BBS Name	Nodeid	Site	Sysop Name	BBS Number
Club 36-15	CLUB	793	Serge Ecoiffier	(519) 798-3062
Club PC BBS	CLUBPC	108	Jim Kreyling	(804) 357-0357
Cambridge Micro BBS	CMICRO	451	Armand Michaud	(519) 621-0561
Coffee Cup	COFCUP	5155	Tom Graham	(519) 751-0832
The Coffee Shop	COFFEE	572	Jim Murphey	(407) 830-5316
The Colosseum	COLOSSEUM	5194	Walt Martin	(301) 258-8151
Colossus	COLOSSUS	5161	Craig Wright	(614) 885-9829
Commnet-386	COMMNET	823	Stephen King	(909) 359-3189
Communication Systems BBS	COMMSYS	923	David Harding	(804) 285-7231
The Communicator Network BBS	COMMUNICATOR	5036	Roy Stevens	(614) 366-5672
Compart BBS	COMPART	1240	Ulf Sandas	35 80 506 332
Computers and Dreams BBS	COMPNDREAMS	1638	William Stewart	(212) 888-6565
Computronics Comm Link	COMPTRON	74	Ken Hunt	(813) 526-1265
Comp-U-Ease	COMPUEASE	90	Stuart Smith	(408) 286-8332
CompuNet Online	COMPUNET	1779	Shawn Bogardus	(301) 963-4453
CompuSpec	COMPUSPEC	1797	Ken Polsson	(604) 727-2362
Computer World Connection	COMPWORLD	5276	Gordon Cavanaugh	(406) 721-6484
Com-Sec	COMSEC	1311	Hans Von Braun	(415) 495-4642
Comstar	COMSTARI	593	Roger Dye	(216) 661-9065
COM Systems MajorBBS	COMSYSTM	5063	Thomas Mahnke	(414) 289-0162
Connectivity	CONNECTIVITY	5302	Ray Crittenden	(804) 499-8934
The Consultant BBS	CONSULTANT	5049	Jay Caplan	(718) 837-3236
Consumer Board	CONSUMER	1787	Charles Swett	(703) 759-2001
CoolBaby BBS	COOLBABY	5244	Mark Krieg	(717) 755-1859
Bob's Corner Board	CORNER	272	Robert Cox	(904) 361-9094
Cor Unum	CORUNUM	1719	Joe Gallegos	(714) 531-7255
The Electronic Cottage	COTTAGE	1464	Sam Gorstein	(617) 738-5196
Country Lane	COUNTRY	1259	Harold Murphy	(207) 499-2999
Country Link	COUNTYLINK	1080	Steve Husk	(216) 236-6126
The CPA's BBS	CPABBS	5070	Rob Richmond	(202) 882-9067
Platinum Express Online Service	CPRINT	462	Glenn Jarvis	(519) 579-9939
The Computer Master	CPUMASTR	1824	Jim Grimsby	(909) 355-1404
Cracker's Paradise	CRACKERS	1771	Bob Brumley	(707) 838-4483
Cravings BBS Network	CRAVINGS	1778	Steven DeTrafford	(718) 956-3874
Sound Blaster BBS	CREATIVE	5339	Raymond Loh	65 776 2423
The Crenshaw County BBS	CRENSHAW	5337	Ed Welch	(205) 335-3968
Croatia PCBoard BBS	CROATIA	1443	Goran Reinspach	38 54 127 118
The Crooked Blade	CROOKED	1368	Jay Vanvalkenberg	(503) 838-4059
The Crooked Blade II	CROOOKED2	5310	Jeff Spradling	(206) 822-0902
CROSS n CROWN BBS	CROSSCROWN	5349	Tim McIntosh	(606) 754-8650
Crossroads	CROSSRDS	603	Mike Feinberg	(703) 590-0049

BBS Name	*Nodeid*	*Site*	*Sysop Name*	*BBS Number*
The Crow's Nest	CROWNEST	303	Kenny Gardner	(714) 493-3819
CRS Online	CRS	118	Rick Munro	(416) 213-6002
The Crystal Ball	CRYSTALBALL	5256	Brett Morris	(502) 271-2500
The Crystal Palace	CRYSTALPAL	1789	Shane Barth	(407) 774-5964
Clear to Send	CTSBBS	5323	Kent Tyrell	(712) 325-8202
City Corner BBS	CTYCRNR	1613	Daniel Kempton	(503) 838-4551
CyberBoard - Rye Brook	CYBERBOARD	5373	Marc Steinberg	(914) 934-8125
CyberQuest	CYBERQUEST	5305	David Brunell	(407) 969-0056
Cyber Zone	CYBERZONE	1780	Bob Fayne	(401) 732-0258
The Rib N' Rall	DADELUS	78	David Logan	(519) 264-2919
Dalriada BBS	DALRIADA	5438	Sammy McSkimming	44 0770 302532
The Dark Shadows BBS	DARKSHADOWS	5352	Todd Rauch	(609) 782-8205
The Dark Side	DARKSIDE	888	Mike Dukeman	(609) 391-0987
Dark Side of the Moon	DARKSIDEMOON	5402	Peter Cacchioli	(914) 621-2865
The Dark Star	DARKSTAR	470	Bill Oliver	(716) 668-3396
Da Rucci BBS	DARUCCI	1662	Steve Rucci	(904) 743-7052
Dasan I Sandefjord	DASAN	352	Hans Gether	47 34 595 30
Data-Base BBS	DATABASE	1251	Michael Walter	(908) 735-2180
DataBoard][BBS	DATABRD	1074	Marvin Blackburn	(817) 297-6222
DataByte Computer Services	DATABYTE	468	Jim Kornegay	(619) 367-9208
Data Connection	DATACONNECT	5416	Jeffrey Callaway	(317) 299-8696
Data-Link BBS	DATALINK	5084	Gary Fisher	(609) 299-2935
Dataport Network Information	DATANET	1507	Michael Simmons	(619) 864-1468
DatStream BBS	DATASTREAM	245	Dean Lake	(309) 688-7713
Data Tamers BBS	DATATAME	168	William Waldheim	(502) 857-2548
Data Terminal Ready BBS	DATATERM	1532	Stephen Clarke	(602) 993-4753
The Dataexchange BBS	DATEX	5126	Don Morris	(318) 239-2122
DAT Information Exchange	DATINFOEXCH	1714	Dale Sullivan	(708) 426-9563
Dave's Arcade	DAVESARCADE	5428	Dave Prows	(904) 353-2335
Daytona Beach	DAYTONABEACH	1912	Todd Utrup	(904) 257-0706
The DC Info Exchange	DCINFO	16	Bill Walsh	(703) 836-0748
The Dead Board	DEADBOARD	120	Klaus Bender	(717) 677-9573
Dead of Night	DEADNITE	5240	Donald Mehrtens	(703) 644-7667
The Dead Zone	DEADZONE	5316	Scott Garrett	(515) 684-5418
Uncle "D"'s Directory	DEAFNET	5039	Dave Spensley	(415) 364-3001
The Deal Makers BBS	DEALMAKERS	5358	Ted Kraus	(908) 730-9002
The Decker's BBS	DECKERS	5264	Adam Roycraft	(715) 839-0942
The Modems Delight BBS	DELIGHT	5149	Ronald Dishon	(310) 944-1221
deltaComm Online	DELTA	22	Jeff Woods	(919) 481-9399
Deltona PCBoard BBS	DELTONA	66	Wayne Barrett	(407) 789-5028
Design BBS	DESIGN	1735	Jeff Smart	65 44 281 58
The Devil's Advocate	DEVIL	5170	Ron Vass	(519) 756-7988
The Dew Drop Inn	DEWDROP	1886	Doug Frank	(412) 854-0619

BBS Name	Nodeid	Site	Sysop Name	BBS Number
David's Express PCBoard	DEXPRESS	1304	David Keener	(404) 963-5514
Dextra Customer Support BBS	DEXTRA	5391	Robert Wakefield-C	886 2 718 3589
DFW Programmer's Exchange	DFWPGMR	1033	Ric Naff	(214) 398-3112
The Elusive Diamond	DIAMOND	373	Gregg Snyder	(703) 323-6423
The Digital Connection	DIGICON	5429	Brian Williams	(316) 792-3314
Digital Schoolhouse	DIGISCHL	873	Chris Shaw	(416) 458-5820
Digital Systems BBS	DIGISYS	1383	David Flood	(708) 307-9097
Digital Spectrum BBS	DIGITAL	953	Rhett Dail	(410) 266-7343
The DIGITAL X-Connect BBS	DIGITALXCONN	1335	Andrew Walding	(214) 517-8443
Directory Assistance	DIRASNT	91	Jim Goodenough	(707) 579-8234
Distributed Information Serv.	DIS	418	Joseph Bianco	(718) 722-1456
Dis Iz Dis	DISDIS	1078	Mike Downie	(408) 227-1583
Late Nite DIVERSIONS	DIVERSIONS	5301	Jon Vidler	(519) 332-0241
Danish Key Board BBS	DKBBBS	1117	Jens Hummelmose	45 32 473 040
DK Online	DKONLINE	276	Jorgen Jensen	45 44 993 860
Don's BBS	DONSBBS	5218	Don Sharp	(609) 435-1663
Doppler Base BBS	DOPPLER	5344	Dan Myers	(410) 922-1352
Members Only	DOTCOMPUTERS	1142	Dan Graves	(913) 762-4841
The Double-D BBS	DOUBLED	1794	Doug Davis	(214) 492-8090
The Downey BBS	DOWNEY	1435	Mark Motley	(310) 806-2226
Down The Hole BBS	DOWNTHEHOLE	5105	John Huston	(316) 721-5528
Dragon Citadel	DRAGCIT	5287	Dave Kubasiak	(517) 279-7530
Dragnet BBS	DRAGNET	5419	Dale Wood	(619) 940-1985
Jim's Dream	DREAM	121	James Wall	(301) 248-0906
Dream Land BBS	DREAMLAND	1652	Ron James	(904) 837-2567
Electric Dreams	DREAMS	5036	Dave Bannerman	(714) 489-1734
Dreamscape	DREAMSCAPE	5258	Scott Brennan	(315) 458-3482
Datamax/Statalink Connection	DSC	308	Ron Brandt	(215) 443-9434
Delaware Tech Engineering Lab	DTEL	871	Sam Guccione	(302) 739-2818
The DVUG BBS	DVUG	1401	Barry Connolly	(302) 324-8091
Downloader's Dream	DWNLDRSDREAM	5330	Chuck Engstrom	(410) 544-8126
D.W.'s Toolbox	DWTOOLBOX	1035	David Willoughby	(404) 471-6636
Dx Connection BBS	DXCONN	1692	Cosimo Delrosso	(201) 692-3705
The Eagle's Nest	EAGLE	8	Michael Labbe	(401) 732-5290
The Eagle BSS	EAGLEBBS	1905	Ralph Moore	(317) 889-4274
The Earth Art BBS	EARTHART	1646	Bob Chapman	(803) 552-4389
The Nor'Easter Premium BBS	EASTER	151	Gardiner Jones	(603) 432-6711
Executive Computers	ECTECH	687	Jim Pierce	(714) 780-5672
Eden	EDEN	1096	Tim Chen	88 62 504 8111

BBS Name	Nodeid	Site	Sysop Name	BBS Number
Edgelight On-Line	EDGELIGHT	824	Greg Miller	(201) 305-9042
Collector's Edition	EDITION	79	Leonard Hult	(214) 351-9859
The Electric Dream BBS	EDREAM	5200	Bud Lucas	(318) 397-1996
EDS Development Support	EDSDEVELOP	1620	Eric Scales	(812) 423-3394
Eds Home	EDSHOME	780	Ed Bachmann	(410) 730-2917
The College Board	EDUCATION	5441	Ron Pappas	(803) 878-7340
Eternal Equinox BBS	EEBBS	1360	Doug Taylor	(703) 370-7326
EFFIGY Systems	EFFIGY	766	John Francis	(617) 288-1117
Port EINSTEIN	EINSTEIN	5090	John_P Lynch	(410) 774-4641
Electric Dreams!!!	ELDREAMS	1644	Dwayne Terry	(217) 544-1022
Electric Magazine	ELECTRICMAG	5272	Robert Shannon	(707) 961-0735
Electric Knights BBS	ELECTRIK	1001	Bill Brown	(519) 442-6449
Fuzzy Bear's Electronic Forest	ELF	929	Michael Wishnietsk	(703) 356-9487
Emerald Online BBS	EMERALD	644	Chuck Orton	(503) 942-7014
EmmaSoft BBS	EMMASOFT	5281	Dan Veaner	(607) 533-4685
The Empire BBS	EMPIRE	999	Martin Ryder	(516) 325-0827
The Ham Radio Emporium	EMPORIUM	1101	Chester McCarter	(918) 272-4327
The Difference Engine	ENGINE	1122	Patrick Nobles	(803) 576-7194
THE USS Enterprise	ENTER	77	Fred Purnell	(301) 663-3129
End of The Line	EOLN	5392	Duane Brown	(703) 720-1624
Ephesus Online	EPHESUS	5461	Kim Demers	(514) 426-0110
The Equinox BBS System	EQUINOX	5261	Bob Malus	(312) 631-2172
Executive Region Premium BBS	ERBBS	791	Randy Gautier	(312) 267-4749
The Escape	ESCAPE	247	Mark Turner	(714) 698-9568
ExpresSearch	ESEARCH	5444	Frank Pisarski	(708) 304-9807
Essex Wildcat!	ESSEX	674	Doug Peterson	(519) 736-3659
BBS Haugesund	EURONET	1431	John Nordbor	47 47 160 21
The EVANGELIST BBS	EVANGELIST	1041	Cope Jonkman	(519) 448-3223
Evergreen BBS	EVERGREEN	556	Bob Lawton	(201) 398-2373
Excalibur BBS	EXCAB	817	Ken Ready	(219) 923-7611
Excelsior	EXCELSIOR	5156	Joe Golembiewski	(518) 566-7009
The Falcon's Nest BBS	FALCON	1812	Ed Niemczyk	(716) 677-2528
Falcon RBBS-PC	FALCONRBBPC	5324	Lee Wallace	(509) 575-6862
Family BBS	FAMILY	1729	Marilyn Terry	(801)
Family Fun BBS	FAMILYFUN	799	Roy Gurley	(910) 364-4996
The Fanatics BBS	FANATICS	1479	David Dempsey	(718) 967-6827
Fantasy Land	FANTASY	1567	Steve Horrighs	(217) 566-3775
Agric<+>Food Think Tank	FARMFOOD	1611	Danny Gottlieb	(209) 527-2944
Farpoint Station	FARPOINT	5146	Kevin Wilkinson	(215) 272-6244
FatherBoard North	FATHERII	389	Don Clevenger	(302) 737-6041
Faxmachine	FAXMAN	5364	Wei Weng	(408) 295-7526
Fractured Femur Software's BBS	FFSBBS	5455	Ross Contino	(717) 630-8860
F.I.A.W.O.L	FIAWOL	977	Bobb Waller	(214) 790-6472

BBS Name	Nodeid	Site	Sysop Name	BBS Number
The File Bank	FILEBANK	246	Bob Laszko	(619) 728-4318
The File Connection	FILECONN	5279	Derek Darby	(618) 997-3503
The File Depot	FILEDEPOT	1843	Bill Masella	(708) 202-1516
File-Link BBS	FILELINK	1604	Bill Marcy	(212) 777-8282
First Due BBS	FIRSTDUE	5280	Francis Fowler	(301) 949-1927
Fligth 642	FLIGHT642	5213	Bruce Forbes	(416) 642-5295
Flightline BBS	FLIGHTLINE	5333	Grandvell Lindsey	(803) 762-3060
The Royal Flush	FLUSH	988	Marion Royal	(703) 361-4872
The French Flyer	FLYERBBS	1867	Greg French	(310) 597-2235
The Fortress BBS	FORTRESS	1116	Jay Sheperd	(419) 524-6528
Fountain BBS!!	FOUNTAINBBS	699	Calvin Dumas	(904) 448-5574
Fox Online BBS	FOXONLINE	1306	Glenn Fox	(407) 324-1700
The FPXchange	FPX2	1617	Kevin Freeman	(212) 627-0531
Freedom Infonet	FREEDOM	1381	Peter Skorupsky	(609) 586-4847
Freedom Lounge	FREEDOMLOUNG	586	Terry Hanson	(904) 778-1644
The User Friendly BBS	FRIENDLY	5088	Don Shackelford	(317) 784-0520
Friends and Family BBS	FRIENDS	112	Jim Neargarder	(214) 250-7697
The Frisky Coco	FRISKYCOCO	379	Jerry Oliver	(816) 746-5987
Frogpond by the Sea	FROGPOND	581	Donald Erkfitz	(904) 249-8368
Faster-Than-Light (FTL)	FTL	93	Robert Vostreys	(404) 292-8761
ZARNO Board	FUBAR	604	Tim Saari	(706) 860-2927
Fun Investing BBS	FUNINVST	1414	George Meno	(203) 834-0490
Film & video Domain	FVD	5456	Ben Howard	(703) 538-7148
Gadge'-Tronics Computer Cons.	GADGET	5193	Wayne Anderson	(808) 682-4648
Galaxy BBS	GALAXYl	5182	Howard Mahady	(609) 691-8701
Galaxy	GALAXY2	5183	Al Massari	(609) 678-5360
Galway On-Line	GALWAY	1660	Barry Flanagan	35 39 127 454
Game Master BBS	GAMEMASTER	1758	George Kuhl	(909) 889-3219
SoCal GameOver(tm) Chatlink	GAMEOVER	5389	Shanon Fernald	(714) 646-6094
The Game Peddler BBS	GAMEPEDDLER	860	John Sirabella	(516) 493-0785
The Games and Graphics BBS	GAMGRAFX	1731	Larry Tyler	(410) 672-5360
The Gap Chasm	GAPCHASM	1603	Jim Harding	(609) 467-0244
The Garden Spot	GARDEN	157	Karl Johnson	(617) 545-6239
Boston Gas BBS	GAS	154	Jon Anderson	(617) 235-6303
The Gastank BBS	GASTANK	1423	Richard Kenney	(609) 886-3717
Gateway BBS	GATEWAY	54	David Todd	(401) 849-9205
The Gearbox	GEARBOX	5398	Edward Fuhrman	(201) 692-1315
The General BBS	GENERAL	917	Marc Teitler	(619) 281-1581
Genesis PCBoard	GENESIS	494	Gary Thurlow	(717) 697-3717
GFSA Online	GFSA	5059	Tony Reynolds	(214) 690-5701
Giant BBS	GIANT	1601	Joseph Castagno	(508) 692-4708
Giant Steps BBS	GIANTSTEPS	5140	George Hamilton	(202) 588-0819
The Gold Mine	GLDMINE	1825	Dave Teller	(414) 458-0767

BBS Name	*Nodeid*	*Site*	*Sysop Name*	*BBS Number*
The Great Northern BBS	GNBB	680	David King	(207) 325-4103
The N. American Confederation	GOVTFREE	5369	Michael Adams	(201) 746-3935
Grace + Base	GRACE	235	Sean Isham	(901) 452-0168
Grady's BBS	GRADY	1862	Tim Grady	(301) 424-1057
The Grainstore	GRAINSTORE	650	Simon Schaanning	44 09 05770470
The Grapevine BBS	GRAPEVINE	318	Jim Wenzel	(501) 753-8121
The Great Escape BBS	GREATESC	889	Ed Ohlson	(619) 775-3930
The Green Machine	GREENMAC	5041	Thomas Green	(504) 394-1592
GreyBeards Castle	GREYBEARDS	949	Kimberly Smith	(904) 783-5637
Greyfriars Bobby BBS	GREYFRIARS	5430	Alan Seymour	(519) 455-9462
The World of GreyHawk BBS	GREYHAWK	837	Walter Ames	(410) 461-9943
The GRID BBS	GRID	5366	Ken Nash	(305) 321-2410
The Greenwich Connection	GRNCNNT	5434	Rob Glasener	(203) 869-7742
Ground Zero PCBoard	GROUND0BBS	5208	Jerry Hubbard	(415) 964-4143
Group One BBS	GROUPONE	493	Dan Parsons	(312) 752-1258
Golden Triangle BBS	GTBBS	1223	Fred Allen	(409) 899-1249
The Glendale Tower BBS	GTOWER	5390	Fred Algarin	(718) 417-8601
Hades BBS	HADESBBS	500	Mark Paris	(201) 261-0127
The Halibut	HALIBUT	95	Mark Smith	(415) 961-9635
Ham-it-up BBS	HAMITUP	966	Joseph Isbell	(516) 878-4906
Hammond BBS	HAMMOND	5222	Sidney Egnew	(504) 542-9600
The Cutting Edge BBS	HANDYNET	1366	Brian Marx	(219) 873-1035
The Hangar BBS	HANGAR	5411	Jason Hyland	44 934 511751
Hangar 18	HANGAR18	5354	Bob Dunlap	(513) 435-8481
Tandy Harbor	HARBOR	14	Jack Daugherty	(313) 455-3977
The Escape Hatch	HATCH	1610	Steve Lowery	(303) 690-0436
the Haven of Rest	HAVEN	9	Bryan Pike	(612) 474-0724
HAWG! WILD! BBS	HAWGWILD	5008	Nate Chase	(402) 493-2737
The Hawk's Hill BBS	HAWKHILL	1492	Mark West	(904) 462-5589
Hispanic Bell Management Assoc.	HBMA	900	Tony Herrera	(312) 727-4868
Hard Disk Cafe BBS	HDCAFE	5228	Charles Cunningham	(909) 269-9150
Kauai Health Net	HEALTH	5128	Stephen Tuell	(808) 822-1889
Health & Education BBS	HEALTHED	5388	Jama Lucas	(705) 424-5505
The HideOut	HIDEOUT	5332	Derek Crager	(319) 839-9103
Hillbilly Meeting Place	HILLBILLY	1663	Curtis Lange	(317) 897-4183
Hillside BBS	HILLSIDE	1245	Dave Pletsch	(519) 821-6389
Hints BBS	HINTS	467	Ernest Hintz	(415) 572-8219
His Board	HISBOARD	1542	Bob Harris	(805) 652-1478
Hobbynet	HOBBYNET	5034	Jim Knapp	(517) 336-4242
Hobby Shop	HOBBYSHOP	5179	John Murphy	(508) 572-2632
The Hole In The Wall	HOLEINWALL	5433	Mike Fergione	(303) 841-5515
The Holistic BBS	HOLISTIC	88	Mike McCarthy	(310) 531-3890
Holly City BBS	HOLLY	1690	Frank Norman	(609) 825-1621

BBS Name	Nodeid	Site	Sysop Name	BBS Number
Hollywood News/Info System	HOLLYWOOD	106	Brandon Hayden	(301) 373-3530
HomeNet	HOMENET	5242	Ronald Bowden	(619) 249-4743
Homer's Palace	HOMERSPALACE	5204	Jeff Willaims	(812) 471-5939
Dream Home BBS	HOMES	1654	Richard Camba	(908) 888-3959
Hotline BBS	HOTLINE	210	Piet Ebbes	31 20 689 1014
Hottips BBS	HOTTIPS	487	Mike Callaghan	(818) 248-3088
HomeLine	HOUSENET	1533	Gene Hamilton	(410) 745-2037
The Boost Connection	HUBTBC	1698	Mark Boost	44 499 2463851
The Happy Hunting Ground	HUNTNET	5291	Dennis Mullins	(206) 228-1734
Hudson Valley BBS	HVBBS	1608	John Perz	(914) 876-1450
The HY-IT EXPRESS BBS	HYITEXPRESS	5263	John Creamer	(407) 295-0594
IBM-NET Connection	IBMNET	5	Rex Hankins	(317) 882-5575
The Spartanburg IBMPcUg BBS	IBMPCUG	5108	Johnnie Turner	(803) 542-1658
Innovative Computer Services	ICSBBS	309	Greg Carman	(516) 226-3727
IDC BBS	IDCBBS	918	Mike King	(510) 865-7115
The Idea Link	IDEALINK	125	Andrew Miller	(301) 949-5764
Ideal Studies BBS	IDEALS	166	Peter Longo	(508) 757-1806
The Idle Gossip	IDLE	1054	Lee Goldberg	(818) 342-7808
Infinite Data Source	IDSONLINE	5032	John Choi	(703) 642-8704
The I.H.S. BBS	IHS	1266	Lucky Hughes	(909) 785-4586
Illusions	ILLUSIONS	883	Ralph Maya	(703) 803-0382
The Image Center	IMAGECENTER	1388	Larry Clive	(914) 693-9100
The Immortal! BBS	IMMORTAL	886	Jamey Hopkins	(602) 926-0281
Sudden Impact	IMPACT	5091	Randy Martin	(317) 457-5957
Indy-PC BBS	INDYPC	720	Mark Dutton	(317) 257-5882
Portal To Infinity	INFINITY	1466	Anthony Bisesi	(317) 887-6043
Visions InfoLine	INFOLINE	797	Jeffrey Morgan	(908) 769-1779
Info_Nation BBS	INFONAT	5435	Chuck Hoeltje	(609) 235-0183
Ino-Net	INFONET	1884	Bob Fehn	(609) 628-4311
The Ink and Paint Club	INKANDPAINT	5306	Christopher Harrow	(717) 295-4633
Inn On The Park	INNPARK	1037	Jim Jusko	(602) 970-0105
The Temporary Insomniac's	INSOMNIAC	1021	Gery Magalong	(408) 866-0640
Interact BBS	INTERACT	1904	Jeff Walters	(813) 745-1865
Inter-Coastal BBS	INTERCOASTAL	350	Randy Gasser	(904) 272-4305
Intriga Internacional	INTRIGA	1103	Afonso Vicente	35 11 435 2629
the Investment Club BBS	INVESTMENT	1517	Neil Dunn	(619) 476-0692
The Information Resource Sys.	IRS	1803	Chuck Jacques	(401) 783-7559
The Irish Shanty	IRSHANTY	5235	Tim Richissin	(216) 362-7733
Islington BBS	ISINGTONBBS	781	Edward Cowling	44 71 359 3121
Information System of Queens	ISOQ	5466	Steven Bunin	(718) 268-5025

BBS Name	Nodeid	Site	Sysop Name	BBS Number
I Spy BBS	ISPY	5405	Peter Spies	27 31 215 704
Info Tech	ITECH	535	Pierre Doucet	(819) 375-8452
Ivy Tech's BBS	IVYTECH	488	Philip Brown	(812) 299-9306
JackPot	JACKPOT	5271	Eric Buhr	(219) 493-2963
Janis II - Tokyo	JANIS	482	Pete Perkins	81 33 252 7224
JBJ Systems PCBoard BBS	JBJ	262	John Berardelli	(412) 341-9323
Jbs-BBS	JBSBBS	1111	John Schulte	(312) 583-1674
The Jellicle Cate	JELLICLE	1036	Ken Jacobs	(301) 779-5946
Jim's Place BBS	JIMSPLACE	1691	Jim Loos	(904) 757-0281
John's House	JONHSE	1030	John Bohman	(201) 893-8082
JP's Place	JPPLACE	5285	John Palazzolo	(703) 237-5786
Jungle Land BBS	JUNGLAND	5453	Danny Miller	(412) 343-3137
Just For Fun	JUSTFORFUN	5345	Della Moore	(314) 374-9039
KA9LQN	KA9LQM	5020	Michael Anderson	(812) 428-3352
Kalich's Kargo	KALKAR	5290	Robert Kalich	(313) 281-1138
The Kat's Lair	KATSLAIR	5245	Bobby Hitt	(703) 754-1755
Kendall Park PCBoard	KENDALL	5212	John Reinke	(908) 821-8015
Kerbside Software	KERBSIDE	732	Ed Berger	(301) 564-4035
The Killer Bee	KILLERBEE	5336	Shawn O'Connor	
Kilroy's Zer0 BBS	KILROYS	1728	Al Forte	(915) 530-0227
The King's Palace	KINGSP	1144	Paul Gamber	(404) 781-8435
Knightec BBS	KNIGHTEC	5216	Phil Knight	(519) 940-0007
San Diego's Know Ware BBS	KNOWWARE	1355	Jim Lewis	(619) 223-7111
Koinonia! BBS	KOINONIA	1697	Bob Korch	(609) 625-4475
The Krystal Palace BBS	KPALACE	5073	Michael James	(302) 652-8993
Quicksilver's Kruwle World BBS	KRUWLEWORLD	5326	Chris Sanburn	(219) 268-9913
Space Command	KWAJ	1237	George Witter	unlisted
Lancaster Area BBS	LABB	32	Jerry Shenk	(717) 394-1357
Motown - L.A. BBS	LABBS	279	Mike Kruss	(714) 535-1319
Lakes Region BBS	LAKESREGION	229	John Hodal	(708) 872-8086
LanternRock BBS	LANTERNROCK	5175	Paul Binns	(416) 690-1407
The Laser Board	LASERBOARD	1009	Shawn Higgin	(408) 268-4863
Last Dayz	LASTDAYZ	5397	Dennis Johnson	(417) 673-4623
Late Night Las Vegas	LATELV	1615	David Knudson	
The Late Night BBS	LATENIGHT	5335	Alif Ambler	(801) 377-8919
The Lavet	LAVET	5315	Bob Wieters	(318) 449-1012
Lazy Day's BBS	LAZYDAYSBBS	1471	Bob Bush	(703) 659-2227
Long Beach ibm users Group	LBIBMUG	1329	Mark Flo	(310) 420-1000
The Locker Room	LCKERROOM	1653	John Foley	(609) 889-8374
The Legend Graphics BBS	LEGEND	1267	Joey Marquez	(909) 689-9229
Leo Technology	LEOTECH	1343	Eric Poole	(603) 432-2517
Designated Letters	LETTERS	748	Jim Sura	(201) 299-7914
E.P. Levine BBS	LEVINEBBS	5446	Steven Brettler	(617) 439-0399

BBS Name	Nodeid	Site	Sysop Name	BBS Number
LexiCom BBS	LEXICOM	5421	Sean Orandi	(301) 869-7743
The Liberty BBS	LIBERTY	5443	William Zakreski	(407) 253-3959
Life Link 2 Drug Awareness BBS	LIFELINK	827	Ian Beed	65 77 802 10
The Lightning Board	LIGHTNIN	851	Tony Ledbetter	(205) 745-4515
The Little Place BBS	LILPLACE	5232	Tom Houska	(216) 341-6568
The Lima Exchange	LIMEXCH	1911	Michael Schoenberg	(419) 228-5633
The Outer Limits	LIMITS	5341	Daniel Chlarson	(801) 964-2885
LinchPin	LINCHPIN	5219	Kathleen Lynch	(617) 577-7931
Lincoln's Cabin BBS	LINCOLNCABIN	5238	Steve Pomerantz	(415) 752-4490
The LIne Driver	LINEDRIVER	5209	James Parks	(303) 465-5476
Lip Service	LIPSERVICE	1151	Debbie Davis	(816) 765-0764
Lisa BBS	LISA	383	Alyssa Baird	(702) 452-8309
The Littlest BBS In Town	LITTLEST	818	Carl Morvant	(504) 785-1848
Loboland BBS	LOBOLAND	716	Mike LeMire	(519) 979-1921
The Locker Room	LOCKERROOM	1213	Ed Golka	(714) 542-5917
Locksoft BBS	LOCKSOFT	981	Carl Curling	(909) 654-5625
The Legend of Roseville	LOR	1842	Richard Leneway	(313) 776-1975
Land of the Pharoahs	LOTP	5355	Andy MacGugan	(519) 570-9821
Land of the Unicorn	LOTU	1243	Steve Sambor	(914) 961-0399
The Lunatic Fringe BBS	LUNATIC	1282	John Stewart	(214) 235-5288
MAC's Place BBS	MAC	53	John Mcnamara	(919) 891-1111
MA/COMM	MACOMM	1651	Brice Wellington	(617) 926-0673
Magic BBS	MAGICBBS	5226	David Bauer	(210) 648-3702
Magnetic Bottle BBS	MAGNET	128	Bill Mertens	(814) 237-3825
Fort Worth Mailbag	MAILBAG	176	Scott Fritz	(817) 244-3850
The Mail House BBS	MAILHOUSE	5103	Carlos Santos	35 11 988 1183
The Electronic Mail Man	MAILMAN	1155	Jack Morgan	(808) 689-4559
The Mail Room BBS	MAILROOM	1445	Scott McPheeters	(317) 644-5029
the Main Frame BBS	MAINFRAM	1000	Andrew Bilski	(301) 654-2554
Malibu Ultraverse	MALIBU	1591	Chris Ulm	
Mallard Software	MALLARD	5353	Aaron Massey	(214) 539-2913
The Megabyte Mansion	MANSION	5189	Todd Robbins	(402) 551-8681
The Market	MARKET	131	Alan Sislen	(201) 467-3269
Martin Creek	MARTINCREEK	5357	Phil Cook	(903) 836-4654
The Mass Running Board	MASSRNBD	1770	Barry Devine	(617) 828-0868
MasterNet	MASTER	5334	Don Meldrum	(303) 444-9230
Master BBS	MASTERBBS	5380	Margarita Marin	
Max-BBS	MAX	1503	Magne Krutnes	47 87 723 11
The McHenry BBS	MCHENRY	316	Bob Walker	(815) 385-5031
Moring Computer Systems BBS	MCS	1870	Billy Moring	(904) 375-7860
MDS Support BBS	MDATA	5317	Michael Parello	(814) 724-6644
Metro. Communications Agency	MECAB	1895	Joseph Crone	(317) 327-5508
MEDCAT	MEDCAT	870	Steve Moore	(615) 343-8172

BBS Name	Nodeid	Site	Sysop Name	BBS Number
Mediccom BBS	MEDICCOM	954	Churton Budd	(419) 389-6642
Medical Information Systems	MEDINFO	585	Peter Booras	(904) 246-1481
MegaMedia MultiMedia BBS	MEGA	5198	Raaj Menon	(408) 428-9901
The MegaMixers BBS	MEGAMIXERS	5143	Geoffrey Nolasco	(301) 949-0183
The Mege-ROM BBS	MEGAROM	5096	Marcial Moreno	(310) 944-2327
Mega-Source BBS	MEGASOURCE	5180	Steve Laris	(718) 545-3990
Memory Prime	MEMPRIME	5467	Joe Sadlek	(412) 627-3227
The Cat's Meow	MEOW	225	Ray Herold	(703) 439-3060
Merrifield PC BBS	MERRIBBS	1123	Gilbert Pence	(218) 829-6340
MetroNet BBS	METRONET	1489	Brian Carner	(410) 720-5506
MetroPitt BBS	METROPITT	5225	Emery Sediak	(412) 487-9223
Metroplex BBS	METROPLX	1786	Rick Van Hooser	(901) 327-1895
The Micks BBS	MICKS	349	George Garvin	(818) 810-0615
Manassas IBM Club PC Users GP	MICPCUG	1461	Owen Carlson	(703) 367-3674
Microcom/Topcat II	MICROCAT	5234	Terry Tillman	(216) 431-9174
Micro Effects	MICROFX	5282	Steve Hansen	(916) 771-2405
Micro-Images	MICROIMAGES	111	Manual Ordona	(804) 471-0806
Micro-Link][	MICROLINK	1914	Craig Beible	(717) 393-9913
The Midas Touch	MIDAS	887	Marc Medow	(312) 764-0591
The Midnight Connection	MIDCONN	938	Gary Wolf	(312) 594-0813
Midnight Express	MIDEXPRESS	1859	Ryan Potts	(216) 867-8727
The Midnight BBS	MIDNIGHTBBS	1915	David Yancy	(502) 442-7514
Mid-Nite Rendezvous	MIDNITER	5440	bill Rupert	(319) 752-1189
Mike's Host Mode BBS	MIKESHOST	5137	Michael Hoffman	(219) 873-1949
Millenium	MILLENIUM	1130	Stephen Haas	(201) 374-2730
The Magic Mindbender BBS	MINDBEND	1589	Jeff Clarkson	(308) 632-5234
Mindless One's BBS	MINDLESS	5266	Mike Perkins	(304) 748-0491
The Mind's Eye BBS	MINDSEYE	5257	Chris Cook	(704) 322-1681
Mirage Network-VA	MIRAGEVA	1764	Tully Mars	(703) 264-3962
The Missing Link BBS	MISSLINK	1505	Thomas Conley	(312) 221-2879
MMS Online	MMSNEJM	5262	Bill Good	(617) 893-2170
ModemNews Express!	MODEMNEWS	465	Jeff Green	(203) 969-1183
Modem Zone	MODEMZONE	23	Don Cheeks	(513) 424-7529
The Mog-Ur's EMS	MOGUR	323	Thomas Tcimpidis	(818) 366-1238
The Monsoon BBS	MONSOON	1055	Sunil Gupta	(410) 235-2365
Moonbeam System's	MOONBEAM	1016	Dennis Moon	(404) 945-2185
Moondog	MOONDOG	35	Don Barba	(718) 692-2498
M.O.R.E.	MORE	6	JThomas Howell	(401) 849-1874
The Motorcyclist	MOTORCYCLIST	5412	Dale Coyner	(703) 903-5527
Memphis PC Users Group	MPCUG	368	Larry Slavick	(901) 365-1764
Mr. Crowley's Corner	MRCROWLEYS	5331	Roddy Bowen	(410) 257-6362
Mr. Rick's Neighborhood	MRRICKS	624	Rick Fry	(714) 260-1913

BBS Name	Nodeid	Site	Sysop Name	BBS Number
Moore Stephens infoline	MSINFOLINE	857	Martin Brampton	44 71 334 0337
MSmac BBS	MSMAC	933	Luis Silva	35 16 131 935
Midieval Times BBS	MTIMES	1722	Sam Evans	(208) 368-0365
The Motorcyclists BBS!	MTRCYC	5142	Dale Sokoloski	(203) 793-2024
Mushin BBS	MUSHIN	819	Brad Chesbro	(619) 452-8137
Pittsburg Midi-Music BBS	MUSIC	985	Arthur Doud	(412) 882-3703
The Music Ladder Network	MUSICLADDER	5343	George Germain	(201) 471-4913
Music Connection BBS	MUSICONNEX	1547	David Coleman	(404) 936-0550
MWB-BBS	MWB	1059	Malia Boaz	(806) 352-6523
Mystery Board	MYSTERY	1236	Richard Klein	(301) 588-8142
Mythical Kingdom Tech BBS	MYTHKING	466	Mark May	(513) 237-7737
The Electronic Grapevine	NAPAVINE	1338	Dick Wolff	(707) 257-2338
No Anchovies PC	NAPCOHIO	803	Frank Capo	(216) 466-1152
Narcoossee Connection BBS	NARCONN	65	Frank Walker	(407) 892-8483
Acropolis Nation	NATION	1751	Kelvin Khoo	65 76 351 30
The National Archives BBS	NATIONAL	1882	Ed Gibson	(703) 978-7929
New England Online	NEONLINE	5415	Michael Flood	(617)
Straight Board BBS	NEPTUNE	1475	Ray Sulich	(708) 689-1980
The NERC BBS	NERC	1396	Mike Gent	(609) 452-7669
PC's Nest BBS	NEST	345	Erlend Moen	47 78 813 71
The Nest Egg BBS	NESTEGG	5414	Tom Frye	(913) 492-2739
Network East	NETEAST	132	Howard Hartman	(301) 738-0000
Network Help! BBS	NETHELP	1131	Steven London	(617) 332-6599
The Network Market BBS	NETMARKET	5400	Kent Mulford	(816) 239-4808
Network Link BBS	NETWORKI	1502	Larry Maclellan	(317) 573-9414
Newberry Bulletin Board System	NEWBERRY	5370	Ken Anderson	(210) 233-4877
The New Future BBS	NEWFUTURE	5382	Mark Cox	(303) 438-9420
New World	NEWWORLD	5294	John Jones	(803) 795-9350
The Nexus BBS	NEXUS	590	Bob Andrews	(703) 898-7205
Nezuld's Domain	NEZULD	908	Edward Dluzen	(708) 559-0513
Nick's Folly	NICKSFOLLY	5447	Nick Ebner	(609) 764-2243
Niflheim BBS	NIFLHEIM	5173	Kurtis Lindqvist	35 82 817 924
Night Hawk BBS	NIGHTHAWK	5174	Jeff Ernsberger	(419) 525-3301
Night Magic BBS	NIGHTMAGIC	5319	Mary Mauro	(309) 786-2095
Night Owl's Publisher	NIGHTOWL	5462	Richard Graham	(716) 483-3917
Nitelog BBS	NITELOG	635	Karl Van Lear	(408) 655-1096
New Jersey Computer Connection	NJCOMPCONN	1407	Brian Kramer	(609) 895-0398
Node 66 East	NODEEAST	1516	Brian Buffell	(914) 352-6121
The Power Connection	NODEPOWER	5030	Jerry Aves	(316) 221-6782
No-Frills BBS	NOFRILLS	1299	Robert Bakley	(703) 538-4634
NoHo	NOHO	5053	Brian Parker	(619) 949-4021
New Orleans Mensa Society	NOLAMENSAey	5395	Phil Wilking	(504) 456-6704

BBS Name	Nodeid	Site	Sysop Name	BBS Number
The NoName BBS	NONAMES	1724	Robert Miller	(703) 754-0884
Nookies in the Crater	NOOKIES	1885	Shawn Muldowney	(808) 833-6862
Nordic Enterprises EDMS	NORDIC	84	David Patterson	(508) 356-1767
Northern Maine BBS	NORMAINE	749	David Collins	(207) 496-2391
Great Northern	NORTHERN	5071	Mike Wilson	(708) 634-9368
Northern Exposure BBS	NORTHERNEXP	5075	Mike McEachran	(612) 263-3320
Northfield BBS	NORTHFIELD	1906	Allan Miller	(203) 742-6400
Northern Lights	NORTHLITE	5321	Terrance Sprys	(313) 784-9872
The Northern Exchange	NORTHNEX	5325	Gary Hammer	(907) 479-3292
NorthPaul BBS	NORTHPAUL	5410	Paul McKinnon	44 236 458256
Norse Sea Operations BBS	NORTHSEA	1901	Timothy Doran	(516) 283-9631
Windsor Spitfire BBS	NORTHSTAR	673	Mike Adamson	(519) 735-1504
The Nuthouse	NUTHOUSE	5436	Stanley Klick	(412) 229-9560
Night*Watch BBS	NWATCH	1704	Tim Rush	(803) 553-1047
The New World BBS	NWORLD	5284	Cindy Millhollin	(209) 323-0638
The NY Amateur Computer Club	NYACC	5192	Hank Kee	(718) 539-3064
NYPC BBS	NYPC	5086	Michael Steinberg	(212) 679-6972
The OASis	OASIS	916	Marshall Brown	(404) 627-2662
The Old Town BBS	OLDTOWN	203	David Dean	(602) 344-2621
Omaha Network	OMAHANET	19	Rick Kingslan	(402) 392-2613
Onwards and Upwards BBS	ONANDUP	1600	Merlin DePeel	(402) 553-7390
OmniScope PCBoard	ONMISCOP	5169	Mark Compton	(704) 825-2778
The OpenWindow BBS	OPENWIN	1695	Mike Riley	(508) 927-3459
Orion Message Board	ORIONCONSULT	5176	Cliff Corcoran	(206) 485-0196
The OS/2 Solution BBS	OS2SOLUTION	5329	Jeffrey Komar	(708)
Osceola Horticulture BB	OSCHORT	1850	Eleanor Foerste	(407) 846-1723
Other World BBS	OTHERWORLD	98	Nick Short	(408) 256-5119
Escape To Other Worlds BBS	OTHERWORLDS	5130	Brett Frymire	(408) 956-1750
The Outhouse	OUTHOUSE	5013	James Wendeln	(209) 634-5395
Outnet	OUTNET	5385	John Rokes	(402) 496-9987
Church Chatters BBS	OUTRIDER	693	Tom Hansen	(402) 593-8863
Padan BBS	PADANBBS	1455	David Fogle	(410) 667-6592
Generation 5	PALTECH	5221	Paul Lazar	(301) 588-0770
Panama Shareware	PANAMASW	5470	David Wilhite	(904) 235-3634
Panda's Den BBS	PANDA	5417	Patrick Rosenheim	(508) 750-0250
Pandora's Box BBS	PANDORA	1493	Dorothy Gibbs	44 70 766 4778
Paradise Connection Micro Syst.	PARACON	1438	Stan Brown	(812) 925-7864
Paradise City BBS	PARADISE	5361	Jim Reed	(408) 280-6630
Paradise Station: Phoenix	PARADISESTA	5450	Wayne McCreight	(409) 866-5217
PARADOX Online BBS	PARADOXBBS	5023	Keith Bratton	(216) 686-7900
Parameters Info Service	PARAMETERS	774	Bob Pauls	(618) 549-8448
The Party Line	PARTY	7	Mike Glenn	(901) 873-2328
The Party BBS	PARTYBBS	1273	Napoleon Smith	(608) 258-9555

BBS Name	Nodeid	Site	Sysop Name	BBS Number
Passaic Valley BBS	PASSAIC	5058	Charlie Stivali	(201) 256-4509
Passing Fancy	PASSING	5460	Bill Forlines	(615) 270-7765
FTB's Passport BBS	PASSPORT	1716	Karina Wright	(301) 662-9134
Pavlov's Dog BBS	PAVLOV	1389	Robert Hayward	(703) 771-9771
PC Assist	PCASSIST	5267	Douglas Litten	(703) 264-1826
PC BBS	PCBBS	27	D.K. Lee	(516) 795-5874
PC Connect	PCCONNECT	989	John Scarfone	(416) 733-9052
PC-Exchange	PCEXCHANGE	859	Mike Simmons	(404) 977-6686
PC-Help	PCHELP	86	Duke Ducote	(214) 680-2693
PC Info System	PCINFOSYSTEM	1903	Peter Whitelaw	(516) 922-5153
PC-Ohio	PCOHIO	1869	Norm Henke	(216) 381-3320
The PC Place BBS	PCPLACE	1309	Jim Dirkes	(803) 762-7023
The Pegasus BBS	PEGASUS	36	Raymond Clements	(502) 684-9896
The Peg-board	PEGBOARD	1588	Chuck Mitchell	(703) 444-4718
PerryHall BBS	PERRYHALL	930	James Chmielweskyi	(410) 529-1822
The Phoenix Islands BBS	PHXISLND	5383	Phan Tran	(408) 270-4077
Pick's Place	PICKS	1301	Greg Pickering	(201) 765-0110
Poetry In Motion BBS	PIM	1064	Inez Harrison	(212) 666-6927
Plan B	PLANB	5241	Jerry Lauer	(615) 339-3246
Planet DX	PLANETDX	5367	Joseph Slawsky	(201) 933-8061
The Plymouth BBS	PLYMOUTH	696	Bruce Haefemeyer	(612) 553-0150
Port-of-Call	PORTOFCALL	995	Sam Coleman	(301) 249-4193
The Portrait Shoppe BBS	PORTSHOP	1283	Wayne Gilbert	(916) 243-4533
The Potter's House	POTTER		Nancy Powers	(706) 637-9276
Power Windows! BBS	POWERWINDOWS	5052	Cyrus Cathey	(205) 881-8619
Premier BBS	PREMIER	243	Curtis Kowalski	(615) 588-9407
The Privy ledged BBS	PRIVYLEDGED	5448	David Tigner	(801) 966-6270
Procyon	PROCYON	495	Barrie McConnell	(419) 524-7825
Programmer's Corner	PROGCRNR	1520	Gary Smith	(301) 596-1180
The "us" Project BBS	PROJECT	1563	Walt Mateja	(302) 529-1650
ProPC BBS	PROPCBBS	288	Robert Malakoff	(412) 321-6645
Pro-Vue	PROVUE	1449	Steven Nickle	(301) 490-1824
Pscychodrome BBS	PSYCHODROME	992	Patrick Briscoe	(713) 488-6817
The PUB Desktop Publishing BBS	PUBDTP	1659	Steve Gjondla	(312) 767-5787
Puma Wildcat BBS	PUMA	1026	Chuck McMillin	(318) 443-1065
The Punkin Duster BBS	PUNKIN	284	David Ludwig	(714) 522-3980
'Puter Fever	PUTERFEVER	5270	Randy Kosarik	(412) 228-0475
Gamma Quadrant	QUADRANT	5350	Tim Grove	(517) 546-2696
Information Access Network	QUADTECH	5196	Richard Dennis	(412) 262-4794
The Quest BBS	QUEST	5449	Al Carrero	(909) 789-0265
The Radio Board	RADIO	310	Ron Chase	(806) 352-9365
The Radio Wave BBS	RADIOWAVE	1478	Tyler Myers	(609) 764-0812
Random Access Information Net	RAIN	1526	Janice Stevens	(503) 695-3250

BBS Name	Nodeid	Site	Sysop Name	BBS Number
The Rainmaker	RAINMAKER	1839	Matthew Giles	(404) 587-4515
John 3:16	RAMELA	5457	Chris Range	(301) 208-0855
Rams' Island BBS	RAMSISLE	1235	Rudy Ramsey	(303) 841-6269
RNBB Technologies BBS	RANDOM	369	Gary Smith	(404) 516-7150
Random Walk Investment BBS	RANDOMWALK	1798	Mike Higgs	(416) 274-2381
Randy's Home Project	RANDYHP	566	Randy Finster	(904) 223-4060
Rose and Crown BBS	RC	214	David Ellison	(615) 892-0097
R.C. consulting BBS	RCCONSULTING	5304	R.E. Christian	unpublished
The Ranch & Cattle Metro BBS	RCMETRO	1760	Peter Raymond	(602) 943-1497
The Real Deal	REALDEAL	1320	Steven Myers	(919) 425-5414
The Flying Dutchman BBS	REDBARON	1077	Chris Von Motz	(408) 294-3065
The Red Phone BBS	REDPHONE	504	Chris Welber	(212) 924-1138
Reflex BBS	REFLEX	965	Danny Van Onselder	31 20 689 1790
Remote Host BBS	REMHST	940	John Schumacher	(201) 539-4544
Renaissance BBS	RENAIS	1476	David Pollard	(817) 467-7322
Christian Resource BBS	RESOURCE	661	Mike Olah	(804) 543-3459
Right Track Computer	RIGHTRACK	5153	Roger Tsai	(818) 443-0086
The RoadHouse BBS	ROADHOUZ	5056	Richard Holler	(317) 784-2147
Rock Island Communications	ROCILND	1521	Mike Greene	(206) 378-6028
The Rocking Chair Connection	ROCKING	100	Frank Crispell	(415) 364-7884
PC Rockland BBS	ROCKLAND	1052	Charlie Innusa	(914) 353-2157
Rockledge Systems BBS	ROCKLEDGE	1308	James Phillips	(407) 639-2546
Rock & Roll - Atlanta	ROCKROLL	391	Bob Helbush	(404) 982-0960
Rocky Mountain Software	ROCKYMTN	1384	Ray Snow	(801) 963-8721
The Lightning Rod BBS	ROD	13	Rod Renner	(301) 622-0708
RoJack BBS	ROJACK	5406	Jack Chapman	(909) 276-0007
Ronin	RONIN	1375	Chuck Mattern	(214) 938-2840
Rose Media	ROSE	1047	Vic Kass	(416) 733-2285
RoseNet	ROSENET	1580	Charles Rose	(703) 799-2536
Ruby's Joint	RUBYSJOINT	5215	David Freeman	(305) 856-4897
Runesword BBS	RUNESPIT	5201	Lyle Barrow	(707) 526-4969
The Running Board	RUNNINGA	2	Bonnie Anthony	(301) 229-5342
The Running Board	RUNNINGB	3	Howard Belasco	(718) 654-1349
Salt Air BBS	SALTAIR	1720	Dave Terry	
Salt City II	SALTCITY	473	Brandon Bachman	(801) 359-1820
Sam-I-Am BBS	SAMIAM	5185	Dave Sacerdote	(203) 741-6736
Santa Cruz BBS	SANTACRUZ	5445	Adolfo Justiniano	(591) 336-7046
Satellite TV Board	SATEL	947	J.M. Dolan	(713) 623-4899
The Savannah BBS	SAVANNAH	134	Michael Herin	(912) 920-8070
SCCM Comm Link	SCCM	296	Darin May	(714) 282-6055
The Score Board BBS	SCORE	325	David Taylor	(801) 269-9575
Scottsdale BBS	SCOTTS	1244	Tony VanRoon	(519) 821-7261

BBS Name	Nodeid	Site	Sysop Name	BBS Number
Script On-line BBS	SCRIPTS	967	J.J. Greene	(909) 685-1371
Super Deformed BBS	SDBBS	1852	Gary Olhava	(404) 978-9065
The Seaside BBS	SEASIDE	1223	Les Jones	(805) 964-4766
Second Opinion BBS	SECONDOP	394	Terry Baun	(414) 873-7807
The Secret Service	SECRET	313	Mike Wilson	(304) 429-6838
Semware Support	SEMWARE	330	Sammy Mitchell	(404) 641-8968
The Seven Keys BBS	SEVENKEYS	739	Jim Condon	(914) 747-2836
The Seven Seas BBS	SEVENSEAS	1065	Michael Rolow	(909) 247-2972
Seven Seas BBS	SEVENSEAS	1065	Mike Rolow	(714) 247-2972
Share City	SHARECITY	5379	John St. Clair	(801) 569-0897
Sherman's Shelter BBS	SHELTER	5109	Daniel Sherman	(415) 872-2142
The Electronic Shopper	SHOPPER	666	Peter Anderson	(301) 530-5962
The Shoreline BBS	SHORELINE	1205	Dan Shore	(301) 946-2771
Allen's Space Shuttle	SHUTTLE	1570	Allen Stone	(609) 953-5612
In-Side In-Fo BBS	SIDEFO	1085	Chuck Eisenmenger	(519) 756-8079
SideWayz BBS	SIDEWAYZ	5351	Paul Cutrona	(703) 352-5412
Sights and Sounds BBS	SIGHTS	5014	Donald Younker	(209) 925-9529
Sigma Industries BBS	SIGMAIND	1199	Randy Sun	(707) 263-8582
Sigma Iotia II RBBS	SIGMAIOTIA	961	Delmar Bice	(509) 965-2023
Silent Circle BBS	SILENT	5318	Tom Markiewicz	(312) 685-1136
The Silhouetter BBS	SILHOUET	5111	Daniel Hagerty	(209) 472-0843
The Silver Bullet BBS	SILVERBULLET	1913	Frank Semeraro	(201) 812-9352
The Sinewave BBS	SINEWAVE	1550	David Perkowski	(814) 237-2117
Sing Sing Sing	SINGSING	26	Ira Lichtenstein	(914) 762-4679
SkyLab BBS	SKYLABBBS	5197	Miguel Alves	35 11 726 2849
Skyship BBS	SKYSHIP	638	Mario Pozzetti	35 11 352 7623
Slekts-Forum BBS	SLEKT	255	Gunnar Aaboe	(473) 990-991
Silver Eagle	SLVREGLE	1509	Charles Watson	(404) 438-0725
Small Town BBS	SMALLBBS	5339	David Jaco	(903) 364-5144
SMARTalec	SMARTALC	972	Glenn Menzie	(416) 253-5900
COM Systems BBS	SMUGR	790	Thomas Mahnke	(414) 835-7754
The Port of Call	SNAPPER	5452	John Hunter	(081) 391-5779
The High Society BBS	SOCIETY	5231	Chuck Frieser	(508) 927-6951
Software Creations	SOFTC	777	Dan Linton	(508) 365-2359
The Software Exchange	SOFTEXCH	155	Don Eklund	(508) 949-3590
The Software Exchange	SOFTWAREXCH	5243	Bob St. Cyr	(717) 243-9620
Solid Rock BBS	SOLIDROCK	812	Ron Hossack	(909) 785-9176
Southern On-Line Services	SOSINC	505	Russell Jackson	(504) 356-0790
The Sounding Board BBS	SOUND	575	Pat Nefos	(303) 444-7942
Sound Advice Information Serv	SOUNDADVICE	5072	Roy Timberman	(816) 436-4516
Sound Town	SOUNDTOWN	5377	Bob Braun	(812) 235-1692
Selective Source	SOURCE	1369	Roger Messer	(804) 430-3584
The South Pole BBS	SOUTHPOLE	5274	Jim Ames	(707) 643-6284
Space BBS	SPACE	606	Owen Hawkins	(415) 323-4193
Spartan Computer Systems	SPARTAN	5363	Buddy Grimsley	(803) 587-8948

BBS Name	Nodeid	Site	Sysop Name	BBS Number
The SpeakEasy	SPEAKESY	978	Steve Page	(407) 291-4626
Special Appointment BBS	SPECIALA	1450	Dan Bermejo	(914) 965-4980
Sound Power Systems	SPS	5292	Ron Gage	(517) 792-4680
Spud's World	SPUDWRLD	5236	Ray Kolman	(216) 238-3130
Second Sanctum	SSANCTUM	759	Mark Robbins	(817) 784-1178
Star of Life BBS	STAROFLIFE	1373	Beth Dodge	(203) 669-2089
Stars and Stripes	STARS	5035	Paul Gluszek	65 73 872 78
The Starting Gate BBS	STARTING	1002	Ed Clifford	(502) 423-9629
NAFBBS	STATION	1210	Mark Justman	(619) 352-9354
ST Com-Link	STCOMLINK	987	Clint McBee	(501) 394-1454
The Step Club	STEPCLUB	5295	Michael Falba	(301) 593-8992
Stonehenge	STONEHENGE	1138	William Daley	(609) 238-1587
Straight Street BBS	STRAIGHTST	5171	Darin Johnson	(317) 482-0011
Struppi's BBS	STRUPPI	1086	Carol Carmichael	(703) 478-9380
Studs	STUDS	551	Hans Von Braun	(415) 495-2929
Suburban Software BBS	SUBSOFT	715	Chuck Valecek	(708) 636-6694
SunLight Through the Shadows	SUNLIGHT	5320	Joe Derouen	(214) 620-8793
Sunrise-80 BBS	SUNRISE	868	Al Lawrence	(404) 256-9525
Express (tm) Shareware Report	SUPPORTU	507	Patrick Grote	(314) 256-0507
Surreal BBS	SURREAL	5229	Marcus Breese	(219) 262-9371
SWIndy BBS	SWINDY	1209	Garry Courtney	(317) 856-7562
The Swingers Connection BBS	SWINGCON	1849	John Kutas	(215) 724-5324
SWL Private Exchange (PEX) BBS	SWLPEX	1853	Rick Nakroshis	(703) 506-0567
Shareware South	SWS	1015	Steve Rohrer	(404) 370-0736
Syllables	SYLLABLES	1834	Jackie Jones	(401) 848-9925
Synapse BBS	SYNAPSE	1112	Daniel Coulombe	(819) 561-5268
Synergy	SYNERGY	20	Jim Boxmeyer	(201) 829-7460
Systematic BBS	SYSTEMATIC	5210	Mufutau Towobola	(718) 716-6198
Timmins Area Bulletin Board	TABB	826	Gary Lapierre	(705) 264-5941
Tacotel PC	TACOPC	1358	Bart Van Dijk	31 20 634 4490
TandyLand Exchange	TANDYLAND	1483	Ricky Schradin	(513) 398-8218
The Tao BBS	TAO	1377	Bob Watson	(609) 587-2672
The Tardis II BBS	TARDIS	29	Andrew Borrs	(914) 478-5107
The Byteline BBS	TBL	1634	Bernard Poisson	(801) 773-1101
The Christian Connection BBS	TCCBBS	639	Walt Benson	(219) 464-9164
The Computer Room	TCR	5085	Marshall Thompson	(614) 861-8377
Team H BBS	TEAMH	5394	Steven Karp	(510) 236-5114
Tea Room	TEAROOM	5420	Piotr Starzynski	(718) 626-8087
Tech Connect BBS	TECHCONN	1307	Tiff Reardon	(703) 551-0002
Tech Data Connection	TECHDATA	1795	Dan Kyburz	(813) 538-7090

BBS Name	Nodeid	Site	Sysop Name	BBS Number
Techie Tavern	TECHIE	1496	Huey Hammontree	(318) 387-8264
The Technical Forum	TECHNICAL	5342	George Germain	(201) 933-2363
TeleLink Network BBS	TELELINK	5426	Shawn Nicholson	(216) 633-2808
The Telephone Exchange	TELEPHNE	222	Doug Haire	(407) 791-2474
Telestar BBS	TELESTAR	5463	Robert Kruss	(313) 274-4989
Terminal Velocity	TERMVEL	1494	Jason Koller	(503) 390-6538
Terrapin Flyer BBS	TERRAPIN	719	Mark Chickering	(703) 886-7825
The Door BBS and Info. Network	THDOOR	895	Neil Peiman	(407) 682-3132
The Back Door	THEBACKDOOR	1417	Barry Bottger	(402) 553-7445
The Border Renegade	THEBORDER	5311	Rudy Borjon	(915) 778-0487
The Boss	THEBOSS	760	Mark Seiden	(201) 568-7293
The Break RBBS	THEBREAK	5021	Bruce Jackson	(703) 680-9269
The Caverns BBS	THECAVERNS	5051	Michael Goetz	(407) 521-9886
The Chair TOO!	THECHAIR	104	Mike Stewart	(408) 866-7370
The Club BBS	THECLUB	5359	Din Ebrahim	(609) 748-1728
The Computer Room South	THECOMPROOM	1426	Sandifer Platt	(904) 347-4319
The Chicken Coop BBS	THECOOP	740	Brian Carlson	(708) 658-1545
The Detour BBS	THEDETOUR	1222	Bill Roman	(609) 896-3112
The Dungeon BBS	THEDNGN	1678	Peter Paulekat	(416) 926-8734
The Dock BBS	THEDOCK	1454	Cindy Duryea	(219) 848-7200
The Gig BBS	THEGIG	5237	George Warish	(216) 267-3410
The HUB BBS	THEHUB	319	Irve Towers	(703) 685-0019
The Main Shop	THEMAIN	326	Tony Summy	(714) 288-1320
The Oasis BBS	THEOASIS	1119	Robert Hall	(410) 882-4942
The Outhouse	THEOUTHOUSE	5387	John Stewart	(409) 295-1760
Pier 1 Exchange	THEPIER	1376	Greg Armenia	(716) 875-0283
The Rock of Gibraltar	THEROCK	1750	Paul Bonifacio	44 81 678 6087
The Swing BBS	THESWING	738	Scott Brown	(914) 834-7830
TQM BBS	THETQMBBS	5104	Tom Glenn	(301) 585-1164
The Tree BBS	THETREEHUB	726	Frank Fowler	(904) 732-0866
The Vault BBS	THEVAULT	1861	Keith Ketcham	(614) 387-2762
The Voice	THEVOICE	5437	Debbi Morgen	(914) 664-1844
The Computer Connextion	THEWEB	162	Tim Meade	(513) 436-9036
The Who Knows BBS	THEWHOKNOWS	1415	David Ainsley	(301) 934-4963
Creative Thoughts BBS	THINKER	5312	Paul Hildmann	(708) 382-3904
The Image Bank BBS	TIB	5314	Jose Almeida	351-1-778-6640
Technical Information - USA	TIFSDBU	1258	Cindy Chiang	(301) 926-4367
The Time-Out BBS	TIMEOUT	765	Larry Edwards	(303) 751-7064
	TIMEX	1313	Lynn Walker	
Tiny Board	TINYBOARD	1072	Alvin Combs	(703) 569-8075
Tippy BBS	TIPPY	5277	Mark Atkinson	(219) 453-4046
Toad Hall BBS	TOADHALL	1379	Gordon Anderson	(415) 595-2427
The Token Ring BBS	TOKEN	343	Glen Fredericks	(201) 546-1468

BBS Name	Nodeid	Site	Sysop Name	BBS Number
Tom Cat Pictures	TOMCATPIX	1241	Roger Campagnoni	(805) 482-8030
Total Access	TOTALACC	1013	Scott Lagos	(508) 342-2200
Technoid's Toybox	TOYBOX	832	Rick Kuban	(214) 226-6017
Tin Pan Alley	TPALLEY	1285	Steve Walcher	(206) 742-7782
The Panic Zone	TPZ	5469	Dave Muench	(716) 473-5204
The Trading Post	TRADINGPOST	5413	Ralph Howard	(803) 827-1735
Transcom-1 BBS	TRANSCOM	292	Dean Mason	(302) 325-2337
TransMountain BBS	TRANSMTN	5340	Dave Havron	(904) 645-0431
Travel Online	TRAVEL	736	Rik Brown	(314) 973-4073
Treasures BBS	TREASURES	69	Jim Daly	(407) 831-9130
Freezing Point Systems	TRIAD	1546	Ron Woods	(612) 525-9632
Tri-City Network	TRICITYNET	5408	John Tarasko	(519) 621-3261
Tridon	TRIDON	5119	Joe Vasconcelos	(416) 575-2986
Triway BBS Systems Group	TRIWAY	197	Dann Way	(216) 945-9068
Troll's Cave PCBoard	TROLLSCAVE	1302	Dennis Wynne	(615) 872-0757
The Right Place(tm)	TRP	564	Roger Sligar	(404) 476-2607
The Round Table BBS	TRT	490	Dan McCoy	(215) 678-0818
Trying Hard BBS	TRYHARD	1679	Karl Ulrich	(404) 509-7464
The Sports Complex 'net 386	TSCNET	1607	Al Charpentier	(206) 692-2388
Technical Support Resources	TSRBBS	5141	Gerry Vratanina	(312) 282-4851
Terrapin Station dBBS	TSTATION	971	Howard Ekman	(612) 623-0152
Tsunami - Catch the wave!	TSUNAMI	82	Chet Wilkinson	(904) 273-9738
The Hub! BBS	TULSAHUB	5166	Warren Farrimond	(918) 627-0923
The Tumbleweed BBS	TUMBLEWEED	5211	Jesse Goplen	(608) 647-4820
NEMC	TUNEIN	1350	Stephen Pauker	(617) 350-8513
The Wish Book BBS	TWB	1032	Lorne Shantz	(602) 340-9516
The "Techno-Weenie"	TWEENIE	5347	Marshall Van Wagne	(301) 963-4262
The Exchange BBS	TWEXCHANGE	110	Steve Haynes	(804) 552-1014
World Data Exchange	TWWDE	1051	James Thomas	88 62 695-2320
The Twilight Zone	TWZONE	237	Robert Jackson	(609) 921-0354
User-to-User	U2U	83	Kevin Carr	(214) 492-6565
The USERS Choice	UCHOICE	660	Martin Scolaro	(317) 894-1378
CB's Underwater Bar	UNDERWATER	5374	Christopher Baye	(808) 455-8758
Unibase TBK	UNIBASE	381	Torbjorn Mjos	47 59 48 298
The Union Lake BBS	UNION	274	George Cuccia	(609) 327-5553
USA-Net Online	USANET	5371	Dirk Hilbig	(602) 966-5155
USR USA	USRUSA	174	Adam Strack	(708) 982-5092
The United States Veterans BBS	USVETS	1029	Glen Kepler	(612) 588-7563
Unconventional Thoughts	UTBBS	5423	Mike Kovach	(904) 221-1657
Utopia	UTOPIA	1256	Doug Moore	(404) 978-0603
Valhalla	VALHALLA	5224	Sean Martin	(619) 598-3545
The Valley BBS	VALLEY	57	Larry Daymon	(813) 322-2587
Valley PC Clone	VALLEYPC	1066	Earl Albin	(502) 937-6143

BBS Name	Nodeid	Site	Sysop Name	BBS Number
Bargain Board BBS	VASN	959	James King	(703) 730-0950
Veterans Benefits and Research	VBARNET	113	Barry Davis	(410) 761-3406
Vertraven	VERTRAUEN	5115	Rob Swindell	(714) 529-9525
VideoPro	VIDEOPRO	390	Tom Hackett	(703) 455-1873
The Virginia Connection	VIRGINIA	448	Tony McClenny	(703) 648-1841
The Virtual Dimension	VIRTUALDIM	5284	Ernie Jackson	(619) 722-8041
Visus BBS	VISUS	267	Jose Camara	35 11 793 5839
Vocations Central BBS	VOCATION	1263	Bill Leaming	(210) 423-1574
Vox Populi	VOXPOP	1696	Bryan Devaney	(206) 895-1376
Voyager BBS	VOYAGER	1868	Edmund Tan	65 35 221 00
Voyager BBS	VOYAGER1	5022	Dan Allennder	(412) 746-1447
Vulture Nest	VULTURE	1247	Roy Reyer	(602) 684-3974
Virtual Worlds	VWORLDS	1848	Ricky Rhoden	(904) 388-4614
WThreeJP	W3JP	75	Lucas Spiros	(301) 831-5954
Wally's World Wacky Hackers	WACKYHACKERS	5043	John Masoner	(509) 529-3726
Wall Street Connection	WALLST	5159	Keith Nakata	(808) 521-4356
Wamblyville	WAMBLY	5328	John Borowski	(213) 380-8188
The Warped Board BBS	WARPED	1875	Rick Welshans	(703) 660-5028
Washington PC-Board	WASHPCB	240	Mike Keelon	(412) 746-0109
The Watch Word	WATCHW	813	Jim Edwards	(317) 247-1382
Watership Down	WATERSHIP	5442	Jim Nobles	
West Coast Connection	WCC	702	Don Presten	
The Westonia BBS	WESTONIA	1347	David E. Smith	(416) 241-9793
Whaler's Walk	WHALERS	5099	Patrick Bresnahan	(508) 627-3285
Maranatha BBS	WHEELIE	138	Dan Nance	(904) 353-3807
Who Knows	WHOKNOWS	105	Johnny Bowen	(408) 262-3634
The Wicked Scherzo	WICKED	356	Michael Part	(818) 508-0881
The Wild Thing	WILDTHING	1836	Sheldon Gerber	(305) 587-3496
Wildwood BBS	WILDWOOD	5409	Gary Head	(604)
Windraker International	WINDRAKER	1271	Robert Thompson	(904) 388-5297
The Windy City	WINDYCITY	5078	Dave Zmeyr	(312) 275-7492
Wingit	WINGIT	1060	Charlie Yontz	(904) 386-8693
The Wings BBS System	WINGS	5081	Mike Shearer	(206) 876-6735
The Wireless BBS	WIRELESS	1759	Conrad Harteloo	(503) 692-7097
Wishbone	WISHBONE	1212	Neil Hoffman	(718) 441-1262
A1A West	WITS	1284	Betty Duckworth	(904) 781-6744
The Wizard's BBS	WIZARDSBBS	5378	Andy Hermanson	(508) 481-4693
Windows OnLine	WOL	1579	Frank Mahaney	(510) 736-8343
Wolverine	WOLVERINE	5288	Rick Rosinski	(517) 631-3471
Woodlawn Manor	WOODLAWN	5278	Henry Stryker	(301) 948-8504
The Woodshed	WOODSHED	1023	Steve Wood	(704) 847-8177
WorldComm	WORLDCOM	1860	Matt Clement	(301) 656-8313
Window on Windows BBS	WOWBOARDERIE	5372	Don Shriver	(814) 452-6900
La Palma Communications	WPE	1043	Kelly Tompkins	(310) 865-7374

BBS Name	Nodeid	Site	Sysop Name	BBS Number
Wright_Access_BBS	WRIGHT	5432	Raymond Wright	(213) 389-9183
Welcome to the MACHINE! BBS	WTTM	847	Chris Trifari	(914) 833-2746
The Wizard's World	WWORLD	952	Bill Rogge	(508) 975-1924
Excalibar Bulletin Board	XCALIBAR	1564	Paul Croteau	(519) 758-1173
Arc Xchange BBS	XCHANGE	1501	Rick De Pinho	(201) 429-1317
Xevious	XEVIOUS	159	Nels Anderson	(508) 875-3618
"Ya! WEBECAD!"	YAWEBECAD	608	Don Habegger	(812) 428-3870
The Year 2000 Network	YEAR	611	Bart Flint	(801) 547-0607
Your Software Resources	YOURSOFTWARE	5190	John Woodstock	(516) 736-6662
Zion's Cache	ZIONSCACHE	1823	Dan Bachman	(801) 752-5059

CHAPTER 12

The MajorNet Bulletin Board System Network

Majornet is a bulletin board system network with nodes located throughout the United States and many foreign locations. An important part of MajorNet is MailLink, which is a system which provides bulletin board system users with the ability to transmit messages around the U.S. and internationally as long as you know the address of the intended recepient.

A MajorNode MailLink "address" is a combination of the MailLink System Node-Id, and the recipient's User-Id. For example, the Downtown LA BBS system has a MailLink System Node-Id of "DWN". The author's User-Id on that system is "Treblig." Thus, you would address messages to the author using the MajorNet address of "Treblig@DWN", without the quotation (") marks, of course. The "address" is not case-sensitive, therefore capitalization is unimportant.

If you know the "address" of a person, you can send them a private letter, by entering that "address" when the "write e-mail" function asks you for a User-Id. Then, continue with composing the "subject" and body of your letter normally. Currently, file attachments can NOT be sent over the MajorNet. Also, at the present time you can NOT Private reply to a MajorNet forum/newsgroup message. The message will be sent, but as Public. Private replies should be made from the E-mail section as a new message.

The MailLink system supports a "return receipt" capability and, when requested, a receipt will be sent back to the mail originator when the addressee's system receives the letter (and your addressee exists on that system), not when the addressee personally reads the letter.

To read from a MajorNet newsgroup, read the messages in the Forum which is attached to the newsgroup, just the same as a Local newsgroup. To post to a MajorNet newsgroup, post a message as normal to the Forum attached to the desired newsgroup. It is not necessary to "address" the message, but it is best to sign it with your "address."

Messages you post will be sent worldwide and messages posted on other systems will be received and placed in the appropriate Forum for you to read.

MajorNet News Group

MajorNet Newsgroups carried on each bulletin board can vary by system. The following table lists the MajorNet Newsgroups carried by the Downtown BBS in Los Angeles, CA to include the forum name on that bbs, the Newsgroup name and a brief description of the Newsgroup.

Forum	Newsgroup/Description
/MISSING	MISSING [NET] Missing persons bulletins
/ForSale	FORSALE [Net] National FOR SALE newsgroup
/ForSaleW	FORSALE.WEST [Net] Western U.S. FOR SALE newsgroup
/Graphics	GRAPHICS [Net] Computer graphics discussions
/Hardware	HARDWARE [Net] Computer hardware discussions
/HardAds	HARDWARE.ADS [Net] Ads for computer hardware
/Modems	HARDWARE.MODEMS [Net] Modems & terminal software
/IBMDOS	IBMDOS [Net] Discussions of DOS of all flavors
/IBMOS2	IBMOS2 [Net] Discussions about OS/2
/IBMPC	IBMPC [Net] IBM & compatible PC's discussions

/COMICS	COMICS
	[Net] Discuss/trade comic books
/Humor	HUMOR
	[Net] Funny stuff for all ages
/MJRFAQ	MAJORNET.FAQ
	[Net] MajorNet frequently asked questions
/MSYSAD	MAJORBBS.SYSTEMS
	[Net] BBS Ads for major BBS Systems
/WINDOWS	MSWINDOWS
	[Net] Microsoft Windows discussions
/LASale	ANX!LASALE
	[NET] Los Angeles area for sale/buy newsgroup

MajorNet Modem Type Legend

CS1	= 9600 CompuCom CSP	[CompuCom Champ]
CS2	= 9600 CSP & 9600 v.32	[CompuCom Storm]
CS3	= 9600 CSP & 14.4k v.32bis	[CompuCom Star]
DS	= 14,400 HST & 9600 v.32	[US Robotics Dual Standard]
DS2	= 14,400 HST & 14.4k v.32bis	[US Robotics v.32bis Dual Standard]
DS3	= 16,800 HST & 14.4k v.32bis	[US Robotics 16.8k HST/v.32bis DS]
DS4	= 16.8 HST/v.32bis/21.6 v.32terbo	[US Robotics 16.8k HST/v.32bis DS]
HST	= 9600 or 14,400 bps HST	[US Robotics HST]
HST4	= 14,400 bps HST (if known)	[US Robotics HST]
HST6	= 16,800 bps HST (if known)	[US Robotics HST]
TB	= Telebit PEP	[Telebit Trailblazer]
TB2	= Telebit PEP & v.32	[Telebit T-2500]
TB3	= Telebit PEP & v.32bis	[Telebit T-3000]
ULT	= 9600 Hayes V & 9600 v.32	[Hayes Ultra]
ULT2	= 9600 Hayes V/14.4k v.32bis	[Hayes Ultra 14400]
VFC	= 14.4k v.32bis/28.8 v.fast class	Brands will vary
VH	= 9600 Hayes V Series	[Hayes Express 96 V-series]
V32	= 9600 ITU v.32	Brands will vary
V32A	= 9600 ITU v.32/12k v.32bis	Brands will vary
V32B	= 14,400 ITU v.32bis	Brands will vary
V32T	= 19,200 AT&T v.32terbo	Brands will vary
ZYX6	= 14.4k v.32bis & 16.8 ZyXEL	ZyXEL

ZYX9 = 14.4k v.32bis & 19.2 ZyXEL   ZyXEL
2400 = 2400 bps DEFAULT MODEM TYPE   Brands will vary
24EC = 2400 bps w/Error Correction   Brands will vary

United States MajorNet Node List

State	City	Node ID	Name	Phone	Modm
AK	Anchorage	L&L	Leather & Lace	907-258-1528	
AK	Anchorage	SWC	SoftWorks BBS	907-522-2900	V32B
AL	Birmingham	GOI	Genesis Online	205-620-4144	
AL	Huntsville	IO1	InterQuest	205-461-6681	
AZ	Phoenix	ROK	The Rock Garden	602-220-0001	
AZ	Phoenix	TGD	THe GaRBaGe DuMP BBS	602-331-1112	24EC
AZ	Sedona	GFX	GraF/X	602-282-9035	V32B
AZ	Tucson	DIG	Digital Concepts BBS	602-292-0065	DS
AZ	Tucson	DIG	Digital Concepts BBS	602-292-9333	ZYX6
CA	Agoura	KBB	KBBS	818-889-2546	
CA	Alhambra	LIB	The Liberty BBS	818-570-0695	24EC
CA	Altadena	TC1	The Castle BBS	818-794-0302	
CA	Anaheim	LIB	The Liberty BBS	714-996-7777	ZYX6
CA	Arcadia	KBB	KBBS	818-445-5051	
CA	Azusa	AOS	Avatar Online Systems	818-969-8227	
CA	Beverly Hills	KBB	KBBS	310-278-7810	V32B
CA	Beverly Hills	TC1	The Castle BBS	213-936-9951	
CA	Channel Islands	FNZ	The FunZone	805-988-0549	
CA	Compton	KBB	KBBS	310-532-1700	
CA	Compton	LIB	The Liberty BBS	310-609-1443	24EC
CA	Corona	LIB	The Liberty BBS	909-278-0924	ZYX6
CA	Covina	AUZ	AuSSie Bbs	818-337-9701	
CA	Culver City	ECN	E & C Network (ECN)	310-204-6007	
CA	Culver City	KBB	KBBS	310-558-0145	
CA	Cypress	LIB	The Liberty BBS	714-827-7458	ZYX6
CA	Davis	DAV	The Compass Rose - Davis	916-758-0292	
CA	Diamond Bar	LIB	The Liberty BBS	909-861-7613	ZYX6
CA	El Cajon	SCP	Scoop BBS	619-449-8430	V32B
CA	El Cajon	SCP	Scoop BBS	619-449-9157	V32B
CA	El Toro	PSM	Prism	714-583-7039	V32B
CA	El Toro	PSM	Prism	714-583-9649	DS3
CA	Escondido	DRM	Dream Net BBS	619-747-4048	V32B
CA	Fremont	LIB	The Liberty BBS	510-793-9019	
CA	Fresno	BBS	BBS Technologies	209-277-3333	
CA	Fullerton	BUR	The suBurbs BBS	714-871-9000	

State	City	Node ID	Name	Phone	Modm
CA	Gardena	TC1	The Castle BBS	310-527-7380	
CA	Glendale	KBB	KBBS	818-507-1365	
CA	Glendale	TC1	The Castle BBS	818-409-9365	
CA	Hayward	LIB	The Liberty BBS	510-264-0708	
CA	Huntington Beach	PSM	Prism	714-897-8075	24EC
CA	Huntington Beach	RNK	Realty Network	714-969-9624	
CA	Irvine	LIB	The Liberty BBS	714-854-4235	ZYX6
CA	Isla Vista	GSS	Gaiasys	805-562-8355	
CA	La Puente	LIB	The Liberty BBS	818-961-4895	ZYX6
CA	Lake Forest	CAL	California Online Systems	714-707-1839	
CA	Lake Forest	PSM	Prism	714-454-9242	24EC
CA	Lompoc	GRA	The Granola Board BBS	805-735-3315	
CA	Lompoc	GRA	The Granola Board BBS	805-737-7346	ZYX6
CA	Long Beach	PSM	Prism	310-799-0380	24EC
CA	Long Beach	SPC	Spectrum Online Systems	310-597-0858	
CA	Los Angeles	DWN	The DownTown BBS	213-484-0260	V32B
CA	Los Angeles	DWN	The DownTown BBS	213-484-0287	ZYX6
CA	Los Angeles	DWN	The DownTown BBS	213-484-0331	DS2
CA	Los Angeles	LIB	The Liberty BBS	213-732-2300	24EC
CA	Los Angeles	PL1	Pro-Line BBS	818-592-6993	
CA	Los Angeles	TC1	The Castle BBS	213-953-0040	
CA	Los Angeles	TC1	The Castle BBS	213-953-0066	V32B
CA	Mira Loma	LIB	The Liberty BBS	909-685-1939	ZYX6
CA	Modesto	AG1	Friends Agric/Food/Trade	209-527-2944	V32B
CA	Monrovia	ODY	Odyssey	818-358-6968	
CA	Montebello	KBB	KBBS	213-725-3047	
CA	Newport Beach	PSM	Prism	714-642-6256	24EC
CA	North Hollywood	KBB	KBBS	818-505-8459	V32B
CA	North Hollywood	KBB	KBBS	818-505-9848	
CA	North Hollywood	LIB	The Liberty BBS	818-506-5228	24EC
CA	North Hollywood	PT1	Prime Time BBS	818-982-7271	
CA	North Hollywood	TC1	The Castle BBS	818-985-2392	
CA	Northridge	HDC	The Hard Drive Cafe	818-993-5516	
CA	Northridge	KBB	KBBS	818-886-0872	
CA	Northridge	KBB	KBBS	818-886-3965	V32B
CA	Northridge	LIB	The Liberty BBS	818-727-0367	24EC
CA	Northridge	SPC	Spectrum Online Systems	818-773-1738	
CA	Oakland	LIB	The Liberty BBS	510-553-0124	
CA	Orange	LIB	The Liberty BBS	714-974-8601	ZYX6
CA	Palo Alto	LGR	Legal Recourse(sm) BBS	415-856-2820	
CA	Palo Alto	LIB	The Liberty BBS	415-325-6781	
CA	Pasadena	KTV	Knight Vision BBS	213-344-3600	
CA	Poway	NEX	The Nexus Point	619-486-0529	DS3
CA	Riverside	LIB	The Liberty BBS	909-275-9716	ZYX6
CA	Sacramento	GE1	Genesis Network #1	916-965-9361	

State	City	Node ID	Name	Phone	Modm
CA	Sacramento	SAC	The Compass Rose - Sac	916-447-0292	
CA	San Carlos	LIB	The Liberty BBS	415-802-0820	
CA	San Francisco	LIB	The Liberty BBS	415-468-5124	
CA	San Francisco	TCE	The Cutting Edge	415-751-0588	DS3
CA	San Jose	ATB	Atlantis BBS	408-377-8510	
CA	San Mateo	LIB	The Liberty BBS	415-347-9592	
CA	Santa Ana	PSM	Prism	714-531-3091	24EC
CA	Santa Clarita	KBB	KBBS	805-255-5006	
CA	Santa Maria	GRA	The Granola Board BBS	805-928-7221	
CA	Santa Monica	BYT	Nite Byte's BBS	310-820-6597	
CA	Santa Monica	LIB	The Liberty BBS	310-396-8793	24EC
CA	Santa Rosa	XCL	The Party Line BBS	707-588-8055	V32B
CA	Sherman Oaks	CBX	ChatterBox! BBS	818-995-6959	V32B
CA	Silverado	LIB	The Liberty BBS	714-649-3283	ZYX6
CA	Simi Valley	BRN	BrainStorm	805-584-6088	
CA	Simi Valley	KBB	KBBS	805-520-7323	
CA	Simi Valley	LIB	The Liberty BBS	805-581-6089	24EC
CA	South Los Angeles	TC1	The Castle BBS	213-293-0070	
CA	Sunnyvale	LIB	The Liberty BBS	408-733-7600	
CA	Sunnyvale	MKS	Magic Kingdom Systems	408-245-3961	
CA	Trabuco	LIB	The Liberty BBS	714-858-0759	ZYX6
CA	Van Nuys	ANX	Annex! BBS	818-786-5600	
CA	Van Nuys	KBB	KBBS	818-994-0442	
CA	Van Nuys	TC1	The Castle BBS	818-785-6920	
CO	Colorado Springs	KIX	KICK'S - U.S.A.	719-577-0000	
CO	Denver	TGD	The GaRBage DuMP BBS!	303-457-1111	24EC
CT	Bolton	K-W	The Keystone WareHouse	203-649-9675	
FL	Cape Coral	TTT	The Tandy Tane	813-574-2301	
FL	Clearwater	MBM	NetworX	813-541-5876	
FL	Cocoa Beach	GXY	Galaxy Station	407-868-0344	
FL	Deerfield Beach	SON	The House of ICHTHYS	305-360-2991	
FL	Enterprise	ASK	SOLUTIONS-Net	407-321-6119	
FL	Fort Lauderdale	AAA	Always All Adult BBS	305-584-4080	
FL	Fort Lauderdale	BSI	BSI Technologies BBS	305-434-5619	
FL	Fort Lauderdale	COM	CITICOM	305-486-5969	
FL	Fort Lauderdale	GCM	Galacticomm Demo System	305-583-7808	
FL	Fort Lauderdale	IOS	The GRID	305-321-2410	
FL	Fort Myers	AST	Astro	813-277-0906	
FL	Gainesville	DKM	Dragon Keep	904-375-3500	
FL	Largo	RGC	Baudville Social Club	813-593-0061	
FL	Leesburg	PNO	Prometheus NET OnLine	904-469-4384	V32B
FL	Leesburg	RFL	RFL	904-365-9088	
FL	Melbourne	MAG	MagiComm, Inc./AEN	407-724-1226	
FL	Miami	NET	The Networker	305-638-7982	

State	City	Node ID	Name	Phone	Modm
FL	New Port Richey	GUM	Gumbyland	813-846-1140	
FL	Orlando	ISS	Infinite Space Systems	407-856-0021	
FL	Orlando	PNO	Prometheus NET OnLine	407-648-5454	V32B
FL	Orlando	TEN	The Entrepreneur Network	407-426-8451	V32B
FL	Palm Harbor	CSI	Crime On-Line	813-784-1104	
FL	Sarasota	S&S	S & S	813-751-1896	
FL	Sunrise	ROL	Realm of Legends	305-748-9700	
FL	Tallahassee	CPA	Computer Patch	904-668-6129	
FL	Tampa	TPA	The NETWORKER II	813-920-4954	
FL	Tarpon Springs	RFI	The Rain Forest	813-943-8000	
FL	West Palm Beach	EPS	Electronic Publishers Svc	407-640-9195	
GA	Athens	QPW	Quiet Place In The Woods	706-769-9933	
GA	Atlanta	ATL	Atlanta Chatline	404-922-2937	
GA	Atlanta	FUN	Fun Factory BBS	404-985-5061	
GA	Rincon	WCE	Wildd Cardd BBS	912-728-4107	V32B
GA	Savannah	WCE	Wildd Cardd BBS	912-356-1600	V32B
GA	Statesboro	STS	The Protocol BBS	912-871-6578	
HI	Honolulu	HNL	Pacific Velvet	808-532-6002	
HI	Maui	GIL	Gilligan's Island BBS	808-244-5575	
HI	Oahu	TAN	The Aloha Network	808-621-8845	V32B
ID	Boise	A-H	After Hours BBS	208-345-6121	
ID	Boise	IDI	Idaho Interactive BBS	208-345-4987	
IL	Addison	MAR	Mail Advertising Resource	708-628-0330	V32
IL	Buffalo Grove	UFP	Ultimate Fantasy Playgrnd	708-215-6612	
IL	Chicago	ONE	COM ONE	708-717-9379	V32
IL	Chicago	ONI	The Wild Onion!	708-993-0461	V32B
IL	Chicago	STZ	STZ	312-345-3508	
IL	Chicago	THU	Thunderbolt BBS, Inc	312-248-0109	
IL	Franklin Park	TVL	Crystal Carousel BBS	708-928-0281	
IL	Mundelein	MUL	Mulligan's Place	708-566-6183	V32B
IL	Naperville	ONE	COM ONE	708-717-9370	
IL	Pekin	F4U	Corsair On-Line	309-925-5916	
IL	Peoria	FLC	Future Link	309-676-0387	
IL	Quincy	PMQ	ProfitMaker BBS	217-224-3203	ZYX6
IL	Rockford	BCI	BCI InfoNet	815-636-2702	
IL	South Beloit	WRE	Whiskey Road	815-654-0504	
IL	Springfield	AVI	The Ultimate BBS	217-792-3663	
IL	Springfield	GOV	Government Witness	217-789-6290	
KS	Lawrence	BRT	BART	913-832-0320	
KS	Lawrence	MET	Metropolis	913-832-0041	
LA	New Orleans	PNT	The Point	504-391-7119	
MA	Athol	CMB	Crystal Mountain BBS	508-249-2156	

State	City	Node ID	Name	Phone	Modm
MA	Bridgewater	PZM	PriZm BBS	508-697-3508	V32
MA	Plymouth	C-L	Communications-Link	508-746-3465	
MA	Plymouth	TAH	The Adult Hangout BBS	508-746-6010	
MA	Quincy	GCQ	Games Complex	617-773-3910	
MA	Worcester	MHD	Mithril Hall	508-852-4807	
MD	.....	INF	InfiNetwork	301-498-6183	
MD	Beltsville	GLO	1! GlobeNet Place! BBS	301-595-5776	V32B
MD	Churchville	DAC	Deluxe Accommodations	410-836-2692	
MD	Frederick	ADS	Advanced Data Services	301-695-9116	
ME	York Beach	SCU	The Scuttlebutt E.E.S.	207-363-2660	
MI	Bay City	CRC	CRIS	517-895-0510	
MI	Dearborn	STA	Central Station BBS!	313-730-0888	
MI	Detroit	UCB	Ultimate Computers BBS	313-538-9823	
MI	Grand Rapids	CBR	Cyberspace BBS	616-454-3704	V32
MI	Grand Rapids	CBR	Cyberspace BBS	616-454-7800	
MI	Jackson	SRH	Live-ON-Line	517-789-9826	
MI	Kalamazoo	AML	AML	616-343-1346	
MI	Lansing	CSC	CSC's High Density BBS	517-394-2552	
MI	Lansing	MIP	MI PSC E&R Matters BBS	517-882-1421	
MI	Muskegon	PLA	Playboard	616-798-7557	
MI	Taylor	GCI	Gateway Online	313-291-5571	
MI	Taylor	MHL	Michigan HOT-Line	313-292-4934	
MI	Traverse City	CAT	The Cathead Bay Mining Co	616-946-5885	
MI	Troy	E_L	Electronic Lucidity	313-680-8861	
MN	Albert Lea	TRJ	PC-Monitor	507-373-1100	
MN	Minneapolis	CCI	Minnesota BBS	612-851-7060	
MN	Minneapolis	TFE	The Friendship Express	612-566-5726	
MN	Sauk Rapids	OUT	The Outpost!	612-259-0801	
MN	Twin Cities	PCL	PC-Library TeleComm	612-895-8775	24EC
MN	Twin Cities	PCL	PC-Library TeleComm	612-895-9084	V32B
MO	Kansas City	BAL	The Crystal Ball	816-453-0100	
MO	Kansas City	MET	Metropolis	816-763-7000	
MO	Springfield	C-M	ChatMaster BBS	417-886-6639	
MO	St. Louis	STL	SLACC STACK	314-367-1903	
MS	Kosciusko	Z-1	Zone 1	601-289-7837	V32B
MS	Laurel	RND	The Round Table BBS	601-649-0540	
NC	Asheville	WNC	The Arena BBS	704-687-3608	
NC	Winston-Salem	ETH	Earth-Link	919-777-0022	
NE	Omaha	OMA	The CHATisfACTION BBS	402-453-5356	
NE	Omaha	TMI	The Mages Inn	402-734-4748	
NE	Papillion	SGP	StarGate INN	402-339-4341	V32

State	City	Node ID	Name	Phone	Modm
NE	South Sioux City	THE	THEM	402-494-1175	
NH	Candia	NHA	Adaptive Technology	603-483-0534	
NH	Manchester	WIZ	Whiz Data Network	603-647-3068	V32B
NJ	Bergen County	TIS	Trilogy On-Line Services	201-439-1555	
NJ	Caldwell	FIS	The Forest	201-228-0009	
NJ	Cherry Hill	L-1	Logic One BBS	609-429-6232	
NJ	Clifton	TLC	The LaserConnection	201-472-7785	
NJ	Fairfield	DIN	Dreamline Info Network	201-765-9090	
NJ	Highland Park	HWM	Renasci BBS	908-249-1818	
NJ	Maple Shade	CGN	Computer Gaming Network	609-778-4442	
NJ	Marlboro	CHR	Cheers Online!	908-972-2387	
NJ	Secaucus	DCS	Digital Consulting Supprt	201-865-1783	ZYX6
NJ	Sparta	REM	Remote Host BBS	201-729-7046	
NJ	Toms River	COS	CyberComm Online Services	908-506-7637	
NJ	Union City	DEA	Beacon Studios BBS	201-863-5253	
NM	Albuquerque	ALB	Kaffe' Werks	505-268-0796	
NM	Albuquerque	ET1	The Electronic Trib	505-823-7700	
NM	Albuquerque	ET1	The Electronic Trib	505-823-7701	V32B
NM	Albuquerque	ET1	The Electronic Trib	505-823-7702	24EC
NM	Albuquerque	GGB	GigaBaud BBS	505-271-2848	
NM	Albuquerque	PAN	Pandamonium BBS	505-298-7000	
NM	Albuquerque	P_L	A Paradise Lost BBS	505-298-4234	
NM	Albuquerque	TGD	The GaRBage DuMP BBS!	505-294-0803	V32B
NM	Albuquerque	TGD	The GaRBaGe DuMP BBS!	505-294-5675	
NM	Farmington	IND	Indigo CIS	505-326-2436	
NM	Rio Rancho	FEX	Fantasy Express	505-891-2200	
NV	Las Vegas	MCM	Multi-Comm	702-362-9224	
NY	.....	NCS	The Second Foundation	315-393-6504	
NY	Brooklyn	BAY	Bay Cafe	718-769-6787	
NY	Elmira	HUS	Destination CPU	607-737-6901	
NY	Jamestown	MMB	Modem Madness BBS	716-483-2851	
NY	Long Island	PBB	Point Blank	516-371-5764	V32
NY	Long Island	PBB	Point Blank	516-371-5767	V32B
NY	Long Island	PBB	Point Blank	516-371-9039	V32B
NY	Long Island	PBB	Point Blank	516-371-9643	
NY	Mt. Kisco	NYM	New York Metro Chat	914-242-8227	V32B
NY	New York	FFN	Free Financial Network	212-752-8660	
NY	New York	SN1	SPARK*Net - New York	718-447 5544	
NY	New York	SN1	SPARK*Net - New York	718-447-5544	
NY	New York	ANY	Access New York	212-580-6473	
NY	Staten Island	NWB	Northern World BBS	718-987-8786	
OH	Canton	HAM	Ham Radio BBS	216-492-1577	

State	City	Node ID	Name	Phone	Modm
OH	Canton	TCC	The Canton Connection	216-455-2446	V32
OH	Cincinnati	BRW	BrainWaves BBS	513-641-2203	
OH	Cincinnati	L-L	Liberty Line BBS	513-891-2032	
OH	Cincinnati	SAS	Stars and Stripes BBS	513-521-1510	
OH	Columbus	CTK	CompuTrek	614-338-8400	
OH	Columbus	HRT	Heartland Multiline BBS	614-846-7669	
OH	Columbus	POL	Phantasy On-Line	614-871-8063	
OH	Grove City	EXP	The Electronic Explorer	614-875-3808	
OH	Holland	O-L	Omni-Link	419-867-9271	
OH	Toledo	911	MedicCom	419-389-6642	
OK	Oklahoma City	CEC	Cardin Electronic Comm	405-749-9906	
OR	Eugene	TKP	The KEEP BBS	503-343-5015	
OR	Eugene	TKP	The KEEP BBS	503-343-6010	V32B
OR	Portland	RIP	Rip City BBS	503-234-6218	
PA	Allentown	CBB	C.B.B.S.	215-433-3370	
PA	Ambler	MBS	The Magic Bus	215-628-2646	
PA	Bradford	BRA	Bradford Information Net	814-368-8318	
PA	Guys Mills	MOL	Machinery Online	814-789-4336	
PA	King of Prussia	ONX	ONIX BBS	610-992-1021	DS2
PA	King of Prussia	ONX	ONIX BBS	610-992-1720	V32B
PA	Lancaster	201	2001:CommunicationsOdysey	717-293-9023	
PA	Philadelphia	CWK	ClockWork	215-546-7088	
PA	Philadelphia	ETI	Entertainment Technologie	215-335-9850	
PA	Philadelphia	ONX	ONIX BBS	215-879-6616	V32B
PA	Philadelphia	TEC	Technomanna	215-558-9600	
PA	Pittsburgh	BBD	The Bargain Board	412-341-4607	
PA	Pittsburgh	BBD	The Bargain Board	412-341-4904	V32B
PA	Pittsburgh	BBD	The Bargain Board	412-655-7038	
PA	Wyomissing	TMP	The Mercury Project BBS	215-670-8725	DS3
PR	Carolina	CAR	MATRIX SYSTEM	809-276-7368	
RI	Portsmouth	TMH	The Meeting House BBS	401-848-2200	
SC	Beaufort	ZON	The Zone BBS	803-846-5201	
TC	Memphis	MON	The Mongoose's Shadow	901-382-5972	
TN	Nashville	SOS	The Sounds Of Silence	615-449-5969	
TX	Austin	AFP	Austin Free Press	512-447-7703	V32B
TX	Austin	TX1	After Hours BBS	512-320-1650	
TX	Beeville	STC	South Texas ConneXion	512-362-2160	24EC
TX	Corpus Christi	CDS	Computer Data Services	512-887-0787	V32B
TX	Corpus Christi	STC	South Texas ConneXion	512-882-8395	24EC
TX	Dallas	DFW	Argus Information Service	817-481-0097	

State	City	Node ID	Name	Phone	Modm
TX	Dallas	TGD	THe GaRBaGe DuMP BBS	214-644-6060	24EC
TX	Fort Worth	FTW	Micro-Mall BBS	817-237-0050	
TX	Killeen	3PM	The PC Connection	817-690-9105	
TX	Laredo	TRI	Tri-COM Data Network	210-725-5398	
TX	San Antonio	HRC	UTSA HRC BBS	210-561-8030	V32
TX	San Antonio	SAF	San Antonio Forum	210-615-3503	
TX	Victoria	STC	South Texas ConneXion	512-576-9495	24EC
TX	Woodsboro	STC	South Texas ConneXion	512-543-5811	
TX	Woodsboro	STC	South Texas ConneXion	512-543-5813	V32
UT	Salt Lake City	BNN	Bulletin News Network	801-562-9488	
VA	Arlington	CQI	Crystal Quill	703-241-7100	
VA	Charlottesville	VBS	The V.I.N.E. System	804-978-7182	V32B
VA	Fort Myer	!02	2! GlobeNet Place! BBS	703-527-9056	
VA	McLean	TPE	The Power Exchange	703-749-9150	V32
VA	Portsmouth	ORN	Orion	804-397-2030	
VA	Roanoke	ONL	Online! CIS	703-774-0842	
VA	Virginia Beach	CAF	The Creative Cafe' BBS	804-471-1472	HST
VA	Virginia Beach	CAF	The Creative Cafe' BBS	804-471-7151	24EC
VA	Virginia Beach	CAF	The Creative Cafe' BBS	804-471-9669	DS3
WA	Auburn	PRO	ProStar Plus	206-941-0317	V32B
WA	Auburn	UPD	MajorNet Central Hub	206-351-0561	DS3
WA	Battle Ground	TLF	Foundation Earth BBS	206-687-9700	
WA	Bellevue	MPC	MasterPiece MBBS	206-281-3676	DS3
WA	Everett	MPC	MasterPiece MBBS	206-776-2327	DS3
WA	Everett	SCO	Pacific Exposure	206-337-2744	
WA	Gig Harbor	H-P	The Hodge Podge	206-884-9747	
WA	Kent	MPC	MasterPiece MBBS	206-639-0899	DS3
WA	Kent	MPC	MasterPiece MBBS	206-639-1156	ZYX6
WA	Kent	WIN	WinPlus!	206-630-8203	
WA	Kent	WIN	WinPlus!	206-938-0213	
WA	Kirkland	ESC	East Side Chatline	206-828-9600	V32B
WA	Kirkland	ESC	East Side Chatline	206-889-CHAT	24EC
WA	Oak Harbor	ISL	Island-CONNECT	206-675-5550	
WA	Olalla	ATJ	All That Jazz	206-857-4981	
WA	Olympia	EIC	Electric Ideas Clearinghs	206-586-6854	
WA	Pullman	COM	The Complete BBS	509-332-7777	
WA	Seattle	ESC	East Side Chatline	206-937-5244	
WA	Seattle	PYL	The Pylon	206-633-2905	
WA	Seattle	QIC	Computer User Info Exchng	206-547-2393	
WA	Seattle	RTZ	The Ritz Hotel	206-248-3020	
WA	Spokane	PLX	Planet X	509-468-0664	
WA	Spokane	SRM	Minerva	509-459-5233	
WA	Tacoma	BGS	Badlands Gaming System	206-584-2039	

State	City	Node ID	Name	Phone	Modm
WA	Tacoma	GRZ	Ground Zero BBS	206-474-6839	
WA	Tacoma	MPC	MasterPiece MBBS	206-926-2365	DS3
WA	Vancouver	GML	GameLand PLUS!	206-260-0957	
WI	Appleton	TVC	The Valley Connection	414-733-3882	
WI	Marinette	PID	CompuLine/PIDS	715-732-1036	
WI	Marshfield	TPL	The Promised Land	715-387-0105	V32B
WI	Marshfield	TPL	The Promised Land	715-387-1339	24EC
WI	Menomonee Falls	OTE	Over The Edge!	414-253-7600	
WI	Milwaukee	ODS	Online Data Systems	414-761-5120	
WI	Milwaukee	ODS	Online Data Systems	414-761-5143	ZYX6
WI	Milwaukee	PIN	ProLink Info Network	414-241-2400	
WI	Milwaukee	UDN	Ultima Data Network	414-241-3301	
WI	Milwaukee	UDN	Ultima Data Network	414-241-8328	V32B
WI	Racine	ODS	Online Data Systems	414-835-2180	
WI	Stevens Point	TPL	The Promised Land	715-341-5775	24EC
WI	Waukesha	MOD	InfoMOD BBS	414-896-2660	
WI	Wausau	TPL	The Promised Land	715-675-4257	24EC
WY	Casper	SIR	Sirius Software Support	307-472-4656	ZYX6

Canadian MajorNet Node List

Prov	City	Node ID	Name	Phone	Modm
AB	Calgary	NUC	Nucleus Info Service	403-531-9353	
AB	Calgary	NUC	Nucleus Info Service	403-531-9365	ZYX
AB	Edmonton	MLM	Malum Information Network	403-473-8875	
AB	Edmonton	MLM	Malum Information Network	403-478-4547	V32B
BC	Cranbrook	AIS	AIS Multiline	604-489-4206	V32B
BC	Vancouver	684	684-PLAY	604-784-7529	
BC	Vancouver	ALT	Alternatives BBS	604-430-8080	V32B
BC	Vancouver	WCC	NightLine	604-732-9622	
BC	Victoria	FAR	Farwest BBS	604-381-3934	V32B
BC	Victoria	FAR	Farwest BBS	604-381-7623	HST
BC	Victoria	FAR	Farwest BBS	604-381-7958	DS2
MB	Winnipeg	ESS	Essential Service System	204-253-9399	
NS	Sydney	CTC	CHIP to CHIP	902-567-2262	
ON	Brockville	REV	Revelation	613-498-2811	
ON	Burlington	JET	The Flight Deck BBS	416-332-7075	

Prov	City	Node ID	Name	Phone	Modm
ON	Cayuga	LTS	Line-Tap	905-772-5420	
ON	Markham	MJS	MajorSoft	905-477-7053	
ON	Mississauga	COL	Continental On-Line	416-858-4400	
ON	Mississauga	VCO	Virtual City Online	905-279-6442	
ON	Oxford Mills	CVT	Curvet Press	613-258-1560	
ON	Toronto	CML	Computer Link	416-233-5410	
ON	Toronto	OPT	OptiComm	416-921-6366	
QU	Montreal	GMS	The GameMaster	514-858-7777	
QU	Montreal	PSC	Power Shift BBS	514-486-2899	V32B
SK	Caronport	TMB	TechnoMedia BBS	306-756-2523	V32B
SK	Caronport	TMB	TechnoMedia BBS	306-756-2526	V32B
SK	Regina	777	Micro City Systems	306-569-2886	

MajorNet International Nodes

Australia	Melbourne	Nemesis BBS +61-3-331-1155	NEM
Czech Republic	Praha	INFIMA Praha +422 782 00 34	PHA
England	Hemel Hempstead	MDIS ISE BBS +44-442-274539	MDI
England	London	CyberSpace Gateway +44-81-944-8026	CYB
England	Oxford	Direct ConneXion +44-4945-35858	DCX
Meerbusch	GOLEM	Warehouse CBBS +49-2132-80051	HTW V32B
Greece	Athens	Forum Online Info Network +301-6450566	ARS
The Netherlands	Hilversum	Dutch Info Center +31-035-239301	DIC 24EC
The Netherlands	Hilversum	Dutch Info Center +31-035-248214	DIC V32B
The Netherlands	Kerkrade	CPC BBS +31-45-458899	CPC

The Netherlands	Spijkenisse	STER BBS +31-1880 40035	STR V32B
United Arab Emr	Dubai	HCT/Dubai Men's College +971-5005406	DMC

CHAPTER 13

Federal Bulletin Board Systems Accessible to the Public

The focus of this chapter is to provide readers with a list of bulletin board systems operated by the United States Federal Government that are accessible to the general public. The bulletin board systems listed in this chapter provide a variety of information that can be very valuable to readers, ranging from information concerning the availability of Federal Government jobs to scientific, economic and statistical information.

Access to all of the bulletin boards listed in this chapter require a communications setting of 8 data bits, 1 stop bit and a parity setting of NONE. Some of the listings in this chapter may require fees for use or a voice registration via telephone.

Agriculture Department/Human Nutrition Information Service Nutrient
Data Bank: 301-436-5078
for: Public data on food composition, messages, dietary analysis software

Agriculture Department - Office of Public Affairs' Computerized Information
Delivery Service: 202-429-7800
for: Public, fee-based service contains press releases, reports, publications and variety of on-line databases

Army/Information Systems Engineering Command
  Computer Support Center: 703-285-9637
    for: Public, but new users must request upgrade for full access to bulletins about major military contracts and user messages

Census Bureau/Data User Services
  Economic Analysis Electronic Forum: 301-763-7554
    for: Public shareware to use Census CD-ROMs; information exchange

Census Bureau/Personnel
  Census Personnel: 301-763 4574
    for: Public job vacancies and personnel messages

Commerce Department
  Economic BBS: 202-482-3870
    for: Full access by paid subscription. Contains monthly GNP and corporate profits; Consumer Price Index; personal incomes and other economic data

Commerce Department
  Information Infrastructure Task Force: 202/501-1920
    for: Speeches, documents and papers released by the National Information Infrastructure

Consumer Information Center
  Consumer Information Center BBS: 202-208-7679
    for: Public news for consumers, publications information, media oriented

Defense Communications Agency
  DCA Acquisition: 618-256-8200
    for: Plans and solicitations for DOD communications

Defense Department
  ADA Information: 703-614-0215
    for: Public, validated compilers; Ada bulletin boards; other Ada information

Defense Mapping Agency
  Navinfonet: 301-227 4424
    for: Public, information for mariners; marine advisories; global positioning

Defense Technology Security Administration
  Export License Status Adviser: 703-697-6109

for: Export license applicants, status reports on export licenses and other export information

Education Department
   OERI BBS: Long Distance: 1-800-222-4922 / Local: 202-219-1511
   for: Public access

Energy Department
   Minority Impact: 202-586-1561
   for: Public, procurement and education opportunities for minorities through DOE labs

Energy Department
   Remote BBS: 301-903-4892
   for: Public, messages and software for micro users

Energy Information Administration
   EIA BBS: 202-586-2557
   for: Public, statistics on energy production; short-term energy outlook; survey prices

Energy/Office of Fossil Energy
   FE Telenews: 202-586-6496
   for: Public, coal, oil, gas reserves and other related information

Environmental Protection Agency
   Cleanup Information: 301-589-8366
   for: Public, information exchange on hazardous waste removal

Environmental Protection Agency
   Office of Research and Development: 513-569-7610
   for: Public, environmental database and electronic conferences

Export-Import Bank
   Eximbank: 202-566-4699
   for: Requires subscription, programs and policies; news releases; staff list

Federal Communications Commission
   Public Access Link: 301-725-1072
   for: Those who have applied for equipment approval status on equipment applications

Federal Emergency Management Agency State and Local Emergency Management
  Users Group: 202-646-2887
  for: Public, how computers can support emergency management

Federal Energy Regulatory Commission
  Commission Issuance Posting System: 202-208-1397   202-208-1781
  for: Public, Commission agenda, filings, findings

Federal Highway Administration
  EEBS: 202-366-3764
  for: Public, open forum on FHWA topics and computer technology

Federal Register Electronic News Delivery
  (FREND):   202-275-1538/0920
  for: Public, law numbers, federal register table of contents

Food and Drug Administration
  Center for Devices and Radiological Health: 301-443-7496
  for: Public, meeting announcements; draft reports; researcher messages

Geological Survey
  USGS Information Systems Division BBS: 703-648-4168
  for: Public can access CD-ROM, conferences

GSA/IRM Service
  GSA Schedule BBS: 202-501-2661   202-501-2014
  for: Public, information on GSA schedule contracts

Head Start
  Resource and Training Center BBS: 301-985-7936
  for: Public, notices for Head Start participants and E-mail

Housing and Urban Development
  Public Affairs BBS: 202-708-3460   202-708- 3563
  for: Public

Internal Revenue Service
  BXR Information Corner: 703-756-6109
  for: Public, micro technology conferences; information on integrated soft
    ware. Federal Users Group

Justice/Bureau of Prisons
  Office of Information Systems BBS: 202-514-6102
  for: Public, software and conference for computer specialists

Justice/National Institute of Justice
  Criminal Justice Reference System: 301-738-8895
  for: Public, Institute news; Bureau of Justice Statistics data; conference information

Labor Department
  Office of Information and Public Affairs BBS: 202-219-4784
  for: Public, full text of press releases, Consumer Price Index and real earnings
    reports, text of officials speeches, fact sheets, text of selected publications/
    reports, federal job opportunities (nationwide and overseas).

Labor Department
  Wage Appeals Board
  "Computerized Reference Library":   1-800-735-7396
  for: Public, over 425 files of Wage Appeals Board and Administrative Law
    Judges decisions.

Library of Congress
  Automated Library Information Exchange: 202-707-4888
  for: Public, BBS lists and information on federal agency libraries

NASA/Marshall Space Flight Center
  NASA Spacelink: 205-895-0028
  for: Public, scientific and education programs; teachers leave questions for
    NASA

National Institute of Standards and Technology
  Data Management Information Exchange: 301-948-2059   301-948-2048
  for: Public, summaries of standards reports; information on data management

National Institute of Standards and Technology
  Center for Fire Research: 301-921-6302
  for: Public, fire simulation programs and lab information

National Oceanic and Atmospheric Administration
  Forecast and Advisory: 303-497-5000
  for: Public, highlights and forecasts of geomagnetic and solar activity

National Science Foundation
Science Resource Studies: 202-634-1764
for: Public, OTA reports, bulletins on R&D fundinq

National Technical Information Service
703-321-8020
for: Public, bulletins, conferences, files, gateway to 50 other Federal Bulletin Boards

National Technical Information Service
FedWorld BBS: 703-321-8020
for: Access to the ASCII text version of the 1995 Federal budget, with charts provided in TIFF format.

National Weather Service
Climate Dial-Up Service: 301-899-0827
for: Public, but user fees charged short-term climate conditions worldwide

Naval Computer and Telecommunications Station
CTS BBS: 301-238-2131
for: Public, DDN newsletter; Navy datacom policy; micro tips

Naval Data Automation Command
NAVDAC BBS: 202-475-7885
for: Public, software; messages

Naval Observatory
Automated Data Service: 202-653-1079
for: Public, time measurement from the observatory atomic clock

Navy/David Taylor Naval Research Center
Office Automation Systems: 301-227-5200   301-227-3700
for: Public, microcomputer support

Navy Leadership Policy Bulletin Board
703-695-6198, 703-695-6388,   703-697-2442,   703-697-2446
   800-582-2344, 800-582-6940
for: Access to the 1995 Navy budget, President's budget message and the National Defense and International Affairs section of the overall 1995 budget.

Navy Regional Data Automation Center
  Norfolk ARDAC Remote BBS: 804-445-1627
  for: Public limited, DOD unlimited. Micro contracts; software for DOD

Office of Government Ethics
  TEBBS: 202-523-1186
  for: Ethics legistlation, regs, policies, opinions

Office of Personnel Management
  Mainstreet BBS: 202-606-4800
  for: Special interest forums, Internet E-mail and file transfers and access to other OPM bulletin boards.

  Mainstreet access to other OPM bulletin boards:

PayPerNet	Washington, DC	202-606-2675
FedJob	Macon, GA	912-757-3100
FedJobs	Philadelphia, PA	215-580-2216
Federal Job Information Center	Detroit, MI	313-226-4423
OPM Express	Dallas, TX	214-767-0565
OPM Federal Jobline	Los Angeles, CA	818-575-6521

Office of Personnel Management
  Federal Job Opportunities: 912-757-3100
  for: Public, job listings, also POSH (info on RIFS, VETS, etc.)

Small Business Administration
  SBA BBS: 202-205-6269
  for: Public, software; messages

Small Business Administration
  1-800-859-4636 (2400)   1-800-687-4636 (9600)
  for: Public, data on small business development, publications, programs and services.

Social Security Administration
  BBS: 410-966-5051
  for: Public

CHAPTER *14*

The K12Net

K12Net was established in September, 1990, through a loose collaboration of FidoNet System Operators who shared an interest in telecommunications for educators and students in grades K through 12. Conference areas in K12Net focus on traditional curriculum areas, such as science, math, and social studies, as well as foreign language practice with native speakers in four languages. Projects between designated classes are coordinated through a unique concept of rotating channels, which are assigned as needed for short or longer term exchange of data.

The K12Net network currently extends to more than 150 systems throughout the United States and Canada, with significant links to Australia, the Soviet Union, and most northern European countries. Students and teachers can access local K12Net systems using any microcomputer and software which is either public domain or inexpensive shareware; this virtually free access as well as the versatility of connection options is widely considered the reason for its explosive growth. The information provided in this chapter is based upon the generosity of Mr. Jack Crawford of Stanley, New York who can be reached at the Internet address crawford@nysaes.cornell.edu.

K12NET: THE FREE INTERNATIONAL EDUCATIONAL NETWORK

List of Participating BBS's

AUSTRALIA

New South Wales

Clontarf	MacConnection BBS	61-2-907-0355	3:714/914
Mt. Druitt	Prophet BBS & Mail Centre	- mail only -	3:54/54
Neutral Bay	The Bay	61-2-954-5412	3:711/508
Parramatta	OzWorld BBS	61-28-91-1886	3:713/601
Pymble	3M Australia	61-2-498-9184	3:711/409
St. Ives	Heaven's Door	61-2-440-8364	3:711/927
Stanmore	The Runway	61-2-569-5130	3:712/506
Sydney	Education Database	61-2-660-8272	3:712/628
West Lakes	Vector X	61-49-50-4942	3:622/405
Westleigh	The Bush Telegraph	61-2-481-8275	3:711/454
Wyong	EDUCATE BBS	61-4-353-2163	3:711/447

North Victoria

Bayswater	Dark Crystal	61-3-720-1169	3:633/105

Queensland

Brisbane	The Galaxy GateWay Computer	61-7-812-0727	3:640/316
Brisbane	madHouse Inc.	- mail only -	3:640/820
Jimboomba	The Flying Scotsman	61-7-297-5315	3:640/297
Redcliffe	Electronic Library	61-7-284-6853	3:640/202
Redcliffe	Redcliffe Library	61-7-283-0315	3:640/203
Redcliffe	Swiss Connection	61-7-283-0314	3:640/204
Sandgate	Soft-Tech	- mail only -	3:640/201
Tingalpa Brisbane	SuPaCom	61-7-890-1844	3:640/890
Townsville	Coral Sea	61-7-779-2250	3:640/706
Townsville	Grammar BBS	61-7-772-6052	3:640/702

South Australia

Flinders Park	Hub-One	- mail only -	3:800/1
Flinders Park	Oracle PC Network	61-8-234-0791	3:800/804
Whyalla	Whyalla Schools BBS	61-86-45-9458	3:800/813

Victoria

	Emerald Primary		3:633/369 OR
	Kilsyth East Primary		3:633/369 OR
	Preston NE Primary		3:633/369 OR
Bayswater	Bayswater South Primary	61-3-720-4147	3:633/369.7

Bentleigh	Ezycom HQ	61-3-578-0968	3:633/152
Burwood	Bennettswood Primary	-unpublished-	3:633/155.20
Burwood	Mt. Scopus School	-unpublished-	3:633/155.7
Clayton	SECAP BBS	61-3-544-1513	3:633/155
Elsternwick	Yavneh College BBS	61-3-523-7120	3:634/380
Keilor	Outer Limits	61-3-367-2951	3:633/369.6
Lower Templestowe	The Spare Parts BBS	61-3-852-0404	3:633/209
Melbourne	COMET BBS	61-3-879-0108	3:633/377
Melbourne	Cloud Nine	61-3-803-1326	3:635/552
Mt. Waverley	Offline	61-3-808-4510	3:633/374
Mulgrave	Northvale Primary	61-3-546-9291	3:633/369.11
Ringwood	City Limits BBS	61-3-876-3353	3:633/369
Syndal	Glen Waverley SC	-unpublished-	3:633/155.3
Syndal	Jeff's Point	-unpublished-	3:633/155.2

BELGIUM

Brussels	Mail Center Brussels	32-2-5827177	2:291/799
Lennik	In Limbo	32-2-5826650	2:291/702

Antwerp

Antwerp	Horse Power	32-3-2355144	2:292/850
Mortsel	S-Team	32-3-4552073	2:29/777

Eastern Flanders

Brugge	TURBOCOM_BBS	32-50-370735	2:291/901

Hainaut

Biercee	Rapid Mail BBS	32-71-59-1663	2:293/3205

Liege

Embacom	Mail Center Liege	32-41-653311	2:293/2201
Fleron	Teachers' Forum	32-41-587752	2:293/2206
Welkenraedt	Extasy	32-87-890488	2:293/4002

Limburg

Maasmechelen	Tripod	- mail only -	2:292/100

Luxemburg

Florenville	Gaume BBS	32-61-313750	2:293/2401

Walloon Brabant

Genappe	Carpe Diem	32-67-790033	2:293/2901

CANADA

Alberta

Calgary	K12 Connection	403-284-9149	1:134/136
Calgary	Lester B Pearson High School	403-299-7156	1:134/118
Calgary	Senator Patrick Burns School	-unpublished-	1:134/500.1
Calgary	The Student Exchange BBS	403-283-5261	1:134/49
Edmonton	Edmonton Catholic School	403-421-1742	89:701/202
Edmonton	SPQR	403-472-1796	1:342/45
Edmonton	The Loony Bin	403-789-2234	89:701/205
Edmonton	The Root Celler	403-436-1918	89:701/203
Elk Point	Elk Point BBS	403-724-4173	89:707/0
Fort McMurray	Father Mercredi High BBS	403-791-5527	1:3402/2
Fort McMurray	JDM BBS	403-791-2841	1:3402/20
Fort McMurray	NMD Maximus	403-743-9330	1:3402/6
Fort McMurray	The Twin Towers Node 1	403-790-2341	1:3402/22
Fort McMurray	The Twin Towers Node 2	403-743-8698	1:3402/28
Fort McMurray	Westwood High BBS	403-791-2038	1:3402/10
Hay Lakes	Hay Lakes School	403-878-3896	89:701/236
Leduc	Science Network	403-986-8616	89:701/204
Lethbridge	The Terminal BBS	403-327-9731	1:358/1
Medicine Hat	Lunatic Haven Node	403-526-6957	1:134/3002
Medicine Hat	Praxis Society K12 BBS	403-529-1610	1:134/3003
Medicine Hat	The Orion Project	403-528-2787	1:134/3004
Morrin	Starboard BBS	403-772-3898	1:134/5002
Olds	Technology Exchange	403-556-2712	1:134/4002
Stavely	Western Canada DATA LINK!	403-549-2284	1:134/85

British Columbia

Dawson Creek	DarkSide BBS	604-782-4845	1:3405/106
Grand Forks	Sunshine Valley BBS	604-442-2386	1:353/400
Lower Nicola	Uplink BBS	604-378-9613	1:353/810
Vancouver	ED-NET	604-732-8877	1:153/734
Vernon	Electric Ladyland	604-542-9658	1:353/330
Westbank	The Polish Connection	604-768-3278	1:353/240

N.W. Territories

Yellowknife	The Really Board	403-920-7239	1:3402/30

New Brunswick

Fredericton	NEWBED	506-453-2147	1:255/2

Ontario

Bowmanville	Compro Systems	416-623-5219	1:229/615
Hamilton	Programmer's Guild	416-522-2379	1:244/117

Hamilton	Renzo's Roost	416-529-7569	1:244/118
Hamilton	Spectrum BBS	905-388-2542	1:244/111
Lindsay	Faraday On-Line	705-328-2632	1:229/710
Oshawa	Net 229 EC	416-579-6302	1:229/2
Peterborough	Download Dungeon SuperBBS	705-749-3233	1:229/318
Thunder Bay	On-Line Now	807-345-7248	1:229/510
Trenton	Viking's Cove BBS	613-394-0685	1:249/304
Whitby	The Durham Board BBS	416-666-4896	1:229/116
Windsor	The Staff Room BBS	519-977-0410	1:246/12

Quebec

Kahnawake	Igloo Station	514-632-5556	1:167/502
Laval	L'Ecole Virtuelle	514-661-1625	1:167/130
Montreal	DELTACOM	514-877-4964	1:167/535
Terrebonne	Ecole Leopold-Gravel	-unpublished-	1:167/130.1

Saskatchewan

Prince Albert	SaskTel P.A.C.M.I.D.	306-763-4403	1:140/51
Regina	Big Bang Burger Bar	-unpublished-	1:140/23.86
Regina	Ganshirt at Home	306-777-5370	1:140/18
Regina	TeeWunKay	306-779-1237	1:140/37
Regina	Titan's Realm	306-949-8692	1:140/52

FRANCE

Paris	Lycee le Rebours	-unpublished-	2:320/1.2
Toulouse	ERANA's PEACE	33-61399198	2:324/102
Wervicq-Sud	The Lys Valley #1	33-20392225	2:322/2

Nord
| Halluin | LIF-Net Gate | 33-20-033922 | 2:2/701 |

GERMANY

Augsburg	Zentralstelle fuer Computer	49-821586074	49:860/1
Aurich	Ulricianum	49-494161296	49:305/12
Brandenburg	Niedersorbisches Gymnasium	49:30/1	
Elze	JCS-Elze	49:305/1.30	
Esens	Hauptschule Esens	49-49714113	49:305/10
Essen	Gymnasium Bad Essen	49-54723769	49:305/40
Frankfurt/Main	Gila's Node	49-69-776679	2:244/1101
Goettingen	Max Planck Gymnasium	49-5514004903	49:305/35
Goslar	RS-HoherWeg	49:305/1.20	
Hameln	Schiller Gymnasium	49-51202636	49:305/4
Hannover	Helene Lange Schule	49-51144786	49:305/2
Hannover	Kultusministerium Hannover	49:305/1.10	
Hannover	Lutherschule	49:305/2.1	
Hildesheim	Nieders Landesinstitut	49-5121760349	49:305/30

Holzminden	Campe Gymnasium	49-55315023	49:305/5
Lindau	Fachoberschule Lindau	49:860/1.10	
Lueneburg	Bezirksregierung Lueneburg	49:305/1.1	
Moers	Berufsbildende Schulen	49-284135992	49:400/1
Neustadt	Gymnasium Neustadt	49-50324025	49:305/1
Neustadt	Informatik-Netz Gymnasium	49:305/99	
Nienburg	Hindenburgschule	49-50217010	49:305/3
Ottersberg	Schule Ottersberg	49-42052178	49:305/20
Rinteln	Gymnasium Ernestinum	49-575146292	49:305/6
Soest	Landesinstitut Soest	49:400/4770	
Wildeshausen	Gymnasium Wildeshausen	49-443172710	49:305/11
Wunstorf	Hoelty Gymnasium	49-50314955	49:305/7

Bavaria

Thannhausen	Realschule Thannhausen	49-82812027	49:860/1.2
Untermeitingen	the gool ol' BLUE	49-8232-74390	2:2/212

ISRAEL

Rishon Le Zion	Galaxy BBS	972-3-9658585	2:403/141
Rishon Le Zion	Rudy's Place	972-3-9667562	2:403/138

NETHERLANDS

			2:500/31.107
			2:500/31.209
			2:500/31.216
Amersfoort	Amersfoort 1	31-33-753273	2:500/13
Amsterdam	Dutch Free Echomail	31-20-6969489	2:2800/999
Amsterdam	Nethost Totaal Net	31-20-6893869	2:2801/0
Appledoorn	Oost 1	31-55-410095	2:500/4
Ede	Tip Top Gateway	- mail only -	2:2/777
Emmen	HCC Emmen 1	31-5910-21000	2:500/31
Heerhugowaard	West 2	31-2207-42101	2:500/3
Hoogland	Electric BBS	31-33-807900	2:500/264
Kerkrade	Zuid 1	31-45-425518	2:500/5
Leusden	Tip Top Gateway	31-33-950750	2:28/777
Leusden-C	Tele Comm BBS	31-33-952596	2:500/300
Monster	Europe-USA Gateway	31-1749-44958	2:28/6
Randstad	Zoetermeer	31-79-427002	2:500/8
Sneek	DOS gg HUB	31-5120-19382	2:500/7
Utrecht	Freenet Hub 777 (TipTop)	31-30-358673	2:2802/777
Utrecht	West 1	31-30-932896	2:500/2

Groningen

Groningen	Boudicca's Bard	31-50-144906	2:282/506

NEW ZEALAND

| Hamilton | Waikato Net | 64-7-846-6918 | 3:774/605 |

Auckland

Auckland	Auckland College of Ed	-unpublished-	3:772/1.62
Auckland	De La Salle College	-unpublished-	3:772/1.52
Auckland	Dominion Road Primary	-unpublished-	3:772/1.55
Auckland	IBM NZ Ltd Gate	64-9-358-8635	3:772/20
Auckland	Kings College A.O.	64-9-276-0680	3:772/95
Auckland	Manurewa High School	-unpublished-	3:772/1.59
Auckland	Marist Sisters College	-unpublished-	3:772/1.65
Auckland	Murrays Bay Primary	-unpublished-	3:772/1.57
Auckland	NZ Micro Club Gateway	64-9-444-0989	3:772/1
Auckland	NZMC International Gateway	64-9-443-2657	3:772/40
Auckland	Onehunga College	-unpublished-	3:772/1.53
Auckland	Pakuranga College	-unpublished-	3:772/1.54
Auckland	Parnell District School	-unpublished-	3:772/1.61
Auckland	St Peters College	-unpublished-	3:772/1.51
Auckland	Te Atatu North Primary	-unpublished-	3:772/1.58
Auckland	Timatanga Community School	-unpublished-	3:772/1.64
Auckland	Waimakoia School	-unpublished-	3:772/1.63
Auckland	Waitakere College	-unpublished-	3:772/1.60

Canterbury

Christchurch	Burnside High	-unpublished-	3:770/115.43
Christchurch	Cashmere Primary	-unpublished-	3:770/115.40
Christchurch	Middleton Grange	-unpublished-	3:770/115.41
Christchurch	Rangi Ruru Girls	-unpublished-	3:770/115.42
Christchurch	Remote Access	64-3-349-6008	3:770/115

North Auckland

Bream Bay	Bream Bay College		3:772/270 OR
Bream Bay	Marsden Christian		3:772/270 OR
Taipa	Taipa Area		3:772/270 OR
Waipu	Waipu Primary		3:772/270 OR
Whangarei	Kamo High		3:772/270 OR
Whangarei	Northern Polytech	64-9-438-6485	3:772/600
Whangarei	Opus North	64-9-438-8689	3:772/270
Whangarei	Pompallier College		3:772/270 OR
Whangarei	Tikipunga High		3:772/270 OR
Whangarei	Whangarei Girls High		3:772/270 OR

North Otago

| Oamaru | 45 South | 64-3-437-1580 | 3:770/455 |

Otago

Dunedin	Bayfield High School	-unpublished-	3:770/530.11
Dunedin	Bradford	-unpublished	3:770/530.17
Dunedin	College Street School	-unpublished-	3:770/530.4
Dunedin	College of Education	64-3-477-3219	3:770/530
Dunedin	Correspondence School	-unpublished-	3:770/530.8
Dunedin	Kaikorai Primary	-unpublished-	3:770/530.2
Dunedin	Lee Stream	-unpublished-	3:770/530.16
Dunedin	Port Chalmers School	-unpublished-	3:770/530.9
Dunedin	School Advisory Services	-unpublished-	3:770/530.10
Dunedin	Southern Lights	64-3-455-6016	3:770/515
Dunedin	Southern Vortex	64-3-388-6655	3:770/505
Dunedin	St. Bernadette's	-unpublished-	3:770/530.15
Dunedin	St. Mary's School	-unpublished-	3:770/530.6
Dunedin	Strath Taieri School	-unpublished-	3:770/530.13
Dunedin	Tahuna Normal Intermediate	-unpublished-	3:770/530.3
Dunedin	Taieri Beach Primary	-unpublished-	3:770/530.5

South Auckland

Rotorua	Beast Mk II	64-7-357-5355	3:774/600
Rotorua	John Paul College	-unpublished-	3:774/600.10
Rotorua	Rotorua Girls High	-unpublished-	3:774/600.11
Rotorua	Rotorua Lakes High	-unpublished-	3:774/600.2

Southland

Invercargill	Cargill H.S. (No Carrier)	64-3-216-8076	3:770/625

Taranaki

New Plymouth	Informex	64-6-757-5584	3:771/400

Wellington

Wellington	GenBOARD/2	64-4-499-0490	3:771/160
Wellington	Te Wahapu	64-4-388-5552	3:771/210

RUSSIA

St. Petersburg	Asy's Unicorn	7-812-100-1590	2:5030/19
St. Petersburg	Exchange	7-812-275-8727	2:5030/56
St. Petersburg	Spider's Nest Line 3	7-812-271-1395	2:5030/88
Zelenogorsk	The Communication Tube	7-812-315-1158	2:5030/10

SOUTH AFRICA

Cape

Grahamstown	Settler City Fido	27-461-311085	5:7104/4
Herold	Diakonos	27-044-81652	5:7104/7
Port Elizabeth	The Catalyst BBS	27-41-342859	5:7104/2

Transvaal

Kempton Park	Goldfields EL	27-11-393-3624	5:7101/3
Pretoria	Novell User Group	27-12-333-0612	5:7106/22.10
Pretoria	Novell User Group	27-12-333-1642	5:7106/22
Pretoria	Pyramid Software	27-12-662-1720	5:7106/61
Pretoria	Suthies BBS, Sutherland High	unpublished-	5:7106/37.2
Pretoria	Unisa Editorial	27-12-429-8641	5:7106/20
Van der Bijl Park	Iscor Hub	- mail only -	5:7101/4

West Rand

Lenasia	Educare BBS	27-11-854-2184	5:7107/74
Roodepoort	Layout de Marillac	27-11-768-2435	5:7107/1

SPAIN

Elx_A	No Man's Land	34-6-666-1325	2:346/4
Elx_A	ZAS Two	34-6-542-5968	2:346/9
Granada	Atlantis I	34-58-123848	2:345/801
Jaen	Dragon	34-53-253526	2:345/301
Madrid	Rafa I	34-1-5447282	2:341/14
Madrid	Sakery Fox	34-1-4169751	2:341/5
Madrid	Virtual Software I	34-1-3207878	2:341/8
Monforte	Galicia I	34-82-410902	2:348/201
Pontevedra	Rias Baixas	34-86-864575	2:348/603
Zaragoza	Public NME	34-76-531807	2:343/4

Huelva

Valverde	ONUBA	34-55-553199	:345/501

SWEDEN

Huddinge	Kvarnbergs Skolan	46-8-7791023	2:201/357
Ornskoldsvik	Nolaskolans TCL	46-660-54819	2:205/418
Solna	The Globe #3	46-8-835130	2:201/301
Stockholm	Lesson 1	46-8-217015	2:201/113

TAIWAN

HsinChu	Secret Lover BBS	886-3-571-1348	6:724/13
Taipei	Digital Library	886-2-203-6327	6:720/107
Taipei	English Teachers BBS	886-2-778-6484	6:720/603
Taipei	Ray Tracer Mailer	886-2-356-8419	6:720/1024
Taipei	World Data Exchange	886-2-695-2320	6:720/921

UNITED KINGDOM

Hampshire

Southampton	Video Movement Sound BBS	44-489-570202	2:252/131

UNITED STATES

Alabama

Mobile	The World According TO	205-633-5875	1:3625/462
Montgomery	Ken's BBS	205-244-0296	1:375/22

Arizona

Phoenix	Falcon's Nest BBS	602-581-7827	1:114/205
Tucson	Edge of Forever	602-881-3769	1:300/8

Arkansas

Rogers	Rogers Public Schools BBS	501-631-3618	1:3823/60

California

Berkeley	IISME-NET	510-643-6258	1:161/470
Claremont	Gentle Rain Forum	909-593-6144	1:218/501
Diamond Bar	Castle of the Four Winds	909-861-3213	1:103/315
San Diego	Pacific Rim Information	619-278-7086	1:202/701
San Diego	Teachers Resource Exchange	619-462-6587	1:202/910
Ventura	HIS BOARD	605-652-1478	1:206/2505
Visalia	Tulare County Office of Ed.	209-627-5572	1:214/33

Colorado

Colorado Springs	Air Force Academy HS	-unpublished-	1:128/17.30
Colorado Springs	CSDB BBS	719-632-8180	1:128/93
Colorado Springs	Challenger Middle School #1	-unpublished-	1:128/17.3
Colorado Springs	Challenger Middle School #2	-unpublished-	1:128/17.6
Colorado Springs	D-20 Ed Network	719-472-1037	1:128/18
Colorado Springs	Eagleview Middle School	-unpublished-	1:128/17.4
Colorado Springs	Grey Haven	719-282-1630	1:128/81
Colorado Springs	Palmer High School	-unpublished-	1:128/17.20
Colorado Springs	RAM Net	719-594-9476	1:128/14
Colorado Springs	Rivendell	719-472-0745	1:128/17
Colorado Springs	Sci-Line	719-578-9127	1:128/48
Colorado Springs	Timberview Middle School	-unpublished-	1:128/17.5
Golden	LES-COM-Net (Lesley Col Net)	303-526-2047	1:104/232
Littleton	Regency Datasource	303-972-1222	1:104/58

Delaware

Wilmington	The Busted Flush BBS	302-323-0176	1:150/175

Florida

Fort Walton Beach	Lysistrata ERPO	904-244-4637	1:366/844
Ormond Beach	Worlds Imagined BBS	904-677-9562	1:3623/10

Sarasota	Global Vision	813-359-5808	1:137/126
Sarasota	Kid's Korner BBS	813-955-5956	1:321/109.5

Georgia

Norcross	The Wizard's Castle	404-921-8900	015/004

Hawaii

Hickam AFB	Enchanted Garden	808-423-9852	1:345/10
Maui	The Daily Planet	808-572-4857	1:345/111
Pearl City	Friendly Users BBS	1:345/6	

Idaho

Boise	Compulink Northwest	208-375-4073	1:347/1
Bonners Ferry	Room 5 BBS	208-267-8964	1:346/14

Illinois

Edwardsville	The 90th Meridian	618-692-2169	1:2250/18
Wheaton	Beezodog's Place	708-668-8287	1:115/668

Indiana

Anderson	The I.O. Board	317-644-3039	1:231/60
Brown County	Brown County School Corp.	-unpublished-	1:2230/129
Evansville	EVSC BBS	812-985-7823	1:2310/40
Evansville	Perry Heights BBS	-unpublished-	1:50/300
Evansville	West Terrace BBS	-unpublished-	1:50/200
Indianapolis	Some Place BBS	317-357-1222	1:231/120

Louisiana

Baton Rouge	Eagle BBS		504-346-0296
Hammond	ChA.D.D./K12NET BBS	504-542-0380	1:394/5

Maine

Bath	Street Corner BBS	207-442-0997	1:326/208

Maryland

Columbia	Maryland Catholic	410-997-5262	033/110
Germantown	Tinkering BBS	301-428-0233	033/033
Rosedale	Rosedale Data Line	410-866-1755	1:261/1119
Silver Spring	Odysseus Board	301-460-4659	1:109/455

Massachusetts

Amherst	Pioneer Valley PCUG #1	413-256-1037	1:321/109
Amherst	SpaceMet Central	413-545-4453	1:321/110
Amherst	SpaceMet Internet	413-545-8801	1:321/120

Bernardston	SpaceMet Bernardston	413-648-5250	1:321/162
Buckland	SpaceMet Buckland	413-625-2034	1:321/161
Dalton	Field Street BBS	- mail only -	1:321/212
Dalton	Vern's Point at School	-unpublished-	1:321/212.1
Easthampton	Shangrila	413-527-7260	1:321/305
Greenfield	SpaceMet North	413-772-1020	1:321/152
Hancock	Hancock Schoolhouse	413-738-5676	1:321/224
Hatfield	SpaceMet Hatfield	413-247-5974	1:321/164
Hawlemont	SpaceMet Hawlemont	413-339-5760	1:321/163
Holliston	Cul De Sac	508-429-8385	1:322/360
Holyoke	SpaceMet South	413-536-7526	1:321/302
Lanesboro	SchoolHouse BBS	413-443-2108	1:321/223
Ludlow	SpaceMet Ludlow	413-583-5691	1:321/321
Norton	School Forum	508-285-9635	1:322/725
Pittsfield	K12Net Mail Server	413-443-6725	1:321/218
Pittsfield	The Cracker Barrel	413-447-9086	1:321/220
Pittsfield	The Friendly BBS	413-443-4567	1:321/231
Turners Falls	SpaceMet Great Falls	413-863-3703	1:321/165
Williamstown	Aslan's Lair	413-458-5899	1:321/238

Michigan

Gladstone	The * ! Lighthouse ! *	906-428-3425	1:139/930
Kalamazoo	Node 2201/13	616-329-4936	1:2201/13
Muskegon	K12 Educator	616-722-8200	1:228/65
Saginaw	Classroom Earth	517-797-2737	1:239/230
Warren	Flight of the Phoenix	313-751-4057	1:120/80

Mississippi

Natchez	Trinity School BBS	601-442-5978	1:3632/42

Missouri

Farmington	Black Knight PC Board	314-756-3934	1:297/2
Gladstone	Sound Advice	816-436-4516	1:280/333

Montana

Billings	Rimrock BBS	406-255-3754	1:3400/9
Butte	Mountain Valley BBS	406-782-3405	1:3400/16
Butte	Silver Bow BBS	406-723-5870	1:3400/4
Dillon	Beaverhead BBS	406-683-4809	1:3400/10
Dillon	Tiny Sky BBS	406-683-7696	1:3400/3
Hamilton	Bitterroot BBS	406-363-5451	1:3400/19
Helena	METNET BBS	406-444-2068	1:3400/17
Hobson	The Russell Country BBS	406-423-5433	1:3400/7

Nebraska

Beatrice	Southeast Community College	402-223-2889	1:285/115
Columbus	Central Community College	402-564-3913	1:285/112

Grand Island	Central Community College	308-389-6495	1:285/116
Hastings	Central Community College	402-461-2442	1:285/117
Lincoln	Nebraska Dept of Education	402-471-0897	1:285/101
Norfolk	Northeast Community College	402-644-0685	1:285/113
North Platte	Mid Plains Community College	308-532-8306	1:285/110
Wayne	Wayne State College	402-375-7564	1:285/111

Nevada

Reno	Library Com	702-785-4191	1:213/742
Reno	The Daily Planet	702-322-6555	1:213/111
Sparks	N. Nevada Mail Machine	- mail only -	1:213/213

New Hampshire

Londonderry	New England Tech Info Serv	603-432-0922	1:132/189

New Mexico

Albuquerque	The Electronic Trib	505-823-7706	1:301/200
Las Cruces	The Eclectic Company	505-523-2954	1:305/104
White Sands	Border Connection	505-678-8491	1:381/401

New York

Albany	Capital Hub (South)	518-482-7623	1:267/200
Bloomfield	Bloomfield High School	716-657-4790	1:2613/518
Bloomfield	The Log Inn	716-657-7660	1:2613/505
Bronx	Fordham Prep's BBS	718-367-9090	1:278/721
Bronx	The Electric Line BBS	718-822-6997	1:2603/501
Bronx	The Electric Line BBS	718-824-6818	1:2603/504
Brooklyn	Blacknet BBS	718-692-0943	1:278/618
Buffalo	Eric County Medical Center	716-898-4366	1:260/1
Buffalo	Med TechNet/WNY Micro	716-688-1552	1:260/10
Canandaigua	Canandaigua City Schools	716-396-3840	1:260/630
Central Valley	Monroe-Woodbury HS BBS	914-928-8660	1:272/89
Eldred	The Main Frame BBS	914-557-3567	1:272/85
Elmira	SCT BOCES Instr. Support	607-739-9399	1:260/650.2
Elmira	The Barracks Rat BBS][	607-737-6984	1:260/801
Farmingdale	SUNY Farmingdale	516-420-0818	1:107/270
Geneva	Geneva High School BBS	315-781-4153	1:260/625
Honeoye	TechRoom	716-229-2934	1:2613/516
Hornell	Hornell City Schools	607-324-3785	1:260/650
Ithaca	Forum BBS	607-272-1371	1:260/701
Levittown	Utopia Technologies Ltd.	516-579-7507	1:107/203
Livonia	School Board BBS	716-346-4055	1:2613/256
Marlboro	Acorn I - Marlboro CSD	914-236-3265	1:272/32
Marlboro	Acorn II	914-236-3609	1:272/102
Millbrook	Bear Heaven BBS	914-677-6948	1:272/53
Monroe	Monroe Electronic Mail & BBS	914-294-7264	1:272/95
Monroe	Monroe Electronic Mail & BBS	914-783-0992	1:272/94

Monroe	SENY NEC	- mail only -	1:272/2
Monroe	The Particle Board 3	914-783-2455	1:272/60
Monticello	MHS:BBS	914-794-8904	1:272/82
New Windsor	APFL - Two	914-565-2407	1:272/20
Newark	Newark Central Schools	315-331-9258	1:260/670
Norwood	Norwood Elementary School	315-353-4565	1:2608/75
Palmyra	Scholasticom	315-597-3439	1:260/615
Phoenix	Galaxia!	315-695-4436	1:260/328
Phoenix	Phoenix High School	315-695-4070	1:2608/20
Phoenix	Phoenix K12Net BBS	-unpublished-	1:2608/30
Phoenix	Phoenix Middle School	-unpublished-	1:2608/19
Poughkeepsie	The Purple Rose of Cairo	914-473-1697	1:272/58
Poughquag	Horse Head	914-227-6503	1:272/96
Queens	Holman's World	718-529-8890	1:278/402
Red Creek	New Age BBS	315-754-8239	1:2613/604
Rhinebeck	The Druids Grove BBS	914-876-2237	1:272/54
Rochester	Door Into Summer	716-473-7312	1:2613/229
Rochester	Infosite BBS	716-442-9590	1:2613/117
Rochester	Knight Moves	716-621-1735	1:2613/313
Rochester	Net 2613 Mail Server	- mail only -	1:2613/5
Rochester	Shack TOO	716-288-5848	1:2613/150
Rochester	The Holodeck BBS	716-865-0256	1:2613/336
Rochester	The Panic Zone	716-473-0252	1:2613/220
Rochester	The Panic Zone	716-473-5204	1:2613/220
Rushville	Marcus Whitman High School	716-554-3414	1:260/610
Shortsville	Red Jacket High School	716-289-3926	1:260/690
Stanley	W-FL Teacher Resource Cntr	716-526-6495	1:260/620
Walworth	Gananda Central Schools	315-986-7466	1:260/680
Williamson	Auto Mania! BBS	315-483-9455	1:2613/601

North Carolina

Charlotte	The Mounties BBS	704-393-7338	1:379/38

Ohio

Columbus	The Tele-Forum Network	614-471-9185	1:226/540
Rocky River	Nerd's Nook II	216-356-1772	1:157/2
Rocky River	Rocky River	216-356-1431	1:157/3

Oklahoma

Norman	The O. U. BBS	405-325-6128	1:147/2051
Warr Acres (OKC)	The Teacher's Pet	405-728-8228	1:147/70

Oregon

Bend	Grand Illusion BBS	503-382-3212	1:105/702
Coos Bay	Blossom Gulch Elementary	503-269-9736	1:356/1010

Coos Bay	Bunker Hill Elementary	503-267-4747	1:356/1011
Coos Bay	Charleston Elementary	503-888-6366	1:356/1012
Coos Bay	Coos Bay Public Schools	503-269-6952	1:356/1000
Coos Bay	District Office	503-269-6952	1:356/1001
Coos Bay	Eastside Elementary	503-267-2020	1:356/1013
Coos Bay	Madison Elementary	503-888-6577	1:356/1014
Coos Bay	Marshfield High	503-269-2453	1:356/1018
Coos Bay	Millicoma Middle	503-269-0134	1:356/1016
Coos Bay	Milner Crest Elementary	503-269-0349	1:356/1015
Coos Bay	Sunset Middle	503-269-0521	1:356/1017
Coos Bay	The College BBS	503-888-6676	1:356/11
Gaston	Gaston Elementary School	-unpublished-	1:105/23.77
Grants Pass	The Eclectic BBS	503-479-4482	1:349/20
Gresham	Et Cetera BBS	503-663-1459	1:105/405
Hillsboro	HilHi BBS	503-648-8566	1:105/323
Lincoln City	Lincoln County School Dist.	503-765-4305	1:105/732
McMinnville	McMinnville K12Net	503-434-9478	1:105/721
Newberg	Chehalem BBS	503-538-0539	1:105/791
Newport	Lincoln County School Dist.	503-265-4796	1:105/732
Port Orford	FarWest BBS	503-348-2391	1:152/104
Portland	Bink of an Aye	mail only -	1:105/42
Portland	Cascade Echomail Server	- mail only -	1:105/30
Portland	Computer Wizard BBS	503-256-2574	1:105/57
Portland	HI TECH TOOLS for Librarians	503-245-4961	1:105/23
Portland	Marshall High School	unpublished-	1:105/23.12
Portland	Online Mutual Fund News	503-244-8535	1:105/32
Portland	Terminal Velocity	503-280-5107	1:105/13
Portland	The Catlin Gabel School BBS	503-292-7772	1:105/29
Portland	Wilson High K12Net	503-280-5644	1:105/22
Salem	Earth Kids Net	503-363-7787	1:3406/6
Salem	Salem Educators Online	503-399-2645	1:3406/3

Pennsylvania

Milford	Der Haflinger BBS	717-296-4181	1:268/14

Rhode Island

Woonsocket	Mise en Place	401-461-2605	1:323/112

Tennessee

Nashville	DuPont Elementary School	615-847-7305	1:116/41.8
Nashville	DuPont Hadley Middle School	615-847-7303	1:116/41.1
Nashville	Granbery Elementary School	615-333-5113	1:116/41.3
Nashville	Lakeview Elementary School	615-360-2912	1:116/41.6
Nashville	METRO-NET BBS	615-883-3585	1:116/41
Nashville	Meigs Magnet School		1:116/41.5

Texas

Austin	TECHnet II	-unpublished-	1:382/3
Brownsville	Morningside K12 BBS	210-982-2783	1:3820/83
Brownsville	The Lyceum	210-546-4812	1:3820/2
Corpus Christi	Inspired Designs	512-547-3923	1:160/401
Edinburg	Dr. Watkins, Come Quickly!	210-381-2321	1:397/9998
El Paso	Academy K12Net	915-598-1987	1:381/64
El Paso	College of Education	915-747-5041	1:381/94
El Paso	Del Valle High BBS	915-858-4458	1:381/800
El Paso	Eagle BBS	915-598-7215	1:381/104
El Paso	Hawks BBS	915-594-3408	1:381/105
El Paso	Stallion BBS	915-599-1585	1:381/90
El Paso	The Anytime School BBS	915-590-1588	1:381/71
El Paso	Wolverine BBS	915-533-0938	1:381/89
Houston	Collinwood	713-486-4751	1:106/832
Killeen	Bill's Try	817-690-5859	1:395/3
Richardson	MACS 'R US	719-597-9040	1:128/114

Vermont

Burlington	Wintermute	802-656-1182	1:325/111

Virginia

Great Falls	The Consumer Board	703-759-2001	1:109/231
Virginia Beach	Southeast Virginia Net	804-496-3320	1:275/0

Washington

Auburn	Auburn Ed-Net	206-931-4821	1:343/80
Bothell	Silver Lake	206-338-3723	1:343/58
Bremerton	Ground Zero	206-377-0907	1:350/10
Everett	Northern Hub	- mail only -	1:343/500
Federal Way	South Seattle Hub	206-838-7908	1:343/600
Marysville	The Quest	206-653-4881	1:343/55
Mount Vernon	The Hole in the Wall	206-445-5444	1:3401/10
Mukilteo	The Precedent	206-355-1295	1:343/9
Olympia	Dimension 23	206-456-6073	1:352/23
Richland	The Wishing Well	509-375-0507	1:3407/4
Seattle	Programmer's Information	206-283-5978	1:343/27
Seattle	Seattle West Hub	- mail only -	1:343/300
Spokane	Mac BBS	509-924-5364	1:346/6
Tacoma	Black 424	206-589-0997	1:138/174
Tacoma	Keithley Komputer Korner	206-759-5550	1:138/118
Tacoma	The Phoenix Reborn	206-759-7601	1:138/206
Tacoma	The Right Place	206-565-8853	1:138/131
Vancouver	Taboo BBS	206-254-5071	1:105/105
Washougal	The Electronic Educator	206-837-3299	1:105/114
Yakima	Threshold of Origin	509-453-3283	1:3407/101

West Virginia

| Dunbar | Project Enable | 304-766-7807 | 1:279/14 |

Wisconsin

| Marshfield | The Promised Land | 715-387-1339 | 1:238/500 |
| Neenah | Homebuilt Flyer | 414-725-7598 | 1:139/600 |

Wyoming

| Gillette | Lone Tree BBS | 307-686-3181 | 1:316/24 |
| Gillette | Lone Tree BBS | 307-686-8042 | 1:316/23 |

"K12Net" is the trademark and servicemark of Jack Crawford.

CHAPTER *15*

The GlobalNet Bulletin Board
System Network

This chapter contains two detailed tables related to GlobalNet. The first table is a list of GlobalNet echos, a term used by this bulletin board system to reference the subjects carried by conferences. The second table lists bulletin board systems affiliated with GlobalNet at the time this book was prepared

The author is indebted to Mr. Joe Smolinski, the North American coordinator for GlobalNet and the operator of Joe's Code BBS for permission to provide readers with the tables contained in this chapter.

GLOBALNET ECHOS

GN.4DOS – This echo is talk about the 4DOS shareware program and utils.
  Available   : Global   Access   : All

GN.4SALE – This echo is for people who want to sell/buy items.
  Available   : Global   Access   : All

GN.BBS.DOORS – This echo is discussions about BBS doors.
  Available   : Global   Access   : All

GN.BINK – This echo is discussions about the Binkley front-end mailer.
   Available   : Global   Access   : All

GN.CD-ROM – This echo is discussions about CD-ROMs and discs/utils.
   Available   : Global   Access   : All

GN.COMP.AMIGA – This echo is discussions about the Amiga line of computers.
   Available   : Global   Access   : All

GN.COMP.APPLE – This echo is discussions about the Apple line of computers.
   Available   : Global   Access   : All

GN.COMP.ATARI – This echo is discussions about the Atari line of computers.
   Available   : Global   Access   : All

GN.COMP.IBM – This echo is discussions about the IBM/Compatable computers.
   Available   : Global   Access   : All

GN.COMP.OS2 – This echo is discussions about the OS 2 operating system.
   Available   : Global   Access   : All

GN.COOKING – This echo is discussions about cooking.
   Available   : Global   Access   : All

GN.COORD – This echo is for *C talk only. Read access for GN sysops.
   Available   : Global   Access   : GlobalNet Sysops

GN.DB – This echo is discussions about the Dbridge front-end mailer.
   Available   : Global   Access   : All

GN.ECHOS – This echo is for GlobalNet Sysops discussing echos.
   Available   : Global   Access   : GlobalNet Sysops

GN.ECHOTEST – This echo is for echo tests.
   Available   : Global   Access   : GlobalNet Sysops

GN.ETC.CHATTER – This echo is talk around the world.
   Available   : Global   Access   : All

GN.ETC.MILITARY – This echo is discussions about US and non US military.
   Available   : Global   Access   : All

GN.ETC.TRAVEL – This echo is discussions about travel.
   Available   : Global   Access   : All

GN.ETC.WEATHER – This echo is for discussions about weather.
 Available   : Global   Access : All

GN.EUROPE – This echo is zone 52 GlobalNet sysops talking.
 Available   : Zone 52   Access   : GlobalNet Sysops

GN.FD – This echo is discussions about the Frontdoor front-end mailer.
 Available   : Global   Access : All

GN.FILES.DIST – This echo is for GlobalNet file announcements.
 Available   : Global   Access : All

GN.FIREARMS – This echo is discussions about firearms and laws.
 Available   : Global   Access : All

GN.GAMES.RPG – This echo is discussions about Role Playing games.
 Available   : Global   Access : All

GN.JOBS.MISC. – This echo is discussions about jobs available etc.
 Available   : Global   Access : All

GN.JOBS.PROGRAMMER – This echo is discussions about jobs available
for programmers.
 Available   : Global   Access : All

GN.MODEMS – This echo is discussions about modems.
 Available   : Global   Access : All

GN.NEWS.EARTHWIDE – This echo is discussions about any news around
the world.
 Available   : Global   Access : All

GN.POLICE – This echo is discussions about police.
 Available   : Global   Access : All

GN.PROG.BASIC.AMI – This echo is discussions about the Amiga Basic programming.
 Available   : Global   Access : All

GN.PROG.BASIC.ATA – This echo is discussions about the Atari Basic programming.
 Available   : Global   Access : All

GN.PROG.BASIC.DOS – This echo is discussions about the DOS Basic programming.
 Available   : Global   Access : All

GN.PROG.BASIC.DOS.C – This echo is discussions about the DOS C programming language. Lessons are offered in this echo.
    Available : Global   Access : All

GN.PROG.DOS.PASCAL – This echo is discussions about the Pascal programming language. Lessons are offered in this echo.
    Available : Global   Access : All

GN.PROPOSAL – This echo is discussions and proposals of the GlobalNet Network.
    Available : Global   Access : GlobalNet

GN.SHAREWARE – This echo is discussions about shareware programs.
    Available : Global   Access : All

GN.SPORTS.NFL.FOOTBALL – This echo is discussions about NFL Football.
    Available : Global   Access : All

GN.SPORTS.NHL.HOCKEY – This echo is discussions about NHL Hockey.
    Available : Global   Access : All

GN.SPORTS.USA.BASEBALL – This echo is discussions about USA Baseball.
    Available : Global   Access : All

GN.SYSOP.DEAL – This echo is discussions about deals for sysops.
    Available : Global   Access : All

GN.TALK.ADULT – This echo is discussions for ADULTS over 18 years old.
    Available : Global   Access : 18+ Only

GN.TALK.BBS.SYSOPS – This echo is discussions for BBS Sysops.
    Available : Global   Access : All

GN.TALK.BBS.WILDCAT – This echo is discussions about the Wildcat BBS.
    Available : Global   Access : All

GN.TALK.COMPUTER.GAMES – This echo is discussions about computer games.
    Available : Global   Access : All

GN.TALK.CRISIS – This echo is discussions for people having a rough time.
    Available : Global   Access : All

GN.TALK.DISABLED – This echo is discussions about disabled.
    Available : Global   Access : All

GN.TALK.EDUCATION – This echo is discussions about education.
    Available : Global   Access : All

GN.TALK.ELDER – This echo is discussions about elderly people.
    Available : Global   Access : All

GN.TALK.LOVE – This echo is discussions about love.
    Available : Global   Access : All

GN.TALK.MEDICAL.GENERAL – This echo is discussions about medical questions etc.
    Available : Global   Access : All

GN.TALK.MOVIES – This echo is discussions about movies.
    Available : Global   Access : All

GN.TALK.MUSIC – This echo is discussions about music.
    Available : Global   Access : All

GN.TALK.PARENTS – This echo is discussions about and for parents.
    Available : Global   Access : All

GN.TALK.PETS – This echo is discussions about animals.
    Available : Global   Access : All

GN.TALK.TV – This echo is discussions about television.
    Available : Global   Access : All

GN.THINGS.INFO – This echo is discussions about things you always wanted to know.
    Available : Global   Access : All

GN_USA – This echo is zone 51 GlobalNet sysops talking.
    Available : Zone 51   Access : GlobalNet

GN.VOTE.51 – This echo is for public voting in zone 51.
    Available : Zone 51   Access : GlobalNet Sysops

GN.VOTE.52 – This echo is for public voting in zone 52.
    Available : Zone 52   Access : GlobalNet Sysops

GN.WINDOWS – This echo is discussions about window type applications.
    Available : Global   Access : All

GN.WORDPERFECT – This echo is discussions about Wordperfect.
    Available : Global   Access : All

GN.WRITERS – This echo is discussions for writers.
    Available : Global   Access : All

GN.490 – This echo is for region 490 sysops talking.
Available   : Region 490 – Germany   Access : GlobalNet Sysops

GN.ZONE.54 – This echo is discussions in Zone 54 for GN sysops.
Available   : Zone 54   Access : GlobalNet Sysops

GN.GER.4SALE – This echo is German for sale.
Available   : Region 490 – Germany   Access : All

GN.GER.CHATTER – This echo is German chatter.
Available   : Global   Access : All

GN.GER.MEDICAL – This echo is German Medical.
Available   : Global   Access : All

GN.GER.PASCALE – This echo is German Pascal programming.
Available   : Global   Access : All

GN.GER.PROPOSAL – This echo is German GlobalNet proposal area.
Available   : Region 490 – Germany   Access : GlobalNet Sysops

GN.GER.SYSPROB – This echo is German computer system problems area.
Available   : Region 490 – Germany   Access : All

GN.INFO.4SALE – This echo is German for sale.
Available   : Region 490 – Germany   Access : Ready-Only

GN.INFO.REZEPTE – Kochrezepte - MealMaster-Format.
Available : Region 490 - Germany   Access : Read-Only

GN.TALK.KOCHEN – Diskussion zu GN.INFO.REZEPTE.
Available   : Region 490 – Germany   Access : All

GN.TALK.KOSMETIC – Kosmetik, Wellness, Koerperpflege.
Available   : Region 490 – Germany   Access : All

GN.TALK.ELTERN – Erziehung, Schule, Kindergarten.
Available   : Region 490 – Germany   Access : All

FMAIL_HELP – This echo is discussions/support for the F-mail echo tosser.
Available   : Global   Access : All

HP – This echo is discussions about HP computers and accessories.
Available   : Global   Access : All

SCOUTER – This echo is discussions about Boy/Girl scouts.
Available   : Global   Access : All

GN.FR.CHATTER – This echo is French chatter.
Available   : Global   Access : All

GlobalNet BBS Listing

9600 implies 9600 or greater

"We are looking forward to your visit!"

Area	Service	Coordinator	Data Number	
	North America	Joe Smolinski	313-855-0894	
Area 110	NJ NY RI DE	Mark Astarita	201-509-7851	
Area 120	PA VA WVA DC MD	Don Papa	215-887-0171	
Area 130	FL GA SC NC AL	Ed Shemanski	407-897-6022	
Area 140	MI IN OH KY TN	Jeff Kaplow	313-661-2511	
Area 150	WI MN IL MO IA AR MS	Stuart Click	608-838-8439	
Area 160	TX LA OK KS NE SD ND	Phil Root	402-558-5104	
Area 170	CO NM AZ WY MT ID UT	Chris Millikin	303-373-5140	
Area 180	CA NV OR WA	Steve Souza	408-227-4865	
Area 190	HI	Wyatt Barbee	808-396-2420	
Area 210	QUE ONT NB NS PEI NFLD	John Momy	613-684-6187	
Area 220	BC ALB SASK MANTA	Kenneth Langley	604-421-6519	

GlobalNet Area 110 BBS's

Service	Location	Data Number	Speed
Video Game Info. Ser.	Montclair NJ	201-509-7851	9600
Panorama BBS	Binghamton NY	607-723-6957	2400
The Programmer's Cove	Montclair NJ	201-509-0430	2400
The Maven's Roost	Kendall Park NJ	908-821-4533	9600
Self Help	Elizabeth NJ	908-289-3981	9600

GlobalNet Area 120 BBS's

Service	Location	Data Number	Speed
Mechanix Choice BBS	Glenside PA	215-887-0171	9600
AirPower_BBS	Lansdowne PA	215-259-2198	9600
Scott's House BBS	Havertown PA	215-789-5748	9600
The Keep In Touch BBS	Philadelphia PA	215-333-0540	9600

GlobalNet Area 130 BBS's

Service	Location	Data Number	Speed
The Virtual Groove	Orlando FL	407-897-6022	9600
The Rush Room	Orlando FL	407-678-0749	2400
Compu-Link II	Orlando FL	407-240-7864	9600
Nite Games	Orlando FL	407-382-8251	2400

Level V	Altamonte Springs FL	407-339-6858	9600
Sensible Software	Orlando FL	407-298-5830	9600
Exotica's Pets & Stuff	Crystal River FL	904-563-0358	9600
E-Mail Central	Ponce de Leon FL	904-836-5143	9600
Sunshine Online Service	Miami FL	305-378-6828	9600
Ye Olde Collectable Shoppe	Miami FL	305-220-6301	9600
Ramblin' Roots	Miami FL	305-221-1571	9600
SOX! The SysOp eXchange	Hialeah FL	305-821-3317	9600
The Rookie_BBS	Miami FL	305-595-7491	9600
PC_Connect	Marietta GA	404-565-8250	9600
The Legions Of Valhalla	Midland NC	704-784-2428	9600
The Family SmorgasBoard<tm>	Pleasant Grove AL	205-744-0943	2400

GlobalNet Area 140 BBS's

Joes CODE BBS	West Bloomfield MI	313-855-0894	9600
Lightning Bolt!	Farmington Hills MI	313-661-2511	9600
Ground Zero!	Dearborn MI	313-561-9274	9600
The College Board	Livonia MI	313-478-9647	9600
The King's Palace	Bloomfield Hills MI	313-737-4765	9600
The /Flux/ Line	Bloomfield Hills MI	313-851-3509	9600
MetroMagic	Southfield MI	313-353-9543	9600
CDS Mega BBS	Southfield MI	313-478-8922	9600
The Edge Of Sanity	Dearborn MI	313-584-1253	9600
V.O.I.C.E. BBS	Redford MI	313-532-8410	9600
The Flying Circus	Royal Oak MI	313-549-4214	9600
Bruce's Place BBS	Dearborn MI	313-562-0051	9600
PBCS	West Bloomfield MI	313-932-8725	9600
B & P Inc.BBS	Detroit MI	313-255-8084	9600
The Emergency Scene	Romulus MI	313-941-2176	2400
CyberOptic Junction (tm)	Redford MI	313-255-9129	9600
The Rif-Raf BBS	Detroit MI	313-897-4340	2400
THE BASEMENT	Taylor MI	313-295-6865	9600
The Beam Rider	Lansing MI	517-394-4874	9600
The Oratory BBS	Paw Paw MI	616-657-6306	9600
Ad Board	Paw Paw MI	616-657-6150	9600
The BIBLE STUDY BBS	Kalamazoo MI	616-372-9946	9600
The Evans BBS	Greenville MI	616-754-6180	9600
Data Management BBS	Ionia MI	616-527-0705	9600
Hill Top	Hamilton IN	219-488-3812	9600
Walden Pond	Angola IN	219-665-8767	9600
Semper Fi	Fort Wayne IN	219-424-4292	9600
Play Board	Fort Wayne IN	219-744-4908	9600
The Christian Star	Columbus OH	614-841-9991	9600
Rockin' BBS!	Columbus OH	614-267-9436	9600
The Comm * Port	Columbus OH	614-870-6544	9600
The Mists of Avalon!	Grove City OH	614-539-1748	9600

Mystic Life BBS	Columbus OH	614-279-7709	9600
IBM Classic BBS	Eaton OH	513-456-9051	9600
Living Air BBS	Irvine KY	606-723-3370	9600
Bible Study II	Winchester KY	606-744-6079	9600
Alpha Colony CBCS	Memphis TN	901-323-6429	9600
Naden EBBS	Memphis TN	901-366-7221	9600
Crystal Clear Ideas EBBS	Memphis TN	901-324-8511	9600
The Smile Line	Memphis TN	901-685-0017	2400

GlobalNet Area 150 BBS's

AXCess BBS	McFarland WI	608-838-8439	9600
JW PC DataFlex	Sun Prairie WI	608-837-1923	9600
JW PC DataFlex.ZYX	Sun Prairie WI	608-837-2550	9600
Trolls Den BBS	Poynette WI	608-635-7948	9600
Connect 2400 BBS	Madison WI	608-222-0410	9600
Moonlight BBS	Madison WI	608-271-5397	2400
The Gallow's Poll	Janesville WI	608-756-9191	9600
The Parody	Madison WI	608-277-8597	2400
TRS BBS	Waunakee WI	608-849-4259	9600
The King's Court BBS	Bensenville IL	708-860-2496	9600
Soap Suds BBS	Saint Louis MO	314-771-7954	2400
DOC in the BOX CBIS	Lohman MO	314-893-6099	9600
The Rarely Called BBS	Arnold MO	314-282-0017	2400
The Gathering BBS	Florissant MO	314-839-2978	9600
Short Circuit BBS	Walls MS	601-781-1886	9600

GlobalNet Area 160 BBS's

Planetary Defense	Tyler TX	903-597-0712	9600
The Barn Owl	Elkhart TX	903-764-2803	9600
Delicate Sounds Of Thunder	TX	903-877-4447	9600
Comtel One BBS	Tyler TX	903-592-9821	2400
Solar Soyuz Zaibatsu	Austin TX	512-458-6084	9600
Cobra's Den	Tyler TX	903-592-1299	9600
Lightning Strike BBS	Bullard TX	903-894-7133	9600
The Software Library	Omaha NE	402-558-5104	9600

GlobalNet Area 170 BBS's

SEC-COM International	Denver CO	303-373-5140	9600
VALUE LINE Multi-BBS	Denver CO	303-373-5140	9600
SPECTRUM BBS	Denver CO	303-373-5204	9600

GlobalNet Area 180 BBS's

West-World BBS	San Jose CA	408-227-4865	2400
INTEREX BBS	Sunnyvale CA	408-747-1158	2400
Communication Breakdown	San Jose CA	408-297-8383	9600
ZyXEL USA Technical Support	Anaheim CA	714-693-0762	9600
The FLASH POINT bbs,	Pomona CA	714-625-4920	9600
The WARP ZoNE bbs	Pomona CA	714-624-0140	9600
Gentle Rain Forum	Claremont CA	714-593-6144	9600
Lincoln's Cabin bbs	San Francisco CA	415-752-4490	9600
The Oasis	Springfield OR	503-747-5818	9600
Neverland BBS	Vancouver WA	206-696-1250	2400
The WANTED	Spokane WA	509-838-1974	2400

GlobalNet Area 190 BBS's

The Splicer	Honolulu HI	808-396-2420	9600
Coconuts BBs NODE1	Honolulu HI	808-845-7054	9600
Coconuts BBs NODE2	Honolulu HI	808-841-8661	9600
Coconuts BBs NODE3	Honolulu HI	808-845-7066	9600

GlobalNet Area 210 BBS's

The Northern Connection	Hudson ON	807-582-3880	9600
Samms Addiction BBS	Windsor ON	519-255-9272	9600
The New Guy On The Block	Windsor On	519-776-4996	2400
Digital Wasteland	Windsor On	519-972-6828	9600
Czarland BBS	Windsor On	519-256-1020	9600
Beyond The Realm Of Chaos	Windsor On	519-736-2394	9600
Sweet Water Mountain	Windsor On	519-971-2756	9600
PRACTICAL B.B.S	Windsor On	519-979-1876	9600
Voice Of Windsor BBS	Windsor On	519-969-0747	2400
Giants Castle	Windsor On	519-974-1342	9600
The Cartoon BBS	Windsor On	519-944-9405	9600
B CUBED GENEALOGY BBS	Thamesville On	519-692-5855	9600
THE OUT POST BBS	ST Mary's On	519-284-4855	9600
Gaia/Galaxia BBS	Aylmer PQ	819-684-6187	9600
Neighbours's BBS	Ottawa ON	613-821-7998	9600
King Majestix Court	Nepean ON	613-225-0057	2400
Mostly Harmless	Orleans ON	613-830-8160	2400
The Fantasy BBS	Nepean ON	613-224-4505	9600
The Pixel Palace	Prescott ON	613-925-3086	2400

GlobalNet HQ BBS	Montreal PQ	514-487-7086	9600
The Chrono Zone	Lasalle PQ	514-363-6298	9600
Tony's Madhouse	Montreal PQ	514-630-5923	9600
The Black Hole BBS	Montreal PQ	514-962-4410	9600
Mike's Place BBS	Pierrefonds PQ	514-684-4658	9600
No Way Out BBS	St-Leonard PQ	514-255-6627	9600
ToD2	Montreal PQ,	514-528-8977	9600
Le Vignoble SBE	Ste Julienne PQ	514-831-8412	9600
TechnoBytes BBS	Montreal PQ	514-278-1963	9600
Marshal Law	Montreal PQ	514-684-0843	9600
Marshal Law	Montreal PQ	514-684-0843	9600
XON/XOFF Information Serv	Montreal PQ	514-683-6729	9600
ABS International (Canada)	Montreal QC	514-937-7451	9600
Brian's BBS	Verdun PQ	514-769-5023	9600
Super_Ultrason	Montreal PQ	514-259-0213	9600
Light Star BBS	St Leonard PQ	514-727-4297	9600
Transition Point BBS	Nova Scotia	902-742-3399	9600

GlobalNet Area 180 BBS's

Shalom	Burnaby BC	604-421-6519	9600

CHAPTER *16*

Bulletin Board System Listings

In this chapter readers will find several comprehensive listings of bulletin board systems classified into three major categories.

The first listing, provided by the generosity of Ken Sukimoto, Sysop of the DownTown BBS, consists of bulletin board systems that provide a data transmission capability of at least 9600bps. Readers should note that this list of BBSs, referred to as the 96LIST, provides a list of bulletin board systems throughout the United States that support different operating rates up to and including 9600bps and, when noted, data rates beyond 9600bps. Based upon the type of modem connected to the bulletin board you may be able to communicate with the BBS at data rates as low as 300bps. In any event, all of the bulletin board systems in the 96LIST support the V.24bis modem protocol for operation at 2400bps, which means you can access those systems at 2400bps if you do not have a modem capable of supporting their 9600bps method of modem modulation.

The second listing in this chapter consists of bulletin boards that operate Andrew Miller's RemoteAccess bulletin board system software. This list describes many of the services offered by each bulletin board system, such as hardware, electronic mail and affiliation with one or more bulletin board system networks. The author is indebted to Mr. Gary Barr of Digicom for permission to include this list.

The third and concluding listing in this chapter is provided by the courtesy of

523

Mr. Bob Breedlove, Sysop of BOB's BBS. Referred to as the US BBS, this list consists of bulletin board systems located throughout the United States that operate 24 hours per day every day of the week, support a minimum modem dial-in connection of 2400bps and offer at least 80M bytes of on-line storage capacity.

96LIST BULLETIN BOARD SYSTEMS

The 96LIST list is a collection of telephone numbers reported as belonging to US BBSes with one or more lines supporting CONNECT speeds of 9600bps or higher. This list is compiled and maintained by Ken Sukimoto, SysOp of the DownTown BBS as a service to DownTown BBS subscribers and other callers and is published on an irregular basis.

   This list is provided to readers with the permission of Mr. Sukimoto who dedicates the development of the 96LIST to the SysOps who install high speed modems, enabling users to access systems at higher and higher speeds. He also dedicates the list to users who motivated SysOps to install high speed modems through their contributions; material, inspirational and otherwise.

ABBREVIATIONS USED:

Modem Type Legend

CS1	= 9600 CompuCom CSP	[CompuCom Champ]
CS2	= 9600 CSP & 9600 v.32	[CompuCom Storm]
CS3	= 9600 CSP & 14.4k v.32bis	[CompuCom Star]
DS	= 14,400 HST & 9600 v.32	[US Robotics Dual Standard]
DS2	= 14,400 HST & 14.4k v.32bis	[US Robotics v.32bis Dual Standard]
DS3	= 16,800 HST & 14.4k v.32bis	[US Robotics 16.8k HST/v.32bis DS]
DS3	= 16.8 HST/v.32bis/21.6 v.32terbo	[US Robotics 16.8k HST/v.32bis DS]
DS4	= 16.8 HST/v.32bis/21.6 v.32terbo	[US Robotics 16.8k HST/v.32bis DS]
HST	= 9600 or 14,400 bps HST	[US Robotics HST]
HST4	= 14,400 bps HST (if known)	[US Robotics HST]
HST6	= 16,800 bps HST (if known)	[US Robotics HST]
TB	= Telebit PEP	[Telebit Trailblazer]
TB2	= Telebit PEP & v.32	[Telebit T-2500]
TB3	= Telebit PEP & v.32bis	[Telebit T-3000]

ULT	=	9600 Hayes V & 9600 v.32	[Hayes Ultra]
ULT2	=	9600 Hayes V/14.4k v.32bis	[Hayes Ultra 14400]
VFC	=	14.4k v.32bis/28.8	Brands will vary
		v.fast class	
VH	=	9600 Hayes V Series	[Hayes Express 96 V-series]
V32	=	9600 CCITT v.32	Brands will vary
V32A	=	9600 CCITT v.32/12k	Brands will vary
		v.32bis	
V32B	=	14,400 CCITT v.32bis	Brands will vary
V32T	=	19,200 AT&T v.32terbo	Brands will vary
ZYX	=	14.4k v.32bis & 16.8 ZyXEL	ZyXEL
ZYX9	=	14.4k v.32bis & 19.2 ZyXEL	ZyXEL
2400	=	2400 bps line for Multi-node 96LIST systems.	
24EC	=	2400 bps w/Error Correction line for Multi-node 96LIST systems.	

DISCLAIMERS:

- Because these numbers have not been verified, the Compiler of 96LIST will not be responsible for erroneous information.
- Inclusion/exclusion of a BBS is NOT an endorsement/condemnation of the BBS.

ERRORS & ADDITIONS:

- If you should find a number on the list that is NOT a modem number, please notify the DownTown BBS so it can be noted & removed from the next release.
- If there is an error or if a BBS updates/modifies modem[s], please contact the DownTown BBS.
- If you are a SysOp and wish to be included in the next release of 96LIST, please contact the DownTown BBS with the applicable information. Leave your board info in private e-mail addressed to User_ID "Sysop" with the subject of "96LIST" or to the address below via US Mail.
- Please do not send PUBLIC messages to Ken Sukimoto on networks with your correction, new entry or comment. Although he will act upon the information, many networks frown upon sending PUBLIC messages for this purpose.
- Mr. Sukimoto can be reached by PRIVATE e-mail on several networks that offer this feature. The networks and his address on them are listed below.
- 96-USA.DB should not be modified to modify/add/delete entries!

THE DOWNTOWN BBS
LOS ANGELES, CA
213-484-0260 [3/12/24/96/14.4k bps v.32bis]
9 Gigabytes of Adult Graphics
3.6 Gigabytes of Hard Drive Library Storage
7 Gigabytes of CD-ROM Drive Storage On-line
14.4k HST/v.32bis & 16.8k ZyXEL lines available
PCP via CALAN or CAGLE – Starlink via Vernon

US-SnailMail Address
DownTown BBS
1008 N. Rosemont Avenue; #113
Los Angeles, CA 90026-3032

Network E-mail Addresses
MajorNet: Sysop@DWN
Internet: Ken.Sukimoto@Panasia.Com

US BBS's Supporting 9600 bps CONNECT Rates

Compiled and Distributed by:
The DownTown BBS - Los Angeles, CA
(213) 484-0260
[3/12/24/96/14.4k v.32bis - Public Access]
9600 v.32/14.4k v.32bis/14.4k HST/16.8 ZyXEL Lines Available

See 96MODEM.LST for Modem abbreviations used below.

AC/Phone	BBS Name	City	State	Modem
201-228-4708	Dragon's Cave	Caldwell	NJ	HST
201-228-7704	The Forest Fidonet	Caldwell	NJ	V32
201-239-1151	MicroSellar BBS	Verona	NJ	V32B
201-239-1331	MicroSellar BBS	Verona	NJ	DS3
201-239-1484	The VIC BBS	Cedar Grove	NJ	HST
201-265-7855	CCSBoard	Emerson	NJ	VH
201-288-9076	The Wizard's Tower	Teterboro	NJ	HST
201-293-7778	Shadow Spawn BBS	Montague	NJ	HST
201-305-9042	Edgelight On-Line	Lincoln Park	NJ	DS3
201-307-9225	The Quantum Zone	Park Ridge	NJ	HST
201-313-0002	Tower BBS	Fairview	NJ	DS
201-326-9870	TMMNET	Parsippany	NJ	TB
201-327-5775	The Arrow Tack BBS	Saddle River	NJ	DS
201-332-5306	Syntax BBS	Jersey City	NJ	HST4

AC/Phone	BBS Name	City	State	Modem
201-338-5265	The Golden*Dane BBS	Bloomfield	NJ	DS2
201-347-2652	Danger Zone BBS	Budd Lake	NJ	HST
201-362-5768	Hard Rock Cafe] [	Blairstown	NJ	V32
201-373-1131	Millenium BBS	Newark	NJ	2400
201-374-2730	Millenium BBS	Newark	NJ	V32B
201-385-2874	Menti's Bay	Dumont	NJ	HST
201-387-7995	County Jail] [BBS	Dumont	NJ	HST
201-387-9232	The Rock Pile BBS	Bergenfield	NJ	HST
201-393-0988	Merlin's Castle	Hasbrouck Hts	NJ	HST
201-398-1133	Microcosm BBS	Hopatcong	NJ	HST
201-398-2373	Evergreen BBS	Hopatcong	NJ	HST
201-403-0338	Camelot BBS	Caldwell	NJ	HST
201-420-8434	The Ogate	Jersey City	NJ	DS
201-423-0762	The Direct Connect] [	Hawthorne	NJ	HST
201-437-4355	Bytes 'n Bits BBS	Bayonne	NJ	DS
201-437-5706	The Depths of Hell	Bayonne	NJ	HST4
201-444-1822	Flash Fire RBBS	Glen Rock	NJ	ULT
201-467-3269	MARKET Investment BBS	Short Hills	NJ	DS
201-471-6391	The Passaic/NJPCUG BBS	Passaic	NJ	ULT
201-487-7556	The Game's Afoot BBS	Hackensack	NJ	HST
201-509-7324	The Gamer's Exchange	West Orange	NJ	V32B
201-515-8557	Chessboard	Parsippany	NJ	HST
201-535-0655	The Crime Syndicate	Livingston	NJ	HST
201-567-6994	APFL-The BBS	Tenafly	NJ	DS
201-568-1826	Optimum BBS	Tenafly	NJ	ULT4
201-573-9262	Splitting Atom	Rivervale	NJ	DS
201-612-0394	Informatix 2	Ridgewood	NJ	2400
201-612-0559	Informatix 1	Ridgewood	NJ	DS
201-617-8054	Binary Information Network	Union City	NJ	V32B
201-626-3550	Newport Centre	Jersey City	NJ	DS
201-628-7287	REACT System 1	Mountain View	NJ	HST
201-641-5950	The Aviator	Moonachie	NJ	HST
201-652-7349	Third Stone From The Sun	Ridgewood	NJ	HST
201-654-0477	Files Unlimited	Westfield	NJ	DS
201-656-5273	Happy Station BBS	Jersey City	NJ	DS
201-661-3694	The Pacific Islander BBS	Nutley	NJ	V32B
201-666-2013	MacIntosh BBS	Westwood	NJ	DS
201-678-1367	UNITEX Communications	Bloomfield	NJ	DS
201-729-0097	Zardan BBS	Sparta	NJ	HST
201-729-1494	Chuck's Attempt 3	Sparta	NJ	HST
201-729-1713	The Demon Pit	Hainesville	NJ	DS
201-729-2602	Chuck's Attempt 1	Sparta	NJ	V32
201-729-2606	Chuck's Attempt 2	Sparta	NJ	V32
201-729-2652	Chuck's Attempt 4	Sparta	NJ	VH
201-730-7328	Arrakis BBS	Annandale	NJ	HST
201-731-9425	SportsBoard BBS	West Orange	NJ	DS
201-742-1860	Trailblazer BBS	Paterson	NJ	HST
201-765-0164	Pick's Place	Green Village	NJ	DS2
201-770-2414	Cruise Ship BBS	Stanhope	NJ	V32B
201-772-4835	Zap	Garfield	NJ	HST
201-791-7471	Blue Ribbon BBS	Fair Lawn	NJ	HST

AC/Phone	BBS Name	City	State	Modem
201-794-9529	Prism BBS	Fairlawn	NJ	CS1
201-796-6890	Starship Enterprise	Elmwood Park	NJ	ULT
201-798-0065	Computer Connections	Hoboken	NJ	HST
201-806-8856	OuterLimits BBS	Flemington	NJ	HST
201-808-5574	Rivendell	Fairfield	NJ	HST
201-831-8152	The SailBoard BBS	Ringwood	NJ	DS2
201-835-8273	Rob's Wildcat!	Pompton Lakes	NJ	ULT
201-866-3721	Best Buy BBS	Secaucus	NJ	V32B
201-866-6952	Realm of Possibilities	Union City	NJ	ULT
201-881-7421	RES-Q	Paterson	NJ	HST
201-884-2795	End of the Universe	Whippany	NJ	DS
201-896-8718	The Flight-Deck	Carlstadt	NJ	HST
201-934-0861	Harry's Place	Mahwah	NJ	DS
201-935-1104	The BillBoard BBS	Lyndhurst	NJ	ULT
201-935-7008	The Galileo 7	Lyndhurst	NJ	TB
201-948-3428	Poison Pete's	Branchville	NJ	HST
201-956-7703	Operation ANARCHY!	Paterson	NJ	HST
201-984-5555	Atrium Way	Morris Plains	NJ	DS
201-989-8323	Eureka	Dover	NJ	DS
202-282-2723	NAVDAC BBS	Washington	DC	DS
202-466-5353	NGC/PERMANENT/Synergy	Washington	DC	DS
202-544-4285	RRA BBS	Washington	DC	HST
202-863-1493	Baron Carlos's Castle	Washington	DC	HST4
203-228-9578	The Library	Hebron	CT	V32B
203-231-8700	Bruce's Bar & Grill	W Hartford	CT	HST
203-235-5908	Meriden Adult BBS	Meriden	CT	DS2
203-238-0462	SDnet/Works-Eastern Star	Meriden	CT	HST
203-250-7899	Equinox	Cheshire	CT	DS2
203-259-6770	Fast-Track BBS	Fairfield	CT	HST
203-261-6434	Trumbull Mini-BBS	Trumbull	CT	TB
203-263-2573	Green Acres	Woodbury	CT	HST
203-263-4542	Gateway To Hell	Woodbury	CT	HST
203-268-3111	Lil Frog	Trumbull	CT	HST
203-271-1579	The Hole in the Woods	Cheshire	CT	HST
203-274-4639	Socialism Online!	Watertown	CT	HST
203-295-8384	Info-Link	Marlborough	CT	DS
203-335-7742	The Planet Earth	Bridgeport	CT	DS
203-344-0495	Storm Haven	Middletown	CT	DS
203-344-1991	K&T's	Middlefield	CT	V32
203-345-2111	The Big Byte	Higganum	CT	V32
203-375-1751	The Stratford Spitfire	Stratford	CT	HST
203-384-9728	Pleasure Palace][	Bridgeport	CT	HST
203-387-8626	New Haven Kitten/Seadog	New Haven	CT	DS
203-389-8426	Amiga Connection	Hamden	CT	HST
203-431-4687	Source of Magic	Ridgefield	CT	HST
203-438-4721	The Dark Side	Ridgefield	CT	HST
203-438-9908	Orions Nebula	Ridgefield	CT	V32
203-444-7607	LineNoise BBS	Waterford	CT	HST
203-445-2703	Chronicles Info Network	Groton	CT	DS
203-445-6069	Ghandeel's Fortress	Groton	CT	DS
203-449-8100	Chalkboard II BBS	Groton	CT	HST

AC/Phone	BBS Name	City	State	Modem
203-466-1625	Fritz BBS	East Haven	CT	HST
203-468-6619	The Ultimate BBS II	North Branford	CT	HST
203-481-6827	PgDn BBS	Branford	CT	HST
203-483-0348	Fernwood	Branford	CT	DS
203-484-4621	Hippocampus BBS	Branford	CT	HST
203-488-1115	Alice's Restaurant	Branford	CT	HST
203-523-1987	WGM Computer Consulting	West Hartford	CT	DS
203-528-7181	Dean's Machine	East Harford	CT	HST
203-531-4289	Angelus ComputerConsultant	Greenwich	CT	DS
203-531-4780	OS-Bullet	Greenwich	CT	DS
203-535-4284	Bits & Bytes BBS	N. Stonington	CT	DS
203-563-6455	Hart-Metro Fido	Wethersfield	CT	TB
203-564-5318	The Plainfield New II	Plainfield	CT	HST
203-564-8579	The Plainfield News	Plainfield	CT	HST
203-582-5462	First Encounter	Bristol	CT	DS
203-582-9791	The Eclipse	Bristol	CT	HST
203-598-3934	The Storm Front RBBS-PC	Middlebury	CT	HST
203-620-0351	The NEW Farm at Milldale	Milldale	CT	HST
203-621-1930	DownStairs	Southington	CT	HST
203-621-3461	The Dragons' Lair	Southington	CT	HST
203-628-9702	Cygnus X-I	Southington	CT	HST
203-634-0370	The SDN Project	Meriden	CT	HST
203-663-1147	The Hub	Killingworth	CT	HST
203-666-5685	The Daily Planet	Newington	CT	V32
203-688-0675	The Twilight Zone	Windsor	CT	DS
203-738-0342	HH Info-Net BBS	New Hartford	CT	DS
203-740-7249	The Far Side Outpost	Brookfield	CT	HST
203-743-4044	The Creative Edge	Danbury	CT	DS
203-746-4826	Electro's Den	New Fairfield	CT	HST
203-749-6103	Death's Domain	Enfield	CT	DS
203-753-8351	A Place in the Sun	Waterbury	CT	HST
203-763-3485	The Earth Network	Enfield	CT	HST
203-779-2683	Doc's BBS	East Killingly	CT	HST
203-779-3173	Mystical Madrigal	Killingly	CT	HST
203-779-3320	The Club	Danielson	CT	HST
203-791-8532	Treasure Island	Danbury	CT	DS
203-791-8838	Rocky Road	Danbury	CT	DS
203-794-1653	The Abyss	Danbury	CT	HST
203-799-7454	TeleTalk	Orange	CT	HST
203-826-1153	Phone Henge	New Britain	CT	DS
203-826-5438	Polish-American BBS	New Britain	CT	V32
203-846-3522	NORAD Opus	Norwalk	CT	HST
203-854-9716	T.S.C.	Norwalk	CT	DS
203-874-1919	Fr. John's BBS	Devon	CT	HST
203-875-7071	The Water Hole BBS	Ellington	CT	DS
203-878-6355	Mission Ctl II	Milford	CT	HST
203-878-6768	Excalibur IV	Milford	CT	HST
203-886-1441	Sea of Noise	Norwich	CT	V32B
203-924-5603	The Soft Parade	Shelton	CT	HST
203-926-6168	The Handicap News BBS	Shelton	CT	V32B
203-928-4212	The Help File BBS	Woodstock	CT	HST

AC/Phone	BBS Name	City	State	Modem
203-932-6236	Ascii Neighborhood	West Haven	CT	DS
203-933-2690	The Library	West Haven	CT	HST
203-934-6159	Twilight BBS	West Haven	CT	HST
203-934-9852	Ascii Neighborhood II	West Haven	CT	TB
203-949-0375	Ultimate BBS	Wallingford	CT	DS
203-963-7015	Brain Damaged	Pomfret	CT	V32
205-238-0012	The Golden Club	Anniston	AL	HST
205-260-9904	The Com Port	Montgomery	AL	DS2
205-262-3735	The Speed of Light	Montgomery	AL	V32
205-271-3545	The GATEWAY	Montgomery	AL	DS2
205-277-3882	The Idea Board	Montgomery	AL	HST
205-277-6502	YABBS	Montgomery	AL	V32
205-279-7313	StarScan	Montgomery	AL	HST
205-281-6902	Late Night Entertainment	Montgomery	AL	HST
205-340-9440	Just For Fun	Decatur	AL	HST
205-341-5055	On-Line After Late Night	Mobile	AL	HST
205-345-0998	DataWorks BBS!	Tuscaloosa	AL	HST
205-353-3278	Tom's Swap Shop	Decatur	AL	HST
205-355-2983	Byte Swap	Decatur	AL	HST
205-435-1480	Alabama-On-Line	Jacksonville	AL	DS
205-435-2477	Alabama-On-Line	Jacksonville	AL	2400
205-452-3897	ProTech	Chickasaw	AL	DS
205-539-2710	Motherboard BBS	Huntsville	AL	HST
205-556-5417	Spectrum WWIV	Tuscaloosa	AL	V32
205-569-1333	The Unicorn	Slapout	AL	HST
205-575-3474	Digital Escape BBS	Monroeville	AL	V32B
205-663-6015	Central Quest BBS	Helena	AL	HST
205-664-5589	Joker's Castle	Alabaster	AL	DS
205-671-0092	Computer Works	Dothan	AL	V32B
205-671-0468	The Southern Pride	Dothan City	AL	HST
205-680-9680	Abject Poverty BBS	Pinson	AL	CS1
205-739-1469	Frontier	Cullman	AL	HST
205-745-3989	SmorgasBoard	Opelika	AL	HST
205-745-4515	The Lightning Board	Opelika	AL	HST
205-774-6989	The Out-Post RBBS 1	Ozark	AL	DS3
205-774-7427	The Out-Post RBBS 2	Ozark	AL	DS3
205-796-5957	Exchange of Bytes	Cullman	AL	HST
205-821-4664	Xignals PCBoard	Auburn	AL	HST
205-822-0956	The DUCK Pond	Hoover	AL	DS
205-837-2871	The Aim High BBS	Huntsville	AL	HST
205-852-1100	The Trading Pos	Huntsville	AL	DS
205-871-3356	Programmer's Shack	Birmingham	AL	HST
205-880-7723	Gateway	Huntsville	AL	HST
205-880-8031	NASAU Beach CBIS	Huntsville	AL	V32
205-881-0889	The Bird's Nest	Huntsville	AL	DS
205-882-6886	Publishers' Paradise BBS	Huntsville	AL	DS2
205-969-0007	Little Kingdom	Birmingham	AL	DS
205-969-5733	The Lions Den BBS	Birmingham	AL	DS
205-974-5123	Cyclone	Moulton	AL	HST
205-979-0367	The Light	Birmingham	AL	V32B
205-985-1725	The Outer Limits	Birmingham	AL	HST

AC/Phone	BBS Name	City	State	Modem
205-995-6590	ISA-BBS Birmingham	Birmingham	AL	HST
206-222-6224	Pascal Alley	Snoqualmie	WA	HST
206-242-8028	Mac-A-Mania Nut	Seattle	WA	HST
206-243-7145	Erotic Nirvana	Seattle	WA	DS
206-243-7309	Erotic Nirvana	Seattle	WA	2400
206-244-9661	BECS Tandy Heath	Seattle	WA	HST
206-248-7647	Cyberspace BBS	Seattle	WA	HST
206-253-9770	Pacifier BBS	Vancouver	WA	DS
206-254-5071	Taboo BBS	Vancouver	WA	DS
206-263-1117	Country Computing	La Center	WA	V32B
206-277-1689	Starfinder I	Renton	WA	HST
206-282-3065	Bumbershoot BBS	Seattle	WA	HST
206-283-5978	Programmers Info Exchange	Seattle	WA	HST
206-322-0814	Northwest PC Link	Kent	WA	DS
206-338-3168	Silver Lake Too	Everett	WA	DS
206-338-3723	Silver Lake	Everett	WA	DS
206-338-9361	Mark's Point! BBS	Everett	WA	2400
206-347-3286	Tin Pan Alley 2	Mukilteo	WA	HST
206-353-6966	ProVision	Mukilteo	WA	DS
206-367-9131	Pony Express	Seattle	WA	V32B
206-377-0907	Ground Zero	Bremerton	WA	HST
206-391-1425	NW Images BBS	Issaquah	WA	V32
206-391-2330	Real Batchin' Board	Issaquah	WA	DS
206-391-2339	Futzer Avenue PCBoard	Issaquah	WA	HST4
206-392-5037	NW Images BBS	Issaquah	WA	V32
206-438-6716	Squad Room BBS	Olympia	WA	CS1
206-451-1274	BECS Opus	Bellevue	WA	DS
206-452-2012	Evergreen Micro Net	Port Angeles	WA	DS
206-456-6073	Dimension 23	Olympia	WA	HST
206-464-5222	The Four Horsemen	Seattle	WA	DS2
206-474-6839	Ground Zero BBS	Tacoma	WA	V32B
206-486-0160	Crystal Cavern	Bothell	WA	HST
206-486-2415	Mark's Point! BBS	Seattle	WA	DS
206-524-4811	Letters RBBS	Seattle	WA	HST
206-524-8037	Games BBS	Seattle	WA	HST
206-526-7143	Westways	Seattle	WA	DS
206-528-1941	Grey Matter BBS	Seattle	WA	V32B
206-532-9220	Techline BBS	Aberdeen	WA	HST
206-565-9740	ArcticNet	Steilacoom	WA	HST
206-566-1155	AmoCat BBS	Tacoma	WA	HST
206-573-8503	Illuminatus!	Vancouver	WA	V32
206-578-1157	Darkstar System	Longview	WA	DS
206-582-3212	Group Medical BBS	Tacoma	WA	HST
206-582-5579	Awakening	Tacoma	WA	HST
206-584-7895	The Cat's Paws	Tacoma	WA	HST
206-628-0427	The Resource	Bremerton	WA	DS
206-631-6185	The Files Depot	Kent	WA	DS
206-637-2398	Seattle Software Exchange	Bellevue	WA	DS
206-639-0899	MasterPiece MBBS	Kent	WA	DS3
206-641-6767	Pacific Macintosh	Bellevue	WA	DS
206-653-4881	The Quest	Marysville	WA	HST

AC/Phone	BBS Name	City	State	Modem
206-675-4234	The Files Bank	Oak Harbor	WA	HST
206-682-3552	CIS Independant Studies	Seattle	WA	HST
206-694-5661	End Times BBS	Vancouver	WA	V32
206-698-1044	The Jimby BBS	Brownsville	WA	DS
206-725-6629	SEA/MAC	Seattle	WA	HST
206-742-7782	Tin Pan Alley 1	Mukilteo	WA	HST
206-745-6340	Puget Sound TBBS	Edmonds	WA	DS
206-756-9689	North End Skyscraper	Tacoma	WA	HST
206-762-7294	Real Batchin' Board	Seattle	WA	DS
206-771-1730	French Connection	Edmonds	WA	HST
206-820-4771	10 Forward BBS	Seattle	WA	V32B
206-822-4615	SeaEast PC Exchange	Kirkland	WA	DS
206-822-7498	Silicon Harvest	Kirkland	WA	DS2
206-822-8520	SeaMist SDS Archive	Kirkland	WA	HST
206-828-9600	East Side Chatline	Kirkland	WA	V32
206-830-9319	My Electronic Dungeon	Bremerton	WA	DS
206-848-9232	Puget Sound Gateway	Tacoma	WA	HST
206-850-0809	The Wee Hoose	Kentt	WA	HST4
206-852-4364	Northwest PC Link	Kent	WA	CS1
206-854-5646	Northwest PC Link	Kent	WA	DS
206-854-8714	The Wee Hoose 2	Kent	WA	DS2
206-863-5877	The Racer's Edge	Sumner	WA	V32
206-869-4152	The Four Horsemen	Seattle	WA	DS2
206-869-4430	The Four Horsemen	Seattle	WA	DS2
206-878-1096	NorthWest ENTER-Tainment 1	Des Moines	WA	HST
206-882-0110	Alpine Trails Service	Bellevue	WA	ZYX
206-883-2203	Horsefeathers	Kirkland	WA	HST
206-888-9249	Sno-Valley S/W Exchange	North Bend	WA	DS
206-889-2428	East Side Chatline	Kirkland	WA	400
206-937-5800	Alki Express	Seattle	WA	HST
206-939-6337	NorthWest's Best BBS 1	Auburn	WA	V32B
206-939-6813	NorthWest's Best BBS 2	Auburn	WA	V32
206-939-7876	Racer's Edge	Sumner	WA	ZYX
206-941-3124	The Boardwalk	Auburn	WA	HST
206-943-1513	Radio Point BBS	Olympia	WA	HST
206-957-1124	Norseman Conqueror BBS	Bellevue	WA	DS2
207-325-4103	Great Northern BBS	Limestone	ME	HST
207-363-6584	Montreal Express	York	ME	HST
207-363-8774	Ocean BBS	York Beach	ME	HST
207-429-8019	N. Maine Educators	Bridgewater	ME	HST
207-439-5466	The Grove BBS	Kittery	ME	HST
207-490-3624	The Hobbit Hole	Sanford	ME	HST
207-693-3810	Nix Pix East BBS	Naples	ME	HST
207-725-8533	I-95 Hub	Topsham	ME	HST
207-727-3065	Addiction Bulletin Board	West Buxton	ME	CS1
207-727-5989	Addiction Bulletin Board	West Buxton	ME	HST4
207-773-5791	Wolf's Moon BBS	Portland	ME	HST
207-780-6567	OPUS DEI BBS	Portland	ME	V32B
207-799-2374	The Lyons Den	So Portland	ME	V32
207-799-4088	Maine PC COnnection 3	Westbrook	ME	VH
207-799-9080	GS Connection	Cape Elizabeth	ME	V32B

AC/Phone	BBS Name	City	State	Modem
207-833-6597	Dataease BBS	Harpswell	ME	VH
207-854-1015	Maine PC COnnection 2	Westbrook	ME	VH
207-854-3928	Maine PC COnnection 1	Westbrook	ME	HST
207-882-4152	The Nucleus	Wiscasset	ME	DS3
207-941-0805	The Lobster Buoy 1	Bangor	ME	V32B
207-942-7803	Bangor ROS	Bangor	ME	HST
207-945-9346	The Lobster Buoy 2	Bangor	ME	DS2
208-322-5227	Greater Boise BBS	Boise	D	HST
208-362-6068	The Idaho Root Cellar	Boise	D	HST
208-368-0644	Medieval Times BBS	Boise	D	V32
208-664-2983	The Third Millennium	Coeur d'Alene	ID	ULT4
208-667-2606	Coeur d'Alene BBS Private	Coeur d'Alene	ID	DS2
208-762-2549	Norton's Alley Private	Hayden Lake	D	V32B
208-765-0180	Coeur d'Alene BBS Public	Coeur d'Alene	ID	2400
208-772-6218	Norton's Alley Public	Hayden Lake	ID	V32B
209-225-6824	Dark Side of the Moon	Fresno	CA	DS
209-226-7162	Fresno Amiga eXchange	Fresno	CA	DS
209-239-5133	Hornets Nets	Manteca	CA	HST
209-297-8790	Stingray! II	Clovis	CA	HST
209-298-9461	Stingray!	Clovis	CA	HST
209-299-3734	Take-Two	Clovis	CA	HST
209-439-6921	West-Net 1	Fresno	CA	HST
209-477-9502	Software Silo	Stockton	CA	DS
209-551-2227	Flight Line of Dbase	Modesto	CA	HST
209-577-3081	MJC Info Net	Modesto	CA	VH
209-582-5177	Murr Barn BBS	Hanford	CA	DS
209-599-7435	TurboCity	Ripon	CA	HST
209-661-5355	West Coast Pyro Board	Madera	CA	DS
209-732-6394	Midnight Express BBS	Visalia	CA	HST
209-823-0093	Bertha Board	Manteca	CA	HST
209-823-6133	FreeAccess OnLine	Manteca	CA	HST
209-825-3103	Cross Roads	Manteca	CA	HST
209-826-1900	The Haunted Castle BBS 1	Los Banos	CA	DS
209-826-1911	The Haunted Castle BBS 2	Los Banos	CA	DS
210-672-2219	The Ranger Station	Gonzales	TX	DS3
212-289-3965	AmerIServe	New York	NY	CS1
212-371-5462	Granny's BBS	New York	NY	HST
212-397-1576	The Beginner's BBS	New York	NY	HST
212-477-7072	The Braintree Bookshelf	New York	NY	DS
212-496-7946	DataCom Software	New York	NY	HST4
212-496-8324	Aardvark BBS	New York	NY	DS2
212-579-2869	Fordham Jesuit BBS	Bronx	NY	DS
212-597-9083	Metro Area M.U.G. BBS	Bron	NY	HST
212-645-8673	Communication Specialties	New York	NY	HST
212-727-3213	AMAGINATION	New York	NY	HST
212-734-1090	ACE BBS	New York	NY	DS
212-777-8282	The File-Link BBS	Manhattan	NY	V32B
212-824-5512	Patch House	Bronx	NY	HST
212-831-4920	Boom Boom BBS	New York	NY	DS
212-842-2033	The Tardis BBS	Bronx	NY	HST
212-876-5885	AmerIServe	New York	NY	DS

AC/Phone	BBS Name	City	State	Modem
212-964-8090	NYC Fire Dept.	New York	NY	HST
212-995-0059	Manhatten Transfer	New York	NY	HST
213-223-6901	Megabytes BBS	Los Angeles	CA	V32B
213-223-9285	PhotoPro! BBS	Los Angeles	CA	DS
213-224-3925	Puppet BBS	Los Angeles	CA	V32B
213-225-5474	ThunderVolts BBS	Los Angeles	CA	V32B
213-387-5901	Little Angels PCB	Los Angeles	CA	DS2
213-484-0260	DownTown BBS v.32bis	Los Angeles	CA	V32B
213-484-0287	DownTown BBS ZyXEL	Los Angeles	CA	ZYX
213-484-0331	DownTown BBS Dual Standard	Los Angeles	CA	DS2
213-653-4077	12 Steps BBS	Los Angeles	CA	HST
213-654-7337	Charlatan's Cabin	Los Angeles	CA	DS
213-665-5332	Rediffusion	Los Angeles	CA	HST
213-666-6937	Hollywood Christian	Los Angeles	CA	HST
213-778-6450	Southside Info Exchange	Los Angeles	CA	V32B
213-779-3414	Collaboration BBS	Los Angeles	CA	32
213-874-9484	Expiring Mind	W Hollywood	CA	HST
213-933-4050	The Westside	Los Angeles	CA	400
213-935-9600	The Westside	Los Angeles	CA	ZYX
213-953-0040	THE CASTLE bbs	Los Angeles	CA	2400
213-953-0066	THE CASTLE bbs	Los Angeles	CA	V32B
213-962-1428	The Crow's Nest	Hollywood	CA	HST
213-962-2902	BSC BBS	Los Angeles	CA	DS3
214-221-8931	Mainframe Exchange	Coppell	TX	HST
214-222-2510	Amiga LANd	Dallas	TX	HST
214-231-3841	Nibbles & Bytes	Dallas	TX	HST
214-234-4952	Rabbit and Snake's BBS	Richardson	TX	V32
214-235-5288	Lunatic Fringe	Plano	TX	S3
214-235-7973	The Hitching Post	Richardson	TX	DS2
214-238-1168	Master Control	Richardson	TX	HST
214-239-7607	The Chai Way	Dallas	TX	DS
214-252-5120	The Fantasi Corner	Irving	TX	HST
214-254-4775	Attitudes	Irving	TX	HST
214-254-7664	Hambone's Opus Cop Shop	Irving	TX	TB
214-258-1832	The Interocitor	Dallas	TX	V32
214-259-3366	Modem Addicts Anonymous	Irving	TX	DS2
214-288-1537	Amiga Scope	Mesquite	TX	HST
214-307-8119	Live-Wire	Dallas	TX	DS
214-315-0420	ACCESS	Lewisville	TX	DS2
214-340-6393	Proximate Cause	Dallas	TX	HST
214-392-7312	OPUS Centerville	Richardson	TX	HST
214-394-1929	User-To-User PCBoard	Dallas	TX	HST
214-394-4837	The KoZmiK KaTHouSe	N. Dallas	TX	HST
214-394-9324	Mac Exchange	Carrollton	TX	HST
214-412-9660	Optomeyes	Rowlett	TX	HST
214-416-2162	The Diplomat	Carrollton	TX	HST
214-422-0632	Software Mechanics	Plano	TX	HST
214-423-6992	The P.I.G.	Plano	TX	DS
214-436-8753	Code 3 BBS	Lewisville	TX	DS2
214-437-0914	Verbose Ink	Richardson	TX	HST
214-437-2734	Palindrome ONLINE	Richardson	TX	HST

AC/Phone	BBS Name	City	State	Modem
214-437-2906	Fool's Errand	Dallas	TX	HST
214-437-3247	UTD Student Connection	Richardson	TX	DS2
214-458-2620	The Inns of Court	Dallas	TX	DS
214-475-3610	The County Line	Carrollton	TX	HST
214-487-9053	The Bailiwick 2	Garland	TX	DS2
214-487-9422	The Bailiwick 1	Garland	TX	DS3
214-492-5695	User To User #2	Dallas	TX	V32
214-492-6565	User To User #1	Dallas	TX	DS
214-495-5980	Shock Treatment BBS	Garland	TX	DS
214-530-5526	The Carrier Pigeon	Dallas	TX	HST
214-573-3649	The Blue Flame BBS	Dallas	TX	DS2
214-594-7911	Squirrel Talk	Irving	TX	HST
214-620-0192	HardWired	Dallas	TX	DS
214-641-1136	The Chess Board	Grand Prairie	TX	HST
214-669-2960	Turbo Opus	Dallas	TX	DS
214-680-2693	PC Help	Richardson	TX	V32
214-680-3155	Omniverse	Dallas	TX	ULT
214-771-3226	NCC-1701	Rockwall	TX	DS2
214-823-1579	JaxBBS	Dallas	TX	HST
214-867-6630	Texas Twister	Plano	TX	HST
214-881-2627	MY BBS	Plano	TX	DS
214-881-2628	MY 2nd BBS	Plano	TX	DS
214-890-0262	Llama Bob's BBS	Dallas	TX	HST
214-923-2610	Ronin BBS	Waxahachie	TX	DS3
214-938-2840	Ronin BBS	Waxahachie	TX	DS3
214-988-0124	DeadHead's	Grand Prairie	TX	DS2
214-988-1053	The Castle	Grand Prairie	TX	HST
215-237-1281	The Seeker's Place BBS	Darby	PA	HST
215-244-4640	Horse Talk BBS	Bensalem	PA	HST
215-245-5926	The Ravens Nest	Bensalem	PA	HST4
215-245-5927	The Ravens Nest	Bensalem	PA	HST4
215-255-0610	Landenberg Wildcat!	Landenberg	PA	HST
215-264-1481	The Wishing Well BBS	Catasauqua	PA	HST
215-269-1660	BusiLink (tm) USA/RBBS-PC	Downingtown	PA	HST
215-269-9729	KEYSTONE Net Exchange	Downingtown	PA	HST
215-272-6244	Farpoint Station BBS	Norristown	PA	V32
215-279-9799	Ophiophile Maximus	Blue Bell	PA	DS
215-287-7689	The 5th Dimension BBS	Chester Springs	PA	DS
215-289-6940	Philadelphia Fire Films	Philadephia	PA	V32
215-295-2625	Mother(b)Board BBS	Morrisville	PA	DS2
215-322-9193	The Datamax	Warminster	PA	DS
215-326-9774	Cruise'in City BBS	Pottstown	PA	DS2
215-331-2590	Wombat's Wagon	Philadelphia	PA	V32B
215-337-5815	GVP BBS	King of Prussia	PA	HST
215-356-1630	HYPERLINC East BBS	Philadephia	PA	DS
215-363-6625	Del Ches Systems BBS	Lionville	PA	DS3
215-368-5289	STINGRAY	Lansdale	PA	HST
215-391-8951	Planet of Magrathea	Trexlertown	PA	HST
215-425-0713	Graphics Array	Philadelphia	PA	HST
215-434-6225	The Micro Cottage BBS	Whitehall	PA	DS
215-443-5830	DSC BBS	Ivyland	PA	DS

AC/Phone	BBS Name	City	State	Modem
215-443-7390	DSC BBS	Ivyland	PA	V32B
215-443-9434	DSC BBS	Ivyland	PA	24EC
215-446-8923	The Bazaar at Deva	Upper Darby	PA	DS
215-469-6050	The Dying Planet	Elverson	PA	DS
215-493-5242	Bucks Telematics	Yardley	PA	DS
215-535-5816	Tower BBS	Philadelphia	A	HST
215-540-0141	The UnNamed BBS	Ambler	P	V32
215-540-0329	ELLIOT	SpringHouse	PA	HST
215-544-3757	Philly Gamers PCBoard	Springfield	PA	HST
215-551-1485	Tri-Star Amiga BBS	Philadelphia	PA	HST
215-567-2417	Val'Dragonsongs	Philadelphia	PA	HST
215-583-9784	COPY-CAT BBS	Folcroft	PA	DS2
215-598-8122	DREAMLINE	Wrightstown	PA	HST
215-623-6203	RunWay BBS	Lansdowne	PA	DS
215-628-0878	The Big Board	Dresher	PA	HST
215-631-0685	System-2 BBS	Norristown	PA	V32
215-635-0664	First Sighting	Elkins Park	PA	HST
215-635-2341	StarLine	Elkins Park	PA	V32
215-639-3242	SecTec	Bensalem	PA	HST
215-641-0270	U.S.S. Intrepid	Spring House	PA	HST
215-659-0711	Galileo's Grove Opus	Willow Grove	PA	DS
215-675-7850	CyBoard Lobe	Hatboro	PA	HST
215-678-9854	The File Cabinet BBS	Wyomissing	PA	DS
215-691-0491	The Locker Room	Bethlehem	PA	HST
215-721-0363	The Foxes Den	Hatfield	PA	HST
215-721-4556	DREAMLINE II	Souderton	PA	HST
215-721-7039	DREAMLINE II	Souderton	A	DS
215-725-9134	Walsh MicroSystems RBBS	Philadelphia	PA	HST
215-741-6077	Sophist. S'ware	Yardley	PA	HST
215-741-9893	The 32 Bit Bus BBS	Bensalem	PA	DS3
215-755-0166	The Batcave	Philadelphia	PA	DS
215-770-0774	Keystone Info-Net	Allentown	PA	HST
215-783-6352	NPN	King of Prussia	PA	V32B
215-785-0895	Refuge BBS	Bristol	PA	V32B
215-788-4339	The Storm Front BBS	Croydon	PA	V32B
215-788-4662	The Storm Front BBS	Croydon	PA	V32B
215-848-5728	TRS-Link BBS	Philadelphia	PA	S
215-868-0565	The Main Sequence	Bethlehem	PA	DS2
215-871-0394	Future Tech	Philadelphia	PA	HST
215-884-6122	Rydal Board	Rydal	PA	HST
215-896-9240	Kingswood TYPENET	Ardmore	PA	HST
215-922-1729	ONIX	Philadelphia	PA	HST4
215-923-8026	Cyberdrome	Philadelphia	PA	V32B
215-938-1322	Opaque Prism BBS	Huntingdon Valley	PA	DS3
215-942-3874	Threshold BBS	Honeybrook	PA	HST
215-944-6269	Schizophrenia	Fleetwood	PA	DS
215-948-7734	TFS Luckey Thirteen	Royersford	PA	HST
215-968-4998	Sophisticated Software BBS	Newtown	PA	HST
215-992-1720	ONIX	King Of Prussia	PA	32B
216-225-6130	Buggie Works	Brunswick	OH	HST
216-273-1340	Appleholic's BBS	Hinckley	OH	HST

AC/Phone	BBS Name	City	State	Modem
216-337-0133	L & L BBS	Salem	OH	HST4
216-343-7717	On-Demand!	Dover	OH	HST
216-356-1431	Nerd's Nook	Rocky River	OH	HST
216-356-1772	Nerd's Nook II	Rocky River	OH	DS2
216-356-1872	Nerd's Nook III	Rocky River	OH	HST
216-461-4639	OHIO Graphics	Cleveland	OH	V32B
216-461-5930	OHIO Graphics	Cleveland	OH	ZYX
216-461-5949	OHIO Graphics	Cleveland	OH	HST
216-494-0684	Eclectic Chair	No. Canton	OH	HST4
216-526-9480	AMCOM	Cleveland	OH	2400
216-526-9485	AMCOM	Cleveland	OH	HST
216-526-9489	AMCOM	Cleveland	OH	DS
216-526-9490	AMCOM	Cleveland	OH	DS
216-527-2186	The Odyssey BBS	Garrettsville	OH	DS2
216-529-0019	NEOPC BBS	Lakewood	OH	HST
216-544-4022	Host - State Line <HST>	Niles	OH	HST
216-545-0093	Steel Valley II	Niles	OH	HST
216-545-2318	Steel Valley	Girard	OH	DS2
216-562-1110	West Branch Connection	Aurora	OH	ZYX
216-562-1129	West Branch Connection	Aurora	OH	HST
216-593-3446	The Mad House BBS	Conneaut	OH	HST4
216-593-4438	The Mad House BBS	Conneaut	OH	DS
216-628-4860	Patriot BBS	Mogadore	OH	HST
216-637-8397	Love Board	Cortland	OH	HST
216-699-1547	Tribute Test Point	Uniontown	OH	DS2
216-752-4921	The Monstrous MAC BBS	Shaker Hts	OH	HST
216-823-6658	Night Moves	Alliance	OH	DS
216-837-9592	Massillon TeleNet	Massillon	OH	HST
216-842-5911	OHIONet Express	Cleveland	OH	HST
216-845-7948	Q$$	Parma	OH	HST
216-867-6984	The Buckeye Hamshack	Akron	OH	HST
216-928-8565	Northampton Data ConneXion	Cuyahoga Falls	OH	DS2
216-946-3161	Dr. ZING'S	Cleveland	OH	V32B
216-949-5581	Online BBS	Sheffield Lake	OH	DS
216-951-6693	Dr. ZING'S	Cleveland	OH	V32
216-969-1985	Dragons Den BBS	Ashtabula	OH	VH
216-972-6504	U of Akron	Akron	OH	HST
216-992-4774	Mystic Rhythm BBS	Ashtabula	OH	V32
217-244-6954	The Check Source	Urbana	IL	DS
217-328-6015	StageDoor	Urbana	IL	DS
217-344-7773	Lucid Dream	Urbana	IL	TB2
217-352-6168	The Workshop	Champaign	IL	HST
217-356-0278	Alliance	Champaign	IL	HST
217-359-6165	CappMail	Champaign	IL	V32
217-367-8429	The Cloud Chamber	Urbana	IL	DS2
217-384-4311	Programmer's Toolbox	Urbana	IL	DS
217-398-2800	Wolfram Research Inc	Champaign	IL	DS
217-422-2585	Computer Corner	Decatur	IL	DS
217-425-7051	Smokin' Joe's	Decatur	IL	DS
217-431-1695	The Relative Connection	Danville	IL	HST
217-643-2396	The Satellite/SDNet/Works	Thomasboro	IL	HST

AC/Phone	BBS Name	City	State	Modem
217-774-5978	Hudson Softsides BBS	Shelbyville	IL	V32B
217-789-5080	BEC BBS 1	Springfield	IL	HST
217-789-5970	BEC BBS 2	Springfield	IL	DS
217-789-5971	BEC BBS 3	Springfield	IL	V32
217-877-1138	2/3 Board	Decatur	IL	DS
218-739-2296	Latenite's at the Lake	Fergus Falls	MN	CS1
218-924-206	The Bertha BBS	Bertha	MN	DS2
218-924-2060	The Bertha BBS	Bertha	MN	DS2
219-256-2255	Radio Daze BBS Public	Mishawaka	IN	2400
219-256-2398	Radio Daze BBS Private	Mishawaka	IN	HST4
219-262-0648	The SALT BBS	Elkhart	IN	V32B
219-262-1370	After Five' BBS	Elkhart	IN	DS
219-282-1054	Michiana Computer Network	South Bend	IN	HST
219-293-6465	Beta Connection	Elkhart	IN	DS2
219-493-2193	New Files Express BBS	Fort Wayne	IN	V32
219-663-3107	The Bad Connection	Crown Point	IN	HST
219-665-8767	Dark Shadows BBS	Angola	IN	HST
219-696-3415	The Toolkit BBS	Lowell	IN	DS
219-728-9598	Hoosier Hideaway West	Decatur	IN	HST
219-736-9170	The Board-Walk	Merrillville	IN	HST
219-824-5628	The Jokerman BBS	Bluffton	IN	V32
219-882-3213	Lighthouse BBS	Gary	IN	HST
219-884-9508	The LANS BBS	Gary	IN	HST4
219-923-2377	Datacom of Highland	Highland	IN	DS2
219-925-5524	The Loft	Auburn	IN	DS
219-926-2060	Restoration Rock	Chesterton	IN	V32B
219-929-5574	Lake Effect BBS	Chesterton	IN	HST
301 645-8624	Lighthouse II	Waldorf	MD	V32B
301-206-9162	The Flying PC AT	Montpelier	MD	DS2
301-262-9650	Money Matter$ BBS	Mitchellville	MD	V32
301-283-0917	Free Spirit BBS	Suitland	MD	HST
301-424-3614	CannonFodder BBS	Rockville	MD	HST4
301-428-8998	The Addict's Attic	Germantown	MD	V32
301-460-9134	ENIAC	Rockville	MD	DS
301-490-1935	Pro-Vue RBBS	Jessup	MD	V32
301-499-0896	Corp. Press	Landover	MD	S
301-593-9323	SilverSoft Micro	Silver Spring	MD	V32
301-596-1180	The Programmer's Corner	Columbia	MD	V32
301-622-2247	Silver Bullet	Silver Spring	MD	HST
301-627-4953	Pleasure Palace	Lothian	MD	DS
301-630-2492	The Jhereg's Den	Hillcrest Hgts	MD	HST
301-654-2969	Bit Stream BBS	Chevy Chase	MD	DS
301-670-9621	3 WINKs BBS	Gaithersburg	MD	DS
301-718-4690	Europa BBS	Chevy Chase	MD	DS
301-735-8124	AFSC MCCR BBS	Andrews AFB	MD	V32
301-737-1786	John's Workshop	Lexington Park	MD	DS
301-737-1979	The Niether World	California	MD	HST
301-776-8259	Brazen's Hell! BBS	Laurel	MD	V32B
301-831-9012	Thunder Bay	Mt. Airy	MD	V32
301-863-5312	Combat Zone	Lexington Park	MD	HST
301-869-7743	LexiCom	Gaithersburg	MD	V32B

AC/Phone	BBS Name	City	State	Modem
301-894-8516	The Thieves Guild	Suitland	MD	HST
301-924-0398	Perspectives BBS	Greenbelt	MD	DS
301-935-4941	Foundation BBS	College Park	MD	HST
301-949-1927	First Due BBS	Wheaton	MD	V32B
301-995-1134	The Programmer's Corner	Columbia	MD	V32
302-322-4863	Royal Castle BBS	New Castle	DE	V32A
302-323-1604	AmigaNetwork	New Castle	DE	DS
302-324-8619	The Hotline	New Castle	DE	HST
302-328-3993	Hackers BBS	New Castle	DE	HST
302-427-8093	Eastern C Board	Wilmington	DE	HST
302-475-1572	Motherboard	Wilmington	DE	HST
302-633-4797	The Phantom II	Wilmington	DE	HST
302-645-2658	Paradox BBS	Rehoboth Beach	DE	HST4
302-645-7264	Paradox BBS	Rehoboth Beach	DE	DS
302-652-0942	The Phantom	Wilmington	DE	HST
302-678-0141	Mayhem Unlimited	Dover	DE	HST
302-678-2335	Ed's Place	Little Creek	DE	HST
302-731-1998	Black Bag BBS	Newark	DE	HST
302-738-2026	Space Station Alpha	Newark	DE	HST
302-738-6813	DelaMarPenn Opus	Newark	DE	HST
302-984-2238	Singing Bear	Wilmington	DE	HST
303-229-9719	HP-BBS (North)	Ft. Collins	CO	DS
303-237-8575	Microlink D	Denver	CO	HST
303-278-8369	Fantasy Mountain	Golden	CO	DS
303-287-8267	Phoenix's Egg	Denver	CO	HST
303-289-6864	Midrash	Denver	CO	DS
303-320-4153	Little Byte	Denver	CO	HST
303-320-4822	World Peace BBS	Denver	CO	ULT
303-322-4078	CMOS-BBS	Denver	CO	V32
303-337-0219	Right Angle BBS	Aurora	CO	V32B
303-343-4234	Information Society	Denver	CO	V32
303-343-4235	Information Society	Denver	CO	V32
303-352-5013	Christian Connection II	Greeley	CO	HST
303-360-6340	Rocky Cabin BBS	Denver	CO	HST
303-361-6965	Fort Mac	Aurora	CO	DS
303-367-9701	The Silver Hammer	Aurora	CO	DS
303-373-5370	The Love Boat BBS	Arvada	CO	HST
303-377-2371	Jaguar's Networking Labs	Denver	CO	DS
303-420-3568	L&L Support & Sysops Xchg	Arvada	CO	ULT
303-422-2149	RBase Users Group BBS	Westminster	CO	HST
303-426-0623	Mojave Net	Westminster	CO	HST
303-426-1866	TelePeople Members Only	Federal Heights	CO	HST
303-429-2208	The CyberZone	Westminster	CO	HST
303-431-1404	Mile High BBS	Arvada	CO	DS
303-431-8797	ParaNet Info Service	Arvada	CO	HST
303-433-2648	Tommy's Toys BBS	Denver	CO	V32
303-438-1120	The Cutting Board	Broomfield	CO	HST
303-443-8292	Adelante	Boulder	CO	DS
303-449-5251	OnLine Consult	Estes Park	CO	DS
303-449-7274	Chidvilas	Boulder	CO	TB
303-450-0822	The WatchDesk	Thornton	CO	HST

AC/Phone	BBS Name	City	State	Modem
303-469-4842	The Rec Room	Denver	CO	HST
303-469-7161	The Monkey Boy BBS	Broomfield	CO	HST
303-469-9359	System Support BBS	Westminster	CO	HST4
303-484-6483	The Temporal Alliance	Ft Collins	CO	DS
303-534-4311	The Comm-Post	Denver	CO	HST
303-642-0703	Pinecliffe HST/DS	Boulder	CO	DS
303-651-7745	The Eighth Dimension	Longmont	CO	V32
303-652-3595	The Dinosaur Board	Niwot	CO	DS
303-665-6091	King's Market BBS	Louisville	CO	HST
303-665-6092	King's Market 2	Louisville	CO	DS2
303-666-0304	The Circuit Board	Lafayette	CO	HST
303-671-5976	HP Haven	Englewood	CO	HST
303-678-8439	Knowledge Resource BBS	Longmont	CO	V32B
303-680-0509	The Peacock's Nest	Aurora	CO	DS2
303-752-9641	P-N-P BBS	Aurora	CO	DS2
303-758-7589	WestWind BBS	Denver	CO	HST
303-771-8107	Computer Care BBS	Littleton	CO	HST
303-777-1357	RMGC	Denver	CO	V32
303-790-4266	The Weyr	Englewood	CO	HST
303-794-5065	The Byte Shop	Littleton	CO	HST
303-797-0296	InterConnect	Littleton	CO	HST
303-831-1704	CO State Judicial BBS	Denver	CO	DS
303-840-9862	21st Century BBS	Parker	CO	DS2
303-841-9571	Rocky Mtn Info Exchange	Parker	CO	VH
303-841-9572	Rocky Mtn Info Exchange	Parker	CO	DS
303-933-0701	The Eagle's Nest	Littleton	CO	HST
303-933-2286	Boardwatch Magazine	Littleton	CO	DS
303-933-3472	The Discordian Society	Littleton	CO	HST
303-933-4087	USA Today Distribution	Littleton	CO	HST
303-935-6323	Electronic Library	Denver	CO	HST
303-936-2791	D-Link 1	Denver	CO	HST
303-945-4041	Roaring Forks	Glenwood Springs	CO	VH
303-949-3253	Master Control (NSN)	Avon	CO	VH
303-972-1222	Regency Data	Littleton	CO	ULT
303-972-6575	Dehnbase	Littleton	CO	DS
303-972-9023	Chatfield Armory BBS	Littleton	CO	HST
303-973-1002	Computer Consulting	Littleton	CO	VH
303-973-7852	SnarfQuest I	Denver	CO	DS
303-973-8554	Club Micro HST	Littleton	CO	DS
303-978-9229	Microlink B Fast 1	Denver	CO	HST
303-978-9301	Microlink B Fast 2	Denver	CO	HST
303-979-9418	The Vulcan Way	Littleton	CO	HST
304-264-0280	CASA West	Martinsburg	WV	V32B
304-296-3649	The Back Door QBBS	Morgantown	WV	DS2
304-429-6838	Secret Service	Huntington	WV	HST
304-487-3558	Fantasy Sports Central	Athens	WV	CS1
304-599-6083	The Full Spectrum	Morgantown	WV	DS2
304-728-0884	The BitBank	Charles Town	WV	VH
304-733-1338	JNS Software Support BBS	Barboursville	WV	DS
304-748-1377	The Final Frontier	Weirton	WV	HST
304-757-0530	Miskatonic University	Hurricane	WV	V32

AC/Phone	BBS Name	City	State	Modem
304-766-7807	Project Enable	Dunbar	WV	HST
304-768-5036	21st Century Connection	Dunbar	WV	DS
304-776-5037	Hillbilly Haven Christian	Cross Lane	WV	DS
305-220-8752	The Southern Cross BBS	Miami	FL	HST
305-221-1571	Ramblin' Roots	Miami	FL	HST
305-232-8000	Shareware Online	Miami	FL	DS
305-233-4196	The Library BBS	Miami	FL	DS2
305-238-6390	The Weatherman BBS	Miami	FL	DS2
305-238-8851	S.T.A.R. BBS	Miami	FL	HST
305-245-7601	Backpacker's Wilderness	Homestead	FL	HST
305-247-1305	TURBO-Soft	Homestead	FL	HST
305-251-2698	CAP-BBS	Miami	FL	HST
305-271-2146	Kendall BBS	Miami	FL	HST
305-321-8168	PipeLine BBS	Plantation	FL	HST
305-341-6919	Doorway BBS	Coral Springs	FL	HST
305-370-3528	The Catwalk BBS	Davie	FL	HST
305-378-1307	The Devil's Place BBS	Miami	FL	HST
305-378-2571	Metro Data Group BBS	Miami	FL	DS2
305-384-0970	Freddy's Funland	Sunrise	FL	HST
305-384-9566	2032	Fort Lauderdale	FL	DS
305-386-9130	The Black Hole BBS	Miami	FL	HST
305-388-3858	Whatnow BBS	Miami	FL	HST
305-425-4304	Rock'n Roll Harbour	Deerfield	FL	V32
305-432-2223	Sunshine PCBoard	Pembroke Pines	FL	HST
305-432-8210	Bitsy's Place	Pembroke Pines	FL	HST
305-436-1085	The InterZone Cafe	Pembroke Pines	FL	HST
305-436-5070	Data Center BBS	Pembroke Pines	FL	V32B
305-437-1284	CYGNUS	Pembroke Pines	FL	HST
305-444-5615	Coral Gables MEDTERM	Coral Gables	FL	DS2
305-467-6712	Nightmare BBS	Fort Lauderdale	FL	DS2
305-474-6429	Silicon Beach BBS	Fort Lauderdale	FL	DS
305-474-6560	Data Center BBS	Plantation	FL	V32B
305-480-6758	The InnerSight Connection	Deerfield Beach	FL	HST
305-523-1717	The DrawBridge	Fort Lauderdale	FL	DS
305-551-5868	The REDMAN BBS	Miami	FL	HST
305-554-1114	The Boardwalk	Miami	FL	HST
305-559-4018	The Sanctum BBS	Miami	FL	HST
305-581-1248	The Unknown	Fort Lauderdale	FL	DS2
305-598-3785	Micro-Link	Miami	FL	HST
305-599-3004	The USA	Miami	FL	HST
305-621-0103	AMS Support	Miami	FL	DS2
305-624-6631	Home of the 135 NEC	Miami	FL	DS2
305-628-3455	BBS1-PC!	Miami	FL	HST
305-642-0754	The Software Cuisine	Miami	FL	V32B
305-720-3307	Unique Connections	Tamarac	FL	DS
305-722-8037	The Pelican's Roost	Fort Lauderdale	FL	V32
305-733-8930	Scipes BBS!	Fort Lauderdale	FL	HST
305-754-5477	Town Crier	Miami Shores	FL	HST
305-755-0127	Waves in the Cesspool	Coral Springs	FL	V32B
305-757-4108	DevPalMiami	Miami	FL	HST
305-763-7743	Fluid Power BBS	Fort Lauderdale	FL	HST

AC/Phone	BBS Name	City	State	Modem
305-785-9596	CrossFire BBS	Pompano Beach	FL	HST
305-822-4673	Miami Infomatics	Hialeah	FL	HST
305-827-3702	The CORE BBS	Hialeah	FL	HST
305-828-7909	Telcom Central	Miami Lakes	FL	HST
305-944-6271	The Jailhouse	North Miami	FL	HST
305-948-4382	The Firehouse BBS	North Miami	FL	HST
305-961-6916	Bits and Pieces	Hollywood	FL	HST
305-964-1896	PROMEON	Hollywood	FL	DS
305-964-7267	The Hughes Network	Hollywood	FL	HST
305-971-6118	The TiTanic BBS	Margate	FL	HST
305-978-0556	Station Tender BBS	Coconut Creek	FL	HST
305-979-2073	The Branch Office	Pompano Beach	FL	DS2
305-981-9927	MASH 4077	Hollywood	FL	HST
305-985-9605	Lost in Space BBS	Miramar	FL	HST
305-987-7873	Midnight BBS	Pembroke Pines	FL	HST
307-472-3615	Oregon Trail Crossroads	Casper	WY	ULT
307-635-8366	International Computer BBS	Cheyenne	WY	HST
307-638-1917	Cowboy Country RAS	Cheyenne	WY	HST
307-686-0940	Black Diamond BBS	Gillette	WY	DS
308-487-5505	Panhandle Connection	Hemingford	NE	HST
309-346-2074	Treasure Island BBS	Pekin	IL	HST
309-452-2838	Adventurer's Corner	Normal	IL	DS
309-662-2017	Desktop Micro's BBS	Bloomington	IL	DS2
309-663-8354	Midwest InforNetwork	Bloomington	IL	DS2
309-672-4405	Hacker's World BBS	Peoria	IL	HST
309-676-0360	The Bavarian BBS	Peoria	IL	HST
309-688-7713	The Data Stream BBS	Peoria	IL	HST
309-691-5416	Buzzard's Roost	Peoria	IL	DS
309-694-7725	EPE Onlin	East Peoria	IL	DS
309-755-8409	Quad City Amiga Forum	Moline	IL	V32
309-786-9518	The Ancient Mariner	Rock Island	IL	V32
309-788-1956	The DangerZone!! BBS	Rock Island	IL	HST
309-788-2029	The Danger Zone	Rock Island	IL	HST
309-788-9811	The Genealogy Workshop	Rock Island	IL	V32
309-828-6941	Prairie BBS	Bloomington	IL	DS
310-204-3249	The I.B.S.A. BBS	Los Angeles	CA	DS3
310-204-6155	Camelot Private	Culver City	CA	DS
310-204-6158	Camelot Public	Culver City	CA	V32B
310-207-0568	Quantum Connection	Pacific Palisades	CA	ULT
310-212-3472	Sabre Mail	Torrance	CA	HST
310-306-5134	Skeleton Crew BBS 1	Venice	CA	V32B
310-306-9775	Skeleton Crew BBS 2	Venice	CA	V32B
310-370-3452	Cyberdyne Software	.....	CA	HST
310-370-4113	Long Island RBBS	Los Angeles	CA	HST
310-370-5832	Cyberdyne Software	.....	CA	HST
310-371-1803	Source BBS Subscription	Torrance	CA	DS3
310-371-1870	CrossLinked FAT	Redondo Beach	CA	HST
310-371-3737	Source BBS Public	Torrance	CA	DS2
310-372-4800	Manhattan Transfer	Manhattan Beach	CA	HST
310-376-2150	Kirks BBS	Hermosa Beach	CA	DS
310-376-9567	Beach Cities RBBS	Redondo Beach	CA	HST

AC/Phone	BBS Name	City	State	Modem
310-391-1351	MicroSource	Mar Vista	CA	HST
310-391-5302	The Mac Zone BBS	Los Angeles	CA	DS
310-391-7372	The Batchelor Pad	Mar Vista	CA	V32B
310-404-9116	The TOWER BBS	Norwalk	CA	HST
310-419-0931	PC Workshop	Inglewood	CA	HST
310-421-4788	Paradise Cove BBS	Long Beach	CA	DS
310-430-0079	Ground Zero	Seal Beach	CA	DS
310-434-0401	The Q Continuum BBS	Long Beach	CA	HST
310-452-3374	The Xchange	Los Angeles	CA	V32
310-459-6053	DPS #1	Pacific Palisades	CA	ULT4
310-459-6846	DPS #2	Pacific Palisades	CA	DS
310-459-8220	DPS #3	Pacific Palisades	CA	DS
310-474-8309	Topology System Service	West Los Angeles	CA	DS
310-498-6346	The French Flyer BBS	Long Beach	CA	DS
310-518-9524	MASATEK	Torrance	CA	DS
310-532-0278	Specta Graphix BBS	Carson	CA	V32B
310-542-0350	Source BBS Private	Torrance	CA	DS
310-545-5146	Ursa Major BBS	Manhattan Beach	CA	2400
310-545-7216	Ursa Major BBS	Manhattan Beach	CA	DS
310-549-9640	Mac-HACers BBS	Carson	CA	HST
310-559-5333	West Los Angeles BBS Pvt	Los Angeles	CA	DS2
310-559-5334	West Los Angeles BBS Pvt	Los Angeles	CA	V32B
310-595-1488	Sense/Ne	Long Beach	CA	HST
310-597-2235	The French Flyer BBS	Long Beach	CA	DS
310-630-7090	Equiping The Saints	Lakewood	CA	DS
310-634-4885	SoCalNet EC	Los Angeles	CA	HST
310-634-8993	Target Range BBS	Paramount	CA	HST
310-676-2219	The Great Escape Private	Gardena	CA	DS3
310-676-3534	The Great Escape Public	Gardena	CA	DS2
310-676-4282	The Great Escape Private	Gardena	CA	DS3
310-677-4007	RoofTop! Connection	Inglewood	CA	V32
310-677-4389	RoofTop! Connection	Inglewood	CA	V32
310-806-2226	The Downey BBS	Downey	CA	V32
310-822-6729	StormGate Aerie	Los Angeles	CA	HST
310-827-8171	L.A. Computer Society BBS	Los Angeles	CA	V32T
310-838-9229	West Los Angeles BBS Pub	Los Angeles	CA	V32B
310-859-2453	Sleepy Hollow #2 Private	Los Angeles	CA	DS
310-859-2454	Sleepy Hollow #3 Private	Los Angeles	CA	HST4
310-859-9334	Sleepy Hollow #1 Public	Los Angeles	CA	2400
310-920-3631	The MegaByte System	Bellflower	CA	DS
310-927-8352	Arco Products BBS	South Gate	CA	DS3
312-225-9711	The Bog	Chicago	IL	HST
312-275-1785	20/20 TBBS	Chicago	IL	DS
312-342-0015	BBS-Chicago][	Chicago	IL	HST
312-376-9872	The PUB	Chicago	IL	DS
312-561-6140	Anonymous Wonder BBS	Chicago	IL	HST
312-581-1111	Village Adult BBS	Chicago	IL	V32
312-583-1674	JBS-BBS	Chicago	IL	V32B
312-594-0643	The Power Palace	Chicago	IL	V32B
312-631-2172	Equinox BBS System	Chicago	IL	DS2
312-661-1740	LawMug RBBS	Chicago	IL	HST

AC/Phone	BBS Name	City	State	Modem
312-665-7319	Home Again	Chicago	IL	V32B
312-685-1136	Silent Circle BBS	Chicago	IL	DS
312-736-7526	Innovations BBS	Chicago	IL	DS
312-743-6116	Krishna Yoga Foundation	Chicago	IL	HST
312-767-5787	The PUB DTP BBS	Chicago	IL	DS
312-871-8426	ALTERNET BBS	Chicago	IL	V32B
312-935-6809	BIT WIZ Opus	Chicago	IL	DS3
312-973-0428	The Chicago Mensa BBS	Chicago	IL	HST
313-228-7383	Glass City BBS	Mt Clemens	MI	CS1
313-232-1905	The Ultimate Connection	Flint	MI	HST
313-232-7815	Flight of the Raven	Flint	MI	DS
313-242-3612	Computer Alley BBS	Monroe	MI	HST
313-243-0944	Fast Eddie's BBS	Monroe	MI	HST
313-247-0094	The Tool Box	Utica	MI	HST
313-247-1838	North Sterling BBS	Sterling Hts	MI	HST
313-264-7051	The Dart Board	Sterling Hts	MI	DS
313-268-0028	NIGHT Gallery II	Sterling Hts	MI	DS2
313-332-3625	Altair Business Systems	Pontiac	MI	DS
313-338-4482	North Pole	Pontiac	MI	HST
313-364-5157	HomePlate BBS	Marysville	MI	DS2
313-381-2931	The Nut House	Taylor	MI	HST
313-385-9969	The Land of Nul	Port Huron	MI	HST
313-391-6856	Les's Place The Mansion	Lake Orion	MI	HST
313-398-3078	Atari Advocate	Madison Heights	MI	DS
313-421-3254	The Abyss BBS	Livonia	MI	DS
313-427-0223	Suburban Computer ConnXion	Garden City	MI	HST
313-427-4727	Paradise City BBS	Garden City	MI	HST
313-429-2150	The Falcon's Lair	Saline	MI	DS2
313-435-5766	Son of The Royal Joke	Royal Oak	MI	TB2
313-435-7556	The Royal Joke	Royal Oak	MI	DS
313-482-4388	Wyld Stallyns	Ypsilanti	MI	HST
313-482-4436	SomeWare In Time	Ypsilanti	MI	HST
313-483-1359	Builders Workshop	Ypsilanti	MI	HST
313-521-0330	Facillium	Detroit	MI	DS
313-537-2520	One Way Christian BBS	Redford	MI	HST
313-542-9615	LAN Solutions BBS II	Ferndale	MI	HST
313-543-2911	TRILOGY II	Hazel Park	MI	HST
313-545-1931	LAN Solutions BBS I	Ferndale	MI	HST
313-548-2159	TRILOGY I	Hazel Park	MI	HST
313-548-3889	TRILOGY]I[	Hazel Park	MI	HST
313-553-9274	Milliways I	Farmington Hills	MI	HST
313-558-7689	Technician's Corner	Center Line	MI	HST
313-563-1390	Nightmare	Dearborn	MI	HST
313-582-6671	CRIMP BBS	Dearborn	MI	HST
313-584-1253	The Edge of Sanity	Dearborn	MI	V32
313-588-3487	Mike's TAG/TAGMAIL	Madison Hts	MI	HST
313-626-9006	Graffiti Bridge BBS	Birmingham	MI	HST
313-629-6967	The TigerPaw BBS	Linden	MI	HST
313-646-5632	Death Vale BBS	Birmingham	MI	HST
313-651-4009	The Blind Ambition BBS	Rochester	MI	HST
313-658-1110	The Shark's Mouth	Flint	MI	HST

AC/Phone	BBS Name	City	State	Modem
313-665-2832	The Programmer's Pit Stop	Ann Arbor	MI	TB2
313-685-3313	Charlie's Roost	Milford	MI	HST
313-689-1657	The OZoNE BBS	Troy	MI	HST
313-739-1193	UtiCom	Utica	MI	HST
313-754-1131	Tony's Corner	Warren	MI	HST
313-769-6346	Valhalla	Ann Arbor	MI	DS2
313-773-6959	East Detroit Amiga	East Detroit	MI	HST
313-775-6097	The Crash Landing	Roseville	MI	DS
313-776-6082	Grand Central Station	Roseville	MI	HST
313-776-8928	Electric Eye][BBS	Roseville	MI	HST
313-795-0523	Horizons BBS	Sterling Hts	MI	DS
313-826-9411	Firebox Express 1	Sterling Heights	MI	DS3
313-826-9412	Firebox Express 2	Sterling Heights	MI	DS3
313-836-8275	CALnet @node.1	Detroit	MI	V32B
313-854-5600	Russ's Corner	Temperance	MI	HST
313-879-2318	ARTHUR	Troy	MI	HST
313-879-7387	The Black Hole	Troy	MI	HST
313-886-7756	The Foxgate BBS	GrossePointe Wood	MI	HST
313-972-1446	The Christian Crossroads	Detroit	MI	HST
313-977-5880	Access Denied BBS	Sterling Hts	MI	DS
314-227-6885	Messianic Jewish CN1	St. Louis	MO	DS
314-281-4362	The HARTZ Foundation	St. Peters	MO	V32
314-334-6576	The 'In My Room' BBS	Cape Girardeau	MO	HST
314-343-9736	DataCentral BBS	Fenton	MO	V32
314-434-3470	The B.S. Box	St. Louis	MO	HST
314-434-4873	Angel Station	St. Louis	MO	HST
314-436-0120	ISCBBS	St. Louis	MO	DS
314-443-2668	The Bios BBS	Columbia	MO	HST
314-521-8290	Flight Control	St. Louis	MO	HST
314-537-9238	The Banana Republic BBS	Chesterfield	MO	DS
314-553-4086	HELITOW(A)	St. Louis	MO	TB
314-553-6068	Optometry OnLine	St. Louis	MO	HST
314-581-6717	The Bearly Bored	Mexico	MO	HST
314-625-4045	Travel Online	Lake St. Louis	MO	ULT
314-635-7588	Night Shift	Jefferson City	MO	HST
314-636-7375	Chris Byrd Software	Jefferson City	MO	HST
314-774-2736	Waynesville BBS	Waynesville	MO	DS
314-774-5327	Writer's Biz BBS	Waynesville	MO	V32B
314-774-5957	EightUp! BBS	Waynesville	MO	HST
314-831-7469	The Wallstreet Raiders BBS	St. Louis	MO	HST
314-843-0001	EMC/80	St. Louis	MO	DS
314-869-9330	The Countryside BBS	St. Louis	MO	HST
314-893-9166	Fun City USA	Jefferson City	MO	HST
314-896-5393	Summit Forum BBS	Holts Summit	MO	DS
314-897-2178	The GENESIS Project	Bonnots Mills	MO	HST
314-928-7262	QwikCom	St. Charles	MO	DS
314-928-9228	First Capitol BBS	St. Peters	MO	HST
314-941-3672	KnightsOfTheSquareTableBBS	Wentzville	MO	HST4
314-941-9151	Knights Square Table	Wentzville	MO	HST
314-961-2246	Reach-Out BBS	St. Louis	MO	HST
314-965-1385	Cheswick's	St. Louis	MO	DS

AC/Phone	*BBS Name*	*City*	*State*	*Modem*
314-965-5296	Cheswick's BBS	St. Louis	MO	DS
314-973-4073	Travel Online	St. Louis	MO	ULT
315-245-0510	Kadet PCBoard	Camden	NY	DS
315-245-3815	Kadet PCBoard	Camden	NY	DS
315-331-1556	T.O.I.L. BBS	Newark	NY	DS
315-337-4093	BrookSide Trader	Rome	NY	HST
315-339-6713	Odies PCBoard	Rome	NY	DS2
315-353-4565	Norkids BBS	Norwood	NY	HST
315-393-6504	The Second Foundation	Ogdensburg	NY	HST
315-451-5088	The Bassett BBS	Liverpool	NY	HST
315-458-8602	Rivendell TAP/NA	Syracuse	NY	DS2
315-492-8765	Digital Visions	Syracuse	NY	HST
315-592-7300	Late Night BBS	Hannibal	NY	DS
315-593-1589	Backstreet BBS	Fulton	NY	DS
315-597-3439	Scolasticom	Palmyra	NY	DS
315-598-8106	Gary's BBS	Fulton	NY	HST
315-652-5367	Central Station BBS	Liverpool	NY	HST
315-673-4894	Shockwave Rider	Marcellus	NY	DS2
315-695-4070	Phoenix High School	Phoenix	NY	HST
315-695-4436	Galaxia!	Phoenix	NY	HST
316-684-3010	MGBBS	Wichita	KS	HST
316-686-0870	Flatlands BBS	Wichita	KS	HST
316-687-0719	InformationLink	Wichita	KS	HST4
316-689-3779	TWSU BBS	Wichita	KS	DS
316-689-3890	TWSU BBS	Wichita	KS	V32
316-721-0581	Night Flight	Wichita	KS	HST
316-721-3773	Midwest Info Exchange	Wichita	KS	HST4
316-788-1907	The GraveYard BBS	Derby	KS	V32B
316-943-6030	Wichita BBS	Wichita	KS	HST
317-251-8063	The Twin Towers	Indianapolis	IN	HST
317-253-1573	Portable Hole BBS	Indianapolis	IN	HST
317-257-5882	INDY PC BBS	Indianapolis	IN	DS
317-284-0796	Muncie MicroLink	Muncie	IN	HST
317-353-2973	The Paladen BBS	Indianapolis	IN	HST
317-353-9981	Someplace BBS	Indianapolis	IN	HST
317-447-9653	Napierville File Exchange	Laffayette	IN	DS2
317-457-5957	Sudden Impact	Kokomo	IN	V32B
317-535-9097	The SouthSide BBS	New Whiteland	IN	HST
317-547-6204	Media Net ProLine	Indianapolis	IN	HST
317-644-3039	The I.O. Board	Anderson	IN	DS2
317-784-8401	User Friendly BBS	Indianapolis	IN	V32B
317-831-1827	Handy Magazine BBS	Bethany Pk	IN	HST
317-848-1701	OPUS Pocus	Indianapolis	IN	HST
317-849-4007	IndyServe	Fishers	IN	DS
317-881-2743	The Motherboard	Greenwood	IN	HST
317-889-6669	RCS BBS	Greenwood	IN	HST
317-895-0976	The CTS BBS	Indianapolis	IN	HST
318-222-3455	The Pit	Shreveport	LA	V32
318-235-3207	CajuNet	Lafayette	LA	DS
318-345-0334	Direct Online System	Monroe	LA	DS
318-367-9916	BINAN	New Iberia	LA	HST

AC/Phone	BBS Name	City	State	Modem
318-424-9260	Dan's Den	Shreveport	LA	HST
318-436-2992	Duffey's Tavern MJCNA#21	Lake Charles	LA	DS
318-436-5219	Micro Link	Westlake	LA	HST
318-527-0238	Maiden Voyage	Sulphur	LA	HST
318-537-3620	Fort Polk Info Board	Fort Polk	LA	HST
318-797-8310	Dawn Patrol	Shreveport	LA	HST
318-981-3373	The Lawboard	Lafayette	LA	DS2
318-988-1404	The Twilight Zone	Lafayette	LA	DS2
319-277-1484	Trader's Paradise	Cedar Falls	IA	HST
319-335-6409	ISCA	Iowa City	IA	V32
319-337-6723	The Computer Plumber	Iowa City	IA	HST
319-337-9878	Icarus	Iowa City	IA	DS
319-377-9257	WB9MCJ BBS	Cedar Rapids	IA	HST
319-393-4588	Cedar Valley DataNet	Cedar Rapids	IA	HST
319-556-4536	Tri-State Data Exchange	Dubuque	IA	HST
319-752-0953	Catfish Bend BB	Burlington	IA	HST
401-351-0719	The Prometheus System	Providence	RI	HST
401-421-9614	ACME BBS	Providence	RI	DS
401-539-8636	The Information Resource	Carolina	RI	DS2
401-725-7863	The Bloom Beacon	Pawtucket	RI	DS2
401-822-3060	ImageNet BBS	Coventry	RI	DS
402-291-2896	The Atomic Dustbin	Omaha	NE	DS
402-292-1360	EDGE	Bellevue	NE	V32
402-593-1192	The Inns Of Court	Papillion	NE	V32
404-228-7524	Sharp's Corner	Griffin	GA	DS
404-256-9525	Sunrise-80 BBS	Atlanta	GA	DS
404-279-8936	NASPA Systems SE	Norcross	GA	VH
404-292-7797	White Wolf Connect	Atlanta	GA	V32B
404-296-6038	The Swamp	Stone Mountain	GA	HST
404-296-9681	Centurion	Atlanta	GA	HST
404-327-3450	AMI-GeorgiA BBS	Columbus	GA	HST
404-351-2975	Swizzle Stick	Atlanta	GA	DS2
404-354-0817	Athens IBM-PC Users Group	Athens	GA	HST
404-355-5625	Visions	Atlanta	GA	HST
404-368-1652	Southern Comfort	Norcross	GA	VH
404-381-0430	Astralite	Norcross	GA	V32
404-429-1714	Mainframe Exchange	Marietta	GA	HST
404-443-0366	H.A.B.I.T.S.	Marietta	GA	DS
404-446-1252	Mortgage Network	Norcross	GA	V32
404-454-8795	Byte Flight BBS	Atlanta	GA	HST
404-466-3994	The Eagle Line	Loganville	GA	V32B
404-471-1549	Information Overload	Riverdale	GA	HST
404-487-5329	Midnight Madness	Peachtree City	GA	HST
404-499-2532	Great British Take-Away	Marietta	GA	VH
404-509-7813	The Base BBS	Marietta	GA	V32B
404-532-1978	Ed's Place	Gainesville	GA	DS2
404-535-1754	Living Water BBS	Gainesville	GA	HST
404-548-0130	Classic City #2	Athens	GA	HST
404-548-0726	Classic City #1	Athens	GA	DS
404-561-6106	BackWoods BBS	Upatoi	GA	HST
404-569-9651	PC Valley Remote BBS	Columbus	GA	HST

AC/Phone	BBS Name	City	State	Modem
404-636-2136	Hangar 15	Atlanta	GA	ULT
404-664-1075	Star Trek Atlanta	Atlanta	GA	HST
404-671-1024	Galaxy Info System (GIS)	Atlanta	GA	V32
404-685-1455	Adult Fun Castle BBS	Ft. Benning	GA	HST
404-687-7309	Columbus Connection	Columbus	GA	DS
404-705-9104	Sunrise-80	Atlanta	GA	2400
404-717-7835	Software Dimensions	Lawrenceville	GA	ULT
404-739-1216	Bear Cat BBS	Atlanta	GA	V32B
404-742-7736	Express Line BBS 2	Winterville	GA	DS2
404-742-8313	Express Line BBS 1	Winterville	GA	DS2
404-749-0680	MPC BBS	Cedartown	GA	DS3
404-769-0318	Route 66 BBS	Bogart	GA	HST
404-790-0671	The Lion's Den	Augusta	GA	HST
404-793-8619	Wizard's Workshop	Augusta	GA	DS2
404-796-2867	The Final Assault	Augusta	GA	HST
404-798-3864	The Beehive RBBS	Hephzibah	GA	DS
404-860-0367	CannonFodder	Martinez	GA	HST
404-863-3450	Soldier's Bored	Augusta	GA	DS
404-869-3410	Phoenix StarFighter BBS	Lula	GA	HST
404-879-1600	R.'s Little BBS	Stone Mountain	GA	V32
404-881-8319	Our House BBS	Atlanta	GA	V32
404-907-4361	Abject Poverty BBS	Riverdale	GA	V32B
404-920-0621	Total Recall BBS	Douglasville	GA	V32
404-921-1186	The Data Dimension	Norcross	GA	HST4
404-923-0792	CyberSpace Nexus	Norcross	GA	HST
404-924-3987	INDEX	Woodstock	GA	ULT
404-924-8414	INDEX Line 2	Woodstock	GA	ULT
404-924-8472	INDEX System	Woodstock	GA	DS
404-926-0905	Woodstock BBS 1	Woodstock	GA	HST4
404-926-1043	Woodstock BBS 2	Woodstock	GA	DS
404-929-1291	Atlanta Connection	Conyers	GA	HST
404-933-9253	Digital Wasteland	Atlanta	GA	DS
404-939-1158	Atlanta Info Systems 2	Atlanta	GA	V32
404-939-1248	Atlanta Info Systems 1	Atlanta	GA	V32B
404-955-6715	Programmer's Connection	Marietta	GA	HST
404-957-8115	Connect One	Stockbridge	GA	HST4
404-965-7836	Lunar Photon	Ringgold	GA	DS
404-975-7176	U.H.F. BBS	Acworth	GA	V32
404-978-6736	Android BBS 1	Snellville	GA	2400
404-978-9636	Android BBS 2	Snellville	GA	V32B
404-987-3972	Bare Bones	Decatur	GA	HST
404-993-2316	Paul's Place	Atlanta	GA	HST
404-994-9714	Abject Poverty BBS	Riverdale	GA	CS1
404-996-9957	Abject Poverty BBS	Riverdale	GA	DS
405-243-3200	PC-Oklahoma	Elk City	OK	DS
405-248-9884	DarkStar	Lawton	OK	DS2
405-277-3603	LATTICE	Luther	OK	HST
405-321-0642	The Family Tree	Norman	OK	HST
405-325-6128	The O.U. BBS	Norman	OK	DS
405-329-4262	The Family Roots	Norman	OK	HST
405-354-1986	TurboLink West	Yukon	OK	HST

AC/Phone	BBS Name	City	State	Modem
405-354-6024	ModemLink BBS	Yukon	OK	DS
405-357-2473	Bink's Barn	Lawton	OK	HST
405-360-4391	The 49'er	Norman	OK	DS
405-360-9622	ORPA	Norman	OK	HST
405-366-1449	Seeing Impaired Technology	Norman	OK	HST
405-376-0905	TallBoy's BBS	Mustang	OK	HST
405-391-3865	Teleco USA TBBS	McLoud	OK	V32B
405-477-0920	Dueling Dragons Inn	Altus	OK	HST
405-478-1144	M.I.S.E.	Edmond	OK	HST
405-482-2536	Majik Shoppe BBS	Altus	OK	DS
405-624-0301	Amiga Frontier 1	Stillwater	OK	DS
405-670-1100	Will's House	Oklahoma City	OK	HST
405-672-0326	Sagittarius I	Midwest City	OK	HST
405-672-3973	Mach 3+ BBS	Oklahoma City	OK	HST
405-685-4688	OmegaCom	Oklahoma City	OK	HST
405-686-0458	OKCCC BBS	Oklahoma City	OK	HST
405-691-3437	The Recovery BBS	Oklahoma City	OK	HST
405-737-7565	Torii Station	Midwest City	OK	HST
405-751-8096	The CD-ROM Electronic News	Oklahoma City	OK	HST
405-765-0167	The Aztec BBS	Ponca City	OK	DS2
405-765-0951	The WordShop	Ponca City	OK	HST
405-799-2043	Moore's Pro System 1	Moore	OK	HST
405-842-4766	Yellow Stone BBS	Oklahoma City	OK	DS
405-842-6831	Yellow Stone II BBS	Oklahoma City	OK	HST
405-843-3545	Fort Knox Fido	Oklahoma City	OK	HST
405-843-5002	American Fido	Oklahoma City	OK	HST
405-943-8638	Okie Mavenware	Oklahoma City	OK	HST
405-946-5222	The Nineteenth Hole	Oklahoma City	OK	HST
405-946-6279	Engineering HQ	Oklahoma City	OK	HST
406-232-0046	Signal Butte BBS	Miles City	MT	DS3
406-257-5432	PC-Mania!	Kalispell	MT	DS
406-423-5433	The Russell Country BBS	Hobson	MT	DS
406-543-4978	The Joyous Occasion	Missoula	MT	V32B
406-549-1318	BikeNet	Missoula	MT	HST
406-721-6647	Micha U.S. Computers	Missoula	MT	DS
406-756-8296	MO's Back Door	Kalispell	MT	HST
407-239-4213	The Simpsons House	Orlando	FL	DS
407-269-2169	Space Coast BBS	Titusville	FL	DS2
407-269-5188	TechTalk	Titusville	FL	DS
407-292-3211	Debbie's Couch BBS	Orlando	FL	HST4
407-330-7002	Village BBS	Sanford	FL	HST
407-365-9809	The Listening Post	Oviedo	FL	DS
407-366-3335	Online X-press	Orlando	FL	DS3
407-380-0204	Thunderdome QuickBBS	Orlando	FL	HST
407-380-1093	Micro-Tech Solutions	Orlando	FL	HST
407-380-6446	NCC-1701	Orlando	FL	HST
407-380-7680	The Generic BBS	Orlando	FL	HST
407-383-1372	Rights On!	Titusville	FL	DS2
407-383-9372	The Bear's Cave	Titusville	FL	DS
407-383-9820	StarShip Enterprise	Titusville	FL	DS2
407-394-5308	S.A.R.C.A.S.M. BBS	Boca Raton	FL	HST

AC/Phone	BBS Name	City	State	Modem
407-439-0341	The FireHouse BBS	Lake Worth	FL	HST
407-454-3779	Electric Island BBS	Merritt Island	FL	HST
407-483-1097	The Twilight Zone	Boca Raton	FL	HST
407-496-7468	Brave New World	Delray Beach	FL	DS
407-521-9886	The Caverns EBBS	Orlando	FL	DS
407-571-1354	Robert's Roost	Fellsmere	FL	HST
407-574-9246	Deltona Lakes BBS	Deltona	FL	HST
407-575-3853	Jupiter BBS	Jupiter	FL	V32B
407-624-5998	Cecil's Nite Owl	Palm Beach Garden	FL	DS
407-639-9123	Programmers World	Cocoa	FL	DS2
407-644-9712	The Abyss	Winter Park	FL	DS
407-645-4929	Cornucopia TBBS	Winter Park	FL	HST
407-649-4136	Gourmet Delight	Orlando	FL	HST
407-649-9834	Electronic Arts BBS	Orlando	FL	DS
407-671-0464	CDS Computers	Orlando	FL	HST
407-679-6238	Big Blue	Orlando	FL	DS
407-682-2018	The Business	Altamonte	FL	DS
407-682-3132	The Door BBS	Altamonte Springs	FL	DS2
407-682-3417	The Graphic Approach	Longwood	FL	HST
407-694-1008	The Court of Last Resort	Palm Beach Garden	FL	DS
407-699-6613	Black Cauldron	Winter Springs	FL	HST
407-773-0831	The SaddleBag BBS	Satellite Beach	L	DS
407-777-1114	The Palace BBS	Satellite Beach	FL	HST
407-778-4834	Ghostcomm BBS	Vero Beach	FL	HST
407-783-2338	The Rapture Connection	Satellite Beach	FL	HST
407-788-8178	The Love Connection BBS II	Longwood	FL	DS
407-788-8552	The Q Continuum BBS	Altamonte Springs	FL	HST
407-791-2474	The Telephone Exchange	Royal Palm Beach	FL	ZYX9
407-831-1613	The Twilight Zone BBS	Longwood	FL	HST
407-831-2359	Ultimate S/W Tech Support	Orlando	FL	DS
407-832-8971	Trojan Express II	West Palm Beach	FL	DS
407-834-6466	FABulous BBS	Orlando	FL	DS
407-862-9040	The Data Bus	Orlando	FL	HST
407-878-9800	The Dragon's Lair	Port St Lucie	FL	V32
407-880-4598	The DataExchange	Orlando	FL	DS
407-880-4968	TopRock BBS	Apopka	FL	V32
407-894-9641	The Lone Wolf	Orlando	FL	DS
407-896-0494	The Digital Connection	Orlando	FL	HST
407-951-4031	Microtech BBS	Indialantic	FL	HST
407-951-7681	The Space Coast BBS	Palm Bay	FL	HST
407-964-8450	Econo-SOFTS BBS	Lake Worth	FL	HST
407-994-3690	PC-Emporium	Boca Raton	FL	DS
408-226-1052	The Haunted Castle	San Jose	CA	DS2
408-227-1583	Mike's 'Dis iz Dis' BBS	San Jose	CA	DS
408-229-0706	The Village	San Jose	CA	DS
408-229-0709	The Village	San Jose	CA	HST
408-244-0813	Excalibur!	Santa Clara	CA	HST
408-244-4250	The Rocking Chair	San Jose	CA	HST
408-246-7002	Silicon Valley BBS	San Jose	CA	V32B
408-246-7854	Crumal's Dimension	Santa Clara	CA	HST
408-247-1717	The Micro Foundry	San Jose	CA	DS2

AC/Phone	BBS Name	City	State	Modem
408-248-9213	Club Zen	Santa Clara	CA	HST
408-248-9704	Carl's DV Corner	San Jose	CA	HST
408-249-7916	The Realm of Wonder	Sunnyvale	CA	VH
408-253-3926	MacDaze	Cupertino	CA	HST
408-257-9606	Fido's Kennel	Cupertino	CA	DS
408-259-2223	ASM-Lang & CFS Board	San Jose	CA	HST
408-266-3490	Collinwood	San Jose	CA	TB2
408-270-2678	The Falcon BBS	San Jose	CA	V32B
408-294-3065	The Flying Dutchman BBS	San Jose	CA	V32B
408-298-2740	American PECS HQ	Sunnyvale	CA	HST
408-338-6860	House of Ill Compute	Boulder Creek	CA	HST
408-370-3139	Award Software's BBS	Campbell	CA	HST
408-395-1402	Saratoga Clone	Saratoga	CA	HST
408-432-3424	The Next Generation	San Jose	CA	V32
408-435-2886	Automation Central	San Jose	CA	V32B
408-438-8513	Seagate Technology	Scotts Valley	CA	HST
408-438-8514	Seagate Technology	Scotts Valley	CA	V32
408-438-8771	Seagate Technology	Scotts Valley	CA	V32
408-438-8772	Seagate Technology	Scotts Valley	CA	HST
408-456-0339	Gifted Urban Yuppies	San Jose	CA	DS
408-578-5325	Wild Thang	San Jose	CA	HST
408-578-6704	The Lion's Den	San Jose	CA	TB2
408-578-7954	My Scummy Run-Down Hovel	San Jose	CA	V32B
408-626-2655	Dream World BBS	Carmel	CA	V32B
408-655-1096	Nitelog BBS	Monterey	CA	2400
408-655-5555	Monterey Gaming System	Monterey	CA	V32B
408-655-8294	Nitelog BBS	Monterey	CA	V32B
408-655-8297	Nitelog BBS	Monterey	CA	HST
408-733-3034	Mongoose BBS	San Jose	CA	DS2
408-737-9447	Higher Powered BBS	Sunnyvale	CA	DS2
408-738-4679	The NEBULA	Sunnyvale	CA	V32B
408-745-0127	Lynns Live Wire	Sunnyvale	CA	DS
408-847-2495	Garlique Graphics	Salinas	CA	HST
408-865-1560	MicroBBS	San Jose	CA	HST
408-866-4933	MaCS1ience BBS	San Jose	CA	DS2
408-883-0744	Two Birds/One Stone BBS	Marina	CA	V32
408-922-0988	TIPS BBS	San Jose	CA	V32
408-922-0989	TIPS BBS 2	San Jose	CA	V32A
408-923-6321	The Serenity BBS	San Jose	CA	V32B
408-997-8591	The Major League BBS	San Jose	CA	TB
409-364-2968	Muddy Creek's BBS	Calvert	TX	HST
409-693-7832	The White House	College Station	TX	HST
409-693-8764	Aggie Mac	College Station	TX	HST
409-696-0982	Silent Warrior	College Station	TX	HST
409-696-3477	C.A.M. BBS	College Station	TX	HST
409-762-2761	DragonNet	Galveston	TX	HST
409-764-0056	My Word 2	College Station	TX	DS2
409-764-0713	PhlatLiner BBS	College Station	TX	HST
409-765-6632	Beacon Terra 1	Galveston	TX	HST
409-846-4480	Starfleet PCBoard	College Station	TX	HST
409-945-4358	Fast Eddie's Adult BBS	Texas City	TX	HST

AC/Phone	BBS Name	City	State	Modem
410-247-3797	The NetWork BBS	Baltimore	MD	V32B
410-252-0717	AviTechnic	Lutherville	MD	HST
410-252-5518	AviTechnic II	Lutherville	MD	DS
410-256-0170	Wit-Tech	Baltimore	MD	V32B
410-256-7314	PerryHall BBS	Perry Hall	MD	DS
410-256-7638	Dave's Doghouse	Perry Hall	MD	HST
410-327-9263	Pooh's Corner	Fells Point	MD	V32B
410-332-7386	Maryland Med-SIG	Baltimore	MD	HST
410-343-1102	Fisherman's Cove	Parkton	MD	DS
410-437-3463	The Puffin's Nest	Pasadena	MD	V32B
410-466-0949	The Science Lab BBS	Baltimore	MD	DS
410-476-5098	Computer Consulting BBS	Easton	MD	V32
410-488-7461	PainFrame	Baltimore	MD	HST
410-531-5748	Polar Bear's Lair	Clarksville	MD	V32B
410-544-4629	The Grimace BBS	Ft. Meade	MD	HST
410-551-9631	CENTMAR Corridor	Odenton	MD	HST
410-561-0789	Law Line	Baltimore	MD	HST
410-566-1336	John's BBS	Baltimore	MD	DS
410-566-6059	Writer's Block ECHO Hub	Baltimore	MD	HST
410-655-4708	Nerve Center	Pikesville	MD	DS
410-665-1855	Outside the Wall	Baltimore	MD	V32
410-666-9109	Dark Side of the Moon	Cockeysville	MD	V32
410-686-0286	Waterfront East BBS	Baltimore	MD	HST
410-757-1479	The Scrap Board BBS	Annapolis	MD	VH
410-761-2362	Other Worlds BBS	Glen Burnie	MD	HST
410-766-9756	Robin's Nest BBS	Baltimore	MD	V32
410-787-8077	Kyle's Office	Baltimore	MD	HST
410-821-8930	Castle Cafe	Timonium	MD	V32
410-827-8789	Eastern Shore On-Line	Queenstown	MD	V32
410-833-8933	Liberty Hall	Reisterstown	MD	HST
410-880-0965	The Trilogy	Glen Burnie	MD	DS
410-882-4481	The Wright Place	Baltimore	MD	V32B
410-945-1540	Writer's Block BBS	Baltimore	MD	HST
410-997-7204	Double Nut Board	Simpsonville	MD	DS
412-247-4610	Behavioral Vision Project	Pittsburgh	PA	DS2
412-264-2692	Anything Goes	Pittsburgh	PA	HST
412-322-6548	No Gurus Here	Pittsburgh	PA	DS
412-366-5208	NSS Satellite	Pittsburgh	PA	HST
412-373-8612	Ecclesia Place	Monroeville	PA	HST
412-482-4721	Info Exchange RBBS-PC #1	Butler	PA	HST
412-482-4722	Info Exchange RBBS-PC #2	Butler	PA	DS
412-621-4604	SoundingBoard	Pittsburgh	PA	HST
412-653-7540	AutoBoss	Bunola	PA	DS
412-682-7057	The Meeting Place	Pittsburgh	PA	DS2
412-683-1235	Mac at Night	Pittsburgh	PA	DS
412-745-4185	The Cyberspace BBS	Canonsburg	PA	TB2
412-766-0732	BlinkLink	Pittsburgh	PA	HST
412-766-1086	Milliways	Pittsburgh	PA	DS3
412-824-6566	Astral Board	Pittsburgh	PA	HST
412-832-8185	Marcom Engineering Access	Greensburg	PA	HST
412-834-1128	E*COM	Greensburg	PA	DS

AC/Phone	BBS Name	City	State	Modem
412-834-7964	Post Road Inn	Greensburg	PA	HST
412-843-5592	The Fountainhead BBS	New Brighton	PA	DS
412-856-1428	First Sanyo Opus	Trafford	PA	DS2
412-864-2294	Pitt Xpress	Pittsburgh	PA	DS
412-881-1749	NorthStar Pitt	Whitehall	PA	HST
412-881-7757	DOCTOR'S Inn	Whitehall	PA	HST
412-962-9514	Beacon Hill CBIS	Transfer	PA	HST
412-981-3151	Mabel's Mansion	Sharon	PA	HST
413-243-0034	JonesNose	S Lee	MA	HST
413-256-1037	Pioneer Valley PCUG1	Amherst	MA	HST
413-323-8652	B-Town BBS	Belchertown	MA	HST4
413-443-6313	VETLink#1	Pittsfield	MA	HST
413-443-6725	Schoolhouse BBS	Pittsfield	MA	HST
413-445-7310	The B.A.U.D. BBS	Lanesboro	MA	HST
413-499-1327	Berkshire Estates BBS	Pittsfield	MA	HST
413-545-4453	Physics Forum	Amherst	MA	HST
413-562-1870	Baudville	Westfield	MA	HST
413-568-2829	The U.S.S. Light Speed][	Westfield	MA	HST
413-568-4466	PVCC User Group BBS!!	Westfield	MA	DS2
413-586-2925	Joe's Bar And Grill	Northampton	MA	DS
413-592-9208	Career Systems BBS	Chicopee	MA	HST
413-684-1938	Field Street BBS	Dalton	MA	HST
413-743-1111	Berkshire Hills BBS	Adams	MA	HST
413-747-7937	Dan's Drive-In	Springfield	MA	HST
413-772-1020	SpaceMet North 2	Greenfield	MA	HST
413-782-2158	Signal Hill	Springfield	MA	V32B
413-967-9541	Quaboag Valley	Ware	MA	HST
414-231-6886	Hunt 'N Peck	Oshkosh	WI	DS
414-251-2580	The Anonymous BBS	Menomonee Falls	WI	ULT
414-258-3373	The BillBoard BB	West Allis	WI	ULT
414-271-0576	Special Times	Milwaukee	WI	DS2
414-282-9580	Ye Olde Pawn Shoppe]I[	Milwaukee	WI	DS2
414-327-4104	PC-Express	Greenfield	WI	HST
414-351-2075	Worthwhile Unltd.	Glendale	WI	HST
414-352-6176	Radio Free	Milwaukee	WI	HST
414-353-1576	SciQuest BBS	Milwaukee	WI	ULT
414-384-1701	Modern Pastimes	Milwaukee	WI	DS
414-426-1306	The Back Fence BBS	Oshkosh	WI	DS
414-445-6969	Starcom	Milwaukee	WI	DS
414-445-7835	Penguin Point	Milwaukee	WI	HST
414-462-2874	The Wheelchair Ramp	Milwaukee	WI	DS2
414-476-8468	The County Line BBS 1	West Allis	WI	DS2
414-476-8469	The County Line BBS 2	West Allis	WI	ULT
414-545-6178	The End of the Galaxy BBS	West Allis	WI	DS2
414-563-9361	NightOwl Connection	Fort Atkinson	WI	HST
414-682-8679	Mystery Manor	Manitowoc	WI	HST
414-725-7598	Homebuilt Flyer	Neenah	WI	DS2
414-733-3882	Applegate South	Appleton	WI	DS
414-738-1219	Applegate	Appleton	WI	DS
414-739-8226	Foxy's Place	Appleton	WI	DS
414-749-0010	Homebuilt Flyer II	Appleton	WI	HST

AC/Phone	BBS Name	City	State	Modem
414-762-0813	ClearWaters	Oak Creek	WI	HST
414-764-9346	The Castle	Oak Creek	WI	DS
414-796-8408	Top Gun][	Brookfield	WI	V32
414-878-5223	SourceCode BBS	Union Grove	WI	HST
414-964-0386	Digital Future	Milwaukee	WI	HST
414-966-3552	Sirius Cybernetics	Oconomowoc	WI	DS
415-255-2188	RECOVERY	San Francisco	CA	HST
415-323-4193	SPACE BBS	Menlo Park	CA	TB3
415-323-4197	SPACE BBS	Menlo Park	CA	ULT2
415-323-4198	SPACE BBS	Menlo Park	CA	DS3
415-331-6241	Marin County Net	Sausalito	CA	DS3
415-337-5416	The PC GFX Exchange	San Francisco	CA	DS2
415-337-5599	The PC GFX Exchange	San Francisco	CA	ULT
415-340-7261	Trade Center BBS	Millbrae	CA	HST4
415-343-5160	Run Of The Mill	San Mateo	CA	HST4
415-349-5676	CHARISMA BBS	Foster City	CA	DS
415-349-6576	CHARISMA BBS	Foster City	CA	HST4
415-349-8408	Wally World	San Mateo	CA	V32
415-359-6036	Chemist ComPort	Pacifica	CA	HST
415-359-8327	My Brother's Board	Pacifica	CA	DS
415-398-6171	The Boundary Line	San Francisco	CA	V32B
415-431-0227	SeaHunt BBS Public	San Francisco	CA	2400
415-431-0473	SeaHunt BBS Subscriber	San Francisco	CA	DS2
415-467-8966	Harv's Hideout	San Francisco	CA	HST
415-469-5809	Draken's Keep	San Francisco	CA	HST
415-474-4523	The Network 2000	San Francisco	CA	DS
415-479-8328	Stonehenge BBS	San Rafael	CA	V32
415-494-3116	AHA Hydrogen BBS	Palo Alto	CA	V32B
415-550-8027	The Lost Realms	San Francisco	CA	HST
415-572-9563	PCBL BBS	San Mateo	CA	HST
415-572-9626	PCBL TOO	San Mateo	CA	V32
415-573-5473	HINTS BBS	San Mateo	CA	DS
415-573-8709	The Anxiety Closet	San Mateo	CA	V32
415-595-5843	Geno's Place	Belmont	CA	HST
415-595-5844	Geno's Place	Belmont	CA	2400
415-598-0398	The Micro Foundry	San Carlos/Blmt	CA	DS2
415-621-2609	SF PCUG BBS	San Francisco	CA	DS
415-626-7812	Gillian/Craig Asso.	San Francisco	CA	DS
415-637-9324	Toad Hall	San Carlos	CA	HST
415-641-9862	The Ultramagnetic Empire	San Francisco	CA	DS2
415-681-5862	NU-BBS	San Francisco	CA	DS2
415-681-9594	Macademe/Emma	San Francisco	CA	V32B
415-692-7721	The Skull	San Francisco	CA	HST4
415-695-0759	Late Night Software	San Francisco	CA	DS
415-737-9939	VidGame BBS	San Bruno	CA	HST
415-742-6441	VidGame BBS	San Bruno	CA	DS3
415-751-9308	ThelemaNet	San Francisco	CA	TB
415-756-5098	Bun's BBS	San Francisco	CA	DS2
415-861-8290	Coconino County	San Francisco	CA	DS
415-863-2739	Fido Software	San Francisco	CA	HST
415-876-0299	The Dragon's Lair	S. San Francisco	CA	DS

AC/Phone	BBS Name	City	State	Modem
415-965-4097	GameMasters BBS	Mountain View	CA	VH
415-968-4781	Unofficial HSA-UWC BBS	Mountain View	CA	DS
415-968-7481	Unofficial HSA-UWC BBS	Mountain View	CA	DS3
415-969-5486	Telesoft RBBS PC	Mountain View	CA	HST
415-969-6321	Haltek Electronics	Mountain View	CA	V32
415-989-9804	Generic CG's BBS	San Francisco	CA	DS
415-991-2995	Bun's BBS	San Francisco	CA	HST4
415-992-2140	Writers Block	San Jose	CA	DS
415-992-3780	The Micro Foundry	San Francisco	CA	DS2
417-334-3885	Branson's Remote Access	Branson	MO	HST
417-624-3815	The PC Depot	Joplin	MO	HST
417-624-7300	The Crawly Crypt	Joplin	MO	HST
417-673-2283	LANStar	Joplin	MO	DS
417-732-8720	The Entry Point	Republic	MO	V32
417-820-3514	The Oak Tree BBS	Springfield	MO	DS
417-886-2563	Tele-Quest BBS	Springfield	MO	DS
417-887-1790	Plaza Communications BBS	Springfield	MO	HST
417-887-9616	The TriStar BBS	Springfield	MO	TB
419-222-6676	The Black Hole	Lima	OH	HST
419-353-8397	The Bellfry BBS	Bowling Green	OH	HST
419-448-1421	NorthWest Ohio RBBS	Tiffin	OH	DS
419-475-6003	Toledo's TBBS	Toledo	OH	DS
419-476-0389	Toledo Home Education BBS	Toledo	OH	V32
419-826-1218	The Data Point	Swanton	OH	V32
419-882-2697	QRV de W8GRT	Sylvania	OH	HST
501-327-0405	Toadsuck Country BBS	Conway	AR	HST
501-329-9419	Thunder BBS	Conway	AR	DS
501-444-8080	NoWeARkNet	Fayetteville	AR	DS
501-470-0624	Computer Information Assoc	Mayflower	AR	HST
501-521-4734	Ozark Connection	Fayetteville	AR	HST
501-532-5641	MCS1ott's BBS	Blytheville	AR	DS2
501-532-5821	The Computer Terminal	Blytheville	AR	HST
501-563-6829	RiverBend	Osceola	AR	HST
501-646-5812	The Rainbow QuickBBS	Fort Smith	AR	HST
501-735-9980	The Midnight Hour BBS	West Memphis	AR	VH
501-753-4428	Ferret Face	North Little Rock	AR	CSP
501-753-6859	Ferret Face	North Little Rock	AR	V32B
501-753-8121	Ferret Face	North Little Rock	AR	V32B
501-756-0335	Razorback BBS	Springdale	AR	HST
501-791-0124	Ferret Face	North Little Rock	AR	V32
501-791-0125	Ferret Face	North Little Rock	AR	V32B
501-862-3976	Da Connection	ElDorado	AR	DS
501-864-0640	The U.S.A. BBS	ElDorado	AR	DS
501-886-1701	Phil's BBS	Walnut Ridge	AR	DS
501-931-7274	ROBBS	Jonesboro	AR	HST
501-932-6949	JUG BBSLS	Jonesboro	AR	HST
501-932-6961	The Wizard's Domain	Bono	AR	HST
501-932-7355	The Gameing BBS!	Jonesboro	AR	HST
501-932-7932	Freedom One	Jonesboro	AR	HST
501-935-7349	The Dragon's Lair BBS	Jonesboro	AR	HST
501-968-3910	Karate & Comics	Russellville	AR	V32B

AC/Phone	BBS Name	City	State	Modem
501-972-1156	The Cat's Meow BBS	Jonesboro	AR	HST
501-972-8381	Total Chaos!	Jonesboro	AR	HST
501-985-0059	The Courts of Chaos	Jacksonville	AR	HST4
502-223-6610	Leased Squares	Frankfort	KY	HST
502-423-8690	The Fifth Dimension	Louisville	KY	DS
502-458-0511	Reciprocity Rules!	Louisville	KY	DS3
502-575-3359	Hangar 18 BBS	Paducah	KY	V32B
502-762-3140	Fido-Racer	Murray	KY	V32
503-228-5866	Barristers' BBS	Portland	OR	V32
503-233-0850	Big Larry's RBBS-PC	Portland	OR	V32
503-245-0229	Atarian BBS 2	Portland	OR	V32
503-245-2006	Sadie's Swingshift	Portland	OR	DS3
503-245-4961	Hi Tech Tools/Librarians	Portland	OR	V32
503-245-9730	Atarian BBS	Portland	OR	DS
503-249-6949	1st Choice Communications	Portland	OR	DS2
503-249-6967	D'Bridge Support West II	Portland	OR	TB2
503-269-1935	MarshField Exchange	Coos Bay	OR	HST
503-285-9907	SMI's 3X/400 BBS	Portland	OR	HST
503-286-2802	Sea Breeze BBS	Portland	OR	DS
503-287-7091	Future Tech	Portland	OR	V32
503-296-1957	Cherry City Opus	The Dalles	OR	HST
503-297-8667	Trade Winds	Portland	OR	DS
503-297-9043	Bink of an Aye	Portland	OR	TB2
503-342-6581	Nightline	Eugene	OR	HST
503-343-1483	Baudville	Eugene	OR	DS
503-343-4520	Pandora's Box	Eugene	OR	DS
503-345-2582	Out In The Styx	Eugene	OR	HST
503-346-9674	The PC ToyShop	Eugene	OR	HST
503-364-2791	Gamorian Vortex Project	Salem	OR	DS
503-370-9739	Purgatory BBS	Salem	OR	DS
503-386-2903	T&E Verbal Abuse Network	Hood River	OR	HST
503-390-9051	Chemeketa OnLine	Salem	OR	CS1
503-393-5580	Chemeketa Online	Salem	OR	DS
503-452-9291	Ghost Walker BBS	Portland	OR	V32
503-461-2219	Dimension 7	Eugene	OR	HST
503-484-9754	ORTLAND	Eugene	OR	HST
503-485-5860	The Boulder	Eugene	OR	HST
503-582-4860	Three R's	Rogue River	OR	HST
503-591-5103	The Bare Bones BBS	Aloha	OR	V32
503-629-0517	Pass-IT-On Software Supp	Beaverton	OR	HST
503-635-8841	ET SCRIBE<M>	Lake Oswego	OR	V32
503-636-9562	CyBorg Systems BBS	Lake Oswego	OR	DS2
503-640-0728	Com-Dat	Portland	OR	V32
503-640-1241	Compulink Northwest I	Hillsboro	OR	TB
503-642-5548	Points R Us	Aloha	OR	V32
503-643-1891	The Omega Quadrant	Beaverton	OR	TB2
503-643-8249	The Silver Falcon	Beaverton	OR	V32
503-646-4312	The Bear's Den	Beaverton	OR	V32
503-648-3976	Compulink Northwest II	Hillsboro	OR	DS
503-649-5833	Images BBS	Portland	OR	DS
503-650-8727	AfterBurner!	Oregon City	OR	V32

AC/Phone	BBS Name	City	State	Modem
503-656-9790	Blue Lake System	West Linn	OR	V32B
503-659-9691	Mad BBS	Portland	OR	V32
503-663-1459	Et Cetera	Gresham	OR	DS
503-681-0543	COM-DAT BBS	Hillsboro	OR	HST
503-682-1511	The Realm/AnyNet HomeBase	Wilsonville	OR	TB2
503-687-2355	Blind Leap	Eugene	OR	DS2
503-690-7581	SCP Services	Hillsboro	OR	V32
503-691-0927	Spectrum BBS	Tualatin	OR	DS
503-741-1829	Well Of Souls	Springfield	OR	DS
503-746-5725	Cheezy Data Systems	Eugene	OR	HST
503-747-7636	The Buffer Board	Springfield	OR	HST
503-761-3003	Eastside Data Services #2	Portland	OR	V32
503-769-4394	C-King Knowledge CBCS	Marion	OR	HST
503-771-0732	The Electric Eye	Portland	OR	V32
503-771-4773	Busker's Boneyard	Portland	OR	TB2
503-777-1578	Event Horizons	Portland	OR	HST
503-777-5389	Phaze RBBS	Portland	OR	HST
503-786-2869	Wally World	Milwaukie	OR	HST
503-826-9290	Safe Sex	White City	OR	HST
503-881-1733	The Dark Star System	Ontario	OR	DS2
503-928-9535	Around The Klock Software	Albany	OR	DS2
504-244-1417	Pontchippi	New Orleans	LA	DS
504-273-3116	HelpNet #1	Baton Rouge	LA	DS
504-275-7389	HelpNet #2	Baton Rouge	LA	DS
504-282-0273	Grampa's House	New Orleans	LA	DS
504-282-5753	The Dungeon	New Orleans	LA	DS
504-283-2817	RAM On Line BBS	New Orleans	LA	HST
504-294-5027	The River's Edge	Ponchatoula	LA	HST
504-386-8827	The Movie Man	Ponchatoula	LA	HST
504-387-4015	Antelope Freeway BBS	Baton Rouge	LA	HST
504-391-2925	High Concepts	New Orleans	LA	HST
504-436-1887	N.O.P.C. Club	New Orleans	LA	DS
504-455-8665	Minas Tirith	New Orleans	LA	HST
504-466-0126	Center of The Cosmos	Metairie	LA	HST
504-466-0908	The Bowling Alley RBBS	New Orleans	LA	HST
504-527-0022	Ozone BBS	New Orleans	LA	DS2
504-542-0380	Ch.A.D.D./K12net BBS	Hammond	LA	V32B
504-563-2603	Players Palace	Houma	LA	HST
504-641-4789	The Fire Scene	Slidell	LA	HST
504-649-7101	The Flying Dutchman	Slidell	LA	HST
504-652-7014	Tri-Parish Exchange	LaPlace	LA	HST
504-738-7080	LA Medsig	Harahan	LA	DS
504-756-9658	Cajun Clickers BBS	Baton Rouge	LA	DS
504-764-0449	The Eagle's Nest	Norco	LA	DS3
504-767-0681	Hell BBS	Baton Rouge	LA	DS
504-769-4969	Arkham Asylum BBS	Baton Rouge	LA	V32
504-796-5860	NorthLake Data Exchange	Folsom	LA	DS
504-837-8188	New Orleans MUG	New Orleans	LA	TB2
504-851-4473	Computer Associates of LA	Houma	LA	HST
504-851-4857	Curtain Call	Houma	LA	HST
504-866-5765	Amiga Gateway	New Orleans	LA	HST

AC/Phone	BBS Name	City	State	Modem
504-868-1440	Databank Message Center	Houma	LA	HST
504-878-3023	Christian Distribution Net	Loranger	LA	HST
504-885-0118	The Generic BBS!	New Orleans	LA	DS
504-885-5928	The Southern Star	New Orleans	LA	DS
504-886-2157	Washington/StTammanyConnX	Sun	LA	HST
504-888-6515	The Silver Streak RBBS	New Orleans	LA	HST
504-926-7903	The Alternatives BBS	Baton Rouge	LA	DS
504-947-6761	The RedLight BBS	New Orleans	LA	DS
505-266-0697	The Tech Source	Albuquerque	NM	V32B
505-293-0010	THe GaRBaGe DuMP BBS!	Albuquerque	NM	V32
505-294-5675	THe GaRBaGe DuMP BBS!	Albuquerque	NM	2400
505-434-0724	The ROCK BBS	Alamogordo	NM	V32
505-434-3224	The Tech Net	Alamogordo	NM	HST
505-437-2280	Fast Kode	Alamogordo	NM	HST
505-437-8267	Casa de La Luz	Alamogordo	NM	HST
505-479-4023	Kustom Kastle	Alamogordo	NM	HST
505-479-4732	Foundation's Edge	Alamogordo	NM	HST
505-523-2811	Desert Dolphin	Las Cruces	NM	HST
505-527-7668	Dona Ana Branch CommCntr	Las Cruces	NM	HST
505-589-0319	Randy's Basement	Anthony	NM	DS
505-646-2868	NASW New Mexico	Las Cruces	NM	HST
505-662-0659	Construction Net #6	Los Alamos	NM	HST
505-822-0836	Land of Enchantment BBS	Albuquerque	NM	DS
505-822-0837	Land of Enchantment BBS	Albuquerque	NM	V32B
505-843-9597	Hackers Den BBS	Albuquerque	NM	DS3
505-865-4082	Paula's House of Mail	Los Lunas	NM	HST
505-865-8385	High Mesa Publishing	Los Lunas	NM	V32
505-891-3840	The Call	Albuquerque	NM	HST
505-899-9282	Night Magic BBS	Albuquerque	NM	ZYX
507-281-1989	Medical Software Exchange	Rochester	MN	HST
507-281-8292	The Castle BBS	Rochester	MN	DS
508-222-5875	FirePlug II	N. Attleboro	MA	V32
508-279-1552	PriZm BBS	Bridgewater	MA	HST
508-283-5712	The Twin Lights BBS	Gloucester	MA	V32B
508-352-7603	Rogers & Blake	Georgetown	MA	HST
508-356-2469	The Fire Fly BBS	Ipswich	MA	HST
508-373-0486	Joshua BBS!!!	Haverhill	MA	HST
508-373-3845	ECIS TBBS	Haverhill	MA	HST
508-429-8857	Cul De Sac	Holliston	MA	DS
508-441-9215	Adventure Unlimited	Lowell	MA	DS
508-454-0356	Space Station	Lowell	MA	DS
508-465-3198	The MASS Hysteria BBS	Newburyport	MA	HST
508-474-0328	Aeolus BBS	Andover	MA	DS2
508-475-8344	Druzhba BBS	Andover	MA	TB
508-481-7147	WayStar	Marlborough	MA	DS
508-481-7293	WayStar	Marlborough	MA	HST
508-520-1516	The Apogee II	Franklin	MA	DS
508-528-2295	Computer Confident	Franklin	MA	DS
508-531-8416	Lost In The Supermarket	Peabody	MA	HST
508-562-3230	The Fun Fun BBS	Hudson	MA	HST
508-568-0957	The Imperium	Hudson	MA	DS

AC/Phone	BBS Name	City	State	Modem
508-588-2210	Tandy Tavern RBBS	Brockton	MA	HST
508-626-2481	MSI SW BBS	Framingham	MA	DS
508-652-9334	HMM BBS 2	Natick	MA	V32
508-655-8927	HMM BBS 1	Natick	MA	V32B
508-658-8185	The Concept BBS	Wilmington	MA	HST
508-668-7792	GNUs Board	Walpole	MA	HST
508-682-0133	BlackMarket BBS	Methuen	MA	HST
508-682-5279	Electric Dreams	Methuen	MA	HST
508-682-5329	The Business Card	Lawrence	MA	DS2
508-689-4493	The Mystic Tribunal	N. Andover	MA	HST
508-697-3508	PriZm BBS	Bridgewater	MA	VH
508-697-7771	PriZm BBS	Bridgewater	MA	DS
508-699-9357	FirePlug	N. Attleboro	MA	V32
508-750-0250	PandA's Den BBS	Danvers	MA	V32B
508-752-1227	Paddy's Place	Worcester	MA	HST
508-759-9596	Bungalow Cape Cod	Monument Beach	MA	HST
508-772-6373	Denis OPUS	Ayer	MA	DS
508-777-2352	Danvers Software Support	Danvers	MA	HST
508-788-1603	The SKATEboard BBS	Framingham	MA	DS
508-839-4597	Paragon STar Net	S. Grafton	MA	HST
508-840-8017	TC-Trader	Leominster	MA	DS2
508-865-0498	Davy Jones Locker #2	W Millbury	MA	HST
508-865-0499	Davy Jones Locker #3	W Millbury	MA	DS
508-865-3290	Davy Jones Locker #1	W Millbury	MA	HST
508-865-7207	Davy Jones Locker #4	W Millbury	MA	TB
508-875-3618	Xevious BBS	Framingham	MA	HST
508-877-0768	The Apocalypse BBS	Framingham	MA	HST
508-877-8756	FoReM PC	Framingham	MA	HST
508-883-0795	The PC Library	Bellingham	MA	HST
508-897-1963	Tour de Force BBS	Maynard	MA	VH
508-927-2537	Titan BBS	Beverly	MA	HST
508-975-1924	Wizard's World	Lawrence	MA	HST
508-975-2340	Amiga Attic	Methuen	MA	HST
508-991-6058	Dreamer's BBS	New Bedford	MA	HST
509-276-6431	TouchStone	Deer Park	WA	HST
509-328-8770	Futurist's RoundTable	Spokane	WA	HST
509-483-0042	The Garage	Spokane	WA	HST4
509-487-6572	Gonzaga Law BBS	Spokane	WA	V32B
509-534-7924	EWARG	Spokane	WA	HST
509-545-1789	The SunDial BBS	Pasco	WA	HST
509-545-3742	Sundial III	Pasco	WA	CS1
509-582-9493	The Data Shop BBS	Kennewick	WA	HST4
509-586-0104	The Hide Away BBS	Kennewick	WA	HST
509-624-6799	Inland Empire Archive	Spokane	WA	DS
509-663-2888	Wenatchee Area BBS	Wenatchee	WA	HST4
509-663-3618	Apple Capitol BBS	Wenatchee	WA	HST
509-663-5232	Electronic Library	Wenatchee	WA	DS
509-758-6248	STARWEST-BBS	Clarkston	WA	V32
509-766-0380	The CrossRoads BBS	Moses Lake	WA	V32
509-783-5526	Tri-Cats BBS	Kennewick	WA	HST
509-783-8260	Under Construction	Pasco	WA	HST

AC/Phone	BBS Name	City	State	Modem
509-884-7803	The Hartmann Medical BBS	East Wenatchee	WA	DS
509-922-4568	Interdoor	Spokane	WA	HST
509-943-0211	OneStop PCBoard	Richland	WA	DS2
509-965-2345	The Yakima Atari ST BBS	Yakima	WA	HST
510-215-7430	Firebird	El Cerrito	CA	HST
510-373-6583	Windraker II	Livermore	CA	VH
510-452-0350	ClawMarks	Oakland	CA	HST
510-452-3551	ShadowFox/Furverts! 3	Oakland	CA	VH
510-458-6404	The Tiffany Touch	Pittsburg	CA	V32
510-483-4823	The Black Circle	San Leandro	CA	DS
510-484-0998	MacCircles	Pleasanton	CA	HST
510-505-9047	Online Bible Reference	Newark	CA	VH
510-549-0311	Dragon's Cave	Berkeley	CA	V32B
510-582-6743	GADM	Hayward	CA	HST
510-685-0644	Sempervirens BBS	Concord	CA	DS2
510-687-0236	OnlineComputerResources	Concord	CA	DS
510-689-4378	The GIFt Shop (tm)	Concord	CA	HST6
510-689-4686	The GIFt Shop (tm)	Concord	CA	V32B
510-689-6811	The Sinking Ship BBS	Concord	CA	V32
510-706-0904	Cheers	Antioch	CA	V32
510-736-8343	Windows OnLine(tm) IDS	Danville	CA	DS2
510-741-6442	VidGame BBS	San Bruno	CA	DS
510-754-2440	Seekers Haven	Antioch	CA	V32
510-778-5929	Infolinc BBS	Antioch	CA	V32
510-792-3210	The Midnight Express	Fremont	CA	DS2
510-795-8862	MacInfo	Newark	CA	HST
510-830-4616	Guardian's Gateway	San Ramon	CA	HST
510-838-7687	Diablo BBS	Danville	CA	HST
510-849-1795	BMUG	Berkeley	CA	DS
510-849-9118	BMUG	Berkeley	CA	DS
510-865-7115	IDC BBS	Alameda	CA	HST
510-881-5427	Bust Out BBS	Hayward	CA	DS
510-937-0156	Walnut Creek BBS	Walnut Creek	CA	ULT2
510-938-5836	Walnut Creek BBS	Walnut Creek	CA	ULT2
512-219-0737	Perfect Square	Austin	TX	HST
512-241-1120	WireLine	Corpus Christi	TX	HST
512-258-3643	LoneStar CBCS	Austin	TX	DS
512-258-8831	Austin Code Works	Austin	TX	HST
512-259-4896	Far Point Station	Leander	TX	HST
512-295-4710	Micro-Link	Buda	TX	DS
512-298-3693	The Computer Connection	Del Rio	TX	HST
512-322-0265	The Zen Wedgie BBS	Austin	TX	DS2
512-323-3276	Tex-A-Caid	Austin	TX	HST
512-327-5376	River City MailBox	Austin	TX	HST
512-335-7949	Crystal Palace	Lake Travis	TX	DS
512-338-9369	Scotts Excellent BBS	Austin	TX	DS2
512-339-9426	Bon Appetit	Austin	TX	HST
512-343-1612	The Bull Creek BBS	Austin	TX	HST
512-346-8075	RagBBS v.69	Austin	TX	V32B
512-346-8175	RagBBS v.69	Austin	TX	2400
512-357-6904	Lounge Lizard's Retreat	San Marcos	TX	DS

AC/Phone	BBS Name	City	State	Modem
512-383-9898	Soft World BBS	Edinburg	TX	DS
512-385-8321	Rumours	Austin	TX	DS
512-387-6638	SeaBat	Corpus Christi	TX	DS
512-389-2839	The Lighthouse	Austin	TX	HST
512-396-0252	Martin's Domain Telegard	San Marcos	TX	V32
512-434-1557	APCO Public BBS	San Antonio	TX	HST
512-442-6091	Button and Dietz	Austin	TX	V32
512-443-5441	Red Wheelbarrow	Austin	TX	V32
512-445-6000	The ACADemy	Austin	TX	HST
512-451-0891	Future Quest	Austin	TX	DS
512-451-4349	DataQuest	Austin	TX	HST
512-451-4610	Pair-O-Dice BBS 1	Austin	TX	2400
512-451-7117	Pair-O-Dice BBS 2	Austin	TX	DS2
512-454-9488	Connect America	Austin	TX	HST
512-467-7621	GIF Land	Austin	TX	HST
512-467-9180	Systems Consulting	Austin	TX	V32
512-496-6550	FliegWeg BBS	San Antonio	TX	HST
512-496-9373	The Rampant Griffin	San Antonio	TX	HST
512-521-9307	Jim's RBBS	San Antonio	TX	DS
512-556-2524	Tex*Star BBS	Kempner	TX	DS2
512-590-7227	The TITAN RBBS	San Antonio	TX	HST
512-590-9423	The Ansi Touch	San Antonio	TX	DS
512-618-3219	InterPhaze	McAllen	TX	HST
512-631-5841	The Dragon's Den	McAllen	TX	HST
512-643-7858	Garfield	Portland	TX	HST
512-643-8196	Papa Shmurf's Place	Portland	TX	HST
512-647-8189	ACS People Connection	San Antonio	TX	HST
512-654-8349	The Gathering BBS	San Antonio	TX	HST
512-670-8595	Puzzle Palace	San Antonio	TX	HST
512-684-6531	The Retreat House	San Antonio	TX	HST
512-688-3753	B&B BBS	San Antonio	TX	HST
512-692-0730	NUL 1	San Antonio	TX	DS2
512-754-7715	Jacob's Well	San Marcos	TX	DS
512-778-6246	The Auto Control	Liberty Hill	TX	HST
512-781-3506	Wildcat BBS	Pharr	TX	HST
512-822-4050	Last Chance II	San Antonio	TX	HST
512-822-7519	Last Chance TBBS	San Antonio	TX	HST
512-827-9377	QUARK BBS	New Braunfels	TX	HST
512-835-4848	Middle Earth	Austin	TX	HST
512-836-6383	The Omicron	Austin	TX	HST
512-837-0953	JimNet	Austin	TX	HST
512-853-8509	Mirage BBS	Corpus Christi	TX	HST
512-855-7564	Ye MailRoom	Corpus Christi	TX	HST
512-882-2997	Sparklin City	Corpus Christi	TX	HST
512-887-0787	Computer Data Services BBS	Corpus Christi	TX	V32B
512-924-8179	The Playground	San Antonio	TX	HST
512-926-0670	HyperCache! BBS	Austin	TX	V32B
512-929-3855	Sonic Boom	Austin	TX	HST
512-929-9107	Heart O' Texas BBS	Austin	TX	HST
512-937-8907	The Probe	Corpus Christi	TX	HST
512-993-0178	Data One Systems	Corpus Christi	TX	HST

AC/Phone	BBS Name	City	State	Modem
513-231-7013	MultiSystem TBBS	Cincinnati	OH	HST
513-233-1200	The Pit-Stop BBS	Huber Heights	OH	HST
513-236-0917	J&J's BBS 4	Huber Heights	OH	V32B
513-236-1229	J&J's BBS 3	Huber Heights	OH	HST4
513-236-3087	J&J's BBS 2	Huber Heights	OH	HST4
513-236-3448	The Darkroom	Dayton	OH	HST
513-236-4788	J&J's BBS 1	Huber Heights	OH	V32B
513-237-7737	Myth Kingdom Tech	Huber Heights	OH	HST
513-244-2255	Access!	Cincinnati	OH	DS2
513-252-8891	The Arena BBS	Dayton	OH	HST
513-253-2476	CURRENTS	Dayton	OH	HST
513-256-0399	FireHouse BBS	Dayton	OH	HST
513-258-0971	Trader's Cove	Dayton	OH	HST
513-259-0806	D.M.U.G BBS	Dayton	OH	HST
513-294-8064	Kettering BBS	Kettering	OH	V32
513-298-3006	Decker's Board	Dayton	OH	HST
513-299-8910	D'Bridge Support/OH USA	Kettering	OH	DS2
513-376-9711	PW&M BBS	Xenia	OH	V32
513-383-2264	D.N.R Connection	Wilmington	OH	V32B
513-398-0928	Train Board	Mason	OH	HST
513-429-5818	DAYHUG	Dayton	OH	DS2
513-436-0400	Genealogy Ohio	Dayton	OH	HST
513-438-8376	MIDI MATRIX BBS	Dayton	OH	V32
513-439-5021	Dayton West Chapter	Dayton	OH	HST
513-446-3108	Barn Owl	Georgetown	OH	HST
513-474-2985	CINTUG TBBS	Cincinnati	OH	HST
513-528-7018	Showcase TBBS	Cincinnati	OH	HST
513-563-6475	NGPK Shareware Board	Cincinnati	OH	HST4
513-732-0984	Fishing Hole	Batavia	OH	HST
513-751-4009	Peace Net	Cincinnati	OH	HST
513-752-1055	Cincinnati Comp Conn	Cincinnati	OH	DS
513-761-2084	Rolling Stone	Cincinnati	OH	HST
513-762-1115	KIC	Cincinnati	OH	HST
513-821-1387	D'Bridge/North America	Cincinnati	OH	HST
513-844-8557	The Upper Room	Fairfield	OH	HST
513-845-2484	Bulldog Express	New Carlisle	OH	HST
513-860-1340	MIDI Inn	Cincinnati	OH	HST
513-860-2277	Basselope West	Cincinnati	OH	DS2
513-860-2728	ACORN	Cincinnati	OH	HST
513-864-1143	The Blue Byte	Enon	OH	HST
513-898-3393	Hooterville BBS	Dayton	OH	DS2
513-921-5568	Mountain Top	Cincinnati	OH	HST
513-968-6900	Design & Data Systems	Union City	OH	VH
513-987-2417	Dragon BBS	Wilmington	OH	DS
513-987-2418	Dragon BBS	Wilmington	OH	DS
515-255-2567	TSI BBS	Des Moines	IA	DS
515-279-3073	ZSys BBS	Bagdad	IA	V32
515-279-6769	Enchanted Mansion	Des Moines	IA	HST
515-285-1190	Alternatives	Des Moines	IA	DS
515-752-6554	Horseless Carriage	Marshalltown	IA	DS2
515-964-7937	FOG Line BBS	Des Moines	IA	HST

AC/Phone	BBS Name	City	State	Modem
516-283-9631	North Sea Operations BBS	Southampton	NY	DS3
516-321-4893	EarthNet Environmental Inf	West Islip	NY	HST
516-325-0827	Empire BBS	Westhampton	NY	DS
516-331-5562	The Symbolic Stack Dump	Miller Place	NY	V32
516-364-4450	Substation BBS	Long Island	NY	CS2
516-367-6387	D2 Systems BBS	Melville	NY	HST
516-474-1472	Take-Out	Port Jefferson Stn	NY	DS
516-481-2004	Jack & Jill's LI ConneXion	East Meadow	NY	DS
516-536-1546	Big Apple BBS	Rockville Centre	NY	ULT
516-536-8723	SOM Premium Info-Net	Long Island	NY	ULT
516-561-6590	LICA Limbs BBS	Valley Stream	NY	DS
516-579-0050	Tele-Net Online	Seaford	NY	V32B
516-579-7507	Utopia Technologies Ltd.	Levittown	NY	DS2
516-581-6540	Captain Jack's	Brentwood	NY	DS
516-626-3804	ShadowRun	Old Westbury	NY	HST
516-689-5833	The Realm of the Unknown	Stonybrook	NY	DS
516-694-3623	The Expressway BBS	Farmingdale	NY	V32B
516-731-1094	Fort Z BBS	Levittown	NY	DS
516-736-3403	King Diamond's Realm	Coram	NY	DS
516-737-8217	Logylink BBS	Ronkonkoma	NY	HST
516-741-6914	The Rail Road	Garden City Park	NY	HST
516-767-5189	ImageSoft BBS	Port Washington	NY	HST
516-791-1407	The File BBS 1	Long Island	NY	ULT
516-867-4445	Intelec Online	Freeport	NY	HST4
516-867-4446	Intelec Online	Freeport	NY	HST4
516-867-4447	Intelec Online	Freeport	NY	DS2
516-867-4448	Intelec Online	Freeport	NY	DS3
516-868-1741	Intelec Online	Baldwin	NY	V32B
516-889-3036	Your WhereHouse BBS	Oceanside	NY	DS2
516-922-5153	PC Info System BBS	Oyster Bay	NY	DS2
516-957-1465	MORDOR BBS	Lindenhurst	NY	V32
517-321-0788	The Lighthouse BBS	Lansing	MI	HST
517-332-0472	The Program Exchange	East Lansing	MI	HST
517-337-0624	The Lansing FORUM	East Lansing	MI	HST
517-337-8132	Microsystems	East Lansing	MI	DS
517-349-0743	The Gamer's Forum	Okemos	MI	HST
517-349-9491	The Kollection Konnection	Okemos	MI	HST
517-374-1088	Jenny's Dog House I	Lansing	MI	HST
517-641-4801	The Rec Room	Bath	MI	HST
517-641-4802	The Rec Room II	Bath	MI	DS
517-645-0026	The Abacus II	Potterville	MI	HST
517-645-7343	The Abacus	Potterville	MI	HST
517-655-3347	The Programmers Attic	Williamston	MI	HST
517-695-6859	Flying Circus	Kawkawlin	MI	HST
517-695-9952	Wolverine	Midland	MI	HST
517-783-5471	The Flaming Dragon	Jackson	MI	HST
517-797-2737	Classroom Earth BBS	Saginaw	MI	V32B
517-797-3740	Delight The Customer BBS	Saginaw	MI	V32B
517-865-6173	MicroCosm	St. Charles	MI	HST
518-383-2282	Fantasy Land	Clifton Park	NY	DS
518-437-1267	Computer Group Ltd 1	Albany	NY	HST

AC/Phone	BBS Name	City	State	Modem
518-583-2841	The Final Frontier II	Saratoga Springs	NY	DS
518-584-8187	ALLIES BBS	Saratoga Springs	NY	HST
518-761-0869	The Final Frontier	Glens Falls	NY	HST
518-785-1715	Pain & Pleasure BBS	Latham	NY	HST
518-785-6643	Pain & Pleasure BBS	Latham	NY	HST
518-793-9574	The HOST BBS	Glens Falls	NY	HST
601-268-8871	Camelot BBS	Hattiesburg	MS	HST4
601-289-7837	Zone 1 BBS	Kosciusko	MS	V32B
601-328-2278	The Wizzards Inn	Columbus	MS	HST
601-332-9453	!PSYCHOBABBLE!	Greenville	MS	V32
601-362-9958	Berserker BBS	Jackson	MS	V32
601-366-1664	Big Bang Theory	Jackson	MS	DS2
601-371-8597	Infinite Limit	Jackson	MS	V32
601-372-6998	Electronic Dreams	Jackson	MS	V32
601-373-0018	HyperDrive	Jackson	MS	V32B
601-437-2108	Grand Gulf Connection	Port Gibson	MS	HST
601-634-1625	The Southern Belle	Vicksburg	MS	HST
601-636-1119	The Cat's Meow	Vicksburg	MS	HST
601-638-7056	The Wishing Well	Vicksburg	MS	HST
601-856-8337	Heliport	Madison	MS	V32B
601-875-2355	DataSync BBS	Ocean Springs	MS	V32B
601-896-3970	On-line Systems	Gulfport	MS	HST
601-924-4174	Xanadu BBS	Clinton	MS	V32
601-925-4380	Binary Bros	Clinton	MS	ULT
601-956-9943	The Connector	Jackson	MS	DS2
601-957-0843	Irrelevant BBS	Jackson	MS	ULT
601-957-3016	Cont'l Divide	Jackson	MS	V32
601-981-1394	StarNet BBS	Jackson	MS	2400
601-981-8220	StarNet BBS	Jackson	MS	V32B
601-992-4023	MCS Micronet	Brandon	MS	HST
601-992-9459	MacHaven	Brandon	MS	DS
602-235-9653	St Joes Hospital	Phoenix	AZ	DS
602-242-3158	Answering Mach	Phoenix	AZ	HST
602-242-4784	The Open Door West	Phoenix	AZ	HST4
602-245-2946	Hidden Cavern BBS	Phoenix	AZ	VH
602-252-1426	Mac's Place	Phoenix	AZ	HST
602-258-8347	Construction Net 1	Phoenix	AZ	DS
602-264-2328	Migrant BBS	Phoenix	AZ	HST
602-271-2492	CHHS BBS	Phoenix	AZ	DS
602-275-3284	The CAD-alog BBS	Tempe	AZ	V32B
602-279-0793	Cheese Whiz Wildcat! BBS	Phoenix	AZ	V32
602-290-9854	Eternity! BBS	Tucson	AZ	DS2
602-326-2999	The Hour Glass	Tucson	AZ	DS2
602-326-9345	New Parents Network	Tucson	AZ	DS
602-458-0451	The Analog Gate	Sierra Vista	AZ	DS
602-458-8342	The Hometown BBS	Sierra Vista	AZ	HST
602-459-2412	The New Way BBS	Fort Huachuca	AZ	V32B
602-488-0656	Construction Net 5	Cave Creek	AZ	HST
602-495-1713	AZ MAC UG	Phoenix	AZ	DS
602-524-2032	Animal Pharm BBS	Holbrook	AZ	DS
602-526-5805	Ramcom Technology BBS	Flagstaff	AZ	HST

AC/Phone	BBS Name	City	State	Modem
602-527-8404	The High Mountain BBS	Flagstaff	AZ	DS2
602-548-0513	Anime Archive 2	Phoenix	AZ	DS2
602-571-9063	Comm-Post	Tucson	AZ	V32
602-577-6393	Tucson Apple Core	Tucson	AZ	ULT
602-578-0842	Add Net	Tucson	AZ	HST
602-579-0869	Meridith Place	Tucson	AZ	DS2
602-582-1549	Aslan's Roar Distr Ctr	Phoenix	AZ	DS
602-584-7395	Sunwise	Sun City West	AZ	DS
602-624-5125	Community Resource On-Line	Tucson	AZ	DS2
602-730-0119	Megabytes	Mesa	AZ	HST
602-730-8943	The CADalog BBS	Tempe	AZ	V32B
602-741-7851	Tucson On-Line	Tucson	AZ	ULT
602-744-2314	Old Pueblo BBS	Tucson	AZ	DS2
602-745-3638	Clearwater #1	Tucson	AZ	DS2
602-745-3639	Clearwater #2	Tucson	AZ	HST
602-747-1269	Dave's Mailbox	Tucson	AZ	HST
602-747-5236	Solitude	Tucson	AZ	V32
602-749-5968	BigFoot's RBBS-PC	Tucson	AZ	DS2
602-750-0016	Black Dragons Lair #1	Tucson	AZ	DS2
602-756-2855	Rare Readers BBS	Mesa	AZ	HST
602-757-1125	PrimeNet (tm)	Kingman	AZ	HST
602-780-1839	The Shire	Phoenix	AZ	HST
602-780-9180	The Ranch	Phoenix	AZ	DS
602-788-7144	Amiga City	Phoenix	AZ	HST
602-789-0091	The BatBoard	Phoenix	AZ	V32B
602-789-5088	Iasd Eng Bbs	Phoenix	AZ	HST
602-792-3772	Nine Star	Tucson	AZ	DS
602-814-0123	AMC Net	Chandler	AZ	HST
602-820-6237	The Anarchy Connection	Mesa	AZ	DS
602-820-7861	Conceptual CAD Design BBS	Tempe	AZ	V32B
602-840-4752	Nat'l. Congress For Men	Phoenix	AZ	HST
602-846-4420	Land Of Nomad	Glendale	AZ	DS
602-848-0732	Ed's Place	Phoenix	AZ	HST
602-848-9902	InfoSpectrum BBS	Glendale	AZ	HST
602-866-9229	Valley Of The Sun	Glendale	AZ	TB2
602-872-9148	Broadcaster's BBS	Phoenix	AZ	DS2
602-881-3769	Edge of Forever	Tucson	AZ	DS2
602-885-4004	PC Consulting Agency BBS	Tucson	AZ	DS2
602-886-7943	Bigfoot's RBBS-PC	Tucson	AZ	DS
602-886-8650	Midnight Oil	Tucson	AZ	DS2
602-887-1329	The Home RCS	Tucson	AZ	DS
602-888-0819	Aztec BBS	Tucson	AZ	DS2
602-892-3198	The Coconut Telegraph	Mesa	AZ	HST
602-898-1603	NCC-1603	Mesa	AZ	DS
602-899-3386	The Hog Trough!	Chandler	AZ	DS
602-921-1651	Flatland Center	Tempe	AZ	DS
602-926-4026	AMUG Preferred	Phoenix	AZ	ULT
602-933-1768	TJ's	Peoria	AZ	HST
602-937-2304	Exterminator BBS #2	Phoenix	AZ	HST
602-939-2134	Exterminator BBS	Phoenix	AZ	DS
602-943-1497	Ranch & Cattle Metro BBS	Phoenix	AZ	V32B

AC/Phone	BBS Name	City	State	Modem
602-945-0869	Genoa City	Tempe	AZ	HST
602-947-0587	AZ MAC UG 2	Scottsdale	AZ	ULT
602-965-3648	Construction Net 2	Tempe	AZ	HST
602-994-9882	Swamp Gas	Scottsdale	AZ	HST
602-996-0078	The Tiger's Den	Phoenix	AZ	HST
603-228-0705	Easy Does It	Bow	NH	HST
603-335-5640	Barrington BBS	Barrington	NH	HST
603-424-0923	VAXCat	Merrimack	NH	TB
603-424-4915	Outer Limits	Merrimack	NH	HST
603-429-2052	Starship's Shuttle Craft	Manchester	NH	HST
603-433-1859	Quagmire BBS	Portsmouth	NH	HST
603-434-5842	Gateway Communications	Windham	NH	ULT
603-448-0198	Guru Mountain	Lebanon	NH	HST
603-474-8915	The Nuke Zone	Seabrook	NH	HST
603-523-7676	The Dead Pool BBS	Canaan	NH	HST
603-524-8600	Alter-Net	Laconia	NH	HST
603-527-0862	Alter-Net IV	Gilford	NH	HST
603-528-2149	Alter-Net II	Gilford	NH	HST
603-529-3395	Manchester EchoMail City	Manchester	NH	DS
603-529-4290	Granite State Connection 2	Weare	NH	HST
603-547-6485	InterVision	Francestown	NH	HST
603-595-7739	The Danger Zone	Nashua	NH	HST
603-595-9677	The Starship	Amherst	NH	DS
603-624-9451	Amiga Venom BBS	Manchester	NH	HST
603-635-3738	George's Place	Pelham	NH	HST
603-641-2017	Computer Solutions	Manchester	NH	HST
603-647-3177	Boardtalk BBS	Manchester	NH	HST
603-672-8041	The Ultimate Realm	Merrimack	NH	V32
603-673-2781	Dave's Swimmin Hole	Brookline	NH	HST
603-880-1658	Cuckoo's Nest BBS	Hudson	NH	HST
603-881-9741	Kat(h)'s Meow	Nashua	NH	HST
603-882-2099	The Ballpark RBBS	Nashua	NH	HST
603-883-4466	Legal Beagle	Nashua	NH	HST
603-886-5722	The Toy Room BBS	Hudson	NH	HST
603-888-3840	The Outpost	Nashua	NH	HST
603-891-1386	The Imperial Palace	Nashua	NH	HST
603-898-2349	My House BBS	Salem	NH	HST
603-899-3335	The Cereal Port BBS	Rindge	NH	HST
605-232-4648	The Voyager BBS	McCook Lake	SD	DS2
605-331-5831	YEE BBS	Sioux Falls	SD	DS3
605-335-7288	PrairieNet BBS	Sioux Falls	SD	DS2
605-336-3578	Dakota InfoNet	Sioux Falls	SD	DS2
605-338-8333	Youth Education EBBS	Sioux Falls	SD	DS
605-348-4113	The Time Portal	Rapid City	SD	DS
605-923-1185	The Crows Nest	Rapid City	SD	HST
605-923-2111	Cowboy's Corral	Rapid City	SD	DS2
606-269-1565	PROF-BBS	Lexington	KY	HST
606-283-2040	The ZOO	Independence	KY	DS2
606-283-2455	Fifth Dimension	Independence	KY	HST
606-371-0570	Hellfire Club	Florence	KY	HST
606-376-3747	Black Angel	Marshes Siding	KY	HST

AC/Phone	BBS Name	City	State	Modem
606-586-5202	InfoNet	Petersburg	KY	HST
606-727-3638	DataNet	Erlanger	KY	DS2
606-727-9666	Nobody's Here Now	Erlanger	KY	DS2
606-781-2956	Camelot	Ft. Thomas	KY	HST
606-836-1267	The Penal Colony	Worthington	KY	HST
607-256-0200	The Lowlands	Ithaca	NY	V32
607-256-5466	Shark's Basin	Ithaca	NY	DS2
607-687-6193	Walden Puddle	Owego	NY	V32
607-722-1689	The Great Outdoor	Binghamton	NY	HST
608-256-5697	NineJackNine	Madison	WI	HST
608-273-9894	Experimental RBBS	Madison	WI	HST
608-274-7483	Der SaugenGrube BBS	Madison	WI	V32
608-325-7994	The Swiss Bull BBS	Monroe	WI	HST
608-837-1923	JW-PC DataFlex	Sun Prairie	WI	DS2
609-232-1245	Compu-Data	Turnersville	NJ	DS2
609-327-5553	Union Lake BBS	Millville	NJ	HST
609-327-9133	The Towers BBS	Millville	NJ	V32B
609-383-9369	Academia BBS	Northfield	NJ	CS1
609-383-9392	Academia BBS	Northfield	NJ	DS3
609-383-9400	Academia BBS	Northfield	NJ	2400
609-386-1989	Capital City BBS	Burlington	NJ	DS2
609-392-5953	Polymath One 1 Public	Trenton	NJ	CS1
609-394-5414	Polymath One 2 Private	Trenton	NJ	HST
609-435-4410	Dark Shadows BBS 1	Lindenwold	NJ	HST
609-467-3898	The Beckett BBS	Swedesboro	NJ	HST
609-482-1336	The Next Generation BBS	Maple Shade	NJ	V32B
609-482-6916	The Happy Hour BBS	Cherry Hill	NJ	HST
609-482-7345	The Next Generation BBS	Maple Shade	NJ	V32
609-482-8604	Maple Shade Opus	Maple Shade	NJ	DS
609-488-4398	The Dark One's Domain	Pennsauken	NJ	HST
609-530-1427	CentraLink	Ewing	NJ	HST
609-546-5808	The APT To Be BBS	Haddon Heights	NJ	HST
609-561-3377	Casino BBS	Atlantic City	NJ	DS2
609-582-4753	The Programming Lynk	Sewell	NJ	DS
609-582-9618	Lestershire Country Club	Turnersville	NJ	HST
609-586-4847	Freedom InfoNet BBS	Mercerville	NJ	DS3
609-625-2453	Dynalogic Product Support	Mays Landing	NJ	HST
609-627-8369	Dark Shadows BBS 2	Lindenwold	NJ	DS
609-645-7080	Online In D'Hood	Pleasantville	NJ	V32B
609-646-2011	Nirvana	Pleasantville	NJ	V32B
609-654-0999	RTC-BBS	Medford	NJ	HST
609-697-2976	Microshare II BBS	Newfield	NJ	HST
609-751-3847	Memory Link BBS	Cherry Hill	NJ	HST
609-784-9404	Computer Co-op	Voorhees	NJ	HST
609-786-3475	Allen's Space Shuttle	Riverton	NJ	DS
609-786-8601	Allen's Space Shuttle	Riverton	NJ	V32
609-799-0628	The Switch Room	Plainsboro	NJ	HST
609-825-1621	Holly City BBS	Millville	NJ	DS2
609-825-5223	Union Lake BBS	Millville	NJ	V32B
609-825-5717	Towers BBS Intn'l	Millville	NJ	CS1
609-825-6057	Union Lake BBS	Millville	NJ	HST

AC/Phone	BBS Name	City	State	Modem
609-825-7776	Towers BBS Intn'l	Millville	NJ	2400
609-829-1395	Marquee Systems BBS	Cinnaminson	NJ	2400
609-829-5601	Marquee Systems BBS	Cinnaminson	NJ	DS2
609-859-1910	Pinelands RBBS	Vincentown	NJ	DS
609-866-2551	The Livewire BBS	Mt. Laurel	NJ	DS
609-871-7484	JB BBS	Edgewater Park	NJ	V32B
609-875-9759	Hurricane Alley BBS	Williamstown	NJ	HST
609-877-0703	Tomcat BBS	Willingboro	NJ	HST
609-895-0398	The NJCC	Lawrenceville	NJ	DS3
609-953-5612	Allen's Space Shuttle	Medford	NJ	DS3
609-953-5621	Allen's Space Shuttle	Medford	NJ	DS2
609-953-5623	Allen's Space Shuttle	Medford	NJ	2400
609-985-4750	The Armoury II	Marlton	NJ	HST
612-252-1116	The Outpost!	Sauk Rapids	MN	DS2
612-259-0801	The Outpost!	Sauk Rapids	MN	2400
612-259-5139	The Outpost!	Sauk Rapids	MN	CSP1
612-332-5217	Telegraph Road	Minneapolis	MN	HST
612-426-6687	MacRefuge	St. Paul	MN	HST
612-474-0724	Haven of Rest	Minneapolis	MN	DS
612-493-4943	The Mirror Exchange	Champlin	MN	HST
612-535-7153	The Senate Chamber	Crystal	MN	HST
612-544-5118	FlightLine BBS	Minneapolis	MN	DS2
612-546-2490	WalkInTheShadowsOfNight	Minneapolis	MN	V32B
612-571-6280	The Enterprise Board	Fridley	MN	V32
612-591-7767	The O-Zone BBS	New Hope	MN	DS
612-593-4083	WalkInTheShadowsOfNight	Minneapolis	MN	V32B
612-593-5081	WalkInTheShadowsOfNight	Minneapolis	MN	DS2
612-593-5107	WalkInTheShadowsOfNight	Minneapolis	MN	TB2
612-623-0152	Terrapin Station	Minneapolis	MN	V32B
612-624-4318	U-of-MN Libraries BBS	Minneapolis	MN	V32
612-636-7580	DTP Exchange BBS	New Brighton	MN	TB2
612-654-8194	Granite BBS Public 2	St. Cloud	MN	V32B
612-654-8372	Granite BBS Public 1	St. Cloud	MN	HST
612-654-8516	Fort Weyr BBS	Sauk Rapids	MN	HST4
612-656-0678	Granite BBS Private 3	St. Cloud	MN	V32B
612-721-8967	Terraboard	Minneapolis	MN	HST
612-825-5231	Nightlife BBS	Minneapolis	MN	V32
612-832-5127	Odyssey BBS	Edina	MN	DS2
612-885-0537	The File Cabinet BBS	Bloomington	MN	HST
612-938-1875	TC-AMS TBBS	Minnetonka	MN	DS
612-938-8924	Dark Knight's Table	Minnetonka	MN	DS
612-944-3358	The Freezing Point	Eden Prairie	MN	V32
614-224-1635	The Wizard's Gate	Columbus	OH	DS3
614-259-5822	Kitty City BBS	Lucasville	OH	V32
614-268-1982	Ginger's Port Limited	Columbus	OH	DS
614-268-5606	Ginger's Port Limited	Columbus	OH	2400
614-268-9456	Ginger's Port Limited	Columbus	OH	DS2
614-333-6343	OdieLink Music BBS	Washington C.H.	OH	DS4
614-335-3627	PC-Connection	WashngtnCrtHouse	OH	HST
614-363-4204	Patriot Network System	Delaware	OH	V32
614-374-6910	Flying High!	Marietta	OH	DS

AC/Phone	BBS Name	City	State	Modem
614-382-3534	Marion Software Connection	Marion	OH	DS
614-387-3524	Marion Software Connection	Marion	OH	DS
614-423-6308	MELTDOWN	Belpre	OH	HST
614-436-2414	Briefcase BBS	Columbus	OH	V32
614-442-6695	Utilities Exchange BBS	Columbus	OH	HST
614-442-6696	Utilities Exchange BBS	Columbus	OH	DS
614-457-1701	MARDUK III	Upper Arlington	OH	DS2
614-478-3611	AveMaria	Columbus	OH	DS
614-523-1105	Ginger's Port	Westerville	OH	V32
614-772-5520	The Outer Limits	Chillicothe	OH	DS2
614-773-2423	South of the Bauder	Chillicothe	OH	HST
614-775-3370	MCINET	Chillicothe	OH	HST
614-784-8555	Ginger's Port Limited	Columbus	OH	V32B
614-837-3896	Aspencade BBS	Pickerington	OH	DS2
614-846-1274	Compu-Link	Columbus	OH	HST
614-855-2958	The KrackerLine	New Albany	OH	HST
614-861-5825	The Computer Room II	Pickerington	OH	HST
614-861-8377	The Computer Room	Pickerington	OH	DS
614-864-0092	Pets Elite BBS	Columbus	OH	HST
614-870-6544	The CommPort BBS	Columbus	OH	V32
614-875-3552	MARDUK IV	Grove City	OH	HST
614-882-4478	MARDUK	Columbus	OH	DS2
614-885-9829	Colossus	Worthington	OH	DS
614-891-0255	Twilight Zone	Columbus	OH	DS
614-928-2339	The Mother Board!	Buckeye Lake	OH	HST4
615-227-1768	Dandy Line BBS	Nashville	TN	DS
615-245-1364	The Commo Bunker	Kingsport	TN	HST
615-265-2629	The Old Folk's Home	Chattanooga	TN	HST
615-297-5611	The Transfer Station	Nashville	TN	HST
615-331-6664	The SHMC BBS	Nashville	TN	HST
615-331-7819	ShareWorld BBS	Antioch	TN	HST
615-333-1458	WorkBench BBS	Nashville	TN	HST
615-353-0514	Control Systems	Nashville	TN	DS
615-353-3476	EET BBS	Nashville	TN	DS
615-356-0453	UltraTech	Nashville	TN	HST
615-356-8016	The M.C. Photographers	Nashville	TN	DS
615-366-0064	The Ace of Spades BBS	Nashville	TN	HST
615-377-3419	Genesis BBS	Brentwood	TN	HST
615-381-3201	Computer Concepts	Columbia	TN	HST
615-385-4268	Dawg Byte (ANSI Club HQ)	Nashville	TN	HST
615-385-9328	Strawberry Fields	Nashville	TN	DS
615-385-9421	Promises	Nashville	TN	HST
615-453-0780	C Delight	Pigeon Forge	TN	HST
615-472-9748	Nova BBS	Cleveland	TN	HST
615-478-2890	PC Junction BBS	Cleveland	TN	HST
615-479-3686	Inner Circle	Cleveland	TN	HST
615-482-5138	Beginners BBS	Oak Ridge	TN	V32B
615-526-3347	Cumberland BBS	Cookeville	TN	HST
615-531-2177	Volunteer PC BBS	Knoxville	TN	DS
615-546-5401	The Hitchin' Post	Knoxville	TN	HST
615-552-8783	The GTR	Clarksville	TN	HST

AC/Phone	BBS Name	City	State	Modem
615-646-2842	The Rx Shop 2	Nashville	TN	DS
615-646-5550	The Fishing Hole	Nashville	TN	HST
615-662-0371	The Humanities Forum	Franklin	TN	HST
615-662-0632	Transformations BBS	Nashville	TN	HST
615-671-1732	Data Bank BBS	Knoxville	TN	V32B
615-671-4695	Data World BBS	Knoxville	TN	ZYX
615-671-4696	Data World BBS	Knoxville	TN	ZYX
615-675-3282	Data World BBS 4 Private	Knoxville	TN	DS2
615-675-4577	Data World BBS 3 Private	Knoxville	TN	DS2
615-675-4753	Data World BBS	Knoxville	TN	DS
615-675-6994	Data World BBS 5 Private	Knoxville	TN	DS2
615-675-6995	Data World BBS 1 Private	Knoxville	TN	ULT
615-744-0024	The Tutorboard	Decatur	TN	DS
615-842-9225	MAXspeed BBS	Hixson	TN	HST
615-870-5238	The P.T. Connection!] [	Chattanooga	TN	HST
615-870-5876	The P.T. Connection!	Chattanooga	TN	HST
615-875-4131	Starfire Command	Chattanooga	TN	HST
615-889-0948	Rendezvous BBS	Nashville	TN	HST
615-894-8825	The District Car	Chattanooga	TN	HST
615-899-3899	Glenn's GIF World	Chattanooga	TN	DS
615-899-5578	The Ragged Edge BBS	Chattanooga	TN	HST
615-966-3574	Data World BBS 2 Public	Knoxville	TN	ULT
615-970-7418	Data-Comp BBS Private	Maryville	TN	DS2
615-982-6512	Data-Comp BBS Private 3	Maryville	TN	DS2
615-982-6537	Data-Comp BBS Public 2	Maryville	TN	ULT
615-982-8723	Data-Comp BBS Private 1	Maryville	TN	ULT
615-983-8232	The Disk Fix	Maryville	TN	DS
616-235-2313	RIP	Grand Rapids	MI	HST
616-285-9002	Fort Knox BBS	Grand Rapids	MI	HST
616-372-3547	The Amigans BBS	Kalamazoo	MI	V32B
616-383-0337	Lightning Zone	Kalamazoo	MI	DS
616-455-0168	Fort Knox	Grand Rapids	MI	2400
616-455-2252	Fort Knox	Grand Rapids	MI	DS
616-456-1845	Ryan's Bar BBQ	Grand Rapids	MI	HST
616-456-5342	Post Office	Grand Rapids	MI	V32
616-534-7093	Crystal Palace	Grand Rapids	MI	HST
616-791-2109	SuperService	Grand Rapids	MI	HST
616-896-7820	DJ's Country	Dorr	MI	V32
616-897-4953	River City	Lowell	MI	HST
616-897-6647	Spiteos	Lowell	MI	V32
616-940-6026	Covered Bridge	Grand Rapids	MI	HST
616-963-9092	The Final Frontier	Battle Creek	MI	ULT
617-237-1511	Heath Users Group	Westwood	MA	HST
617-286-1807	Total Confusion III	Revere	MA	HST
617-326-4676	BINEX II	Westwood	MA	HST
617-331-1070	Navigator BBS	Weymouth	MA	HST
617-335-2238	The Complete Sports BBS	Weymouth	MA	2400
617-335-6842	The Complete Sports BBS	Weymouth	MA	DS2
617-354-0470	Channel 1 (R)	Cambridge	MA	TB2
617-354-3137	Channel 1 (R)	Cambridge	MA	HST4
617-354-3230	Channel 1 (R)	Cambridge	MA	V32B

AC/Phone	BBS Name	City	State	Modem
617-354-4443	Channel 1 (R)	Cambridge	MA	CS1
617-354-5776	Channel 1 (R)	Cambridge	MA	ULT
617-395-4317	Total Confusion	Medford	MA	HST
617-471-0542	Tom's BBS	Wollaston	MA	DS2
617-472-8612	Photo Talk BBS	Squantum	MA	HST
617-494-0565	4th Dimension BBS	Cambridge	MA	HST
617-497-6463	Number Nine Graphics BBS	Cambridge	MA	HST
617-551-0495	Rainbows Edge	Westwood	MA	HST
617-595-5626	NewWorld Magic1	Swampscott	MA	HST
617-598-6646	Baystate PCBoard	Lynn	MA	HST
617-621-0882	BCS Info Center	Cambridge	MA	HST
617-625-0381	BCS Macintosh TBBS	Somerville	MA	DS
617-631-3304	Island Logistics	Marblehead	MA	HST
617-631-4029	Cambridge DataWorks	Marblehead	MA	V32
617-767-2909	VI/BUG	Holbrook	MA	HST
617-786-9788	BCSnet Telecomm OPUS	Quincy	MA	HST
617-828-0868	American Playhouse	Canton	MA	HST
618-233-1659	EchoMania	Belleville	IL	HST
618-253-3608	Crimson Cross BBS	Harrisburg	IL	V32B
618-346-9164	Comm Central	Maryville	IL	HST
618-548-3637	Channel Z BBS	Salem	IL	ULT4
618-549-1129	Mac UnderGround HQ	Carbondale	IL	DS
618-549-6918	Mac UnderGround	Carbondale	IL	VH
618-624-6578	USS Hexum	O'Fallon	IL	CS1
618-684-3889	The Hard Disk Cafe	Murphysboro	IL	DS3
618-684-3990	Hard Disk Cafe! BBS	Murphysboro	IL	DS3
618-744-1458	The BackChannel BBS	Belleville	IL	HST
618-932-6927	Channel II	W. Frankfort	IL	HST
619-221-0311	JBBS	San Diego	CA	HST
619-223-7111	Know Ware BBS	San Diego	CA	DS
619-228-1781	Electronic Universe BBS	Yucca Valley	CA	CS1
619-240-6200	Tana BBS	Apple Valley	CA	DS
619-243-9422	WPGS	Victorville	CA	HST
619-270-8779	Information Exchange 386	Pacific Beach	CA	V32
619-272-2059	Mac Underground San Diego	San Diego	CA	HST
619-273-0514	Lost Bytes	San Diego	CA	DS2
619-275-6129	The RATS Nest	San Diego	CA	HST
619-278-7086	Pacific Rim Information	San Diego	CA	DS
619-278-7361	Pacific Rim Information II	San Diego	CA	DS
619-279-5240	Dan's BBS	San Diego	CA	HST
619-280-3819	Chaos	San Diego	CA	DS
619-281-2622	The General	San Diego	CA	CS1
619-281-5538	The General BBS	San Diego	CA	DS
619-284-8729	Trader's World	San Diego	CA	DS
619-291-0544	Hillcrest Community BBS	San Diego	CA	DS
619-291-6746	Pea's Keep	San Diego	CA	HST
619-345-5838	The T&L BBS	Indio	CA	DS2
619-361-5527	The Stumps II WC! BBS	Twentynine Palms	CA	DS
619-371-1665	Computing Technology BBS	Ridgecrest	CA	DS
619-423-9352	Data Works	Imperial Beach	CA	HST
619-435-0036	Daily Calendar BBS	Coronado	CA	V32B

AC/Phone	BBS Name	City	State	Modem
619-440-6038	Don's House	El Cajon	CA	HST
619-446-4452	Mr. C's BBS 1	Ridgcrest	CA	V32B
619-446-4453	Mr. C's BBS 2	Ridgcrest	CA	V32B
619-447-5489	Suburbia?	San Diego	CA	HST
619-449-8333	West Coast Connection	San Diego	CA	DS
619-461-0982	I.D.I.C BBS	Lemon Grove	CA	HST
619-461-3415	$ound of Money	San Diego	CA	HST
619-464-2134	The Mouse-Trap	San Diego	CA	HST
619-466-9505	Gandalf's	San Diego	CA	HST
619-467-0335	The SW/SE Connection	San Diego	CA	DS2
619-469-1354	The Chief's Mess	San Diego	CA	HST
619-479-3006	Starhelm Greystaff	San Diego	CA	HST
619-497-0541	USS Enterprise	San Diego	CA	HST
619-542-0906	About Town	San Diego	CA	HST
619-560-2996	Starbase 23	San Diego	CA	HST
619-562-3646	Foys' Trading Post	Santee	CA	DS
619-562-8735	The Santee Micro	Santee	CA	CS1
619-565-1728	Plain Vanilla	San Diego	CA	HST
619-566-0328	Classified Connection III	San Diego	CA	CS1
619-566-1745	Classified Connection III	San Diego	CA	HST
619-571-7791	Casa de Cricket	San Diego	CA	HST
619-583-1626	Central City Hub	San Diego	CA	HST
619-587-9825	Tunnels Of Vesarius	San Diego	CA	DS
619-588-8931	DOOGER'S Place	El Cajon	CA	DS
619-593-1341	D J M BBS	La Mesa	CA	HST
619-632-8287	Cornucopia	San Diego	CA	HST
619-665-8028	Public Access BBS	Big River	CA	V32B
619-670-3969	Bauhaus	San Diego	CA	HST
619-695-3011	Adventure Games Of America	San Diego	CA	HST
619-698-5715	The Morgue	Lemon Grove	CA	HST
619-746-1455	Time Traveler BBS #2	Escondido	CA	HST4
619-746-7511	Time Traveler BBS #1	Escondido	CA	DS3
619-747-4040	Dream Journal BBS	Escondido	CA	V32B
619-775-3930	Great Escape	Indio	CA	DS
619-949-4021	NOHO BBS	Hesperia	CA	DS
619-949-4025	NOHO BBS	Hesperia	CA	HST
619-949-4026	NOHO BBS	Hesperia	CA	2400
701-228-2908	The Academy BBS	Bottineau	ND	V32
701-239-6048	Text BS	Fargo	ND	HST
701-266-5463	The N.E.R.D. Board	Rock Lake	ND	V32B
701-746-0441	Wild West BBS	Grand Forks	ND	HST
701-772-5399	City Lites PCB	Grand Forks	ND	DS3
702-253-9917	dBest In The West	Las Vegas	NV	DS2
702-254-8601	Absolutely Temporary	Las Vegas	NV	DS2
702-358-7233	The Danger Zone	Sparks	NV	HST
702-359-4999	Nevada Mac	Reno	NV	HST
702-368-0846	Shortwave-Scanner Infonet	Las Vegas	NV	HST
702-431-2031	Corvette BBS 2	Las Vegas	NV	V32B
702-431-2284	Corvette BBS 1	Las Vegas	NV	V32
702-431-8589	Tuesday Night BBS	Las Vegas	NV	DS2
702-435-0786	The Rebel BBS	Las Vegas	NV	DS2

AC/Phone	BBS Name	City	State	Modem
702-435-8407	Reservations Only	Las Vegas	NV	DS2
702-453-5866	Software-A-America	Las Vegas	NV	CS1
702-453-6981	Caddis BBS	Las Vegas	NV	HST
702-454-6340	Click Me Twice BBS	Las Vegas	NV	DS
702-463-5346	Black Rock BBS	Yerington	NV	DS
702-463-5754	The Control Tower BBS	Yerington	NV	DS
702-565-4800	The Late Show Of Las Vegas	Las Vegas	NV	DS2
702-588-0315	Lightning System III	Stateline	NV	DS2
702-597-1932	The Las Vegas Center BBS	Las Vegas	NV	DS
702-644-1537	Nighthawk BBS	Las Vegas	NV	HST
702-644-3289	Nighthawk BBS	Las Vegas	NV	DS
702-647-4427	The $in City Bit Pit	Las Vegas	NV	DS2
702-738-4177	The Image Club	Elko	NV	V32
702-796-7134	Dust Devil BBS	Las Vegas	NV	V32B
702-825-3981	Evolutions End BBS	Reno	NV	DS2
702-873-4476	The South Poll	Las Vegas	NV	DS2
702-878-1490	Desert Dreams	Las Vegas	NV	HST
702-882-4846	Sherwood Forest 702	Carson City	NV	CS1
702-882-7761	Earth Rescue	Carson City	NV	HST
702-882-9305	M&M Computers BBS	Carson City	NV	HST
703-241-5492	Craig's Place	Falls Church	VA	V32
703-257-1583	The Outpost	Manassas	VA	DS2
703-264-3962	The Coral Reefer BBS	....	VA	DS
703-264-9698	Board On Boards	Reston	VA	DS
703-323-7654	The Systems Exchange	Fairfax	VA	HST
703-335-9064	Wheels & Spokes	Manassas	VA	HST
703-339-0847	Last Frontier BBS	Lorton	VA	V32
703-352-1502	Brewster's Barn	Fairfax	VA	HST
703-354-1104	The Info Exchange	Springfield	VA	DS
703-358-9112	Sara's Outpost	Arlington	VA	HST
703-368-5429	The Time Portal	Manassas	VA	HST
703-370-7054	TIDMADT	Alexandria	VA	DS
703-373-7742	Journey QuickBBS	Falmouth	VA	HST
703-373-8215	Jack's Emporium	Falmouth	VA	HST
703-373-9289	The Thunderbolt BBS	Falmouth	VA	HST
703-385-4325	OS/2 Shareware	Fairfax	VA	DS2
703-385-8450	OS/2 Shareware	Fairfax	VA	HST
703-389-2495	Wonko The Sane's ASYLUM	Salem	VA	DS
703-406-0073	Pencil Pusher 2	Sterling	VA	ULT
703-406-0074	Technical Hangout Private	Sterling	VA	V32
703-406-0117	IDIC	Sterling	VA	HST
703-425-6638	Hallucination	Fairfax	VA	DS
703-427-2138	Mountain Air BBS	Roanoke	VA	V32
703-427-2258	Mountain Air BBS	Roanoke	VA	HST
703-430-5824	Pencil Pusher 1	Sterling	VA	2400
703-433-6903	The MoonGate	Harrisonburg	VA	HST
703-444-3366	The Hat's Place BBS	Sterling	VA	HST4
703-444-6765	Technical Hangout Public	Sterling	VA	ULT
703-450-9456	Small Business Graphics	Sterling	VA	V32B
703-471-7111	The PINNACLE!	Reston	VA	HST
703-471-8010	HBX	Herndon	VA	HST

AC/Phone	*BBS Name*	*City*	*State*	*Modem*
703-478-9380	Struppi's BBS	Herndon	VA	V32
703-491-5445	Milliways BBS	Woodbridge	VA	HST
703-494-1713	The RENEX BBS	Woodbridge	VA	HST
703-494-8331	Network Connections BBS	Woodbridge	VA	HST
703-528-2612	NGS/CIG	Arlington	VA	DS
703-532-7143	Arlington SoftwareExchange	Arlington	VA	V32
703-534-0177	GreyEagle	Falls Church	VA	DS
703-548-1507	ITS Online	Alexandria	VA	V32B
703-573-8652	To HIS Glory	Vienna	VA	V32B
703-591-5744	The Midnite Rider	Fairfax	VA	HST
703-620-5418	Washington ZEPHYR	Oakton	VA	HST
703-631-8597	Insight Computer Graphics	Leesburg	VA	DS
703-642-8704	Infinite Data Source	Alexandria	VA	CS1
703-642-8705	Infinite Data Source	Alexandria	VA	CS1
703-642-8706	Infinite Data Source	Alexandria	VA	CS1
703-642-8707	Infinite Data Source	Alexandria	VA	CS1
703-642-8708	Infinite Data Source	Alexandria	VA	CS1
703-642-8709	Infinite Data Source	Alexandria	VA	CS1
703-642-9882	Infinite Data Source	Alexandria	VA	V32
703-642-9883	Infinite Data Source	Alexandria	VA	V32
703-642-9884	Infinite Data Source	Alexandria	VA	DS2
703-642-9885	Infinite Data Source	Alexandria	VA	DS2
703-662-6964	Zhentil Keep	Winchester	VA	HST4
703-667-3530	Another Dimension	Winchester	VA	DS
703-670-5037	Connect! BBS	Dale City	VA	HST
703-680-5970	K4NGC BBS	Woodbridge	VA	TB
703-689-3355	The Hat's Place BBS	Sterling	VA	V32
703-719-9646	Data Bit NETWork Private	Alexandria	VA	DS
703-719-9648	Data Bit NETWork Public	Alexandria	VA	HST
703-771-1830	Pavlov's Dog BBS	Leesburg	VA	HST4
703-777-2690	Insight Computer Graphics	Leesburg	VA	DS
703-785-0422	Data Empire	Fredericksburg	VA	HST
703-793-3307	Paragon Systems	Herndon	VA	DS3
703-802-2251	The Joker's Wild	Fairfax	VA	ULT2
703-802-6885	The Transporter	Centreville	VA	DS
703-815-3244	Sentry Net BBS	Centreville	VA	HST
703-823-6591	The ABySS BBS	Alexandria	VA	V32
703-845-1162	Zonzr	Fairfax	VA	DS
703-866-3739	CCIB	Burke	VA	DS2
703-892-1921	The Art's Place BBS	Arlington	VA	V32B
703-892-2189	Bob's BBS	Somewhere	VA	HST
703-899-0020	The Cracker Barrel BBS	Falmouth	VA	HST
703-938-9738	Lumberjack SNUBBS	Vienna	VA	DS
703-941-4041	The Warped Board BBS	Alexandria	VA	DS3
703-941-8291	ShanErin	Alexandria	VA	DS
703-951-2708	Sybil BBS	Blacksburg	VA	DS
703-951-9461	The TARDIS BBS	Blacksburg	VA	HST
703-953-0640	The MBT	Blacksburg	VA	DS2
703-962-9253	The PCSS BBS	Covington	VA	DS2
703-963-2460	The XT Connection!	Richlands	VA	HST
703-971-1783	Indirections!	Alexandria	VA	DS

AC/Phone	BBS Name	City	State	Modem
704-251-5507	The OnLine BBS	Asheville	NC	DS
704-282-0713	The KEYboard	Charlotte	NC	VH
704-326-8948	Silver Bullet BBS	Hickory	NC	HST
704-327-6350	Heffe's Place	Hickory	NC	HST
704-352-5675	The Edderd BBS	Lexington	NC	HST
704-537-7752	The Orphanage	Charlotte	NC	HST
704-541-1180	ComStar Telecommunications	Charlotte	NC	HST
704-544-0010	Programmers Assistant	Charlotte	NC	HST
704-545-7076	AET's BBS	Mint Hill	NC	DS
704-554-1496	The Funny Farm	Charlotte	NC	DS
704-563-5857	Carolina Forum	Charlotte	NC	HST
704-567-9513	Transporter Room	Charlotte	NC	HST
704-567-9594	Transporter Room Pod II	Charlotte	NC	HST
704-598-1139	Dead Letter Queue	Charlotte	NC	HST
704-732-1852	Jacurutu BBS	Lincolnton	NC	HST
704-744-6237	Mega-Byte BBS	Lexington	NC	DS
704-865-3063	Echo Express	Gastonia	NC	HST
704-982-9223	The King's Dominion BBS	Albemarle	NC	V32B
706-375-2196	The Battlefield	Chickamuaga	GA	DS3
706-860-2927	ZARNO Board	Martinez	GA	DS2
707-257-2338	The Electronic Grapevine	Napa	CA	DS
707-257-6502	Napa Valley Fido	Napa	CA	HST
707-263-6612	Clever Endeavor BBS	Lakeport	CA	DS2
707-422-6057	Nordic Computers Inc	Fairfield	CA	V32
707-429-9664	Jim's BETA Surprise	Suisun City	CA	HST
707-437-5389	Aerospace Technology	Fairfield	CA	HST
707-445-4770	Salad Bar Adult Board	Eureka	CA	V32
707-464-3705	Wheel Chair Express	Crescent City	CA	HST
707-485-0987	Mirror BBS	Redwood Valley	CA	HST
707-545-0746	Sonoma Online	Santa Rosa	CA	HST
707-552-2344	Power Station	Vallejo	CA	DS
707-575-0636	The Outland	Santa Rosa	CA	DS
707-677-3871	Trinidad RBBS	Trinidad	CA	HST
707-725-5785	End of the World BBS!	Fortuna	CA	HST
707-746-6091	DCC BBS	Benicia	CA	DS
707-747-0306	Byte out of the Apple	Benicia	CA	V32
707-838-7500	Aerie by the Bay	Windsor	CA	DS
707-938-8843	The Other Woman	Sonoma	CA	VH
708-208-0662	Grey Matter	Chicago	IL	DS2
708-208-4716	Grey Matter	Chicago	IL	V32B
708-291-6660	The Rest of Us MUG	Northbrook	IL	DS
708-295-6926	MACropedia BBS	Lake Forest	IL	DS
708-297-1591	The Chicago BBS	Niles	IL	DS
708-298-4121	O'Hare Oasis	Des Plaines	IL	DS
708-299-1296	Eye Resources Network	Des Plaines	IL	DS3
708-301-2872	BBS USA	Lockport	IL	DS
708-352-9282	Mac-I-Nations	LaGrange	IL	DS
708-382-3904	Creative Thoughts BBS	Chicago	IL	V32B
708-394-0071	Samson	Arlington Heights	IL	DS
708-395-1253	RichWare ShareWare PVT	Antioch	IL	DS
708-395-1254	RichWare ShareWare PUB	Antioch	IL	V32B

AC/Phone	BBS Name	City	State	Modem
708-398-7013	The File Master BBS	Rolling Meadows	IL	HST
708-424-6136	The Electric Estates BBS	Oak Lawn	IL	V32
708-428-0519	BURPs and TOEJAM Bbs	Dundee	IL	V32B
708-439-9679	The Midrange System	Mt. Prospect	IL	DS
708-462-1508	Wheaton File Exchange 1	Wheaton	IL	DS3
708-462-1509	The Wheaton File Exchange	Wheaton	IL	DS3
708-462-1691	Wheaton File Exchange 3	Wheaton	IL	V32B
708-491-3892	Northwestern University	Evanston	IL	HST
708-505-0713	SoftranBBS	Naperville	IL	HST
708-529-1586	Elk Grove Repeater	Elk Grove	IL	DS
708-551-9275	The Emporium System	Carpentersville	IL	DS
708-559-0513	NezulD's DomaiN	Northbrook	IL	HST
708-559-0514	NezulD's DomaiN	Northbrook	IL	HST
708-566-6183	Mulligan's Place BBS	Mundelein	IL	V32B
708-620-8244	FutureSource	Lombard	IL	HST
708-657-1113	Spectrum MACInfo	Glenview	IL	DS
708-657-9543	Terrapin Station	Glenview	IL	DS
708-674-1989	TechLine RBBS	Evanston	IL	HST
708-683-2390	The Red Star	Burlington	IL	DS2
708-734-1177	Sports Connection	Wooddale	IL	HST
708-734-1818	Sports Connection	Wooddale	IL	V32
708-740-2072	The Black Knight BBS	Ingleside	IL	DS
708-741-9628	The Omega BBS	Elgin	IL	HST
708-746-0548	Flat Cat Alley	Zion	IL	HST
708-748-4025	Space City Grafix	Park Forest	IL	DS
708-749-8137	W.B.B.S.	Berwyn	IL	DS
708-759-7908	Magrathea BBS	Bolingbrook	IL	DS
708-790-4688	Information Station	Glen Ellyn	IL	HST
708-799-4790	The Day of the Yuga	Homewood	IL	DS
708-820-8344	Aquila BBS	Aurora	IL	CS1
708-823-4814	The White Star Line	Park Ridge	IL	V32
708-832-7754	Addison DOS Haus	Addison	IL	V32B
708-839-5054	CYCLOPS! Multi-Line TBBS	Willow Springs	IL	DS
708-963-4551	Masquerade BBS	Downers Grove	IL	V32
708-964-8022	The Dragstrip	Westmont	IL	HST
708-967-7157	Rude Attitude BBS	Niles	IL	DS2
708-969-9380	Blood & Guts	Westmont	IL	V32
708-982-5092	USR Tech Support	Skokie	IL	DS2
708-983-4524	AL Product Support BBS	Naperville	IL	DS
712-737-3960	Virtual Reality BBS	Orange City	IA	V32B
712-758-3483	Exegete's Haven RBBS	Ocheyedan	IA	V32
713-251-9757	North Shore BBS	Spring	TX	V32T
713-266-3563	The Swap Shop	Houston	TX	HST
713-277-5465	Keith's Little S/W Shop	Houston	TX	HST
713-292-6787	Grandmaster BBS	Woodlands	TX	V32B
713-331-3056	Ye Olde Inn III	Alvin	TX	HST
713-331-6719	Service Station	Alvin	TX	HST
713-342-1174	Treeshare Genealogical BBS	Houston	TX	HST
713-350-6284	Fulcrum's Edge	Spring	TX	V32
713-355-6107	Data Warp Premium BBS	Spring/Houston	TX	DS
713-355-7201	Data Warp Premium BBS	Spring/Houston	TX	DS2

AC/Phone	BBS Name	City	State	Modem
713-367-1484	The Mormon Opus	Houston	TX	HST
713-367-4008	Nowhere USA	The Woodlands	TX	HST
713-376-4767	Texas Father's BBS	Tomball	TX	HST
713-392-2578	Black Star	Houston	TX	HST
713-395-3101	Bob's File Exchange 1	Houston	TX	V32B
713-395-3901	Bob's File Exchange 2	Houston	TX	V32B
713-424-5456	Ye Sailors Rest	Baytown	TX	HST
713-440-4217	The Domain BBS	Houston	TX	HST
713-441-3080	HomeBoy's Place	Humble	TX	V32
713-442-2811	Phoenix Net Opus	Houston	TX	HST
713-446-5194	Computer Buy/Sell	Houston	TX	ULT4
713-458-7410	Fidos Partner	Houston	TX	HST
713-461-7384	The VeriTech BBS	Houston	TX	HST
713-463-2484	Utopia BBS	Houston	TX	V32
713-463-4434	Far Point Back Door	Katy	TX	DS
713-463-8324	Far Point Relay Ham BBS	Katy	TX	HST
713-470-8987	The Stargazer Opus/BBS	LaPorte	TX	HST
713-479-2184	Deer Park Connection	Houston	TX	DS
713-480-2686	The Black Box RCPM	Houston	TX	DS
713-482-7080	The Roost BBS	Friendswood	TX	DS
713-487-7638	Mail Room	Pasadena	TX	HST
713-488-4589	South o'the Border!	Houston	TX	DS2
713-498-3248	HAL-PC Telecom 1 Service	Houston	TX	V32
713-520-1569	Ye Olde Bailey	Houston	TX	ULT
713-520-5719	Prime	Houston	TX	HST
713-520-9566	Ye Olde Bailey	Houston	TX	ULT
713-521-0698	The Exchange BBS	Houston	TX	DS2
713-541-3910	Software Expressions BBS	Houston	TX	HST
713-568-6401	WCS1NET	Houston	TX	HST
713-578-8155	V-45 Express	Katy	TX	HST
713-579-8979	The Breakfast Club	Houston	TX	DS2
713-584-1821	The Leaders in Control	Houston	TX	DS
713-587-2670	The Bohemian's BBS	Houston	TX	V32B
713-589-0308	The InterMix Chamber	Houston	TX	DS2
713-640-2533	MacEndeavour	Houston	TX	TB2
713-668-3849	Club Megabyte	Houston	TX	DS
713-673-5510	Open Access	Houston	TX	ULT
713-682-6508	Two Wheelers	Houston	TX	HST
713-683-9776	Muscle Beach BBS	Houston	TX	DS
713-688-1729	JW's Laser BBS	Houston	TX	HST
713-726-0445	My New BBS	Houston	TX	V32
713-771-2802	The Abend BBS 1	Houston	TX	V32B
713-771-4661	The Abend BBS 2	Houston	TX	DS3
713-821-4174	The END Adult BBS!!	Houston	TX	HST
713-821-6629	Texxas Star	Houston	TX	DS2
713-849-2659	TEJAS	Houston	TX	ULT
713-855-4382	Cloud Nine BBS	Houston	TX	HST
713-855-4773	Houston SwingShift III	Houston	TX	HST
713-855-6540	The Mechanic Shop BBS	Houston	TX	HST
713-859-6320	The Computer Shop BBS	Katy	TX	V32
713-890-5456	The LAST Stop BBS	Houston	TX	HST

AC/Phone	BBS Name	City	State	Modem
713-890-6257	Southern Oracle	Houston	TX	DS2
713-890-7017	Radar's Little BBS	Houston	TX	DS
713-896-1721	The Archives BBS	Houston	TX	V32
713-947-9866	The ComPort BBS	Houston	TX	HST
713-961-1604	Sands ProBoard	Houston	TX	DS2
713-980-9671	COMM Port One	Houston	TX	DS2
713-984-2782	Bay Area BBS	Houston	TX	V32
714-255-9508	Colossus Galactica	Brea	CA	DS2
714-348-1755	The Barn BBS	Mission Viejo	CA	DS4
714-361-5150	Builders Board	San Clemente	CA	HST
714-367-1755	Electric Dreams	Laguna Hills	CA	DS
714-432-9104	PC-Applications	Costa Mesa	CA	HST4
714-447-4356	Hustler's Corner BBS	Fullerton	CA	HST
714-457-0359	Discovery BBS	Mission Viejo	CA	HST
714-457-1019	The Believer's Board 1	Lake Forest	CA	DS
714-457-1020	The Believer's Board 2	Lake Forest	CA	V32B
714-457-1021	The Believer's Board 3	Lake Forest	CA	HST
714-457-8066	The Safety Net	Mission Viejo	CA	DS2
714-489-1734	Electric Dreams	Dana Point	CA	ZYXL
714-492-1045	The Calypso BBS	San Clemente	CA	DS2
714-492-3035	The Calypso BBS	San Clemente	CA	V32
714-492-8727	InfoMat BBS	San Clemente	CA	DS
714-493-3819	The Crow's Nest	Monarch Beach	CA	HST
714-533-9501	Car-Puter BBS	Anaheim	CA	V32
714-535-1258	Philosopher's Log	Anaheim	CA	HST
714-539-1246	12 & 12 Anonymous BBS	Garden Grove	CA	V32
714-539-2477	The Master's BBS	Garden Grove	CA	HST
714-539-8644	Orange Co North	Garden Grove	CA	HST
714-539-9374	The Black Pine BBS	Garden Grove	CA	DS2
714-545-3175	Clipboard	Costa Mesa	CA	HST
714-552-3515	Software Exchange BBS	Irvine	CA	V32B
714-552-3715	Legends BBS	Irvine	CA	HST
714-559-6862	Beginners Luck BBS	Irvine	CA	V32
714-583-1679	Digital Illusions	El Toro	CA	HST
714-636-2667	The Kandy Shack	Garden Grove	CA	DS2
714-638-2298	F.O.G.	Garden Grove	CA	DS
714-638-8353	F.O.G.	Garden Grove	CA	HST
714-639-1139	Ol' Codger's BBS	Orange	CA	DS
714-642-0561	Bourbon St. West	Santa Ana	CA	HST
714-643-3066	Laguna Hills BBS	Laguna Hills	CA	DS2
714-650-2737	Remote Designs	Costa Mesa	CA	HST
714-651-1050	Master Connection BBS 2	Irvine	CA	HST
714-651-9815	Master Connection BBS 1	Irvine	CA	DS3
714-666-9238	ChristianInfoExchange	Anaheim	CA	V32
714-675-3947	Fire Wheel BBS	Newport Beach	CA	DS3
714-675-9121	The Waterfront	Newport Beach	CA	DS
714-708-2593	The Stand BBS	Costa Mesa	CA	V32B
714-720-1139	The Kernel	Newport Beach	CA	HST
714-730-5739	The Club Board	Tustin	CA	DS2
714-730-6743	The Club Board	Tustin	CA	ZYX
714-738-0841	PC Treasure Chest	Fullerton	CA	V32

AC/Phone	BBS Name	City	State	Modem
714-768-5720	The Carpenter's Workshop	Laguna Hills	CA	V32B
714-786-5736	MadDog! BBS	Irvine	CA	V32B
714-826-0125	The Point After BBS	Anaheim	CA	HST
714-827-2018	NymphoZit	Anaheim	CA	DS
714-827-3728	The Business Store	Buena Park	CA	HST
714-830-0311	Alpha/NET BBS	Lake Forest	CA	DS3
714-830-0402	Alpha/NET BBS	Lake Forest	CA	ZYXL
714-830-1884	California Online!	Lake Forest	CA	HST
714-830-8909	California Online!	Lake Forest	CA	V32B
714-836-8650	Traveller's Outpost	Santa Ana	CA	HST
714-838-4689	Shepherds Flock Family BBS	Irvine	CA	V32
714-838-6539	Mount Silverthorn	Tustin	CA	DS
714-846-4393	1139/South!	Huntington Beach	CA	V32B
714-854-6760	Moving & Shaking	Irvine	CA	V32
714-858-0787	The Other One	Trabuco Canyon	CA	HST4
714-870-4614	Online Exchange BBS	Fullerton	CA	HST
714-870-9624	Aim Online Services	Fullerton	CA	DS
714-879-4052	N.S.T.T.Z. Free 1	Fullerton	CA	V32B
714-879-8411	N.S.T.T.Z. Pay 2	Fullerton	CA	V32B
714-879-8412	N.S.T.T.Z. Pay 3	Fullerton	CA	HST
714-939-1041	Homer	Tustin	CA	DS2
714-952-2110	CA Self-Help Library	Anaheim	CA	HST
714-952-8910	Pleasure Island Chateau	Cypress	CA	DS3
714-956-4878	THE NET!	Anaheim	CA	DS
714-957-2881	The GOOD SAM BBS	Costa Mesa	CA	V32B
714-969-9624	Realty Network BBS	Huntington Beach	CA	V32B
714-992-0716	La Habra Connection	La Habra	CA	HST
714-993-5311	x-Point BBS	Placentia	CA	DS
714-994-4705	JRL Online Services	La Mirada	CA	DS
714-996-0805	Archivist's Scroll	Yorba Linda	CA	HST
714-996-4444	The Liberty BBS	Anaheim Hills	CA	ZYX
714-996-7777	The Liberty BBS	Anaheim Hills	CA	2400
714-996-8996	PC Exchange	Placentia	CA	HST
715-345-1173	Requiem Free Expression	Stevens Point	WI	V32B
715-345-1327	The Point BBS	Stevens Point	WI	HST4
715-387-1339	Promised Land	Marshfield	WI	DS
715-453-7615	Jeaux Garage	Tomahawk	WI	DS
715-539-2950	OutLand!	Merrill	WI	HST
715-652-2758	Twilight Zone	Auburndale	WI	DS
715-732-4134	CompuLine/PIDS	Marinette	WI	HST
715-748-4614	MIBBS	Medford	WI	HST
716-225-7446	The Magic Carpet BBS	Rochester	NY	HST
716-262-2612	The Pigeon Coop BBS	Rochester	NY	DS
716-271-6592	Data Comm	Rochester	NY	HST
716-288-0299	Runt's Madhouse	Rochester	NY	HST
716-288-5848	The Shack TOO	Rochester	NY	DS
716-289-3351	Chris' Amiga	Manchester	NY	HST
716-381-4749	The Mountains of Shadow	Pittsford	NY	DS2
716-381-8538	The Rochester Lab	Pittsford	NY	DS
716-396-2699	EFX Systems	Canandaigua	NY	HST
716-426-5202	Xerox National PC-Board	Rochester	NY	HST

AC/Phone	BBS Name	City	State	Modem
716-436-9497	NightWorX	Rochester	NY	DS
716-442-8144	I'm Crushing Your Head	Rochester	NY	HST
716-461-5201	The Recovery Room BBS	Rochester	NY	DS2
716-475-3044	The Garden South GSBBS	Henrietta	NY	V32
716-482-2592	Crystal Palace	Rochester	NY	V32
716-482-5401	The Wayward Wind	Rochester	NY	DS
716-526-6495	W-FL Teacher Resource Cntr	Stanley	NY	DS
716-554-5372	Interstellar Systems	Vine Valley	NY	HST
716-594-1804	Micro Science	Chili	NY	DS2
716-594-4227	The Oracle BBS	North Chili	NY	DS
716-646-1114	BackScatter BBS	Boston	NY	TB
716-688-1552	Med TechNet	Buffalo	NY	HST
716-695-1937	Cougar's Kingdom BBS	Buffalo	NY	V32B
716-723-0060	Vinnie's BBS	Rochester	NY	HST
716-787-1155	The Viper's Lair	Rochester	NY	DS3
716-865-2106	Knight Moves BBS	Rochester	NY	HST
716-872-0128	Mike's Maze	Webster	NY	HST
716-889-2016	Flower City Central	Chili	NY	HST
716-895-1146	Buffalo Data Systems	Buffalo	NY	DS2
717-243-0055	L & T's Spitfire BBS	Carlisle	PA	DS2
717-245-2847	Micro Medical Center BBS	Carlisle	PA	DS
717-248-2699	KB-NET	Lewistown	PA	HST
717-248-5375	Juniata Valley BBS	Lewistown	PA	V32B
717-323-1457	The Forrest's End	Williamsport	PA	HST
717-354-5027	Rabbit Hutch	East Earl	PA	DS
717-364-5375	Sarver's Output Services	Monroeton	PA	V32B
717-387-5000	BloomsBurg/Shigaraki Net	Bloomsburg	PA	V32
717-397-0538	Mike and Rose's BBS	Lancaster	PA	DS2
717-533-2865	P/T BBS	Cleona	PA	HST
717-561-8150	Megaboard]I[	Harrisburg	PA	VH
717-588-7549	Parallax/ParaNet Omicron	Bushkill	PA	HST
717-622-2421	Coal Cracker BBS	Pottsville	PA	HST
717-653-9621	The BOYS Room	Mt. Joy	PA	DS2
717-657-2223	The Other BBS	Harrisburg	PA	HST
717-686-3037	Al's Cabin	Milford	PA	HST
717-689-3123	Brinkman's Hollow BBS	Hamlin	PA	HST4
717-759-1693	NePa BBS	Berwick	PA	HST
717-795-9636	The Christian BBs	Mechanicsburg	PA	HST
717-828-9416	Jerry's Place BBS	Dingmans Ferry	PA	HST
717-840-0139	Bill and Ted's	York	PA	V32B
717-840-1444	Cyberia	York	PA	DS3
717-853-3599	The Depot RBBS	Susquehanna	PA	DS2
717-853-3999	The Depot RBBS	Susquehanna	PA	V32B
717-876-0152	The Northeast File Bank	Jermyn	PA	HST
717-876-5869	GROUND ZER0!!! BBS	Archbald	PA	HST
717-938-6760	Infinity V BBS	Lewisberry	PA	DS2
717-944-0655	Middletown BBS	Middletown	PA	HST
717-944-6877	Dino][	Middletown	PA	HST
717-992-4467	The Allied Group BBS	Brodheadsville	PA	DS
718-204-7831	Cravings BBS	Long Island City	NY	V32
718-217-0898	PharmStat Systems Public	Bayside	NY	DS

AC/Phone	BBS Name	City	State	Modem
718-251-9346	MORE BBS	Brooklyn	NY	DS
718-252-4529	The Taste BBS	Brooklyn	NY	HST4
718-276-0246	Design Line BBS	Rosedale	NY	V32
718-278-2120	The WALL	Long Island City	NY	HST
718-377-0768	Moondog BBS Private	Brooklyn	NY	HST
718-386-6010	Orphan BBS	Ridgewood	NY	HST4
718-424-1696	The Greek Isles	New York City	NY	V32B
718-444-4555	MAS	Brooklyn	NY	2400
718-444-5090	MAS	Brooklyn	NY	DS2
718-461-9487	The Corner Palace BBS	College Point	NY	HST
718-468-6388	PharmStat Systems Private	Bayside	NY	VH
718-494-8310	Staten Island Exchange	Staten Island	NY	VH
718-494-9273	The Event Horizon	Staten Island	NY	DS
718-529-8890	Holman's World	New York	NY	V32B
718-548-8704	Manhattan College RBBS	Riverdale/Bronx	NY	DS3
718-562-1946	The Promised Land	Bronx	NY	V32B
718-565-1522	The Red Mansion BBS	New York	NY	DS2
718-667-4470	Black Box BBS	Staten Island	NY	HST
718-692-1368	Moondog BBS Private	Brooklyn	NY	HST4
718-692-2498	Moondog BBS Public	Brooklyn	NY	VH
718-692-2942	David's Girls BBS	Brooklyn	NY	HST
718-716-6198	Systematic BBS	Bronx	NY	V32B
718-716-6341	Systematic BBS	Bronx	NY	V32B
718-721-2051	C Shop BBS	Long Island City	NY	V32
718-756-7201	L'chaim BBS	Brooklyn	NY	DS
718-793-4796	The BELFRY(!)	Forest Hills	NY	HST
718-793-8548	The IceBox BBS	New York	NY	V32
718-816-7792	Night Shift	Staten Island	NY	HST
718-853-8957	Brooklyn Perverts BBS	Brooklyn	NY	V32
718-894-2515	Final Frontier	Midl Village	NY	HST
718-934-1843	Shadowdale BBS	Brooklyn	NY	V32
718-939-7686	Squawk 1200 Aviation BBS	New York	NY	HST
718-956-3874	Cravings BBS	Brooklyn	NY	DS
718-972-6099	Star-Link Network BBS	New York	NY	DS2
718-997-1189	NEO Macintosh BBS	New York City	NY	V32B
719-380-8813	Programmers Playhouse	Colorado Springs	CO	HST
719-390-9249	Electric Locksmith	Colorado Springs	CO	HST
719-391-1092	The Crystal Cave	Widefield	CO	HST
719-391-8958	The Wandering Consultant	Security	CO	HST
719-392-6631	Wildcat Orphanage	Fountain	CO	V32
719-550-9305	CS-Depot	Colorado Springs	CO	DS2
719-574-3304	FireNet Leader	Colorado Springs	CO	HST
719-578-9127	Sci-Line	Colorado Springs	CO	HST
719-578-9406	SmartNet	Colorado Springs	CO	HST
719-579-0593	Hornet's Nest	Colorado Springs	CO	HST
719-591-6496	The Dark Crystal	Colorado Springs	CO	HST
719-632-2566	Cosug	Colorado Springs	CO	DS2
719-632-2657	Goldmill BBS	Colorado Springs	CO	HST
719-634-1115	DeskTop Central	Colorado Springs	CO	HST
719-637-1458	Scorpion	Colorado Springs	CO	HST
800-354-2983	Idiot Box RBBS-PC #6	Tucson	AZ	DS2

AC/Phone	BBS Name	City	State	Modem
801-261-8976	Salt Air BBS	Salt Lake City	UT	DS2
801-261-8979	Salt Air BBS	Salt Lake City	UT	ULT
801-269-0795	Nibbles 'n Bits	Murray	UT	DS
801-269-9575	Score Board BBS	Murray	UT	HST
801-373-4473	Rocky Mountain SF	Provo	UT	DS
801-374-8080	FamTies BBS	Provo	UT	HST
801-377-5933	Sanctuary	Provo	UT	V32
801-451-9102	MIC Computer BBS	Farmington	UT	HST
801-486-0929	The Iron Grid	Salt Lake City	UT	DS
801-489-3558	CamSoft, Inc	Springville	UT	DS3
801-563-6348	The Holodeck	Smithfield	UT	HST
801-579-7482	The WareHouse BBS	Salt Lake City	UT	V32B
801-586-2067	BBS-Cedar City	Cedar City	UT	DS
801-586-3935	BBS-Cedar City	Cedar City	UT	DS
801-944-0666	The Concrete Foundation	Sandy	UT	V32
802-334-2057	CUS-VT	New Port	VT	DS2
802-388-9899	Green Mountain Mac BBS	Middlebury	VT	DS
802-425-2139	Micro Corner	Ferrisburgh	VT	HST4
802-479-0551	Sol II System	Barre	VT	V32
802-482-2265	VT Education System	Hinesburg	VT	HST
802-860-1795	High-Z	Burlington	VT	HST
802-860-1875	We Serve Your Drives	Burlington	VT	HST
802-860-1908	Dog Dish	South Burlington	VT	CS1
802-899-4988	The Data Dungeon!	Underhill	VT	V32B
803-229-1747	Late Night Express BBS	Greenwood	SC	HST
803-236-7481	AmiSS	Myrtle Beach	SC	DS2
803-256-3546	ParaSoft BBS	Columbia	SC	HST
803-279-1183	Hero's Guild	Belvedere	SC	DS2
803-279-4124	Augusta Forum	North Augusta	SC	HST
803-299-3668	Door to the South	Greenville	SC	DS2
803-456-2747	Shareware Connection	Ware Shoals	SC	HST
803-525-2665	The Low Country	Beaufort	SC	DS
803-548-0900	Fort Mill BBS	Fort Mill	SC	VH
803-552-0700	Charleston Classifieds	N. Charleston	SC	ULT
803-552-4389	The Earth Art BBS!	North Charleston	SC	DS3
803-556-7485	East Bay X-Change 1	Charleston	SC	HST
803-556-7514	East Bay X-Change 2	Charleston	SC	ULT
803-569-7195	The Crowe's Nest	Goose Creek	SC	HST
803-571-1633	The NUTT House BBS	Charleston	SC	HST
803-572-3353	The UNKNOWN BBS	Goose Creek	SC	HST
803-576-6212	Hyperspace I BBS	Spartanburg	SC	HST
803-577-0545	The B.I.B.S. System	Charleston	SC	DS
803-588-2430	Beyond Reality	Folly Beach	SC	HST
803-593-4391	The Valley Connection	Gloverville	SC	HST
803-648-0283	Keep It Simple	Aiken	SC	HST
803-649-5303	Aiken Transient Authority	Aiken	SC	HST
803-649-9612	The SpeakEasy	Aiken	SC	DS2
803-650-9022	Periscope BBS	Myrtle Beach	SC	HST
803-732-1049	Dragon's Den	Columbia	SC	HST
803-763-4657	Charles Towne BBS	Charleston	SC	HST
803-768-4782	Seabrook Island Board	John's Island	SC	HST

AC/Phone	BBS Name	City	State	Modem
803-797-1930	The Gameland BBS	Goose Creek	SC	HST4
803-821-1363	The General Store	Summerville	SC	HST
803-871-9771	RaceNet	Ladson	SC	HST
803-875-2019	RaceNet	Ladson	SC	HST
803-875-3020	Randy's House	Summerville	SC	HST
803-957-8691	The Enchanted Realm	Columbia	SC	HST
804-261-1819	B&C BBS	Richmond	VA	DS
804-262-9289	Boot Factory	Richmond	VA	HST
804-264-0035	C & C	Richmond	VA	HST
804-264-2107	The Back Door	Richmond	VA	HST
804-293-2400	C.O.M.A.	Charlottesville	VA	V32B
804-293-4710	Freeware Hall of Fame	Charlottesville	VA	DS2
804-295-3581	Data World BBS	Charlottesville	VA	V32
804-296-1242	The Information Exchange	Charlottesville	VA	V32B
804-296-2066	The Midnight Foundation	Charlottesville	VA	HST4
804-296-4450	Into the Shadows	Charlottesville	VA	V32B
804-353-4160	Intercity BBS	Richmond	VA	DS
804-424-0394	Wings and Wheels BBS	Cheasapeake	VA	V32B
804-436-3125	The Apex	Chesapeake	VA	HST
804-456-2971	Pleasure Dome BBS	Virginia Beach	VA	V32B
804-465-5375	Play Pen BBS	Chesapeake	VA	DS
804-489-7450	Terrapin Station	Norfolk	VA	DS
804-490-5878	Pleasure Dome BBS	Virginia Beach	VA	2400
804-491-3192	The Weyr BBS	Virginia Beach	VA	HST4
804-495-4955	Touch of Ireland	Virginia Beach	VA	HST
804-499-5612	Pleasure Dome BBS	Virginia Beach	VA	HST
804-525-2358	Laser TAG	Forest	VA	V32
804-525-5372	BB-P	Forest	VA	V32B
804-525-9760	BB-P	Forest	VA	V32B
804-590-2161	Servant of the Lord	Matoaca	VA	V32B
804-591-0736	The Felicia BBS	Newport News	VA	HST
804-591-8537	Brokedown Palace	Newport News	VA	HST
804-626-0103	The No*Name BBS	Norfolk	VA	HST
804-671-8547	The Skeleton Closet	Virginia Beach	VA	HST
804-721-3320	TEL-COM	Virginia Beach	VA	DS
804-744-0797	The FreeBoard BBS	Midlothian	VA	HST
804-793-0950	The Hugman's BBS	Danville	VA	DS
804-793-6094	Just For Fun BBS	Danville	VA	DS
804-826-1928	Ten Bowl BBS	Hampton	VA	HST
804-846-6518	Starbase 9000	Lynchburg	VA	DS
804-851-7675	The Party Place	Hampton	VA	HST
804-857-4346	TimeLords BBS	Norfolk	VA	DS
804-865-6848	Pier 22 BBS	Hampton	VA	HST
804-877-3539	Virginia Data Exchange	Ft Monroe	VA	DS
804-929-6113	The CCC BBS	Madison Heights	VA	V32
804-973-8235	Pat's Place	Charlottesville	VA	V32B
804-977-9600	C.O.M.A.	Charlottesville	VA	DS3
804-978-7182	The V.I.N.E.	Charlottesville	VA	V32B
804-979-2035	The Amiga Bandwidth	Charlottesville	VA	DS2
804-979-2487	The Amiga Bandwidth	Charlottesville	VA	V32B
804-979-9568	The SPIRIT of '76!	Charlottesville	VA	DS3

AC/Phone	BBS Name	City	State	Modem
805-252-0450	The Space Station BBS	Canyon Country	CA	HST
805-256-6457	Rosamond Astronomical	Rosamond	CA	HST
805-258-0413	The Night Owl BBS	Edwards	CA	DS3
805-258-5304	Desert Connection!	Edwards	CA	V32
805-264-1383	dCOM Support	Lancaster	CA	HST
805-272-1812	Lighthouse BBS	Palmdale	CA	HST
805-296-9056	The Software Station	Saugus	CA	V32
805-322-5587	The Dew Drop Inn	Bakersfield	CA	HST
805-334-2242	MSI HQ BBS Private	Bakersfield	CA	V32
805-334-2243	MSI HQ BBS Private	Bakersfield	CA	HST
805-334-2244	MSI HQ BBS Private	Bakersfield	CA	HST
805-334-2245	MSI HQ BBS Private	Bakersfield	CA	HST
805-334-2246	MSI HQ BBS Private	Bakersfield	CA	DS
805-334-2264	MSI HQ BBS Private	Bakersfield	CA	ULT
805-334-2265	MSI HQ BBS Private	Bakersfield	CA	ULT
805-334-2267	MSI HQ BBS Private	Bakersfield	CA	ULT
805-334-2268	MSI HQ BBS Private	Bakersfield	CA	ULT
805-334-2269	MSI HQ BBS Public	Bakersfield	CA	HST
805-334-2270	MSI HQ BBS Public	Bakersfield	CA	HST
805-374-7373	Conejo Info Services BBS	Thousand Oaks	CA	V32B
805-374-7575	Conejo Info Services BBS	Thousand Oaks	CA	HST
805-395-0250	MSI HQ BBS Private	Bakersfield	CA	V32
805-395-0650	MSI HQ BBS Public	Bakersfield	CA	ULT
805-395-0667	MSI HQ BBS Public	Bakersfield	CA	ULT
805-395-0672	MSI HQ BBS Public	Bakersfield	CA	DS
805-399-1765	KAOS-AMIGA	Bakersfield	CA	DS
805-399-5880	All Sports BBS	Bakersfield	CA	HST4
805-482-8030	Tomcat Productions	Oxnard	CA	HST4
805-483-1467	Surfboard	Oxnard	CA	V32
805-488-7430	RoyaLink	Oxnard	CA	HST
805-488-8973	The R&R BBS	Oxnard	CA	DS
805-492-7642	Joe's Garage BBS	Thousand Oaks	CA	V32B
805-494-9386	Pacific Coast Micro	Thousand Oaks	CA	HST
805-496-7320	Pacific Coast Micro	Thousand Oaks	CA	CS1
805-498-3500	The NOMAD PCBoard	Thousand Oaks	CA	V32
805-499-0865	Alt. Methods BBS	Newbury Park	CA	V32B
805-582-1534	Modem ONE BBS	Simi Valley	CA	HST
805-583-5833	The Grinder	Simi Valley	CA	DS
805-640-0120	Riff Raft	Ojai	CA	V32B
805-652-1478	His Board	Ventura	CA	HST
805-659-3313	805 SysOp	Saticoy	CA	DS
805-832-6173	The Late Show!	Bakersfield	CA	DS
805-871-5414	The Underground BBS	Bakersfield	CA	HST
805-872-5227	MobilNet	Bakersfield	CA	V32
805-937-6205	The Back Door BBS	Orcutt	CA	HST
805-943-5881	CoreDump BBS	Quartz Hill	CA	DS
805-944-2994	Hitchhikers Guide	Littlerock	CA	V32
805-949-8151	The Researcher's BBS	Lancaster	CA	HST
805-962-0122	Network XXIII	Santa Barbara	CA	HST
805-964-4766	The Seaside BBS	Santa Barbara	CA	HST
805-983-4303	The Golden Retriever	Oxnard	CA	HST

AC/Phone	BBS Name	City	State	Modem
806-792-0216	The Windmill	Lubbock	TX	DS2
806-792-0536	The Windmill	Lubbock	TX	DS2
806-792-5947	The Windmill	Lubbock	TX	DS2
806-792-6116	The Windmill	Lubbock	TX	HST
806-792-6447	The Windmill	Lubbock	TX	DS2
806-795-0509	The Crystal Palace	Lubbock	TX	V32
806-795-9003	Agape BBS	Lubbock	TX	DS3
806-797-7512	Club RayD8	Lubbock	TX	V32
806-799-5228	Dark Side Of The Moon	Lubbock	TX	DS
808-338-9999	PeaceKauai	Kauai	HI	HST
808-456-8510	Ghostcomm Tele-Services	Honolulu	HI	DS
808-486-2565	Wire Head	Aiea	HI	DS2
808-531-1355	Musubi BBS	Honolulu	HI	HST
808-732-6909	The Magic Castle	Honolulu	HI	DS
808-845-7054	Coconuts BBS	Honolulu	HI	DS
808-935-1748	Syscon Hilo	Hilo	HI	HST
808-942-2508	The Computer Station	Honolulu	HI	DS
808-956-2626	Coconut Telegraph	Honolulu	HI	DS
809-720-1246	Baron Carlos's Castle	Guaynabo	PR	HST
809-724-0621	Opus Amicus BBS	San Juan	PR	DS
809-751-7728	Mega-D RBBS 2	Rio Piedras	PR	HST
809-752-8713	Midi Land	Carolina	PR	HST
809-756-8863	Cyclone BBS	Rio Piedras	PR	HST
809-783-9542	The Island Sun I	Caparra Heights	PR	HST
809-789-6241	The Warehouse BBS	Puerto Nuevo	PR	HST
809-793-3923	The Island Sun II	Caparra Heights	PR	HST
812-279-2143	The Hotseat	Bedford	IN	HST
812-284-1321	GenevaConvention Adult BBS	Clarksville	IN	HST4
812-284-5465	GenevaConvention Adult BBS	Clarksville	IN	HST4
812-442-5354	ATTEL BBS 1/A	Brazil	IN	HST
812-474-2263	Digicom	Evansville	IN	HST
812-479-1310	Digicom	Evansville	IN	DS2
812-941-9427	Digital Underground	New Albany	IN	V32
813-262-2755	Trail-T BBS	Naples	FL	HST
813-264-0073	Data Exchange 1	Tampa	FL	DS
813-264-6344	Entropy BBS	Lutz	FL	HST
813-267-1215	The Emerald City	Fort Myers	FL	HST
813-275-5410	Mental Floss	Fort Myers	FL	DS2
813-278-5731	ArchonRAINBOW	Fort Myers	FL	DS
813-282-0023	The Godfather BBS Public	Tampa	FL	CS1
813-286-7084	The Godfather BBS Private	Tampa	FL	DS
813-286-7659	The Godfather BBS Private	Tampa	FL	CS1
813-286-7812	The Godfather BBS Private	Tampa	FL	V32B
813-287-2462	The Godfather BBS Private	Tampa	FL	CS3
813-289-3314	The Godfather BBS Public	Tampa	FL	DS
813-321-0734	Mercury Opus	St. Petersburg	FL	DS
813-321-3976	Mercury Opus	St. Petersburg	FL	2400
813-341-2327	Lambda Unlimited BBS	St. Petersburg	FL	V32
813-351-9358	Minas Tirith BBS	Sarasota	FL	HST
813-371-3600	The Grapevine BBS	Sarasota	FL	HST
813-376-6994	Mutt & Jeff's	New Port Richey	FL	HST4

AC/Phone	BBS Name	City	State	Modem
813-376-8229	Mutt n Jeff's	New Port Richey	FL	DS
813-377-1470	The Above Board	Sarasota	FL	HST
813-378-1077	AmericanUnitedBroadcasting	Sarasota	FL	HST
813-392-6718	Beyond 2000	Largo	FL	HST
813-445-4337	CSFSO Telecomm	Clearwater	FL	DS
813-446-7311	AquaScape	Clearwater	FL	DS
813-471-0552	Ancestry TBBS	Sebring	FL	DS2
813-481-5575	The Pegasus Project	Fort Myers	FL	V32B
813-493-7386	The Back Door	Venice	FL	HST
813-497-7186	Crystal Visions 2	Bradenton	FL	HST
813-521-2925	The Jayhawk Amiga BBS!	St. Petersburg	FL	HST
813-521-3664	Jayhawk BBS!	St. Petersburg	FL	HST
813-527-5666	St Pete Programmers Xchg	St. Petersburg	FL	DS2
813-530-0799	New Age	St. Petersburg	FL	HST
813-535-8560	Computer Vision BBS!	St. Petersburg	FL	HST
813-542-5482	ENTREvous II	Cape Coral	FL	HST
813-545-0401	Park Place	Pinellas Park	FL	HST
813-574-2301	Tandy Tane BBS I	Cape Coral	FL	HST
813-585-7082	FREE	Largo	FL	HST
813-596-4999	Happy Hideaway	Seminole	FL	HST
813-596-7034	The Pegboard BBS	Largo	FL	HST
813-625-4740	The Southern State BBS	Port Charlotte	FL	V32
813-625-5636	The Gold Coast RBBS	Punta Gorda	FL	HST
813-647-3624	PC-net BBS	Lakeland	FL	V32
813-675-8812	Byte Size Bits	LaBelle	FL	HST
813-685-6097	The C21 Link BBS	Tampa Bay	FL	V32B
813-693-2390	The Nite Line	Fort Myers	FL	HST
813-693-8095	AquaFlight	Fort Myers	FL	DS2
813-696-2444	Crown Jewel BBS	Lake Wales	FL	V32B
813-745-5677	Chipper Clipper	Bradenton	FL	HST
813-746-7788	Silicon Dreams	Bradenton	FL	V32
813-755-0575	Jos' Lounge	Bradenton	FL	DS
813-772-7585	The PIG Sty	Cape Coral	FL	HST
813-785-3243	The FatherBoard	Palm Harbor	FL	DS2
813-796-2038	Cat House BBS! Systems	Safety Harbor	FL	HST
813-796-2486	Cat House BBS! Systems	Safety Harbor	FL	HST
813-835-0706	Challenger BBS	Tampa	FL	V32
813-855-5163	Mr. Bill's Place	Tampa	FL	HST
813-856-7926	Gulf Coast BBS	New Port Richey	FL	HST
813-862-1809	Studio PC BBS 2	Port Richey	FL	DS
813-862-7946	The Program BBS	Port Richey	FL	HST
813-862-8850	Studio PC BBS 1	Port Richey	FL	HST
813-885-5797	Top Cat BBS! 1	Tampa	FL	ZYXL
813-885-6011	Top Cat BBS! 2	Tampa	FL	2400
813-920-4704	Rivendell BBS 2	Odessa	FL	DS
813-920-4714	Rivendell BBS 1	Odessa	FL	HST
813-924-0499	ZimmComm	Sarasota	FL	HST
813-924-4982	Grand BBS	Sarasota	FL	HST
813-938-7386	The Fatherboard BBS	Holiday	FL	DS2
813-939-3394	ArchonRAINBOW	Fort Myers	FL	HST
813-949-3392	PC-Help! BBS	Lutz	FL	DS3

AC/Phone	BBS Name	City	State	Modem
813-949-4993	PC-Help! BBS	Tampa	FL	DS
813-949-6588	PC-Help! BBS	Tampa	FL	HST4
813-961-6242	T.A.B.B.	Tampa	FL	HST
813-968-3213	Data Exchange 2	Tampa	FL	HST
813-971-2934	Tower Club	Tampa	FL	HST
813-973-3346	PC Consultants BBS	Wesley Chapel	FL	V32
813-977-7065	Southern Systems	Tampa	FL	DS
813-979-7307	HealthSource BBS	Tampa	FL	V32
814-266-9234	Rhythm & Blues BBS	Johnstown	PA	V32B
814-337-0501	Compuphile BBS	Meadville	PA	V32B
814-337-2971	Compuphile BBS	Meadville	PA	DS3
814-459-8901	Erie's WestSide BBS	Erie	PA	DS3
814-539-6648	Cheers BBS	Johnstown	PA	DS
814-725-2713	Hoosier Hideaway	North East	PA	HST4
814-725-8887	Hoosier Hideaway	North East	PA	DS3
814-756-5661	The Gauntlet	Cranesville	PA	HST
815-233-5008	The Gateway Net BBS	Freeport	IL	DS2
815-234-2346	OverBoard BBS	Stillman Valley	IL	HST
815-282-9248	The Eagle's Nest	Rockford	IL	HST
815-385-5031	McHenry BBS 1	McHenry	IL	DS
815-385-7113	McHenry BBS 2	McHenry	IL	DS
815-385-7167	McHenry BBS 9	McHenry	IL	CS1
815-385-7906	McHenry BBS 8	McHenry	IL	CS1
815-385-7956	McHenry BBS 7	McHenry	IL	CS1
815-385-9011	McHenry BBS 3	McHenry	IL	DS
815-385-9013	McHenry BBS 5	McHenry	IL	HST4
815-385-9347	McHenry BBS 6	McHenry	IL	HST4
815-385-9936	McHenry BBS 4	McHenry	IL	HST4
815-434-4430	River City BBS	Ottawa	IL	DS
815-443-2489	The Black Star BBS	Pearl City	IL	HST
815-633-1558	Uncle Spikes Place	Machesney Park	IL	DS2
815-633-6455	The Silver Dragon Inn	Loves Park	IL	HST
815-654-9729	Outlaw Tech Zone	Rockford	IL	HST
815-748-2539	Castle Anthrax	DeKalb	IL	HST
815-868-2422	The Boomtown BBS	McConnell	IL	DS2
815-886-0109	Electric Estates BBS	Romeoville	IL	ULT
816-228-1719	Powertrain BBS	Blue Springs	MO	HST
816-228-3204	BenNETt	Blue Springs	MO	DS
816-231-3002	The Heartbreak Ridge	Kansas City	MO	DS
816-232-2813	HOLLYWOOD Tonite!!	St. Joseph	MO	HST
816-233-1357	CMOS OPUS BBS	St. Joseph	MO	DS
816-239-4808	Network Market BBS	Atlanta	MO	V32B
816-241-8869	Transient Technologies	Kansas City	MO	HST
816-246-5253	The Guru Zone	Lees Summit	MO	HST
816-322-1133	Happy Hour BBS	Raymore	MO	HST
816-322-4547	SOLO-Quest	Belton	MO	HST
816-353-3462	Writers' Block BBS	Raytown	MO	DS
816-356-0901	K C Central BBS	Raytown	MO	DS
816-358-3204	The Power Board - CBCS	Raytown	MO	DS
816-364-1035	MEGA-Link BBS	St. Joseph	MO	HST
816-436-2843	Maple Woods BBS	Kansas City	MO	HST

AC/Phone	BBS Name	City	State	Modem
816-444-4960	Laser Online	Kansas City	MO	DS
816-587-5360	Amiga Central BBS	Kansas City	MO	V32
816-587-9936	The File Shop BBS	Kansas City	MO	HST
816-665-7157	The Cave	Kirksville	MO	V32B
816-746-4747	The BullPen BBS	Parkville	MO	V32
816-761-0860	Infinity BBS	Kansas City	MO	HST
816-761-4039	Rampart General BBS	Kansas City	MO	DS2
816-765-9306	Barsoom BBS	Kansas City	MO	HST
816-822-8233	ProBoard Plus	Kansas City	MO	DS
817-244-7136	The Bone Box	Fort Worth	TX	HST
817-284-1520	GeneSys I BBS	Hurst	TX	VH
817-293-1134	The AIDS Chat Line	Everman	TX	HST
817-326-4101	Chaparral BBS	Grandbury	TX	HST
817-329-1614	The Dew Line	Grapevine	TX	HST
817-367-0401	Automation	White Settlement	TX	HST
817-367-3828	The Mail Drop	White Settlement	TX	HST
817-370-7304	Monty's Place	Fort Worth	TX	DS
817-381-7905	The Moose's Den	Denton	TX	HST
817-382-4388	Golden Triangle BBS	Denton	TX	V32B
817-387-5155	The Big Book BBS	Denton	TX	HST
817-430-5131	The Dandy Tandy BBS	Roanoke	TX	DS
817-447-1969	The ARChive	Burleson	TX	HST
817-447-2598	Incredible BBS	Burleson	TX	V32
817-447-3527	The Speed Way	Fort Worth	TX	DS
817-457-9800	CTR Company	Fort Worth	TX	HST
817-477-4824	The Elite Circle	Mansfield	TX	HST
817-478-0744	Gemini	Arlington	TX	HST
817-485-9969	Laugh Connection	Dallas/FW	TX	V32B
817-491-1516	The Alternative Adult	Roanoke	TX	DS
817-497-4110	The Andromeda Galaxy	Corinth	TX	HST
817-497-6325	[NEC]/[SDN]	Corinth	TX	HST
817-526-2941	Bill's Try	Killeen	TX	HST
817-540-3527	Spare Parts	Bedford	TX	HST
817-547-1734	Virtual Reality BBS	Copperas Cove	TX	DS
817-554-2515	The Land Beyond	Killeen	TX	HST
817-560-9165	Bob's Bear Line	Fort Worth	TX	HST
817-573-0156	Turbo AT! BBS	Granbury	TX	DS
817-656-4282	The Back Door	Fort Worth	TX	DS
817-656-7620	The Third Eye BBS	Fort Worth	TX	HST
817-656-8093	The Gallery	Fort Worth	TX	DS
817-662-2361	File Quest	Waco	TX	DS2
817-666-5137	The Unicorner BBS	Waco	TX	DS2
817-695-0058	The ClipBoard (tm)	Arlington	TX	DS
817-696-9617	The ID/ST Vortex	Wichita Falls	TX	HST
817-731-1754	Obscured By Clouds	Fort Worth	TX	DS
817-732-6157	Shadowdale	Fort Worth	TX	DS
817-735-1626	Bowl Of Chili!	Fort Worth	TX	HST
817-735-8006	The BBN	Fort Worth	TX	HST
817-738-3454	The Pulse	Fort Worth	TX	DS
817-752-4999	Feet First BBS	Waco	TX	HST
817-754-7758	Waco Info Net	Waco	TX	HST

AC/Phone	BBS Name	City	State	Modem
817-756-3123	The Blood Bank II	Waco	TX	V32
817-756-7343	The Blood Bank	Waco	TX	V32
817-756-7565	The Mule Barn	Waco	TX	HST
817-776-0291	The Private EaR III	Waco	TX	DS
817-776-6041	The Private EaR II	Waco	TX	DS2
817-776-9877	The Private EaR	Waco	TX	DS2
817-799-1570	TSTI INFO NET	Waco	TX	HST
817-840-2140	Hello World	McGregor	TX	HST
817-848-5840	Back Stage	Waco	TX	HST
817-857-4241	The Fissure	Waco	TX	V32
817-947-8899	Comland PC-Board BBS	Austin	TX	HST
818-240-5774	Infinity Ltd	Glendale	CA	HST
818-248-1087	BJ's RBBS	La Crescenta	CA	HST
818-248-2304	DeepSky	Montrose	CA	DS2
818-248-3088	HOT TIPS Private	Glendale	CA	CS1
818-248-8974	HOT TIPS Public	Glendale	CA	2400
818-249-3227	The Closet	La Crescenta	CA	V32B
818-284-3554	Alhambra Data Exchange	Alhambra	CA	HST4
818-287-6133	The J-Connection BBS	Rosemead	CA	V32B
818-288-0573	Eclair BBS	Monterey Park	CA	V32
818-330-1739	Medi-Call BBS 1	West Covina	CA	DS
818-330-5849	Medi-Call BBS 2	West Covina	CA	2400
818-352-2993	Central Computer Banks	Tujunga	CA	HST
818-352-6777	Court Jester	Tujunga	CA	ULT
818-352-8874	Court Jester	Tujunga	CA	2400
818-353-2242	KnowledgeBase Of Henry Geo	Tujunga	CA	CS1
818-353-5873	AirConditioned Nightmare	Tujunga	CA	V32B
818-353-8891	Mysteria	Tujunga	CA	DS2
818-366-1238	The MOG-UR'S EMS	Granada Hills	CA	DS3
818-366-6442	The MOG-UR'S EMS	Granada Hills	CA	DS3
818-366-8929	The MOG-UR'S EMS	Granada Hills	CA	DS3
818-441-2625	The Continuum	So. Pasadena	CA	V32B
818-443-0086	Right Track BBS	South El Monte	CA	DS3
818-503-4668	The Wizard of OS/2 BBS	North Hollywood	CA	HST4
818-562-3014	The Night Shift BBS	Burbank	CA	V32B
818-569-3740	Panasia BBS	Glendale	CA	DS3
818-579-3711	Programmers Exchange	Monterey Park	CA	CS1
818-579-9711	Programmers Exchange	Monterey Park	CA	HST
818-683-3438	The Labyrinth	Pasadena	CA	V32B
818-700-9591	Third World	Chatsworth	CA	HST
818-709-6978	Wizard of OsZ PCBoard	Canoga Park	CA	V32B
818-765-1215	Computer Addicts	North Hollywood	CA	HST
818-765-2171	The Crystal Palace	North Hollywood	CA	V32B
818-766-0911	The Annex	Studio City	CA	DS
818-772-0384	MoonBeams BBS	Northridge	CA	DS2
818-791-8680	Infomania BBS	Pasadena	CA	V32B
818-798-2793	Global BBS	Pasadena	CA	HST
818-848-4101	Blue Thunder BBS	Burbank	CA	DS3
818-891-1344	The Tool Shop	Panorama City	CA	VH
818-891-3772	The Tool Shop	Panorama City	CA	HST
818-891-6780	The Tool Shop	Panorama City	CA	2400

AC/Phone	BBS Name	City	State	Modem
818-896-4015	The Ledge PC-Board	Lakeview Terrace	CA	DS2
818-913-6843	Learning Experience	La Puente	CA	V32
818-951-4445	Mac Valhalla BBS	Tujunga	CA	DS
818-953-9063	Personal Computing U.	Burbank	CA	V32
818-955-9681	The Night Shift BBS	Burbank	CA	DS
818-957-5318	DataPhile	Montrose	CA	V32B
818-965-6241	The Drawing Board	Hacienda Heights	CA	DS
818-965-7220	House Atreides	Rowland Heights	CA	HST
818-967-0701	KBTC BBS	West Covina	CA	V32
818-969-9170	Azusa Pacific BBS	Azusa	CA	HST
901-345-0117	CornerStone TBBS	Memphis	TN	HST
901-357-1778	The High Flying BBS	Memphis	TN	HST
901-366-7221	Crystal Clear Ideas Netwrk	Memphis	TN	HST
901-367-0837	The South Poll	Memphis	TN	DS
901-372-3143	The Neutral Zone	Bartlett	TN	HST
901-373-4188	HaditNet	Memphis	TN	HST
901-373-5941	Cheers BBS	Memphis	TN	DS2
901-382-0337	The Labrynth BBS	Memphis	TN	DS2
901-386-1760	The Full Moon BBS	Memphis	TN	HST
901-398-9050	Home-Computer Users Group	Memphis	TN	HST
901-458-3604	Worthington's Computer	Memphis	TN	DS
901-525-5543	Sherwood Forest	Memphis	TN	HST
901-754-9823	The NiteMare BBS	Memphis	TN	HST
901-756-9438	Minnie's Basement	Cordova	TN	HST
901-757-5753	Radio Free Memphis	Memphis	TN	HST
901-761-1147	Mr. Zip BBS	Memphis	TN	HST
901-767-2503	The Think Tank	Memphis	TN	HST
901-872-0426	Tech Line BBS	Millington	TN	HST
901-873-0387	North End BBS	Millington	TN	HST
901-873-2315	Minnie's Satellite	Millington	TN	HST
901-873-2837	Buccaneer's Harbor	Millington	TN	HST
903-432-3584	THE Friendly OPUS	Seven Points	TX	HST
903-432-3586	OPUS USA	Seven Points	TX	HST
903-454-8737	Kev's Korner	Greenville	TX	HST
903-534-1049	Tyler Open Forum! #2	Tyler	TX	DS
903-534-1918	Tyler Open Forum!	Tyler	TX	DS
903-593-6856	Technical Systems	Tyler	TX	HST
903-593-7365	J'Adoube	Tyler	TX	HST
903-593-9056	Off The Wall	Tyler	TX	HST
903-597-1239	The Other Side Of The Hill	Tyler	TX	HST
903-753-0485	Marty's Place	Longview	TX	HST
903-868-2794	Electrode's BBS	Sherman	TX	HST
904-221-9425	Medical Info Health Netwrk	Jacksonville	FL	HST
904-224-8047	The ShadowFax	Tallahassee	FL	DS2
904-243-8376	The Mess BBS	Ft. Walton Beach	FL	HST
904-260-1811	The Final Frontier	Jacksonville	FL	HST
904-282-7125	Mr. Bill's World	Jacksonville	FL	CS1
904-292-9014	The King's Castle RBBS	Jacksonville	FL	HST
904-332-0408	Images Unlimited	Gainesville	FL	2400
904-332-0709	Images Unlimited	Gainesville	FL	DS2
904-332-2848	The Looking Glass	Gainesville	FL	DS

AC/Phone	BBS Name	City	State	Modem
904-332-4100	Images Unlimited	Gainesville	FL	HST4
904-332-6082	Esoteric Oracle	Gainesville	FL	DS
904-334-4798	Time Slice 1	Gainesville	FL	V32B
904-334-4885	Time Slice 2	Gainesville	FL	DS3
904-336-9785	Oubliette BBS	Gainesville	FL	DS
904-368-6945	Smokey's Place BBS	Ocala	FL	HST
904-372-7408	The Political Arena	Gainesville	FL	HST
904-373-5864	Bob's Corner Board	Gainesville	FL	DS
904-377-1325	Black ICE	Gainesville	FL	HST
904-377-2082	The Enchanted Forest	Gainesville	FL	DS
904-378-6403	The WARLOCK's Castle	Gainesville	FL	DS
904-386-8693	Wingit	Tallahassee	FL	DS3
904-389-6125	River City Roots	Jacksonville	FL	HST
904-389-8212	SoftWare Exchange	Jacksonville	FL	HST
904-396-6644	The Shuttle Pad BBS	Jacksonville	FL	V32B
904-398-5270	The Inter-Phase	Jacksonville	FL	HST
904-438-4803	Forty Two	Pensacola	FL	HST
904-474-0167	The Jaded Stairway	Pensacola	FL	HST
904-476-1270	Titan Software Solution	Pensacola	FL	HST
904-479-2440	Titan Software Solution	Pensacola	FL	HST
904-479-2448	Titan Software Solution	Pensacola	FL	2400
904-483-2498	Craig's DATA Exchange! BBS	Eustis	FL	DS3
904-623-5512	OFFCenter	Milton	FL	DS
904-651-8684	The *Hot Muddy Duck*	Shalimar	FL	HST
904-673-3765	Alpha Centuri	Ormond Beach	FL	V32
904-678-3503	U.S.S. Scorpion NCC-4017	Niceville	FL	HST
904-678-4509	Forgotten Realms BBS	Niceville	FL	HST
904-682-8028	The *Ugly Duckling*	Crestview	FL	HST
904-683-3309	Into The Night BBS	Spring Hill	FL	HST
904-688-9124	Toy Shop-PC BBS	Spring Hill	FL	DS
904-730-8799	Jax Online	Jacksonville	FL	HST
904-732-0866	The Tree BBS	Ocala	FL	DS
904-733-4750	Manpower	Jacksonville	FL	HST
904-743-0466	Al's Garage	Jacksonville	FL	HST
904-755-1182	The Nuclear Disaster	Lake City	FL	HST
904-757-8636	Small Business Graphics	Jacksonville	FL	V32B
904-768-3854	Stan's Shack	Jacksonville	FL	HST
904-769-9431	Computer Country	Panama City	FL	HST
904-779-5527	The Generic BBS	Jacksonville	FL	HST
904-786-4176	The Bounty St. BBS	Jacksonville	FL	DS
904-789-4786	Software Pit BBS	Deltona	FL	HST
904-789-7791	King Arthurs Castle	Deltona	FL	HST
904-797-2554	Ancient City BBS	St. Augustine	FL	HST
904-797-4824	Computer Store	St Augustine	FL	HST
904-862-9817	Victoria Station	Fort Walton Beach	FL	HST
904-863-8408	RSBBS/Oliver	Fort Walton Beach	FL	HST
904-863-8697	The Amiga Advantage	Fort Walton Beach	FL	HST
904-871-6536	221B Baker St	Panama City	FL	HST
904-878-4457	The Reactor	Tallahassee	FL	V32
904-897-3956	The Wizards' Oliver BBS	Niceville	FL	HST
904-944-9547	FoneEmporium	Pensacola	FL	DS

AC/Phone	BBS Name	City	State	Modem
904-963-1342	Technical Connection BBS	Wellborn	FL	HST
904-968-3687	Amiga Depot BBS	Cantonment	FL	V32
906-228-6517	Bytes-R-Us	Marquette	MI	HST
906-428-3250	The Intensive Care Unit	Gladstone	MI	HST
906-428-3425	The Lighthouse	Gladstone	MI	HST
906-482-8050	Amiga BitSwap	Houghton	MI	DS2
906-863-8407	Phoenix	Menominee	MI	HST
907-345-0147	The Pipeline	Anchorage	AK	DS
907-349-1857	The Mailman	Anchorage	AK	HST
907-373-5361	Jump Start	Wasilla	AK	V32B
907-452-1460	65'North	Fairbanks	AK	DS
907-479-0197	Doug's Domain	Fairbanks	AK	HST
907-479-8643	Chances Are	Fairbanks	AK	DS2
907-522-2327	Confuserland	Anchorage	AK	V32
907-522-2900	SoftWorks BBS	Anchorage	AK	V32B
907-561-2480	Alaska Smart Homes	Anchorage	AK	ULT
908-245-6614	The Micro Room	Roselle	NJ	HST
908-247-8252	EBBBS	East Brunswick	NJ	DS
908-249-1898	Skating Rink	East Brunswick	NJ	DS
908-249-2502	TibetNet BBS	Milltown	NJ	TB2
908-254-8117	Cop Shop	Sayreville	NJ	HST
908-271-5168	Gypsy Baron	Bridgewater	NJ	DS
908-276-2581	The Club House	Cranford	NJ	HST
908-276-3708	The Door Land BBS	Kenilworth	NJ	HST
908-276-5494	The Bird's Nest	Cranford	NJ	HST
908-291-0788	Selective Source BBS	Atlantic Higlands	NJ	DS2
908-297-3723	Rail News Network	North Brunswick	NJ	TB
908-297-5669	T&S BBS	Franklin Park	NJ	DS
908-324-2617	The Nut House BBS	Perth Amboy	NJ	HST
908-351-5883	Fone Link Support	Elizabeth	NJ	HST
908-381-5682	Heart Throb Adult BBS	Rahway	NJ	HST4
908-388-1676	NJMUG BBS	Clark	NJ	HST
908-418-4354	The Diner	Somerset	NJ	V32
908-463-0315	Parthenon	Piscataway	NJ	DS
908-486-2956	CFONJ	Linden	NJ	DS
908-494-3417	Planet Shadowstar TBBS	Edison	NJ	HST
908-505-8420	This Notes For You BBS	Toms River	NJ	V32
908-506-0472	The Dog's Breakfast	Toms River	NJ	HST
908-525-9440	Central Jersey MicroConnec	Parlin	NJ	DS
908-526-6395	Tranquil River BBS	Bridgewater	NJ	V32
908-544-8193	The University	Shrewsbury Twp	NJ	DS2
908-545-1751	OZ BBS	New Brunswick	NJ	DS2
908-545-2928	OZ BBS - 2400	New Brunswick	NJ	2400
908-566-8267	DZK BBS	Matawan	NJ	DS
908-580-0486	Milky Way RBBS	Millington	NJ	DS
908-602-0427	The SEAMCOlink Maximus	Iselin	NJ	HST
908-627-0318	The Airport II BBS	Middlesex	NJ	V32B
908-637-6336	Back Lounge of the TourBus	Hackettstown	NJ	HST
908-657-2178	The Thieve's Guild	Lakehurst	NJ	DS
908-665-5992	The Summit PCBoard	Summit	NJ	DS2
908-721-3087	Group Side of the Gate	Old Bridge	NJ	HST

AC/Phone	BBS Name	City	State	Modem
908-722-2231	The Sorcery Board	Bridgewater	NJ	DS2
908-727-1914	Hologram	Old Bridge	NJ	HST
908-727-7514	The Phase IV BBS	South Amboy	NJ	HST
908-730-7328	Arrakis 1	Ananndale	NJ	HST4
908-735-2180	Data-Base BBS 1	Annandale	NJ	2400
908-735-2185	Data-Base BBS 2	Annandale	NJ	VH
908-735-2242	Arrakis 2	Ananndale	NJ	HST4
908-735-2707	Data-Base BBS 3	Annandale	NJ	DS2
908-777-7380	Software Society South	Edison	NJ	V32
908-781-5131	The Sky's The Limit	Bedminster	NJ	HST
908-806-8779	The Missing Link BBS	Flemington	NJ	HST
908-806-8856	The Outer Limits BBS	Flemington	NJ	HST
908-821-8015	Kendall Park BBS	Kendall Park	NJ	DS
908-846-7981	Somerset Central BBS	Somerset	NJ	DS
908-872-8028	Selective Source BBS	AtlanticHighlands	NJ	DS2
908-906-7685	Micro-Fone TBBS	Metuchen	NJ	DS
908-920-7981	Steal Your Face	Brick	NJ	DS
908-981-9190	IEEE-Gateway	Piscataway	NJ	HST
908-988-0706	Castle Tabby	Bradley Beach	NJ	HST
909-276-0007	ROJACK's Pentium Palace	Riverside	CA	HST4
909-279-5458	The Board BBS	Corona	CA	HST
909-279-6987	In His Service	Norco	CA	2400
909-350-4418	The Fountainhead	Rialto	CA	V32B
909-352-1905	Baddog's Domain	Riverside	CA	V32B
909-356-3607	Bits and Bytes BBS	Fontana	CA	HST4
909-356-4636	Bits and Bytes BBS	Fontana	CA	ZYX9
909-356-5762	Bits and Bytes BBS	Fontana	CA	DS3
909-356-8345	Bits and Bytes BBS	Fontana	CA	CSP1
909-359-3189	Commnet-386	Riverside	CA	DS2
909-359-3230	Aries PCBoard	Riverside	CA	HST
909-369-9150	Hard Disk Cafe BBS	Riverside	CA	DS3
909-381-6013	The PC Spectrum RBBS-PC	Colton	CA	DS
909-591-5934	Modem Madness	Chino	CA	V32
909-591-6991	The Cloak Of Illusion	Fullerton	CA	HST
909-593-6144	Gentle Rain Forum	Claremont	CA	HST
909-597-7858	Sound Source	Chino Hills	CA	HST
909-657-6804	Quality BBS	Perris	CA	HST4
909-677-9695	Nano Access	Murrieta	CA	DS
909-678-2691	Valley Business BBS	Wildomar	CA	HST
909-681-6221	Attention To Details	Mira Loma	CA	HST
909-682-5940	Teleconnect BBS	Riverside	CA	HST
909-688-2658	Commu.Potential	Riverside	CA	HST
909-689-2762	Legend Graphics	Riverside	CA	DS2
909-689-7049	Legend Graphics	Riverside	CA	V32B
909-689-8895	Legend Graphics	Riverside	CA	DS3
909-689-9229	Legend Graphics	Riverside	CA	DS3
909-736-9548	CompuStar Network	Corona	CA	HST
909-781-4066	Far East Asian Connection	Riverside	CA	V32B
909-783-7802	MicroWave Research BBS	Colton	CA	HST
909-785-4586	The I.H.S. BBS	Norco	CA	DS
909-785-9176	Solid Rock BBS	Riverside	CA	HST

AC/Phone	BBS Name	City	State	Modem
909-824-3254	C.P.U. BBS	Colton	CA	HST
909-825-1854	Access Online	Colton	CA	ZYX
909-862-5388	Air America BBS	Highland	CA	ZYX
909-924-7336	The Seven Seas BBS	Moreno Valley	CA	V32B
909-927-8146	Hemet Nights BBS	Hemet	CA	HST
909-947-7478	Diamond Bar BBS	Ontario	CA	DS
909-986-1525	The Otter's Holt	Ontario	CA	DS
909-989-2603	Chips Unlimited RBBS-PC	Rancho Cucamonga	CA	HST
912-245-7655	The Fox's Den	Valdosta	GA	HST
912-247-6977	The Bad Lands BBS	Valdosta	GA	HST
912-328-6183	TallyBoard	Warner Robins	GA	HST
912-432-2440	Software Designer RBBS-PC	Albany	GA	DS
912-438-1210	Albany AstroLink	Albany	GA	HST
912-471-1243	Dixieland BBS	Macon	GA	HST
912-784-7273	Shorty's Corner BBS	Macon	GA	HST
912-882-3588	Kelsey Tech OnLine	St. Marys	GA	DS3
912-920-1952	The Control Tower BBS	Savannah	GA	V32
912-920-8070	The Savannah BBS	Savannah	GA	V32B
912-927-7323	The TACRBBS	Savannah	GA	V32
913-236-4863	Computer Specialties	Shawnee Mission	KS	HST
913-262-3796	The Golden Key BBS	Kansas City	KS	DS
913-271-2071	The Software Connection	Topeka	KS	HST
913-357-0316	City Limits Proboard HQ	Topeka	KS	HST
913-422-1025	Cosmix Station	Bonner Springs	KS	HST
913-441-3420	NesByte BBS	Bonner Springs	KS	HST
913-478-3229	The Green Acres	Topeka	KS	HST
913-599-6211	3-Times-7 BBS	Overland Park	KS	DS2
913-599-6266	3-Times-7 BBS	Overland Park	KS	DS
913-642-7907	South Of The River BBS	Overland Park	KS	HST
913-651-0400	The Ham Shack	Leavenworth	KS	HST
913-776-0111	Fox Support System	Manhattan	KS	HST
913-897-6667	Colossus]II[Systems	Stilwell	KS	DS2
914-229-8483	InFiniTy I	Hyde Park	NY	HST
914-234-1284	Stromi's Place	Bedford	NY	DS
914-236-3265	Acorn I BBS	Marlboro	NY	DS
914-245-2455	Amawalk Premium PCB	Yorktown	NY	2400
914-245-9115	Amawalk Premium PCB	Yorktown	NY	DS3
914-255-8154	PC-Paradise	New Paltz	NY	HST
914-271-9407	2x4 BBS	Croton	NY	DS
914-279-2514	The Brewster BBS	Brewster	NY	DS
914-297-0665	Rasputin Compute's	Poughkeepsie	NY	HST
914-297-8810	The 5-K BBS	Wappingers Falls	NY	HST
914-332-1983	TeleTech IES	N. Tarrytown	NY	DS
914-354-5463	10 Forward BBS	Pomona	NY	DS2
914-354-7499	TOUP	Spring Valley	NY	HST
914-374-3903	Dix MoJo BBS	New Hampton	NY	HST
914-381-1300	Brentwood BBS	Mamaroneck	NY	HST
914-381-1600	Brentwood BBS	Mamaroneck	NY	V32
914-564-3342	Micro-Mania	Newburgh	NY	HST
914-565-2407	APFL-Two	New Windsor	NY	V32
914-566-0948	TINY	Newburgh	NY	DS

AC/Phone	BBS Name	City	State	Modem
914-576-6139	Smart Office Solution	New Rochelle	NY	HST
914-621-2865	Dark Side of the Moon	Mahopac	NY	DS2
914-628-0535	Dark Side of the Moon	Mahopac	NY	DS2
914-631-7825	PC-Net BBS	Tarrytown	NY	HST
914-665-1725	Go Diamond! BBS	Mount Vernon	NY	V32B
914-667-9385	Joe Brown's BBS	Mount Vernon	NY	DS
914-677-5890	Camelot II	Millbrook	NY	HST
914-686-8091	Pub Info Exchange	White Plains	NY	DS2
914-723-3397	Sex On The Beach BBS	Scarsdale	NY	V32B
914-736-3186	Dark Side of the Moon	Crompond	NY	DS3
914-738-6857	M&M's Pelham BBS	Pelham	NY	DS
914-747-2836	Seven Keys BBS	Thornwood	NY	DS
914-753-8241	The Lanalyst's Asylum	Sloatsburg	NY	VH
914-762-4679	Sing Sing Sing	Ossining	NY	HST
914-783-0992	Monroe Electronic Mall	Monroe	NY	DS
914-796-4566	Dirty Hacker BBS	Rock Hill	NY	HST4
914-834-2973	Powertest BBS	Larchmont	NY	V32B
914-834-7830	Powerboard HQ BBS	Larchmont	NY	HST4
914-887-4651	Summit Data BBS	Long Eddy	NY	V32B
914-961-8749	Hardgoods East	Eastchester	NY	HST
914-965-4980	Special Appointment BBS	Yonkers	NY	DS
915-532-0332	La Cantina BBS	El Paso	TX	HST4
915-566-9100	Trans Mountain ST	El Paso	TX	HST
915-570-7833	Rude Armadillo	Midland	TX	DS
915-585-3628	Palisades Park	El Paso	TX	HST
915-590-9798	Health Professions	El Paso	TX	HST
915-591-1090	Micro Applications	El Paso	TX	DS
915-594-0144	The Clubhouse	El Paso	TX	HST
915-594-7806	Sky's The Limit BBS	El Paso	TX	DS
915-598-1987	Academy K12 Net	El Paso	TX	HST
915-653-3396	Warrior's Path	San Angelo	TX	HST
915-653-9077	HamNET	San Angelo	TX	HST
915-677-5008	The PC-Express	Abilene	TX	HST
915-691-9453	Archives of Oblivion BBS	Abilene	TX	V32B
915-779-0900	Physicians Link	El Paso	TX	V32
915-821-3638	The Pass	El Paso	TX	DS
915-821-5880	Ed's BBS	El Paso	TX	HST
915-821-8952	Palanthas	El Paso	TX	HST
915-944-1436	Tele-Port][	San Angelo	TX	HST
916-265-0338	The Sunbeamers BBS	Nevada City	CA	HST
916-272-5107	The Cosmic Connection	Grass Valley	CA	HST
916-334-4470	Extinguisher BBS	Sacramento	CA	HST
916-338-5227	KBBS	Sacramento	CA	HST
916-342-9239	Time Bender-Long	Chico	CA	DS
916-345-4253	Wildfire	Chico	CA	DS
916-361-1016	Camera Eye BBS	Sacramento	CA	V32
916-362-1755	NightLine I	Mather AFB	CA	HST
916-368-7518	Star BBS	Sacramento	CA	HST
916-381-8788	Capitol City Gateway RBBS	Sacramento	CA	DS
916-383-4560	Fox Propaganda	Sacramento	CA	V32
916-383-9371	Windows BBS	Sacramento	CA	HST

AC/Phone	*BBS Name*	*City*	*State*	*Modem*
916-387-1264	Windows BBS 2	Sacramento	CA	V32
916-424-1727	PrimeTime Network	Sacramento	CA	DS
916-424-1728	PrimeTime Network	Sacramento	CA	DS
916-427-0324	City Lights PCBoard	Sacramento	CA	HST
916-432-3179	Rough & Ready OnLine	Rough & Ready	CA	HST
916-446-0926	Sacramento Telefinder	Sacramento	CA	V32
916-477-9073	Logrus	Grass Valley	CA	HST
916-529-5248	Mega Graphics	Red Bluff	CA	DS2
916-534-5329	The TDEC BBS	Oroville	CA	DS3
916-542-3088	The Cheshire Cat 1	So. Lake Tahoe	CA	DS3
916-544-1682	The Cheshire Cat 2	So. Lake Tahoe	CA	DS3
916-577-4438	HighSierra Online	Lake Tahoe	CA	V32B
916-722-1984	Channel-D BBS	Sacramento	CA	V32B
916-722-1985	Channel-D BBS	Sacramento	CA	V32B
916-722-7223	Channel-D BBS	Sacramento	CA	V32B
916-725-8578	Sirus System BBS	Citrus Heights	CA	DS
916-737-1844	Humanx Commonwealth	Sacramento	CA	HST
916-742-5501	Amber Shadow	Marysville	CA	DS
916-753-8788	Dynasoft	Davis	CA	HST
916-755-1692	The Hideaway BBS	Yuba City	CA	HST4
916-755-3964	The Hideaway BBS	Yuba City	CA	DS2
916-791-4298	Commodore CRC Link!	Roseville	CA	DS2
916-824-1939	Bit Stream	Corning	CA	V32B
916-824-1953	After Hours BBS	Corning	CA	DS2
916-891-1920	Humanity Net	Chico	CA	HST
916-891-3410	Gliff	Chico	CA	HST
916-893-9019	Lazarus	Chico	CA	DS
916-929-7511	BOBsBBS	Sacramento	CA	V32
916-962-1952	Now and Zen Opus	Fair Oaks	CA	HST
916-962-3964	FAO BBS	Sacramento	CA	2400
916-962-3978	FAO BBS	Sacramento	CA	V32
916-965-1619	Robert's Place	Fair Oaks	CA	V32
916-966-4923	Slammer BBS	Fair Oaks	CA	HST
916-969-4043	Another BBS	Citrus Heights	CA	HST
916-985-4041	Starfleet Academy HQ	Rancho Cordova	CA	HST
916-985-4720	The Second Opinion	Folsom	CA	DS
918-234-3617	Time Tunnel	Tulsa	OK	HST
918-250-0936	461 Ocean Blvd.	Tulsa	OK	V32
918-254-6618	The Truckstop BBS	Tulsa	OK	DS2
918-272-4327	The Ham Radio Emporium	Owasso	OK	DS
918-298-1901	MegaByte Image Center	Tulsa	OK	HST
918-355-3113	Thumper's Den	Broken Arrow	OK	DS
918-355-4409	Thumper's Den	Broken Arrow	OK	V32
918-437-4229	Quantum_Leap	Tulsa	OK	DS
918-438-2749	Software America Inc.	Tulsa	OK	DS2
918-438-6918	Hard Drive Cafe	Tulsa	OK	DS2
918-446-1523	The Electric Mall	Tulsa	OK	HST
918-451-3306	Midnight Micro	Broken Arrow	OK	V32
918-493-2137	TechNet One	Tulsa	OK	HST
918-494-4032	Digital Studio	Tulsa	OK	HST
918-585-3840	Techniboard	Tulsa	OK	HST

AC/Phone	BBS Name	City	State	Modem
918-627-0923	The Hub! BBS	Tulsa	OK	V32
918-627-2058	The 7th Inning Stretch!	Broken Arrow	OK	DS2
918-663-5535	SARCO LTD	Tulsa	OK	HST
918-665-2711	Wayne's World BBS	Tulsa	OK	HST
918-682-7337	H*A*L	Muskogee	OK	V32B
918-687-8460	Muskogee BBS	Muskogee	OK	HST
918-742-7893	Midnight Micro II	Tulsa	OK	V32
918-744-0106	TBBS Tulsa	Tulsa	OK	DS
918-749-9036	Hi-Tec	Tulsa	OK	DS
918-832-1462	The Asylum	Tulsa	OK	HST
918-835-4072	Lost Horizons	Tulsa	OK	HST
918-835-8933	Star One	Tulsa	OK	HST
918-838-1615	The Gunner's Mate	Tulsa	OK	HST
918-838-7575	The Looking Glass BBS	Tulsa	OK	DS3
919-226-6984	The Programmer's Oasis	Graham	NC	HST
919-226-7136	The Programmer's Oasis 2	Graham	NC	HST
919-228-7002	Nighthawk BBS	Burlington	NC	HST
919-245-4948	The Sandhills BBS	Cameron	NC	HST
919-274-5760	Alert Data QBBS	Greensboro	NC	DS
919-282-8708	The Towne of Greene	Greensboro	NC	HST
919-286-2100	PreRapture BBS 5	Durham	NC	2400
919-286-3266	PreRapture BBS 3	Durham	NC	DS2
919-286-3606	PreRapture BBS 2	Durham	NC	DS3
919-286-3962	PreRapture BBS 1	Durham	NC	DS3
919-286-4617	PreRapture BBS 4	Durham	NC	DS2
919-286-7738	Psychotronic BBS	Durham	NC	DS
919-326-6613	NSS BBS MNML Annex	Hubert	NC	HST
919-355-0665	The Spectrum	Greenville	NC	HST4
919-355-8833	Precision BBS	Greenville	NC	DS
919-362-1213	The Body Shop	Apex	NC	HST
919-376-8432	Stardate 1990 BBS	Graham	NC	HST
919-383-4905	Durham Center	Durham	NC	HST
919-436-2055	The Federal Post	Spring-Lake	NC	HST
919-444-3023	The Door Zone	Havelock	NC	HST
919-444-3997	ASAHI BBS	Havelock	NC	HST
919-447-2892	Jon's LateNite 1	Havelock	NC	HST
919-447-3321	Dungeon Quest II 1	Havelock	NC	HST
919-447-7211	The Right Choice	Havelock	NC	HST
919-447-8563	2d MAW Comptroller's BBS	Cherry Point	NC	HST
919-455-1933	QX-Connect OPUS	Jacksonville	NC	DS
919-469-1864	Carolina TRACON	Cary	NC	HST
919-469-4838	Mac Tonight	Cary	NC	DS
919-471-2129	Discovery III BBS	Durham	NC	V32B
919-490-8978	TAG Board	Durham	NC	HST
919-553-8745	Carte Blanche BBS	Clayton	NC	HST
919-556-6173	The CAD WorkStation Board	Wake Forest	NC	VH
919-637-3583	Benners' BBS	New Bern	NC	DS2
919-667-7926	The Trading Post	North Wilkesboro	NC	HST
919-670-2846	Opus Supply Central	North Wilkesboro	NC	HST
919-692-6138	WhiTech BBS	Southern Pines	NC	DS
919-736-1388	The FireHouse	Dudley	NC	DS

AC/Phone	BBS Name	City	State	Modem
919-736-1389	800star	Dudley	NC	HST
919-736-3001	386 Powerhouse	Goldsboro	NC	HST
919-751-5085	Strike Eagle	Goldsboro	NC	HST
919-756-2939	East Carolina Connection	Greenville	NC	HST
919-772-0960	The Chalkboard	Raleigh	NC	HST
919-772-1177	Forbidden Tower	Garner	NC	HST
919-772-7806	TBBS Info/Help	Raleigh	NC	HST
919-779-5059	Micro Message Service	Raleigh	NC	HST
919-781-4203	Capitol Opus	Raleigh	NC	HST
919-781-6813	Capitalist Connect.	Raleigh	NC	V32B
919-786-6424	Pure Energy	Mount Airy	NC	HST
919-831-0674	The BoardRoom	Raleigh	NC	HST
919-831-2759	Social Graces	Raleigh	NC	DS
919-833-7435	Z-Board OPUS	Raleigh	NC	HST
919-846-1802	Garden of Stone	Raleigh	NC	HST
919-851-8460	InfoSYS	Raleigh	NC	DS
919-854-7952	NC Triad	Greensboro	NC	HST
919-856-1223	Magic Foam BBS	Raleigh	NC	HST
919-867-0754	Bragg IDBS	Fayetteville	NC	HST
919-872-3984	C: Directory	Raleigh	NC	DS
919-886-8826	NC Public Safety BBS	High Point	NC	HST
919-929-1945	Quantum Tech	Chapel Hill	NC	DS
919-957-4307	The Chicken House	State Road	NC	HST

REMOTEACCESS BBS LISTINGS

This list is dedicated to RemoteAccess Sysops around the world, whose hard work and undying devotion to run a BBS makes the online community a better place to visit. This list is totally comprised of BBS's operating with Andrew Milner's RemoteAccess BBS Software, and offers more than just the normal BBS listing Phone number & modem type. This list also tells you what amount of hard drive capacity they offer, along with if they are offering a CDROM, FidoNet, RelayNet, Visiting Sysop privileges, Adults Only sections, and if they carry RemoteAccess specific files.

If you run a RemoteAccess BBS, and have been left out of this list, you will need to do one of the following options:

1. Send Netmail to Gary Barr at 1:2310/200.
2. Send Private Mail to Gary Barr via RelayNet to ->DIGICOM
3. Call my BBS and fill out the RABBS Q-A in the Applications Section.
4. Call and leave Voice Mail at (812) 453-9100
5. Fax the form in to (812) 474-2264

6. CompuServe E-mail to 70007,4634
7. Or US Mail to Gary Barr, 7624 Syls Drive, Evansville, IN 47712

Please use this format in your message on how you want your BBS to be listed in the file. Failure to keep it in this format might cause delay in getting your BBS listed.

PHONE NUMBER, State, BBS Name, Sysop Name, Modem, Hard Drive Capacity, Notes

(Up to a 76-Character Line on what the system offers. *Brag Line*)

Example:

812-479-1310 IN Digicom BBS   Gary Barr   168DS   2700   ACFMRV
    (RABBS/SUPRT BBS List, Movie News & CDROM Disc List, RANet, SAFNet, Weather)

System Notes:

    A = Adults Only Sections Offered   M = RelayNet EchoMail Offered
    C = CDROM Drive(s) Offered   R = RemoteAccess Support Section
    F = FidoNet EchoMail Offered   V = Visiting SysOp Privileges Offered

****

Verified BBS's   -   (Author Verified or Sent in by Sysop of BBS)

****

203-242-0530 CT Computer Services   Erik Semmel   96 DS   1000   ACFRV
    (Computer Technical Files, Online store)

203-298-8632 CT Other Side Midnight   Thomas Hynes   24   20   V
    (Friendly SysOp, Online Games, Weekend Weather Updates)

203-563-9400 CT The Barber Shop   Mike Malignaggi   24

203-738-2996 CT Excalibur's BBS   Charley Webb   96 DS   200   AFRV
    (Also call node two at 203-738-2084 - 2400 bps)

203-826-1153 CT Phone Henge BBS   Scott Livingston 96 HS   1200   AFMRV
    (Nice collection of BBS Utility Software, plus large variety of files)

203-827-9741 CT Midnight Run   Rick Soderburg   96

203-889-1355 CT Connecticut ADULT Con   Mastter Daniel J.   144V3   680   ACFRV
   (AdultNet-AdultsLink-ThrobNet-WildNet-SwingNet-LuvNet-National Match maker)

207-725-8999 MA Cobra BBS   John Murray   96 HS   CRV
   (Primarily an Amateur radio BBS, access to all on first connection, no fees)

213-850-0459 CA Zone One   Scott Sturgis   96 V3   200   FR
   (1:102/743, Multiline, Windows File, Files for Many BBS Types)

214-228-9173 TX Diamond Lil's Saloon   Diamond Lil   24   A

214-238-1805 TX Master Control   Roger Williams   96 V3   250   FVR
   (Online Games, Multiline, SDN)

214-258-1832 TX Interocitor   Steve Rainwater   96 V3   40   V
   (Artificial Intelligence Oriented BBS)

214-259-1828 TX Charger's Castle   Dean Arthur   96 DS   1300   ACR
   (Adult Games, Matchmakers, ThrobNet,KinkNet,FantasyNet,AdultNet, Live Chat)

214-530-5526 TX Carrier Pidgeon   James Marple   96 HS
   (Desktop Publishing, CADD and other Technical Information)

214-557-6645 TX Giddy-Up-Go   Lady Luv   24   120   AFV
   (Dedicated to Adult's, many online games, also adult online games)

214-641-1822 TX Puss-N-Boots   Unknown   96   AF

214-669-3561 TX Flash BBS   Bob Ratliff   96 DS   40   FRV
   (New SysOp Support, BBS Support files online & offline)

216-671-0850 OH The Dragon's Lair   A. Edens/R. Grove   96 V3   500   ACV
   (Online Games, Large Adult Are with CDROM, MultiNode and lots of files)

216-923-6409 OH The Pig Sty BBS   Danny Smith   24   130   CRV
   (Internation Online Support, Stargate, Friendly, 1/2 RA BBS's in Akron Area)

217-431-1695 IL Relative Connection   Chuck Haine   96 HS   40   FR
   (Genealogy & Health Related Emphasis in Central Illinois)

219-233-8854 IL The Great Beyond   Zak Wolfinger   96 V3   380   CRV
   (RemoteAccess Support Files/Utilities + Large general area)

219-659-2711 IL Magic Lantern   24   F
   (FidoNet Node: 1:230/21)

301-891-2646 DC Animal Bytes/Rights   Paul Nahay   24   40
   (Dedicated to Animals Rights)

302-284-3734 DE Theorem Beach   Lecuyer & Gomolski   96 V3   210   ACFV
   (Adult BBS, 3 CDROMS, 5 Lines (last 3 are pay), Odyssey UFO Network)

303-772-7921 CO Long's Peak BBS   Mike Hawley   144V3   1600   AFRV
   (Large Message Base with FidoNet, SimNet, CFR Net, MUFSNET, 2 Nodes)

304-768-3682 WV Deadly Sins BBS   Edward Crouser   96 V3   1100   ACRV
  (The best BBS in the state of WV! Over 1 gigabyte of storage)

305-271-2146 FL Kendall BBS   Mike Janke   96 HS   30   FR
  (Pascal Oriented, Home of RemoteAccess Utility RACE)

312-588-0587 IL Can We Talk   96 V3

312-648-1981 IL Micrographics   24

317-486-9245 IN Guru Meditation   Matt Barton   24 MN   72   FRV
  (Located in Indianapolis, IN. Offering support for IBM & Amiga)

317-784-2147 IN RoadHouse   Richard Holler   24   180   FRV
  (ASP Software, 1:231/290, Support for Unicorn Software Ltd)

404-351-2975 GA Swizzle Stick   Richard Bollar   96 DS   F
  (Home of FidoNet's Kate Bush Conference, No File sections)

404-422-0110 GA Verbosity   Phil Oberkrom   24

404-458-4924 GA The Dog Bone BBS   Daniel Svanstrom   96 V3   210   RV
  (ChateauNet EchoMail, RodentWare Support, Online games, Files)

404-487-1376 GA USS Republic   Eddie Ferguson   96 HS   80   V
  (Dedicated BBS for StarTrek Fans, a Member of TrekNet, Share # w/ Command)

404-487-1376 GA Command Post   Eddie Ferguson   96 HS   80   V
  (Emergency Service, Fire, EMS, Police & Amateur Radio, Share # w/ USS Rep)

404-590-1969 GA The Outlaw BBS   Randall Baker   24   AFR

404-969-1530 GA The Lost Cause   Andy Head   24   80   F
  (Nice collection of Midi, Adlib, * Soundblaster Files)

404-971-8285 GA Taboo Online   Eric Bowden   96 DS   A
  (Online Games, RA Pro, Adult Files)

404-972-3458 GA Mile's Meadow   Mike Sirmans   24   200   FRV
  (BBS Files for RemoteAccess)

407-438-7093 FL Mystic Pharos   Al Hays   96 DS   170

407-569-0569 FL The Treasure Coast   John Carroll   144V3   590   ACFRV
  (Gif's Galore, Graphics, Animations, Windows Programs! Over 1500 Gif's!)

407-569-6568 FL The Concession Stand   Eric Staufer   96 V3   221   CFV
  (18525+ Files, Over 2.3 Gigs! Tons of RA Utils, INSTAbank betasite)

408-259-3019 CA Data Port BBS   Ian Robertson   96 HS   200   FRV
  (CompuServe/MCI-Mail/BitNet/InterNet/UUCP/FidoNet Line/25+ Doors)

408-435-2886 CA Automation Central   Radi Shourbaji   96 V3   400   ACFRV
  (Home of Enterprise Systems Net, Lots of message areas and entertainment)

409-362-2020 TX Almost Heaven BBS   Woody Angel   96 DS   130   V
(ModemNews stand, Zip Magazine Dist Point, Basic BBS)

409-744-3559 TX The Potpourri   Pamela   96 HS   40   AV
(Just a great FUN board!)

414-251-2580 WI Anonymous   Bob R.   96 V3   676   AFRV
(Science Fiction, Finer Doors, SysOp Support)

414-271-0576 WI Special Times BBS   Kevin Walker   96   A
(Online Game Adult Section)

414-645-9362 WI Starcom BBS   Terry B.   144V3   500   ACV
(Adult BBS with 7 CDROM's Online, Matchmaker, many, many DOORS)

414-649-9361 WI Ye Olde Pawn Shoppe   Scott Hansen   96 DS   1300   AFRV
(IBM & Amiga support, KinkNet Hub, AFDN, USR 16.8 Modems)

414-649-9362 WI Ye Olde Pawn Shoppe 2   Scott Hansen   96 DS   1300   AFRV
(Large Adult Section, FidoNet, KinkNet, UtilNet, AFDN, IBM & Amiga)

414-354-8670 WI PkWare BBS   Phil Katz   96 DS   200   FR
(Support BBS for PKZIP and the other PKWare Software)

414-377-2649 WI Playfully Yours   Joe Maz   24   AFRV
(Adult BBS (Swingers) Fido-Net, Kink-Net, Online Games, RA Files)

414-377-8462 WI Phantom Tollbooth   Steve S.   96   A
(Online Games, ModemNews, Adult Areas)

414-442-0170 WI Priplanus BBS   Jay Jadofsky   96 V3   420   AFRV
(KesherNet & KinkNet Link, Sci-Fi Oriented, Milwaukee's *First* RA BBS)

414-782-2227 WI The Data Cache II   Todd Zabel   96 V3   550   CFRV
(Technical, HAM Radio, Can receive faxes @ same ph. #, Callback verification)

415-255-2188 CA Recovery Alcoholism   Rich Gorin   96   40   FR
(Supports recovering Alcoholic & compulsions)

416-299-1164 ONT The Next Level   James FitzGibbon   96 V3   120   FRV
(Offering Support for RemoteAccess SysOp's running under OS/2)

416-571-4407 ONT Odyssey Systems   Chuck Corvec   96 DS   890   ACFRV
(5 Lines, 500+ Users, 2.2 Gigabytes online)

416-898-3373 ONT The Syruss System][Paul Hunter   96 V3   130   ACFRV
(Very Good BBS... Cdrom is for paying users only)

501-621-9047 AR Power BBS   Erik Berry   96 V3   500   FRV
(Lots of MOD and GIF files. Games and many RA & FD support files. Echomail)

502-425-9941 KY Top Gun II BBS   John Richardson   24   1200   ACFR

502-425-9942 KY Top Gun II BBS   Steve Richardson   96 DS   1200   ACFR
(Support BBS for TopSoft Software Products, RA Beta Test Site)

503-646-0868 OR PC Point   Brian Woodworth   144V3
  (Featuring the latest and greatest in shareware and public domain games)

505-589-0319 NM Randy's Basement   Randy Blackmond   96 DS   100   FMRV
  (Support BBS for RAMail, CCTRX, and other software by Randy)

508-454-3864 MA Dave's RA!   David Layte   96 V3   F
  (FidoNet Node 1:324/278)

509-244-0944 WA Gecko Control BBS   Rodney Lorimor   96 V3   245   FRV
  (US Political New WA Host, News, Many forums)

510-549-0311 CA The Dragon's Cave   Bruce Lane   96 V3   FR
  (SF&F Roleplaying, ham radio/scanner user echos, limited files, FurNet)

514-633-9196 QC Online II Access   Yvon Decelles   96 V3   520   CFRV
  (Newsletter from all over, Media Francophone, Friendly place, Bilingual)

514-937-7451 QC ABS International   Abelardo Garces   96 V3   F
  (RA 1.11+ & D'Bride 1.30, 1:167/136)

516-224-3141 NY Darkstar's Realm   Dom Crispo   96 V3   ACFRV
  (One of New York's oldest BBS's and still retains the old time values)

516-481-3511 NY Island Research Group   Henry Graham   96 V3   200
  (MAGnet messages, On-line doors, Files (Games, Astro, Medical & More))

517-348-2778 MI Sea Space BBS   Ruth Rush   96 V3   AFRV

518-785-6643 NY Three L's BBS Node 1   Bob Norvik   96 HS   600   CFRV

518-785-1715 NY Three L's BBS Node 2   Kimberly Ryan   96 V3   600   CFRV
  (General BBS Support Board, Graphics, Midi, Sound, Doorware, Writing)

519-376-9531 ON Volume Control BBS   Jeremy Kerr   96 CC   190   AFRV
  (Specializing in Sound Files (SB, Covox, Etc) with FREE ACCESS to all)

602-278-1651 AZ Majestic Royalty   John Mendivel   24   165   AFRV
  (Arizona ICN Host - Online Games - Programming Areas - QuickSHARE Point #10)

602-872-9148 AZ Broadcasters   Mark Shander   96 V3   F
  (Dedicated to Broadcast professionals, but open to all)

603-432-5287 NH Our BBS(Yours & Mine) Clyde Sisler   24   600   AFRV
  (SDS, PDN, WindNet, SoundNet)

604-595-4407 BC Quantum Leap   Alex Stuart   96 DS   360   CFRV
  (Multinode * FTN nets plus Intelec and UN'I-Net * H'ware/Software Beta Site)

604-752-5249 BC Shangri-La   Gary Joneson   96 DS   230   ACFR
  (6 CD's, 4+ Gigs Online - Adult Files & KinkNet - HST/DS Modems)

604-948-0275 BC Home HARDware BBS   Hardy Rosenke   24   F
  (SysOp support BBS mainly for RA, iSIG, CRASnet InterSports)

608-277-1376 WI Offline BBS   Tom Landmann   96 V3   F
  (EchoNet 50:5608/777, Win*Net, SDN, PDN, CDN, Files & Messages)

608-356-6569 WI Northern Exposure   Jordan Peterson   24   F
  (Messages, Online Games (25+), Files, FidoNet Node: 1:121/28)

608-752-6762 WI Other Side BBS   Alan Weber   96 V3   600   F
  (Messages, Files, Online Games, in Janesville, WI)

608-755-1449 WI PegaSys BBS   Don Olgeburg   24

608-985-8511 WI Absolute Zero   Tom Jagatic   24   F
  (Messages, Files, Games, FidoNet Node 1:121/29)

609-692-4126 NJ Connections! BBS   Michael Nelson   24   100   FRV
  (Over 50 GeniusNet Conferences. Home of EMPIRE! DoorWare)

612-537-0449 MN The Exchange BBS   Mike McGrane   96 V3   296   AFV
  (SISNet, Online Games, 1 of the largest libraries of BBS software in area)

612-832-5172 MN Odyssey BBS   Stan Hirshman   96   FRV
  (Support BBS for JPSoft products)

612-895-0117 MN A.M.I.G.A. BBS   24
  (Private System, must send letter requesting access)

612-934-2982 MN Beg, Borrow, & Steal   Paul Andre   24   FRV

613-747-7682 ON Digitized Reality   James Chow   96 HS   FR
  (Home of SoundBlaster Network, Large SB/MOD Collection, many conferences)

614-846-1274 OH CompuLink   Chris Bugosh   96 V3   R
  (Midi, Programming, SysOp Support)

615-356-8016 TN Music City Photo BBS   Nelson Charette   96 DS   200   AFRV
  (Photography Files 100+Megs of Gif Files free Access!)

615-441-8478 TN Skyline BBS   Steve Mathews   96 V3   340   ACRV
  (Great access and easy to use BBS. Full access available on first call)

615-442-2833 TN White Lightning BBS   Jeff Cook   96 V3   130   FV
  (Thunderbyte USA Anti-Virus Support/Registration Site)

617-770-9451 MA Cheers!   Scott Greczkowski   96 CC   1300   CFRV
  (Multiline from Quincy MA)

617-965-3036 MA Newton Underground   Joseph Teller   24   RV
  (Support for ARJ, DART-HT, Under-Ware, Roleplaying Aids, Pagan Files)

619-271-6699 CA Astronemers Support   Jonathan Drost   24   60   F
  (1:202/515, Astronomy, Space & Science Echo's, Gif pictures)

703-389-2405 VA Wonko the Sane's Asylum Ric Stverak   96 DS   215   FV
  (FidoNet,YouthNet,RUSHnet,DoorNet Dist Site, Environmental/Earth Day info)

703-720-1624 VA End Of the Line   Duane Brown   96 V3   65   FRV
  (Youthnet RC, PFG Software/Murder Motel Utils, Friendly sysop.6+networks)

703-785-0422 VA Data Empire BBS   Richard Hellmer   144V3   500   FRV
(Data Empire, 100+ Fido Conferences, Support for programmers!)

704-545-9645 NC Computer Systems   Christopher Graham   96   130   F
(1:379/31, Space, Nasa Programs, & GIF Pictures)

704-638-9511 NC The MicroChip BBS   Chad Shoaf   24   171   FRV
(Offers RA/FD Support, SDN, SDS, Sound-Net, Win-Net)

708-297-1591 IL Chicago   96 DS   F
(Part Time BBS 7pm-8am Mon-Fri, 24 hrs on Sat-Sun, FidoNet Node 1:115/396)

708-299-1296 IL Eye Resources Network   Tom Young   96 DS   FRV
(Medical information & disability topics. FidoNet/ADAnet, MultiLine)

708-356-7107 IL Singulatiry Station   96 DS   F
(FidoNet Node: 1:115/356)

708-437-8387 IL Daze Inn   96 DS   F
(FidoNet Node: 1:115/437)

708-439-9679 IL Midrange Systems   96 DS   F
(FidoNet Node: 1:115/439)

708-473-5468 IL Palo I   96 V3

708-517-1898 IL SGS-Thomson Apps Lab   24

708-551-9275 IL Emporium   96 DS   F
(FidoNet Node: 1:115/551)

708-689-2843 IL Caribbean Express   24

708-759-1270 IL Pleaser's Playground   96 V3   F
(FidoNet Node: 1:115/795, Fee Based Board)

708-759-7908 IL Magrathea   96 DS   F
(FidoNet Node: 1:115/708)

708-776-1062 IL The Midrange System   David Gibbs   168DS   1000   CFRV
(For midrange and PC Professionals)

708-892-3449 IL Park Place   96 HS

708-894-1126 IL Bulletproof   96 DS   F
(FidoNet Node: 1:115/894)

708-934-6224 IL Zen Arcade   96 DS   F
(FidoNet Node: 1:115/934)

713-480-6052 TX Maelstrom OS   96 DS   1500   A
(Doors, Online Sales, Adult Areas, Mail, Games)

715-345-5438 WI Spash EBBS   Jason Klismith   96 V3   170   FRV
(FIDO 1:238/400, Modem News, Over 30 Doors, 1000's of Files, MSDOS BBS)

715-839-0942 WI The Decker's BBS   Adam Roycraft   96 V3   130   CFV
(Fido NC of net 2300...always the newest CD's online and offline)

805-494-9386 CA Pacific Coast Micro   Mike Ehlert   96 DS   3000   ACFRV
(3 Lines, RAPro, RA_Support Files, Soundblaster, adult & graphics conference)

812-479-1310 IN Digicom BBS   Gary Barr   168DS   2700   ACFMRV
(Movie News, RANet, SafNet, Magazines, Adult Area/Games, RAPro, 11 Lines)

812-985-7823 IN EVSC BBS   Keith Bobbitt   96 DS   900   CFMR
(K-12 Education Net, CNN Daily Classroom, So Much Shareware CDROM, Multiline)

813-488-7731 FL Alienation BBS   Raymond Fisher   96 V3   F
(FidoNet Node # 1:137/431)

813-748-5380 FL R.B. Enterprises   Bob Brenner   96   230   ACFRV
(Cop & Government Chat, Eviction Search Center, Crime Stoppers, Real Estate)

815-434-4430 IL River City   96 DS   F
(FidoNet Node: 1:11/621)

815-653-3332 IL The Round Table BBS   Michael Toth   24   AFRV
(Many Online Games, SysOp Utilities, MultiLine Chat, Adult Files/Messages)

816-269-3993 MO Stonehenge BBS   Doug Cadmus   96 V3   RV
(The Midwests fastest-growing BBS. Programming, education and entertainment)

816-331-5868 MO Howard's Notebook   Jim Howard   24   40   AFRV
(On-line since 1982. An Enviromental & Freedom of Speech BBS.)

817-662-3177 TX File Quest   Jim Ray   96 DS   1700   CFRV
(1:388/14, RA Beta Test Site - Lots of Files)

817-776-2426 TX The Private Ear   Fred Horner   96 DS   4500   ACFRV
(1:388/10, Multiline - Beta Site for RAPro, FD and many more)

817-840-2140 TX Hello World   Ken Peck   96 HS   40   F
(1:388/21 FidoNet)

819-732-7710 CAN Pro Link BBS   Dave Cloutier   144   CRV
(PLayer's Domain RPG Echomail NET, CDROM, Apogee Games and more...)

904-262-7296 FL Anything Goes   James Bowen   24

904-278-4870 FL Crossroads BBS   Glen Turner   96 CC   120   CFRV
(RemoteAccess Support Files, Easy to use, online CDROM)

904-385-6877 FL The Eliminator   Gregory Wynot   96 V3   295   FRV
(Egg-Net, Chateau-Net & FidoNet. Tons of Messages, files and doors!)

904-422-3606 FL The Warrior's Retreat Jason Valkenburg   96 V3   250   AFRV
(Adult Files, RA Support, Echomail Support in Chateaunet & FidoNet, Doors)

904-678-2667 FL Compu-Assist   Don Anderson   96 DS   65   FRV
(Running RA Professional, Many Forums, Doors, New BBS, User Helpfull)

904-688-9124 FL The Toy Shop-PC BBS   Chuck Curtis   96 DS   213   FR
(Instant Access to all callers and lots of BBS files)

904-778-1622 FL Bridge BBS   Daniel Romero   96 V3   F

908-246-7632 NJ Franklins Tower   Eric Hiby   96 V3   70   FRV
(Online Games, RemoteAccess File Section)

908-273-8709 NJ FunTime BBS   Andrew Tollin   96 DS   880   AFRV
(Over 800 Megs online - 100 megs of RA Support Files 120 Megs of adult)

908-276-4405 NJ The Vector   Joseph Delvecchio   144V3   AFRV
(General File and Message Base areas. Adult Files and Doors. No Fee)

908-463-0315 NJ Parthenon   Paul Papasavas   96 DS   220   A

913-776-0111 KS Fox Support Systems   Jim & Cathy Lund   96 DS   F
(Fido: 1:14/680, ToadNet 86:8016/1, DBNet 201:100/134)

914-965-4980 NY Special Appointment   Dan Bermejo   96 DS   740   FMRV
(Begginner's BBS dedicated to the health)

916-392-3940 CA Microline BBS   Steve Proctor   96 V3   850   ACFRV
(Multiline, Games, WinNet, HamNet, DVNet, OS2, SDS/SDN, Adult, .GIFs)

918-254-6618 OK Truckstop BBS   Bruce Bodgers   96 DS   512   FRV
(RemoteAccess & FrontDoor Support *USA* - Large Collection of RA files)

918-333-6905 OK The Bat Cave BBS   Ted Pugh   96 DS   215   FRV
(Online Games, Many Echo Areas, Tons of Files, Friendly Sysop Support)

919-286-4542 NC Psychotronic   R.E. Lee   24
(PDN - LanNet - OS/2 - WinNet - Ansi Club - SoundNet)

919-579-1672 NC Parity BBS   Pat Finnerty   96 DS   1800   ACFRV
(No fee general use BBS with BBS Support. RANET Hub, 2 CD's, Tech Support)

+27-21-26-1101   Magnum BBS   Joe Rinck   24 MN4   190   FRV
(XRS Support Zone 5, FindoNet 5:7102/111)

+31-35-64563   Nouveau BBS   Raimond Kollman   96 V3   160   FRV
(Turbo Pascal Utils, RemoteAccess Utils, RAFM support)

+31-70-3360795   P.S.S. BBS   Erik Kemper,   96 V3   660   CSRV
(Multitaskers, FroDo, RA, DosGames, Win_games,Online Store DesqView,Sierra)

+31-70-3361380   Interface HQ   Ron Huiskes   96 V3   1200   CFRV

+44-071-733-3992 Starbase One (UK)   Nick Stevens   96 V3   320   CF
(2:440/407, USENet, Astronomy News, Nasa Text)

+44-71-738-5596 Arkham BBS London,UK   Nigel Hardy   96 V3   180   FRV
(Help for new SysOp's, info on multi-user games, carries CyberSpace Echo)

+55-11-247-2899 LucaNet   Flavio Lucarelli   96 DS   340   CFRV
(FidoNet, DataNetLink, RushNet, FreeNet, Free Access for Internation callers)

+55-81-222-2757 BBS Revolution   Guilherme Moura   144V3   150   FRV
   (FidoNet-4:808/16, ANSI, Acad & Music, Brazilian BBS. Call Now! Free Access!)

+972-8-476549   Triple D BBS (Israel)   Roy Udassin   96 DS   250   FV
   (Support of YossiWare Product, FidoNet, Visiting Sysop get high security)

Modem Types:

>   HS - US Robotics HST   HV - Hayes V-Series
>   V3 - V.32 Compatable
>   CC - CompuCom   MN - 2400 MNP

USBBS116.LST

A List of PC Bulletin Boards for DOS Users

Editor: Bob Breedlove
Founder: P.L. Olympia

How to submit update information for this list

Updates can be sent to BOBsBBS at 916-929-7511. The (O)ther BBS (P)hone list feature contains a questionnaire to update list information. The USBBS list is also available directly from that feature on the board. Registration is not required to access this feature or download the list.

Minimum requirements for NEW listings on USBBS include:

(1) Modem(s) supporting 2400 bps or greater operation;
(2) 80 MB of disk capacity devoted to the BBS;
(3) 24hr/7 day service; and
(4) Sysop must give REAL NAME in listing.

The USBBS list is QUITE selective and is for BBS's that are oriented to serious users of DOS computers. BBS's that focus on games, "adults only" topics, dating and similar services or subjects will not be included. These criteria are admittedly subjective and rest in the discretion of the editor of the list. Impolite complaints about these decisions will be politely ignored.

Columns 55–57 show the number of the USBBS list on which a BBS was first listed: 06 = 11/84, 26 = 7/1/86, 55=12/1/88, 88=9/1/91, 100=9/1/92. Cols. 75–79 show the size in 100s of megs and number of nodes. For example, 1/2 would mean 100 megs, 2 nodes and 50/ would be 5 Gigs and only 1 node (the default).

| | | | | | | First on List # \| v | | |
Phone	State	City	Sysop	T/S		(see above)	Name, Features	
201-209-1857	NJ	Hamburg	Thomas Guadagno	B$	09V	105	Fast Data	20/2
201-223-0485	NJ	Secacus	Mike Lostutter	W	19V	116*	Labor Board	2/1
201-228-0009	NJ	Caldwell	Greg Sussex	X$	2	86	The Forest(tm)	4/16
201-239-1151	NJ	Verona	Mark Rapp	B	29DV	36	MicroSellar	7/11
201-261-0127	NJ	River Edge	Mark Paris	U	U	88	Hades	3/
201-261-6848	NJ	River Edge	Barry Pearlman	F	2	82	Modem Pit	1/2
201-262-6612	NJ	River Edge	Cliff Saint	Q$	9D	83	Heaven'sGate	7/2
201-265-7364	NJ	Emerson	Peter Williams	B	2	56	CCS	1/2
201-279-7048	NJ	Clifton	Frank Relotto	B	9H	45	Dean's Office	2/
201-283-1806	NJ	Butler	Chas Lekowski	B	09DB	60	StarshpEntrprse	25/2
201-299-8650	NJ	Boontown	James Sura	B$	9U	33	DesignedLetters	20/14
201-305-9042	NJ	Lincoln Pk	Greg Miller	G	29D		EdgelightOnline	3/1
201-307-1452	NJ	Park Ridge	Wayne Robinson	S$	9U	64	Quantum Zone	12/4
201-313-0002	NJ	Fairview	Albert Aponte	W	9D	84	Tower	15/
201-327-5775	NJ	SaddleRiver	Joshua Abrams	S	9U	91	ArrowTack	7/2
201-331-1797	NJ	Parsippany	Jim Boxmeyer	B	09V	114	Synergy Online	12/30
201-337-7336	NJ	Franklin Lks	Dave Krouse	X	19C	114	Metal Connx	2/1
201-338-3569	NJ	Bloomfield	Matt Bryda	L	2	89	Realm/Imagntn	2/
201-338-5265	NJ	Bloomfield	Max Bruhn	B	9D	62	Golden Dane	2/
201-340-2394	NJ	Clifton	Al Arango	T	2	83	SynerSys	1/
201-342-5659	NJ	Hackensack	Robert Curtis	R	9V	99	The Laboratory	2/1
201-347-0465	NJ	Budd Lake	Michael Deacon	W	9V	91	The Outer Limit	2/
201-347-9284	NJ	Stanhope	Donna & S.Griff	B	9V	56	OtherSide,women	2/
201-361-4131	NJ	Wharton	Ron Allison	W	9V	89	Quantum Leap	3/2
201-374-2730	NJ	Newark	Steve Haas	W	09V	89	Millenium	2/2
201-378-3218	NJ	South Orange	N. Nicholson	X	2	96	Classic Car	1/
201-391-3209	NJ	U.SaddleRiv	Jon Schulman	B	9HV	83	Saddle River	3/2
201-398-2373	NJ	Hopatcong	Bob Lawton	W	9U	72	Evergreen	2/
201-423-4258	NJ	Hawthorne	Jim Wheater	B	9U	29	ComputerNookery	10/2
201-437-4355	NJ	Bayonne	MariusKirschner	B	9U	80	Bytes'n Bits	12/2
201-444-1822	NJ	Glen Rock	Danny Vanino	B	9HV	87	Flash Fire	7/
201-444-8052	NJ	Glen Rock	Joe Tirserio	B	29?	106	Meeting Place	5/1
201-467-3269	NJ	Short Hills	Alan Sislen	B	9U	15	The Market,inv	3/
201-471-1832	NJ	Wallington	Nickalf Grey	X	19VO		Nickalfs Kastle	12/2
201-471-6391	NJ	Passaic	Jim Roy	B	9H	56	Passaic	/

					First on List # | v		
Phone	*State*	*City*	*Sysop*	*T/S*	*(see above)*	*Name, Features*	
201-472-7785	NJ	Clifton	M. Herrmann	M$	09VO	111	Laser Conntion	12/10
201-478-1016	NJ	Clifton	C. Florescu	D$	9V	85	Int'lTrade	4/
201-503-0929	NJ	Parsippany	Mike Low	S	2	81	Videopolis	
201-514-1949	NJ	Chatham	Greg Lowe	B	19V	95	Lowe's Plaza	2/1
201-523-1162	NJ	Paterson	Carole Capuano	W	9D	101	Butterfly	7/1
201-523-2058	NJ	Paterson	Rev T. Williams	W	2	101	The Last Word	1/1
201-523-8212	NJ	W. Paterson	Walter Gould	Y	19V	115	Caretakers	3/1
201-538-6087	NJ	Morristown	Kent Manno	W	9V	93	Maple Leaf	2/
201-543-9326	NJ	Mendham	Shawn Smith	B	19?	86	NullPointer	3/
201-546-1468	NJ	Clifton	Glen Fredericks	B	9U	45	Token Ring	3/
201-568-1826	NJ	Tenafly	Naz Keleshian	S	09BV	109	Optimum	12/1
201-568-7293	NJ	Tenafly	Mark Seiden	B	09V	26	BOSS	30/4
201-569-6685	NJ	Cresskill	John Jacobacci	W	09V	110	PlainBrownWrap	4/1
201-573-0719	NJ	Montvale	Peter Zurich	S	2	87	Over the Edge	8/
201-575-8991	NJ	Montville	Mike Cocke	B	29D	113	Central Core	24/3
201-584-2563	NJ	Randolph	Cherifi/Pafumi	F	2	97	Jug Clod	1/1
201-595-1573	NJ	Haledon	John Prause	W	9V	98	Last Days	1/1
201-605-8117	NJ	Morristown	Jeff Polo	B	9U	75	EastCoastCirBd	3/
201-612-0559	NJ	Ridgewood	J Hulley-Miller	O	9D	103	Informatix	2/2
201-612-8594	NJ	Ridgewood	Gerard Filitti	Q	2	95	Nut House	1/2
201-617-8054	NJ	Union City	G. & B. Eppich	M	09V	84	Hot Tub Chat	81/8
201-626-3550	NJ	Jersey City	Michael Keyles	O	9D	77	NewptCtr	3/
201-641-0493	NJ	Little Ferry	Cono A DelRosso	B	19D	106	Roy Hobbs	12/1
201-641-5375	NJ	Little Ferry	Darrin Hentze	W	29V	115	Waterside	5/1
201-652-6628	NJ	Ridgewood	Jason Woodard	B	9D	58	Phoenix	3/1
201-661-2690	NJ	Nutley	Bob Roncaglio	B	2	89	221-B Baker St	4/
201-664-7217	NJ	Hillsdale	Neil Stewart	B	19VO	108	E. I. B.	1/1
201-667-2504	NJ	Nutley	Cliff Amlung	B	9H	45	Nutley BBS	2/
201-669-9857	NJ	West Orange	John Tracey	W	09V	108	NJ Intel. Agcy	3/2
201-672-8969	NJ	Orange	Rob Rosenhouse	W	29D	116*	Hdq Info Svc	2/1
201-675-2154	NJ	E. Orange	Gene Deans	B	9U	64	Deans Info Cntr	1/
201-678-1367	NJ	Bloomfield	James Waldron	O	9T	79	Unitex,the UN	
201-678-1721	NJ	Orange	Pete Newman	B	9D	95	Rivendell	1/
201-680-1336	NJ	Bloomfield	Rick De Pinho	B	9HV	45	Arc Xchg	10/2
201-691-5500	NJ	Stanhope	Tom Boyer	R	9V	56	InfoExchange	1/2
201-692-1110	NJ	New Milford	Mark Paris	X$	19VO	115	GearBox	40/5
201-692-3705	NJ	Teaneck	Cosimo DelRosso	B	9O	100	The Dx Connect	2/1
201-694-5081	NJ	Wayne	Marc Frega	X$V	2	100	Jungle STS #12	1/15
201-694-6835	NJ	Wayne	Ed Gelb	X	2	99	Gelb's BBS Dir	16/1
201-694-7425	NJ	Wayne	Ed Gelb	X	2	99	Ed Gelb's DBase	16/1
201-694-8122	NJ	Wayne	Jim Sadur	T	09V	50	SonNet Center	15/1
201-729-2186	NJ	Sparta	Michael Repasch	B	19V	105	Lily of Alley	1/1
201-729-2602	NJ	Sparta	Chuck Ammann	B	9UF	34	Chuck'sAttempt	15/4
201-729-7046	NJ	Sparta	John Schumacher	M$	09V	112	Remote Host	2/4
201-729-9538	NJ	Sparta	Joe Dumanov	B	9HV	70	New World	3/2
201-731-9425	NJ	West Orange	Glen Johnson	S	9U	80	Sportsbd	3/
201-742-1860	NJ	Paterson	Vito Milito	W	9U	84	Trailblazer	1/
201-748-8643	NJ	Bloomfield	Drew Lorent	B	9U	64	Playroom	3/

Phone	State	City	Sysop	T/S	First on List # ↓ v (see above)	Name, Features	
201-751-5608	NJ	Belleville	Paul Casale	X	29V	110	VORTEX	2/1
201-751-7766	NJ	Belleville	Jim Rogers	B	2	88	Adv Guild	4/
201-765-0164	NJ	GreenVillage	Greg Pickering	B	9V	104	Pick's Place	13/1
201-765-9090	NJ	Florham Park	A. Stramaglia	M$	09V	114	Dreamline	50/16
201-779-5495	NJ	Lodi	Luis Saravia	B	2	89	Masters,Astron	1/
201-796-1827	NJ	Saddle Brook	Keith Sutton	X	02	113	Loading Zone	1/1
201-796-2752	NJ	Fair Lawn	Ron Lotterman	WV	9D	89	Deredain'sRealm	3/2
201-801-9216	NJ	Teaneck	P. Kronenberg	B	02	29	Friends! Too	1/1
201-804-3916	NJ	Lyndhurst	Dennis Warner	L	2	99	Quadrophonia	8/1
201-822-3658	NJ	Madison	Gerhard Bartsch	Q	19VO	15	The Strand	2/1
201-831-8152	NJ	Ringwood	Jeff Sumberg	B	9D	29	Sail Board	5/1
201-886-8041	NJ	Cliffside Pk	Steve Leon	B	9U	42	Cliffside Park	20/5
201-887-7463	NJ	Parsippany	Rich Taft	R	9V	100	Compucon	2/2
201-893-9636	NJ	Bloomfield	John Bohman	B	19D	111	John's House	12/2
201-912-8915	NJ	Millburn	Will Daniels	V	09V	114	Wild Willie's	3/1
201-916-1725	NJ	Clifton	Fred Wehner	B	29D	44*	Lightning Bolt	14/4
201-927-5106	NJ	Succasunna	Tom McDermet	B	9V	58	The Odyssey	2/2
201-933-8061	NJ	Rutherford	Joseph Slawsky	X	09V	112	Planet DX	3/1
201-933-9048	NJ	Wood-Ridge	Keith Lawson	B	9U	84	FawltyTwrs	2/
201-935-1104	NJ	Lyndhurst	Bill Larkin	B	19B	84*	BillBoard	1/1
201-935-1485	NJ	Lyndhurst	Phil Buonomo	T	9U	56	Starship II	
201-941-3302	NJ	Cliffside Pk	Bob Vesey	B	29D	101	B.F.W.K.	12/2
201-943-1209	NJ	Cliffside Pk	J E Monroe	T	19V	107	RED DEER TABLE	2/1
201-989-0528	NJ	Mount Hope	Chris Smith	A	19V	86	Starlifter	2/1
201-989-8107	NJ	Dover	Dennis Bixler	A	29V	87	E-Patrol	14/1
201-989-8323	NJ	Dover	Sean Aldritch	C	9D	91	Eureka	1/
201-998-7337	NJ	N Arlington	John Kleinbauer	B	9	98	Free For All	1/1
202-225-5527	DC	Washington	Rep.Bob Wise	R	2	92	Whistleblower	
202-244-3042	DC	Washington	Maurice Sanders	B	2	45	Wash Fed Rev	
202-546-3633	DC	Washington	Bob Ashe	U	9V	88	Signal	10/
202-547-2008	DC	Washington	Robert Blacher	B	9V	06+	CompConnx	6/4
202-547-8894	DC	Washington	Bill Walsh	B	9U	45	DC Info Xchg	4/
202-562-4517	DC	Washington	Robert Charnock	W	9	100	megabyte	2/1
202-563-1306	DC	Washington	Jeremy Idol	Q	19D	112	Virtual Madness	7/1
202-581-1422	DC	Washington	Jim Wall	B	2	86	Jim'sDream	12/2
202-609-5423	DC	Washington	Vesta Jones	R	9	92	OASH	2/3
202-634-1764	DC	Washington	Ken Brown	R	2	34	SciResStudies	
202-789-2527	DC	Washington	I. Ahmad	O	2	98	AMNet	1/1
202-882-9063	DC	Washington	Rob Richmond	R	19V	108	CPA's	13/3
203-257-1960	CT	Wethersfield	Jim Hock	X	19D	111	Libertarian	2/1
203-261-3130	CT	Trumbull	Frederick Tan	O	09V	116*	Wacko Board][	12/1
203-268-3111	CT	Trumbull	Terry Wodek	O	9U	45	Lil Frog'sPond	3/
203-269-8313	CT	Wallingford	John Melillo	L	9U	84	Vampire Connx	1/
203-270-9017	CT	Newtown	Tim Cronin	O	19U	111	T.S.C.	2/1
203-335-7742	CT	Bridgeport	Joel Lambert	O	9U	85	PlanetEarth,!	3/
203-349-1975	CT	Durham	Ben Ackerman	L	12	107	DreamScape	1/1
203-359-2299	CT	Stamford	Jeff Green	X	19VO	99*	ModemNews Exp.	1/1
203-367-4005	CT	Fairfield	Ed WEinberg	O	09V	116*	EXTRACT!	10/2

					First on List # | v		
Phone	State	City	Sysop	T/S	(see above)	Name, Features	
203-388-0507	CT	Old Saybrook	Joseph Rock	R	09V	116*	Second Ring	18/1
203-399-7271	CT	Westbrook	Lon Seidman	O	9D	96	The Matrix	1/1
203-438-7761	CT	Ridgefield	Ryan Frank	X	19VO	116*	Exavier Castle	22/1
203-449-0527	CT	Groton	Greg Sootoo	X	9	98	HeiroGlyphix	2/1
203-456-1933	CT	Willimantic	Milo Tsukroff	O	2	15	Willi-Bd,UConn	
203-483-0348	CT	Branford	Emmitt Dove	O	9U	55	Fernwood	/2
203-536-1300	CT	Mystic	Garry Elmer	J	29V	100	K-9	1/1
203-536-9549	CT	Mystic	Stu Watson	B	99D	57	Mystic S/WNet	20/3
203-620-0001	CT	Southington	Bill Arlofski	F	9U	82	Rev Polarity	1/2
203-622-4740	CT	Greenwich	Rob Schmaling	O	9U	100	CALADAN OS/2	6/2
203-624-8990	CT	New Haven	Kenny Teel	O	09VO	113	AEGIS/CT	3/2
203-628-9702	CT	Southington	Alan Filandro	O	19D	82	Cygnus X-I	30/2
203-634-0370	CT	Meriden	Ray Kaliss	O	9D	56	SharewareProj	1/
203-635-6569	CT	Cromwell	Les Robertson	X	2	103	Joe's Garage	1/1
203-637-6710	CT	Old G'wich	Jim Bolster	W	9D	47	Observers Dbase	7/1
203-676-1708	CT	Farmington	Eric Knight	R$	9D	87	DownloadAmerica	12/6
203-688-4973	CT	Windsor	Jim Taylor	R	2	91	Windsor Manor	3/
203-738-2996	CT	Winsted	Charley Webb	Q	2	100	Excalibur's	1/2
203-763-0016	CT	Somers	Ric Allan	W	9U	76	Endeavor	
203-791-8532	CT	Danbury	Don Dawson	O	9D	43	Treasure Island	6/2
203-791-8838	CT	Danbury	Gary Snider	O	9D	43	Rocky Road,ansi	3/
203-792-6397	CT	Danbury	Dan Wheeler	T	09V	112	News Times	12/4
203-793-2024	CT	Plainville	Dale Sokoloski	W	99O	105	NE Motorcyclist	1/1
203-826-1153	CT	New Britain	ScottLivingston	Q	9U	77	PhoneHenge	4/
203-826-5438	CT	New Britain	Henry Lukoszek	X	19V	112	Polish-American	2/1
203-827-9741	CT	Berlin	Rick Soderburg	QV	9V	100	Midnight Run	1/1
203-852-1986	CT	Norwalk	Steve Ungvary	O	09VO	104	12th Step	4/1
203-869-7742	CT	Greenwich	Rob Glasener	G	19V	113	Greenwich Conn	10/1
203-888-4980	CT	Seymour	Dan Wheeler	X	29V	112	Pigeon Coop	24/2
203-924-5603	CT	Shelton	Mike Robinson	F	9D	85	SoftParade	8/
203-926-6168	CT	Shelton	Bill McGarry	O	09V	57	Handicap News	1/1
203-926-9504	CT	Shelton	Steve Williams	X	9V	80	ENUF,netware	2/
203-938-8625	CT	Redding	Ola D'Aulaire	O	9V	103	Challenge	2/1
204-338-0272	MB	Winnipeg	Hartley Macklin	B	9D	78	Winnipeg PCUG	2/5
205-222-3097	AL	Andalusia	Emmett Perdue	F	19D	108	Byte House	65/4
205-232-7191	AL	Athens	Jim Kelly	O	29D	111	Magician's Bday	25/1
205-235-2660	AL	Anniston	Jeff Liddle	X	29V	111	LID'S LOUNGE	1/1
205-238-0012	AL	Anniston	Tom Bowerman	B$	2	45	Golden Springs	3/
205-270-5891	AL	Montgomery	Phil Ratliff	BV	9V	45	Hot-DOS & Beer	2/1
205-277-3882	AL	Montgomery	Chuck Wildzunas	T	2	47	Idea Board	1/
205-277-7836	AL	Montgomery	John Griffith	R	19V	93	The 'Q' BBS	5/1
205-323-2016	AL	Birmingham	Rocky Rawlins	B$	09D	15	The MATRIX	147/25
205-335-3968	AL	Luverne	Ed Welch	B	19V	113	Crenshaw County	6/1
205-341-5055	AL	Mobile	Richard Wallen	QV	9D	81	OnLine	2/1
205-348-6686	AL	Tuscaloosa	Richard L. Byrd	V	2	87	BareFacts,music	7/
205-361-9094	AL	Prattville	Robert Cox	B	9U	25	Bob's Corner Bd	7/
205-381-0769	AL	MuscleShoals	Steve Gasque	W	19VO	101	SCC Info Link	5/1

Phone	State	City	Sysop	T/S	First on List # | v (see above)	Name, Features	
205-442-3078	AL	Gadsden	Bert Owens	B$V	9U	80	So.Nights	3/
205-452-3897	AL	Chickasaw	James Rohmer	W$	9U	92	Protech	11/2
205-491-8402	AL	Adger	David Etheredge	O	09V	113	Electro-BBS	4/1
205-525-5629	AL	Cropwell	John McGough	B	9V	104	Executive Board	4/1
205-534-7981	AL	Huntsville	William Tucker	X	09V	109	Pot Of Gold	1/1
205-586-2257	AL	Arab	Rick Brock	B	9D	100	Bit Xchange	1/1
205-598-9509	AL	Daleville	Mike Howe	B	19D	103	Galaxy	16/3
205-626-7447	AL	Daphne	Pepper Myers	B	9H	84	PepsDataSys	19/2
205-650-0107	AL	Huntsville	Timothy Blake	X	02	114	SFE Systems	3/1
205-664-0406	AL	Birmingham	Mike Hamilton	B	99U	76	DataWorks BBS!	65/8
205-671-0092	AL	Ashford	Jim Lambert	F	19V	98	Computer Works	40/1
205-675-8406	AL	Saraland	Jim Wilson	B	29V	114	Anchor Inn	3/1
205-693-2927	AL	Headland	Darrell Hudson	B	9	95	HeadlandHotline	3/
205 744 0943	AL	Pleasant	Grv R. Dickerson	B	09V	114	Family Smorg.	3/1
205-745-4515	AL	Opelika	Tony Ledbetter	B	19DO	65	Lightning Board	85/3
205-753-6620	AL	Arab	M. Whisenant	B	19DV	98	SouthernAllianc	15/2
205-758-5017	AL	Tuscaloosa	Herb McDaniel	R	09D	115	Bulletin Board	8/1
205-774-6989	AL	Ozark	Sam Sill	R	19D	80	Out-Post	76/2
205-774-9946	AL	Ozark	Mark Feller	W	9V	85	FastBytes	3/1
205-794-5699	AL	Dothan	Steve Spicer	Q	2	48	Dothan QBBS	
205-794-6045	AL	Dothan	Mike Clark	R	2	47	Ala Connx	2/
205-821-4664	AL	Auburn	Miles Lester	B	9U	37	Xignals	5/
205-832-9498	AL	Montgomery	Bill Bernhardt	Q	09DV	106	BILLBOARD	50/1
205-841-2790	AL	Birmingham	Lamar Smith	X	2	100	Night Watch	1/1
205-853-6144	AL	Birmingham	Jack Efird	B	9V	26	Bham SperryBd	2/1
205-854-9074	AL	Birmingham	Bill Freeman	B	9V	54	ADANet One	8/4
205-881-8619	AL	Huntsville	Cyrus Cathey	W	9D	103	Power Windows	12/2
205-882-6167	AL	Huntsville	John Minton	B	9U	45	PC HelpDesk	2/
205-883-1308	AL	Huntsville	Conan Dickson	B	9D	98	Occam's Razor	2/1
205-887-5802	AL	Auburn	Robert Anderson	B	9U	26	Alabama PCBd	7/
205-895-6152	AL	Huntsville	Jim McCullars	C	2	26	Access System,!	
205-969-5733	AL	Birmingham	M. Sieniawski	W	09D	113	Lions Den	30/1
205-974-5123	AL	Moulton	Don Thompson	W	9U	75	Cyclone	7/
206-241-8894	WA	Seattle	Jim Becraft	O	9D	85	Cherry City	4/1
206-248-7647	WA	Burien	Michael Brunk	G	9U	79	CyberSpace	2/2
206-263-1117	WA	LA Center	Keith Buckbee	G	19V	98	CountryComputng	4/3
206-277-1689	WA	Renton	Gary Sterr	B	9U	54	Starfinder I	
206-285-5359	WA	Bellevue	Riley Condor	X$	2	43	InvestorsOnline	
206-296-5277	WA	Seattle	Bob Neddo	B	9U	55	KCSS	
206-322-0814	WA	Seattle	Mike Zakharoff	R$	2	57	Interstate	4/
206-367-3837	WA	Seattle	Robert Dinse	X$	2	50	EskimoNorth,!	
206-377-8508	WA	Bremerton	Bruce Kindred	B$	99B	107	PC Pulse	71/4
206-391-2330	WA	Issaquah	Cody Gibson	A	9U	83	Real Batchin'	7/
206-391-2339	WA	Issaquah	Stan Symms	B	9U	44	Futzer Ave	1/
206-438-6716	WA	Olympia	Sam Drake	W	9C	89	Squad Room	1/
206-448-6562	WA	Seattle	Jim Wagemann	B	9V	81	L.A.W.,legal	10/
206-472-9884	WA	Tacoma	Dick Fairchild	T	9U	79	TotalAccess	40/8

Phone	State	City	Sysop	T/S	First on List # | v (see above)	Name, Features	
206-478-4067	WA	Bremerton	Cory Freed	X	19VV	110	Symposium	4/1
206-486-2415	WA	Everett	Mark Marean	W	9D	100	Mark's Point!	40/
206-489-1931	WA	Bothell	Ken Mitcham	W	09D	111	KGB-BBS	8/2
206-514-0264	WA	Everett	John Markor	X	22	107	Cascade Comp.	1/1
206-524-4811	WA	Seattle	Chas Arden	R	9U	75	Letters	2/2
206-528-1941	WA	Seattle	Dave Halliday	W	9V	98	Grey Matter	2/3
206-566-1155	WA	Tacoma	Rich Langsford	W	9U	63	AmoCat	
206-573-9411	WA	Vancouver	John Nelson	Q	9V	87	Don'tPanic,ems	1/
206-581-6361	WA	Tacoma	Eric Hermes	V	2	100	PC Madhouse	1/1
206-581-9088	WA	Tacoma	I.Arslangiray	Q	2	71	Medical & Tech	
206-582-1185	WA	Tacoma	John Haste	Q	9V	97	Vanguard II	1/1
206-644-1882	WA	Redmond	Jon Badeaux	B	9D		Hotline	9/2
206-661-7335	WA	Federal Way	Rich Greene	B	9U	93	Evergreen Xchg	4/2
206-676-5787	WA	Seattle	Dave Doughty	B	2	75	BBQd RiBBS	1/2
206-698-9206	WA	Bremerton	D. Kleinschmidt	R	2	34	Circuit Board	1/
206-725-9233	WA	Seattle	Sal Manaro	X	2	24	Underdog's MNet	
206-742-7782	WA	Mukilteo	Steve Walcher	B	9U	96	Tin Pan Alley	2/1
206-745-6340	WA	Edmonds	Dean Johnson	T$	9U	08	PugetSound TBBS	
206-784-7508	WA	Seattle	Will Hansen	Q	9	99	ChristianResch.	12/1
206-822-7498	WA	Kirkland	Bill Ruediger	B	9D	92	SiliconHarvest	3/2
206-830-9319	WA	Bremerton	Bill Hippe	O	9U	83	ElecDungeon	3/
206-848-2831	WA	Puyallup	David Reed	Q	9D		CrossRoads	1/
206-854-0420	WA	Kent	Norman Hamer	X	9V	98	The Mavenry	1/1
206-964-4726	WA	Fort Lewis	Randy Davila	B	9D	103	Snake's Den	3/1
206-964-5311	WA	Fort Lewis	Blaine Brost	B	29V	116*	FreeFall	3/1
207-247-6225	ME	E.Waterboro	Matthew Webster	F	9V	100	8th Wonder	1/1
207-469-3585	ME	East Orland	Laurie Duvefelt	J	22	108	Laurie's Garden	11/1
207-469-6732	ME	Bucksport	Ken Bouchard	J	19V	88	(TPinnacle Club	1/1
207-496-2391	ME	Caribou	David Collins	B$V	9U	89	No. Maine	28/4
207-594-0844	ME	Rockland	Rick Winslow	X$	19V	110	Bit of Maine	1/1
207-627-4169	ME	Oxford	Bruce Prindall	F	9U	72	Gt White North	1/
207-657-4423	ME	Gray	Doug Roberts	R	9V	92	Moveable Image	2/1
207-698-1853	ME	Berwick	Ranguette/Clark	W	29V	112	CYBERSPACE	6/1
207-727-5989	ME	W. Buxton	M. Scribner	B	9U	74	The Addiction	2/3
207-761-4782	ME	Portland	Jack Kilday	B	9D	26	No. Lights	7/4
207-766-2467	ME	Portland	Jack Kilday	B	9U	26	Northern Lights	/4
207-777-3465	ME	Auburn	Jon Meier	R	9V		L/A Blues	2/2
207-777-7782	ME	Auburn	P. Delahanty	R	2	100	L/A Blues	2/2
207-786-2926	ME	Lewiston	Brian Caouette	X	09V	107	Dream Link	7/3
207-799-3547	ME	S.Portland	David Pratt	B	9V	45	S. Maine Tech	
207-799-4088	ME	Windham	Herb Edgecomb	B	9U	44	Maine PC Connx	7/
207-799-9080	ME	CapeElizabth	Theo Van Dinter	X	29V	114	GS Connection	3/1
207-854-3928	ME	Westbrook	Dave Parks	B	9D	68	ME PC Connx	7/3
207-873-1937	ME	Winslow	Anne Arnold	W$	9	88	Bits n Bytes	6/2
207-878-3476	ME	Portland	Jeff Richard	L	19U	107	Rolling Thunder	4/1
207-878-8336	ME	Portland	Russ Darling	B	99D	114	Alternative	8/1
207-883-0039	ME	Scarborough	George Caswell	L	09V	114	Test Pattern	2/1

Phone	State	City	Sysop	T/S	First on List # | v (see above)	Name, Features	
207-941-0805	ME	Bangor	Mark Goodwin	X	19D	95	Lobster Buoy	12/3
208-237-5707	ID	Chubbuck	Val Larsen	R	19V	108	V&K After Hours	10/3
208-368-0365	ID	Boise	Sam/Chris Evans	B	19D	115*	Future Times	28/2
208-385-3354	ID	Boise	Skip Knox	B	2	56	Boise St Univ	
208-524-7416	ID	Idaho Falls	David Reavill	R	2	85	DR Computing	
208-587-9367	ID	Mtn Home	Dave Elliott	B	9H	89	Daves Diversion	
208-684-3526	ID	Blackfoot	Steven Purvis	B	99V	115	SuperNET of ID	1/1
208-726-1435	ID	Ketchum	S. Schowengerdt	B	19D	112	Connections	8/1
208-772-4046	ID	C. d'Alene	Dave Pulsipher	B	9U	79	FileSource	30/10
208-785-1185	ID	Blackfoot	Scott Bertwell	R	2	84	Final Circuit	
208-934-5605	ID	Gooding	Shane Hall	W	19V	109*	Tattooed	50/1
209-222-0227	CA	Fresno	John Bevins	W	2	97	BBS Tech	1/2
209-226-3476	CA	Fresno	S. Francis	O	19D	113	Walk Wild Side	10/1
209-239-9853	CA	Manteca	Kenneth Roach	X	9	58	BerthaBd,C	/
209-274-0909	CA	Ione	Mike Holgate	V	19D	113	BONKS WORLD	5/4
209-274-9106	CA	Ione	Warren Benson	V	09V	116*	AmadorHamShack	5/1
209-323-6144	CA	Clovis	Aubrey Barnett	F	2	85	Barney's Wksp	2/
209-323-7583	CA	Clovis	Rod Jessen	W	9V	100	Clovis Connect	1/1
209-339-0220	CA	Woodbridge	Dave Tracewell	O	2	99	STARBASE	1/1
209-357-0103	CA	Atwater	Tim Strickland	R	2	103	Lazy Raven	1/1
209-357-1217	CA	Winton	Mike Dunn	B	2	60	Elegant Applic	
209-357-4230	CA	Atwater	Bill Paez	W	2	92	Ace's Place	2/
209-358-6891	CA	Atwater	K, Grimlore	F	9H	97	Fantasy Wldrlnd	2/1
209-369-1397	CA	Lodi	Tracy Saunders	L	19V	110	Progmer's Link	1/1
209-383-6417	CA	Merced	Clinton Cook	W	9C	77	Merced WC	3/2
209-432-2487	CA	Fresno	John Pickens	O	2	60	StarBase III	2/
209-527-2944	CA	Modesto	Danny Gottlieb	X	9V	93	Argic<+>Food	2/4
209-549-0423	CA	Modesto	Chris Yarnell	V	9		Anything Goes	1/
209-576-1606	CA	Modesto	Larry Beyers	X	29V	113	Root Connection	5/1
209-591-8753	CA	Dinuba	Chuck Sadoian	B	2	73	MicroLink	3/
209-599-7435	CA	Ripon	Pam Lagier	Q	9U	50	TurboCity	3/
209-634-5395	CA	Denair	James Wendeln	B	19V	93	OutHouse	5/1
209-635-8561	CA	Visalia	Michael Smith	X	19V	114	New World Order	1/1
209-734-9412	CA	Visalia	Tony Ermie	Q	2	79	OnLine	
209-781-1344	CA	Porterville	Richard Kelley	C	9		KPS Micro	3/
209-826-1900	CA	Los Banos	David Clifford	W	19V	107	Haunted Castle	15/2
209-826-8107	CA	Los Banos	Andy Nachbaur	W	99V	107	Wild Bee's	10/1
209-832-7895	CA	Tracy	Myles Olson	B	29D	93	Acme	30/6
209-833-3615	CA	Tracy	Mark Bauman	X	19V	114	Sinking Ship	30/1
209-935-2494	CA	Coalinga	Dwayne Gabriel	O	29D	102	West Valley	12/1
209-943-1880	CA	Stockton	Chuck Hague	B	2	79	WrongNumber	8/2
209-982-1297	CA	Manteca	Tracy Pengilly	W	02	105	Construct.Hotln	1/2
209-997-0224	CA	Lemoore	Mark Williamson	Q	29V	110	Software Soltns	2/1
210-421-2670	TX	Harlingen	Doug Couch	X	09V	109	RECCE II	5/2
210-423-1574	TX	Harlingen	Bill Leaming	B	19D	109	Vocations Cntrl	1/1
210-672-2219	TX	Gonzales	Mark Henneke	W	09D	105	Ranger Station	55/1
210-674-1242	TX	San Antonio	Mike Demski	B	9D	103	Soul Connection	2/2

Phone	State	City	Sysop	T/S	First on List # | v (see above)	Name, Features	
210-775-7236	TX	Del Rio	Jose Frias	B	09D	110*	Joe's Place	4/2
212-242-7814	NY	New York	Chris Welber	B	9U	76	Red Phone	13/2
212-353-8415	NY	New York	Ted Young	F	9U	71	DigitalZero[tm]	3/
212-371-5462	NY	New York	Pat Wolfert	R	9U	55	Granny's RBBS	
212-406-9108	NY	Manhattan	Andi Anderson	T	2	75	TentraRedFlag	2/
212-427-1805	NY	New York	Daniel Doman	D	9HV	15	DannySoft,pgm'g	2/
212-431-1273	NY	New York	Michael Sussell	B$	9H	06	InventionFact'y	30/
212-486-0118	NY	RooseveltIsl	Ducu Ionescu	X	9V	97	The MasTRE	1/1
212-519-1791	NY	New York	Howard Belasco	B	2	47	Running Board	
212-579-2869	NY	Bronx	Fr Lombardi	T$	9V	58	Fordham Jesuit	
212-580-3615	NY	New York	Michael Lehman	X	22	115	Needful Things	2/1
212-594-4425	NY	New York	Philip Perlman	O	29D	91	BlueDog	15/1
212-627-0531	NY	New York	Kevin Freeman	Q	19V	103	FPX2	20/1
212-628-5486	NY	New York	Staff	T$	9V	82	Network One	12/?
212-679-6972	NY	New York	M. Steinberg	B	9H	95	NYPC BBS	2/2
212-685-8309	NY	New York	Tom Murphy	B	9V	92	PosterBd Net	2/3
212-691-2679	NY	New York	Joey Havlock	W	19OV	109	Real Exposure	10/4
212-696-0360	NY	New York	Chris Parker	X	2	26	PC Mag I.R.S.	
212-727-9046	NY	New York	Debbie Hart	B	2	68	Natl DPjobs lst	/2
212-734-1090	NY	New York	Jim Moran	B	29V	113	ACE	1/1
212-752-8660	NY	New York	Alex Nason	M	9D	76	Free Fin. Netw	6/64
212-876-5885	NY	New York	David Shapiro	B$	9U	88	Amer.Info.Svcs	4/3
212-888-6565	NY	New York	William Stewart	B	29D	88*	Computers&Dream	36/14
212-924-9627	NY	New York	Jamie Popken	Q	29U	107	BluePhishen'	24/3
212-962-1920	NY	New York	Ron Chibnik	S	9U	45	Wise Byte	1/
212-989-8411	NY	New York	Stacy Horn	X$	09D		Echo	18/30
213-465-9486	CA	Hollywood	Kevin Walker	Q	9D	104	Special Times	1/1
213-654-7337	CA	Los Angeles	Michael Conley	W	9U	60	Charl'sCabin	4/
213-778-6450	CA	Los Angeles	Rudy Lopez	W	19V	116*	Southside Info	3/1
213-874-9484	CA	W. Hollywood	Richard Martz	Q	9U	26	W.Hollywood BBS	
213-876-5661	CA	Hollywood	Leonard Kane	B	29HB	116*	FunTime	21/1
213-933-4050	CA	Los Angeles	Dave Harrison	X$	2	89	MetroOnline	50/60
213-953-0040	CA	Los Angeles	Steven de Mena	M$	09V	112	CASTLE	50/32
214-226-6017	TX	Garland	Rick Kuban	B	9U	79	Technoid'sTB	6/
214-234-4952	TX	Richardson	Don Brandt	O	9V	86	Rabbit/Snake	2/2
214-235-5288	TX	Richardson	John Stewart	B	19V	86	Lunatic Fringe	7/3
214-238-1805	TX	Dallas	Roger Williams	Q	9U	86	MasterControl	3/2
214-250-3778	TX	Greenleaf	Helen Moreira	W	2	26	Greenleaf supt	
214-252-6717	TX	Irving	Mark Elson	W	9U	91	Blues Cafe	3/
214-258-1832	TX	Irving	Steve Rainwater	Q	9V	73	Interocitor	1/
214-259-3366	TX	Irving	Bill Miller	Q	29D	112	Modem Addicts ?	15/1
214-271-8899	TX	Dallas	Jon Hutto	U	2	59	PC-Tech,Ultra	1/
214-306-7218	TX	Dallas	Charles Reiss	R	99D	34	24hr ticket agy	12/2
214-306-8269	TX	Dallas	Rick Wadatz	B	19DU	105	Planet	6/2
214-317-0149	TX	Lewisville	Fred Gardner	W	9V	93	Techline	6/
214-351-9859	TX	Dallas	Len Hult	B	9U	45	CollectorsEd	3/2
214-393-7090	TX	Dallas	Jeffrey Kay	R	9U	26	Central Aerosp	12/

					First on List # | v		
Phone	*State*	*City*	*Sysop*	*T/S*	*(see above)*	*Name, Features*	
214-394-7438	TX	Carrollton	Jeff Wallach	B$	9V	50	DRIG	10/10
214-394-8021	TX	Carrollton	Bryan Erickson	X	19V	107	KoZmiK KaTHouSe	10/2
214-398-3112	TX	Dallas	Ric Naff	F	9V	84	Prgmr Xchg	2/
214-436-6089	TX	Lewisville	Mike Sheppard	F	19DH	112	Graphics Plus	1/1
214-436-8753	TX	Lewisville	Tracy Perry	Q	9U	92	Code 3,cops	1/
214-458-2620	TX	Dallas	Arthur Geffen	C	9D	73	InnsofCourt	3/
214-487-9422	TX	Garland	Danny Cummings	W	9D	91	Bailiwick	18/
214-490-8107	TX	Dallas Area	Bill Hummel	T	9U	26	Computer Sol'n	25/
214-492-2420	TX	Carrollton	Bob Butler	O	2	86	Ogre'sRevenge	
214-492-6565	TX	Carrollton	Wm. Pendergast	B$	9D	50	User-to-User	25/6
214-495-3287	TX	Garland	John Cailloux	B$	9	95	After Hours	16/4
214-495-5980	TX	Garland	Mike Shockley	W$	19D	93	Shock Treatment	10/3
214-517-8443	TX	Plano	Andy Walding	W$	9U	80	Digital	1/
214-517-8553	TX	Plano	Mike Bloom	O	2	72	The Exchange	
214-530-5526	TX	Garland	James Marple	Q	9U	73	CarrierPidgeon	1/
214-541-0201	TX	Irving	Larry Mundy	O	19V	112	Win*Net Library	4/1
214-562-7034	TX	Dallas	T. Rossbottom	X	09D	115	Chips & Dips	3/2
214-573-3649	TX	Dallas	Pat Spreng	B	29D	68	Blue Flame	4/4
214-578-7618	TX	Plano	John Wagoner	F	09D	108	Stargate	9/1
214-613-6975	TX	Mesquite	Warren Nobles	P	2	92	Mesquite'sBest	2/2
214-620-8793	TX	Dallas	Joe DeRouen	X	19VO	109	SunlightShadows	1/1
214-641-1136	TX	GrandPrairie	Ken Givens	Q	9U	42	ChessBoard	6/
214-650-1452	TX	Irving	H. Glantzberg	X	19V	106	Hughes' Power	3/1
214-660-8613	TX	Dallas	Mark Elson	W$V	9D	91	Blues Cafe	3/2
214-669-9052	TX	Dallas	Dustin Nulf	Q	29V	116*	Overkill WHQ	1/1
214-680-2693	TX	Richardson	B. A. Ducate	B	2	54	PC-Help	
214-732-7643	TX	Dallas	C. Satterwhite	X	19D	111	Ratiocination	9/1
214-790-6472	TX	Irving	Bobb Waller	F	2	86	FIAWOL,s.f.	1/
214-808-7801	TX	Dallas	Leo Wrobel	B	9	94	Magic Mansion	2/
214-867-6630	TX	Plano	Don Turner	O	9U	55	Texas Twister	
214-881-0313	TX	Plano	Ron Spatafora	X	9D	15	Rbase 5000	8/
214-881-9346	TX	Plano	Mike Davis	R$	9U	49	Horizon	8/3
215-237-1281	PA	Darby	AnthonyPhillips	W	9U	86	Seeker'sPlace	6/2
215-245-7684	PA	Trevose	Charles Horsey	F	9U	84	Horse Talk	3/
215-255-0610	PA	Landenberg	Jack Murray	W	9D	83	L'berg WCat	3/
215-273-2606	PA	Honey Brook	Bill Hamel	R	2	79	TechConn	1/
215-279-9722	PA	Norristown	K. Sridharan	B	2	83	Starbase 10	2/
215-328-2877	PA	Swarthmore	Nick Martin	W	02	116*	Jack AllTrades	1/1
215-331-2590	PA	Philadelphia	David Pierron	F	9U	86	Wombat'sWagon	2/
215-356-1630	PA	Newtown Sq.	Peter Essl	B	9D	26	HyperLinc East	6/6
215-363-6625	PA	Exton	Peter Rucci	T	2	47	Del Ches	6/2
215-364-2409	PA	Holland	Brian Kerr	Q	9HV	88	MysticIsles sf	1/2
215-364-3324	PA	Hunt'Valley	Ron Brandt	B$	9UHV	67	Satalink	25/10
215-376-1819	PA	Reading	Allen Cravener	W$	19V	91	Glass Menagerie	50/3
215-391-0185	PA	Allentown	Hiram Cook	R	09V	111	Bit Bucket Sys	25/1
215-395-9823	PA	Allentown	Gary Puzzella	B	9D	86	Computer Shop	2/
215-432-5699	PA	Allentown	Bill Earnest	V	9V	104	Allentown Tech	1/1

					First on List # | *v*	
Phone	*State*	*City*	*Sysop*	*T/S*	*(see above)*	*Name, Features*
215-434-4972	PA	Allentown	Stu Jones	V	9U	86	NuclearMedicine	2/
215-443-9434	PA	Ivyland	Ron Brandt	B$	9D	101	DSC	60/16
215-449-7479	PA	Havertown	Larry Hawk	X	9V	103	DownLoad Drive	1/1
215-463-9433	PA	Philadelphia	Mardi Burden	W	9	89	Dragon-1 Sys	8/
215-464-3562	PA	Philadelphia	Mark Miller	T	2	85	Satronics	4/6
215-493-5242	PA	Yardley	Richard Press	T	9D	43	U.S.Telematics	2/
215-524-2459	PA	Exton	Bill Probeck	Q	19V	116*	Telegraph Hill	1/2
215-533-4072	PA	Philadelphia	Tom Welsh	WV	9D	101	TESSERACT	21/3
215-535-6579	PA	Philadelphia	Barbara Dibuono	T	9D	102	Direct ConnectS	3/2
215-536-5157	PA	Quakertown	Robert Myers	O	2	73	MY-COMM	3/
215-563-8109	PA	Philadelphia	Doug Laine	B	9U	77	Philly Xchg	10/4
215-568-1390	PA	Philadelphia	Sean Robins	F	2	84	PhilaLawLink,!	2/
215-580-2216	PA	Philadelphia	June Summers	B	19V	44	OPM FedJobs-Phi	1/2
215-584-1412	PA	Conshohocken	Ed Barboni	O	2	26	System-2	1/
215-586-8705	PA	Collingdale	Tom Guilfoyle	T	9D	102	Carrier Detect	2/2
215-622-3569	PA	Lansdowne	Biff Webb	W	2	104	Maritime Online	2/1
215-623-6203	PA	Lansdowne	Ray Novino	B$	9U	67	RunWay	15/6
215-626-3862	PA	Drexel Hill	Mark Rostein	W$	2	64	Camelot	3/3
215-657-7773	PA	Willow Grove	Wolff & Spotts	B	9HV	56	WDS,applic	
215-678-0350	PA	Reinholds	Ken Regenfuse	W	9U	92	Docksider	2/
215-678-0818	PA	Reading	Brown & McCoy	B	9U	75	Round Table	13/4
215-692-7392	PA	West Chester	Paul Emmons	B	19D	111	Bauding House	2/1
215-698-7677	PA	Philadelphia	Perry Stephens	W	9V	84	Perry-1,Tandy	6/2
215-721-0363	PA	Hatfield	Warren Foxe	O	9U	34	Foxes Den	
215-759-1376	PA	Easton	Bill Snell	V	9V	87	Bits & Bytes	1/
215-779-9562	PA	Reading	Wilson Rogers	W	2	87	WINS	1/
215-783-6352	PA	King Prussia	Steven Rogers	B	9V	102	NPN	35/1
215-788-4339	PA	Croydon	Bill Dennison	W	9V	98	Storm Front	3/2
215-796-9249	PA	Shillington	Brad Leiphart	X	9D	96	Quantum	1/1
215-797-4740	PA	Allentown	Garofalo/Shea	B	2	72	City Lights	2/2
215-797-9378	PA	Allentown	Scott Miller	W$	19D	89	ProgrammersHavn	5/2
215-860-9724	PA	Newtown	A. Maglietta	B	9D	102	Newtown Express	43/6
215-926-1213	PA	Hamburg	Daryll Henrich	L	2	96	U.F.O.	1/1
215-949-2701	PA	Levittown	Bob Bernstein	B$	29D	102	32 Bit Bus	55/2
215-949-3141	PA	Levittown	Tom Maurizi	B$	29V	110	32 Bit Bus S&G	25/4
215-970-2029	PA	Pottstown	Bernie Kosar	V	2	103	Atlantis	2/1
215-989-8436	PA	Philadelphia	Glenn McAtee	B	19V	107	Micro Center	5/1
216-232-2834	OH	Cleveland	Jack D'Angelo	X	29V	111	Chromatic Prism	1/1
216-236-6126	OH	Col. Station	Steve Husk	S$V	2	99	County Link	1/4
216-237-7727	OH	Cleveland	Dave Joyce	W	2		HomeVacationNet	2/2
216-243-0990	OH	Cleveland	John Fisher	P	9U	66	Database Portal	1/
216-273-9196	OH	Brunswick	Andrew Tollin	Q	9D	104	FunTime BBS	9/1
216-296-4446	OH	Ravenna	Joe Rinehart	R	09V	96	Blue Parrot	12/3
216-321-5994	OH	Cleveland	Tim Rossiter	S	2	64	FlipFlop	1/
216-332-2712	OH	Salem	Macy Bergoon	W	99D	103	Tech-Line	14/1
216-366-1935	OH	Elyria	Kevin Worden	B	9U	72	HackersUnltd	
216-381-3320	OH	Cleveland	Norm Henke	B$	9V	26	PC-Ohio	150/35

Phone	State	City	Sysop	T/S		First on List # | v (see above)	Name, Features	
216-397-9966	OH	Univ Hts	Karl Weller	R	19V	112	WellerWare	2/1
216-421-2548	OH	Cleveland	Paul Rebeta	MV	2	100	Foot Talk	1/4
216-449-7036	OH	Cleveland	Glenn McAtee	B	19V	107	Micro Center	5/1
216-526-9480	OH	Cleveland	Bill Poissant	B	9V	34	Amcom	30/8
216-534-3739	OH	Hubbard	Carl Kesner	G	9C	73	2-Bros East	1/
216-544-8802	OH	Niles	Patrick Glunt	B	9U	89	PatricksPlace	4/
216-545-0093	OH	Girard	Orren Zook	X	9U	55	SteelValley	2/
216-562-1110	OH	Aurora	Steve Leu	B$	19D	86	West Branch Con	45/8
216-637-8397	OH	Cortland	Carl Deleo	Q	9U		Love Board	15/
216-639-9508	OH	Concord	Soo Kurz	B	19VU	114	"Scientist's"	20/3
216-661-9065	OH	Cleveland	Roger Dye	W$	29	86	Comstar	10/1
216-674-0144	OH	Millersburg	Rick Nash	W	9U	92	Valkyrie,pgming	34/1
216-686-7900	OH	Stow	Keith Bratton	B	19D	112	PARADOX Online	20/2
216-731-4769	OH	Euclid	Richard Pressl	S	9U	80	Bizhost	6/2
216-745-3451	OH	Akron	Tony Limbert	X	2	97	White Star	1/1
216-769-2091	OH	Seville	Josh Vince	F	09V	115	Admiral's Realm	6/1
216-792-0981	OH	Austintown	Mike Gollner	B	9U	63	Austintown	2/
216-794-1194	OH	Akron	Murry Francis	Q	99D	89	Big Rig	18/2
216-823-3242	OH	Alliance	Richard Bacorn	W	9H	81	Red Eagle	2/
216-923-6409	OH	Akron	Danny Smith	Q	02	111	Pig Sty	1/1
216-941-9420	OH	Cleveland	Tom Swimmer	G	19V	103*	Night Shift	2/1
216-942-7516	OH	Willoughby	Dave Foran	R	9U	85	ClevelandHamnet	1/
216-944-5639	OH	Cleveland	Keith Ross	B$	9V	97	BBS-OHIO	1/1
216-946-3161	OH	Cleveland	Bob Brancheau	G$	19V	98*	Dr. ZING'S	10/2
216-967-9457	OH	Vermillion	Geo Harizal	R	9V	83	WareHouse	21/1
217-384-4311	IL	Urbana	Wayne Hamilton	O	09D	70	Prgmrs Toolbox	1/1
217-422-2585	IL	Decatur	Dennis Kreher	B	29D	83	CompCorner	12/4
217-425-7052	IL	Decatur	Joe Prosser	B	19D	84*	«Smokin'Joe's»	13/3
217-428-9803	IL	Decatur	David Klitzsch	B	19DB	104	Operating Room	12/3
217-522-8680	IL	Springfield	Joseph Pope	B	9V	92	White House	2/
217-566-3775	IL	Williamsvlle	Steve Horrighs	F$	19D	105	Fantasy Land	14/2
217-593-6545	IL	Camp Point	Dale Shank	X	19D	116*	LTM Computer	9/1
217-735-2251	IL	Lincoln	Glen Buckley	B	19V	105	»LIGHTHOUSE«	2/1
217-762-2847	IL	Monticello	Ed Maroon	B	9U	91	BackDoor	12/3
217-875-7114	IL	Decatur	Robert Williams	B	9V	95	The Data Hut	1/
217-877-1138	IL	Decatur	James Jones	B	19D	87*	2/3 Board	45/3
217-935-6144	IL	Clinton	Steve Meade	W$	09V	108	"MANIAC BBS"	5/1
218-254-4921	MN	Chisholm	Philip Johnson	S	2	77	Taconite	
218-389-6800	MN	Mahtowa	Gary Peterson	R	19D	59	***BIGTOP***	45/2
218-449-4715	MN	ThiefRiver	Andy Filer	X	22	108	NCS-NET	1/1
218-624-5853	MN	Duluth	Ben Standley	B	9U	47	MicroSimul(tm)	21/3
218-724-3805	MN	Duluth	Joe Kimbler	O	09VO	106	Duluth	18/1
218-724-9626	MN	Duluth	Kevin Raihala	BV	9D	93	PC Support	10/1
218-729-7072	MN	Hermantown	Bob Slowinski	Q$	99D	76	Info Central	6/2
218-739-2296	MN	Fergus Falls	Perry Mertz	X	9V	99	LatenitesatLake	3/2
218-829-6340	MN	Merrifield	Gil Pence	G$	9V	97	Merrifield PC	1/1
218-924-2060	MN	Bertha	Craig Stevenson	R$	9U	97	Bertha,TIPS	8/2

Phone	State	City	Sysop	T/S	First on List # ↓ (see above)	Name, Features	
219-256-2255	IN	Mishawaka	Mike Shannon	W$	09D	76	RadioDaze,bcstg	63/9
219-262-0910	IN	Elkhart	C. Lambright	B$	9U	96	US-BBSofElkhart	5/1
219-262-1370	IN	Elkhart	Dan Roemer	B$	9U	84	After Five	20/3
219-262-9371	IN	Elkhart	Marcus Breese	B	9O	103	Windchill Factr	5/1
219-295-7710	IN	Elkhart	Tim O'Brien	B	19V	114	Computer Nut	5/1
219-356-6297	IN	Huntington	Mark Timbers	R	9D	102	Timbers	1/1
219-424-4292	IN	Fort Wayne	Dave Doehrman	O	9V	95	Semper Fi	2/1
219-453-4046	IN	LkTippecanoe	Mike Atkinson	B	09D	116*	Tippy	5/1
219-482-4205	IN	Fort Wayne	Gary Hall	X$	19V	106	Pool Room	10/2
219-484-9740	IN	Fort Wayne	Larry Kilgore	X	19V	111*	GeoFract	27/1
219-485-3551	IN	Fort Wayne	Ed Rose	X$	19D	113	EMPLOYMENT LINE	2/3
219-493-2193	IN	Fort Wayne	Mark Pease	W	9M	80	New Files Xpres	5/
219-563-1738	IN	Wabash	Norm Benjamin	B$	2	78	Wabash	2/
219-659-0112	IN	Whiting	Rick Catania	W	2	77	SpecNeeds,Disab	
219-663-3107	IN	Crown Point	Jeff Wahlberg	S	9U	81	BadConnx	3/
219-696-3415	IN	Lowell	Ken Prevo	B	9D	49	Toolkit	12/
219-728-9598	IN	Decatur	Mike Allison	B	9U	87	HoosierHideaway	1/
219-762-5620	IN	Portage	Ralph Shaffer	B	9U	54	Dune Hi-Tech	8/
219-763-2031	IN	Portage	Dennis Matney	B	9D	91	Sometimes	2/1
219-848-7200	IN	Bristol	Cindy Duryea	B	9D	104	Dock	13/3
219-873-1035	IN	MichiganCity	Brian Marx	B	9D		Cutting Edge	4/
219-884-9508	IN	Gary	Philip Stults	B$	9	15	LANS BBS No.1	
219-923-7611	IN	Griffith	Jeff Ready	B	2	72	Excalibur	2/
301-217-3913	MD	Rockville	Charlie Eason	R	9U	85	Friends Forum	
301-229-5342	MD	Bethesda	Bonnie Anthony	B	9U	50	Running Board	1/2
301-230-1214	MD	Bethesda	Jeff Wunderlich	B	99V	116*	Aurora Support	3/1
301-251-9206	MD	Gaithersburg	P. L. Olympia	B	9H	01+	DARWIN	
301-258-1858	MD	Rockville	Bob Lau	W	19V	92*	IICS-DC	33/6
301-261-5644	MD	Shady Side	Jim Hildwine	X	2	90	Vetlink#4	
301-294-5182	MD	Rockville	Exiled Martian	W	2	97	Mars Stn, Abuse	1/1
301-299-1196	MD	Potomac	Hugues Scarlata	X	09V	110	Player One	2/1
301-320-6748	MD	Bethesda	Fritz Finley	X	2	95	Nitrous Cloud	1/
301-322-8678	MD	Landover	William Watson	X	2	26	Wizard's Wrkshp	
301-340-2212	MD	Gaithersburg	Bob Schniebolk	B	29V	29	CONTECH	7/2
301-345-3441	MD	College Park	Jack Mallinger	B	9D	75	Happy Hour	9/2
301-353-1003	MD	Germantown	Pete Raumann	P	19D	100	Pete's Place	9/1
301-373-3503	MD	Hollywood	Brian Miller	X	2	103	Hillville Tradg	4/1
301-373-3859	MD	Hollywood	Lew Adams	Q	19V	113	My Toy	7/1
301-373-5965	MD	Hollywood	Brandon Hayden	B	9U	87	Hollywood News	7/3
301-373-8793	MD	Hollywood	Gene Talley	R	2	26	Southern MD	
301-384-8751	MD	SilverSpring	Gus Padron	F	2	47	Bit Bucket	1/
301-384-9302	MD	Burton'vle	LarryMcGoldrick	R	2	72	Real Estate	
301-417-9341	MD	Gaithersburg	Scott MacLean	X	09V	114	HST Artif Horiz	9/3
301-424-3614	MD	Rockville	Michael Dew	B	19V	77*	CannnonFodder	8/1
301-431-0647	MD	SilverSpring	Angla Babe	B	19D	98	Womens World	10/8
301-460-9134	MD	Rockville	Mr. C. Peters	O	9U	63	Eniac,MIDI	1/
301-468-0175	MD	Rockville	Craig B. Laub	X	02	108	Pronto InfoSys	2/5

Phone	State	City	Sysop	T/S		First on List # | v (see above)	Name, Features	
301-473-5952	MD	Middletown	Jay Alexander	G	9D	78	MachineShop	7/
301-473-8781	MD	Middletown	Roger Gray	Q$	9U	77	Mr.Gray'sToy	7/
301-474-1702	MD	College Park	E.Burleyson	R	2	70	Programming Pl	
301-498-8205	MD	Laurel	NumisNet(sm)	W$	2	67	NumisNet(sm)	
301-499-4671	MD	Mitchellvlle	Raymond Wood	P	9U	104	Capitol Area	14/1
301-513-0163	MD	Greenbelt	Chris Davies	Q	19D	112	Message Ctr E.	2/1
301-530-5962	MD	Bethesda	Peter Anderson	W	9D	66	ElecShopper	2/
301-540-3654	MD	Germantown	Paul Hirsch	X	19V	112	North Pole	4/1
301-568-1679	MD	Camp Springs	Robin Turner	W	2	98	Robin's Nest	1/1
301-585-6697	MD	SilverSpring	Daniel Wendling	B	12	105	Coin of Realm	1/1
301-588-0774	MD	SilverSpring	Paul LaZar	X	2	45	Comm Center	12/5
301-590-9629	MD	Gaithersburg	Stan Staten	R	2	06	3WINKs	/2
301-593-8992	MD	SilverSpring	Michael Falba	W	09D	106	Step Club	20/1
301-593-9323	MD	SilverSpring	Vince Wilding	R	29V	114	SilverSoftMicro	4/1
301-595-5776	MD	Beltsville	Lesley Williams	M	09V	101*	GlobeNetPlace	23/9
301-596-6450	MD	College Park	Mark Oberg	J	2	15	NoPlaceLikeHome	1/
301-596-7693	MD	Columbia	Gary Smith	X	9V	48	Programmer'sCor	28/15
301-601-8710	MD	Germantown	Bruce Marusich	R	9U	91	Street Noise	31/2
301-621-7785	MD	Ft. Meade	Jeff Martin	W	19V	98	Martin's Domain	2/2
301-622-0708	MD	SilverSpring	Rod Renner	BV	9V	10	Lightning Rod	2/1
301-627-4246	MD	Lothian	Jerry Messineo	B	?9V	115	Dark Star Domn	20/1
301-649-1050	MD	Wheaton	Nathan Moschkin	· Q	29D	111	Cascades Etc	2/
301-652-0032	MD	Takoma Park	F. Velasquez	X	9H	26	VF Assoc suppt	
301-654-2554	MD	Germantown	Andrew Bilski	B$	19V	61	Main Frame	46/12
301-654-6462	MD	Chevy Chase	Tim Sawyer	B	9HV	92	Broadcasters	2/
301-662-8948	MD	Frederick	Curtis Campbell	O	9V	95	CyberSystems	3/
301-694-7108	MD	Frederick	A. Bartorillo	Q	9U	15	Baudline II	
301-695-9118	MD	Frederick	B. Brodka	B$	9U	77	AdvDatSys	28/10
301-696-1968	MD	Frederick	Abner Santiago	W	9U	95	Paradise	4/
301-705-6907	MD	Waldorf	Tom Watson	X	29V	114	Mended Vessels	1/1
301-705-7115	MD	Waldorf	Timothy Ward	F	2	98	TimsHouseofFun	12/1
301-738-9060	MD	Rockville	CPCUG MIX	R$	9D	26	Members only	2/8
301-773-0822	MD	Cheverly	Bob Harper	F	9	101	Greystone Manor	4/1
301-776-8259	MD	Laurel	James Mullen	X	29V	114	Brazen's HELL!	2/2
301-779-5946	MD	Riverdale	Ken Jacobs	B	9V	97	Jellicle Cat	5/1
301-794-6496	MD	Sea Brook	Robin Matthew	W$	19U	112	Adv Sftw Concpt	82/13
301-831-5954	MD	Mt. Airy	Lucas Spiros	B	9	56	The WJ3P Xchg	
301-839-0705	MD	Oxon Hill	Lee Pollard	R	9M	34	Deathstar	4/
301-843-1548	MD	Waldorf	Joe Sartori	B	9U	45	Waldorf Connx	4/
301-843-5247	MD	Waldorf	Donald Poole	S	9U	93	Crow'sNest,CDR	5/
301-843-5732	MD	Waldorf	Dave Brodmann	R	2	81	Brodmann's	2/2
301-855-9420	MD	Prince Fred.	Paul Naley	W	19D	111	Little Rascals	38/2
301-862-3160	MD	California	Buggs Bugnon	B	9U	48	So MD Christian	3/
301-884-3686	MD	Charlotte Hl	Dave Lockard	Q	2	95	Dog House	1/
301-884-4507	MD	Charlotte Hl	Jeff Daigle	Q	2	96	Diacom	1/1
301-891-2646	MD	Takoma Park	Paul Nahay	Q$	2	89	Animal Bytes	
301-907-0349	MD	Bethesda	Michael Pearl	W	9D	103	ProfEx BBS	2/3

						First on List # | v (see above)	
Phone	*State*	*City*	*Sysop*	*T/S*			*Name, Features*
301-924-2877	MD	Rockville	Zach Benz	P	2	89	The Benez BBS	1/
301-942-5571	MD	Wheaton	SteveSpottswood	W	2	60	PrivateCorner	
301-946-8677	MD	Rockville	Paul Heller	R$	9D	82	TwilightClone	10/10
301-948-8504	MD	Gaithersburg	Henry Stryker	B	19D	114	Woodlawn Manor	3/1
301-948-8966	MD	Gaithersburg	Dave Bettwy	R	2	86	CALS	1/6
301-949-1927	MD	Wheaton	Frank Fowler	B	19V	107	First Due	2/2
301-949-3828	MD	Kensington	Joe Hayes	W	19V	108	Hat Trick	3/1
301-949-5764	DC	Washington	Andy Miller	B	09V	74	Idea Link	3/1
301-949-8848	MD	Rockville	Rich Schinnell	H	9	06	CPCUG S/W Libr	4/
301-963-4453	MD	Gaithersburg	Shawn Bogardus	B	19V	93	DynamicHorizons	12/2
301-989-9036	MD	Colesville	Norm Saunders	X	2	87	Osprey'sNest	1/
301-990-7565	MD	Gaithersburg	Angi Wigle	W$	19V	111	C'mon Inn	12/3
302-322-8215	DE	New Castle	John Kelley	F$	9U	88	Hacker's	3/
302-324-8091	DE	New Castle	Barry Connolly	F	9U	84	DVUG	3/
302-378-2277	DE	Odessa	WarrenWhiteside	X	9HV	84	ST BBS Delaware	1/
302-436-4780	DE	Selbyville	Greg Parsons	B	9U	89	Paradise Cove	2/
302-529-1650	DE	Wilmington	Walt Mateja	F	9U	99	"us" Project	1/1
302-645-7264	DE	Rehoboth Bch	Keith Cochran	B	9U	66	Paradox	7/2
302-678-1579	DE	Dover	John De Cola	L	19D	113	WhiteKnight	3/1
302-737-6041	DE	Newark	Don Clevenger	B	9U	72	FatherBd	
302-739-3693	DE	Dover	M. Mahaffie	B	19V	113	DNREC On-Line	1/1
302-739-6757	DE	Dover	Ed McCormick	N	2	81	DE's Fire Svc	1/
302-836-7145	DE	Bear	Bob Chalmers	F	19D	107	Obsession	3/1
302-875-7216	DE	Laurel	C. Shockley	F	2	97	Brainwave	1/1
302-892-9953	DE	Wilmington	David Hudson	B	9V	98	ITL-Net	8/1
302-994-3772	DE	Newark	Ed DelGrosso	O	2	48	Black Bag,med,!	4/4
303-241-1966	CO	Grand Jnctn	Mike Bruno	B	9U	50	Colo. West UG	2/
303-242-7977	CO	Grand Jnctn	Allan Worley	B	9H	56	SquirrelNest	3/
303-245-1147	CO	Grand Jnctn	Jason Franklin	J	09V	111	Hot Line	1/1
303-254-8073	CO	NorthGlenn	Ron Costa	R	9U	91	Data-Link	1/
303-258-7739	CO	Nederland	Mike Cook	R	19V	105	DiscoveryPlace2	1/1
303-280-1007	CO	Thornton	Curtis Little	A	9HV	66	Lost at C	1/1
303-287-5274	CO	Denver	Daniel Vachon	X	9U	84	RockyMt MIDI	
303-429-0597	CO	Westminster	Gary Carr	P	2	99	Star One	1/1
303-434-5492	CO	Grand Jnctn	Zak Speakman	B	9U	64	Backboard	7/
303-434-7515	CO	Clifton	Buddy Driever	R$	9D	82	PC Addiction	3/1
303-444-7942	CO	Boulder	Pat Nefos	W$	9D	90	SoundingBd	14/2
303-457-1111	CO	Denver	Dean Kerl	M$	09V	107	GaRBaGe DuMP	50/69
303-458-6774	CO	Denver	Mark Pearsall	P	12	105	RefrigeratorDr	1/1
303-469-9359	CO	Westminster	Barry Young	B	9D	104	System Support	11/4
303-534-4646	CO	Denver	Brian Bartee	T$	9D	96	Comm-Post	25/8
303-642-7463	CO	Pinecliffe	Craig Baker	O	9U	75	Pinecliffe	12/6
303-671-7669	CO	Denver	Jay Melnick	T	2	34	CO Travel Bank	
303-678-8439	CO	Longmont	Larry Gibes	B	9V	104	Knowledge Resce	30/1
303-740-2223	CO	Denver	Bob Voorhees	T	2	26	ADP Audit	
303-752-2943	CO	Denver	Jim Kochmann	Q	9U	80	MicroWire	1/
303-789-4610	CO	Englewood	Phil Kaiser	O$	2	15	PC INFO	

						First on List # | v (see above)		
Phone	**State**	**City**	**Sysop**	**T/S**			**Name, Features**	
303-858-4045	CO	Fruita	Eric Angus	L	29V	112	Shadowen's Lair	3/1
303-864-2227	CO	Nucla	Keith Thomson	Q	19VV	111	USS Alcun	2/1
303-933-7747	CO	Denver	Kevin McCarthy	X	9U	102	Kat's Korner	1/2
303-945-4041	CO	GlenwoodSpg	Connie Lewis	W	9U	92	RoaringFork	1/2
303-972-6575	CO	Littleton	Joe Dehn	O	19V	111	Dehnbase Opus	6/1
303-973-4222	CO	Littleton	Jack Rickard	T	2	60	USA Today Distr	
303-980-8486	CO	Lakewood	Paul Johnson	B	19V	105	Wizards Mansion	1/1
304-264-0280	WV	Martinsburg	Tony L. Cooper	B	19V	108	CASA West	3/2
304-233-4199	WV	Wheeling	Robert Ducker	F	2	84	WV\Online	1/
304-264-8749	WV	Martinsburg	Keith Lehman	Q	09V	104	MountainTrails	4/1
304-348-6327	WV	Charleston	Sam Snead, etc	R	2	26	WV Educ Net	
304-592-3390	WV	Shinnston	Doug Moore	B	19D	107	Cat Eye	2/1
304-636-3907	WV	Elkins	Travis King	W	2	92	Teleph Tech	2/
304-675-2549	WV	Pt. Pleasant	Keith Biggs	B	19V	100	Valley Board	3/1
304-683-9192	WV	Sophia	Larry Wood	Q	9V	101	Alpha-I	2/1
304-728-0884	WV	Charles Town	J. Willingham	Q	09V	95	Bit Bank	7/1
304-736-9169	WV	Barb'ville	John Johnson	M	9U	78	Hotline	15/
304-748-0491	WV	Weirton	Mike Perkins	B	19D	99	MindLess One's	50/3
304-768-5036	WV	Dunbar	Bob Vaughan	T$	9U	62	21stCent Connx	20/2
304-823-3052	WV	Philipi	Jos Boutwell	T	2	79	Ramsbbs	2/
304-845-1108	WV	Moundsville	Robert Wagner	S	02	115	Interfaith Exp	1/1
305-221-5533	FL	Miami	M. Hubschman	X	19D	114	KomputerKollege	3/1
305-232-8000	FL	Miami	Craig Merwitzer	W$	19D	85	SharewareOnline	21/4
305-321-8168	FL	Plantation	RichVandenBosch	B	9U	89	Pipeline	4/3
305-346-8524	FL	CoralSprings	Kenneth Wiren	W	9D	100	Looking Glass	3/1
305-361-4524	FL	Miami	Jim Hendee	R	9	91	Coastal RBBS	2/
305-389-8507	FL	Miami	Bob Pianka	O	9D	87	Rock & Roll	9/
305-432-2223	FL	Pembrk Pines	Michele Stewart	B	19D	77	SunShine	12/2
305-435-0990	FL	Hollywood	Joe Brunson	M$	2	81	Apollo Files	12/4
305-442-6000	FL	Miami	Dan Bernasconi	W	9U	98	Blue Water	1/1
305-447-6668	FL	Miami	Tom Bernasconi	W$	29D	97	Mole Hole	5/1
305-472-2314	FL	Davie	Sherry Levine	QV	9V	99	Misty Moonlight	3/2
305-472-7715	FL	Plantation	Bob Patten	W	19V	98	Bashful Pervert	3/1
305-474-6512	FL	Davie	Lautenschlager	R	9U	62	SiliconBch	5/
305-523-1717	FL	FtLauderdale	Rich Waugh	W	9U	86	DrawBridge,ansi	4/
305-559-9151	FL	Miami	Alex Rubio	W	9U	88	Whatnow	3/1
305-572-1819	FL	Lauderhill	Jim Robbins	X	29V	108	Logic Probe	2/1
305-581-4983	FL	FtLauderdale	Terry Woodward	W	9U	91	The Library	24/4
305-583-7981	FL	Plantation	E.Wolf & L.Boxx	B	9U	29	Plantation	
305-724-4297	FL	FtLauderdale	Steve Fraioli	B$	19D	105	PCBBS Onl Sys	4/2
305-752-0435	FL	Parkland	Huy Tran	R	9M	85	Parkland PC BBS	
305-854-8776	FL	Miami	Ronald Imhoff	Y	19U	114	Infinite Sys	1/1
305-922-4597	FL	L'dale Lakes	Mark Calzaretta	R	9HV	83	IBM Whouse	4/
305-945-4887	FL	No. Miami	Dan Heath	W	2	88	Miami Exchange	1/
305-949-6098	FL	Miami	Eric Santelices	J	9V	96	The Pub	14/1
305-960-1011	FL	Pompano Bch	Mike Moore	R	9U	91	QuickSilver	3/
305-972-1901	FL	N Lauderdale	Eric Leitner	B	19VB	106	FL Byte Exch	12/2

						First on List # | v		
Phone	*State*	*City*	*Sysop*	*T/S*		*(see above)*	*Name, Features*	
305-987-5688	FL	Hollywood	David Bennett	B	19V	74	CAROUSEL	6/2
307-637-5930	WY	Cheyenne	David Hutton	F	19V	115	File Hog	3/1
307-638-7448	WY	Cheyenne	Lowell Stewart	W	9V	98	ElectronicExprs	10/1
307-638-8506	WY	Cheyenne	Jim Taylor	O	2	86	RockyMtRendezv	
307-674-8434	WY	Sheridan	Joseph Savino	X	29V	114	Technopolis	5/1
307-742-8830	WY	Laramie	Fred Wollbrinck	R	09D	74	The Gate	5/2
307-856-3601	WY	Riverton	Mike Lieberman	X	9D	26	Wyoming,dB+	4/2
307-856-5072	WY	Riverton	Elmer Robinson	Q	9D	76	InTech BBS	4/
308-487-5505	NE	Alliance	Keith Herald	O$	9U	59	PanHandle Connx	1/
309-342-3275	IL	Galesburg	Tony Swanson	X$	19V	106	MEGA-PHYLE	3/1
309-343-6659	IL	Galesburg	D. Massingill	R	2	56	Toolbox	
309-343-8503	IL	Galesburg	Darrin Seats	F	2	99	PSYCHO-VISION	3/1
309-438-7370	IL	Normal	David Doss	R	2	08	ISU BBS,CompSci	1/
309-444-3978	IL	Washington	Matt Ostanik	X	2	103	Bart's Tale	1/1
309-452-2838	IL	Bloomington	S. Kuntzelman	V	9D	79	Advr Crnr,!	
309-662-2017	IL	Bloomington	Doug Sharp	W	9D	82	DTMicros	4/2
309-663-8354	IL	Bloomington	Michael DeBerg	B	9D	85	MidwestInfo Net	7/
309-672-4405	IL	Peoria	Martin Belcke	W$	9D	100	Hackers World	19/2
309-694-7725	IL	Creve Coeur	Quentin Smith	W	9D	81	EPE Online	7/2
309-786-2096	IL	Rock Island	Dave Calmer	B$	9D	99	DangerZone!!	16/3
309-786-9518	IL	Rock Island	Bill Keehn	F	9V	100	AnchientMariner	5/1
309-792-2543	IL	Green Rock	Ron Bryant	R	9D	55	Phoenix,astron	6/
309-827-2433	IL	Bloomington	James Jenks	R	09O	107	Hermes	3/1
309-828-0100	IL	Bloomington	Scott Ward	W	9D	100	Midwest Online	3/2
309-828-6941	IL	Bloomington	Garth Bock	T	9D	81	Prairie,+CDR	2/
309-852-2165	IL	Kewanee	Kevin Clarke	R	02	112	CyberHawg	1/1
309-862-4918	IL	Normal	Drew Hunt	V	29VO	116*	Aethelwulf's	3/1
310-208-6689	CA	Los Angeles	Wayne Bell	V	9U	60	Amber,WWIV	
310-212-7179	CA	Carson	Rudy Hartmann	T	9U	65	Leo Electronics	3/
310-306-5134	CA	Venice	Bruce Vigil	B$	19V	111*	Skeleton Crew	25/2
310-370-4113	CA	Los Angeles	George Dahlco	O	9D	100	Long Island RB	8/1
310-371-0007	CA	Torrance	Paul Laufer	Q	09V	110	Learning Curve	2/1
310-371-3737	CA	Torrance	Chip North	W	9D	104	The Source	13/6
310-379-8817	CA	Santa Ana	Chuck Crayne	X	2	26	Chuck's	
310-392-3981	CA	Santa Monica	Joe Fasbinder	R	12	105	Moroni	1/1
310-421-0785	CA	Long Beach	David Hart	V	9V	83	Club Dave	1/
310-421-4788	CA	Long Beach	John Gardiner	T$	29D	108	Paradise Cove	55/8
310-434-2933	CA	LongBeach	Mike Zed	B	9D	54	PlanetZed,Music	2/2
310-436-1311	CA	Long Beach	David Scott	R	9D	86	Why Not RBBS	6/
310-474-8309	CA	Westwood	Andy Lee	B	9U	82	TopologySysSvc	8/
310-531-3890	CA	Seal Beach	Daniel Rall	B	9U	72	Rall Computer	
310-545-5146	CA	ManhattanBch	Scott Robb	W	9D	92	UrsaMajor	7/
310-597-2235	CA	Long Beach	Greg French	W	09D	101	French Flyer	34/4
310-609-2176	CA	Dominguez	Dick Martin	W	9U	77	Maverick	5/
310-671-7335	CA	Lennox	Michael Alves	B	29V	105	APR	1/2
310-823-3609	CA	Venice	Kevin Williams	W	9	80	Compu-Net	12/
310-823-4978	CA	MarinaDelRey	Richard Gross	Q	29V	116*	Quantum Connx	6/1

Phone	State	City	Sysop	T/S		First on List # I v (see above)	Name, Features	
310-838-9229	CA	Los Angeles	Gary Inman	B$	29D	67*	West L.A.,tech	26/3
310-920-3631	CA	Bellflower	Tom Paine	B$	9U	84	Megabyte	20/2
310-944-2327	CA	Whittier	Marcial Moreno	L	9D	92	Mega-Rom	9/
310-978-0024	CA	Hawthorne	Rich Schwartz	B	9U	55	PPC	
310-985-8737	CA	Long Beach	Mark Bishop	T	2	90	CSULB	1/
312-263-0924	IL	Chicago	Richard Kelps	R	9U	82	AssemNotNeeded	3/
312-267-4749	IL	Chicago	Randy Gautier	B	9U	61	Executive Regn	15/3
312-274-6128	IL	Chicago	Frank McNeill	R	02	89	Farpoint	3/4
312-275-0848	IL	Chicago	Norman Nithman	X	9U		Free! Board	1/
312-276-4159	IL	Chicago	JohnRosengarten	B$	2	77	Am Archive,+CDR	9/
312-283-4035	IL	Chicago	Pat Stenberg	F	9U	86	ChiMegaphile	3/
312-583-8481	IL	Chicago	David Lucas	B	9	99	Paradise Towers	2/1
312-589-0508	IL	Chicago	John F. Prior	R	9	95	SQLBBS	1/
312-589-2377	IL	Chicago	P. Janiszewski	R	02	114	SCSI Periphs	1/1
312-631-2172	IL	Chicago	Bob Malus	F	9D	84	Equinox	3/2
312-661-1740	IL	Chicago	Paul Bernstein	R	9U	15	LawMUG	
312-736-5415	IL	Chicago	Larry Teren	W	29D	98	Bu$inessmanSpec	14/2
312-745-7800	IL	Chicago	Kenny Jason	B	19D	112	File Cabinet	40/6
312-761-4480	IL	Chicago	Mitzi Ponce	F	9V	101	ArchimedesScrew	1/2
312-777-2574	IL	Chicago	Pete Koski	X	19V	114	East Village	4/2
312-777-9480	IL	Chicago	Kevin Keyser	S	2	73	RoundTable	1/
312-784-3019	IL	Chicago	James Reames	F	9V	100	Chess Board	8/1
312-786-5525	IL	Chicago	Dwight Ringdahl	B	9U	80	STI	6/
312-879-0921	IL	Chicago	Kevin Reidinger	R	19D	08	Chi Compu Soc	8/6
312-889-6813	IL	Chicago	Ed Rakowiecki	F	9V	101	Chi Byte House	2/1
312-935-6809	IL	Chicago	Michael H. Katz	O	09D	114	BIT WIZ Opus	8/1
313-255-2575	MI	Redford	Hopkins & Gray	T$V	2	100	Creative Cafe'	4/24
313-269-2859	MI	Ida	Jim Bartel	W	29V	114	The PiT	6/1
313-291-5571	MI	Taylor	Bill Mullen	M	9V	87	Gateway	10/4
313-426-0528	MI	Dexter	Jay Blethen	W	9	80	Shack,ham	1/
313-449-8195	MI	Whitmore Lk	Jim Chapman	O	29V	105	GATEWAY	2/1
313-455-3977	MI	Canton	Jack Daughtery	B	29D	55	Tandy Harbor	60/6
313-532-8410	MI	Redford Twp.	Jim Samples	F	9D	104	V.o.i.c.e.	1/2
313-541-2325	MI	Berkley	C. Marracco	T	29U	116*	Redline Exprs	4/1
313-582-6671	MI	Dearborn	Paul Williams	Y	9D	100	CRIMP	40/2
313-663-4173	MI	Ann Arbor	Victor Volkman	B	19B	72	Hal 9000	15/6
313-885-3956	MI	Detroit	Dave Hardy	B$	9U	67	DetroitDownload	15/
313-885-4222	MI	Detroit	Jim Wallace	X$	19V	90	DetroitDataExch	12/2
313-894-2923	MI	Detroit	Rick Baker	W	9D	102	Rick's Corner	12/1
314-230-8368	MO	St. Louis	Brian Smith	W	9	91	ThinkTank	7/
314-256-0507	MO	St. Louis	Patrick Grote	X	9U	96	Express(tm)	2/1
314-281-4362	MO	St. Peters	Nick Hartz	B	19V	85	Hartz Fdn	4/1
314-343-4759	MO	Fenton	Mike Babcock	V	2	100	AmericanLiber	1/1
314-434-4236	MO	Chesterfield	Fred McClaren	B	9V	97	True Blue	2/1
314-442-2922	MO	Columbia	Chris Anderson	X	19O	109	Dark Tower	1/1
314-442-6023	MO	Columbia	Charlie Turner	B	9V	26	Charlie's,wine	7/
314-443-1874	MO	Columbia	Kim Palmer	L	09D	109	IWLA 2X4	2/1

						First on List # | v (see above)		
Phone	*State*	*City*	*Sysop*	*T/S*			*Name, Features*	
314-443-7518	MO	Columbia	Ken Hough	X	19B	108	UnderGround	50/2
314-446-0475	MO	Columbia	Mark Chambers	T	9U	83	Batboard	2/
314-544-4628	MO	St. Louis	John Askew	X	19V	113*	Family Connx	1/1
314-581-6717	MO	Mexico	Linda Glover	W	9U	64	BearlyBored	7/
314-625-4054	MO	Lake StLouis	Rik Brown	B	9H	41	Travel Online	12/2
314-635-7675	MO	JeffersonCty	Fred Framus	R	9D	100	Mid-MO RBBS	1/1
314-636-7375	MO	JeffersonCty	Chris Byrd	W	9D	86	C.B.S/W,uts	2/
314-832-9469	MO	St. Louis	Jeff Link	B	9U	102	Links Network	16/1
314-845-7937	MO	St. Louis	Jerry Olney	T$	09V	116*	Party Line	25/15
314-862-1253	MO	St. Louis	Chris Quinn	R	29V	111	LOOP	8/2
314-875-0503	MO	Columbia	Mike Robertson	T	9	50	Datastorm	
314-893-5106	MO	JeffersonCty	Rick Wolters	W$	9U	46	Modem Zone	9/2
314-942-4758	MO	St.Louis	Gary Johnson	W	99U	108*	Night Owl	22/3
314-961-2242	MO	St. Louis	Jerry Queen	B$	9HV	26	EpsonNewsLine	/2
314-973-4073	MO	St. Louis	Rik Brown	B	29D	114	St.LouisOnline	76/9
315-221-2570	NY	Winfield	Mark Williams	B	9D	89	M.I.S.,files	12/3
315-245-3815	NY	Camden	Lance Williams	B	9U	58	Kadet,pgming	3/
315-331-1556	NY	Newark	James Zapetis	B$V	9U	88	T.O.I.L.	13/2
315-339-5668	NY	Rome	Eric Martin	Q	09V	112	MidnightMadness	1/1
315-339-8831	NY	Rome	Ken DeZotell	W	9D	93	Nite-Air,CDR	7/
315-428-3373	NY	Syracuse	Tony Barrett	W	19B	116*	Tony's Place	1/1
315-474-5568	NY	Syracuse	Pat Gleason	M$	9V	100	N.A.S.I.X.	15/4
315-564-5700	NY	Hannibal	Carter Downer	N	99D	75	Late Night	20/2
315-642-1013	NY	Philadelphia	Vincent Everett	X	02	111	North Country	1/1
315-642-1220	NY	Philadelphia	John Meyer	Q	?9U	106	Dots-N-Dashes	3/1
315-773-2099	NY	Fort Drum	Ken Yinger	J	19DV	110	SeaBIN	16/1
315-733-6694	NY	Utica	Bill Raymond	S	2	78	New Horizons	1/
315-736-3792	NY	Whitesboro	Ed Gray	X	9U		Excalibur	10/2
315-769-0165	NY	Massena	Trudy Zobel	F	2	99	MCHS-BBS	5/1
315-785-8098	NY	Watertown	T. Hammerquist	W	99V	112	Cyberealm	3/2
315-786-0778	NY	Watertown	T. Feisthamel	S	9D	83	StarNet	12/2
315-866-1725	NY	Herkimer	Bob Wilkerson	B$	9D	54	Sierra PCBoard	
316-251-2761	KS	Coffeyville	Ken Collins	W	19V	89	ACS - ham,gif	15/2
316-262-1829	KS	Wichita	Steve Meirowsky	W	99VO	109	NWIS	15/1
316-269-7116	KS	Wichita	Mike Muth	W	2	91	DCMAO Wichita	
316-321-5933	KS	El Dorado	Dale Storm	R	12	107	LINKER	1/1
316-365-7631	KS	Iola	Robin Boyer	T	9U	26	Nautilus	9/200
316-652-7734	KS	Wichita	Tom Boucher	V	2	89	Final Frontier	3/
316-684-8744	KS	Wichita	Mike Yaklin	B	9F	34	InformationBth	
316-687-0578	KS	Wichita	Bradley J Brown	W	99V	116*	Statistics	3/2
316-689-3890	KS	Wichita	Charles Burdsal	B	9V	104	TWSU	35/5
316-788-7520	KS	Derby	Jim Kelland	U$	9U	93	Griswold's,bsns	2/
316-788-9913	KS	Derby	Brian Stockton	W	19V	109	Jet Stream!	3/1
316-942-3021	KS	Wichita	Bill Harvey	R	9U	87	Sharelink,+CDR	1/
316-942-4080	KS	Wichita	Bob Hogan	B	9U	74	BytebrosDen	4/
317-243-0755	IN	Indianapolis	Doug Moore	B	9U	70	CircleCity	3/3
317-251-2067	IN	Indianapolis	Dee Saul	B	2	71	I'polisCompSoc	2/

Phone	State	City	Sysop	T/S		First on List # | v (see above)	Name, Features	
317-291-7827	IN	Indianapolis	Vince Caldeira	B$	2	60	Direct Access	
317-326-4747	IN	Greenfield	Bret Waddy	B	19DD	111	Point Blank	12/1
317-353-9981	IN	Indianapolis	Mike Shepard	Q	9U	60	Someplace	
317-395-8203	IN	Amboy	JB Brown	S	19U	93	JB's BBS	3/1
317-397-8504	IN	Covington	Dave Smith	Y$	19V	105	StarshipEntprse	2/1
317-457-9100	IN	Kokomo	Mike Hebert	R	9U	34	Kokomo,pgmg	10/
317-462-1672	IN	Greenfield	Gary Clift	B	9O	102	Communicator II	2/2
317-471-4067	IN	Indianapolis	Damon Richards	M$	02	107	GabLine	1/8
317-525-7164	IN	Waldron	Mike Phillips	O	9U	89	Catacombs	2/
317-543-2007	IN	Indianapolis	Doug Scott	B$	9U	87	Data Central	40/22
317-578-8533	IN	Indianapolis	Chris Congdon	F	9U	79	Cape Lost Hope	2/
317-644-0006	IN	Anderson	Mike Flanigan	Q	09V	105	BeyondEventHorz	1/1
317-644-3039	IN	Anderson	Bert Happel	O	09D	113	I.O. Board	7/1
317-644-5029	IN	Anderson	S. McPheeters	Q$	29D	115	Mail Room	10/1
317-773-7316	IN	Indianapolis	Paul McLear	R	09D	08	Indy Net One	10/1
317-784-2147	IN	Indianapolis	Richard Holler	Q	2	89	RoadHouse,music	1/
317-856-2087	IN	Indianapolis	Tony Moleta	B$	9D	15	PBS-BBS	6/
317-862-5966	IN	Indianapolis	Tony Moleta	B	2	15	PC-Den	
317-881-4369	IN	Greenwood	Dave Julius	X	9	68	GraftedBranch	1/
317-882-5575	IN	Indianapolis	Rex Hankins	B	9D	34	IBM-Net Connx	12/3
317-885-0820	IN	Indianapolis	David Dorsett	B	2	75	CompuAdd	1/
317-894-1378	IN	Indianapolis	Martin Scolaro	B$	9U	75	UsersChoice	13/
317-925-7273	IN	Indianapolis	Bob Predaina	B	9U	44	Prof'ls Choice	2/
318-255-7345	LA	Ruston	Jake Manning	B$V	9D	100	ComputersUnl'td	8/1
318-343-5247	LA	Monroe	Jerry Scroggin	F	9D	99	Bayou BBS	2/2
318-442-5694	LA	Pineville	Don Hutson	F	9D	91	LinkingRings	72/4
318-443-0271	LA	Alexandria	Tom Palko	M$	2	83	AmSilver$,CDR	/2
318-443-0271	LA	Alexandria	Tom Palko	B	9	98	AmerSilverDollr	10/2
318-443-1065	LA	Alexandria	Chuck McMillin	W	9U	93	Puma	14/2
318-474-4550	LA	Lake Charles	Ken Royer	W	9U	89	New Obsolete	2/
318-487-0800	LA	Alexandria	John Chwatal	U	29D	90*	Chwatal Devlp.	6/2
318-527-0238	LA	Sulphur	Jimmy Woolford	O	9D	67	MaidenVoyage	
318-528-2107	LA	Sulphur	M. D. Hunter	R	2	42	Forum	
318-537-3122	LA	Fort Polk	David Silver	W	9U	77	Silverado	1/
318-798-1008	LA	Shreveport	Paul Rino	G$	29V	79	Software Cafe	8/1
318-865-4503	LA	Shreveport	Patty Pickett	S$	19D	75	MySecretGarden	12/3
318-865-9408	LA	Shreveport	James Pottorff	B	9U	62	Genesis BBS	7/2
318-949-1456	LA	Shreveport	Tony Capoccia	R	9D	26	Bible BBS	2/
318-982-7668	LA	Downsville	Louis Bartet	F	19U	112	GENESIS ONE	10/1
319-232-5627	IA	Waterloo	Larry Edler	W	2		Litter Box	1/
319-233-6719	IA	Waterloo	Mark Steel	P	19D	115	Realm of Shades	5/1
319-234-3527	IA	Waterloo	Greg Cory	B	9D	81	C-Shift Phnx	5/
319-235-0772	IA	Waterloo	Charlie Braatz	W$	19D	95	Missing Link	4/2
319-264-0013	IA	Muscatine	Brian Pressler	F	2	91	Dark Avenger	1/
319-337-6723	IA	Iowa City	Art Petrzelka	W	9V	97	ComputerPlumber	2/1
319-363-3314	IA	Cedar Rapids	Ben Blackstock	R$	9V	06	Hawkeye BBS	/2
319-582-3235	IA	Dubuque	Fay & Bussan	Q$	2	26	Elec Cottage	

Phone	State	City	Sysop	T/S		First on List # ↓ v (see above)	Name, Features	
319-752-1881	IA	Burlington	Jimmy Essex	F	29V	101*	LATE NIGHT...	10/1
319-927-4474	IA	Manchester	Duane Atteberry	Q	19OV	115	VISIONARY	1/1
401-333-3451	RI	Cumberland	Fred Barra	B$	9D	95	Modern Tech.	9/3
401-364-0524	RI	Charlestown	Frank Faubert	X	9V	104	Necropolis	2/1
401-364-9788	RI	Richmond	Jack Gordon	B	09O	73	South Shore	10/1
401-683-5312	RI	Portsmouth	Eric Bishop	F	19V	106	The Source!	1/1
401-683-7763	RI	Portsmouth	Heidi Agin	R	02	91	EarthWorld	1/1
401-732-0258	RI	Warwick	Glen Moorehead	W	9D	11	Cyber Zoner	/1
401-732-5292	RI	Warwick	Mike Labbe	B	9V	26	Eagles Nest,!	/5
401-739-4100	RI	Warwick	David Paolo	B	19V	107	Log On America	0/10
401-782-4264	RI	Wakefield	Mark Schieldrop	X	V	96	Mystic Illusion	4/1
401-823-0176	RI	Coventry	Chris Trainor	F	9V	86	Fleet HQ	1/1
401-823-9256	RI	Warwick	Jerry Leveillee	W	19V	108	CompUSA Tech	8/1
401-841-3990	RI	Newport	John Sawyer	B	9V	84	NavyLawyers	1/
401-846-1763	RI	Newport	Bill Fink	B	9V	87	NCC386	20/1
401-848-9069	RI	Middletown	Chris Mathis	B	O	97	TerminalMadness	/2
401-849-4346	RI	Middletown	David Kahan	Q	9	100	Twilight Zone	/1
401-884-9002	RI	E. Greenwich	Andy Green	B	9V	83	IDS World Net	15/1
402-292-1890	NE	Bellevue	Rob Davis	B	9U	87	DataBoard	/2
402-292-8290	NE	Bellevue	Curt White	F	19D	85	AbortRetryFail?	5/2
402-292-8924	NE	Bellevue	Robert Beagle	B	29D	100	Online Pitstop	2/10
402-371-1472	NE	Norfolk	Kevin Day	W	09DO	89	The Kevin BBS	0/2
402-376-3120	NE	Valentine	Dick Roosa	F	19V	109	Badger's BYTE	2/1
402-391-0488	NE	Omaha	Jeremy Brown	F$	09V	112	Jammin	7/1
402-392-6736	NE	Omaha	Floyd Pretz	W	2		HDR Omaha	0/5
402-444-4873	NE	Omaha	PublicLibr	R	2	76	Public Library	
402-453-1504	NE	Omaha	Rick Kingslan	G	U	51	Omaha Net	4/2
402-474-2900	NE	Lincoln	Bill Richman	M	2	97	Cyberspace	/10
402-493-2737	NE	Omaha	Nate Chase	W$	9	92	HAWG WILD!	0/9
402-593-8863	NE	Papillion	Tom Hansen	R	9U	72	Church Chatters	0/
403-242-5453	AB	Calgary	Dan J. Rudiak	Q	02	110	Penalty Box	1/1
403-633-4364	YT	Whitehorse	Seamus Venasse	O	09V	106	Polaris Remote	2/2
404-279-0717	GA	Norcross	Liane Benway	W	9U	71	RunningWild	2/2
404-288-6174	GA	Atlanta	Dan Pritchett	B	29V	107	X-Link	2/2
404-288-6858	GA	Atlanta	Tom Brady	W$	9U	56	Decibel	12/2
404-292-8761	GA	Atlanta	Robert Vostreys	B	9D	67	F-T-L	/3
404-294-0237	GA	Atlanta	Lee Nelson	B$	9D	06	PC-Forum	12/
404-296-9681	GA	Stone Mtn	Steve Antonoff	O	9U	44	Centurion	
404-336-9701	GA	Kingston	Johnny Bunch	X	19V	108	Warrior Base	2/1
404-365-0641	GA	Atlanta	Bill Sideris	W$	09V	113*	CyberSpace Conn	11/1
404-366-1436	GA	Forest Park	Chris Bradford	W	2	68	So. Crescent	
404-370-0736	GA	Decatur	Steve Rohrer	B$	9U	65	Shareware So.	10/12
404-381-1947	GA	Lilburn	Mike Sabot	B$	9F	34	AESC	1/
404-396-3630	GA	Doraville	Lou Hlad	B	2	62	Bulletronics	
404-410-9139	GA	Atlanta	Keith Harrell	W	29V	101	Express Net	17/2
404-435-9608	GA	Smyrna	Keith Griffin	B	19V	113	No Frills	2/2
404-445-2583	GA	Dallas	Kenny West	W	2	95	Danger Zone	1/

					First on List # | v			
Phone	State	City	Sysop	T/S	(see above)	Name, Features		
404-446-6650	GA	Atlanta	Marshall Magee	B	9HV	13	BigPeach	/3
404-459-8487	GA	Villa Rica	M. Kauffmann	X	19V	113	Radio Free VR	7/1
404-461-5947	GA	Atlanta	Cam DeBuck	W	2	71	Cam's Wildcat	3/
404-466-3994	GA	Loganville	Joe Domaleski	O	02	108	Eagle Line	1/1
404-471-1773	GA	Jonesboro	Ron Shattles	F	09V	114	Peaches	12/1
404-476-2607	GA	Duluth	Roger Sligar	B	2	29	TheRightPlace	4/
404-482-5753	GA	Atlanta	Jess Pimentel	F	9V	80	HomeBasedBsns	
404-498-9646	GA	Atlanta	P. Doolittle	W	02	106	Chaos Inc...	1/1
404-509-7813	GA	Marietta	Ben Alexander	W	29V	116*	Base	10/2
404-516-0048	GA	Woodstock	Warren Royal	R	9V	85	AtlantaWindows	1/
404-521-0445	GA	Atlanta	Chris Camacho	X	9H	79	Undermind	
404-548-0726	GA	Athens	Charles Harper	W	9U	26	Classic Athens	
404-565-4258	GA	Marietta	Ted Monitz	W	9U	75	DrDisk	3/
404-569-9651	GA	Columbus	Ed Willoughby	B	9U	45	PC Valley	
404-587-4515	GA	Marietta	Matthew Giles	B$	9V	101	Rainmaker	3/1
404-596-8126	GA	Columbus	Scott Burkett	X$	9V	88	LaterDaze	10/3
404-627-2662	GA	Atlanta	Chris Camacho	B	9U	71	OASis,Sysops'Bd	1/
404-641-8968	GA	Atlanta	Sammy Mitchell	B	9U	70	SemWare	/2
404-667-0885	GA	Cumming	Brent Cantrell	B	19D	107	Prime Time	35/4
404-717-9867	GA	Atlanta	Kevin Whitney	W	9V	90	AtlantaCOM	10/1
404-723-9150	GA	Atlanta	Paul Mayberry	B	19H	112	Game Room	7/2
404-730-2370	GA	Atlanta	Jim Slone	B	19?	113	OPM ATLANTA	4/2
404-740-8428	GA	Alphareeta	Mark C. Miller	B	9U	80	DCA Connx	/4
404-742-8313	GA	Winterville	Tim Wool	W	9D	86	Express Line	5/2
404-762-0923	GA	East Point	Jerry Frost	B	2	29	PC Plus,Airline	/
404-798-4006	GA	Augusta	Jack Hazel	P	9U	66	Jack's	1/
404-813-0286	GA	Atlanta	David Knight	X	29V	114	D&B Publ	1/1
404-835-6600	GA	Atlanta	Wyn Easton	B	9U	75	IBM PCUG	/18
404-859-1557	GA	Marietta	Glenn McAtee	B	19V	107	Micro Center	5/1
404-867-2307	GA	Winder	Frank Mead	Q	19V	110	Krystall Palace	12/1
404-879-1600	GA	Stone Mtn	Robert Seely	BV	9V	99	R.'s Little BBs	5/1
404-879-5985	GA	Atlanta	Paul Sponaugle	B	9U	26	Atlanta PCUG	3/5
404-920-0621	GA	Atlanta	Roger Cravens	W	2	79	TotalRecall	
404-921-1186	GA	Norcross	Ricky Lacy	B	29DB	39	Data Dimension	15/3
404-921-4395	GA	Atlanta	Ken Cherry	B	9HV	51	Atlanta Xchg	5/
404-921-8900	GA	Norcross	Ken Kirkland	P	9U	74	WizardCastle	7/
404-934-4515	GA	Atlanta	Harvey Pierce	B$	19D	26	Flagship	41/5
404-938-2213	GA	Tucker	Jim Kerr	Y	9U	26	PC-Link	12/3
404-941-0746	GA	LithiaSpring	Raeann Thompson	B	19V	110	Thompson Towers	2/1
404-945-2185	GA	Buford	Dennis Moon	B	9	89	MoonBeam Sys	3/
404-974-0460	GA	Acworth	Jim Torgerson	B	19V	108	Club Torgy	2/1
404-962-5116	GA	Auburn	Joe White	B$	9D	15	GA BBS	2/2
404-964-4483	GA	Fayetteville	Billy Brand	B	2	57	SoftwareShop	1/
404-971-3768	GA	Marietta	Mike Steinman	R	9U	72	Disc-pak,graphx	6/
404-972-3458	GA	Snellville	Mike Sirmans	Q	2	26	Milo'sMeadow	1/
404-977-6686	GA	Atlanta	Mike Simmons	B	9U	24	PC Exchange	
404-982-0960	GA	Atlanta	Bob Helbush	B	9D	84	Rock&Roll	1/

| | | | | | | *First on List*
#
\|
v | | |
Phone	State	City	Sysop	T/S		*(see above)*	Name, Features	
404-985-4022	GA	Grayson	Dave Pointer	B	9U	92	PC-Connection	4/
405-222-0555	OK	Chickasha	Bryant Ingram	O	9U	93	Programming	2/
405-233-2547	OK	Enid	B. Luetkemeyer	R	2	60	Pandoras Box	1/
405-233-7474	OK	Enid	Matt Jackson	W	9V	101	Funny Farm	1/1
405-234-6822	OK	Enid	David Gibson	R$	09O	115	No-Name	10/1
405-243-3200	OK	Elk City	Glen Neal	B	19D	104	PC-Oklahoma	18/2
405-256-9876	OK	Woodward	Lance Nelson	W	19V	112	File Not Found	8/1
405-372-7204	OK	Stillwater	Scott Wilkins	W	9D	102	Ninth Bit	1/1
405-436-3602	OK	Ada	Chris Scott	B	99UV	105	Melange	8/2
405-436-4386	OK	Ada	Wayne Hancock	Q	2	99	Wayne's World	1/1
405-536-8056	OK	Lawton	Robert Kalchik	W	09VO	111	LOTTO EXchange	10/1
405-564-3081	OK	Kingston	Jeff Schrunk	X	09V	116*	Ready Room	6/1
405-722-4231	OK	OklahomaCity	Ed Simich	W	9D	101	49er	20/2
405-733-7084	OK	Midwest City	Jim Oxford	T$	9V	29	Torii Sta	50/
405-920-7494	OK	Durant	Alan Cost	M	09VO	108	Transcendntl	7/1
405-927-2541	OK	Coalgate	Chris Scott	B	9U	72	Coalgate	2/
406-227-8678	MT	East Helena	Steve Utick	B$	29D	112	HUGE	45/1
406-252-7224	MT	Billings	Dave Williams	R	19V	112	APPOKOLIPS	3/1
406-256-3160	MT	Billings	Jay Bohn	B$	29D	116*	Sunshine Soft	24/2
406-265-4184	MT	Havre	Howland&Stone	T	9	87	NMC TBBS	/8
406-543-6356	MT	Missoula	Justin Case	L	99V	116*	dISCO hOSPITAL	2/1
406-756-8296	MT	Kalispell	Gregg Maroney	W	9U	92	Mo's Back Door	3/
407-240-7864	FL	Orlando	Bill Wenzel	X	29V	114	Compu-Link II	20/4
407-255-2973	FL	Melbourne	Mike Whitehurst	X	19V	105	TriCompCircuits	2/1
407-269-5188	FL	Titusville	Jerry Russell	T	9V	50	Tech Talk	3/
407-293-3523	FL	Orlando	Richard Wilson	G	19OV	116*	Wiltechs	6/1
407-295-2749	FL	Orlando	Bob French	M$	9U	47	CompCommOrlando	/2
407-327-8421	FL	Winter Spgs	Jim Lockhart	B	9U	81	Page3	7/2
407-331-1070	FL	Longwood	Richard Hardoon	B$	9U	73	I/O Bd	8/
407-339-6964	FL	Fern Park	Bill Hendrix	F$	19V	115	Birthday Board	1/1
407-348-2006	FL	Kissimmee	Brian Keck	W$	99D	116	*NO NAME!!!	24/2
407-380-0204	FL	Orlando	Max Vonderhorst	Q	9V	98	Thunderdome	3/1
407-391-4884	FL	Boca Raton	John E. Waller	S	9U	78	BocaRatonBytes	7/
407-395-2810	FL	Boca Raton	Norman Kelly	T	2	70	Bisnet,bsns	1/
407-397-0467	FL	Kissimmee	Keith Wolfe	W	9V	98	Space Age	32/4
407-397-2356	FL	Kissimmee	Keith Wolfe	W	9	98	Space Age	15/4
407-433-9351	FL	W.Palm Beach	Bob Whitcomb	V	09O	100	E&B Comp.Svcs	5/2
407-434-0844	FL	WPB	Bianca Thomas	S	29V	105	Chathouse-Exch	2/4
407-438-7093	FL	Orlando	Al Hays	Q	9D	92	Mystic Pharos	9/
407-439-1110	FL	W.Palm Beach	Erynn LeRoy	Q	9V	94	ScreamingInDigt	1/
407-452-6980	FL	Merritt Is.	Halkovic/Cronen	M	9U	50	New Horizons	3/
407-459-0969	FL	Merritt Is.	Tom McKeever	W	19V	112	SPACECON	3/2
407-479-1696	FL	Boca Raton	Steven Baxter	B	9D	51	OtherSide	6/2
407-487-3441	FL	P.BeachGard	Doug Azzarito	R	2	56	TCI	
407-487-4754	FL	Boca Raton	Bill Dwinell	R	9D	45	B.R.InfoXchg	6/
407-496-7468	FL	Delray Beach	Michael Robert	U	2	85	BraveNewWorld	3/
407-533-5216	FL	W.Palm Beach	Buzz Nelson	W	09DD	107	Christian Connx	2/1

Phone	State	City	Sysop	T/S		First on List #	Name, Features	
						v (see above)		
407-533-8885	FL	W.Palm Beach	Vanessa Nelson	W	09V	107	LadyHawk Talk	1/1
407-568-8774	FL	Orlando	Kevin Hoffman	W	2	90	MoonRose,tech	2/
407-575-3853	FL	Jupiter	Ted Parsons	Q	19V	100	JUPITER	11/2
407-624-5998	FL	PBchGdns	L. Osteryoung	B	9U		Cecil'sNiteOwl	6/
407-635-8833	FL	Cocoa	Jerry Russell	T	9D	104	TechTalk	50/8
407-642-9939	FL	Lake Worth	John Lindenberg	W	19D	113	Slipped Disk	44/1
407-657-1033	FL	Orlando	Ray McKeand	F	9D	70	Tele-Commr	2/
407-657-8904	FL	Orlando	Dave Steinman	F	9U	50	CDS Central	1/
407-672-0676	FL	Orlando	Rich Davies	Q	19V	111	OutBound	3/1
407-676-3022	FL	Melbourne	Stan Balcauskas	Q	19D	89	CENTRAL STATION	3/1
407-678-7213	FL	Winter Park	Richard Roldan	S	19V	113	SYSTEMLINK	3/1
407-682-3132	FL	AltamonteSpr	Neil Peiman	GV	9D	100	DOOR/Info. Net.	12/5
407-687-8712	FL	W.Palm Beach	Linda Bloom	X	09V	105	Bloomunit BBS	2/1
407-687-9355	FL	W.Palm Beach	John Benjamin	W$	19D	110*	My Cozy Kitchen	13/1
407-690-0032	FL	Rockledge	Danny Burdick	Q	9C	89	Energy	2/
407-722-9675	FL	MelbourneBch	Tim Yandell	B	9V	103	ACCESS AMERICA	25/8
407-731-1675	FL	BoyntonBeach	Charles Bell	Q	19V	107	College Board	1/1
407-732-7457	FL	Boca Raton	Todd Ferich	L	9	40	SARCASM	6/
407-777-5989	FL	Ind.Harb.Bch	Louis Cohen	X	9U	43	BeachRealtyROS	2/
407-783-6572	FL	Cocoa Beach	Rick Watson	X	02	110	Mary's WorkShop	3/1
407-791-2474	FL	RoyalPlmBch	Doug Haire	B	19V	108	Telephone Exch	5/1
407-795-2099	FL	Wellington	Rich Driggers	B	19V	111	Sparta	16/4
407-831-9130	FL	Longwood	Jim Daly	B	2	48	Treasures	8/
407-833-0878	FL	W.Palm Beach	John Toombs	X	19O	116*	ArrowHead	42/1
407-834-6466	FL	Orlando	Hewie Poplock	B$	9V	34	FABulous	45/2
407-856-0021	FL	Orlando	Herb Scherker	M$	19V	115	Infinite Space	6/32
407-859-2961	FL	Orlando	Jim Russ	B	2	49	DataGate Connx	7/
407-879-4823	FL	Pt.St.Lucie	Bill Wright	W	9MV	50	PcLogic	1/
407-951-4031	FL	Indialantic	Jack Lawrence	Q	9U	86	MicroTech	1/
407-964-4891	FL	Palm Beach	Luis Veras	Q	29O	107	GR Euroline	1/2
407-964-9308	FL	W.Palm Beach	Andrew Fuller	S	2	84	ElecStrawbry	3/
407-994-3644	FL	Boca Raton	Dave Gendle	O	09V	45	PC-Emporium	35/3
408-223-9821	CA	San Jose	Bill Smith	B	9D	87	Eagle's Nest 2	12/
408-226-6150	CA	San Jose	David Hayr	X	09V	112	Dimension Y?	1/1
408-227-1583	CA	San Jose	Mike Downie	F	9	96	Mike'sDisizDis	13/
408-227-1635	CA	San Jose	Jon Frisby	X	12	113	CyberPort Info	1/1
408-227-4865	CA	San Jose	Chas Bolton	R	2	62	West-world	
408-229-0706	CA	San Jose	Michael Wilson	W	9U	94	The Village	4/
408-244-5129	CA	San Jose	Frank Crispell	F	29DU	115	Rocking Chair	6/2
408-245-3961	CA	Sunnyvale	Mike Kalai	M	19V	113	Magic Kingdom	3/18
408-245-7726	CA	Sunnyvale	T. E. Dell	X	2	72	DarkSideMtn	1/
408-248-5938	CA	Santa Clara	Gery Magalong	F	29D	81	TempInsomniac's	8/1
408-248-9252	CA	San Jose	Mike Stewart	F	29D	115	Chair Too!	3/1
408-255-9742	CA	San Jose	Rocky Awalt	W	9U	67	HighGate Dsgn	1/
408-261-3329	CA	Santa Clara	John Curtis	Q	99V	112	Pack Rat	7/1
408-265-3353	CA	San Jose	Robert Griffith	W	9	89	Engineers,tech	1/
408-266-9835	CA	San Jose	Bret Tragni	W	2	98	Spider's Den	2/1

							First on List *#* *|* *v*	
Phone	*State*	*City*	*Sysop*	*T/S*			*(see above)*	*Name, Features*
408-267-6396	CA	San Jose	Travis Wise	W	2	91	HamBBS	
408-268-4863	CA	San Jose	Shawn Higgin	W	2	90	LaserBoard	4/2
408-270-4078	CA	San Jose	Phan Tran	F	?9V	110	Phoenix Islands	12/2
408-270-4085	CA	San Jose	Bob Allen	B$	9U	26	PDS-SIG,allcomp	100/
408-274-0965	CA	San Jose	Jason White	X	19V	105	Parallax View	1/1
408-274-5550	CA	San Jose	Shawn McCullar	B	9U	65	NewDimensions	20/2
408-280-1610	CA	San Jose	Duane Davis	B	9U	51	Micro-Medic	20/4
408-286-8332	CA	San Jose	Stuart Smith	B	2	57	CompUEase,Eng	6/4
408-335-4595	CA	Felton	John Jamieson	Q	9D	78	Mtn Retreat	6/1
408-363-9766	CA	San Jose	Sam Johnston	Q	19V	105	Burn This Flag	2/1
408-365-1881	CA	San Jose	Stewart Tate	M	2	91	CodeCrafters	12/4
408-371-7654	CA	Campbell	Brown Bag Softw	B	9	39	Brown Bag	
408-373-3773	CA	PacificGrove	Jim Robeson	B	9D	49	Cricket	12/2
408-375-5455	CA	Monterey	Mark Pickerill	F	09V	113	HACKER HEAVEN	1/1
408-379-0547	CA	San Jose	Bob Baker	W	02	110	Blue Caller	2/1
408-394-8842	CA	Seaside	George Layton	R	2	60	jUMPIN,pcjrs	
408-395-1402	CA	Saratoga	Chuck Metz	W	9U	64	Saratoga Clone	
408-426-5362	CA	Santa Cruz	Scott Smith	Q	2	97	Program World	1/1
408-428-9901	CA	San Jose	Raaj Menon	B	29D	116*	Megamedia	35/2
408-439-9367	CA	ScottsVal	Paul Curtis	T	2	58	Assoc PCUG	3/
408-559-0253	CA	San Jose	JDRMicrodevices	T	9V	89	JDR Micros supp	50/6
408-645-1304	CA	Monterey	John Wicks	W	09V	112	Mont Pen Colge	2/1
408-655-1096	CA	Monterey	Karl Van Lear	B$	9D	63	Nitelog	30/8
408-655-5555	CA	Monterey	David Janakes	X	09V	110	Gaming System	6/20
408-656-0501	CA	Monterey	Rich Dufour	X	19V	114	M. I. S.	1/1
408-659-3676	CA	CarmelValley	Patrick Briscoe	G	2	82	Psychodrome	3/
408-683-0282	CA	Bay Area	Jim Acker	W	2	34	Bay Area BBS	
408-683-0963	CA	San Martin	Aaron Bromagem	X	9V	97	Badlands	2/2
408-720-1152	CA	Sunnyvale	Ron Schultz	F	19V	112	The Zone	1/2
408-732-0463	CA	Sunnyvale	Gary Araki	G	2	26	Computer Tyme	
408-737-7040	CA	Sunnyvale	Bob Jacobson	B	29D	68	HigherPowered	10/3
408-773-9573	CA	Sunnyvale	John Giever	A	9V	62	Moose is Loose	2/
408-866-7370	CA	San Jose	Mike Stewart	F	9D		Chair Too!	1/1
408-899-3104	CA	Monterey	Mark Herrick	W	09V	116*	Breakwater	1/1
408-899-4552	CA	Seaside	Dan Byrnes	R	9U	64	Logos,Bible	4/
408-922-0988	CA	San Jose	Wm Duemler	B	9V	83	TIPS	3/3
408-946-5642	CA	San Jose	Mark Shapiro	B	19O	102	BerryessaCentrl	3/1
408-988-4004	CA	San Jose	John McAfee	T	2	42	HomeBase	2/
409-265-0971	TX	Lake Jackson	Paul Manck	R	2	72	Paul'sPlayroom	2/
409-265-5958	TX	Richwood	Bob Henderson	J	9U	88	Richwood	2/
409-297-5466	TX	Lake Jackson	Armando Caceres	Q	9V	92	Treehouse	8/2
409-632-1883	TX	Lufkin	Kermit Seubert	BV	9D	101	TeleComp West	1/1
409-696-0413	TX	College Stn	Bobby Carpenter	T	9D	96	General Store	14/2
409-696-8722	TX	College Stn	Kit Cragin	X	9D		Maelstrom	2/4
409-724-1037	TX	Nederland	James Miller	B	19D	*	Hole in Wall	15/1
409-724-6659	TX	Port Neches	David Moore	V	19D	114	Tech BBS	2/1
409-727-0887	TX	Nederland	Ilene Hebert	B	29VO	92	Wizard's Domain	4/2

						First on List # | v		
Phone	State	City	Sysop	T/S		(see above)	Name, Features	
409-727-8141	TX	Port Neches	Timothy Wilson	L	09V	111	Stargate Seven	4/1
409-735-7561	TX	Bridge City	Donald Cart	R	9U	87	Dream Machine	14/
409-798-0905	TX	Brazoria	James Kennemer	Q	9V	88	Brazorian	2/
409-833-6056	TX	Beaumont	Ron Westphal	B$V	9		Daddy's Toy	2/1
409-842-3044	TX	Beaumont	Mike Chambers	R	29B	101	Triple Threat	14/1
409-842-3251	TX	Beaumont	Tim Beard	W	09V	114	BROAD REACH	3/1
409-842-5449	TX	Beaumont	Russ MacDaniel	B$	9U	72	GraphicsUnltd,!	
409-885-2629	TX	Sealy	Troy Scheh	X	02	112	SealyConnection	1/1
409-892-1977	TX	Beaumont	Larry Lesher	W	19V	106	TECH RESOURCE	2/1
409-925-2764	TX	Santa Fe	Kevin Griffin	Y	9V	102	Santa Fe Specl	1/1
410-235-2365	MD	Baltimore	Sunil Gupta	W	9U	89	Monsoon	4/
410-239-8379	MD	Manchester	Kevin Brown	R	2	85	Quantum	7/
410-247-3797	MD	Baltimore	H. Michalski	B	19V	106	NetWork	16/5
410-252-0717	MD	Lutherville	T. R. Hendricks	O$	9D	34	Avi-Technic	35/2
410-256-3631	MD	Baltimore	Hank Volpe	R	09V	112	Modem Doctor	1/1
410-263-4394	MD	Annapolis	Trujillo/Nickle	R	2	91	Pro-Vue	/2
410-266-5939	MD	Annapolis	Wally Babbitt	B	2		Generic	/2
410-266-7343	MD	Annapolis	Rhett Dail	G$V	9U	95	DigitalSpectrum	20/2
410-273-6449	MD	Edgewood	Earl Settle	W$	9U	62	CompConx	2/
410-285-4032	MD	Baltimore	Ed Davis	O$	2	39	Power Tools	
410-290-3260	MD	Columbia	Walter Ames	R$	09V	116*	GreyHawk	45/4
410-357-5574	MD	Freeland	Michael Huggins	R	9D	88	Fishermans Cove	7/2
410-360-8007	MD	Pasadena	Gerald Todd	R	09V	112	Modem Ready	1/1
410-466-0949	MD	Baltimore	Mitch Hobish	B$	9U	67	ScienceLab	2/
410-476-5098	MD	Easton	Bob Willey	B	9H	62	CCS Tech Supp	2/
410-526-7243	MD	Reister'tn	Tony Nadalin	X	9V	77	BlueEdge,OS/2	2/
410-531-5748	MD	Clarksville	Bill Anton	W	9D	90	PolarBear'sLair	3/
410-544-1297	MD	Arnold	Larry Grim	O	9U	72	Grimace BBS	5/1
410-551-4643	MD	Odenton	John Bartley	Q	9D	104	Outland's 4	3/1
410-592-2568	MD	Hydes	Paul Lopez	X	99VO	110	LOPEZVILLE	2/1
410-628-7243	MD	Cockeysville	Steve Cain	B$	19D	99	File Exhange	8/1
410-643-1466	MD	Kent Island	Darren Albert	X	09VO	104	SailingInfoCtr	25/
410-655-4708	MD	Pikesville	Alan Hess	O	9D	46	NerveCenter,Med	
410-676-4521	MD	Aberdeen	S. Hendricks	O	9D	96	Rolling Thunder	9/
410-686-0286	MD	Rosedale	Mike McCullough	B	9U	104	Waterfront East	12/2
410-686-7337	MD	Baltimore	Jason Culler	U	19V	105	The Culler BBS	3/1
410-721-8073	MD	Annapolis	George Brungot	R	09D	26	George's	14/1
410-740-9595	MD		Ed Shore	X	2		Trade Data Exch	10/8
410-744-4692	MD	Catonsville	John P. Lynch	Q	19VO	111	Port EINSTEIN	14/1
410-758-4023	MD	Centreville	Nick LaBrie	W$	29V	106	Lions Den	6/1
410-792-7208	MD	Laurel	Roger Wood	T	29V	111	Crescendo	1/1
410-795-4987	MD	Eldersburg	Dan Sereduick	Y	29OV	112	Dandelion Cult	1/1
410-822-6438	MD	Easton	Mike Leonard	B	19D	98	Atomic Comet	16/1
410-827-8789	MD	Queenstown	Ben Hammock	W$	?9V	106	Eastern Shore	2/3
410-866-4554	MD	Rosedale	Gordon Malone	B$	19D	66	Rosedale Data	75/4
410-882-4481	MD	Baltimore	Ron Wright	B$	19V	67	Wright Place	7/3
410-922-1352	MD	Baltimore	Dan Myers	Q	19V	93	Doppler Base	15/1

					First on List # | v		
Phone	*State*	*City*	*Sysop*	*T/S*	*(see above)*	*Name, Features*	
410-956-3396	MD	Davidsnvle	Andy Smith	R	9U	06	Annap. SW Guild	
410-969-1914	MD	Glen Burnie	Gordon Ogletree	W	09V	110	Windows BBS	4/1
410-987-3542	MD	Millersville	Bob Lloyd	W	29V	107	General Store	20/2
410-995-5423	MD	Columbia	Mark Oberg	T	09D		No Plc Lk Home	30/6
410-997-5262	MD	Columbia	Mike O'Donnell	P	2	93	MD Catholic	
410-997-7204	MD	Columbia	David Elliott	X	9U	81	DoubleNut	2/
412-277-0548	PA	Dunbar	Kristi Crocetti	B	9V	34	Fayette Area	3/1
412-348-6624	PA	Pittsburgh	Dennis White	R	19O	113	Buy/Sell UsedSW	1/1
412-481-5302	PA	Pittsburgh	K. McQuillin	X$	09V	112	Telerama	15/12
412-482-4721	PA	Butler	Dave West	R	19D	107	Info Exchange	6/1
412-523-4269	PA	Jeannette	Rich Beaver	N	2	83	Firefox	
412-563-5416	PA	Pittsburgh	Dan Deady	B$	9U	77	PGH So.	2/
412-746-0107	PA	Canonsburg	Mike Keelon	B$	19D	34	Washington PCBd	10/2
412-766-0732	PA	Pittsburgh	William Wilson	O	9U	90	BlinkLink,blind	1/
412-824-6566	PA	Pittsburgh	G. Stanislav	O	9U	34	Astral Board	
412-854-0619	PA	Library	Doug Frank	B$	19V	107	Dew Drop Inn	60/2
412-856-6322	PA	Monroeville	Tom Doyle	W	2	60	OpenDoor	16/4
412-928-8577	PA	Pittsburgh	Robert Pierce	X	2	93	BoardWalk	
412-934-3061	PA	Pittsburgh	M. Schmelzer	T	2	67	Mt ViewElecMall	
413-527-8977	MA	Easthampton	Hank Hurteau	B$	29D	113	Uncle Hanks	7/3
413-568-4466	MA	Westfield	Dave Orcutt	B	9D	72	PVCC UG	22/6
413-568-7669	MA	Westfield	Eric Willcox	B	09D	34	Westfield	5/1
413-596-6684	MA	Wilbraham	Terry Jamro	LV	2	99	Mercatorius	3/1
413-782-2158	MA	Springfield	Ed Thompson	BV	19V	100	Signal Hill	26/2
414-233-5926	WI	Oshkosh	Dana Laude	O	09D	89	InterLinkData	15/2
414-251-2580	WI	Meno. Falls	Bob Rapp	Q	19B	62	Anonymous	17/2
414-295-4301	WI	Princeton	Alan Beck	B	9HV	74	Connection	7/
414-337-9374	WI	DePere	Reed Hardy	R	9	80	LearningTree	3/
414-352-7176	WI	Glendale	Phil Katz	Q	2	58	PKWARE	
414-353-1576	WI	Milwaukee	Jeff Otto	Q	9H	68	SciQuest	3/
414-462-1400	WI	Milwaukee	Pat Canter	R	9U	75	DiamLaserSvc	2/
414-466-9983	WI	Milwaukee	Jack Becker	Q	9V	104	Edit Suite	1/1
414-476-8468	WI	West Allis	Ron Johnston	Q	9U		County Line	19/2
414-677-4499	WI	Richfield	H. Koskovich	F	09D	112	Computer Plus	15/2
414-681-1123	WI	Racine	Al Maynard	S	9U	66	HarborMaster	
414-722-6996	WI	Neehan	Chris Reagan	W$	99V	115	Back Alley	30/8
414-725-7598	WI	Neenah	Bruce Casner	O	09D	50	Homebuilt Flyer	2/1
414-761-2582	WI	Oak Creek	J. Robins-Wells	W	19V	91	C.A.T.C.H.(tm)1	1/2
414-761-5120	WI	Milwaukee	Mike Wesolowski	M$V	2	101	Online Data Sys	4/25
414-764-6706	WI	Cudahy	D. Christensen	W	09DO	115*	NETWORK CABLING	19/8
414-789-4210	WI	Elm Grove	Bob Mahoney	X$	9D	06	EXEC-PC	70/250
414-789-4400	WI	Elm Grove	Tim Semo	X$	2	84	Exec-PC Chat	/32
414-797-8984	WI	Waukesha	BrandonKostolni	M	9U	72	CAD	1/
414-961-1674	WI	Shorewood	BrandonKostolni	X	9U	72	Battlezone	3/
414-964-5111	WI	Milwaukee	Joe Weinshel	W	09V	108	Disc Golfer	1/1
415-255-2188	CA	Richmond	Rich Gorin	Q	9U	65	Recovery	
415-255-2981	CA	SanFrancisco	Ken Hunter	W	2	72	QU-AN-TO	2/

Phone	State	City	Sysop	T/S		First on List # | v (see above)	Name, Features	
415-323-2616	CA	Atherton	Kelvin Yen	W	19V	105	Last Resort	5/1
415-323-4193	CA	Menlo Park	Owen Hawkins	B	9D	37+	SPACE	36/10
415-334-7393	CA	SanFrancisco	George Salet	T	12	112	Contractors Exc	1/2
415-337-5416	CA	SanFrancisco	Lawrence Liu	B	9U	57	PC GFX Exch 96	
415-340-7261	CA	San Mateo	Gabriel Turk	L	19V	104*	Trade Center	11/2
415-343-5160	CA	San Mateo	Don Silva	R	9U	93	Run of the Mill	1/
415-343-5692	CA	San Mateo	Joe Stennet	P	29VO	110	Creekside BBS	2/1
415-349-6576	CA	Foster City	Tom Swegles	B	9V	26	Charisma,dB3	20/4
415-364-3001	CA	RedwoodCity	Dave Spensley	Q	9C	93	UncleD'sDir	5/2
415-364-7884	CA	Redwood City	Frank Crispell	F	9U	84	RocknChair Cnx	6/2
415-368-0790	CA	Redwood City	Lorin Wilson	F	19V	115	Salt and Light	1/1
415-382-8530	CA	Novato	Mark Montgomery	B	19U	105	Wulihan	1/1
415-382-9195	CA	Novato	Al Kalian	A	9U	47	Palladin, utils	6/3
415-474-4523	CA	SanFrancisco	Helton Lim	B	9V	64	Network2000	
415-479-8328	CA	San Rafael	John Chipps	X	9	96	Stonehenge	1/
415-488-1461	CA	Woodacre	Rick Johnson	W	09V	116*	BREATH FRESHAIR	2/1
415-494-3116	CA	Palo Alto	Howard H. Smith	W	9V	104	AHA HYDROGEN	1/1
415-564-9440	CA	SanFrancisco	Margery Chia	X$	09D	116*	IBBS West	18/5
415-571-6912	CA	San Mateo	Dave Jones	T$	9U	83	PDSE San Mateo	2/4
415-584-0697	CA	SanFrancisco	B. Mavrogeorge	O	2	08	Roots	
415-595-2427	CA	San Carlos	Gordon Anderson	B	9D	+	Toad Hall	20/4
415-595-5843	CA	Belmont	Gene Newcomb	BV	9U	76	GENO'S PLACE	9/2
415-598-0498	CA	San Carlos	Tom Nelson	W	9U	49	MicroFoundry	16/
415-621-2609	CA	SanFrancisco	Richard Couture	R	9U	56	SF PCUG	
415-641-9862	CA	SanFrancisco	M.Fleischman	R	9D		UltraMag Empire	7/2
415-665-7918	CA	SanFrancisco	John Suelen	W$	9V	99	The Classifieds	3/2
415-737-9939	CA	San Bruno	George Hassmer	B	9U	89	VidGame	13/2
415-752-4490	CA	SanFrancisco	Steve Pomerantz	W	9V	102	Lincoln's Cabin	4/4
415-755-1524	CA	SanFrancisco	Jon Carmichael	B	2	06	Continuum	
415-756-5098	CA	SanFrancisco	Bundy Chanock	WV	9	101	BUN'S	15/2
415-802-9011	CA	San Carlos	Robert Maverik	B	19DV	109	Charisma II	22/2
415-875-4196	CA	S.San Fran	Chuck Spear	W	29V	103*	Fox_Hole	3/1
415-897-3073	CA	Novato	Paul Ward	P	2	66	PlayPen,Libtn	
415-927-1216	CA	San Rafael	Leistner & Ward	B	2	26	GoldenGate	3/4
415-927-2435	CA	Corte Madera	Steve Wingate	W	2	100	CIA	1/1
415-941-5384	CA	Los Altos	Greg Whiting	F	2		Mental Hospital	1/
415-948-8928	CA	Los Altos	Jim Heiliger	W	9	91	Compool	12/3
415-961-9635	CA	Los Altos	Mark Smith	F	2	81	Halibut	3/
415-965-3556	CA	Mtn View	Ron Schultz	F	2	77	The Zone	1/
415-968-7369	CA	Mtn View	Jim Switz	A	2	58	SigSig	4/
415-968-7481	CA	Mtn View	Gary Fleisher	B	09D	115	HSA-UWC	3/1
415-969-6321	CA	Mtn View	Mike Goodnight	B	9V	85	Haltek Elec	7/
415-994-2944	CA	Daly City	Vern Buerg	B	2	26	Buerg Utils	
416-450-8030	ON	Brampton	Greg Cazabon	F	9D	88	Northern	2/
416-572-2307	ON	Hamilton	Chris Moore	T	09D	105	OSH Exchange	6/4
416-698-7395	ON	Toronto	C. Kalaboukis	B$	9D	100	BizBase	2/2
416-733-9052	ON	Willowdale	John Scarfone	B	2	77	PC Connect	3/3

					First on List # | v		
Phone	*State*	*City*	*Sysop*	*T/S*	*(see above)*	*Name, Features*	
416-751-6337	ON	Toronto	Steve Johns	B$	9V	06	CD Access	20/
416-773-6109	ON	RichmondHill	Jeff Gerschkow	B	9	98	CAP/AnalysisSpt	2/1
416-778-4193	ON	Toronto	Stew Francis	B	19D	107	Structures	16/
416-793-1411	ON	Brampton	Thomas Thayer	B	09V	112	Streamline	6/3
416-884-4088	ON	Richmond	Glenn Jarvis	F	9U	74	CompuPrint	3/2
416-894-2503	ON	Ridgeway	Shawn Mazzuto	J	9U	100	PrimeDirective	3/1
417-673-2283	MO	Joplin	Tim Pearson	Q	9U	55	LAN Star	
417-738-4341	MO	Seymour	Mike Redman	F	9U	84	SEE-MORE	18/2
418-682-8128	PQ	Quebec	Claude Blouin	Q	9D	103	MEDIC	2/1
419-244-8040	OH	Toledo	Anthony Yockey	Q	9	96	Nebulous System	1/1
419-286-2414	OH	Ft. Jennings	Randy Gasser	B$	9D		RC Comp/Cnslt	1/
419-299-3707	OH	McComb	Shawn Huffman	L$	09V	108	Blue Moon	1/1
419-389-6642	OH	Toledo	Churton Budd	M	9C	92	MedicCom,+CDR	/4
419-422-9742	OH	Findlay	Adam Perry	V	2	95	Elm Street	1/
419-448-1421	OH	Tiffin	Don Smith	R	9U	15	Northwest Ohio	13/7
419-478-7333	OH	Toledo	Peter Barney	T	09V	111	Prog. Tech Shop	3/2
419-524-0948	OH	Mansfield	Randy Conrad	J	9V	100	Side Alley	1/1
419-524-6418	OH	Mansfield	Warren Walker	R	9U	34	Kork Board	2/
419-524-6528	OH	Mansfield	Jay Shepherd	B$	9V	103	The Fortress	12/1
419-524-7825	OH	Mansfield	B. McConnell	B	9D	66	Procyon	7/
419-529-5906	OH	Mansfield	Gary Levelius	W	9	93	A&B Comp	8/2
419-529-5930	OH	Mansfield	Gary Levelius	W	9	93	A&B Comp	8/2
419-655-3798	OH	Cygnet	Michael Cupp	J	02	108	ForgottenFort	1/1
419-673-9259	OH	Kenton	Randy Hattery	W	09VO	107	PointofNoReturn	3/1
419-691-1125	OH	Northwood	John Krytus	R	09D	57	Jet-Lag	3/1
419-691-7884	OH	Sylvania	John Buckley	X	02	116*	Illumination	3/4
419-732-8237	OH	Port Clinton	Matt Whitted	L	2	104	Core Meltdown	1/1
419-756-4958	OH	Mansfield	Tom Rothe	R	2	26	Mid Ohio	7/
501-234-3361	AR	Magnolia	Mike Gee	R	9U	97	Alumax Online	1/1
501-234-5604	AR	Magnolia	Ken Squyers	W	9D	98	DataShop	10/1
501-247-1141	AR	White Hall	Bob Harmon	X	9V	100	File Cabinet	2/1
501-247-2681	AR	Pine Bluff	Dee Perdue	A	9V	84	Gateway	1/
501-273-1755	AR	Bentonville	Bruce Gabbard	D	2	102	Night Hawk	1/1
501-329-7227	AR	Conway	Tim Stone	Q	2	96	Conway PCUG	5/1
501-364-8731	AR	Crossett	Ray Haney	B	9D	85	FireHouse,EMS	3/
501-442-0436	AR	Fayetteville	Terry Brown	Q	02	109	Wizard's Tower	1/1
501-484-0944	AR	Ft. Smith	Fred Ayers	W	?9D	114	Paradox of AR	12/2
501-493-2451	AR	Belleville	Wagner/Shewmake	W	9U	83	PetitJean,med	
501-521-4734	AR	Fayettev'le	Greg Langham	Q	9U	81	OzarkConnx	2/
501-521-5639	AR	Fayettev'le	Kurtis Jones	Q	9D	91	Spectrum/CAD	2/
501-631-5976	AR	Rogers	Jerry Hunter	D	2	102	DARKSTAR SysHub	2/1
501-751-3714	AR	Springdale	Bert Edens	Q	2	93	HillbillyKorner	
501-753-8121	AR	N.LittleRock	Jim Wenzel	B$	9D	72	Grapevine	52/5
501-756-0335	AR	Springdale	William Stewart	B	9U	87	Razorback	36/4
501-791-2994	AR	N.LittleRock	James Hastings	B	9	73	Crossfire GFX	14/6
501-863-0311	AR	El Dorado	J. S. Chandler	T	09D	106	U.S.A.	60/4
501-932-7932	AR	Jonesboro	Kevin Watkins	Q	9U	90	Freedom OneHST	2/

Phone	State	City	Sysop	T/S	First on List # | v (see above)	Name, Features	
501-967-8709	AR	Russellville	Mark Williams	B	99DH	108	MINX	50/4
501-968-1931	AR	Russellville	Michael Gray	W	9U	85	ArkRivVal	2/
502-244-3439	KY	Louisville	Mark Van Dyke	X	9B	104	Realm	3/2
502-281-9686	KY	Owensboro	James Kelley	W	09V	97	PC UNIVERSE!	10/2
502-339-8978	KY	Louisville	Bill Phelps	W	09V	112*	Bill Board	7/2
502-499-8238	KY	Jtown	Dave Hommel	Q	2	86	Common Cents	3/
502-554-7727	KY	Paducah	Tom Gehrke	X	09U	114	Valiant Univ	2/1
502-561-0742	KY	Louisville	Beach Craigmyle	B	2	55	LegNet	
502-684-9855	KY	Owensboro	S & R Clements	B	9U	26	Pegasus,DoorPch	7/2
502-686-1320	KY	Owensboro	Carl Sparks	R	9C	91	TrestleBd	1/
502-732-6693	KY	Carrollton	Dennis Goff	W	2	104	Atcher-Serv!	1/2
502-732-8554	KY	Carrollton	Mark Davis	W	09V	104	Great Scott!	2/1
502-575-3359	KY	Paducah	Yancy & Burton	G	09V	106	Hangar 18	8/1
502-886-7664	KY	Hopkinsvle	Eddie Owen	B$	19D	81	Banana Republic	6/3
502-937-5450	KY	Louisville	Tom Currie	P	09V	98	Volunteer	1/1
502-968-3714	KY	Louisville	Glenn Sheffield	B	19D	114	DaraFactor	45/1
502-942-2848	KY	Fort Knox	Dan Elder	X$	19V	105	Nat'l Data Exch	10/1
503-221-1777	OR	Portland	Richard Bash	W	9V	65	Combat Arms	1/1
503-232-4089	OR	Portland	Hal Schnedler	W	09V	114	Elect Fellowshp	1/1
503-232-5783	OR	Portland	Dan Gannon	Q	09V	95	Banished CPU	6/3
503-236-4945	OR	Portland	Bernie Richards	X$	029V	114	Heartbeat	2/30
503-244-7967	OR	Portland	Gleason Pace	Q	19V	112	Noah's Kitchen	2/1
503-286-5577	OR	Portland	Ted Daniel	X	02	107	Elvira's Club	1/1
503-286-0893	OR	Portland	L & H Kachold	G	19V	62	Utopias	3/2
503-296-5396	OR	The Dalles	Bill Greenland	B	02	104	Open Mind	1/1
503-297-4070	OR	Portland	David Lutjen	W	9U	80	TradeWinds	2/2
503-298-5361	OR	The Dalles	S. Proffitt	O	09V	106	Graphic Express	4/1
503-335-3053	OR	Portland	Dale Weber	O	29D	105	Joyful Noise	5/2
503-336-1039	OR	Toledo	Don Bindley	W	19V	116*	Fireburners	5/1
503-343-6383	OR	Eugene	Drake Koefoed	R	2	77	[assemblypgmg]	
503-346-9833	OR	Eugene	Adrian Ng	B$	9U	90	PC Toyshop IE	13/6
503-362-1602	OR	Salem	David Madding	X	02	105	St.Pauls Church	1/1
503-363-0171	OR	Salem	Jim Page	T	9U	63	PageElecBBS	4/2
503-364-9998	OR	Salem	Anthony Albrich	W	9U	104	OregonSoftware	81/2
503-371-3640	OR	Salem	Kerry Rogers	W	?9	114	EL Shaddai	2/1
503-389-5404	OR	Bend	M. Gerlicher	X	9	100	Metropolis	1/1
503-393-5580	OR	Keizer	Bob Hunter	W	9V	79	Chemeketa	25/6
503-484-9754	OR	Springfield	Paul Ortman	O	9U	55	Ortland OPUS	
503-485-8609	OR	Eugene	Thom Hoyle	X	19V	115	A KlassM BBS	3/1
503-591-7701	OR	Hillsboro	Jerry Barham	W	29V	114	Crimson I.C.E.	4/1
503-620-5910	OR	Portland	Skip Guyer	W	2	76	NWCS	3/3
503-621-3746	OR	Portland	Chuck Forsberg	X	2	15	Pro-YAM,HomeDSZ	
503-635-3138	OR	West Linn	JP Jones	X	12	112	Theory of Kaos	1/2
503-636-4947	OR	Portland	Mike Gottlieb	Q	9U	74	DiskJockey	7/
503-636-9586	OR	Portland	John Bartley	M$	19V	107	Novell UG	1/2
503-653-9068	OR	Portland	Raymond Keith	R	2	83	Real Est NW	
503-656-9790	OR	West Linn	Mark Adkins	B$	19V	50+	Blue Lake	60/3

					First on List # | v		
Phone	State	City	Sysop	T/S	(see above)	Name, Features	
503-682-1619	OR	Wilsonville	Bud Russell	W$	09V	105	Computer Time	12/2
503-697-0845	OR	Lake Oswego	John Luong	F	19V	114	FuNny FaRM	6/1
503-734-0546	OR	Medford	Brent McRoy	B	29V	112	Software Galore	38/1
503-761-8100	OR	Portland	Janice Stevens	T$	9V	76	RAIN	25/
503-777-4931	OR	Portland	Tom Glover	XV	9V	100	Cuckoo's Egg	1/1
503-786-0458	OR	Milwaukie	Jeff Davis	B	9V	109	THE KEEP	2/2
504-271-5307	LA	Chalmette	Mark Hambrice	F	9V	87	Treasure Chest	3/1
504-273-3238	LA	Baton Rouge	Randall Lassabe	B	29V	111	Cutting Edge	15/1
504-340-7027	LA	New Orleans	Jim Sterrett	L	9D	90	Padded Cell	
504-356-0790	LA	Baton Rouge	Russell Jackson	B$	19D	87*	Southern Online	44/4
504-456-6704	LA	New Orleans	Phil Wilking	W	09V	104	NO Mensa Soc	2/1
504-466-0908	LA	New Orleans	Roy Musacchia	R	9V	56	Bowling Alley	
504-542-9600	LA	Hammond	Sidney Egnew	B	19D	114	Computer Solutn	80/10
504-649-7388	LA	Slidell	Tom Miller	W	19V	110	Miller's Xing	2/1
504-738-5100	LA	Harahan	Charles Sea	B	9	57	La. Medsig	15/6
504-756-9658	LA	Baton Rouge	Michael Vierra	B	19D	111	Cajun Clickers	44/4
504-764-0449	LA	Norco	John Perilloux	F	19V	62*	Eagle's Nest	4/1
504-778-1943	LA	Baker	Mark A. Silver	M$	09VO	114	Silveril's Deme	7/4
504-835-0085	LA	New Orleans	Mike Perry	C	9V		The Dungeon	
504-845-0889	LA	Mandeville	Gary Giffin	O	19V	107	Twilight Phone	3/1
504-851-4230	LA	Houma	Rick Luquette	Q	9U	75	CompAssocLa.	3/2
504-878-3023	LA	Loranger	Ray Waldo	O	19D	114	ChristianNetHQ	3/1
504-885-5928	LA	New Orleans	John Souvestre	O	19D	56	Soouthern Star	15/6
504-886-2157	LA	Sun	Nolan Lee	O	9D	98	WSTPC	25/2
504-889-0450	LA	Metairie	R. Porter	X	02	106	ProNet	1/2
504-891-1888	LA	New Orleans	D. Charbonnet	R	2	56	DCI Computers	
504-891-3142	LA	New Orleans	Michael Mathews	B	19D	102	Ozone Hole	10/3
504-891-7579	LA	New Orleans	Tom Lezniak	W	9C	88	Tom's BBS	6/
504-895-7365	LA	New Orleans	Justin Kraft	X	2	101	Computer Shop	2/1
505-255-0697	NM	Albuquerque	Marc Limmany	W	29V	108	Tech Source	4/1
505-255-3623	NM	Albuquerque	Dan Mancuso	P	2	80	AnotherBBS?	2/5
505-268-1669	NM	Albuquerque	Cy Stanton	R	19D	104	Cavern ofCyborg	13/2
505-281-2525	NM	Sandia Park	Gary Chellis	R	9D	100	Mile+ High	1/1
505-293-0059	NM	Albuquerque	Gary Burks	M	09V	106	4th Street	3/10
505-293-8907	NM	Albuquerque	Jim Cloud	B	9V	84	Modern Times	3/
505-294-5675	NM	Albuquerque	Dean Kerl	M	9V	83	Garbage Dump	50/36
505-296-7672	NM	Albuquerque	John Maio	R	2	15	ALBQ,Util/Lang	
505-299-5974	NM	Albuquerque	Steve Fox	X	09D	69	Albuq ROS	20/12
505-326-2906	NM	Farmington	Rich Anderson	W	9U	81	Computer Lynx	5/2
505-345-1912	NM	Albuquerque	Richard Gieske	X	19VU	112	Hyper Zone	1/1
505-434-4670	NM	Alamagordo	Harry Bouma	B$	9U	55	Alamo-PC	
505-523-4528	NM	Las Cruces	Art Pike	W	9U	64	Waterfront West	1/
505-525-8626	NM	Las Cruces	Gordon LaGrow	J	19OV	110	Cruise Trek's	4/2
505-589-0319	NM	Anthony	Randy Blackmond	Q$	9D	65	RandyBsmt	7/3
505-662-0659	NM	Los Alamos	Pam Trexler	O	9D	81	Constr Net	3/
505-672-0427	NM	Los Alamos	Daniel Olsher	Q	02	110	ExplodoModeM	1/1
505-678-0902	NM	WSMR	Keith Shinkle	F	19DD	111	Wolf's Den	25/2

Phone	State	City	Sysop	T/S	First on List # | v (see above)	Name, Features	
505-762-0116	NM	Clovis	Rex Osborn	W	9V	96	Computer Touch	7/
505-763-1795	NM	Clovis	Dan Drinnon	R	9V	102	Cellar Door	2/1
505-784-3275	NM	Cannon AFB	Dan Smith	Y	9V	102	Colosseum	1/1
505-823-7700	NM	Albuquerque	David Carlson	M$	9V		Electronic Trib	3/12
505-824-0049	NM	Chaparral	Roger Avers	Q	9D	74	Abacus	7/
505-857-0836	NM	Albuquerque	Frank Lerner	B	19D	100	LandofEnch'tmnt	22/3
505-877-8354	NM	Albuquerque	Kenn Ozmun	X	9U	81	MAD M.A.X.	18/2
505-891-4498	NM	Rio Rancho	Joe Niderost	B	22	112	LittleOne!!TWO	15/2
505-891-5332	NM	Rio Rancho	Buz Schauer	W	9V	104	Traders	3O/1
506-459-0973	NB	Fredericton	A. Cogswell	W	09V	113	Omni Net	2/2
506-735-3831	NB	Edmundston	Paul Cormier	W$	9V	104	CompuBBS	13/2
507-281-1989	MN	Rochester	Richard Kaplan	O	9U	76	Med S/W Xchg	
507-288-6347	MN	Rochester	Wayne Evans	R	9U	62	PC-ProFile(tm)	13/3
507-433-7017	MN	Austin	Jeremy Hinkle	R$	2	86	Formula,+CDR	
507-533-9356	MN	Stewartville	Zak Metz	X$	09B	116*	Structure	21/1
508-261-9214	MA	Mansfield	Michael Savoy	B	2	84	GreatWoods	2/
508-263-2541	MA	Boxborough	Ben Boyden	B	19V	110	Phantasmal Gtwy	3/3
508-285-7240	MA	Norton	Sal Tuzzo	B$	9H	62	TuzzoEngineer	
508-365-2359	MA	Clinton	Daniel Linton	B	9D	72	SoftwareCreatns	10/5
508-366-7827	MA	Westborough	Jan Bogdanovich	B	19V	107	Proteon, Inc.	2/4
508-368-8456	MA	Lancaster	Dave White	T	29D	110	CyberScape	14/4
508-369-5371	MA	Carlisle	Kenneth Baker	L	9V	100	SUPER LINK	7/1
508-373-7929	MA	Haverill	Scott Goudsward	Q$	9M	59	The Matrix	7/
508-385-3427	MA	Dennis	Bob Baker	B	9U	86	CapeCod,ham	3/
508-393-1213	MA	Northboro	T. DiPasquale	W	9	83	T&T ComEng	2/
508-428-6082	MA	Cotuit	Gary Townsend	W	9U	91	Peeps Place	4/
508-433-8540	MA	Pepperell	Dave Rondeau	WV	2	99	THE HANGOUT	2/2
508-435-4656	MA	Hopkinton	William Suarez	B	2	72	Avatar	
508-465-3198	MA	Newburyport	Brian Tardiff	Q	9U	71	MassHysteria	2/
508-468-4596	MA	Hamilton	D. Mastrianni	W	19D	110	Trauma Room	16/2
508-478-0153	MA	Milford	Wayne Anderson	B$	29VO	111	Gadge'-Tronics	3/1
508-481-7147	MA	Marlborough	Kevin Porter	O	9U	60	WayStar	5/2
508-521-6883	MA	Haverhill	Jim Spheekas	X	9		Cerberus	20/
508-528-2295	MA	Franklin	Edward Zdrok	O	9D	99	COMP. CONFIDENT	60/3
508-529-0801	MA	Upton	John Kelly	B	12	105	AGRA-Net	1/3
508-535-0446	MA	Peabody	Steve Keith	B$	29D	112	Base Line	7/1
508-537-4007	MA	Leominster	Sam Gudgel	B	29D	104	REAL-TIME	35/4
508-537-0719	MA	Leominster	Lenny Bernard	B	19V	107	Vipers	4/1
508-537-5148	MA	Leominster	Mike Ciccolini	B	19V	107	Software Centrl	4/1
508-568-0957	MA	Hudson	Al Goodniss	W	9U	81	Imperium	1/
508-583-7693	MA	Brockton	Larry Gallant	BV	9	99	Cnsumr'sShowcse	10/1
508-588-2210	MA	Brockton	John Rock	R	9	72	Tandy Tavern	2/
508-620-7105	MA	Framingham	Michael Holt	W	2	92	V.F.W.	2/
508-630-3720	MA	Gardner	Nathan Taylor	B	9V	103	InfoNet BBS	10/1
508-634-3695	MA	Milford	Ned Lovely	X	12	111	Medusa's Parlor	2/1
508-651-3470	MA	Natick	Stan Feinberg	W	9	98	Natick VFW	2/1
508-655-3848	MA	Natick	Bill Heiser	Q	9U	70	ThinkTank	

Phone	State	City	Sysop	T/S	First on List # | v (see above)	Name, Features	
508-655-8927	MA	Natick	Scott Szretter	Q	9D	98	HMM BBS	2/2
508-667-7234	MA	Billerica	Daniel Shapiro	Q	09V	105	Chicken Coop!	7/1
508-675-5493	MA	Fall River	Larry Santos	B	9U	56	DataCentral	
508-682-5279	MA	Methuen	Paul Gosselin	Q$	9U	42	ElecDreams	20/
508-686-5994	MA	Methuen	Mike Dube	W	19V	114	GRYPHON's Lair	26/5
508-693-7396	MA	VineyardHavn	Garth Bigelow	S	19V	108	TopherSoft	3/1
508-697-3508	MA	Bridgewater	Gunnar Rieger	M$	9U	72	priZm ImageCtr	2/
508-746-6010	MA	Plymouth	Tom Whynott	M	09D	104	Adult Hangout	55/9
508-750-0250	MA	Danvers	P. Rosenheim	B	19V	116*	PandA's Den	7/1
508-765-9387	MA	Southbridge	Bob Poirier	G	9U	96	Parrot's Den	15/1
508-771-1090	MA	Hyannis	Pepe Evans	X	19V	105	! Two J's !	51/2
508-778-0515	MA	Centerville	Jeb Fulham	T$	09V	114	Bunker	24/2
508-788-1603	MA	Framingham	Perry Lowell	L	09D	77	SKATEboard	7/1
508-791-3303	MA	Worcester	Bob Mckeegan	X	09H	113	Minority	1/2
508-799-6545	MA	Worcester	Phil Carson	B$	2	97	Metropolis Onl.	2/1
508-832-0201	MA	Auburn	Paul Outerson	B$	9U	55	DataCore	3/
508-833-0508	MA	Plymouth	Milton Shaw	B	9	66	AutoExec	12/
508-840-3043	MA	Leominster	Tim Hargreaves	Q	2	93	SENACUS	20/
508-875-3618	MA	Framingham	Nels Anderson	B	9U	66	)(evious BBS	10/
508-879-8531	MA	Framingham	Chris Saia	B	19V	110	MetroWestLinkUp	1/1
508-881-5209	MA	Ashland	Micah Imparato	X	09V	110	IMPosium	2/2
508-883-6812	MA	Millville	R. Desjourdy	B	19V	106	Nasus Nibble	2/1
508-897-1963	MA	Maynard	Frank Gladu	B	09V	95	Tour De Force	10/2
508-898-9995	MA	Marlboro	Stephen Bigelow	W	09VO	113	TechNet BBS	1/1
508-921-4864	MA	Beverly	Jim Allen	B	9U	72	Software Connx	20/
508-927-3459	MA	Beverly	Mike Riley	W	99V	86	TheOpenWindow	12/3
508-927-3757	MA	Beverly	Chuck Frieser	G	09D	110	High Society	40/4
508-948-2921	MA	Rowley	Ron Bergeron	Q	9D	86	The Machine	3/
508-949-3590	MA	Webster	Don Eklund	B	9U	67	S/W Exchg	7/
508-975-9779	MA	N. Andover	Mike Magnuson	B	2	72	Modicon	
509-326-3238	WA	Spokane	W J Sorcinelli	B	9U	56	LegalEase	9/
509-457-0206	WA	Yakima	Mike Shannon	X	09V	112	Starvector	5/1
509-482-2016	WA	Spokane	Larry Taylor	B$	19D	112	MicroData	90/3
509-487-6572	WA	Spokane	Daryl Rodrigues	V	09V	110	DATA*NORTH*WEST	2/1
509-544-0113	WA	Pasco	John Allen	B	9V	102	Arid Acres	25/2
509-576-9397	WA	Yakima	Lee Wallace	R	09V	115	FALCON	3/3
509-624-6799	WA	Spokane	Jeff Albrecht	O	9U	58	Inland Empire	5/
509-758-6022	WA	Clarkston	Ben Davis	X	19V	108	CEO & Chairman	1/1
509-758-6248	WA	Clarkston	Jess James	R	09V	69	STARWEST-bbs	15/2
509-765-7847	WA	Moses Lake	John Jurovich	W	99V	84	Northwest	18/1
509-783-5526	WA	Kennewick	Doug Jones	B	9U	85	Tri-Cats,pgms	2/
509-891-6789	WA	Spokane	Pete Link	X	19VO	113	MOONFLOWER	55/3
509-924-5179	WA	Spokane	Tim Storrs	X	09V	113	Squirrels Nest	1/1
509-943-0211	WA	Richland	Gary Hedberg	B$	19D	102	One Stop	68/7
509-965-0467	WA	Yakima	Del Bice	R	9D	84	Sigma Iotia][	12/4
510-235-3273	CA	El Cerrito	Bill Guggemos	W	2	100	ECPD Pub.Safety	2/1
510-235-6839	CA	Richmond	Kanon Kubose	W	2	98	KanonTech	1/1

Phone	State	City	Sysop	T/S		First on List # | v (see above)	Name, Features	
510-278-1966	CA	San Lorenzo	Dave Wright	N	9U	46	Cafe'Corner	
510-339-1045	CA	Oakland	Julie Mcgrew	W	9V	100	Bay List,!	5/4
510-426-0470	CA	Pleasanton	Bill McCauley	T	2	26	Records Dept	
510-432-2461	CA	Pittsburg	Pete Nelson	W	9V	100	Terminal One	3/1
510-432-7579	CA	Concord	Nancy H. Miller	B	9U	88	Sempervirens	4/1
510-481-9774	CA	San Lorenzo	Dan Hornback	W	19V	113	Night Creature	3/1
510-494-0122	CA	Newark	Kevin Sibley	W	09D	59	Anyody's BBS	5/2
510-524-9330	CA	Albany	Jake Essl	B	9U	75	HyperLinc West	2/2
510-538-2040	CA	CastroValley	Richard Yim	T	2	29	Compu-Pal	1/
510-581-3019	CA	Hayward	Dave Gentry	T	2	40	GADM	1/
510-651-4740	CA	Fremont	Bill Garrison	W	9D	103	Jetstream	10/1
510-659-9169	CA	Fremont	Jim Thomas	Q	2	15	RSVP	
510-670-2940	CA	Hayward	Cliff Wilson	Y	22	111	New Big Board	3/1
510-672-9325	CA	Concord	Eric Cozzi	W	9O	101	Computer Comm	2/1
510-676-7872	CA	Concord	Mark Cowan	W	19V	116*	Motorcycle Hapg	3/1
510-682-1371	CA	Concord	Bill Plein	A	19D	72	HDM OS/2	2/1
510-689-2090	CA	Concord	Jon Martin	R	2	06	HQ RBBS-PC West	
510-689-4686	CA	Concord	Waik Gan	W$	99D	108	GIFt Shop	70/9
510-736-8343	CA	Danville	Frank Mahaney	B$	9U	81	WindowsOnline	15/3
510-770-0630	CA	Fremont	Charlie Floyd	R	9V	76	TheWall	1/
510-778-5929	CA	Antioch	John Palmer	B	9D		Infolinc	3/2
510-785-1123	CA	Hayward	Tim Wilcox	Q	19V	107	Clubhouse	12/1
510-791-0832	CA	Fremont	Noreen Cwick	W	2	89	DiamondMind	3/
510-793-0284	CA	Fremont	John Ferra	P	9D	51	Litter Box	5/1
510-794-0170	CA	Fremont	Scott Whitney	B$	19D	106	WhitCom InfoNet	40/2
510-794-4029	CA	Fremont	Scott Mercer	R	9V	83	Compu-Ace,TP	4/1
510-794-9624	CA	Fremont	Bernie Belew	A	9HV	15	SDA	1/
510-797-3648	CA	Fremont	Larry Davis	B	9	99	Gone Fishin	18/2
510-828-8012	CA	Dublin	Don Odle	B	9U	77	GamesMaster	2/
510-829-6062	CA	Dublin	Young&Gardner	A	9HV	45	ATT-PAC	2/
510-829-7627	CA	San Ramon	Tony Waddell	B	09BV	49	Easy Access BBS	5/2
510-837-4610	CA	Danville	Kevin Fong	B	9V	100	Transfer Stn	8/2
510-838-7687	CA	Danville	Philip Berretta	W	9U	06	Diabolo	3/
510-865-7115	CA	Alameda	Mike King	B	9U	75	IDC,Intelec	1/
510-881-5427	CA	Hayward	Alex Riggs	W	9U	83	BustOut,games	16/
510-895-5985	CA	San Leandro	Mike Hildum	B	9V	36	Moe	5/2
510-937-0156	CA	Walnut Creek	Wes Meier	A	9HV	44	WalnCrk	/2
510-937-6570	CA	Walnut Creek	Don Reid	B	19D	115	ClanDONNACHAIDH	1/1
510-938-9470	CA	Walnut Creek	Werner Gumpert	A	9HV	83	CoEd Assoc	
510-938-9656	CA	Walnut Creek	Wilma Meier	A	9HV	58	AlternateRealty	
510-943-6238	CA	Walnut Creek	Henry Shaw	T	09D	45	DVPCUG	7/3
510-946-1049	CA	Walnut Creek	Eric Kempter	S	9D	91	Knight Court	1/1
510-946-1227	CA	Walnut Creek	Forrest Litke	R	19D	62	LGB	9/1
512-218-1699	TX	Austin	F. Zappone	M$	09H	116*	OPPORTUNITY	4/2
512-280-1980	TX	Austin	Chris Lott	R	19V	112	BUSINESS HUB!	8/2
512-285-5028	TX	Elgin	Peter Banz	W	9C	83	GameSt,windows	9/
512-323-3276	TX	Austin	Jim Westbrook	Q	9U	26	Tex-a-Caid	3/1

Phone	State	City	Sysop	T/S		First on List # I v (see above)	Name, Features	
512-335-5803	TX	Austin	Daniel Thompson	X	2	34	Star's End	
512-346-1852	TX	Austin	John Dierdorf	O$	9D	34	CenTex PCUG	12/3
512-346-8075	TX	Austin	Ross Goldberg	Q	19V	114	RagBBS v.69	5/2
512-388-1445	TX	Round Rock	Jack E. Moore	B$	29DO	44	Accolade!	30/4
512-388-2888	TX	Austin	Gene Chesser	O	2	26	CTSA Unlimited	
512-436-4210	TX	San Antonio	Ron Gonzales	W	2	95	Gonzo's Place	1/
512-442-8198	TX	Austin	Cathy Keller	W	9V	102	Dingle Delaware	2/2
512-443-5441	TX	Austin	Joe Barr	O	9V	98	RedWheelbarrow	2/1
512-462-0207	TX	Austin	Daniel Aiken	R	2	34	Den of Iniquity	
512-491-9034	TX	San Antonio	Forest Newman	B	2	43	Diversions	
512-496-9373	TX	San Antonio	Sean Graig	Q	9U	56	Rampant Griffin	
512-556-2524	TX	Kempner	Pete Theer	B	9U	88	Tex*Star BBS	10/2
512-561-8150	TX	San Antonio	Gregory Shaheen	M	9U	100	Emerald Palace	40/128
512-578-8656	TX	Victoria	Jeff Cameron	R	9	100	The Bearnery	13/1
512-623-1395	TX	San Antonio	Joseph Voigt	X	9V	101	Danse Macabre	1/1
512-648-3874	TX	San Antonio	Joe Pyland	S	2	101	X-Factor	2/1
512-690-4437	TX	San Antonio	Jerry Cooley	Q	9	92	Top Choice	2/
512-696-1270	TX	San Antonio	Mike Warden	B	2	45	ComputerAspects	
512-754-7715	TX	San Marcos	R. Zabbage	Q	9V	83	Jacobs Well	8/
512-835-4848	TX	Austin	Jim Roe	Q	9U	72	MiddleEarth	1/
512-837-0953	TX	Austin	Jim Westbrook	Q	9U	26	JimNet	4/1
512-887-0787	TX	CorpusChrist	Wade Fjeld	M$	19V	107	CDS	12/25
512-930-3414	TX	Georgetown	H. Glantzberg	X	19V	113	Help Desk	8/1
512-993-8876	TX	CorpusChrist	Rudy Reyes	W$	2	104	CAUG-PC	1/1
513-231-7013	OH	Cincinnati	Craig Baker	T	9D	80	MultiSys	36/5
513-233-0807	OH	Huber Hts	Guy Hunter	Q	19V	111	Hunter's Point	4/1
513-233-1200	OH	Dayton	John Wright	J	9D	88	Pit-Stop	2/
513-233-7993	OH	Huber Hts	Robin Reston	W$	19V	111	Perfect Visions	30/2
513-236-1229	OH	Hubert Hts	Joe Caplinger	W	9U	69	J&J's	5/
513-236-3448	OH	Huber Hts	Diane Pencil	Q	9	96	Darkroom	1/
513-236-4954	OH	Huber Hts	J and P Webb	W	02	109&	My Candy Store	2/1
513-237-7737	OH	Huber Hts	Mark May	Q	9U	68	MythicalKingdom	4/
513-274-0821	OH	Dayton	John Cooper	B	9V	34	The Annex	2/
513-383-2081	OH	Wilmington	Brian Powell	X	09V	110	Front Line	1/1
513-383-2264	OH	Wilmington	David Gordley	G	09V	106*	D.N.R.Connectn	1/1
513-390-1093	OH	Springfield	F. Hertenstein	W$	29V	110	A S A D Hdq	2/1
513-393-0075	OH	Hillsboro	Rick Morris	B	09D	113	Highland CtyCmp	40/4
513-393-8378	OH	Hillsboro	Joe Hochstuhl	X	29V	95	APC Softwares	5/2
513-398-0928	OH	Mason	Decker Doggett	Q	9U	26	Train Board	
513-398-6202	OH	Mason	Ken Opdycke	B	29D	110	FinishLine	12/1
513-398-8218	OH	Mason	Ricky Shradin	P	9U	87	Tandy Land II	
513-422-9652	OH	Middletown	Peter Mengel	X	9D	103	Wolverines Lair	1/1
513-424-1860	OH	Middletown	Bill Raines	B$	19UO	108	ConsultantForum	16/3
513-424-2495	OH	Middletown	Paul Sink	X	9C	90	ComplCompSolns	15/
513-424-7529	OH	Middletown	Don Cheeks	B$	9U	63	ModemZone	21/3
513-451-8990	OH	Cincinnati	Mike Nelson	F$	12	110	Type Too!	1/1
513-436-0400	OH	Dayton	Mark Cottom	O	9U	56	Shermark	

Phone	State	City	Sysop	T/S	First on List # ↓ (see above)	Name, Features	
513-446-2133	OH	Sardinia	Rick Donley	Q	9U	75	Compunet	1/1
513-451-1237	OH	Cincinnati	Lee Fitterer	F	9U	65	CoffeeShop	4/
513-489-4405	OH	Cincinnati	Mark Donner	F	9U	85	Warehouse	3/
513-563-6475	OH	Cincinnati	Bob Mace	P	19D	114	Epsilon Comp	4/1
513-574-3536	OH	Cincinnati	John Schmidt	F	2	75	Cincinnati	1/
513-583-0033	OH	Cincinnati	John Leighton	F	09OV	115	Moonshadow	1/1
513-624-0552	OH	Cincinnati	Tarry Shebesta	T	2	81	ACS Onl,autos	
513-667-6016	OH	Tipp City	Josh Borton	J	09V	114	Sword/Shield	1/1
513-752-8248	OH	Cincinnati	Bob Emerson	B$	9U	72	CinnCompConnx	27/2
513-782-8536	OH	Cincinnati	Glenn McAtee	B	19VV	110	Micro Center	5/1
513-779-9717	OH	Cincinnati	Eric Sakurai	W	9V	89	SpocksAdventure	2/
513-793-9257	OH	Cincinnati	Walt Bush	F	9U	74	RossmoyneMall	10/
513-797-6011	OH	Lindale	John Troher	F	29V	112	Micro Systems	20/2
513-831-0246	OH	Milford	Jim Bernges	F	9U	88	Queen City	5/
513-833-6093	OH	Brookville	Jerry Millikin	W	09VO	104	Family	7/1
513-851-9207	OH	Cincinnati	Jim Pierce	B$15	9U	54	SilverBullet	
513-856-9101	OH	Hamilton	Mike Rickman	W	9D	104	Basic Concept	1/2
513-863-0204	OH	Hamilton	D. Severance	B	9	99	TiTan's Empire	6/1
513-864-9914	OH	Springfield	Scott Baker	X	19U	106	Scream'gDigital	3/1
513-868-3383	OH	Hamilton	Rob Smith	F	9U	84	FireBd	2/
513-878-5491	OH	Fairborn	Bill Gibson	W	9	88	ForColltorsOnly	1/1
514-735-4340	PQ	Montreal	M. Heroux	B	29V	112	Op. Prometheus	10/2
515-225-8496	IA	W.Des Moines	Mike Woltz	F	9U	50	BuffCrk	3/2
515-432-4472	IA	Boone	Ryan Myers	X	19V	116*	Oasis	6/1
515-573-5494	IA	Fort Dodge	Kevin Friesth	X	09B	110	Star Frontier	84/4
515-752-6554	IA	Marshalltown	Warren Miller	F	29D	112	HorselessCarrge	5/1
515-964-7937	IA	Ankeny	Dan Buda	O	9U	50	Midwest FOG	4/
516-226-3895	NY	Farmingdale	Gregory Carman	B	12	46	LI File Exch	40/9
516-244-7064	NY	Bohemia	David Hoelzer	X	09V	108	Shadowguard	3/1
516-293-7540	NY	Farmingdale	Keith Goodman	W	19OV	101	Leisure & Bus	20/3
516-352-7475	NY	Elmont	James Dev	R	2	70	Wingnut	1/
516-364-4450	NY	Woodbury	Paul Cangialosi	B	2	45	Substation	
516-371-0539	NY	Inwood	Paul Saponaro	R	19VO	107	Midnight Star	3/1
516-374-0551	NY	Woodmere	Ray Cheverez	B$	9	99	PenDragon'sLair	3/1
516-420-0818	NY	Farmingdale	Gary Glueckert	R	2	85	SUNY College	
516-471-8625	NY	Ronkonkoma	Joe Jerszynski	T	9D	96	SuggestionBox	5/4
516-483-3975	NY	Garden City	Jeff Matthews	B$	19OB	26*	Unicorn BBS	8/3
516-486-4705	NY	S.Hempstead	David Johnson	R	2	26	The Unknown	
516-488-4325	NY	Floral Park	Larry Kiewra	P	09O	116*	MetroFire/Resc	1/1
516-488-6528	NY	Lake Success	David Wells	T	9	50	Canon	
516-493-0186	NY	Commack	John Sirabella	W	9V	73	GamePeddler	3/
516-536-1546	NY	Rockv'l Cntr	Barry Miller	B	9H	56	Big Apple	11/
516-536-8723	NY	Oceanside	Paul Waldinger	B	9H	26	SoundofMusic	43/
516-546-8025	NY	Baldwin	Alan Linker	R	2	26	So. oftheBauder	
516-561-3801	NY	ValleyStream	Hank Selah	B	9HV	81	PCPlace	1/
516-561-6590	NY	ValleyStream	Dave Minott	B	09V	50*	LICA Limbs	3/1
516-579-7507	NY	Levittown	Bob Glasser	W	09D	65	Utopia Tech	34/3

					First on List # | v		
Phone	*State*	*City*	*Sysop*	*T/S*	*(see above)*	*Name, Features*	
516-579-7929	NY	Levittown	Rich Molinelli	X	9V		Small Time	3/
516-589-4984	NY	Bohemia	Michael Colucci	W	9V	102	Software Store	2/1
516-627-6910	NY	Manhasset	Tim Millis	P	9U	89	PrintShoppe,dtp	6/
516-632-8000	NY	Stony Brook	Jeff Fiegel	X	02	106	Eagle's nest	2/
516-643-0747	NY	Melville	Philip Alloca	S	2	89	The Campus	
516-669-8577	NY	No. Babylon	Ken Ostracho	L	2	26	Metro Board	4/
516-674-4033	NY	New York	Dave Friedman	R	9D	72	Star's End	8/3
516-679-0674	NY	East Meadow	Jeff Green	W	2	76	ModemNews mag	
516-689-2566	NY	StonyBrook	Frank LaRosa	S	9U	45	Searchlt Home	1/
516-694-2318	NY	Farmingdale	Enzo Alduino	B	29D	116*	Paradigm Legal	40/2
516-694-3623	NY	Farmingdale	Stan Schwartz	X	09V	86	Expressway	4/1
516-736-6662	NY	Selden	John Woodstock	B	9U	89	Your S/W Resce	1/1
516-783-3228	NY	Wantagh	Ken Merting	M	09VV	106	KESCO	7/10
516-796-7686	NY	Seaford	Neil Chodkowski	B$	19D	62	Hard Disk Cafe	20/2
516-868-1741	NY	Baldwin	Cliff Watkins	B	99V	65	Intelec Online	20/2
516-889-4586	NY	Long Beach	Jim Carter	B	19V	116*	Wizards Domain	12/2
516-922-5153	NY	Oyster Bay	Peter Whitelaw	WV	9V	101	PC Beginner	2/1
516-922-9445	NY	Oyster Bay	P Gildersleeve	B	19	109	Pampered Parrot	2/3
516-935-5704	NY	Plainview	A. Orentlicher	W	19D	96	MicroQuick	12/1
516-938-6722	NY	Hicksville	Jim Toro	T$	2	41	PDSLO,!	15/
516-968-7824	NY	BayShore	Erik VanRiper	O	9U	81	SourceForSource	2/2
517-263-0273	MI	Adrian	Chris Bourne	Y	19V	115	Law & Order	18/2
517-263-3590	MI	Adrian	John A. Crouse	W	09V	101	Ghetto	4/1
517-263-6313	MI	Adrian	Tom McCurdy	F	09VO	116*	Shazam	2/1
516-266-5182	NY	Holbrook	Chris LLoyd	B	9U	93	Time Slice	10/3
517-337-0261	MI	Lansing	Warren Wolfe	R	2	26	Data Basics	
517-356-3478	MI	Alpena	Jesse W. Godsey	X	19D	110	Micro Assets	12/2
517-463-8474	MI	Alma	Jim Olson et al	W	2	77	Mainstream	
517-546-3948	MI	Howell	Dave Gould	B	2	88	4th Dimension	2/
517-676-0272	MI	Mason	Ron Sutterfield	G	29D	114*	Ron's Roost	5/1
517-695-9952	MI	Freeland	Rick Rosinski	S	09D	73	Wolverine	75/5
517-797-3740	MI	Saginaw	Dennis Hauser	T	9V	98	DelightCustomer	5/2
517-799-1304	MI	Saginaw	Jon Hozeska	C	9U	60	DynamiteHill	16/
517-839-0169	MI	Midland	Jeff Weinberg	L	09V	111	Fortress	6/1
517-865-6173	MI	St. Charles	Loyd Craft	Q	9U	89	MicroCosm	1/
518-233-7949	NY	Troy	John Sheehan	L	2		Great Disaster	1/
518-283-5716	NY	E. Greenbush	Larry Miller	B	19D	116*	ACCESS Network	12/2
518-371-6078	NY	Clifton Park	Doug Harple	W	02	111	Shenendehowa	1/1
518-442-5738	NY	Albany	Art Thompson	B	2	15	Rockflr College	7/2
518-452-0897	NY	Guilderland	Rick Brennan	X	9U	93	Pineview	3/
518-462-6134	NY	Albany	Maureen O'Brien	J$	02	110	DissociationNet	1/1
518-479-2051	NY	Rensselaer	Mike Gunderloy	M$	9V	80	AlbCompEnt	1/
518-483-9129	NY	Malone	Mike Hellijas	W	9V	103	Troll Bridge	6/2
518-486-6631	NY	Albany	Thomas Irvin	X	2	93	RAIN,E71	2/5
518-563-8981	NY	Plattsburgh	Don Jewell	R	2	26	GigWhse	10/
518-747-5330	NY	Hudson Falls	Eric Colomb	Q	29V	112	Dream Theater	3/2
518-773-8143	NY	Gloversville	Brett Hayes	V	9O	102	SpeedyTradingPt	1/1

Phone	State	City	Sysop	T/S	First on List # | v (see above)		Name, Features	
518-785-4189	NY	Albany	Doug Kameck	B	2	44	Night Flight	
518-846-8803	NY	Chazy	John Rigby	B	19BD	48*	Tavern	10/3
518-885-4192	NY	Ballston Spa	Maureen Allen	O	19H	113	Access	5/2
519-352-7010	ON	Chatham	Avery Wagg	B	9	74	SW Connect	2/
519-421-1940	ON	Woodstock	Kevin Layne	Q$	9U	89	Cubic BBS,files	2/
519-442-6449	ON	Paris	Bill Brown	F	2	92	Elec Knights	1/
519-658-0069	ON	Guelph	B. & R. Spencer	B$	9U	50	RGB Computing	17/
519-862-5663	ON	Corunna	David Empey	B	29V	113	Mandate Systems	11/1
519-925-2642	ON	Shelburne	Steve Henry	W	2	87	Ambassador	4/4
601-264-0539	MS	Hattiesburg	Craig Brown	F	2	76	Citadel	1/
601-264-0589	MS	Hattiesburg	Chuck Hosey	F$	9	72	PrometheusDesgn	3/
601-268-8871	MS	Hattiesburg	Thomas Pullens	B$2	9U	62	Camelot	1/
601-287-1336	MS	Corinth	Cliff Dalton	W	9U	81	Omega-One	1/
601-328-6486	MS	Columbus	Bob Beebe	F	19V	106	Ranch&CattleSth	1/1
601-362-9958	MS	Jackson	Richard Vaughan	R	99V	87	Berserker	5/1
601-366-1664	MS	Jackson	Jack Ridgway	S	9	81	BigBangTheory	3/
601-372-6998	MS	Jackson	Jim Head	W	9V	82	Electric Dreams	2/
601-373-0018	MS	Jackson	Derryl Steib	Q	2	66	HyperDrive	
601-388-1809	MS	Biloxi	John Holzer	P	19D	113	Web	3/1
601-427-9032	MS	Burnsville	Chris Timbes	W	9V	96	Miss. SuperBd	2/1
601-489-8734	MS	Pontotoc	Dan Dye	S	2	83	Player,sh/w	
601-497-5303	MS	Gautier	Ms Jim Pefley	Q	9V	102	Suffolk News	9/2
601-638-7120	MS	Vicksburg	Charles Lamere	W	9U	88	Chuckie's Place	2/2
601-626-7033	MS	Collinsville	Jason James	W$	09O	110	Zollex Empire	80/1
601-824-0379	MS	Brandon	Tim Gilmore	W	9	99	Elliott's Next	3/1
601-841-0595	MS	Tupelo	Robert Leech	Y	09V	116*	OLEPUT BBS	2/1
601-842-9255	MS	Tupelo	Steve Bishop	Y	9V	100	Buswacker	37/1
601-844-7052	MS	Tupelo	Ray Johnson	B	19U	109	Home/Hobby	2/1
601-853-2688	MS	Ridgeland	Geoff Lewis	B	9V	100	Oasis BBS	10/1
601-856-8337	MS	Madison	James Burns	W	9U	86	Heliport,aviat	3/
601-875-2355	MS	Ocean Sprgs	Mark Gehres	X	09V	105	DataSync	15/1
601-892-6334	MS	CrystalSprgs	John Anderson	W	9V	100	WareHouse	12/1
601-896-3970	MS	Gulfport	Rick Maddox	B	9U	90	On-line Systems	3/
601-924-4174	MS	Clinton	Chris Brown	S	9V	91	Xanadu	2/
601-925-4380	MS	Clinton	F&R Black	S	9D	91	BinaryBros	2/2
601-957-0843	MS	Jackson	Mike Forester	A	9HV	80	Irrelevant	2/2
601-957-3016	MS	Jackson	Mike Seal	A	9V	80	Cont'lDiv.	1/
601-969-1190	MS	Jackson	John MacKenzie	V	9V	103	Patriot Games	8/1
601-981-1394	MS	Jackson	Jimmy Pipkins	W	29V	98	StarNet	79/4
602-220-0001	AZ	Phoenix	Rick Johnson	M$	2	49	Sho-Tron	/20
602-222-5491	AZ	Phoenix	Ray Moore	B	19U	110	Phoenix PCUG	4/2
602-230-8644	AZ	Mesa	Shawn Fergason	B$	9U	62	Genesis II	
602-241-0256	AZ	Phoenix	Mike Scott	F	9U	92	Mac's Place	3/2
602-279-0793	AZ	Phoenix	Sue Widemark	W	2	98	Cheese Whiz	8/1
602-292-0065	AZ	Tucson	Jeff Coleman	X	19D	107	DigitalConcepts	17/2
602-326-2999	AZ	Tucson	Lyn Borchert	QV	9D	101	Hour Glass	8/1
602-326-9345	AZ	Tucson	Karen Lange	R	2	85	NewParents Net	

				T/S		First on List # ↓ v (see above)	Name, Features	
Phone	State	City	Sysop					
602-344-2621	AZ	Yuma	David Dean	WV	19D	73	Old Town	15/1
602-458-0451	AZ	Siera Vista	Mike McGuire	O	9D	90	Analog Gate	2/
602-458-8206	AZ	Sierra Vista	Duke Renwick	B	9D	76	Duke'sDghs	17/
602-459-2412	AZ	Ft Huachuca	Tom Held	Q	09B	72	New Way	10/2
602-527-8895	AZ	Flagstaff	Scott Fell	Q	9V	95	Quandra: TIE	2/2
602-581-6918	AZ	Phoenix	Nick Roberts	B	19DB	111	Cop Shop	95/1
602-582-6760	AZ	Phoenix	J. Engebretson	Q	12	107	Dark Tunnel	3/1
602-584-7395	AZ	Phoenix	Keith Slater	T	9D	104	SUNWISE	2/1
602-682-7443	AZ	Tucson	Ron Herring	X	09V	116*	Hambone	3/1
602-730-8943	AZ	Tempe	Michael Clark	W$	19V	112	CADalog	30/1
602-744-2314	AZ	Tucson	Lee Levin	Q	2	81	OldPueblo	1/
602-747-5236	AZ	Tucson	Jeff White	QV	9V	100	Solitude	1/1
602-749-5968	AZ	Tucson	Gene Lowry	R	9U	15	Bigfoot's BBS	6/2
602-757-0385	AZ	Kingman	Doug Preston	W	9U	89	GoldenValley	2/
602-757-1125	AZ	Kingman	Craig Barnett	B	9U	78	PrimeNet(tm)	40/
602-774-0017	AZ	Flagstaff	Ron Moore	B	29V	73*	Ramcom Tech	4/1
602-790-6230	AZ	Tucson	Ken Salois	Q	9D	104	SouthWEST Data	2/1
602-820-7861	AZ	Mesa	Michael Masters	W	99V	114	Conceptual CAD	14/2
602-831-7979	AZ	Chandler	Jim Mitchell	Q	19V	107	Empty Pockets	2/1
602-840-4752	AZ	Phoenix	Bob Hirschfeld	W	2	34	Natl Cong 4 Men	
602-846-9633	AZ	Phoenix	Michael Abmont	X	19V	107	Mustang's Ranch	2/1
602-866-9229	AZ	Phoenix	John Erikson	W	9D	72	Valley of Sun	8/3
602-868-4889	AZ	Florence	Mike Myers	B$	9D	84	GIF City	20/2
602-870-6004	AZ	Phoenix	Wayne Church	W	19V	116*	Safe 'n Secure	1/1
602-872-9148	AZ	Glendale	Mark Shander	Q$	9V	74	Broadcasters	
602-877-8748	AZ	Phoenix	Michael Prothro	W	2	98	MikeSunshineRst	1/1
602-881-3769	AZ	Tucson	Jerry Cain	X	9U	87	Edge of Forever	2/
602-888-0819	AZ	Tucson	Don Appleton	X	9D		Aztec	4/
602-894-6526	AZ	Tempe	Thane Smith	X	9D	79	Zephyr	3/
602-899-4876	AZ	Chandler	David Cantere	B	2	26	Technoids Anon	
602-937-3796	AZ	Phoenix	John Quently	W	19D	112	LAST BBS	8/1
602-937-5055	AZ	Glendale	Stan Kapala	F	9V	74	ShortCircuit	3/
602-947-4283	AZ	Scottsdale	Dennis Davis	B	9V	86	Resume Xchg	2/
602-964-1788	AZ	Mesa	James Parker	W	2	97	FILEWORKS	8/1
602-970-0105	AZ	Scottsdale	Jim Jusko	B$	19D	110	Inn on The Park	11/7
602-997-9323	AZ	Phoenix	Michael Ingram	W	09V	110	Private Reserve	3/1
603-226-3344	NH	Concord	K. Kalloch	F	12	111	Starlite	1/1
603-228-0705	NH	Bow	Mark Sawyer	O	19VU	111	Easy Does It	2/1
603-256-6147	NH	Hinsdale	John Boden	X	19D	106	Emerald City	1/1
603-298-9872	NH	West Lebanon	R. Johnson	W	19V	111	Nite Owls	5/1
603-332-0419	NH	Gonic	Don Foster	F	09V	104*	BrickYard BBS	2/1
603-335-5640	NH	Barrington	Al Wheeler	B	19U	111	Barrington BBS	5/1
603-352-0194	NH	Keene	Hal Brown	Q	19UO	111	Tactical Edge	4/1
603-357-8941	NH	Keene	Paul Painchaud	Q	2	78	RandomAccess	13/
603-382-6938	NH	Newton	John Mcnally	Q	9D	98	Computer Castle	12/4
603-429-2419	NH	Litchfield	Quentin Lewis	Q	9V	100	The Big QUEUE	1/1
603-431-7229	NH	Portsmouth	Myles Bratter	T$	09D	112	Botnay Bay, EIS	2/16

Phone	State	City	Sysop	T/S	First on List # | v (see above)	Name, Features	
603-432-2517	NH	Londonderry	Eric Poole	W	9V	55	Leo Tech,Ada,C	/1
603-432-6711	NH	Londonderry	Gardiner Jones	B	9U	51	Nor'easter	5/
603-464-4176	NH	Hillsboro	Gil Mitchell	B	19V	108	Blue Knights	8/2
603-529-4290	NH	Weare	Jim Webb	Q	9D	85	GraniteStConnx	2/
603-623-2436	NH	Manchester	Matt Craig	X	12	111	Toxic Jungle	2/1
603-641-2017	NH	Manchester	Paul Roemer	W	9U	89	Comp Solns	7/
603-644-0042	NH	Manchester	Eric Peterson	W	19D	111	Camelot	4/1
603-666-0108	NH	Manchester	Ron LeBlanc	W	9V	84	Cosmopolitan,C	2/
603-666-0935	NH	Manchester	G. Morgan	X	12	111	Tiger Eyes	4/1
603-742-5201	NH	Rollinsford	Walter Stewart	W$	9D	98	Bull Board	12/4
603-753-9716	NH	Penacook	Al Hitchmoth	Q	19D	111	Quiet Revolutn	1/1
603-772-7803	NH	Exeter	Edward Greene	B	9U	61	The Shop	2/
603-882-2099	NH	Nashua	Pat Vallier	Q	9U	34	Ballpark	
603-899-3335	NH	Rindge	Bill Esposito	O	9D	72	Cereal Port	9/1
603-938-5265	NH	Bradford	Mike Pugliese	X	09V	113	V-GER	2/1
604-370-1761	BC	Victoria	David Pottier	B$	9U	79	Bush-Whackers	2/
604-383-7681	BC	Victoria	Mike Doyle	X	29D	111	SARBC HQ	1/1
604-451-0092	BC	Burnaby	Robert Lassiter	A	9O	95	Random Access	1/2
604-563-2469	BC	PrinceGeorge	Joe Tailleur	R$	2	85	Hidden Hideaway	
604-888-5152	BC	Abbotsford	Aaron Wass	Q	9U	54	No.Lights	3/
605-232-4648	SD	McCook Lake	Jeff Preston	Q	2	89	Voyager	2/
605-256-2812	SD	Madison	Mike Waldner	B	9U	55	Dakotan	
605-256-5195	SD	Madison	Bob Blom	B	2	26	Dakota State Bd	
605-331-5831	SD	Sioux Falls	Ray Christensen	B	19D	101*	YEBB	9/6
605-336-3578	SD	Sioux Falls	Rory Binkerd	O	2	76	DakotaInfoNet	
605-341-5062	SD	Rapid City	Burton Landman	X	9U	93	PC Worlds	15/3
605-743-2912	SD	Sioux Falls	Gary Meade	W	2	97	Tiger Run	8/1
605-996-8619	SD	Mitchell	Greg Martinek	W	9V	104	Palace City	4/1
606-261-2971	KY	Newport	Jeff Kidwell	W	2	73	JollyRoger	2/
606-269-0709	KY	Lexington	David Evans	U	19V	108	Pulsators Tavrn	2/1
606-269-1565	KY	Lexington	Don Bodley	W	19D	66	PROF	8/1
606-272-0499	KY	Lexington	Ron Nutter	R$	9U	40	Bluegrass PCUG	38/
606-273-8785	KY	Lexington	Chas Baldridge	B	19D	77	AdventureComm	4/1
606-274-4125	KY	Somerset	David Palmer	V	2	99	PC Gateway	2/1
606-277-2882	KY	Lexington	Scott Wills	B	19D	105	Channel 69	3/2
606-371-0570	KY	Florence	Chuck Baker	Q	9U	81	HellfireClub	3/
606-432-0879	KY	Pikeville	Terry West	B	19V	34	StrawberryPatch	22/4
606-437-4321	KY	Pikeville	Tim Trimble	B	9D	86	BearWallerHollr	15/2
606-437-7983	KY	Pikeville	Jim Draughn	B	9D	85	Graphics Plus	35/2
606-745-6044	KY	Winchester	Wayne Ware	B	9U	26	Eastern Gate	/2
606-784-9865	KY	Morehead	Andy Price	B$	29V	111	A&E's Comp Conn	7/1
606-836-1267	KY	Worthington	C. R. Carter	Q	9U	80	PenalColony	5/
607-272-4060	NY	Ithaca	Jim Laux	Q	09V	80	TotPersVtx	1/1
607-293-6015	NY	Mount Vision	Rich Flathmann	B	19V	105	Silicon SysOp	12/3
607-324-6169	NY	Hornell	Scott Clark	X	09V	105	Demon's Abyss	1/1
607-433-2313	NY	Oneonta	Dick Wooden	Y$	9HV	80	UserGroup	1/
607-533-7072	NY	Lansing	Dan Veaner	B	2	86	Home Emmasoft	

						First on List # | v		
Phone	**State**	**City**	**Sysop**	**T/S**		**(see above)**	**Name, Features**	
607-562-3652	NY	Corning	Alan Tabb	W$	29VB	116*	PC Fanatic!	18/1
607-625-2378	NY	Apalachin	Mike Peck	Q	2	84	Best Spot	
607-687-3470	NY	Owego	Thom McElveen	Q	9U	55	NiteWing	2/
607-687-6193	NY	Oswego	Kevin Brokaw	W	9V	84	WaldenPuddle	2/
607-732-4565	NY	Elmira	Bill Wereley	W	09D	86	Sugar Mountain	4/2
607-797-4522	NY	Johnson City	Craig Green	W$	9HV	84	Toys/Attic	2/
607-798-0315	NY	Binghamton	John Morrison	R	9D	85	The Mail Box	6/
607-798-1734	NY	Johnson City	Chuck Ray	R	9U	58	BroomeCompUn	
607-936-0229	NY	Corning	William LaBarre	B	9U	78	CrystalVisions	1/
608-222-8842	WI	Madison	Sarah Thaler	X	9U	34	PowerBoard	
608-233-0286	WI	Madison	Marty Shannon	B	19D	26	Madison PCUG	15/4
608-271-3685	WI	Madison	Ken Flee	S	2	26	Jamestown Sftw	/1
608-655-3806	WI	Marshall	Francis Selje	B	9HV	83	Madison Tandy	4/
608-655-4012	WI	Marshall	Mark Simmons	R	9U	63	Romany	3/
608-752-7840	WI	Janesville	David Wendt	T	9U	67	J.A.D.E.	2/
608-833-9743	WI	Madison	Larry Herzog	V	09D	115	Miss-Cue	1/1
608-836-9473	WI	Madison	Maurice Thaler	X	9U	34	AudioProj	
608-837-1923	WI	Sun Prairie	Jim Wargula	R	9D	67	JWPC Dataflex	7/2
608-849-5842	WI	Dane	John Fox	R	9U	72	Springfield	5/
608-849-9796	WI	Dane	Ron Mainguth	R	9U	75	K-9 Corner,cops	3/
609-232-1245	NJ	Turnersville	Phil Gordemer	B	9D	26	Compu-Data	24/22
609-232-2258	NJ	Deptford	Howard Abel	W	9U	86	OverlandXprs	3/
609-239-1587	NJ	Burlington	Bill Daley	G	19V	107	Stonehenge	3/1
609-261-5772	NJ	Mount Holly	Joseph Arcieri	X	2	104	Nonprofit Net	2/1
609-263-0406	NJ	SeaIsle City	A. Sorrentino	R	9V	100	After Midnight	16/1
609-275-5663	NJ	Plainsboro	Jim Poulos	F	9U	89	RavensCrest	1/
609-327-5553	NJ	Millville	George Cuccia	B	9U	71	Union Lake	3/
609-327-9133	NJ	Millville	John Towers	B	29V	114	Towers Intl	4/4
609-346-9721	NJ	Pine Hill	Wayne Coates Jr	X	9U	98	Signal Hill	2/1
609-383-9400	NJ	Northfield	Tom McNally	B	9U	78	Academia,+CDR	6/6
609-423-2748	NJ	Paulsboro	Joe Kidd	W	9U	81	LongDarkRd	1/
609-435-1663	NJ	Stratford	Don Sharp	B	19V	106	DON'S	3/1
609-435-2075	NJ	Clementon	Will Thrash	W	9U	91	Antares	1/
609-435-5991	NJ	Voorhees	Jason Cohen	V	2	80	EtherealPlane	3/
609-451-7950	NJ	Bridgeton	Larry Rizzo	W	29V	110	Algorithms Inc.	10/5
609-455-0476	NJ	Bridgeton	Pat Runcie	V	9V	88	PC Maximus	1/
609-455-1665	NJ	Bridgeton	Terry Steele	W	2	96	Lunatics Lounge	2/1
609-461-6254	NJ	Riverside	K. Steinwender	B	12	110	BBS Express	3/1
609-461-6986	NJ	Riverside	Pycik & Smith	B	19V	115	Virt Mkt Place	2/2
609-467-0244	NJ	Swedesboro	Jim Harding	G	09V	95	Gap Chasm	5/2
609-467-3898	NJ	Swedesboro	Jerry Liddle	G	9D	72	Beckett,FAX	7/2
609-467-5372	NJ	Swedesboro	Alex Mastrando	G	9U	68	Alex Wld Comp	5/3
609-467-5540	NJ	Swedesboro	Alex Mastrando	G	09U	112	Alexs World	1/3
609-468-1348	NJ	Wenonah	Al Andrews	W	9H	58	Data Line	
609-478-4806	NJ	Mullica Hill	Chuck Walker	G	9D	102	Chuck's Habitat	1/1
609-482-7345	NJ	Maple Shade	John Carcione	B	9	89	Next Generation	8/2
609-530-0046	NJ	Trenton	Ken Miller	V	19D	90	Haunted Mansion	6/1

Phone	State	City	Sysop	T/S	First on List # l v (see above)	Name, Features	
609-530-1427	NJ	Ewing	Rich Katz	B	9V	56	CentraLink	2/
609-561-3377	NJ	Hammonton	Dave Schubert	B	9D	26	Casino	7/6
609-584-1478	NJ	Hamilton	Andrew Bilak	X	99V	110	Mourning Glory	2/2
609-585-8902	NJ	Yardville	D. Zarodnansky	X	9V	100	Z-Ware Systems	4/1
609-586-4847	NJ	Mercerville	Peter Skorupsky	R	9D	81	FreedomInfo,ham	16/2
609-587-2672	NJ	Mercerville	Bob Watson	B	9D	76	TAO BBS	6/2
609-589-2530	NJ	Sewell	Mark Cusumano	I	19V	87	Dante's Inferno	2/
609-627-3291	NJ	Lindenwold	Joe Barry	V	9U	75	TechLine	2/
609-627-8369	NJ	Erial	Philip Ciccone	V	2	97	Info Express	1/1
609-628-4311	NJ	Petersburg	Bob Fehn	W	9V	102	InfoNet	6/1
609-628-4372	NJ	Petersburg	David Town	N	19BV	113	MENHIR	1/1
609-660-1235	NJ	Manahawkin	Jerry Masefield	Q	9D	101	PIGEON COOP	2/1
609-663-8203	NJ	Pennsauken	Jack Merritt	BV	9D	100	Faculty Lounge	3/1
609-678-5360	NJ	Pennsville	Al Massari	B	19V	112	Galaxy	4/1
609-691-3228	NJ	Vineland	Tom Bocchetti	W	9D		Singles Bar	2/
609-691-4319	NJ	Vineland	HowardLeibowitz	W	2	92	DownloadCityUSA	7/
609-692-9366	NJ	Vineland	Bill Sampson Sr	B	9U	45	Alpha Omega	5/
609-693-9262	NJ	Forked River	R.N. Carling	B	9U	96	Tempest	2/1
609-694-2698	NJ	Franklinvle	Bob Walker	B	19VB	82	Trading Place	12/2
609-694-3069	NJ	Franklinvle	Bob Walker	B	19U	96	Trading Place	12/2
609-695-6130	NJ	Trenton	John Cosolito	W	2	72	IQ+/InfoQuest	3/
609-722-5315	NJ	Moorestown	Glenn Catlin	B	9B	45	Pretzel Zone	12/1
609-734-2158	NJ	Princeton	D. Zarodnansky	X	9V	25	D.SarnoffResCtr	4/1
609-742-8223	NJ	Gloucester	Raymond DeVoe	X	9V	95	Cyclops	1/
609-748-1109	NJ	PortRepublic	Gary Paul	B$V	9U	101	The BBS One	21/2
609-748-1728	NJ	Galloway	Din Ebrahim	B$	19V	103*	CLUB	47/6
609-753-2540	NJ	Atco	Terry Rossi	B	9D	56	PicsOnline!	42/6
609-758-1991	NJ	New Egypt	Jim Panzitta	W$	29V	110	The Wall	40/1
609-764-0812	NJ	Delran	Tyler Myers	B$	19D	87	Radio Wave,ham	60/3
609-768-5689	NJ	Voorhees	Bill Barrett	W	9	93	ElectronSymetry	4/3
609-768-6585	NJ	Atco	Bob Browne	R	09O	40	BB's	6/1
609-771-3177	NJ	Trenton	Michael Richey	B	9V		CJCC Forum	5/2
609-778-5922	NJ	Lumberton	Joseph Arcieri	W	12	105	Vitamin Shop	1/1
609-784-1529	NJ	LaurelSprgs	Paul Porten	B	19V	113	StarPort Omega	12/1
609-784-9404	NJ	Voorhees	Brian Hare	R	9U	26	Computer Connx.	
609-795-7456	NJ	Cherry Hill	Michael Bender	X	02	106	CastleCyberClds	1/1
609-825-4996	NJ	Vineland	Darryl Basner	B	9D	92	Vampyre Bar	2/3
609-829-1395	NJ	Cinnaminson	Albert Afonso	Q	9U	75	Marquee Sys	2/
609-835-1090	NJ	Willingboro	Meg Meyer	B	19V	108	MegaByte	7/1
609-845-7683	NJ	Woodbury	Dave Walker	G	2	87	Kashmire Domain	2/
609-845-9171	NJ	Deptford	Bill Williams	G	9D	88	Bill's	26/3
609-859-1910	NJ	Vincentown	Tom Sundstrom	R	9D	47	Pinelands	
609-866-2551	NJ	Mt. Laurel	Rich Paquette	B	9U	67	Livewire	12/3
609-882-6058	NJ	Ewing	Robert Paller	L	9V	101	Abyss	1/1
609-895-0398	NJ	Lawrencevlle	Brian Kramer	W	9D	99	NJ Comp Conn	1/1
609-896-3256	NJ	Lawrencevlle	Paul Laudanski	B	09V	115	Revision Sys	10/2
609-896-3691	NJ	Lawrenceville	Bill Roman	B$	19V	109	Detour	11/15

Phone	State	City	Sysop	T/S	First on List # | v (see above)	Name, Features	
609-921-0354	NJ	Rocky Hill	Robert Jackson	B	9D	98	Twilight Zone	5/2
609-927-2059	NJ	Linwood	Richard Soucy	T	19D	116*	Linwood TBBS	4/1
609-953-0769	NJ	Medford	Wayne Morton	R	2	70	Praedo	2/1
609-953-5612	NJ	Medford	Allen Stone	B$	19D	108	Space Shuttle	20/3
609-971-9518	NJ	LanokaHarbor	Paul Tricoli	X	19D	105	Paul's Boutique	20/2
609-983-9643	NJ	Circle	Lee Sarama	B	9HV	26	Marlton	1/6
610-376-9883	PA	Wyomissing	Edward Kern	X	29VO	116*	Soul Food Cafe	3/2
610-497-3912	PA	Boothwyn	Bob Martin	B	19VO	116*	Night Wind	5/2
612-231-1726	MN	Willmar	Matthew Young	Q$	19VO	105	DarkSideofMoon	20/1
612-426-0000	MN	Saint Paul	John Desmond	R	09V	106	HAM>link<	1/1
612-435-8058	MN	Burnsville	Nick Sturhk	M	9U	44	PC-Lib	20/18
612-451-3182	MN	West St Paul	Jim Aamot	Q	29V	116*	Jim's Place	11/1
612-460-6056	MN	Farmington	Lew Wurdeman	X	2	93	Dog House	3/1
612-474-0724	MN	Minneapolis	Bryan Pike	B	9U	93	Haven of Rest	3/2
612-553-0150	MN	Plymouth	BruceHaefemeyer	B	9U	55	Plymouth BBS	
612-588-7563	MN	Robbinsdale	Glen Kepler	W	9V	70	U.S. Veterans	42/5
612-623-0152	MN	Minneapolis	Howard Ekman	D	9V	15	Terrapin Sta.	12/
612-654-8372	MN	St. Cloud	ChristineBlount	B	19U	71	Granite City	8/3
612-681-9520	MN	Minneapolis	Chuck Cole	R$	2	15	Star-Net	
612-730-0822	MN	Maplewood	Wayne Copeland	W	2	67	Shadowfax	1/
612-825-0595	MN	Minneapolis	Raul Almquist	Q	9V	91	Walk/Shad/Nite	33/4
612-869-3869	MN	Minneapolis	Bill Wahlstrom	P	9U	75	Billy'sBest	4/
612-942-5614	MN	Bloomington	Mike Bertelson	S	2	84	FileDir	1/
613-257-4276	ON	Carleton Pla	Brian Doucet	R$	2	85	Quasar RBBS	5/
613-523-9816	ON	Ottawa	Tony Smyth	R	9	98	The STREET	1/
613-725-3299	ON	Ottawa	Archi Pelagos	X	29V	110	Capital Offence	16/1
614-236-2028	OH	Columbus	Jim Rhoads	X	2	79	StrangeQuark	4/
614-224-1635	OH	Columbus	Joe Balshone	X	09D	112	Wizard's Gate	12/10
614-268-9456	OH	Columbus	Phill Terry	W	29DV	111	Gingers PortLtd	4/2
614-333-6343	OH	WashCtHse	Mark Gwynn	B	29D	87	OdieLink Music	2/1
614-335-3627	OH	WashCtHse	Dan Michael	B	9U	89	PC-Connection	5/
614-353-7620	OH	Portsmouth	Tim Hileman	W	9U	90	Amazon	2/
614-423-0567	OH	Belpre	Joe Sims	B	19D	107*	Mountain Lair	12/1
614-432-3564	OH	Cambridge	Mark Baker	W	9O	102	Last Byte BBS!	1/1
614-447-2229	OH	Columbus	Dave Noice	W	29V	110	Lets Get Serial	1/1
614-466-1136	OH	Columbus	Terry Dawson	X	09V	107	Ohio Trans Port	10/2
614-476-4058	OH	Gahanna	Jeff Binkley	B	19D	111	ASA CompuHelp	30/5
614-481-0726	OH	Columbus	Glenn McAtee	B	19V	106	Micro Center TS	5/4
614-671-9980	OH	Glencoe	Jim Richards	X$	09V	116*	Small-Trek	1/1
614-756-4685	OH	Carroll	C. Bruckelmeier	R	2	85	The Bbs	
614-773-2423	OH	Chillicothe	Jerry Arnold	WV	9D	101	South of Bauder	8/1
614-837-3896	OH	Pickerington	Fred Forrest	W	9U	55	Aspencade	2/
614-846-1274	OH	Columbus	Chris Bugosh	Q	9D	85	CompuLink	3/
614-878-5772	OH	Columbus	Tom Pugh	L	9V	98	StairwaytoHeavn	1/1
614-885-9829	OH	Columbus	Craig Wright	B	9U	29	Columbus C.Soc	
615-282-3449	TN	Johnson City	Alan Hughes	Q	09V	108	The Rx	1/1
615-292-0639	TN	Nashville	Chris Sherrod	F	2	104	Nashville Conn.	1/1

						First on List # ↓ *(see above)*	
Phone	*State*	*City*	*Sysop*	*T/S*			*Name, Features*
615-334-9800	TN	Ten Mile	Danny Carter	B$	2		Pleasant Hill	8/2
615-337-4628	TN	Sweetwater	Greg McCullough	X	9D	82	CritCondition	1/
615-339-0350	TN	Cleveland	Steve Stanfield	B	9U	63	SkyLine	2/
615-359-5995	TN	Lewisburg	Tony Vinelli	W	02	113	Sons of Liberty	1/1
615-373-2795	TN	Nashville	Bret Teegarden	W	19V	97	SOUNDing BOARD	3/1
615-383-0727	TN	Nashville	B. Cunningham	T$	2	80	Nashvle Xchg	25/20
615-385-9328	TN	Nashville	Glen Harness	O	9U	92	StrawberryFlds	1/
615-399-1801	TN	Nashville	John Farrar	L	9V	103	Basement	1/1
615-458-9099	TN	Philadelphia	Mike Weaver	B	09V	100	NITE-LITE	3/2
615-476-2874	TN	Cleveland	Premo Mondone	B	2	62	PC Solutions	1/
615-478-2890	TN	Cleveland	Doug Carpenter	B	9U	72	PC Junction	3/
615-526-3347	TN	Cookeville	Del Robinson	O	9U	34	Cumberland	
615-526-8463	TN	Cookeville	Rich King	W	2	60	King's Corner	
615-527-3994	TN	Lynnville	Andy Chunn	X	19V	108	RHS "RAIDER"	2/1
615-531-2177	TN	Knoxville	Ed Dial	B	9V	56	Volunteer	16/3
615-531-8789	TN	Knoxville	Cory Wright	P	9H	71	RisingConnx	
615-586-4913	TN	Morristown	James lee	B	19V	110	TECH-NET	8/2
615-586-8260	TN	Talbott	Keith Oakley	B	9HV	81	Talbott	7/3
615-624-1442	TN	Chattanooga	Paul McDougall	B	29V	112	Freestyle	28/3
615-625-0627	TN	Parrot'vle	David Winters	R	2	87	TN Data Xchg	6/
615-626-1620	TN	Tazewell	Ted Freeman	B$	9H		Micronet	3/
615-647-1146	TN	Clarksville	Matt Stanton	GV	9U	99	Andromeda	3/
615-674-8741	TN	White Pine	Michael Manting	W	19VO	116*	On My Honor	2/1
615-723-1867	TN	Manchester	Lee Smith	B$	2		MIDIMaze	11/2
615-727-6214	TN	Mountain Cty	R. Brotschul	W	09D	114	Outer Limits	2/1
615-744-0024	TN	Athens	A.D. Wade	L$	9D	92	TUTORBOARD	36/1
615-775-5449	TN	Dayton	Haydn Doughty	S	09U	116*	StarShip Dayton	8/1
615-824-3871	TN	Nashville	Stephen Tenhet	W	09O	112	Orion's Rift	1/1
615-831-1758	TN	Nashville	Edward Locke	Q	09V	115	Rings of Saturn	2/1
615-869-3657	TN	Harrogate	Brent Ward	W$	29V	110	Boone's Trail	2/1
615-872-0757	TN	Nashville	Dennis Wynne	B	9V	34	Troll'sCave	9/2
615-890-8715	TN	Murfreesboro	Larry Reeves	B	9C	68	Heart of Tenn.	13/3
615-892-8834	TN	Chattanooga	Bill Crawford	S	09V	114	TLR Systems	9/1
516-922-7214	NY	Oyster Bay	P. Gildersleeve	B	19	110	Enclave Book	1/
615-966-3574	TN	Knoxville	Sean Dudley	B	9V	56	DataWorld	16/
615-970-2966	TN	Knoxville	Clay Wynn	R$	2	26	East Tenn PCUG	
615-982-6537	TN	Alcoa	Rickie Belitz	B	9HV	34	Data-CompInfo	2/
615-983-8232	TN	Maryville	Tom Wallace	W	9V	78	DiskFix	10/2
615-984-9396	TN	Maryville	Charles Reed	W	09V	105	Neutron Bomb	1/1
616-235-2313	MI	Grand Rapids	Rodney Fulk	O	9U	90	R.I.P.	1/2
616-243-8663	MI	Grand Rapids	Dave McIntyre	W	9D	86	City Heat	3/2
616-327-8912	M	Portage	Mike Capp	B$	9C	82	Dim.Overview	12/
616-343-1322	MI	Kalamazoo	Curt Gray	M	9V	100	AML	55/64
616-343-7944	MI	Kalamazoo	Bob Runowski	J	19VO	115	Board Walk	2/1
616-373-4231	MI	Kalamazoo	Stephen Barclay	W	09V	116*	Taz's	2/1
616-375-2083	MI	Kalamazoo	Robert Adams	W	9	95	Graphics Shop	3/2
616-429-3414	MI	Wyoming	Dick Castanie	W	2	55	Trillion	1/

					First on List # | v		
Phone	*State*	*City*	*Sysop*	*T/S*	*(see above)*	*Name, Features*	
616-796-8761	MI	Big Rapids	Tom Roberts	R	2	72	PC Connx	7/
616-843-7064	MI	Ludington	Dick Soli	W$	02	113	IBMe	7/1
616-844-0151	MI	Nunica	Rob Kittredge	B	19D	111	7th Heaven	2/1
616-897-4953	MI	Lowell	Clark Jahnke	L	29U	106	River City	2/1
616-946-5885	MI	TraverseCity	Kurt Smith	R$	2	98	CatHeadBayMine	1/6
616-956-7072	MI	Kentwood	Chris Pelton	O	19V	116*	Xest	1/1
616-963-9092	MI	Battle Creek	Peter terSteeg	X	9HV	83	Final Frontier	
616-969-2430	MI	Battle Creek	Byron Plato	X	19V	116*	Plato's Playgnd	3/1
616-969-9416	M	Battle Creek	Warren Witt	W	09V	112	ObSeSSioN bBs	5/2
617-229-2915	MA	Burlington	Jim Little	O	2	26	Alpha Software	
617-235-6303	MA	Wellesley	Jon Anderson	B	9U	86	Boston Gas,med	3/
617-244-7053	MA	Newton	Steve Woodward	B	2	86	BetaBBS	1/
617-288-1117	MA	Dorchester	John Francis	F	2	91	Effigy Sys,med	1/
617-332-5584	MA	Boston	D. Chamberlain	T	2	06	Boston Computer Soc	
617-335-1408	MA	Weymouth	Fred O'Grady	R	09HB	114	WeymouthAirship	2/1
617-354-8873	MA	Cambridge	Brian Miller	B	9V	29	Channel 1<tm>	70/66
617-397-8888	MA	Malden	Ron Doty	W$	29V	104	<BOSTON ROCKS!>	22/3
617-439-0399	MA	Boston	Steve Brettler	B	19V	115	E.P.Levine	3/1
617-451-5327	MA	Boston	Chas Crawford	B	9V	82	Cssn for Blind	1/
617-545-6239	MA	Scituate	Karl Johnson	B	9U	66	GardenSpot	3/
617-631-4029	MA	Marblehead	M. Helfrich	W	19B	96	DataWorks	13/1
617-674-2345	MA	Lexington	Chris White	M	2	85	ArgusCompXch	13/57
617-770-9451	MA	Boston	S. Greczkowski	Q	9	95	Cheers!	6/2
617-786-9788	MA	Boston Area	Robert Gorrill	O	9U	26	BCS Telecom	
617-899-9483	MA	Waltham	Joseph Teller	X$	19?	116	SilverMage's	21/1
617-938-5408	MA	Woburn	Jim Spheekas	M	9U	84	GECS Support	2/
617-961-7870	MA	Randolph	Michael Flood	B	?9V	115	NewEngland Onl	7/1
618-233-2315	IL	Belleville	Tom Morgan	B	2	26	The Phoenix	/2
618-233-9821	IL	Belleville	Robert Pucci	X	2	95	Free World Net	1/
618-234-9260	IL	Swansea	Scott Happel	V	29D	116*	Ice House	7/1
618-244-9565	IL	Mt.Vernon	Jerry Hook	P	9U	80	Engage	3/
618-288-6280	IL	Edwardsville	David Brown	R	2	29	The Asylum	
618-397-1789	IL	Caseyville	Bob Paarlberg	R	2	56	SIL-NET	
618-398-2305	IL	Fairview Hts	Gordon Anson	B$V	9U	46	Wizard's Lair	20/3
618-453-8511	IL	Carbondale	Charles Strusz	R	9U	72	InfoQuest	12/
618-684-3990	IL	Murphysboro	Marc Albrycht	W	9U	73	HardDiskCafe	7/
618-692-6764	IL	Edwardsville	Mike Eberhart	V	09O	116*	Wayne's World	1/1
618-746-0916	IL	Scott AFB	Curt Claybaugh	X	29V	113*	Access	12/2
618-746-9176	IL	Belleville	Robert Pucci	B	09V	114	Free Wld Netwk	13/2
618-942-4508	IL	Herrin	John Lloyd	X	2	68	Taurus	1/
619-243-1332	CA	Victorville	Jon Booth	W	29V	114	HighDesertComp	3/1
619-243-8081	CA	Victorville	Troy Getty	W	9D	89	ETECH-HighDesrt	22/4
619-253-4437	CA	Barstow	Bill Turner	W	9U	87	///AVCOMM\\\	9/
619-256-3545	CA	Barstow	Lyle Skjerve	B	9U	26	Barstow BBS	14/1
619-278-7361	CA	San Diego	Brenda Donovan	W	9U	76	PacRimInfo	3/
619-279-3921	CA	San Diego	Steve Wilmet	W	9U	43	NightOwl,Ham	
619-284-8729	CA	San Diego	Kris Lewis	X	9U	69	Traders' World	1/

						First on List # | v (see above)	
Phone	State	City	Sysop	T/S			Name, Features
619-287-5828	CA	San Diego	Mike Mollerus	P	9H	40	CatholicInfonet
619-298-4027	CA	San Diego	Steve Tom	B$	9U	62	[mediaprfsonly]
619-339-2515	CA	El Centro	Ron Ratliff	W	9U	90	NAFBBS 2/
619-367-9208	CA	29 Palms	Jim Kornegay	W	9U	59	DataByteCompSvc 2/
619-371-1665	CA	Ridgecrest	Rod Kenly	B$	09D	26	Computing Tech 13/2
619-431-5956	CA	Carlsbad	Elden Gaines	B	19D	107	Stac Tech Sup 1/2
619-439-6624	CA	Oceanside	Rainer Mueller	F$	09VO	112	Mainstreet Data 7/3
619-442-3595	C	San Diego	Bob Bailey	B	9U	34	Checkpoint
619-447-1008	CA	El Cajon	Don Presten	B	9C	84	Ballyhoo 2/
619-447-4095	CA	El Cajon	Wm. Westlake	Q	2	85	CajonZone
619-450-2179	CA	San Diego	Dail Fail	B	2	26	Softw Prod Int
619-455-5226	CA	San Diego	John Newlin	W	2	50	New-Ware,sh/w
619-460-6398	CA	La Mesa	Jack Clayton	X	02	106	ToughToPiegonHl 1/1
619-466-9505	CA	San Diego	Gary Ryno	Q	9U	76	Gandalf's 1/
619-532-8022	CA	San Diego	Alex Cook	B	9U	73	BalboaNHosp
619-535-9580	CA	San Diego	Brad Chesbro	B	9U	62	Mushin 3/
619-670-3040	CA	Spring Vly	M. McNelly	S	09VO	116*	Rudy's Place 1/1
619-692-1961	CA	San Diego	Don Saba	B	9U	34	Sabaline
619-728-4318	CA	Fallbrook	Bob Laszko	B	9U	63	File Bank 15/
619-864-1468	CA	Palm Springs	Michael Simmons	B$	9V	104	DataPort NIS 30/5
619-951-5456	CA	Victorville	R.Sullenberger	W	9U	88	Back Door 7/1
701-258-7502	ND	Bismarck	John Roswick	R	2	26	RBBS Bismarck
701-266-5463	ND	Rock Lake	Kevin Krueger	W	9V	99	The N.E.R.D. Bd 14/1
701-293-5973	ND	Fargo	Jim Grettum	R	9U	06	RBBS of Fargo 7/
701-594-8311	ND	Grand Forks	David Moore	V	9D	96	Tech BBS 1/1
701-772-5399	ND	Grand Forks	John Lundell	B	9D	89	City Lites 50/6
701-839-0181	ND	Minot	Steve Swiss	O	9V	100	Blazing Icicle 1/1
701-839-6024	ND	Minot	Dana Amann	B	9U	62	KAT BBS 4/
701-852-8744	ND	Minot	Joe Uhrmacher	R	9U	64	Country Micro 7/
702-242-1794	NV	Las Vegas	J. Denis	B	29D	45*	DPS 6/1
702-334-2257	NV	Reno	Jim Poston	X	2	47	Reno Traffic
702-359-1138	NV	Reno	John Morris	R	9VU	26	AbandonedLand 14/3
702-368-0846	NV	Las Vegas	George Moshier	Q	9U	89	ShW Scanners 1/
702-383-9939	NV	Las Vegas	Rick Cross	W$	9V	92	Pub Access I.S. 88/11
702-431-2264	NV	Las Vegas	Dennis Kesner	G	2	81	2-Bros West 2/
702-433-7940	NV	Las Vegas	Hank Stempien	W	19V	108	Vegas Light 4/1
702-438-3625	NV	Las Vegas	Dennis Makowski	W	2	64	[mail reg]
702-588-0315	NV	Stateline	Bill Martin	B	09V	90	Lightning III 30/2
702-646-0914	NV	Las Vegas	Stephen Gordon	X	19V	107	StarGateSolutns 3/1
702-647-9266	NV	Las Vegas	Dave Hough	R	2	85	The Eyeballer
702-677-8627	NV	Reno	Bob Lucas	QV	2	101	other Side II 1/1
702-747-8411	NV	Reno	Bill Protz	T	2	93	RenoTahoe onlne 1/2
702-825-5357	NV	Reno	Jeff Hyle	O	09V	106	Heavy Metal,! 8/1
702-826-5968	NV	Reno	Steve Beban	R	19V	87	InterSection 3/1
702-849-2207	NV	Carson City	Jeff Grant	B$	09D	26	MegaSystem 45/9
702-871-7983	NV	Las Vegas	Ronda Ryan	W	2	104	!BUY THIS BBS! 1/1
702-875-4037	NV	Las Vegas	Teresa Schoen	M	2	97	Purch.Mgrs.Info 1/2

Phone	State	City	Sysop	T/S		First on List # l v (see above)	Name, Features	
702-876-6478	NV	Las Vegas	Gus Gustavson	R	2	51	DesertWinds	
703-204-8436	VA	Fairfax	Glenn McAtee	B	19V	107	Micro Center	5/1
703-241-7100	VA	Arlington	B. Scarbrough	M$	29?	108	Crystal Quill	6/40
703-241-7980	VA	Arlington	Joe Ahlgren	R	09V	111	GeoClock	1/2
703-254-2099	VA	Buchanan	Fred Balmer	T	09V	116*	Avaitor Heaven	2/1
703-255-1285	VA	Vienna	Frank Dorer	R	2	51	Liberty Hall	3/2
703-256-4777	VA	Arlington	Blaine Korcel	R	2	50	Novac,Astro	1/3
703-257-1583	VA	Manassas	Darin Ramey	B	29D	112	Outpost	10/1
703-257-7524	VA	Manassas	Mark Webster	X	29V	114	BUBBASystems]	18/1
703-276-0904	VA	Ft. Myer	Art Kent	X	2	98	Jackal's Domain	1/1
703-280-5490	VA	Springfield	Arnold Smokler	R$	9M	29	Micro-C	3/
703-322-2529	VA	Bluefield	Mark Turner	V	9V	95	Outer Limits	1/1
703-323-6423	VA	Burke	Gregg Snyder	R	9U	34	DGS Systems	
703-323-7654	VA	Fairfax	Bill Andrus	O	9U	74	SysExch,OS/2	
703-325-0748	VA	Alexandria	Steve Bartlett	B	2	45	JAGNET	
703-328-0028	VA	Wise	Gary Slemp	R	9U	74	6H-HermitHole	3/2
703-328-6915	VA	Wise	David Allio	X	09V	116*	Vivid Images	2/3
703-342-6386	VA	Roanoke	Robert Sink	B	9U	34	16 Bit Exchange	1/
703-348-1423	VA	Lexington	Eddie Gebhard	W	09VV	107	PC PowerHouse	8/1
703-352-5412	VA	Fairfax	Paul Cutrona	X	19D	109	SideWayz	2/1
703-361-4872	VA	Manassas	Marion Royal	R	09V	85	Royal Flush	2/1
703-366-4299	VA	Roanoke	John Campbell	B	19V	113	SparkiesMachine	6/2
703-373-0738	VA	Fred'burg	Dahmen/Surfer	W	9U	86	Bits n PCs	1/
703-373-9289	VA	Falmouth	John Schreiber	B	09V	111	Link!	29/2
703-381-9758	VA	Christiansbg	Bob Brisco	Q	9V	104	I X _ Y _	1/1
703-385-3114	VA	Fairfax	R. Siddiqui	R	02	106	Swap Shop	7/2
703-415-0134	VA	Arlington	S. Greenwald	X	19V	115	<Crystal Aerie>	3/3
703-425-2505	VA	McLean	Jeffrey Morley	B	9	26	Interconnect,!	
703-425-6640	VA	Fairfax	Paul Michaelson	R	2	89	Frostbyte Falls	3/
703-427-2138	VA	Roanoke	Edward Wood	B$	09V	113	Mountain Air	40/4
703-430-5824	VA	Sterling	Moore&Peeples	B	2	79	Pencil Pusher	7/2
703-430-7425	VA	Sterling	Ken Letson	F	2	100	Mid-Atlantic	2/1
703-433-0585	VA	Harris'burg	Tim Brandenburg	Y	2	89	Nocturnal Me	3/
703-451-9509	VA	Burke	Bob Hampton	R	9V	87	S3-Tech	
703-471-8010	VA	Herndon	Raymond Moreau	T	9F	29	HerndonByteXchg	
703-503-9410	VA	Fairfax	Bob Mason	B	2	51	RemJem OnLine	
703-524-1837	VA	Arlington	Kurt Riegel	R	2	34	Enviro,science	
703-525-1458	VA	Arlington	Charles Stuart	W	09V	116*	Ship To Shore	5/1
703-528-7617	VA	Arlington	Dick Holt	O	19V	26	BBS\APL	1/1
703-532-3051	VA	Falls Church	Dan Garnitz	P	2	67	Pedalers	2/
703-532-7143	VA	Arlington	Jay Falvey	B$	19V	107	Arl. Softw Exch	30/5
703-549-2814	VA	Alexandria	Tom Engle	Q	09V	105	Crunchland	3/2
703-560-5616	VA	Dunn	John Burns	B	9U	64	Lifes Like That	1/2
703-590-0049	VA	Woodbridge	Mike Feinberg	R	9U	86	Crossroads	2/
703-591-9380	VA	Fairfax	C. Carmichael	B	9V	99	Struppi's BBS	2/2
703-620-0851	VA	Oakton	Mike Benson	X	9V	83	Electronic Age	2/2
703-620-5418	VA	Oakton	Miles Hoover	T	9U	72	WashZephyr	1/

Phone	State	City	Sysop	T/S		First on List # | v (see above)	Name, Features	
703-641-9218	VA	Falls Church	Ralph Maya	W	9U	83	Illusions	3/2
703-642-8704	VA	Alexandria	John Choi	W$V	9D	99	InfiniteDataSce	100/17
703-642-9573	VA	Annandale	Sirman Celayir	R	19V	112	AsterProAstrol	1/1
703-644-9776	VA	Springfield	Mark Madden	BV	9D	100	BeltwayBandit's	9/3
703-648-1841	VA	Reston	Tony McClenny	B	9U	26+	Va. Connx	19/5
703-658-0250	VA	Annandale	John Gentzel	W	2	73	MyLittleBBS	
703-659-2227	VA	Stafford	Bob Bush	B$	9	101	Lazy Day's	29/10
703-659-9246	VA	Stafford	Jim Riggs	R	2	72	DeadEnd	1/
703-667-3530	VA	Winchester	Miller&Foreman	B	9U	62	Another Dimen	5/
703-679-3009	VA	Norton	Jeff Kiser	R	2	101	EntertainmentUd	1/1
703-680-9269	VA	Dale City	Bruce Jackson	R	29D	46	Break>>>=East=>	40/3
703-685-0019	VA	Arlington	Irve Towers	B	9U	56	The Hub	8/2
703-690-0669	VA	Springfield	Joe Klemmer	X	09V	111	My UnKnown BBS	1/1
703-698-2084	VA	Fairfax	Brian Hardy	W	9V	100	TSS	1/1
703-709-5417	VA	Fairfax	Pete Chandler	F	2	78	Pete's	17/2
703-709-6436	VA	Fairfax	Mike Sullivan	M	2	93	CapitolHillHub	2/5
703-720-1624	VA	Stafford	Duane Brown	Q	09V	110	End of the Line	2/1
703-722-3398	VA	Winchester	Robert Marcus	U	9U	80	RapidStrikeWest	3/
703-731-0601	VA	Radford	Danny Cook	Q	12	107	DockSide BBS	3/1
703-750-7809	VA	Annandale	Wes Merchant	R	2	06	Capitol PCUG	
703-754-7392	VA	Gainesville	Bud Kreiger	W	9D	100	BEST o'the BEST	20/2
703-756-6109	VA	Falls Church	M. Crockford	R	2	83	BXR InfoCorn	2/
703-759-2001	VA	Great Falls	Charles Swett	B	19V	106	CONSUMER BOARD	12/1
703-771-4158	VA	Leesburg	Joe Bartling	B$	19V	87	SQLWare	25/10
703-771-9771	VA	Leesburg	Robert Hayward	B	19V	110	Pavlov's Dog	17/2
703-774-4667	VA	Roanoke	Mike Overacker	B	9U	99	PhotoStar	2/1
703-780-1180	VA	Alexandria	LarryRobertson	R	9V	89	ELECTROTECH	2/1
703-787-9828	VA	Reston	Arline Brecher	W	19V	108	Alt. Med. Conn.	2/1
703-791-6198	VA	Manassas	Dick Miller	R	2	34	DOS Spitzen	
703-803-6420	VA	Fairfax	Allen Roberts	P	2	86	UFOria,confcs	1/
703-823-1162	VA	Alexandria	Scott L. Nelson	X	19V	98	Looking Glass	2/1
703-830-2989	VA	Centreville	D. Sanderson	W	19V	112	NON-REV FLYER	1/1
703-836-0748	VA	Alexandria	Bill Walsh	B	9D	DC	Info Exch	3/2
703-854-6760	VA	Rhoadesville	Andy Hoffman	G	9V	102	Locust Grove	1/1
703-878-0029	VA	Woodbridge	Tiff Reardon	B	29V	111	Tech Connect	12/10
703-878-3664	VA	Woodbridge	Jim Woodhams	R	29V	112*	Woody's Win Whs	4/1
703-886-7825	VA	Staunton	Mark Chickering	B	9U	72	Terrapin Flyer	2/2
703-898-7179	VA	Fred'burg	Jason Taylor	Q	09VB	116*	Bird's Nest	7/1
703-899-0020	VA	Fred'burg	Kevin Graham	Q	9D	84	CrackerBarrel	10/1
703-929-4429	VA	Bent Mt.	John Wilson	X	2	100	FinAide College	1/1
703-931-4902	VA	Arlington	P. Moerschell	X$	02	114	DC Matchmaker	2/18
703-941-3572	VA	Alexandria	Bill Johnson	B	2	50	TechNet	4/
703-941-4041	VA	Alexandria	Rick Welshans	BV	9D	100	Warped Board	2/1
703-951-9066	VA	Blacksburg	boB Gage	B$	19D	116*	Sybil	16/3
703-951-9262	VA	Blacksburg	John Glackin	Q	19OV	111	WildlifePresrve	1/1
703-953-3187	VA	Blacksburg	Smapp & Gooden	B	2	60	Betelgeuse	
703-962-9253	VA	Alexandria	Steve Overton	W	2	74	Indirections	

					First on List # | v		
Phone	*State*	*City*	*Sysop*	*T/S*	(see above)	*Name, Features*	
703-971-2665	VA	Alexandria	Jack Miller	R	2	84	Miller's Light	1/
703-972-3920	VA	Spotsylvania	Shaun Watson	Q	09VB	116*	HyPeD uP	12/1
703-978-6360	VA	Fairfax	Ken Goosens	R	9	15	Your Place	
703-993-2219	VA	Fairfax	W. Grotophorst	W	2	89	GMUtant Online	2/
704-342-2333	NC	Charlotte	Ron Alspaugh	W$	19D	107	Exchange	24/3
704-362-0550	NC	Charlotte	P. Hollowell	X	19V	116*	Gate Euphoria	1/1
704-365-8745	NC	Charlotte	Ross Lafleur	Q	19B	112	Fantasy Island	2/1
704-437-9937	NC	Morganton	Mark Berry	F	2		CaroWare	1/
704-464-7235	NC	Newton	Kevin Teague	S	2	95	The HIDEOUT	1/2
704-492-2081	NC	Mocksville	Rob Roesch	P	9U	68	HOTware	2/1
704-527-3379	NC	Charlotte	Dave Harrison	B	9U	55	Tholian Web	8/3
704-531-7375	NC	Charlotte	Jeff Tucker	W	29V	113	Real Estate Shp	1/1
704-535-7361	NC	Charlotte	Andrew Delisle	J	9V	104	Matrix	2/1
704-541-9842	NC	Charlotte	Blaine Schmidt	W	09D	113	Moobasi Optics	14/2
704-543-6641	NC	Charlotte	Todd Faulkner	Q	9U	64	Comstar	9/4
704-554-1496	NC	Charlotte	Joseph Rybaczek	V	9U	97	Funny Farm East	3/1
704-563-5857	NC	Charlotte	Sam Grier	B	9D	92	CarolinaForum	10/2
704-567-9513	NC	Charlotte	Ed Marquis	Q	19D	63	Transporter Rm	80/8
704-637-6906	NC	Salisbury	Wayne Ashworth	R	9D	55	NC EMS BBS	1/1
704-667-8021	NC	Asheville	Herb Reith	W	9H	67	Armed Forces	
704-739-8093	NC	Kings Mtn	Robert Dalton	R	9U	87	Terminal Zone	2/
705-749-2345	ON	Peterborough	Paul Stewart	Q$	09V	110	DownloadDungeon	20/3
704-784-2428	NC	Midland	Mike Britt	X	29V	113	LegionsValhalla	3/1
704-827-2778	NC	Gastonia	Mark Compton	R	9U	65	OmniScope	18/2
704-859-6985	NC	Tryon	Bill Grubbs	F	2	76	ACC,+CDR	7/2
704-864-2282	NC	Gastoina	Mark Compton	R	2		Omni-Scope	2/
704-982-9223	NC	Albemarle	Chris Cranford	W	09D	100	King's Dominion	1/1
705-327-7629	ON	Orillia	Peter Ellis	B$	2	75	Encode Online	4/
705-722-8194	ON	Barrie	Robin Wells	B$	9D	96	CentralOntario	54/5
705-942-8370	ON	S. Ste Marie	Mario Dulisse	Q	2	45	DogStar	
706-235-7235	GA	Rome	Russell Pool	B	09D	113	Pool Hall	4/2
706-543-2649	GA	Athens	Michael Tift	B	19V	49	S.L.I.M.E.	4/1
706-561-7359	GA	Columbus	Eldon Wakefield	T	19D	10	Country Store	12/2
706-650-8261	GA	Martinez	David Sosnin	Q	29D	110	Genesis	14/2
706-673-4436	GA	Rocky Face	Gary M Hasty	U	19V	107	Comfy Chair!	1/1
706-687-7309	GA	Columbus	Bill Jones	T	19D	47	Columbus Connx	15/4
706-694-3295	GA	Cohutta	Dick Stein	W	19D	112	Hi-Tech Gateway	3/1
706-769-0061	GA	Bogart	Greg Shaffer	X	9D	81	Route 66	40/2
706-798-3864	GA	Hephzibah	Bob Kiernan	R	9D	85	Beehive	12/2
706-820-9157	GA	Lookout Mtn	Paul Elliott	Q$	19VO	102	Intl. Bus. Exch	1/2
706-860-5070	GA	Martinez	Duncan Stewart	J	9H	102	Public's Domain	1/1
707-257-2338	CA	Napa	Dick Wolff	R	09DO	26	Grapvine	19/3
707-257-6502	CA	Napa	Steve Austin	W	9D	83	N.V.W-cat	5/
707-263-6612	CA	Lakeport	George Ramos	B	19DU	114	Clever Endeavor	8/2
707-263-8581	CA	Lakeport	Randy Sun	B	29D	37	Sigma Ind.	63/10
707-263-9517	CA	Lakeport	Danny Hedstrom	U	9D	104	Laser Disc	6/1
707-424-1134	CA	Travis AFB	Ralph Sielaff	W	2	98	60th SecPolice	1/2

Phone	State	City	Sysop	T/S	First on List # | v (see above)	Name, Features
707-427-0277	CA	Fairfield	Chuck Dobbs	U$	09V	96	Dobbs Ent'prise	69/4
707-428-3668	CA	Fairfield	Bill Neal	Q	2	81	BowTieAff'r	1/
707-437-2956	CA	Travis AFB	David Veenstra	W	2	98	D&D Diving Adv.	1/1
707-437-6787	CA	Fairfield	Ed Winters	O	9V	91	Solano Comm PC
707-444-9203	CA	Eureka	Bob Sullivan	T$	9D	34	PDSE home	2/4
707-451-3323	CA		Stephen Cannon	W	9U	88	DarkSideMoon	6/3
707-459-9058	CA	Willits	G. Youngblood	X	09V	113	CompleteSolutn	1/1
707-537-1227	CA	Santa Rosa	Abe Alexander	B	?9V	111	Into The Night	15/1
707-539-4050	CA	Santa Rosa	J. Hochstetler	R	09D	108	A.C.M.E.	9/1
707-545-0746	CA	Santa Rosa	Don Kulha	X	9D	74	Sonoma Online	8/1
707-552-0462	CA	Vallejo	Joe Martin	W	9U	46	Power Station	/7
707-575-4367	CA	Forestville	Don Watkins	A	9HV	34	CC-BBS
707-644-0803	CA	Vallejo	Rich Sornborger	Y	9D	93	Nimrod's Palace	7/2
707-725-9612	CA	Fortuna	Ryan Katri	C	9H	29	M.I.T.	2/
707-746-8490	CA	Benicia	George Thomas	Q	9U	96	GridCom BBS	1/1
707-769-1624	CA	Petaluma	James Boyer	F	19D	115	StarBase 515	13/1
707-769-1732	CA	Petaluma	Abel Jeffcoat	X	19V	116*	Computer Exprs	12/1
707-778-8841	CA	Petaluma	Julie D. Buerg	B	9H	51	Motherboard	2/2
707-778-8944	CA	Petaluma	Vern Buerg	B	9H	26+	VOR BBS	1/
707-795-4939	CA	Cotati	Thomas Tuerke	A	2	72	Gravesend	2/
707-838-4483	CA	Windsor	Bob Brumley	R	09D	108	CrackerParadise	35/3
708-208-0662	IL	Geneva	James Karaganis	W$	29D	108	Grey Matter	20/2
708-223-2344	IL	Grayslake	Bob Zimmerman	F	9D	88	Mainframe	3/2
708-232-1250	IL	Geneva	Ed Curlin	B$	9D	24	Windmill	2/2
708-299-1296	IL	Des Plaines	Tom Young	Q	9D	96	Eye Resources	8/3
708-301-2872	IL	Lockport	Pat Aquino	W	9D	84	BBS USA	7/10
708-352-1035	IL	LaGrange Pk	Loren Jones	R	9D	06	RBBS-PC of Chi	11/9
708-356-7895	IL	Lindenhurst	Keith Moeller	R	2	83	ProfitMargin	1/
708-382-3904	IL	Barrington	Paul Hildmann	M	19V	112	CreativeThought	2/1
708-403-2826	IL	Orland Park	Jordan/Anvin	R	9V	67	Stillwaters
708-423-1468	IL	Oak Lawn	Rich Petroskey	W	09V	106	Rick's Cafe	15/2
708-433-7509	IL	HighlandPark	Tzee-Poor	L	2	83	Squirrels Nest
708-437-8387	IL	Mt Prospect	John Mc Climent	Q	9U	95	Daze Inn	1/
708-470-0199	IL	Morton Grove	Jay Rothschild	R	9V	98	1BBS	3/2
708-513-1034	IL	St Charles	Steve Mills	B	09D	26	MidWest	39/8
708-516-8679	IL	Cary	Curt Zimmerman	W	19D	115*	HOT MIX	32/4
708-530-0194	IL	Elmhurst	Terry Batt	R	2	91	CAEUG BBS	1/
708-548-2481	IL	Grayslake	Ken Buchholz	M	2	75	WashTowneCrier	1/2
708-566-6183	IL	Mundelein	Scott Yaskin	M$	09V	100	Mulligan'sPlace	18/16
708-628-0330	IL	Addison	Rob Hopkins	M	9V	103	Maranatha!	2/2
708-632-0884	IL	ArlingtonHts	Mike Wilson	W	9U	99	Great Northern	3/1
708-674-1638	IL	Lincolnwood	William Knopp	B$	9H	26	Bill's
708-681-4722	IL	Melrose Park	Jim Reed	B	29V	107	SuburbanFileExc	12/1
708-682-9223	IL	GlendaleHgts	Joe Zozzaro	MV	2	101	Collector Conn.	2/4
708-689-0084	IL	Gt Lakes	Steve McCarthy	W	9U	89	Absolute BBS	2/10
708-690-9860	IL	Winfield	Larry Spiegel	W	9V	86	Job-Link,jobs	/2
708-697-1606	IL	Elgin	Rich Dougherty	B	9D	80	Richware,sh/w	3/2

Phone	State	City	Sysop	T/S	First on List #|v (see above)	Name, Features	
708-705-7094	IL	Palatine	Eddy Hicks	G	19V	107	EMTech Systems	1/1
708-705-7263	IL	Chicago	Andrew Patrick	R	19V	114	Home Brew Univ	1/1
708-776-1062	IL	Palatine	David Gibbs	Q	9D	57	Midrange System	1/2
708-820-0704	IL	Aurora	Steve Schacht	M	02	112	FitnessResource	1/4
708-820-8344	IL	Aurora	Steve Williams	B$	9U	77	Aquila	25/
708-843-2809	IL	Hoff Estates	Gene Plantz	X$	09D	115	IBBS #1	60/16
708-872-8086	IL	Zion	John Hodal	B	2	26	Lakes Region	3/
708-882-4227	IL	Chicago	Gene Plantz	X$	9U	06	IBBS,a.-4228	/13
708-916-1200	IL	Glen Ellyn	C. DeConcilis	D	9	48	Lattice,C,DOS	
708-949-6434	IL	Mundelein	Dave Nosek	B$	9U	72	SoundMgmt Midi	2/
708-953-4922	IL	Lombard	John Hines	B$	19V	45*	Scintillation	30/3
708-961-1658	IL	Naperville	Rob Fischer	B	19D	113	OS/2 Solution	4/2
708-964-1084	IL	Downer's Grv	T. Wisnionski	B	9U	34	ServiceMaster	3/
708-969-9380	IL	Westmont	Steve Strunk	BV	9V	100	<Blood & Guts>	4/2
708-972-0628	IL	Chicago	Dick Lain	R$	2	08	Bolingbrook	
708-991-3894	IL	Hoffman Ests	Tony Antonucci	A	9D	84	DigitalDynamics	16/3
709-596-4536	NF	Carbonear	Kenneth Murray	Q	2	96	Cheyennes	23/2
712-111-1111	NB	Note that no fee is charged for this list ever!						
712-737-3960	IA	Orange City	Travis Noteboom	L	09V	106	Virtual Reality	1/1
712-758-3483	IA	Ocheyedan	Richard Jordan	R	29V	104	Exegete's Haven	13/1
712-864-3189	IA	Armstrong	Daniel Sherack	F	9V	95	HOT WIRE	2/1
713-242-6370	TX	Sugarland	Rich Devinney	W$	2	72	Bulldozer	1/
713-355-6107	TX	Houston area	Mike Meyer	B$	9U	54	Data Warp	11/
713-395-3101	TX	Houston	Bob Koscak	B	9V	95	Bob's File Xch	1/2
713-421-3994	TX	Baytown	Bob Carpenter	P	2	45	Plain & Simple	
713-438-1219	TX	MissouriCity	Bill Huther	O	9V	56	Investor$ Edge	1/
713-440-7364	TX	Houston	Joe Lincoln	B	2	55	LINX	
713-466-1525	TX	Houston	David Bonds	B	29D	106	Cutting Edge	3/1
713-470-8987	TX	LaPorte	Danny Wofford	O	2	47	Stargazer	
713-480-8403	TX	Webster	Andrich/Vrooman	R	2	78	Money Pit,GIFs	4/
713-482-7080	TX	Houston	Rob Van Burkleo	W	9V	73	The Roost	2/
713-495-3730	TX	Houston	Roger Wise	A	2	89	Macaw'sRoost	3/
713-520-1569	TX	Houston	Reggy Hirsch	B	9HV	42	YeOldeBailey	12/2
713-530-1166	TX	Houston	Tim Barth	A	2	58	Zeitgeist,!	2/
713-530-5300	TX	Houston	Lonnie Hortick	P	2	58	HoustCatholic	
713-537-0702	TX	Houston	Frank Dear	B	9U	79	Bits&Pieces	4/
713-550-8105	TX	Houston	Gloria Short	X	19V	110	Brain Storm	2/2
713-590-6267	TX	Houston	James Holmes	R	9V	103	Micro Archives	50/3
713-661-3399	TX	Houston	Dana Wood	O	9U	26	Last Stop,!	
713-682-5600	TX	Houston	Stephen Sheward	M	29V	112	Cyber Chat	3/14
713-726-0445	TX	Houston	Roger Williams	O	99V	109	My New BBS	2/1
713-728-2199	TX	Houston	Mike Lenker	R	19V	111	The "X"	2/1
713-771-2802	TX	Houston	Pat Whelton	B	9H	56	Abend,Tandy	
713-781-3875	TX	Houston	J. A. Crossman	O	12	107	Castle of Dream	1/1
713-837-1103	TX	Baytown	Ray Cramer	B	29D	34	DogHouse	15/1
713-856-7010	TX	Houston	Donald Shelton	W	9D	91	Aida's AirBoat	12/4
713-923-6418	TX	Houston	Steve Moore	R	19UV	114	Home Brew Univ	2/1

Phone	State	City	Sysop	T/S		First on List # | v (see above)	Name, Features
713-933-7353	TX	Houston	Bruce Zachary	X	9	26	Zachary Net	
713-947-8489	TX	Houston	Mitch Urquhart	P	2	87	Mandala Obsvtry	2/
713-948-9906	TX	Houston	Terry Horton	T	2	104	I.F.H.C.A.	25/16
713-955-7564	TX	Houston	Area Walter Holmes	R	2	08	PC Eve, Radio	
713-961-1604	TX	Houston	D& S Shelton	B	9D	57	Sands	7/
713-977-9505	TX	Houston	Anne Phillips	X$	2	78	Advantage Houst	
713-980-7733	TX	Sugarland	Gavin McMahon	W	2	63	King'sThrone	
713-997-7575	TX	Houston	Ed Hopper	B$	9U	34	Ed Hopper's	2/2
714-257-1175	CA	Brea	David Unfried	W	9	96	Star Tech III	7/2
714-282-6055	CA	Anaheim	Darin May	G	9D	57	SCCM CommLink	6/2
714-457-0359	CA	Miss'n Viejo	John Sasser	B	9	98	Discovery	4/3
714-457-8066	CA	Miss'n Viejo	John Heath	B	09D	116*	Safety Net	20/2
714-493-1006	CA	Missn Viejo	Beau Bramlett	W	2	99	Cutting Board	3/2
714-493-3819	CA	Lag. Niguel	Kenny Gardner	G	2	26	Crow's Nest	
714-499-2864	CA	Laguna Beach	Jason MacDonald	W	9V	102	TrixiesDoghouse	1/1
714-524-0880	CA	Placentia	John Cannon	G	19V	114	FireBall	12/2
714-535-1319	CA	Anaheim	Mike Kruss	G	9V	62	Motown-LA	
714-552-3515	CA	Irvine	John Coon	W$	9U	93	S/W Xchg,+CDR	10/
714-636-2667	CA	GardenGrove	Mike Bernstein	B	9U	60	KandyShack	1/
714-643-3066	CA	Laguna Hills	Mark Stein	B$	19V	26	Laguna Hills	4/1
714-651-9815	CA	Irvine	Mark Duvall	B	19D	112	Master Connect	3/2
714-675-9193	CA	NewportBch	Duncan Markley	G	9D	92	Waterfront	7/
714-730-6743	CA	Tustin	Bert Langer	B	2	57	Club Bd	2/
714-739-4256	CA	Buena Park	Dan Jubelt	B	9U	62	Business	5/
714-760-3265	CA	Newport Bch	Addison Ching	B	9U	64	Chips Connx	2/
714-773-8240	CA	Fullerton	Phil Holliday	B	09V	115	Beckman	2/2
714-830-0402	CA	Lake Forest	Jamie Wilson	W	19D	114	Alpha/NET	30/2
714-831-4936	CA	Laguna Hills	David Mitchell	X$	2	87	Diaspar	10/25
714-834-0711	CA	Tustin	Douglas Baxter	B	29V	114	SOLITUDE	5/1
714-837-4408	CA	Irvine	Hugh Faulkner	B	9UH	88	Toshiba Support	3/7
714-837-9677	CA	MissionViejo	Peter Guethlein	W	19D	77	Solar System	65/5
714-840-4633	CA	Hunt'gtonBch	Jason Baker	B$	19D	105	Reflections	60/1
714-846-4393	CA	Hunt'gtonBch	Kevin Collins	B	9D	50	1139/South	5/
714-856-7996	CA	Irvine	Steve Clancy	R	9U	62	Wellspring	
714-965-9963	CA	Hunt'gtonBch	Rollin White	U	9U	92	CompEducSvcs	1/
714-968-3965	CA	Fountain Vly	Damian Clark	B	9D	92	Ground Zer0	15/5
715-341-4016	WI	StevensPoint	Jeremy Guthrie	Q	19V	110	Neighborhood	5/1
715-345-1173	WI	StevensPoint	Davey Jones	L$	29V	111	REQUIEM	2/2
715-345-1327	WI	StevensPoint	Tom Lehner	F	19D	88*	The Point	13/1
715-362-3895	WI	Rhinelander	Ryugen Fisher	O$	9U	29	Old Frog Swamp	7/2
715-387-1339	WI	Marshfield	Tim Brown	M$	9V	72	PromisedLand	13/8
715-421-1546	WI	Wis. Rapids	Tom Schara	O	09V	109	Online Exchange	13/1
715-435-3855	WI	Rudolph	Jim Suzda	R	9D	79	RapidRiver	1/
715-652-2758	WI	Auburndale	J. Hrusovszky	R	19D	74	TwilightZone	11/2
715-723-3552	WI	Chip. Falls	Chris Anderson	O	2	84	Inn/LastHome	1/
715-831-0843	WI	Altoona	K.T. McCRARY	R	9V	104	LCS Customer	3/1
715-839-0942	WI	Eau Claire	Adam Roycraft	Q	29V	116*	Decker's	2/1

Phone	State	City	Sysop	T/S	First on List # | v (see above)		Name, Features	
716-264-9382	NY	Rochester	David Soehner	B$	19V	116*	Crystal Palace	20/6
716-342-2673	NY	Rochester	Dave Gregor	Q	2	72	Irond	4/
716-359-4730	NY	Rochester	Ben Schollnick	Q	2	76	MatrixDataBank	3/2
716-367-3652	NY	Hemlock	Lewis Duffing	W	9V	100	CONST. ORION	2/
716-383-1321	NY	Rochester	Paul Remington	S	09VO		Intele–comm	4/1
716-434-1448	NY	Lockport	Allan Bremer	Q	29V	107	Mr. Machinist	7/1
716-461-1924	NY	Rochester	Nick Francesco	Q	19V	106	FROG Pond	2/2
716-473-5204	NY	Rochester	David Muench	U	9V	96	Panic Zone	2/2
716-482-2592	NY	Rochester	David Soehner	B$	2	26	CrystalPalace	2/
716-549-6365	NY	Angola	John P. Miller	G	9U	91	MGG Enterprise	2/
716-594-5440	NY	Rochester	Brian Martin	B	9	100	The Oracle	13/2
716-627-3299	NY	Cheektowaga	Bill Oliver	G	19D	107	Dark Star	70/6
716-688-6537	NY	Buffalo	Nick McCraith	T$	2	62	On-line Sports	3/
716-695-0583	NY	Buffalo	Bass/Bieda/Brown	R	2	54	B-IBM-UG BBS,!	1/2
716-695-1937	NY	Tonawanda	Kevin Beamer	G	19V	110	Cougars Kingdom	1/1
716-728-3896	NY	Wayland	John E. Smith	F	2	101	Professional's	1/1
716-774-8547	NY	Buffalo	Robert Smith Jr	V	09V	111	Niagara Univ	8/4
716-787-1155	NY	Penfield	Erik Harris	U	29DO	112*	Viper's Lair	10/1
716-836-8717	NY	Buffalo	Matt Foster	G$	29V	108	Triton	7/1
716-865-2106	NY	Rochester	Ken Serikstad	W	9U	74	Knight Moves	2/2
716-875-0283	NY	Buffalo	Greg Armenia	G	9U	93	Pier 1 Xchg	8/2
716-881-5380	NY	Buffalo	Rich Graham	B	9U	58	Night Owls	38/5
716-892-8428	NY	Buffalo	Ralph Markwardt	B	9V	91	RAM BBS	13/2
716-895-1146	NY	Buffalo	Bill Deer	G	?9V	110	Buffalo DataSys	3/3
716-964-8475	NY	Rochester	Robert Dean	F	19V	111	Lighthouse	7/1
717-225-7256	PA	SevenValleys	F. Strausbaugh	W	19D	111	Merchantmen	20/
717-243-9620	PA	Carlisle	Bob St. Cyr	F	9D	80	SW Xchg	
717-325-9481	PA	Jim Thorpe	Tom Wildoner	W	19V	98	T&J Software	1/2
717-367-8891	PA	Elizabethtwn	C. Pemberton	X	2	100	Freedom.BBS	3/2
717-387-5000	PA	Bloomsburg	OliverPettebone	C	9H	91	[msgs/ Japan]	1/
717-393-1865	PA	Lancaster	David Hand	S	09B	113	Gen Hosp Biomed	3/1
717-393-2640	PA	Lancaster	Richard Kelly	W	29U	109	Board Room	10/1
717-394-1357	PA	Lancaster	Jerry Shenk	D$	2	44	LABB	23/7
717-488-6551	PA	Honesdale	Randy Gullick	B	2	26	S/W Safari	4/2
717-538-3009	PA	New Columbia	Jim Aikey	B	29V	104	Ike's Place	27/1
717-561-8145	PA	Harrisburg	Bob Lester	R	9D	57	TEC-Board,Unix	6/
717-566-2398	PA	Hummelstown	Amy Moore	R	2	104	Up and Running	1/1
717-587-9060	PA	Clks Summit	T. Hollenberg	V	09V	115	Houses of Holy	1/1
717-588-7549	PA	Bushkill	Paul Faeder	Q	9U	62	PoconoMtn	
717-620-0448	PA	Bartonsv'le	Joe Sukenick	W	9U	80	B'ville	3/
717-652-0874	PA	Harrisburg	Terry Brown	W	19V	107	Network 24	1/2
717-653-0636	PA	Mount Joy	Haven Sommers	M	9U	98	MtJoyInfoSyst	1/4
717-657-8699	PA	Harrisburg	George Peace	T	19V	64	Penna.6Online!	800/16
717-689-3123	PA	Hamlin	Bob Gibbons	W	9D	87	BrinkmansHollow	1/
717-697-0172	PA	Mechs'burg	John Boyer	R	09V	93	Rose Garden	2/1
717-697-3717	PA	Harrisburg	Gary Thurlow	B$	9D	08	Genesis	60/5
717-724-6339	PA	Wellsboro	Karl Kilburn	W	2	98	General Store	1/1

						First on List # | v	
Phone	State	City	Sysop	T/S		(see above)	Name, Features
717-738-1976	PA	Ephrata	Justin Shirk	X	19V	112	Cybernetics	19/1
717-755-2440	PA	York	Mario Mueller	B	29V	115	Antarctica	11/1
717-822-2874	PA	Ashley	Chris Kellock	Q	19V	115	Ravenloft	2/1
717-839-2250	PA	Mt. Pocono	Ken Yerke	X	2	100	Novice	1/1
717-840-1444	PA	York	Adam Viener	T	19D	111	Cyberia	16/6
717-853-3599	PA	Susquehanna	Michael Lurie	R	19D	73	Depot,CAD !	10/2
717-876-0152	PA	Jermyn	Stuart Wilson	Q	9D	71	NE FileBank	9/2
717-932-2104	PA	N.Cumberland	Mike Smeal	R	9	92	Sunburst	1/
717-944-0655	PA	Middletown	Gary Rux	O	9U	34	Mdtn BBS	3/
717-944-6876	PA	Middletown	Tom Wagner	R	19V	44	Dino][	33/3
718-204-7831	NY	L. I. City	S. deTrafford	B$	9V	97	Cravings	11/2
718-251-9346	NY	Brooklyn	Mel Silverman	T	9U	79	More BBS	20/
718-253-2431	NY	Brooklyn	Edward Weiss	V	09V	108	JTSCom	5/1
718-268-0060	NY	Forest Hills	Fernando Ortiz	M$	9V	100	EmpireStateOnln	12/4
718-268-5763	NY	Forest Hills	John Wilson	W	19D	116*	NET-Hack	5/1
718-335-0763	NY	MiddleVill.	Eddie Caffray	B	9U	90	On-line Store	10/3
718-341-3606	NY	Jamaica	Alan Siegal	B$	9D	84	[Int'l Trade]	4/
718-351-7633	NY	Staten Isle	Mark Froese	R$	9U	79	Abstract	12/
718-367-2940	NY	Bronx	Kenneth Topp	B	19V	100	Bronx Science	3/1
718-370-3592	NY	Staten Isle	Pete Picataggio	B	2	80	Crystal Castle	?/2
718-377-0524	NY	Brooklyn	David Adress	B$	9U	77	DataLink	20/8
718-381-3651	NY	Brooklyn	Dave Navarro	B	9D	91	Bard's Lair	24/2
718-439-3116	NY	Brooklyn	M. Swannick	X	22	106	Trans-Continent	15/2
718-444-4555	NY	Brooklyn	Matt Kahn	D$	9D	56	MAS,!	23/5
718-458-0502	NY	Elmhurst	Jim Symbouras	W	9V	98	Jims'PCParadise	2/1
718-460-4373	NY	New York	Howard Altman	S	2	88	TradeWare	2/
718-494-1719	NY	Richmond	Bob Hassler	R$	29D	111	fathernet bbs	32/1
718-531-5223	NY	New York	Neil Leder	B	9U	29	Doctor'sOffice	3/2
718-539-3338	NY	New York	Hank Kee	R	2	26	NY Amat.ComClub	/2
718-592-1095	NY	New York	Gerry Pulver	B	2	15	Friend's	
718-626-8087	NY	Astoria	P. Starzynski	X	29D	110	Tea Room (Zen)	1/1
718-631-8719	NY	Queens	Juan Garcia	B	9U	97	J&L Computer	26/3
718-692-2498	NY	Brooklyn	Don Barba	B	9H	50	MoonDog's	
718-698-1776	NY	Staten Isle	Sam Schuster	B	9V	89	Obscured/Clouds	16/2
718-716-6198	NY	Bronx	M. Towobola	W	9V	102	Systematic	4/2
718-761-9513	NY	Staten Isle	Joe DeBonis	X	09V	105	Sports Connectn	2/1
718-762-1030	NY	Queens	A. Rosenthal	B	29V	112	10:30 BBS	2/1
718-793-4796	NY	New York	Jesse Erlbaum	X	09D	105	the Belfry(!)	3/2
718-833-5949	NY	Brooklyn	Kevin R. Aleman	X	19O	110	Japanese NetSys	96/2
718-837-3236	NY	Brooklyn	Jay Caplan	B	9D	55	Consultant,sh/w	6/2
718-853-8957	NY	Brooklyn	Ed Deringer	Q	9V	102	BrooklynPervert	6/1
718-876-0337	NY	StatenIsl	Ron Janorkar	X	2	98	PhotogrphrsNtwk	2/1
718-876-7009	NY	StatenIsl	John Roccomboli	B$	19V	74	MJF BBS System	56/2
718-882-5683	NY	Bronx	Ray Checko	B	19V	112	BBSLineTraveler	3/1
718-934-1843	NY	Brooklyn	Scott Raymond	LV	9D	100	Shadowdale	2/1
718-939-5462	NY	New York	Clarke Ulmer	B$	9U	72	MovieBBS	10/
718-939-7686	NY	Fresh Meadow	Lewis Kopp	B	9D		Sq1200 Aviation	2/

Phone	State	City	Sysop	T/S	First on List #↓v	(see above)	Name, Features	
718-951-6652	NY	Brooklyn	IsraelSilverman	B	19D	93	Mind Matters	1/2
718-962-2403	NY	Bellerose	Kevin Clark	B	9V	96	dCLipboard	100/3
718-966-8637	NY	Staten Isle	David Heath	B	9U	87	The Forum BBS	85/3
718-972-6099	NY	Brooklyn	Michael Keylin	B	9D	48	Star-Link	42/10
718-979-6629	NY	Staten Isle	Chas Scheffold	U	9U	90	Sound Barrier	3/
718-983-9152	NY	Staten Isle	Rik Line	X	19U	112	Computec Data	5/1
718-984-4511	NY	Staten Isle	Sylvia Carole	B	2	70	Sylvia'sDen	2/
719-488-9470	CO	Monument	Jerry Shifrin	B	9V	92	Monument Board	3/1
719-546-3567	CO	Pueblo	Michael Hughes	X$	9V	102	DIALOG Board	2/1
719-591-7415	CO	Colo Springs	??	O	9U	55	Fire Net	
719-597-8670	CO	Colo Springs	Fred Forrest	B	2	67	Commstar Ent.	
719-598-6746	CO	Colo Springs	Guy Bentley	B$	19V	114	Wizards Lair	5/2
719-846-9140	CO	Trinidad	Walter Hazen	R	02	107	Port 13	4/1
800-932-7459	WV	Univeristy	Brad Maust	B	02	112	Drinking Water	1/2
801-224-4031	UT	Orem	Ed Wilkinson	B	19V	107	Hackers' Haven	20/4
801-261-8974	UT	SaltLakeCity	Fred Clark	B$	2	26	Salt Air	
801-264-1191	UT	SaltLakeCity	Kay Leavitt	B	19V	71*	GraphicsConnx	53/14
801-266-8456	UT	Murray	Kelvin Hyatt	B$	9H	78	CenterPoint	2/
801-269-9575	UT	Murray	Dave Taylor	B$	09D	107	SCOREBOARD	10/2
801-359-0925	UT	SaltLakeCity	F. Jacobberger	B$	19VO	108	Your Roots	1/1
801-374-2880	UT	Provo	Adam Radulovic	G	9	95	Humble Heaven	1/
801-394-9324	UT	Ogden	Hal Wold	B	29D	98	FoundationsEdge	6/1
801-451-7630	UT	Farmington	Mike Blevins	O	9V	99	Mike's BBS	1/1
801-489-0638	UT	Springville	Mike Crane	L$	19V	110	This Old BBS	1/1
801-561-5025	UT	W.Jordan	Marty Greenlief	B	9D	71	RatTrap	2/2
801-586-2067	UT	Cedar City	Ken Hedgecock	B	9D	34	BBS-Cedar City	8/2
801-723-6117	UT	Brigham City	Steve Reichard	B	19V	113	Zion Curtain	3/1
801-752-5059	UT	Logan	Dan Bachman	B	19V	89*	Zion'sCache	3/1
801-825-4571	UT	Clearfield	Bill Gray	O	9M	88	Byte House	
801-963-8721	UT	SaltLakeCity	Raymond Snow	B	9D	88	Rocky Mtn S/W	12/4
801-966-4800	UT	SaltLakeCity	Jeff Case	B	?9?	116*	Utah CompNet	10/1
801-969-5886	UT	SaltLakeCity	Dick Claiborne	S	19V	112	FOVEA Centralis	5/1
802-334-2520	VT	Newport	Jason Russell	X	9V	96	Dawn Patrol	1/1
802-527-1683	VT	St. Albans	Howard Lenmah	W	2	41	St. Albans	
802-860-1908	VT	Burlington	A. Hardesty	C	9C	55	Dog Dish	1/
802-863-5722	VT	S.Burlington	Dave Dube	Q	9V	102	C.M.C.B.B.S.	3/2
802-879-1732	VT	Essex Jct	James Jacob	Q	9	73	VtTradingPost	2/
802-933-2417	VT	Sheldon	Tom Repstad	B	9U	50	Black Creek	1/
803-223-3802	SC	Greenwood	Danny Byrd	W	2	54	TrueBlue BBS	
803-227-9557	SC	Greenwood	David Bonamo	Y	09VV	108	Packet Connx	1/1
803-244-8782	SC	Taylors	Jeremy McClure	B	9U	100	Music Box	4/1
803-268-8679	SC	Taylors	Brian Hess	Q	19V	106	StarBase 8	1/1
803-272-2856	SC	Myrtle Beach	Jay Ward	B	9	99	2112	13/1
803-299-3594	SC	Greenville	Richard Fuller	B	2	65	Door to South	6/2
803-347-8653	SC	Conway	Andrew Wheeler	X	9V	88	Dragon's Lair	2/1
803-365-1467	SC	Conway	Dion Brown	X	2	102	Tiger's Den	1/1
803-393-7399	SC	Florence	Erwin Reyer	V	2	45	Pee Dee Xchg	2/

					First on List # | v		
Phone	State	City	Sysop	T/S	(see above)	Name, Features	
803-469-3814	SC	Sumter	Derek Cosby	W	09VB	105*	Vangaard Keep	18/1
803-538-4084	SC	Walterboro	M & E Farrell	B	19V	109	Main Street	1/1
803-542-1658	SC	Spartanburg	Johnnie Turner	B	2	48	Spart'bg PCUG	3/
803-552-4389	SC	N.Charleston	Bob Chapman	B	09DO	93	Earth Art	9/3
803-556-7485	SC	Charleston	Mike Ratledge	Q	9U	45	EastBayXchg	15/
803-574-2617	SC	Spartanburg	Rick Heyn	Q	99V	110	ReductioAbsurdm	2/1
803-574-2632	SC	Spartanburg	Billy Geier	Q	19VO	106	First Flight	2/1
803-576-7194	SC	Spart'burg	Pat Nobles	B	19V	91	Diff'ce Engine	33/1
803-736-6066	SC	Columbia	John Broome	B	2	06	So.Hospitality	1/2
803-767-4201	SC	Charleston	Rick Cann	B	9U	60	The Roost	3/
803-768-4782	SC	SeabrookIsle	Earl Boone	B	9U	49	SeabIsleBd,!	6/
803-795-6260	SC	Charleston	Bill Jones	B	2	55	Coastal BBS	
803-795-9350	SC	James Island	John P. Jones	G	19V	112	New World	3/1
803-797-3858	SC	Goose Creek	José Zapata	Q	02	115	Gateway B	1/1
803-821-2745	SC	Ladson	Jennifer Credle	B	19V	100	The Agency	1/1
803-824-0070	SC	N.Charleston	Fred Busteed	B	29D	99	Arcs & Sparks	20/1
803-846-8100	SC	Seabrook	Barry Anderson	B$	9U	83	C.S.A.	5/
803-871-3076	SC	Summerville	Paul Dardis	B	19V	111	Byte Bucket	2/1
803-871-8197	SC	Summerville	George Stadler	B	9U	40	Summerville 80	2/
803-879-4364	SC	Greer	Vic Montgomery	W	9U	57	Comax,+CDR	15/
803-895-3536	SC	Greenville	Matthew Cooley	B	2	63	Ultimate	/2
803-899-6940	SC	Pinopolis	Michael Dodge	B	19D	102	Bedrock Cafe	9/2
803-957-7077	SC	Lexington	William Wingard	W	19VO	107	Crossroads	1/1
804-270-0502	VA	Richmond	P. Moerschell	X	22	114	Matchmaker	2/10
804-293-2400	VA	Charlo'ville	Chris Ochoa	B	19D	115	C.O.M.A.	72/4
804-293-4710	VA	Charlo'ville	Rey Barry	B	9D	98	FreewareHall	4/1
804-295-3581	VA	Charlo'ville	Bruce Dubuque	X	19V	104	Data World	1/1
804-353-4160	VA	Richmond	Tyronne Foy	R$	09D	64	Intercity	24/1
804-360-5899	VA	Richmond	Jay Brown	Q$	19V	105	Grand Slam!	5/2
804-379-7731	VA	Richmond	Chuck Watkins	B	9U	67	Under Const	1/
804-421-3571	VA	Chesapeake	David Hoyt	W	9	87	Nite Owl	3/3
804-424-0394	VA	Chesapeake	Scott White	Q$	19V	106	Wings & Wheels	2/1
804-424-1514	VA	Virginia Bch	Shawn Chenault	B	9U	46	Micro Enhancemt	13/6
804-459-2323	VA	Norfolk	David Gabriel	B	2	79	ComputerOutlet	7/4
804-467-1835	VA	Virginia Bch	C. A. Norton	B	9U	81	Phoenix,+CDR	1/
804-468-6454	VA	Virginia Bch	Ray Sulich	B	19D	114	Straight Board	23/2
804-471-3360	VA	Virginia Bch	Jim Rhodes	B$	9U	34	ComForum	12/2
804-481-3090	VA	Chesapeake	Larry Schnitt	M	9U	72	Gathering	3/10
804-488-2595	VA	Chesapeake	Roy McCollum	R	2	74	Megabyte	2/
804-488-4146	VA	Chesapeake	Bill Torbert	X	09V	116*	TDS	5/1
804-491-0152	VA	Virginia Bch	Steph Billings	B$	9U	56	CompCon,a.-2826	8/2
804-526-6471	VA	Chester	Rick Dawson	B$	9D	96	TouchStone	3/2
805-528-2041	CA	Los Osos	Lynn Stokes	Q	12	116*	Night Owl	1/1
804-547-7608	VA	Virginia Bch	P. Moerschell	X$	09V	114	VABch Matchmakr	2/18
804-552-1010	VA	Virginia Bch	Steve Haynes	B$	9U	55	Exchange	
804-590-2161	VA	Matoaca	Dr C.A. Wootten	W	09B	102	Servant of Lord	10/1
804-642-9405	VA	Gloucester	Thomas Arnold	QV	9V	67	Sysabend	1/1

Phone	State	City	Sysop	T/S	First on List # | v (see above)	Name, Features	
804-665-7906	VA	Bloxom	Bob Reynolds	W	19V	111	Hambones Fish	1/1
804-722-2627	VA	Hampton	Richard Wicker	X	2	89	Wicker Basket	1/
804-727-0399	VA	Hampton	Wesley Fralick	B	9V	101	Georgia Peach	7/1
804-732-1189	VA	Ft. Lee	Daniel Slagle	S	29V	113	Cracked Windows	2/1
804-737-3932	VA	Richmond	Don Waybright	O	?9V	116*	G.R.C.	13/2
804-740-1364	VA	Richmond	Barry Lee	W	9V	102	Richmond Conn.	10/3
804-740-2413	VA	Richmond	Wendell Kenney	F	11	114	RainTree	4/2
804-744-0744	VA	Richmond	Bill Hunter	R	9U	72	FreeBd,graf,DTP	4/
804-745-5817	VA	Richmond	Jay Swain	G	19D	76	The Gates	14/5
804-750-1300	VA	Richmond	Jim Tomasello	V	2	99	The Inn	1/1
804-790-1675	VA	Richmond	Webb Blackman	R	09V	26	BlueRidgXprs	30/36
804-827-8726	VA	Hampton	R & L Epley	G	9V	86	DogWood	12/2
804-838-3767	VA	Hampton	E & R Jacobson	J	09V	107	MargaritaVille	1/1
804-846-6518	VA	Lynchburg	Jon Barnhart	O	9U	71	Starbase9000	2/
804-862-4663	VA	Petersburg	Floyd Archer	W	9V	102	Midnite Express	16/2
804-865-6848	VA	Hampton	David Moore	Q	9U	88	Pier 22	2/
804-872-7171	VA	NewportNews	King & Riggins	Q	2	60	Trilogy	
804-973-8235	VA	Charlo'ville	Pat Wilson	B	2	51	Pat's Place	1/
804-978-4134	VA	Charlo'ville	T. Allensworth	M$	9V	89	VINE	2/8
805-259-3475	CA	Newhall	Nick Mitchell	M$	09VO	112	Vaults BBS	1/2
805-273-2360	CA	Palmdale	Dave Norris	W	2	98	Strangers	1/1
805-296-9056	CA	Saugus	Dan Martin	X	9V	100	SoftWare Statn	2/1
805-297-6225	CA	Saugus	Andy Daddario	W	29D	116*	Database	28/2
805-343-6018	CA	Nipomo	Roy Mumaw	Q	09V	99	Chthonic	3/2
805-374-7373	CA	ThousandOaks	Glenn Bomke	B	9D	61	Conejo Info Srv	8/4
805-395-0650	CA	Bakersfield	Steve Crippen	W	9U	40	Mustang Wildcat	
805-466-4712	CA	Atascadero	Carl Thompson	W	?9V	114	Cyber_Gazm	3/1
805-473-2414	CA	GroverBeach	Jerry Ferris	Q	19V	100*	Jerris's	6/1
805-488-7430	CA	Oxnard	Greg King	C	9U	54	RoyaLink,pgming	3/
805-489-1966	CA	ArroyoGrande	Jim Tinlin	Q	09V	114	Message Center	3/1
805-492-5472	CA	ThousandOaks	Trevor Marshall	X	9V	15	Technical RCPM	
805-494-9386	CA	ThousandOaks	Mike Ehlert	Q	29D	112	PACIFIC COAST	50/4
805-498-3500	CA	Newbury Park	Ty Simpson	B	9V	62	NOMAD	5/
805-499-5717	CA	NewburyPark	Eric Lundberg	B	19V	82	Formula 350	19/4
805-525-5278	CA	Santa Paula	Don Cook	W	99V	116*	Lost Space	2/1
805-526-0609	CA	Simi Valley	Alan McDonald	Q	9	34	IBM Data Shop	
805-527-8704	CA	Simi Valley	Greg Smith	B	9U	72	CloneBd,jobs	7/
805-528-7341	CA	Los Osos	Tim Sawchuck	W	9D	98	Nasty Old Lady	2/1
805-543-8227	CA	SanL.Obispo	Chris Ambler	X	2	90	Fubar Sys	2/
805-581-6210	CA	Simi Valley	Steve Hawley	W	02	113	Resume File	2/1
805-582-1621	CA	Simi Valley	G. Bisner	W	9U	89	Farpoint	5/2
805-583-2282	CA	Simi Valley	Howard Coleman	W	09V	108	S.V.A.R.	2/1
805-583-5833	CA	Simi Valley	Larry Stevenson	B	9U	81	Grinder,people	10/
805-649-5314	CA	Oakview	Chas Radley	O	2	80	FinalFrontEar	
805-652-1478	CA	Ventura	Bob Harris	R$	9U	58	HIS BOARD,relig	10/
805-658-8155	CA	Ventura	David Saunders	W	29V	114	XANADU	5/2
805-683-0499	CA	SantaBarbara	Scott Swaine	B	9U	67	Console Command	7/

						First on List # | v (see above)		
Phone	State	City	Sysop	T/S			Name, Features	
805-735-5253	CA	Lompoc	Jim Williams	W$	9U	76	Mt Desert West	7/
805-735-7019	CA	Lompoc	Jim Hill	W	19V	104	Royal Wolf	5/1
805-822-9600	CA	Tehachapi	Ed Brown	B$	9V	93	MiddleofNowhere	2/2
805-834-5539	CA	Bakersfield	Tim Paddock	F	2	84	Turbotron	2/
805-948-8047	CA	Lancaster	Tracy Huston	T	9U	29	LancasterTBBS	1/
805-949-8151	CA	Lancaster	Burns/Taylor	B$	9U	67	Researcher's	14/4
805-964-4766	CA	SantaBarbara	Les Jones	G	19D	93	Seaside	12/4
805-981-0875	CA	Oxnard	Gregory Chester	W	9D	104	House of Cards	2/1
805-983-0281	CA	Oxnard	Peggy Mellinger	W	2	71	Bastille	2/
805-995-1299	CA	S LuisObispo	Dave McCaleb	B$	19D	113	ComputerFactory	55/9
806-273-2407	TX	Borger	Terry Burland	Q	19V	113	RF-Baker	12/1
806-352-5784	TX	Amarillo	Tom Whittenburg	T	2	83#	BurgBd	
806-355-6968	TX	Amarillo	Don White	R	2	83	TeachersPet	
806-359-3542	TX	Amarillo	Ted Johnson	S	2	93	GIRC,educ	
806-742-2917	TX	Lubbock	David Coons	W	2	34	Texas Tech U	
806-792-6116	TX	Lubbock	Lee Stafford	B$35	9D	06	Windmill	14/6
807-468-8226	ON	Kenora	Rod McIver	R	9D	75	Central RBBS	1/
808-396-2420	HI	Honolulu	Wyatt Barbee	R	2	85	Splicer	2/
808-541-2639	HI	Honolulu	U.S. Govt	B	2	34	Uncle Sam No.1	
808-625-5120	HI	Wahiawa	Lou Steinritz	B	29D	112	Paradise	12/1
808-732-7958	HI	Honolulu	Del Wong	S	19V	66	FLEX Plus+	4/2
808-845-1303	HI	Honolulu	Dave DeWald	B$	9U	75	[Chinchillad]	9/
809-751-7728	PR	Rio Pedras	Juan Davila	R	9U	45	MegaD RBBS II	8/2
809-774-7088	VI	St. Thomas	Peter deBlanc	S	29VU	108	Pieces of Eight	6/2
809-779-4066	PR	St. John	Thom MacDonald	W	9	98	COM-DAT	12/2
809-783-9542	PR	Cap.Hts	Luis Salazar	F	9U	66	IslandSun	8/2
809-785-2993	PR	Bayamon	Ben Fernandez	Q	9U	97	Moon Rise	1/1
809-849-5921	PR	Hormigueros	Ricardo Romero	F	9U	89	Tropical Island	2/
810-227-4724	MI	Brighton	Mark C. Boyer	X	9D	78*	InnerSanctum	7/
810-227-6607	MI	Brighton	Mark Newton	X	19V	114*	NEWTONIAN	5/1
810-229-0736	MI	Brighton	Timothy Harder	X	19D	115*	Sev Devastation	16/2
810-229-4465	MI	Hartland	Mike Ryan	X	19VO	109*	Hartland Pride	1/1
810-230-8433	MI	Flint	Jim Schlee	B	9V	100*	F.A.C.E.	3/2
810-231-2366	MI	Brighton	Tim Rappette	Y	9U	62*	UFO Data Coltn	
810-247-0895	MI	SterlingHts	Larry Phillips	Y	9U	81*	Generic	3/
810-349-3408	MI	Novi	Gil Schultz	X	2	41*	007's Runway	
810-352-4112	MI	Southfield	Tom Forest	C	9U	92*	Vanishing Point	1/
810-398-3078	MI	Madison Hts	David Day	W	9U	77*	AtariAdv	4/
810-547-2985	MI	Ferndale	Jeff Howard	Y	2	84*	Wiz/Orchid	1/
810-558-5024	MI	Warren	Chris Kaminski	X	29V	114*	EarthDreamlands	6/2
810-558-7689	MI	Warren	Gary Schultz	P	9U	71*	Tech Corner	
810-559-8604	MI	Southfield	Oscar Petoskey	X	2	93*	Biznet 2000	1/
810-623-9406	MI	Waterford	Bill Thomas	P	9U	104*	Skyliner	1/1
810-623-9804	MI	Clarkston	Dave Uhley	F	9U	75*	Corsair	2/
810-653-1139	MI	Davison	CraigHarrington	B	9U	92*	VehicleCity	2/
810-664-5856	MI	Lapeer	Jamie Prevo	Y	2	83*	Powerhouse	
810-680-9154	MI	Troy	D. MacFarlane	B	9D	34*	Automation Res	

						First on List # ↓ v		
Phone	**State**	**City**	**Sysop**		**T/S**	**(see above)**	**Name, Features**	
810-767-0969	MI	Flint	B. Bissonnette	B	9D	101*	Stoned Circus	7/3
810-772-0522	MI	Warren	Bill Duerr	R	09D	100*	DKUG RBBS	16/2
810-774-9501	MI	StClrShores	Paul DiGiusto	B	29D	112*	Paul's OpenPort	4/1
810-776-1975	MI	Roseville	Richard Leneway	B$	29V	110*	LegendofRosevle	40/6
810-787-0270	MI	Flint	Jeffrey Smith	W	9U	86*	Diamond Club	2/
810-826-9411	MI	SterlingHght	Dan Walford	T	29D	?*	Firebox Express	32/2
810-967-5397	MI	Oak Park	Ron Schreiber	B	9U	91*	Jews forJudaism	
812-275-4689	IN	Bedford	Mike Allen Jr	B	9U	72	HST Express	
812-279-2143	IN	Bedford	Brian Mathis	X	9U	86	Hotseat,files	10/
812-299-9306	IN	Terre Haute	Philip Brown	F	19U	104	Ivy Tech's	7/1
812-332-7227	IN	Bloomington	Taylor/Rumple	X$	09D	15	IndianaOn-line	55/5
812-428-3870	IN	Evansville	Don Habegger	W$	19D	113	"YA! WEBECAD!"	11/3
812-479-1310	IN	Evansville	Gary Barr	Q	9D	74	Digicom	17/7
812-855-7252	IN	Bloomington	Indiana U.	B	9U	26	PC-Link Central	
813-237-8184	FL	Tampa	Don Depue	W	2	67	Jeff Elec,!	9/
813-262-2755	FL	Naples	Alan Dalton	B	19D	62	Trail-T	4/1
813-264-0073	FL	Tampa	Jim Unroe	B$	9U	83	DataXchg	8/
813-265-3256	FL	Tampa	Wes Cowley	X	2		Bird Lake	12/
813-277-0906	FL	Fort Myers	Randy Sherwyn	Q	9D	95	*ASTRO*	6/2
813-287-0001	FL	Tampa	Roger Pearson	B	2	88	USAComp sup.	
813-289-3314	FL	Tampa	Sharrer/Webster	B	9U	78	Godfather	16/
813-299-8778	FL	Winter Haven	M. Wennerstrom	B	9H	45	Micro-World	1/
813-321-0734	FL	St Petersbrg	Emery Mandel	B$	09D	112	Mercury Opus	12/6
813-325-8972	FL	Winter Haven	John Lucas	X	9		Temple Builders	8/
813-327-8842	FL	St Petersbrg	David Mueller	F$	09V	114	C.R.S.	75/2
813-349-0355	FL	Sarasota	Bob Marone	R$	9U	90	FL Info Xchg	30/2
813-372-6621	FL	N Pt Richey	Dale Hutchinson	P	19O	111	Baywatch	1/1
813-376-8229	FL	NwPortRichey	Chris Cady	B$	9D		Mutt n Jeff's	21/2
813-378-0273	FL	Sarasota	Dave Gardner	R	19	106	EXECUSERVE	1/1
813-378-3477	FL	Sarasota	AndrewOberweger	W	2	93	Imitation/Life	2/
813-394-6488	FL	Marco Island	S. Hendricks	O	09UD	105	Island BBS	16/1
813-399-1271	FL	Seminole	James Gaskins	P	9U	68	SightnSound	
813-455-6390	FL	Naples	Glenn Niesen	W	9D	75	CaptCorner	3/1
813-471-0552	FL	Sebring	John Grove	T	9U	71	Ancestry,geneol	13/
813-481-5575	FL	Fort Myers	Chris Michaels	B	09O	107	Pegasus Project	10/2
813-526-1265	FL	St Petersbrg	Ken Hunt	B$	9U	45	Computronics	4/
813-526-3388	FL	St Petersbrg	Thomas Angarano	B$	9U	45	MicroVision	8/
813-527-5666	FL	St Petersbrg	Bill Blomgren	B	9U	74	StPetePgmersXch	7/2
813-531-4493	FL	Clearwater	Tom Kis	B	29	116*	Tradewinds	8/1
813-544-7669	FL	Largo	Larry Wright	M	2	98	Intl Auto&Boat	3/3
813-575-8767	FL	Punta Gorda	Scott Williams	X	99V	110	Friends 'R Us	1/1
813-625-5636	FL	Punta Gorda	Jerry Albert	R	9U	72	GoldCoast	12/
813-646-7347	FL	Lakeland	Alex Magdics	W$	9D	88	Graphics,DTP	35/3
813-653-2937	FL	Brandon	Chris Curran	B	9U	89	QExchange	1/2
813-653-4034	FL	Brandon	John Lake	W	09	107	Lotto Player's	2/1
813-667-0413	FL	Lakeland	Stephen Neas	A	9V	102	DIGITECH	1/1
813-676-7549	FL	Lakes Wales	Bolden/Waldrop	W	2	68	Crown Jewel	

Phone	State	City	Sysop	T/S	First on List # | v (see above)	Name, Features	
813-685-0957	FL	Florida	Robbie Taylor	X	2	98	Budmans	1/1
813-689-3334	FL	Valrico	George Mills	X	19V	110	Colosseum	1/1
813-697-3327	FL	Cape Haze	Jim Kirk	W	19D	116*	USS Enterprise	25/1
813-748-5380	FL	Bradenton	Bob Brenner	Q	9V	101	R.B. Enter.	30/1
813-785-3243	FL	Palm Harbor	Ken Pangborn	B	9U	34	FatherBd	3/
813-785-6563	FL	Clearwater	Steve Melone	W	9U	97	Atrium	12/3
813-795-2793	FL	Bradenton	Dan Cioffi	R	9D	100	Premier BBS	2/1
813-796-5627	FL	Clearwater	Steve Sanders	B$	9D	45	DataCOM	40/3
813-823-2473	FL	St. Pete	Doug Lawrence	W	2	89	Research Center	2/
813-842-8099	FL	Port Richey	Brent Yandell	B	9D	34	YCS Doors	5/2
813-849-4034	FL	NPort Richey	Dave Anderson	X	19D	115	Ground Zero	17/4
813-853-9394	FL	Lakeland	John Lucas	W$	09V	115	ENIAC Prof Sys	4/2
813-856-6534	FL	Hudson	Jeff Coates	O	2	104	Data Bank	8/1
813-862-8850	FL	Pt Richey	Ralph LoBianco	B	9D	75	Studio PC BBS	18/3
813-862-4772	FL	NPort Richey	Richard Ziegler	B	19	105	Board of Trade	6/1
813-863-5934	FL	Hudson	Bernie Koch	W	09V	106	Iron Eagle's	3/1
813-869-3700	FL	Port Richey	Herb Mellinger	G	9D	45	Senior Link	25/3
813-882-0478	FL	Tampa	Bill Weinheimer	Q	9U	96	Entropy	2/1
813-887-3984	FL	Tampa	DavidHacquebord	R	9U	06	Sunshine Bd	6/
813-894-6402	FL	St Petersbrg	Ken Brown	B	9U	50	Litigator,Law	
813-920-4714	FL	Odessa	Tim Rivers	B	9U	93	Rivendell	13/2
813-920-8820	FL	Tampa	John Brock	B$	9V	48	ProfDataXchg	6/
813-922-4125	FL	Sarasota	Steve Ahnen	X	9V		Island Central	6/
813-942-1747	FL	Holiday	Mike Hatala	B	9U	72	TeleComp	2/
813-943-0014	FL	Tarpon Sprgs	Dennis Ditoro	B$	29D	112	I N F I N I T Y	24/1
813-949-4993	FL	Lutz	Walter Zipper	B	9U	98	PC-HELP!	12/4
813-953-5505	FL	Sarasota	Chas Dittell	Q	9V	83	Suncoast City	1/
813-954-3282	FL	Sarasota	Jim Studebaker	X$	09V	107	Southeast Data	7/1
813-960-5169	FL	Tampa	Greg Jones	W	19V	116*	CitySettingSun	10/1
813-961-0788	FL	Tampa	Marianne Love	X	9U	77	Nordevald Softw	2/
813-963-1900	FL	Tampa	Paul Streicher	Q	9U	50	Tampa Info	1/
813-968-1684	FL	Tampa	Mike Fontaine	U	29V	97	TNBBS	6/1
813-968-7604	FL	Tampa	Tom Ballachino	X	09VV	78	ProNet BBS	2/1
813-969-2761	FL	Tampa	Earl Bonser	B	19D	104	GIFfer	99/4
813-971-2934	FL	Lutz	Steve Leigh	B	19V	61	Canine Training	15/2
813-973-2780	FL	Tampa	Dave Miller	R	9U	26	RTA	3/
813-973-3346	FL	WesleyChapel	Ken Johnson	B	19D	74*	CadConnx	10/1
813-984-4426	FL	Polk City	Wayne Steinard	B$	9		GlobalRapidRly	6/2
813-996-7425	FL	LandOLake	John Doak	W	9	90	LOL s/w xchg	2/
814-226-2187	PA	Clarion	Scott Kuehn	A	9V	77	COMCIS	1/
814-231-2568	PA	St. College	Mike Loewen	B	9V	70	ICS Roundtable	1/1
814-237-2664	PA	St. College	Rod Humphrey Jr	R	19D	113	$ecurity BBS	22/2
814-237-3825	PA	St. College	Bill Mertens	B	9D	64	Magnetic Bottle	4/2
814-238-5559	PA	St. College	Alan Claver	B	2	50	Blue&White Lion	
814-239-8323	PA	Altoona	Matt Lightner	A	2	90	Wx-ham	
814-353-0566	PA	Bellefonte	Mike Loewen	X	9D	103	Centre ProgUnit	5/1
814-368-8481	PA	Bradford	Jason Valentine	Q	19D	106	Major Minor	1/1

Phone	State	City	Sysop	T/S	First on List # ↓ v (see above)	Name, Features	
814-371-5881	PA	DuBois	Frank Maczaczyj	B	9U	45	Random Access	1/
814-371-6193	PA	DuBois	Penny Meholick	B	09V	72	Rock Island	6/1
814-432-2476	PA	Franklin	Gary Morford	W	2	97	Sci-Link	2/3
814-452-6900	PA	Erie	Don Shriver	B	19V	107	WindowonWindows	1/2
814-456-0869	PA	Erie	Terry Morrison	B	19V	112	Cobra	12/1
814-459-4631	PA	Erie	Robert Depew	B	9U	50	Lake Erie Vnyd	10/
814-459-8901	PA	Erie	Mike Maynard	B	29D	95	Erie's Westside	4/1
814-825-7905	PA	Erie	Barry Walters	B	29	110	Darby Research	3/2
814-827-1234	PA	Titusville	Mark Harcourt	X	9V	100	TitusvilleConn.	3/1
814-866-2611	PA	Waterford	Kriss Kennedy	W	29O	108	Runway 24	7/1
814-866-6475	PA	Erie	Tom Hughes	B	29D	87	HoosierHideaway	5/1
814-886-2563	PA	Cresson	Richard Lis	S	19D	86	SummitSchlight	5/2
814-898-1732	PA	Erie	Frank Huff	B	9D	97	2nd Amendment	2/1
814-941-9245	PA	Altoona	Chris Stewart	S	29V	114	COMMAND LINE	3/2
815-233-5008	IL	Freeport	Geoff Booher	Q	9V	72	GatewayNet	1/
815-234-2346	IL	Stillman Val	Robin Miller	B	9D	81	OverBoard	3/
815-337-0279	IL	Woodstock	Mather/Brenton	T	29V	116*	ESP-BBS	61/16
815-385-5031	IL	McHenry	Bob Walker	B	9U	50	McHenry BBS	4/
815-395-8154	IL	Rockford	Chuck Renaud	Q	9D	91	Channel 62	3/2
815-729-9793	IL	Shorewood	Mike Bohler	R	2	90	Radio Free IL	1/
815-786-6240	IL	Sandwich	Lee Taylor	W$	19DB	116*	Resting Place	32/3
815-795-6371	IL	Marseilles	Neal Roberts	W$	19BV	114	Squirrel's Nest	3/2
815-868-2422	IL	McConnell	K. Zimmerman	Q	19D	77	Boomtown	5/1
815-874-9737	IL	Rockford	Chris Wood	L	9D	100	Death Star	1/1
815-886-0109	IL	Romeoville	John Damore	R	09B	105	ElectricEstates	28/1
815-963-9717	IL	Rockford	Eric Bergdahl	X$	2	103	Multi-Link PC	21/2
816-229-1841	MO	Blue Springs	Gary Wood	B$	2	45	Passport System	1/
816-233-1357	MO	St. Joseph	Michael Fuson	O	9U	51	CMOS	7/2
816-322-5494	MO	Belton	David Fuller	B	19V	97	Night Watch	1/1
816-331-5868	MO	Belton	Jim Howard	Q	19V	66	Howard's Notebk	3/3
816-436-4516	MO	Gladstone	Roy Timberman	B$	19DH	54	Sound Advice	80/32
816-452-3048	MO	Kansas City	Gary Lincoln	X	2	87	Monarch Softw.	1/
816-454-3787	MO	Kansas City	James Hale	Q	9HV	72	Unicorn	1/
816-459-7327	MO	Gladstone	Jim Boling	B	9U	60	Kittyhawk	3/
816-478-3240	MO	Independence	Glenn Powell	S	29V	108	SI's	1/1
816-632-3297	MO	Cameron	Bob Schmidt	W	19V	100*	PC-LYNX	2/3
816-665-5511	MO	Kirksville	Tyson Treasure	Q$	09V	112	TreasureMansion	2/1
816-796-7980	MO	Independence	Greg Moore	S	2	87	Widowmaker	2/
816-891-8176	MO	Kansas City	Jason Reskin	Q	9V	103	Tyrell Int'l	4/4
817-265-8938	TX	Arlington	Mike Henderson	R	9U	55	GasCompany,med	
817-274-9361	TX	Arlington	John McNeely	Q	09U	113	Possum Joint	3/1
817-297-6222	TX	Crowley	M. Blackburn	B	29D	112	DataBoard][	45/2
817-355-9284	TX	Euless	Boyd Roberson	X	09V	112	Out Of Doors	1/1
817-382-4388	TX	Denton	Kevin Carr	Q	19V	107	Golden Triangle	6/1
817-424-3052	TX	Grapevine	Larry Mundy	O	19V	54	Spare Parts	10/2
817-469-8352	TX	Arlington	David Bradley	X	29D	116*	Workshop	5/1
817-547-1734	TX	Copperas Cv	Ben Hamilton	Q	9D		Comp Connection	1/2

Phone	State	City	Sysop	T/S	First on List # | v (see above)	Name, Features	
817-568-1344	TX	Fort Worth	Danny Brigance	Q	9D	97	Bowl of Chili!	12/1
817-579-6062	TX	Granbury	Kevin Jarrett	W	99D	116*	Junk Drawer	12/1
817-589-2525	TX	Hurst	Larry Short	B$V	9D	100	ComputerGallery	20/2
817-626-3417	TX	Fort Worth	Yann Cortina	F	9D	85	YC-1	
817-662-2361	TX	Waco	Jim Ray	Q	9U	71	FileQuest	5/
817-685-0073	TX	Euless	Scott Fox	J	9V	104	Madhatter's Wld	1/1
817-692-4378	TX	WichitaFalls	Curt Harrelson	W	9V	97	Air Patrol	1/1
817-696-0791	TX	WichitaFalls	Terry Morton	V	9U	89	White House	3/
817-696-5771	TX	WichitaFalls	Bob Lennard	X	9V˙	95	Cold Fire	1/1
817-761-7735	TX	WichitaFalls	C.R. Harrelson	W	9V	97	WFPD	1/2
817-784-1178	TX	Arlington	Mark Robbins	B	9D	104	Second Sanctum	5/2
817-847-9211	TX	Fort Worth	Ronnie Oldham	T$	9V	97	$ales Force	2/2
817-855-7955	TX	WichitaFalls	Nelson Newman	W	9C	91	ChessMaster	2/
818-240-0280	CA	Glendale	Everet Milner	W$V	9U	101	PROBOARD	5/2
818-248-1087	CA	LaCrecenta	Robert Jones	R	9U	34	BJ's	4/
818-248-2304	CA	Montrose	Mark Gallaher	W	99D	114	DeepSKy	2/1
818-248-3088	CA	Glendale	Mike Callaghan	W$	9V	68	Hottips	10/
818-337-9701	CA	Baldwin Park	Mike Szabados	M	9V	86	Aussie	30/10
818-363-8713	CA	GranadaHills	Todd Stephan	V	9U	93	Holodeck	8/
818-366-1238	CA	GranadaHills	Tom Tcimpidis	W	9D	80	MOG-UR'S EMS	24/5
818-441-2625	CA	S. Pasadena	Jon Carmichael	B	2	88	Continuum Onln	/2
818-505-1799	CA	N. Hollywood	Gerhard Reeg	Q	2	101	Information Sys	5/1
818-508-0881	CA	N. Hollywood	Michael Part	G	9U	45	Wicked Scherzo	2/1
818-569-3740	CA	Glendale	William Padilla	BV	9D	101	Panasia	1/2
818-591-8642	CA	Calabasas	Ron Ehrens	L	9U	91	AI Transylvania	4/2
818-727-7639	CA	Chatsworth	Mark Valentine	S$	19V	116*	Sleuth	40/3
818-763-8160	CA	Studio City	Dan Praeger	BW	19V	105	Valley Village	25/6
818-763-9006	CA	N. Hollywood	Ed Baker	W	29V	116*	Computer One	11/1
818-773-0873	CA	Los Angeles	S. Sardana	W	2	81	Bits&Megs	2/
818-786-5600	CA	Van Nuys	Gregory Gooden	M	9	96	The Annex	20/8
818-787-1290	CA	Van Nuys	Richard Godfrey	F	19V	114	Mercury Softwr	1/4
818-791-8680	CA	Pasadena	Frank Keeney	W	9V	83	Infomania	1/2
818-792-0419	CA	Pasadena	Carlos Bazan	W	2	102	INTER-BBS	1/2
818-810-0615	CA	Rowland Hts	George Garvin	F	9D	84	The Mick's	1/
818-854-0797	CA	Industry	Jon Mortensen	G	09D	116*	DTK Tech Supt	1/1
818-858-2783	CA	Covina	R. Belleville	W	29D	114	Compu-Ad Info	25/2
818-882-9058	CA	Canoga Park	Mike Waldron	B	9D	95	Sweet Life	2/
818-884-6799	CA	WoodlandHlls	Myles Wakeham	X	2	95	MUSO-BBS,music	1/2
818-891-6780	CA	Panorama	Samuel Smith	B	9	86	ToolShop,langs	10/3
818-893-1899	CA	North Hills	Patrick Martin	X	2	103	SAHARA CLUB	1/1
818-896-4015	CA	LVT	Joseph Sheppard	B$	9U	34	Ledge PCB	8/3
818-913-7624	CA	La Puente	Doug Padgett	W	9	99	Childs Play	1/1
818-966-3305	CA	Covina	David Levin	X	29D	104	Data Field	8/1
818-967-0701	CA	West Covina	J.Kalinowski	X	9V	104	KBTC BBS	6/1
818-969-9170	CA	Azusa	Geoff Vaughan	Q	9U	63	Azusa Pac	3/
818-988-0452	CA	Van Nuys	Guy Hickey	T	9V	104	Audiophile Net	1/2
818-992-3321	CA	Simi Valley	Guy Nohrenberg	B	09O	91	Tin Shack	15/4

Phone	State	City	Sysop	T/S		First on List # | v (see above)	Name, Features	
818-994-0442	CA	Los Angeles	Dale Porter	X	9	88	KBBS L.A.	10/32
900-370-1994	GA	Atlanta	David Coleman	W$	19D	87	MUSIC	20/7
901-278-7305	TN	Memphis	Jerry Armour	WV	9	99	COTNET, agri.	2/2
901-357-5483	TN	Memphis	Lisa Archer	O	29B	111	FLESH ILLUSIONS	1/1
901-363-7301	TN	Memphis	John Pearsall	B$	9U	75	Stillwater	7/
901-373-5941	TN	Memphis	Bobbie Sumrada	B	9U	56	Cheers	1/
901-382-5583	TN	Memphis	Mark Herring	B	9U	62	Sparky'sMach	
901-382-9466	TN	Memphis	Steve Swanson	W	09D	100	Second Wind	60/5
901-725-7964	TN	Memphis	Darryl Haas	R	9U	67	Network 1	2/
901-767-3040	TN	Memphis	Marc Brawner	Q	2	96	Brawner's	1/1
901-873-2328	TN	Memphis	Mike Glenn	B	9U	48	PartyLine,Tech	13/2
902-539-7554	NS	Sydney	Roger Christmas	Q	2	98	Mi'kmaq	1/1
903-463-6581	TX	Denison	Lee Clayton	B	9U	15	Doc's Office	
903-531-0085	TX	Tyler	Gary Ford	W	09V	107	HamRadioHeaven!	2/1
903-657-7990	TX	Henderson	Jerry Maines	F	2	102	Hometown BBS	1/1
903-723-1727	TX	Palestine	Chuck Yaunk	W	9V	93	Piney Woods	
903-786-2058	TX	Dennison	Robert Smith	T	2	96	ElderCare	4/2
903-838-6713	TX	Texarkana	Mike Dundei	O	9U	34	SplitupMiddle	
903-892-0963	TX	Sherman	Gary Day	Q	9	88	After Hours	2/2
904-236-2320	FL	Ocala	Dale A Cook	O	09D	109	Gargoyle's Plce	8/1
904-249-8368	FL	Jacksonville	Donald Erkfitz	U	9U	101	Frogpond By Sea	2/2
904-260-9283	FL	Jacksonville	George Frena	B$	2	54	Tech'sWarehouse	7/
904-265-4643	FL	Lynn Haven	Jack Pizza	T	2	26	House of Help	
904-276-5417	FL	Orange Park	Kim Namanny	B	9U	78	CSI GigaFree	14/2
904-288-8621	FL	Ocklawaha	Paul Cutright	V	02	113	Magnum	2/1
904-322-0061	FL	Daytona Bch	Doug Barnhart	R	9C	86	BadgerBd,pgmng	1/1
904-322-2503	FL	S. Daytona	Bill Kuhn	R	9H	43	APCO HQ	
904-331-4317	FL	Gainesville	Ray Hines	X	9	98	DreamStates	3/2
904-334-4798	FL	Gainesville	Greg Wrey	B	9V	84	Time Slice	33/2
904-347-5143	FL	Ocala	Carol Rex	F	19U	109	AirShow	5/1
904-353-3807	FL	Jacksonville	Dan Nance	B	9	83	Maranatha	3/2
904-365-1110	FL	Leesburg	Kris Harney Jr.	M$	02	107	Prometheus NET	3/5
904-365-9088	FL	Leesburg	Kevin Lodwick	M	29V	109	Rainforest Lvwr	2/2
904-368-6945	FL	Ocala	Eric Carr	O	09U	40	Smokey's Place	1/2
904-375-3461	FL	Gainesville	Tim Slocum	V	2	99	Chrysalis	1/1
904-377-8169	FL	Gainesville	David Rockey	B$	9U	45	EnchantedForest	10/
904-377-8574	FL	Gainesville	Trent Sherman	F	2	95	Transcom][	1/
904-383-0907	FL	Mt. Plymouth	Steve Burton	B	2	83	Gaia, Neo-Pagan	1/
904-383-7841	FL	Mount Dora	Russ Roush	F	29VO	113	Techno Systems	5/1
904-384-2112	FL	Jacksonville	Sidney Moore	B	9		The BatCave	1/
904-385-2761	FL	Tallahassee	Norman Pettus	S	2	26	Eagles Nest III	
904-386-8693	FL	Tallahassee	Charlie Yontz	B	29D	111	Wingit!	8/1
904-388-5297	FL	Jacksonville	Robert Thompson	A	19B	97	WINDRAKER Int'l	3/2
904-396-3064	FL	Jacksonville	Ed Krayer	B$	29V	29	DEMO(plus)	8/1
904-462-5589	FL	Gainesville	Mark West	B	9D	88	Hawk's Hill	8/
904-468-2862	FL	Hampton	Mike Boynton	X	29V	106	Direct><Conntn	1/1
904-473-9790	FL	KeystoneHgts	Bruce McHollan	B	9D	98	KeystoneConn.	12/3

						First on List # | v	
Phone	State	City	Sysop	T/S		(see above)	Name, Features
904-476-1270	FL	Pensacola	Clayton Manson	W$	9D	92	TITAN S/W Solns	22/4
904-481-2792	FL	Island Grove	Roy Toppino	R	2	100	KludgeWerkes	1/1
904-532-1911	FL	Deltona	Kevin Inscoe	X	09V	114	Refuge	1/1
904-544-0552	FL	Brooksville	Barry Nilsen	W$	9V		Corner Factory	6/
904-563-2547	FL	CrystalRiver	Jim Brewer	B	9D	92	Gulf Coast	1/
904-574-9349	FL	Tallahassee	Russ Evans	Q	9V	92	Circuit Bd,sci	
904-584-8287	FL	Perry	Paul Wilson	W	2	86	askSam db supp	/2
904-591-4559	FL	Mcintosh	Billy Boulware	F	29D	115	Summer Escape	3/1
904-595-5057	FL	Citra	Roy Fralick	B$	29V	107*	Hurry No Mo	36/1
904-625-2737	FL	SilverSpngs	Jim Lewis	T	9U	91	The Light,Chrst	1/
904-637-0152	FL	Inverness	Tom Tobin	B$	9U	77	MicroLand	5/
904-637-3713	FL	Inverness	Mark Beaubien	S	19D	92*	PrimeTime	12/1
904-678-2667	FL	Niceville	Don Anderson	Q	9D	100	Compu-Assist	2/2
904-688-1804	FL	Sprint Hill	Paul Schweiger	W	9V		ForgottenRealms	6/
904-688-9124	FL	Spring Hill	Chuck Curtis	Q	29D	97	TOY SHOP-PC	10/1
904-726-7681	FL	Floral City	Skip Sanders	S	2	92	Paradise Island	1/
904-732-0866	FL	Ocala	Frank Fowler	B	19D	75	TREE	22/3
904-733-5405	FL	Jacksonville	Don McWhirter	F	9U	84	Manpower,bsns	14/4
904-743-7052	FL	Jacksonville	Steve Rucci	X	29V	109	Crusader Castle	2/1
904-749-9937	FL	Pierson	Mart Friend	F	9	95	Marts Undergrnd	2/1
904-751-5416	FL	Jackspnville	BJ Littlejohn	F	2	84	New World	2/
904-753-3643	FL	Lady Lake	Michael Senello	W	2	93	DragonHaulers	2/2
904-757-0281	FL	Jacksonville	Jim Loos	R	19V	96	Jim's Place	3/1
904-757-8636	FL	Jacksonville	Al Segura	B$	12	108	SBG Online!	1/1
904-777-0831	FL	Jacksonville	William Wingard	W$	2	93	Crossroads	1/
904-789-0192	FL	Deltona	Don Geser	S	2	95	Outback	1/
904-789-9640	FL	Deltona	Tim Jones	O	19D	106	Four Towns Info	15/1
904-796-2828	FL	Brooksville	Michael Manting	W	9V	103	On My Honor	1/1
904-878-4413	FL	Tallahassee	Doug Ferrell	T	9HV	26	The Exchange	8/
904-928-9542	FL	Jacksonville	Harold Carney	B	2	93	SuperNET, net	1/
904-939-8027	FL	Navarre	Jeff Norton	FV	19D	101	Terrapin Stn.	13/2
904-942-3913	FL	Tallahassee	Bob OLary	R	09V	92	Tally-Apple	1/2
906-774-8555	MI	Iron Mount	Mark R. Young	R	2	85	Social Work	
906-863-8407	MI	Menominee	Joe Boburka	O	9U	58	Phoenix	
907-248-8130	AK	Anchorage	Blaine Nay	W	2	100	DiscoverySftwre	1/1
907-272-4538	AK	Anchorage	Ralph Harper	X	19V	64	Fireweed	1/1
907-276-2416	AK	Anchorage	Paul Davis	Q	12	111	AlaskaMineshaft	3/1
907-338-7049	AK	Anchorage	Tracy Dreyer	W	29V	103	Play Room	17/2
907-349-4646	AK	Anchorage	Bill Merry	X	19D	111	AnchorageSelect	9/2
907-452-1460	AK	Fairbanks	Peter Stern	O	9U	47	65' North	1/
907-463-5238	AK	Juneau	Gary Irwin	W	19D	111	Treadwell	2/1
907-488-3751	AK	North Pole	Tom Creek	Q	09V	109	T.C.'s ByteBank	2/1
907-561-5436	AK	Anchorage	Todd Savoie	O	9D	84	The Mailman	2/1
907-562-0290	AK	Anchorage	Luke Reed	W	2	49	Alaska OnLine	
907-696-4812	AK	Eagle River	Ron Keech	F	09O	105	Lunatics Asylum	2/1
907-789-1694	AK	Juneau	Matt Anderson	R	2	58	AK EMS RBBS	
908-205-0189	NJ	Metuchen	John Kelley	T$	09B	115	MicroFone Info	14/16

Phone	State	City	Sysop	T/S		First on List # | v (see above)	Name, Features	
908-245-6938	NJ	Roselle	Cliff Blessing	Q	29VV	110	Heaven's Gate	2/1
908-246-7632	NJ	Somerset	Eric Hiby	Q	9D	71	Franklin'sTower	1/
908-247-8252	NJ	E. Brunswick	Fabian Gordon	O	9U	45	E.Brunswick	4/
908-249-4306	NJ	N. Brunswick	Fleet Senseman	R	19V	45	Fleet Street	2/1
908-254-8117	NJ	Sayreville	Bob Kelly	W	9U	67	Cop Shop	3/
908-257-6029	NJ	E. Brunswick	Karan Bhagat	B	9U	62	Brunswick Mart	1/
908-272-6890	NJ	Kenilworth	Chris Sloyan	B	9U	87	The Arena	4/
908-273-7914	NJ	Summit	Alan Freidberg	Q	9D	95	Dmaster's Den	5/1
908-298-9098	NJ	Roselle Park	Matt Korybski	B	9D	54	Just Programs	2/
908-329-3216	NJ	Dayton	Lou Braconi	W	9D	88	AlteredIllusion	6/2
908-354-6979	NJ	Elizabeth	Jeff Shapiro	W	9V	66	Computer Junct	4/2
908-355-3592	NJ	Elizabeth	Mat Androlowicz	Q	2	95	Home Base	2/
908-363-2760	NJ	Lakewood	Steve Hajducek	R	19D	105	ByteWise(tm)	2/2
908-364-0841	NJ	Lakewood	Andrew Adams	R	9V	97	Adams Computer	6/2
908-381-5682	NJ	Rahway	Douglas Kent	B	9U	97	Zooman's Zoo	1/2
908-389-8473	NJ	Tinton Falls	Carolyn Carrock	X	09V	98	Generic	1/1
908-463-0001	NJ	Piscataway	Steve Linhart	O	2	26	Cork Board	
908-463-0315	NJ	Piscataway	Paul Papasavas	Q	9U	44	Parthenon	1/
908-469-0049	NJ	Piscataway	Bob Lindabury	X	9V	103	Graphics BBS	2/1
908-494-3649	NJ	Metuchen	John Kelley	T	2	26	MFTBBS	3/
908-517-1431	NJ	Oakhurst	Rem Hunnewell	R	9T	91	IronHorse	7/
908-525-9440	NJ	Parlin	Fred Seibel	W	9U	84	CentNJMicroConn	3/
908-537-4207	NJ	Hampton	Gray Davis	B	9U	26	Rat City BBS	3/
908-542-7085	NJ	Ocean Twn	Frank Ruhl	W	9	97	DigitalDimen	9/1
908-544-8193	NJ	Eatontown	Mike Quinlan	Q$	9D	84	University,CAD	1/
908-545-2769	NJ	NewBrunswick	Dave Davis	X	2	91	Lake of Fire	
908-548-6253	NJ	NewBrunswick	David Pierce	W	9D		OZ	1/4
908-566-8267	NJ	Matawan	Kenneth Klose	W	9D	82	DZK BBS	6/
908-580-0486	NJ	Millington	Ezra Conger	R	9D	26	MilkyWay	4/
908-583-7894	NJ	Laur.Harbor	Lance Merlen	W	9D	77	Magic Dominion	10/
908-591-2673	NJ	Marlboro	Barry Jay	B	29D	75*	OffHourRockers	20/3
908-627-0318	NJ	Middlesex	Roger Torre	W	09V	112	Airport II	4/1
908-634-1673	NJ	Fords	Dave Dworkin	O	2	34	Dad'sPlc	5/2
908-638-5766	NJ	Glen Gardner	Wayne Ross	B	19U	112	Arrakis	13/2
908-654-3178	NJ	Westfield	Vince Rifici	B	9D	82	No Nonsense BBS	4/
908-665-5992	NJ	Summit	Doug Vohden	B	29D	45	Summit PCB,!	9/1
908-686-7084	NJ	Union	V. Novellino	B	29V	116*	The Place	2/1
908-688-0738	NJ	Union	Bob Simms	B	19V	116*	Union Station	5/1
908-706-0321	NJ	Middletown	Mike Macaluso	B	9D	86	Imperiumms	30/3
908-722-2231	NJ	Bridgewater	B.J. Weschke	Q	9D	85	Sorcery	/2
908-730-9002	NJ	Belle Mead	Ted Kraus	B	19V	110	DEALMAKERS	1/3
908-735-2180	NJ	Annandale	Mike Walter	B	9U	26	Data-Base	4/3
908-739-3693	NJ	Holmdel	David Wrobel	R	9U	76	HighFrontier	1/
908-752-9285	NJ	Middlesex	Chris Mattos	R	19D	88	ACGNJ Main	4/2
908-753-2371	NJ	S.Plainfield	John Glowacki	W	9	89	Raider	2/
908-755-4461	NJ	N.Plainfield	Chris Martis	S	2	55	StarGate	
908-758-5206	NJ	Red Bank	Andrew Verba	X	29V	116*	Switzerland NJ	1/1

Phone	State	City	Sysop	T/S	First on List # | v (see above)	Name, Features	
908-769-1779	NJ	Plainfield	Jeffrey Morgan	W	2	85	[mediaprofonly]	2/
908-777-7380	NJ	Edison	Dave Klein	B	19V	47	SW Soc South	20/2
908-787-8383	NJ	PortMonmouth	John Mendes	W	9V	85	POW/MIA Info	3/
908-806-8856	NJ	Flemington	Kevin Santella	W	9D	81	SophS/W	10/
908-821-3962	NJ	Somerset	Bryan D. Boyle	T$	9V	95	Message Central	5/2
908-821-8015	NJ	Kendall Park	John Reinke	B	9U	79	KendallPark	
908-828-8121	NJ	Somerset	BernieGallagher	X	2	84	Starship,pascal	
908-846-7981	NJ	Somerset	Frank Petillo	T	9D	26	Somerset Centrl	?/4
908-851-2416	NJ	Union	Art Abbondante	M	09V	116*	My Home	2/2
908-874-4104	NJ	Skillman	Brad Presbo	X	9U	75	Logic Gate	2/
908-888-3959	NJ	Hazlet	Richard Camba	B	9D	97	Dream Home	13/3
908-905-8031	NJ	Lakewood	J VanWallendael	B	29V	114	Zipper	30/1
908-905-9066	NJ	Lakewood	John Greenlow	F	9V	104	CAPTIAN HOOKS	6/1
908-914-1922	NJ	S Toms River	Bob Willis	F	19V	109	Ground Zero	4/1
908-925-0845	NJ	Winfield	Sal Crocevera	S	19V	113	NO UPLOADS	30/3
908-974-8317	NJ	Spring Lake	Mark Jackwicz	B	9U	45	Right Choice	3/
909-276-0007	CA	Riverside	Howe & Chapman	G	29U	113	ROJACK'S	3/1
909-336-6080	CA	Cedar Glen	Paul White	X	09D	115	Mountain Air	3/1
909-353-1366	CA	Riverside	William Prince	Q$	29D	107	FOX Central	2/1
909-356-5762	CA	Fontana	Barly Redsar	B	9	93	Bits & Bytes	15/3
909-359-3189	CA	Riverside	Stephen King	B	9U	79	Commnet-386	2/
909-369-9150	CA	Riverside	C. Cunningham	B	19D	107	Hard Disk Cafe	12/1
909-369-9766	CA	San Ber'dino	Norm Patriquin	B	9U	34	Patriquin's BBS	
909-381-6013	CA	Colton	Rod Bowman	R	9	15	PC Spectrum	
909-394-1873	CA	La Verne	Bryan Bowers	Q	12	105	Shield of Faith	1/1
909-428-7601	CA	Fontana	C Moss/B McGrew	B$	29D	106	Sky Gallery	60/10
909-464-2515	CA	Chino	Alan Brenner	B	9U	93	ACR Embassy	8/3
909-597-3004	CA	Chino Hills	Chuck Goss	B	9D	95	After Hours	1/2
909-597-7858	CA	Chino Hills	Chris Epler	Q	9D	85	SoundSource	1/
909-626-1054	CA	Claremont	S. Campden-Main	R	?9V	90	ZoneTwixtBars	1/1
909-676-5324	CA	Temecula	Chad McFall	X$	19V	113	File Conjunctn	1/1
909-681-6221	CA	Mira Loma	Clint Bradford	X	19V	92	ATTN to Details	10/2
909-686-1522	CA	Riverside	Mark Lester	W	9U		MEL's Diner	6/4
909-689-9229	CA	Riverside	Joey Marquez	B$	29DV	105	Legend Graphics	55/6
909-780-5175	CA	Riverside	Jim Pierce	W	9D	101	ECTECHRiverside	80/30
909-780-6365	CA	Riverside	Kim Martin	W	19U	105	Library!	12/3
909-783-6613	CA	Riverside	Tony Summy	G	9U	72	Main Shop	7/
909-790-0079	CA	Yucaipa	Tom Clark	F$	19V	114	Firehouse	5/1
909-822-4003	CA	Fontana	Ed Murray	B	9U	55	Low Desert Inn	2/
909-825-1854	CA	Colton	Brian McGrew	B$	09V	115	Access Online	12/2
909-861-1549	CA	Diamond Bar	Jim Holloway	B	9U	26	Diamond Bar BBS	
909-862-5388	CA	Highland	Mark Rogers	B	29V	116*	Air America	1/1
909-865-2328	CA	Pomona	Rick Foster	W	9V	100	CuriousConnectn	12/3
909-865-8586	CA	Pomona	Steve Posson	B	2	67	Compsea	1/
909-931-0533	CA	Upland	Gary Huff	R	9D	55	Capitol City	10/2
909-982-2200	CA	Upland	Don Sanders	B	2	34	CommCepts	
910-659-9121	NC	WinstonSalem	Jeff Moen	X	29V	108*	PC Solution	18/2

						First on List # | v (see above)	Name, Features	
Phone	**State**	**City**	**Sysop**		**T/S**			
912-245-0610	GA	Valdosta	John Stringham	J$	19VO	87	SouthernEcstasy	22/2
912-247-6977	GA	Valdosta	Andy Smith	Q	9U	90	Bad Lands	7/2
912-249-9124	GA	Valdosta	Aulton White	J	19O	113	HOT South	34/4
912-249-9585	GA	Valdosta	Robert Whitt	R	9U	93	Powerline	1/2
912-264-8326	GA	Waverly	David Little	W	9U	86	Malfn Jnctn	3/3
912-283-1535	GA	Blackshear	Carlous Fralick	B$	9D	96	SEGE	12/1
912-285-5406	GA	WaresBoro	Bruce Kindred	B	9	97	BudgetCompFiles	20/6
912-333-5975	GA	Valdosta	Paul Worth	R	9V	34	Valdosta St.Col	
912-368-8111	GA	Hinesville	Wally Rankin	F	9V	102	TOWER BBS	3/1
912-427-3310	GA	Jesup	Jay Weinstein	F	09B	112	Starshp Entrprs	1/1
912-432-2440	GA	Albany	Warren Muldrow	R	9U	59	SoftwareDesign	1/
912-435-3327	GA	Albany	John Hank	X	09V	116*	Night Lights	7/1
912-471-6833	GA	Macon	Jerry Toler	B	9U	63	Dixieland	13/
912-477-3347	GA	Macon	Ryan Allen	P	19D	86	BROTHERHOOD	6/1
912-538-7950	GA	Vidalia	Michael Brazell	W	19V	110	Cornerstone	3/1
912-673-6459	GA	St. Marys	David Anderson	L	9V	100	Night Shift	2/1
912-729-6125	GA	Kingsland	Wayne Masters	A	9HV	85	Potpourri	4/4
912-786-5888	GA	Tybee Isle	Burke Day	B	9U	87	MicroLink	30/3
912-882-3588	GA	St. Marys	Mark Cirmotich	A	19D	104	Kelsey Tech	2/1
912-920-1952	GA	Savannah	Dave Mednick	S	2	73	ControlTower	
912-920-8070	GA	Savannah	Michael Herrin	G	19D	86	SAVANNAH	15/2
912-927-7323	GA	Savannah	Craig Gagner	R	9D	84	Am Connx	10/
913-266-0067	KS	Topeka	Dave Clark	F	9D	90	Fremont Arsenal	20/3
913-271-2071	KS	Topeka	Mike Ortiz	W	9U	87	S/W Connx	8/3
913-375-9612	KS	Kansas City	Cathy Kerns	Q	19V	112	Funny Farm	3/2
913-469-4401	KS	Overland Pk	Jeff Kosko	B	9F	26	JCCC,MU	
913-541-0120	KS	Lenexa	Gary Nilges	W	9U	72	I Compute	2/
913-642-9895	KS	Leawood	Melisco Mtkg	X	9U	72	Home Pony Exprs	1/
913-722-6577	KS	Mission	Todd Svec	V	9V	101	FoxFire I	18/1
913-842-7744	KS	Lawrence	Bob Oyler	B$	9D	104	DATABANK	12/4
913-897-6667	KS	Kansas City	Frank Neal	B	9U	26	Colossus III	3/
914-229-0197	NY	Hyde Park	Chris Hawkinson	R	09B	92	Solutions	20/1
914-234-1284	NY	Bedford	Antony Arcadi	X	9V	103	Stromi's Place	25/1
914-237-3664	NY	Yonkers	Jim Greenawalt	F	9D	104	Ricochet	12/1
914-245-2455	NY	Amawalk	Richie Cawley	B	9U	93	Amawalk Premium	3/
914-266-8472	NY	Staatsburg	Edward Hudock	W	9D	104	FrenchysHideout	1/1
914-271-9407	NY	Croton	Chris Adams	Q	2	85	2' x 4'	
914-279-2514	NY	Brewster	Rick Durso	W	9D	84	Brewster	1/
914-297-2915	NY	Wapp. Falls	John Simons	W	9D	104	SMBBS NETWORK	5/2
914-297-0665	NY	Poughkeepsie	Ray Hyder	X	2	06	PC-Rain Node1	1/
914-298-8205	NY	Wapp. Falls	Chris Serino	Q	09D	115	Dutchess CoCo	40/2
914-336-4582	NY	Lake Katrine	George Williams	X	29V	114	North Country	12/1
914-336-8269	NY	Kingston	Scott Glass	J	99O	105	Fly With Eagles	2/1
914-342-4585	NY	Wawayanda	S. Fleckenstein	R	2	85	RedOnionExpress	
914-344-0140	NY	Midddletown	Ted de la Mare	B	29DB	108*	Game Room Delx	9/2
914-344-0350	NY	Middletown	Janis Kracht	O	9D	78	<<Prism	2/2
914-352-6121	NY	Monsey	Brian Buffell	B$V	9D	101	Node 66 East	12/3

Phone	State	City	Sysop	T/S	First on List #	v (see above) Name, Features	
914-353-2157	NY	South Nyack	Charlie Innusa	B	9DH	06	PC Rockland	50/24
914-354-5463	NY	Pomona	Glenn Fischer	B	09D	83	10 Forward	10/3
914-361-3887	NY	Circleville	Jedd Jacke	W	9V	95	Bill/TedsExcl	10/
914-365-6176	NY	Orangburg	Ken Whittaker	W	2	86	Gain Share	1/
914-368-4354	NY	Suffern	Mike Sokolov	B	9D	83	Skyline	6/
914-425-2304	NY	SpringValley	Lazer Milstein	B	9D	104	Adv. Comp. Nets	1/2
914-436-5293	NY	Fallsburg	Rich Olsen	Y	02	108	Vampire's Den	1/1
914-439-4681	NY	Lvgstn Manor	James Griffin	Y	02	108	Midnight Hour	1/1
914-452-4753	NY	Poughkeepsie	Dave Harnett	O	9V	104	Rifle Range	1/1
914-462-0363	NY	Poughkeepsie	Scott Wolpert	N	9U	26	OuterLimit	1/
914-462-1536	NY	Poughkeepsie	Paul Corey	B	2	26	PC-PANIC	
914-462-7674	NY	Wapp. Falls	Ray Bobak	X	2	45	PC-Rain Node2	
914-485-3393	NY	Poughkeepsie	Bob Farrell	B	9U	80	HamRadio	1/
914-496-4115	NY	Wash'ville	Ray Albrecht	L	22	110	Glass Manazure	1/1
914-557-3615	NY	Eldred	Paul Paradiso	Q	09V	100*	Main Frame	10/1
914-621-7001	NY	Mahopac	Jeff Lancton	S	19BV	113	Gateway	18/2
914-654-1981	NY	New Rochelle	Skip Ross	B	9U	61	Adv'dCompCpts	8/2
914-665-1725	NY	Mount Vernon	C. Brewington	X	09V	100	Go Diamond!	1/1
914-667-4567	NY	Mount Vernon	Andy Keeves	B$	9D	34	ExecNet,LAN	45/20
914-667-9385	NY	Mount Vernon	Joe Brown	Q	9U	64	Brown's	
914-682-1965	NY	White Plains	S. Drassinower	B	9U	72	Cloud 9 Online	10/
914-693-9100	NY	DobbsFerry	Larry Clive	M	09D	92	Image Center	10/2
914-735-9362	NY	Pearl River	Farokh Irani	X	19VO	34*	Electronic NY	40/1
914-736-3186	NY	Crompond	Peter Cacchioli	B	19D	85	Dark Side Moon	12/3
914-739-8274	NY	Peekskill	Brian Sweeney	X	19VU	107	Laser	8/1
914-747-2836	NY	Thornwood	Jim Condon	B	09D	105	Seven Keys	2/1
914-758-3055	NY	Red Hook	Michael Comeau	X	9V	103	WIZARD's TOWER	6/1
914-782-2080	NY	Monroe	B&B Hassler	B	9V	86	Idle Hour	15/3
914-783-0343	NY	Chester	Bob Biegel	B	9U	50	Hillside	3/
914-794-8904	NY	Monticello	Scott Waschitz	Y	02	108	MHS:BBS	1/1
914-796-1136	NY	Monticello	James Oppenheim	B$	09V	108	CPU:BBS	2/1
914-831-3379	NY	Wapgers Flls	Dominic Bruen	Q	99V	114	Chicago Fire	8/1
914-833-1479	NY	Larchmont	Scott Brown	X	09D	109	Powerboard Supt	3/2
914-835-7898	NY	Harrison	Guy Cappello	B$	9HV	61	Brentwood	30/12
914-876-1450	NY	Red Hook	John Perz	W	2	95	Hudson Valley	6/
914-878-3112	NY	Patterson	Joe Ross	X	9V	100	People Power	1/1
914-887-4651	NY	Long Eddy	Lyle Carey	W	09V	108	Summit Data	2/1
914-888-4295	NY	Wurtsboro	Joe Germann	Q	19U	112	Leading Edge	3/2
914-889-8379	NY	Staatsburg	Mark Long	W	2	74	The Link	4/
914-928-8191	NY	H'land Mills	Ed Czerwonka	R	9HV	91	Laser Light	7/2
914-934-8125	NY	Rye Brook	Marc Steinberg	W	9V	102	The Gateway BBS	3/1
914-941-2246	NY	Ossining	I. Lichtenstein	F	19D	114	Sing Sing Sing	12/2
914-961-8749	NY	Eastchester	John Fix	B	9U	51	Hardgoods-East	2/
914-964-0419	NY	Yonkers	Gerry Schechter	B	9U	99	Lost Carrier	6/1
914-965-4980	NY	Yonkers	Dan Bermejo	Q	9U	89	Spec Apptmt	7/
914-968-2205	NY	Yonkers	John Downey	X	09V	116*	Dome Ideas	2/1
914-969-1266	NY	Yonkers	Steve Bowers	X	29VH	105	T.R.E.K. +	1/1

					First on List # | v			
Phone	*State*	*City*	*Sysop*	*T/S*	*(see above)*	*Name, Features*		
914-986-9341	NY	Warwick	Bill Muller	Y	09VO	108	Mind of WEM	3/1
915-332-4256	TX	Odessa	George Cheney	F	2	84	Centrox	1/
915-530-0227	TX	Odessa	Al Forte	F$	09V	113	Kilroy's Zer0	33/2
915-592-3713	TX	EL Paso	Bernd Jaeger	Q	9O	104	LETHAL X-ESS	3/1
915-594-7645	TX	El Paso	Sean Dunbar	X	19O	108	Sean's BBS	2/1
915-595-8705	TX	El Paso	Thomas Jaeger	R	9U	91	Czar RBBS	2/
915-598-3080	TX	El Paso	Ken Blystone	X	2	75	Academy	/8
915-672-5510	TX	Abilene	Bob McAtee	R	2	71	AG5F Ham Radio	13/
915-698-1332	TX	Abilene	Jim Beverlin	N	2	85	CrashnBurn	1/
915-698-5055	TX	Abilene	Bob Gartner	L	9D	86	Outhouse	2/
915-755-1454	TX	El Paso	Fritz Wilson	Q	9V	101	Outland	7/1
915-857-2656	TX	El Paso	Robert Corbin	F	19U	98	El Diablo	2/1
915-944-3036	TX	San Angelo	Doug Berry	X	2	100	Thomas Paine	1/1
916-275-5361	CA	Redding	R. Noseworthy	U	19V	95	Edison'w Star	1/2
916-327-1208	CA	Sacramento	Ted Smith	W	09V	113	CDMG ONLINE	4/1
916-331-0557	CA	No. Highlands	Mike Weber	W	9O	100	(No Name!) BBS	2/1
916-334-2773	CA	No. Highlands	Brian Gibbons	F	9V	99	Ultimate	1/1
916-334-2961	CA	Sacramento	Dave Luiz	G	09V	102	EndlessHorisons	2/1
916-334-3142	CA	Sacramento	Aaron Bond	T	9U	74	StarshpEnt	3/
916-334-6530	CA	No. Highlands	Matt Feenstra	X	02	109	TempleOfSolomon	1/1
916-344-6727	CA	No. Highlands	Lyle Hintz	R	2	81	BizNet,+CDR	
916-348-8847	CA	Sacramento	Walt Vipond	W	02	107	OLD SACRAMENTO	2/1
916-362-4298	CA	Sacramento	E.T. Bear	W	2	94	Biomed Eng	1/
916-372-3646	CA	Sacramento	Tom Childress	B	2	90	SMUG BBS	1/
916-381-8788	CA	Sacramento	Charles Doughty	R	9D	26	CapCityGateway	1/
916-447-0292	CA	Sacramento	Albert Boyle	M$	09UH	111	Compass Rose	5/13
916-544-1682	CA	S Lake Tahoe	Sally Kosh	B	19V	72	Cheshire Cat [3.4 gigs]	34/3
916-546-2095	CA	Tahoe Vista	Robert Holmes	R	09UH	113*	Racers Net	16/2
916-546-7002	CA	Kings Beach	Kip Gies	R	?9V	109	Dog House	2/2
916-581-5826	CA	Tahoe City	Steven Arnold	B	19V	115	ExecutnerBlock	24/1
916-585-2281	CA	Corning	Greg Smith	B$	29V	100	Golden State	13/2
916-622-2052	CA	Placerville	George Cardoza	O	2	45	El Dorado OfcEd	
916-635-4157	CA	RnchoCordova	Ron Ablang	F$	22	106	Rowdy Ronny's	1/1
916-645-0997	CA	Lincoln	Boyd Naron	B	09V	65	City Lights	6/2
916-649-0750	CA	Sacramento	P.Mc Cormick	X	09D	116*	Woolie Bears with call roll-over	24/16
916-652-5920	CA	Loomis	Jim Brennan	W	9D	86	KingmontObs	5/1
916-674-9675	CA	Yuba City	Ken Gunter	W	9V	96	The Candy Store	8/1
916-682-6951	CA	Sacramento	M. Glessner	F	19D	116*	6-51 Lotto	5/1
916-685-2368	CA	Elk Grove	Mike Markov	F	2	98	Record Place	2/1
916-685-7886	CA	Elk Grove	Karl Okamoto	O	2	96	Elk Grove PC	1/
916-722-2569	CA	Sacramento	Josh Long	L	2	97	Alpha & Omega	1/1
916-722-7423	CA	Citrus Hgts	E.T. Bear	W	2	94	Bear's Byte	1/
916-723-1657	CA	Citrus Hgts	Jeff Fehlman	X	9V	94	The Mind Keep	1/1
916-725-0674	CA	Orangevale	Paul Dyer	L	19V	95	Eclipse,tgd spt.	4/1
916-727-3007	CA	Antelope	Jim Thompson	B	29V	102*	The Break /West	17/2

Phone	State	City	Sysop	T/S	First on List # | v (see above)	Name, Features	
916-741-3504	CA	Marysville	Dave Tudisco	F	9U	89	Millenium BBS	2/
916-742-5501	CA	Marysville	Dave Overton	Q	9U	86	Amber Shadow	3/
916-755-1456	CA	Yuba City	Ken Gunter	W	99D	109	Candy Store	12/1
916-755-3964	CA	Yuba City	Rich Hackney	B	29D	43	R.H. Hideaway	8/1
916-758-0292	CA	Davis	Albert Boyle	M$	09HU	111	Compass Rose	5/16
916-784-9406	CA	Roseville	Mach	L	9U	96	DigitalParadise	1/1
916-852-9273	CA	Rcho Cordova	Brian Place	J	9O	100	The Place	2/1
916-885-1468	CA	Auburn	Rick Stannard	Q	19VV	105	Thief's Keep	5/1
916-921-9949	CA	Sacramento	Michael Crosson	S	29V	99*	Holiday	2/1
916-923-2161	CA	Sacramento	Mark Childs	X	2	99	P.A.T.S BBS	2/1
916-928-0504	CA	sacramento	Jeff Herr	X	2	97	test engr'ing	3/1
916-929-7511	CA	Sacramento	Bob Breedlove	X	29V	26+	BOBsBBS, USBBS	2/1
916-962-3964	CA	Sacramento	Dale DeBord	M$	19D	106	FAO	20/17
916-972-9228	CA	Carmichael	Shane Wooten	F	9O	100	Dragons Nest	4/1
916-974-7046	CA	Sacramento	Lucas Moody	J	19D	105	Source of Magic	2/1
916-991-2784	CA	Roseville	Marc Lewis	Q	2	98	Crypt of Chaos	9/1
918-251-3160	OK	Broken Arrow	Bill Rogers	B	29O	*	FOX ONE	5/1
918-272-4327	OK	Owasso	ChesterMcCarter	Q	19D	85	Ham Radio	88/1
918-423-6165	OK	McAlester	Ron Richter	M$	2	98	Advantage	1/3
918-438-6918	OK	Tulsa	RaymondWillhoite	W	9D		Hard Drive Cafe	2/
918-438-8260	OK	Tulsa	Kelly Drown	Q	9D	86	SoftwareAmerica	
918-493-2137	OK	Tulsa	Mike Johnson	O	9D	15	Technet One	/1
918-627-0923	OK	Tulsa	WarrenFarrimond	W	9V	91	The Hub	
918-665-2711	OK	Tulsa	Wayne Greer	X$	9U	87	Wayne'sWorld	12/2
918-838-7575	OK	Tulsa	Arnie Holder	Q	09D	101	Looking Glass	11/2
919-240-0777	NC	Newport	Lee Starr	L$	09HB	113	Right BBS	17/1
919-278-4198	NC	Long Beach	Robert Cole	M	9H		Globenet	1/2
919-286-4542	NC	Durham	R. E. Lee	Q	2	66	Psychotronic	/2
919-292-1979	NC	Greensboro	Bill Bailey	W	9U	62	BillBoard	2/2
919-326-7839	NC	Hubert	Greg Stilwell	W	9V	89	Cannnon Cocker	10/1
919-354-4753	NC	Emerald Isle	Danny Pridgen	X	09O	66	The Island	3/2
919-362-0676	NC	Cary	Dale Dutcher	M$	2	72	Oracomm	
919-364-7378	NC	Timberlake	Jeffrey Barnes	R	9U	45	The No Games	17/
919-365-0393	NC	Wendell	Lewis Futrell	V	2	103	Cat's Cradle	1/1
919-383-4905	NC	Durham	Tom Faulkner	T	19V	116*	Downtown!	10/2
919-419-1602	NC	Durham	Chris Hipgrave	B	19VO	107	DataGate	14/1
919-423-4774	NC	Fayetteville	Zoltan Bokeny	R$	9D	96	FAPCUG	4/1
919-471-6026	NC	Durham	Allen Dew	T	9V	45	Geneal Board	6/2
919-475-5662	NC	Thomasville	Michael Edinger	X	19V	113	Mach][	2/1
919-476-7747	NC	Thomasville	Steve Boyles	W	9D	66	P.S.O.,law enfc	16/5
919-485-6202	NC	Fayetteville	R. Winstead	F	29V	108	Ricks Place	5/1
919-493-0620	NC	Durham	Bill Foard	X	9V	73	Foard's,OS/2	6/
919-579-1672	NC	Ocean Isle	Pat Finnerty	Q	9M	92	Parity	2/2
919-636-5341	NC	New Bern	Rob Atencio	B	9U	54	MirrorImage	1/
919-667-7157	NC	Wilkesboro	Rick Shelton	Q	9V	96	LifeBegins150	1/
919-692-6138	NC	SouthernPns	John White	W	9U	86	John White's	3/
919-723-4475	NC	WinstonSalem	Gregg Smith	W	09V	108	DarkStar	6/1

					First on List # | v		
Phone	State	City	Sysop	T/S	(see above)	Name, Features	
919-726-9737	NC	Newport	Chuck Katsekes	X	2	62	Dungeon,law enf	
919-733-0486	NC	Raleigh	Greg Wallace	B	9U	74	SCONC,law	1/
919-771-2678	NC	South Mills	William Webb	L	19B	102	doc's box	1/1
919-777-1099	NC	WinstonSalem	Waser&Woitineck	R	2	56	W-S PC Grp	
919-779-6674	NC	Raleigh	Mike Stroud	T	2	47	Micro Msg Svc	2/
919-782-3095	NC	Raleigh	Wayne Aiken	R	9U	69	StarFleet	1/
919-782-8962	NC	Raleigh	James Harris	V	2	101	Castle ARGH!	1/1
919-832-0035	NC	Raleigh	Anon. Jones	X	2	56	AJIS	
919-875-8996	NC	Raeford	Steve Myers	W	09V	111	Real Deal	7/1
919-891-1111	NC	Dunn	John McNamara	B	9U	72	UNIX/DOS C srce	
919-893-5206	NC	Buies Creek	Rick Rodgers	B$	9U	29	Frolic&Detour	
919-897-4940	NC	Angier	Steve Langdon	T	29V	110	Mt.Cuz Obs	3/1
919-922-1047	NC	WinstonSalem	James Slade	F	9	98	Treasure Chest	1/1
919-934-1002	NC	Smithfield	Ned Attayek	W	19D	105	Free Advice	13/1
+31215528096	Netherlands		Arthur Mol	B	29V	109	Owl's Nest	35/3
+45 86131081	Denmark		Jeppe Locht	W	9V	100	BOOSTER	4/1

List accuracy is not assured. Use this material entirely at *your* own risk. NO attempt is made to verify (1) BBS's outside 48 states,(2) CP/M or ROS, or (3) BBS's that charge fees for more than nominal access.

Under FEATURES, cols. 75–79 show the size and number of nodesas follows: default = less than 100 megs; 1/ = 100 megs, 1 line 50/5 = 5 Gigs and 5 nodes.

T/S: BBS Type and Status

Type Codes
A = Auntie
B = PCBoard
C = Phoenix/Collie/Collosus
D = dBBS
F = Spitfire
G = GAP
H = PC-Host
I = Magpie
J = SuperBBS
L = Telegard
M = OraComm/Major/Galacticomm
N = Genesis Deluxe

Status
$ = Subscription required
HOURS (24 hr is default)
(N,W) in FEATURES means
nights & weekends only

O = Opus/Maximus
P = GT PowerComm
Q = QuickBBS/RemoteAccess
R = RBBS
S = Searchlight
T = TBBS or TCOMM
U = UltraBBS
V = WWIV
W = Wildcat
X = BBS-PC,RyBBS,ROS,Fido,Citadel,
    Osiris,etc. or custom,
    unverified or unknown type
Y = T.A.G.
Z = TPBoard

BAUD CODE (col 50=min, 51=max):
0 = 300
1 = 1200
2 = 2400
9 = 9600 or faster

Model of 9600+ modem in use:

    M=Microcom, U=USR, F=FastComm, H=Hayes VSM, V=CCITT V.32 compatible

Modulation type(s) [Boards new/updated after 1/1/93]:

V = V.32 or V.32bis
U = USRobotics HST
H = Hayes VSM

O = Other proprietary method
D = USRobotics Dual Standard (V32 and HST)
B = Hayes Ultra (V32 and VSM)

Note: An asterisk before NAME column means changed since last revision.
! in the NAME,FEATURES column means usually maintains a BBS list.
+ before NAME means personally verified during last update period.
@ before NAME means verified during last update period AND the entry was changed.

CHAPTER 17

Engineering Bulletin Boards

The focus of this chapter is upon engineering-oriented bulletin board systems that should be of considerable interest to persons with a technical background. The author is indebted to Mr. Arthur T. Petrzelka of Iowa City, Iowa for permission to use a considerable portion of his Engineering Oriented Bulletin Board System Directory in this chapter. Mr. Petrzelka is the Sysop of The Computer Plumber BBS and his BBS can be reached at 319©337©6723. Mr. Petrzelka can also be reached at apetrzelka on BIX, 76320,204 on CompuServe, or at apetrzelka@iworks.ecn.uiowa.edu on Internet to provide him with information concerning other engineering or scientifically oriented bulletin boards or provide him with corrections or comments concerning his Engineering Oriented Bulletin Board Systems Directory.

Readers will find two tables of engineering-related bulletin board systems in this chapter. The first table is a quick directory which lists the BBS name and telephone number grouped into several common categories. The second table provides readers with a description of most of the bulletin boards contained in the first table. BBS entries in the quick directory marked with an asterisk (*) did not have a description included in the second table when this book was prepared. Unless otherwise noted, all BBS entries operate 24 hours per day and can be accessed using a communications setting of 8 data bits, 1 stop bit and no parity (8N1).

QUICK DIRECTORY

Engineering-Related BBS's

Sponsored by Technical Societies:

*	ARINC BBS (Aeronautical Radio)	410-266-2120
	AHA HYDROGEN	415-494-3116
	AHA TEMPE BBS	602-894-8403
*	Gulf Coast SPE-BBS	318-267-3228
	IEEE (San Diego) BBS	619-452-3131
*	INTERNATIONAL FLUID HANDLING COMPONENTS ASSOCIATION BBS	713-948-9900
*	ISA Computec BBS	205-995-6590
*	Kansas Geological Society	316-265-6457
	MechEng (ASME)	608-233-3378
	NSPE PEPP BBS	703-684-2871
	SCIQ	313-769-4488
*	Society of Manufacturing Engineers BBS	313-271-3424
*	SNAME BBS	703-684-0233

Sponsored by Individuals or Companies Primarily Engineering-Related:

	AIIN BBS	503-526-1323
	Automation Insight	201-335-7202
	The Biomedical Engineering BBS	201-596-5679
	Bitbus Board	313-229-9072
	BOSTON GAS BBS	617-235-6303
	Broadcaster's Info Center	301-654-6462
	The Cadd Station	205-653-0240
	Central Neural System	509-627-6267
*	The Computer Center BBS	707-746-0827
	Computer Access BBS	919-787-7395
	The Computer Plumber	319-337-6723
	THE CONSTRUCTION HOTLINE	209-982-1297
*	Data Bank	206-868-6434
	The Depot	717-853-3599
	Digital X-Connect BBS	214-517-8443
	EBBS (Engineering Bulletin Board System)	805-253-2917
	ELECTRO.BBS	813-528-1191

	The Engineers' Club	408-265-3353
	The Engineer's Connection	603-497-4381
	ENGINET	513-858-2688
	EVI Titusville	407-268-1949
*	The Eyeballer	702-647-9266
	Finishing Technology	201-838-0113
	Foundations of Science BBS	206-562-7083
	GETNIS	702-651-0516
	Geofuel Geoscience BBS	416-829-4097
	GeoNet BBS	316-265-6457/316-265-1994
	The Interocitor	214-258-1832
	MatChat	510-655-1753
	M&C Magazine BBS	813-377-7032
	Megalon BBS	713-479-3323
	Milwaukee HP48SX BBS	414-362-2020
	The MOG-UR'S EMS	818-366-1238/8929
	MULTI-TECH SUPPORT	305-596-6841
*	NECAD BBS	402-455-4337
*	New-Con (Concrete)	301-687-9417
	Orion's Rift - SAFTEK	615-824-3871
	PC-AUG BBS	602-952-0638
	PCAD USER GROUP (LA/OR)	714-625-2679
	PPC BBS	213-978-0024
	The Preservation-BBS	618-549-8448
	QU-AN-TO	415-255-2981
	ROBOTS R4U BBS	404-978-7300
	Run of The Mill	415-343-5160
	SciQuest	414-353-1576
*	Scooters Scientific Exchange	215-657-5586
	SPACE BBS	415-323-4193
	The Spectrum BBS	501-521-5639
	Statistics BBS	316-265-3036
	Tangent Engineering BBS	206-778-5360
*	The Tech BBS	414-233-4506
	TECH PRO BBS!	619-755-7357

Computer information services which have an engineering section:

	AEC-ONLINE	818-360-7022
*	Cadence Magazine	512-258-9532
	Comp-U-Ease	408-286-8332

	Harris Technology BBS	508-877-7233
*	Nat'l Space Society	412-366-5208
	Santee Micro BBS	619-562-8735
	The Scientist's BBS	216-639-9508
	"YA! WEBECAD!"	812-428-3870
*	H2!net (American Hydrogen Association) Hub:	602-894-8403
*	PCGnet (Professional CAD and Graphics Network) Hub:	908-544-8193
*	FSnet (Foundations in Science Network) Hub:	206-562-7083

Sponsored by Public Bodies:

	Alternative Treatment Technology (ATTIC)	301-670-3808
	Applied Modeling Research	919-541-1325
*	Bureau of Mines	202-501-0373
*	California Division of Mines & Geology	916-327-1208
	CEAM BBS	706-546-3402
	NIU CEET BBS	815-753-2308
	Cleanup Information (CLU-IN) BBS	301-589-8366
*	COGSNET BBS	303-526-1617
	Drinking Water Information (DRIPSS) -EPA	800-229-3737
*	FCC (EMI data)	301-725-1072
	Federal Emergency Management (FEMA) BBS	202-646-2887
	HMIX BBS (Hazmat)	708-972-3275
	IT Annex BBS	612-754-1541
	Non-Point Source (NPS) BBS (EPA)	301-589-0205
	EPA ORD BBS	513-569-7610
	Pesticide Information Network (EPA)	703-305-5919
	Pollution Prevention Info Exchange (EPA)	703-506-1025
	Research and Development BBS (EPA)	513-569-7610
	Solid Waste Information Clearinghouse	301-585-0204
	EPA Technology Transfer Network	919-541-5742
	US Geological Survey	703-648-4168
	VA-Tech College Engineering BBS	703-231-7498

Manufacturer's & Sales Representatives Support BBS's:

*	Allied Computersmith	603-889-9084
*	Altera PLA/PLD BBS	408-249-1100
*	Amaze (Signetics)	800-451-6644
	Ariel Tech Support BBS	201-249-2124
*	AT&T DSP BBS	201-834-6068
	Byte Craft BBS	519-888-7626
*	Burr-Brown BBS	602-741-3978
*	CAD Concepts	408-437-1677
	The CAD Duck	703-631-2559
	The Circuit Cellar BBS	203-871-1988
	CONUG East Coast BBS	407-725-8978
*	Data Circuit Systems	408-280-1613
*	Data I/O	206-882-3211
*	EDN Magazine	617-558-4241
	EEsof MICROWAVE CAE SOFTWARE	818-991-8548
	EMTech Systems' BBS	708-705-7094
	Georgia Power Corporation	404-368-5058
*	Heuristics	(for owners of OnSpec only)
	HP Calculator BBS	503-750-4448
*	Intel Product Support	503-645-6275
*	Int'l Circuit Design Associates	404-242-0266
*	JDR Microdevices BBS	408-559-0297
	Leo Technology BBS	603-432-2517
*	MicroMath Sci Soft	801-943-0397
*	Motorola - Austin	512-891-3733
*	Motorola - DR. BUB (DSP)	512-891-3773
*	Notorola - Europe	49-89-92103-111
*	Notorola - Toronto	416-497-8989
*	Motorola - San Diego	619-279-3907
	National Semiconductor	408-739-1162
	New World Information Service BBS	316-262-1829
	OPTO 22	714-892-8375
*	PADS-PCB	206-859-1744
	PHD BBS	219-478-6615
*	Printed Circuit Design Magazine	404-933-8627 after hours
*	Professional RBBS	702-356-1048
*	R4 Systems	416-289-4554
*	Right Coast (DC CAD)	718 448 1126
	Savannah Power BBS	912-966-3645

	Shilstone Software	214-361-7925R
*	TI's PLD BBS	214-997-5665
	TI TMS320 Hotline BBS	713-274-2323
	WCSCNET	713-568-6401
	XYZ Technologies, Inc.	313-939-4514

Other Related Engineering BBS's:

	Climate Assessment Bulletin Board	
*	Computer Jobs	817-336-8123
*	CTC/IEEE Jobs Database	603-432-2742
	DOC Economic Bulletin Board	202-377-3870
	NIST Computer Security Bulletin Board	301-948-5717
	Preservation BBS	618-549-8448
	Science Resources Studies	202-634-1764
	Triangle Fraternity BBS	317-872-4305

Engineering-Related BBSs

BRIEF DESCRIPTIONS

(In Alphabetical Order)

AEC-ONLINE; 818-360-7022; 1200,2400; Sysop: Lorne Steiner, Northridge, CA.; Sponsored by Los Angeles AutoCAD Users Group; XYZmodem; no subscription or ratios, phone validation; Voice Support Line: 818-366-9407; Tomcat Mail Door, QWK packets; Wildcat! BBS; 80MEGS
Designed for professional users of AutoCAD. Member of ADE-Net, Alacrity Design and Engineering Network.

AEG - Association of Engineering Geologists Sysop: Richard C. Kent, Battle Ground, WA;
Currently under construction: It looks like this will move from a single BBS in Los Angeles to a conference on a geological network that spans North America: GeoInfoNet.
Contents: E-Mail, Geology publications, online advertising, order geology publications, job openings, public bulletins and news on engineering geology, opinion polls, geology programs.

AHA HYDROGEN; 415-494-3116; 1200 - 14400, V.32bis; Sysop: Howard H. Smith, Palo Alto, CA; Wildcat 3.5, 107 MB; Sponsored by: Silicon Valley Chapter of the American Hydrogen Association; No Subscription, Validation or Ratios; Moby Zmodem, Zmodem, Ymodem, Kermit, Xmodem, Xmodem/CRC, Xmodem1k, ASCI; Voice Support Line: 415-494-2915; Mail Door: Tomcat, QWK packets

Hearlding the dawn of the Hydrogen Economy! We intend the BBS to be a meeting place for those interested in production, storage, transport and applications of hydrogen energy. Subjects included the conversion of H20 to H2 by direct solar conversion, electricity from photovoltaic cells, solar heated Stirling engines, wind turbines, ocean thermal energy, tidal energy, etc. One project is to design and build a hydrogen-fueled, electric-powered commuter auto with a range of 1000 miles on a single charge of hydrogen.

AHA TEMPE BBS; 602-894-8403; 14,400 Kbps 8N1 24hrs; Sysop: Rod Gallagher; Tempe, AZ; Tel: (602) 921-0433; Fax: (602) 967-6601; Email:Rod@indirect.com

The main hub on the new H2!net Serving the whole hydrogen industry. Operated by the: AMERICAN HYDROGEN ASSOCIATION, 216 South Clark Drive, Suite 103, Tempe, AZ 85281 USA. This bbs will be the main hub for the H2!net which will connect other bbs's operated by the thirty or more chapters of the American Hydrogen Association and others interested in promoting the hydrogen economy and sustainable, renewable energy systems in general.

! ! !PROSPERITY WITHOUT POLLUTION! ! !

THERE IS A HYDROGEN FUELED, ELECTRIC VEHICLE IN YOUR FUTURE

AIIN BBS; 503-526-1323; 300-14400 bps; Sysop: Russ Davis; Portland, OR; Wildcat! 3.55M; 40 Mb; Sponsored by W&H Pacific, Inc.; No Subscription, On-line call back validation, Ratios: 20 to 1; XYZmodem, h/slink; Voice Support Line: 503-626-0455; Mail Door: Tomcat!, QWK mail packets

File and conferences open to general public with no subscription fees. Conference areas for all engineering diciplines and most all software applications, with a focus on AutoCad and Microstaton. Expect growing areas for Microsoft Windows and Novell Netware support.

Ariel BBS; 908-249-2124; 300-9600 HST; Highland Park, NJ Wildcat; 5 Meg; Sponsored by Ariel; Free Subscription; Voice Support Line: 908-249-2900

Ariel is a leader in Digital Signal Processing (DSP) development system technology. We offer a wide range of DSP development and data acquisition systems which include DSP hardware and software for the IBM PC/AT, Sun SparcStation and 386i, HP-9000 200/300, MAC-II, NeXT, and VMEbus systems. The Ariel DSP BBS is dedicated to provide information and support for these systems, as well as being a venue for DSP information sharing. It is beneficial to those who are using Ariel development systems and to those who are looking for information about

DSP. We currently support DSP chips made by AT&T, Motorola and Texas Instruments.

Alternative Treatment Technology Information Center (ATTIC) BBS; 301-670-3808; 1200-2400; Sponsored by: USEPA's Office of Research and Development, Risk Reduction Engineering Laboratory; PCBoard V14.5; Voice Telephone: 301-670-6294

Services: 4 on-line hazardous waste treatment databases (treatment bibliography, water treatability, technical assistance, calendar of events), bulletins

Automation Insight; 201-335-7202; Sysop: Bill Bentley; PC Board 14.5a;

Specialty: Industrial Automation, Process Control, Instrumentation and related topics. All Aspects. Conference topics on equipment, software, vendors, applications, and professional topics.

Cost: Subscription Only. $150/yr. Half price startup sale! Special charter member offer now also.

The Biomedical Engineering BBS; 201-596-5679, 300/1200/2400 Sysop: John F. Andrews, Newark, NJ, Searchlight BBS; 90 Megs. Independently operated out of the Biomedical Engineering Research Laboratory of the New Jersey Institute of Technology; Xmodem, Ymodem, Kermit, ASCII, ZModem; no fees; validation required, download ratio.

An engineering BBS dedicated to information exchange between engineers and researchers from all backgrounds who are working in the biomedical arena. Emphasis on text files, discussions of research, and interaction between academia and the biomed industry. Over 60M on line for programs and files. Echo site for medical and biomedical newsletters, mailing lists, and bulletins, including the Health Infocom Network, SNM, and Health Physics Society. Forums on Medical Imaging, DSP, and Medical Instrumentation. Regular postings of conferences and seminars of broad scope sorted by region, from "local" through "International." Announcements of professional society activities (EMBS, BMES, others)

Bitbus Board; 313-229-9072; 9600,4800,2400,1200 bps; Sysop: Heath Smith; Brighton, MI; WWIV BBS, 215MB; FREE Subscription, 24 hour Validation, No Ratios; XYZmodem; Voice Support Line: 313-229-9072 (Weekdays) Hours: Weekends ONLY. All day.

This BBS is intended for users of the i8051 and i8044 Microprocessors. It is especially designed for users of DCX51 operating system and the 8044BEM firmware. All manufacturers of products relating to any of the above, are welcome to advertise at no cost. Since the 8044 was created for use with the Bitbus interconnect, that is one of the main subjects. All hardware platforms which support Bitbus may also be discussed.

There are no games, pictures, or general interest files here. Any such files will be immediately deleted. Transfer section is available.

BOSTON GAS BBS; 617-235-6303, 300/1200/2400/9600 HST/DS Sysop: Jon Anderson, Wellesley, Mass.; PCRelayNet, ID = GAS A Specialty BBS for Anesthesia, Engineering, Medicine and Science; PCBoard 14.5 (beta); free access unless an institution/business, Autoverification available; Zmodem/Batch; Ymodem(s) ; Lynx; Kermit; Xmodem(s) and others; 1:20 Upload/Download Ratio; MarkMail, Qmail 3.0, MegaMail, 344M Hard Disk.

Our primary interest is in distribution of information in medicine, science, engineering, including e-mail, relay-echos and shareware/freeware distribution. Our bulletins contain comprehensive descriptions of our activities. Our Sysop is a mechanical engineer/physician. The BBS is open to the public, but private conference areas are maintained.

Broadcaster's Info Center; 301-654-6462; 1200-9600; Sysop: TIM SAWYER, CHEVY CHASE, MD; PCBOARD 14.5, 1.8 GIGABYTE; RIME ->BIC; Sponsored by T.Z. SAWYER TECHNICAL CONSULTANTS; No Subscription, Validation or Ratios; XYZmodem; Voice Support Line 301-913-9287; Mail Door, CAM-MAIL, QWK compatible

Engineering related topics of interest to the communications engineer 1.8 gigabytes on-line, over 32,000 public domain files, New users have limited download rights, upgrades/registration daily. No FEES, member of RelayNet International Message Exchange Network (RIME), node id->BIC Sponsor is communications engineering consulting firm located in the metro Washington DC area. The MASS MEDIA database contains the operating parameters for all AM/FM/TV stations in IFRB Region 2.

Byte Craft BBS; 519-888-7626, 300/1200/2400 bps, Sysop: Walter Banks, Waterloo, Ontario; Wildcat; Sponsored by Byte Craft Limited, no subscription, no ratios, validation required. Voice Support Line: (519) 888-6911

Customer support and demonstration software BBS for Byte Craft Limited's products which are code generation tools for embedded micro computers. They include a C6805 compiler for 6805 family, cross assemblers simulators and symbolic debugging packages.

The CAD Duck; 703-631-2559; 1200-9600 bps; Steven Minton, Centreville, VA; PCBoard 14.5a/2, 100MB; Sponsored by CAD Duck Circuits; No Subscription, Validation, Ratios; XYZModem, HS/Link; Voice Support Line, 703-222-9743 4-7PM

The CAD Duck BBS was opened on Sept 16, 1992. The purpose is first to be a communication port for CAD Duck Circuits, my PCB design service. The second is to be a meeting place for circuit design professionals, CAD users, and the engineering professional. There are no explicit requirements for use of the board, and there are a couple of game doors to occupy the users (Scrabble). The board is affiliated with the American Circuit Design Association, a fledgling group being run from the Washington, DC area. I intend to restrict the available files to those of interest to the engineering community and a few utilities that are necessary for file decompression, viewing, etc. Thank you.

The Cadd Station; 205-653-0240; 2400 bps; Jimmy Fey, Theodore, AL; Telegard 2.7, 130 meg; Fidonet - 1:3625/459.0; Free Access; No File Ratio; XYZmodem; Voice Support Line: 205-653-1777; Mail Door: The Blue Wave, Blue Wave Format; Time Zone: Central

The Cadd Station is a BBS for the people who interact with the Cad Package AutoCAD. This BBS has several file bases and message bases. Being a part of Fidonet, the Cadd Station also carries several CAD echos.

The Cadd Station is not just for the Cad user only. There are also file and message bases for the everyday BBS user.

Center for Exposure Assessment Modeling's (CEAM BBS); 706-546-3402; 300-19200 bps HST; EST; Sysop: Shawn Turk; Athens, GA; Wildcat! BBS software, sponsored by U.S. EPA Environmental Research Laboratory, no fees. Kermit, XYZmodem, MegaLink, Ymodem-Batch Phone: 706-546-3549 or FTS 250-3548 (Person to Person). Athens Environmental Research Laboratory, College Station Road, Athens, Georgia 30613

This BBS is designed and used for the distribution of public domain exposure assessment models supported by the CEAM and for interactive user support. All CEAM models (and Fortran source code) that are available for the personal computer environment can be down loaded from the CEAM BBS file area. The BBS can also be used to deposit questions concerning model theory, application, and installation.

Central Neural System; 509-627-6267; 14.4Kbps HST -> 300 bps; Sysop: Wesley R. Elsberry; Richland, WA; Maximus 2.0; 65M; Network Addresses: 1:347/303 FidoNet; No Subscription or Ratios, but donations are accepted, Validation: First-time; XYZmodem; Voice Support Line: 509-375-6421; Mail Door: QWK format; Mail Packet Format: FidoNet Technology.

Central Neural System is a science-oriented BBS with an emphasis on Artificial Neural Network information. CNS has the largest collection of simulators, source code, tutorials, and announcements pertaining to ANN technology of any direct dial-up BBS. CNS is the home of the International Neural_Net Echo and the Evolution Echo. A collection of critical files for PC experimentation with AI and various science-oriented files is also available. Evolutionary-science-related files include a 15,000-entry bibliography, FAQs from the Usenet talk.origins newsgroups, and FAQs from the SCIENCE Echo.

The Circuit Cellar BBS; 203-871-1988; 300/1200/2400; Sysop: Ken Davidson; Vernon, CT; TBBS 2.1M, 60M Sponsored by: Circuit Cellar INK Magazine; XYMODEM, Kermit, SEAlink; No Ratios, subscription or user validation; Voice Support Line: 203/875-2199

The Circuit Cellar BBS was first established to support the projects presented by Steve Ciarcia in his Ciarcia's Circuit Cellar articles formerly found in BYTE magazine. Upon leaving BYTE, Steve started his own magazine called Circuit Cellar INK. The Circuit Cellar BBS continues its committment to supporting all those involved in computers and electronics at both the hardware and the software level. The BBS hosts numerous conferences containing discussions ranging from embedded controllers to using electronics to induce different dream states. File areas contain collections of engineering and cross-development tools not often available from a single source.

Cleanup Information (CLU-IN) BBS; 301-589-8366; 1200/2400/9600 bps; PCBoard V14.5; Sponsored by: USEPA's Office of Solid Waste and Emergency Response, Technology Innovation Office; Voice Telephone: 301-589-8368

Services: On-line databases (corrective action technology, bibliography, course descriptions), information bulletins, utilities.

Climate Assessment Bulletin Board 301-763-8071 Operating agency: Climate Analysis Center, National Weather Service, Department of Commerce

Contents: Historical climate information: daily, weekly, and monthly, heating degree days, weekly climate bulletins. For further information contact Vernon Patterson, Climate Analysis Center.

COMP-U-EASE; 408-286-8332; 300-9600bps; Sysop: Stuart Smith, San Jose, CA; PCBoard; ~600 MB; COMPEASE on RIME; $25 subscription optional, mail validation; XYZModem; 10:1 ratio; QMail, MarkMail doors

Comp-U-Ease is the San Francisco Bay Area message hub for RIME (also known as RelayNet). It echos the national CAD and engineering message bases, plus over 80 other RIME message conferences. Comp-U-Ease also has a large and varied file base of engineering programs, as well as a huge general interest file library. Membership give you freedom from upload-download ratios, and access to three additional phone lines.

Computer Access BBS; 919-787-7395; 1200,2400,9600,12000,14400 - V.42bis; Zachary Hamm, Raleigh, NC; Wildcat 3.51, 1.3G; Sponsored by Computer Access Consulting; Subscription: contribution or $35 lifetime membership;

Callback Validation; no ratios; XYZmodem, Kermit, HSlink; Tomcat Mail Door; QWK format; Time Zone: Eastern
CAD/CAM/CAE & Graphics BBS with over 6000 files.

Computer Plumber BBS: 319/337-6723; 300-19.2k bps HST DS; Sysop: Art Petrzelka, Iowa City, Iowa; Wildcat! 3.90M; 209 Meg; Donations accepted; questionnaire required for access upgrade; XYZmodem, Hyperprotocol, Lynx. QWK mail door. Member of ILink, FSnet and GeoInfonet.
The Computer Plumber BBS is devoted to those engineers who work with industrial applications of computers, especially data acquisition, supervisory control, process monitoring, operator interface, or SCADA. TCP local conferences include Data Acquisition, PID, and Other BBS's. If it's engineering-related, TCP will carry it. Home of The Engineering BBS List. Sysops Conference available for verified sysops to promote engineering netmail.

NIST Computer Security Bulletin Board; 301-948-5717
Internet: telnet to cs-bbs.ncsl.nist.gov (129.6.54.30); download files available via anonymous ftp from csrc.ncsl.nist.gov (129.6.54.11)

THE CONSTRUCTION HOTLINE; 209-982-1297; 300-2400; Sysop: Tracy Pengilly; Manteca, CA; Wildcat! 3.55m; 120 mb; Subscription: FREE; Validation: Full access within 24 hours; Ratios: None; File Transfer Protocols: All; Voice Support Line: 209-982-1299 FAX 209-982-5169; TOMCAT mail door, QWK mail packets
On-line construction information on Nor-Calif. commercial projects out to bid, arch/eng projects out to bid, mechanics liens, notices of comp., bid results, homeowner projects, free advertising, free M/W/DVBE advertising, general discussion area, constr. related files such as estimating and design programs, certified payroll forms, waiver forms, preliminary notice forms. On-going PEACHTREE accounting software discussion. Meet contractors/architects/engineers/material suppliers from all over the country. Will accept plans on disk (local blueprint shop will plot out conforming files). Plans received are made available for bidding purposes. Future full service plans room.

CONUG East Coast BBS; 407-727-0331; 300/1200/2400/9600/14400 HST, 407-725-8978; 300/1200/2400; Sysop: Alex Soya Concurrent Users Group BBS, sponsored by Logan Industries, manufacturers of software for concurrent operating systems.
System is for computer Professionals interested in Computer Science and multi-user/tasking operating systems, including Digital Research's Concurrent DOS and Microsoft's Windows and OS/2. System access is FREE to CONUG members, from others, however, it is expected that you contribute by either uploading files

or financially supporting the system with contributions based on your download/upload ratio.

The Depot BBS; 717-853-3599; 3-14.4k HST/V.32bis; Sysop: Michael Lurie; Susquehanna, PA RBBS-PC v17.3c; 400Mb; XYZmodem, Kermit; no subscription, validation or ratios; JIMMER Mail Door, QWK packets

The Depot is an RBBS system, open to the public, with an emphasis on Computer-Aided Design, Manufacturing, and Engineering systems. There are 2 message areas, the "Main" message base, and The CAD Conference. The CAD Conference is dedicated to the free exchange of information regarding PC-based (mostly) engineering applications. The collection of downloadable software includes a large selection for CAD/CAM/CAE, Math & the Sciences, Programming, and other engineering-related pgms. There are no fees, and no upload requirements. The Depot, located in Susquehanna Depot, PA, was opened to the public because the Sysop (an engineer and CAD Support Specialist) could find no other BBS like it.

Digital X-Connect BBS; 214-517-8443; 300-9600 bps; Sysop: Andrew Walding; Plano, Texas; RyBBS; 120M; over 35 external protocols; no ratios, validation required, subscription in some areas. Voice Support Line - 214-517-3717

This board is for Engineers, Technicians, Programmers and Technical Managers. Specialized files areas, a free on-line Resume Service, on-line PCPMenu Program support area. They call us "Protocol Heaven" as we support over 35 external ul and dl protocols!

Drinking Water Information Processing Support System (DRIPSS) BBS; 800-229-3737; 1200/2400 bps; PCBoard V14.5; Sponsored by: USEPA's Office of Drinking Water; Voice Telephone: (703)931-8700

Services: Databases, regulations, text files, utilities, bulletins.

The Economic Bulletin Board 202-377-1986/4450 Operating agency: Office of Business Analysis; Office of the Under Secretary for- Economic Affairs, U. S. Dept of Commerce

Contents: Current economic news from DoC Economic Affairs(EA) agencies including press releases, economic indicators, official DoC summaries of economic news, information on how to obtain data tapes, and summaries of reports and studies produced by EA agencies. Also included are press releases issued by the Bureau of Labor Statistics.

EEsof MICROWAVE CAE SOFTWARE; 818-991-8548

For product support of EEsof software for digital board-level design, including ACADEMY (tm), Touchstone (r), Touchstone/RF (tm), Touchstone Sr. (tm),

Libra (tm), Microwave SPICE (r), OmniSys (tm), E-Syn (tm) ANACAT (tm), Xtract (tm), EMSim (tm), MiCAD II (r), Filter Design Programs (tm), The MMIC Design Workstation (tm), GaAs FET Model Library, Foundry Library Options.

ELECTRO.BBS; 813-528-1191; 300-14,400 v.32(bis), v.42, mnp; Sysop: David Etheredge; St. Petersburg, FL; MAXIMUS 2.00; 260 MEG; No Subscription; Validation:CALLER I.D. through Serial Port; Ratios:12:1; XYZmodem, Sealink, Telink; Voice Support Line: 813-528-1999

Oriented toward engineering, science, technology and programming. This Board is operated for the benefit of its users and the technical community in general. Ratios are not currently enforced. Special interest areas for Motorola Processors, Fuzzy Logic, and other technical issues.

EMTech Systems' BBS; 708-705-7094; 14,400 v.32bis; Sysop: Eddy Hicks; Palatine, IL; GAP BBS; Subscription: Free until approx. 3-1-93; Validation: On-Line, immediate access; Ratios: 10:1; XYZModem, Kermit, etc.; Mail Door: GAPQWK, QWK packets

We are dedicated to the exchange of information regarding subjects of Engineering, DOS, Windows, CAD, Multimedia, Rendering, and we welcome exchanges on most topics. We specialize in supporting FastCAD, EasyCAD, AutoCAD and other systems. We develop products for all these systems. After that, established callers will keep their access for a year, new callers will be subject to a low subscription fee or ratios (or some other option of support barter).

ENGINEERING BULLETIN BOARD SYSTEM (EBBS) 805-253-2917 Voice Line: 805-259-6902

Mailing Address is: 25439 Via Nautica, Valencia, CA 91355 FAX: 805-255-7432 EBBS is a subscription service. While mainly of interest to Civil and structural Engineers, it offers programs in a number of engineering fields. Many of the programs are only available to subscribers and will not be found on free bulletin boards. EBBS is very strong on Lotus 123 engineering applications.

The Engineers' Club (TEC); 408-265-3353; 300-9600 bps; Sysop, Robert Griffith; San Jose, CA; Wildcat! BBS; 80M; XYZmodem, Jmodem; 20:1 file ratio, no subscription; Tomcat Mail door, QWK packets

The Engineers' Club is a bulletin board dedicated to electronic and mechanical engineering. Files are mostly engineering related as are the Message areas. TEC carries echoed messages from TechNet (technical and engineering) and WildNet (general interest). Other message folders include Computer Corner, for computer buffs to exchange ideas, and Society Events, which has regular postings of local ASME activities. The Sysop is Robert K. Griffith, a Senior Electronics Engineer specializing in microwave and millimeter wave circuit design. Co-Sysops are Ron Smithson (specializing in computer related topics and problems), Vince Camanga (programming), and Bill Weitze (mechanical engineering).

The Engineer's Connection; 603-497-4381; 300-2400 bps; Sysop: Denis Desharnais; Manchester, NH; Galacticom's MBBS; 300 MEG; Sponsored by Creative Technical Resources; Subscription- .50 per hour; Validation Required; Most Popular Protocols Available; No Ratios; Voice Support Line: 603-497-4866

The Engineer's Connection was established for engineers of most disciplines. There is a wide selection of message forums covering many technologies. With today's technology advancing at a frantic pace, this service gives engineers a common area to share information and solutions. Current rate is 20 hours for $10.00. This service has regular nationwide teleconference link-ups, polls and debates on current events, job market, file library, reference library and entertainment areas.

ENGINET, (513) 858-2688, 1200bps–38.4 kbps, USR HST, P.O. BOX 18505 Fairfield, OH 45018. Sysop: Steve A. Witters, P.E.

ENGINET is an Engineer's Network. This system was designed and is maintained by a Licensed Professional Engineer. Purpose: provide a forum where engineers can work together and share knowledge, ideas, files and resources.

*Each conference is an open forum that allows engineers of that particular discipline to cooperate with others in their field.

*The files area within each conference offer a wealth of engineering programs.

*Job Bank is an online job placement system (contract & direct) that aids engineers and employers in meeting job needs.

You may encounter new associates, download files, find career advancement or contract opportunities, FREE of charge. ENGINET -> #1 in Engineering!

EVI Titusville; 407-268-1949; 300-2400; Sysop: Howard McGinnis, Palm Bay, FL; RemoteAccess BBS; 100 Megs Sponsored by Electronic Visions, Inc.; No Subscription, On-line Validation; Most popular protocols, no ratios; Voice Support Line: 407-632-7530

This BBS is being setup to support users of MODCOMP computers. These computers are (were) used extensively in process control and data acquisition systems. In addition, we hope to maintain files concerning process control and data acquisition for industry.

Finishing Technology Hotline; 201-838-0113; 300/1200/2400 bps; Sysop: Ted Mooney, Kinnelon, NJ; Second Sight BBS software, 105 MB Sponsored by: Finishing Technology; Free Subscription, Immediate Validation, No Ratios; XZMODEM; Voice Support Line: 201 838 1346

Free BBS of interest to those involved in any way in metal finishing: anodizing, coil coating, electroplating, painting, pickling, phosphatizing, powder coating, printed circuit manufacturing, etc. More than 20 forums covering help/sit'n wanted, misc. items for sale, shop capacity, plating problems, environmental issues, and safety. On-line database of firms in the field including finishers, suppliers, labs, waste haulers, contractors, and consultants.

GENERAL ELECTRIC PLASTICS The firm has provided an ENGINEERING DESIGN DATABASE available to interested engineers. The database contains information on stress/strain, creep, fatigue, and other properties of GE plastics. The system runs software to aid in the selection of plastics. It requires 1200 or 2400 baud modem and Tektronics emulation software (or a Tektronics terminal, I presume). For more details call 800-845-0600.

GETNIS (Generic Engineering Technical Information System); 1-702-651-0516; 300,1200,2400,9600,14.4; Sysop: Mark Mims, Las Vegas, NV; Maximus BBS; 200MB; Network Addresses: 209/229 (Internet: first.last@f229.n209.z1.fidonet.org); Donations Accepted; No Validation; XYZmodem; Mail Door: BinkleyTerm

GETNIS is a technically orientated Bulletin Board Systems with primary interest in Embedded Systems Design using various processors & micro-controllers. Also provides Message & File Areas to support different CAD software packages with primary interest on design computations DC/CAD schematic & printed circuit board software. Other software packages include Orcad, Tango, GAV, PADs-PCB, and more. Micro-controller support for the 8051, 68HC11 and others. Generic Engineering also offers services to its users such as PCB routing, circuit reductions, design evaluation & custom design services. Also area to find other users who have same interest.

Geofuel Geoscience BBS; 416-829-4097; 1200-14.4k bps; Sysop: Dr. Dieter Birk; Wildcat! 2.55; 200 meg (growing) Sponsored by: Geofuel Research Inc., 2704 Ashridge Place, Oakville, Ontario, L6J 7K3; Subscription: $25 US/year or $29Cd/year. First month free; Phone validation or give geoscience society I.D.; XYZmodem; Ratios: 5:1; Voice Support Line: (416) 829-2716; Tomcat .QWK Mail Door

Canada's best geoscience BBS dedicated to serious earth science professionals (geology, geography, geotechnical, mining, oil, environmental), hobbyists (rockhounds, naturalists) and students of the Earth. The sysop is a professional geologist with years in Calgary oil, Sudbury nickel, Cape Breton coal, and Toronto $ "gold." File database includes specialist programs (academia, Geol. Surveys of Canada, Ontario) as well as family games, utilities, scientific graphics, etc. Bulletins give geoscience and hobbyist information for Canada (museums, shops, collection sites, societies, meetings, etc.). Try the Geotrivia games; visit the "Gold Mine"; look for a geo-job!

Georgia Power Corporation 404-368-5058; 300/1200/2400 bps Georgia Power's Engineers' & Architects' Information Service. 2 lines & internal phone system plus local dial-in numbers in several Georgia cities.
System was first placed on line on Friday, February 5, 1988. New users are automatically registered in the Engineer, Architect and Software Exchange conferences. Conferences for Georgia Power Marketing personnel and contractors have also been established. For access please leave a comment for the sysop. An additional conference is available for sysops of other BBS's. This BBS supports engineering and construction professionals. It has lots of AutoCAD files as well as electrical and mechanical engineering programs.

HP Calculator BBS 503-750-4448; 300-2400
For those of you who might be interested, HP has a BBS for their calculators. Contents are mostly HP-48SX stuff.

IEEE (San Diego) BBS; 619-452-3131; 300-14.4Kbps (USR DS: HST, V32, V42b); Sysop: Larry Hamerman; San Diego, CA; Fido BBS (version 12.21 as of 12/28/91); 120MB; Network Addresses: 1:202/715 @ FidoNet; Sponsored by IEEE (San Diego Section); No Subscription or ratios; validation required only if you want to POST messages in Conferences; XZmodem, Kermit, etc; Voice Support Line 619-535-7618 (Weekdays, 9am-3pm PST); Mail Door Uses Fido's Built-in Mailer and VPurge Conference Mail Utility to produce ZIPped Packets.
We cater mainly to the Engineering and Computer Science community, but everyone is welcome. We have some technical/engineering/math software (e.g., Fast Fourier Transform, Digital Signal Processing, Bode Plots, etc.), among others, for downloading, and we hope to become a base for these types of software (as they are rare on most boards).
   Our Bulletins feature upcoming IEEE events around San Diego, and we have message areas devoted to conferences (e.g., Artificial Intelligence, Electronics, Jobs Available (from misc.jobs.offered on UseNet), etc.).

IGES (National Bureau of Standards) 301-963-6234; 1200bps. The various committees working on the development of IGES use this system for communications and sharing of results. If you have opinions or questions on IGES this is the place to go.

The Interocitor; 214-258-1832; 300-9600 V.32bis/V.42bis; Sysop: Steve Rainwater, Irving, TX; FidoNet 1:124/2206 Remote Access; 120M; XYZmodem, no fees, no ratios, validation by questionnaire.

The Interocitor is specifically oriented towards artificial intelligence and robotics. There are message and file areas for expert systems, artificial neural networks, voice recognition, natural language processing, robotics, and other, less mainstream topics such as virtual reality. We have what is possibly the largest collection of public domain files related to AI. Users are validated and able to download on their first call after answering a simple questionaire. No download ratios, fees, or other restrictions apply. We also pick up the Fidonet AI, NEURAL_NET, and ROBOTIX echoes right now and will be adding more, related, networked message areas in the future.

IT Annex BBS; 612-754-1541; Sysop: Ryan Olson, Minneapolis, MN; Supports the Institute of Technology at the University of Minnesota and the Hewlett Packard HP-48 Calculator.

Leo Technology BBS 603-432-2517; 300-2400bps; Sysop: Eric Poole: Sponsored by RKT Engineering.

MatChat BBS; 510-655-1753; 300-9600V.32bis; Sysop: Doug Williams, Oakland, CA; Auntie BBS; 211 Meg; No subscription, validation required; XYZmodem, Ymodem-G; Voice Support Line 510-655-6938; Mail Packet Format: QKiK mail
MatChat is a BBS for those who work in or are interested in materials-related fields. Materials folk include those interested in mines, ceramics, NDE, solid-state physics, welding, corrosion, etc. MatChat is intended to provide a forum for this widely divergent community to get together.

Measurement & Control Magazine BBS; 813-377-7032, 300-2400; Sysop: Robert Aronson
MACNET BBS is for all persons involved with instrumentation for measurements & control serving the following fields: temperature, pressure/force/torque, flow/level, moisture/viscosity, electrical/magnetic/spectral, dimensional gaging/proximity sensing, recording/data instrumentation and counters/timing/frequency/tachometers. MACNET will encompass every facet of professional practice involving computers.
    MACNET - $25.00 per year (measurements & control subscribers).
             $40.00 per year (non-subscribers).
             $45.00 per year (combination rate).

MechEng; 608-233-3378; 3/12/24/96 V.32bis and HST; Sysop: Greg Jackson, Madison, Wisconsin; PCBoard, 850m hard disk, 2 CD-ROMs; Sponsored by: The American Society of Mechanical Engineers; No Subscription, Validation or Ratios; XYZmodem and Kermit; Mail Door: Qmail4, QWK packets
MechEng is the BBS of the American Society of Mechanical Engineers. Five

phone lines and 15,000 files on-line. 850 meg hard disk supports a unique engineering, technical, and scientific collection. CD-ROM server supports general interest and Microsoft Windows collections. The system offers instant registration, no upload/dnload ratios, liberal time allowances, and no usage fees. As the leading society supported engineering BBS, many technical authors choose MechEng as their software release point. MechEng offers software authors and user groups their own file and conference areas where approprote to engineering interests. Internet e-mail and Usergroups available soon.

Megalon BBS; 713-479-3323; Sysop: Michael W. Johnson
This BBS is about Engineering and Technical disciplines . . . Instrumentation to be particular. It has the following echos: Telemetry, Instrumentation, Engineering, Autocad, CAD-CAM, Survival, C Programming, DBASE, Science Forum, Electronics. The first call will be a request for validation and then a user gets 60 min. per day each day. Telemetry, Instrumentation, Engineering and Safety echos originate from the MEGALON! Anyone running a fido-compatable mailer can request these echos by netmailing a request to 106/1999 c/o SYSOP. They will have to come get the echo for now.

Milwaukee HP48SX BBS; 414-362-2020; 300-9600bps V.32, V.42; Sysop: Kevin Jessup; Milwaukee, WI; RyBBS; 40M; No Subscription, validation (suggested) or ratios; XYZMODEM, HSLINK, MPt, ASCII; 6PM to 7AM M-F, 24 Hours on Weekends
Dedicated entirely to software and information for the Hewlett-Packard HP48 and HP28 portable professional calculators/computers. Most files have been compressed using PKZIP. Various IBM executables for the HP48 and assorted IBM file compression and file transfer protocols are also available. All HP48 "goodies disks" are available for download.

The MOG-UR'S EMS; 818-366-1238/8929; USR HST & V.32; PST; Sysop: Tom Tcimpidis, Granada Hills, CA; Wildcat! BBS; 676 Mb; RIME address: MOGUR. Sponsored by TGT Technologies; Subscription optional; Mail validation for full access XYZmodem, Bimodem, Puma; no ratios; Voice Support Line 818-366-4837; Mail Door: TomCat & MegaMail Mail Packet Format: .QWK, .TXT and Mega
Many engineering sections catering to Television Broadcast Engineering, HDTV and IDTV, Computer Engineering for the IBM PC and compatibles, and many other diverse engineering interests and disciplines. The system is network affiliated with RIME. Multi-user with four nodes, hundreds of conferences and thousands of files. The system also supports strong programming sections as well.

MULTI-TECH SUPPORT; 305-596-6841; 14400 bps; Sysop: Juan Martinez; Miami, FL; Multinet BBS software; 300 Meg; Subscription: Varies; Validation: Yes;

Ratios: With subscrition; File Transfer Protocols: Most popular; Voice Support Line: 305-342-9667
Support for X-ray Service and sales, also job posting in the medical field, biomed, computers and OS2 area almost ready.

National Semiconductor; 408-739-1162; 300/1200 bps
National Semiconductor Microcontroller Applications Group Welcomes you to the Dial-a-Helper System. Dial-a-Helper is a free service provided by National Semiconductor Corporation for our microcontroller customers and field sales personnel. Files on this system are available for your perusal and for downloading to your system if desired. If you have difficulty using this system, call (408) 721-5582 for help.

New World Information Service BBS; 316-262-1829; 1200/2400/9600 SpeedModem; Sysop: Steve Meirowsky, Wichita, KS; Wildcat! v2.55; 170Meg; No Subscription or Validation, High Ratios; Sponsored by New World Designs; YZmodem, Tmodem, Kermit, Etc; Tomcat v2.9 (QWK) Mail Door
Supporting development of personal engineering applications. Expert software users in embedded systems, DSPs, C,C++, 8bit CPUs(6502,Z80,..), 16bit CPUs (8088,68000), and much more. Expert hardware users with interface experience on IBM PCs, MacIntosh, Amiga, Commodore 64, MIDI. Also home of PathTool IBM PC shareware. Also has a caving message area. Everyone is welcome (novice, students, or professionals)!

NIU CEET BBS; 815-753-2308; 1200/2400/9600 bps; Sysop: Terrance A. Olin; DeKalb, IL; Wildcat! 2.55N; 350M; XYZmodem, Bimodem, Jmodem, Kermit; No subscription, 15:1 ratio; Sponsored by: Northern Illinois University, College of Engineering & Engineering Technology, DeKalb, IL 60115
Desc: Open to all interested parties. Provide professional, college admin & general BBS Services
Mail: Terrance A. Olin c/o Northern Illinois University, College of Engineering & Engineering Technology, DeKalb, IL 60115 815-753-8055 Voice

Non-Point Source (NPS) BBS; 301-589-0205; 1200/2400/9600 bps; PCBoard V14.5; Sponsored by: USEPA's Office of Wetlands, Oceans, and Watersheds, Assessment and Watershed Protection Division; Voice Telephone: (301)589-5318 or (703)385-6000
Services: On-line databases, text files, bulletins.

OPTO 22 BBS; 714-892-8375; 300/1200 bps
This Bulletin board is our no-charge service for customers using computers in industrial control. For your convenience we have included: Software drivers for

OPTOMUX and various computers; application software examples; new product announcements; third party software packages, including Paragon LC.

EPA ORD BBS; 513-569-7610, 1200/2400; Sysop: Jose Perez, Cincinnati, OH; PCBoard, 170MB; Sponsored by U.S. EPA/ORD; No fees, ratios or validation; VoiceSupportLine, 513-569-7272
Created to serve as a forum for the exchange of scientific and technical research information both within and external to EPA.

Orion's Rift - SAFTEK; (615)824-3871; 14.4K (16.8 other ZyXels); Sysop: Stephen Tenhet; Nashville, TN
Dedicated to occupational safety and risk management, science and engineering, computing and fun . . .

PC-AUG BBS; 602-952-0638, 1200/19.2 USR Dual Std V.42bis; Sysop: James Witt, Phoenix, AZ; Wildcat 3.01s; 240 megs; ADEnet; Validation, No Subscription, 3-1 File Ratio; XYZmodem, Kermit; Voice Support Line: 602-840-9230; Tomcat 3.01 Mail Door (QWK) and MA(s)
My primary goals are to develop interactive user discussions related to AutoCAD, AutoDesk products, RayTracing (Vivid) or any other CAD software packages. I'm very interested in developing a MicroStation, CAD/CAM, Civil/DCA, conferences through PC-AUG BBS. PC-AUG BBS will offer interested individual(s) specific conference areas relevant to their discipline, if requested, and enough participation. PC-AUG BBS offers all ADENET (AutoCAD) message conferences, most Intelec application related conferences, including the BIX Microbytes news. Message conferences are open to the general public FREE of charge. There are restrictions imposed to PC-AUG BBS file areas.

PCAD USER GROUP (LA/OR); 714-625-2679; Sysop, JAK OLSON; Pacific Time Zone; 2400 bps; WWIV; 65M; Sponsored by ROYOCAD, INC.; No Subscription or ratios, instant validation; XYMODEM/BATCH Voice Support Line, 714-625-1080 (TAMMY)
Open to all PCAD users, and anyone interested in circuit board design. Hope to add support for users of PADS software soon. Full access on first call. Valuable to both new designers and experienced veterans.
* 3rd-Party utility reviews, announcements, user-written software
* Open-forum design conference, with tips, tricks, and workarounds
* Hardware swap meet, and a new job shop (employment) area
* Discussion on setting standards, CAE/CAM and integration issues
* subdivided file transfer section. Trade components, macros, etc
* Tutorials for most-misunderstood/least-documented design tasks

CALL AS OFTEN AS YOU LIKE. DON'T PANIC. FRIENDLY SYSOP. NOT A SALES TOOL

PHD BBS; 219-478-6615; 300-9600 bps; Sysop: C. Jay Hatter; Fort Wayne, IN; Wildcat! 2.55; 40 meg; Sponsored by PHD, Inc.; No subscription, validation or ratios; XYZmodem, ASCII, Kermit, etc.; Voice Support Line: 219-747-6151 Ext. 202

Intended as a support mechanism for PHD Customers and Distributors, as well as an informational aid to engineers in general. Available files include the company's own Product CAD Drawing Files and Product Sizing/Selection Softwares. Have ideas for additional uses? Leave a comment to the Sysop. . . I'd love to hear from you!

PPC BBS; 213-978-0024; 300/1200/2400/9600; Sysop: Personal Programming Center Bulletin Board Service

Supporting users of Handheld and Portable Computers, Programmable Calculators (mostly HP) and Artificial Intelligence. This bulletin board was established by Personal Programming Center (PPC), an independent user group that, since 1974, has been supporting programmable calculators and handheld computers. PPC was incorporated in California in 1982 and disbanded in 1988. Our main interest is artificial intelligence and its applications. We are also interested in certain technologies related to the latest in handheld computers. These include ham radio, artificial intelligence, forth language (especially HP-71B forth), and other sciences.

Pesticide Information Network (PIN) BBS; 703-305-5919; 1200/2400 bps, 7E1; Sponsored by: USEPA's Office of Pesticide Programs; Voice Telephone: (703)305-7449

Services: On-line databases (pesticide monitoring inventory, restricted use products, and chemical index)

Pollution Prevention Information Exchange (PIES); 703-506-1025 1200/2400/9600 bps; PCBoard V14.5; Sponsored by: USEPA's Office of Environmental Engineering and Technology Demonstration and Office of Pollution Prevention; Voice Telephone: (703)821-4800 or (202)475-7161

Services: On-line pollution prevention databases (program summaries, case studies, publications, contacts, calendar of events, grants, environmental education), short publications, and bulletins

The Preservation-BBS 618-549-8448; 300-2400bps Sysop: Bob Pauls; Carbondale, IL 62901

The Preservation-BBS exists to provide technical and strategic advice to callers regarding the use of historic preservation tools for the development of communities. Preservation is both an art and a science requiring a multi-disciplinary approach to community, building, and site protection. Standards exist by which all historically and architecturally significant structures should be repaired, replaced and adaptively reused. The BBS serves as technical resource as well as a forum for preservation activists to explore creative solutions to the loss of the world's cultural heritage.

QU-AN-TO; 415-255-2981; 1200/2400 bps; Sysop: Dr. Ken Hunter
QU-AN-TO is a BBS for users of QUantitative ANalytic TOols. Major topics supported are mathematics, statistics, engineering, and some of the sciences (e.g., astronomy, electronics, geology). We are a serious BBS, primarily for people who use quantitative techniques in their professions or studies. Access by individuals interested in games, graphics, or utilities is discouraged.

Research and Development BBS (EPA); 513-569-7610; 1200/2400 bps PCBoard
V14.5; Sponsored by: USEPA's Office of Research and Development, Center for
Environmental Research Information; Voice Telephone 513-569-7272
Services: On-line ORD bibliography, public domain software and databases, bulletins.

ROBOTS R4U BBS; 404-978-7300; 3/12/2400; Sysop: JOHN W. GUTMANN,
Lilburn, GA; RBBS-PC VER 17.1; 10 MEG; Sponsored by REAL - Robot
Experimenter Amateur League; No Subscription, Validation, Ratios; XMO-
DEM,YMODEM,ASCII; Voice Support Line, 404-972-7082
ROBOTS R4U BBS is a Hobby Robot building BBS. All Files, Bulletins, Messages, are related to "How to build, program, and operate a Robot." Product information, resources, individuals, locations, supporting or relating to ROBOTS. This is a very focused board. Sysop formed the first Hobby Robot Club in Southeast USA in 1981. The BBS was online Jan 5th 1990. Downloads/Uploads, 60 min on the first call. You can enter and read messages, bulletins and most files after answering a short questionnaire. If you prepare ASCII files in advance you can upload directly into message base. Make your files no more than 72 col 19 lines. Bulletins 79 col any line length.

Run of The Mill; 415-343-5160; 300 to 14.4 HST; Sysop: Don Silva, San Mateo, CA;
RBBS-PC, 460meg; Network Addresses: 1:125/727@fidonet; No Subscription,
Validation: Questionaire, Ratios: Must contribute; ascii, XYZModem, Hslink,
Kermit; Voice Support Line: by prior arrangement; Mail Door: Mail Manager,
QWK Packets
Run of The Mill BBS was started to provide FREE access for ACAD. Later it expanded to be the one stop source for information for practicing engineers. It supports RBBS and network communications. Heavy emphasis on engineering, CAD,

science, and database. Many conferences are being added! Member of Fidonet and SFnet.

Santee Micro BBS; 619-562-8735; 300/1200/2400 bps; Sysop: Dennis Kleinsmith
Conversation, latest files, live Doors reviews, file downloads, sale/want ads, Prometheus 2400 baud Promodem
  The Santee Micro
  10125 Woodpark Dr.
  Santee, CA. 92071

Savannah Power BBS; 912-966-3645, 1200/2400 22 Hrs.; Sysops: William Hamilton, Gary Hodges, Robert Tuck, Tim Venters; Savannah, GA; An independent technical BBS for the instrumentation and control departments; free, verification required
The purpose of this BBS is to allow instrument and controls technicians from around Southern Company and this area to exchange programs, technical info, hints for solving problems, problems associated with equipment, and any other data that may be useful to our individual plants. This BBS is for only I&C shops and other technical crafts.

SCIENCE FACTOR BBS; 206-562-7083; 1200-2400 bps; 1200-19.2K DS; Sysop: Bruce N. Baker; Bellevue, WA; PCBoard 14.5 /E3; 300 Meg; Sponsored by: Science Factor Systems; Donations accepted; Validation Via Mail Registration; Ratios On Free Access only, No ratios on Donators; XYZmodem; Mail Door: QMAIL4 QWK Format
Science Factor is a dedicated Science/Technical/Education/Engineering BBS. The System is run with Lantastic 4.0 on 3 286's and 1 386sx and supports 300 Meg of non-game file space. Free access is available on Node 1, Donations are required for Node 2 access.
 Features:
  * Home of SFNET (Science Factor Science Network) which is an international messaging network.
  * Specialized and categorized File Directories.
  * Space Link updates done periodically (NASA info).
  * SFS and AEC Technical Support.

SCIENCE RESOURCES STUDIES (SRS RBBS) 202-634-1764; Voice line is 202-634-4636
From the National Science Foundation. The system lists federal funds for research and development, scientific and engineering expenditures, and international comparisons of science and technology data. For more information contact Vanessa Richardson at NSF.

The Scientist's BBS; (216)639-9508; 1200-9600mnp5; Sysop: Soo Kurz; Concord, OH; PCBoard 14.5; 330 meg; Subscription $35 per year; Mail Validation, No Ratios; XYModem; Voice Support Line: (216)639-0853

Science, engineering, medicine, C/C++ programming section, many science conferences, MIDI.

SCIQ BBS 313-769-4488; 300–2400bps, 4 lines; Sysop: Robert Tait; Ann Arbor, MI; Sponsored by Industrial Technology Institute; XYZModem, Kermit, ASCII; no subscription or ratios, validation required; Available 4:00 AM to 3:00 AM daily; Galacticomm, 60M; Voice Support Line: 313-769-4498

The SCIQ BBS is dedicated to serving the sensing, quality and vision industry, as it is related to manufacturing of durable goods. Intended to be an information and discussion board, it has a variety of Special Interest Groups, and a News forum, with electronic reprints of select journal articles, and specilized news items. The board is also available as a platform for customer support by manufacturers and vendors. A small technical file library is available. Users can start and moderate SIG's if they are within the mission of the board.

SciQuest BBS; 414-353-1576; 19200 bps; Sysop: Jeff Otto; Milwaukee, WI; DSZ, Bimodem, MPT, SuperK, Jmodem, PcKermit, Megalink, WXmodem; subscription optional, mandatory validation, 15:1 ratio users, 25:1 ratio sysops; Remote Access, 310 meg; RAQMX Mail Door, Fido Mail format; Fido 1:154/32; 22.5 hours/day

SciQuest BBS is a science, math and engineering BBS, dedicated to education and support of these technical areas. Approximately 50% of the 130 meg of online files are in these categories. Support is also give through fidonet echos of related subjects. Offline reading is available through RAQMX, and furthermore all files are freqable. SciQuest allows file transfers up to 19200 bps through the use of a Hayes Ultra 96 V.32/V.42 V.42 bis modem. Although subscriptions are available, they are not mandatory. Registration (validation) for local users can be achieved through a call back verification door. Long distance callers must leave a message requesting validation.

Shilstone Software; 214-361-7925R; Sysop: Jay Shilstone; Dallas, TX; RBBS-PC; 10M; Sponsored by Shilstone Software Co.; Voice Support Line: 214-361-9681; No subscription or ratios, minimal validation; X-modem, 1K X-modem, ASCII

Primarily intended as a support BBS for our customers, we are also trying to accumulate software relating to concrete and construction. Also looking for data files (i.e.'s zip codes, SIC code, anything that might be of use in a database format). Especially like to find database of printer control codes for lots of different printers. You need to put R after phone number for reverse modem detection. If that doesn't work, try ";ATA" and wait about 20 seconds for confirmation.

Solid Waste Information Clearinghouse (SWICH) BBS; 301-585-0204; 1200/2400 bps; PCBoard V14.2; Sponsored by: USEPA's Office of Solid Waste and Solid Waste Association of North America; Voice Telephone: 800-677-9424
Services: On-line SWICH library database, document orders, bulletins.

SPACE BBS; 415-323-4193; 10 Nodes/4 Public; 2400-19,200 DS; Sysop: Owen Hawkins, Menlo Park, Calif; PC board; 4.8 gB; file ratios unless subscriber, no validation; XYZmodem, Kermit, Bimodem; Voice support, 415-323-6693; QMAIL4 - MARKMAIL QWK Doors; SPACE (Relay-Net) spacebbs!uucp (Usenet)
10 lines, 30,000+ files, 1,000+ conferences for computer professionals

The Spectrum BBS; 501-521-5639; 300-14.4k(HST/v.32); Sysop: Kurtis Jones; AR; RemoteAccess 1.10; 200 meg; Network Addresses: 1:391/1110; Free subscription, Validation by Message, Ratios: 1:5 for first-time callers; XYZmodem; Mail Door: MCQwk, QWK Format
The Spectrum BBS offers a wide varity of engineering/science-related files, as well as a large selection of AutoCAD related files. The Spectrum BBS also carries CAD/science/astronomy/physics related EchoMail message areas. First-time callers are given full upload/download privilages. The Spectrum BBS is FREE system running on a Compaq 386 w/ a USRobotics Dual Standard modem (HST/v.32) and 200 megabytes of drive space.

Statistics BBS; (316) 265-3036; Sysop: Brad Brown; Wichita, KS; 2400 bps Wildcat! 2.50; 305meg; No subscription, validation or ratios; Sponsored by Institute for Statistical Applications; Zmodem, etc.; Voice Support Line, 316-648-5093 pager; Mail Door Tomcat!; Mail Packet Format .QWK
The Statistics BBS is a non-profit no fee board established to promote the dissemination of knowledge concerning statistics throughout society. Other subjects, including engineering, math, science and education, are supported. Topics of special interest include chaos theory including fractals, reliability, quality, design of experiments, statistical process control, and industrial statistics. Small business owners, manufacturers, retailers, educators and students are welcome to seek consultation regarding experimental design, SPC, etc. Experienced industrial statisticians and practioners are available for consultation and advisement.

Tangent Engineering BBS; 206-778-5360; Sysop: Lew Merrick; Lynnwood, WA; 300/1200/2400; Wildcat; 15M; Sponsored by Tangent Engineering; no subscription or ratios, validation required; XYZModem, Jmodem; Hours: 6PM–6AM & weekends.
The Tangent Engineering BBS is open to the public from 6:00 PM to 6:00 AM Monday through Friday and 24 hours on Saturday and Sunday. The justification for this BBS is client support. Public access comes secondarily. Validation is re-

quired for uploading privileges and realistic access time. Areas are of interest to engineers and technicians. Areas for files and discussion include: CAD, CAM, FEA, Technology in general and Space.

TECH PRO BBS!; 619-755-7357; Sysop: Al Gordon; Del Mar, CA; 300-9600
    DUAL STD; ORACOMM; 85 MB; No subscription, validation or ratios; XY-
    Modem, CRC, Checksum, Batch, G; Voice Support Line, 619-755-7357
San Diego tech jobs (140 or more at all times, all less than 2 weeks old). Lots of engineering and tech files, math files, windows files, IBM/Apple/Next files and conferences. Match help with other users for technical help. Files screened for quality. Complete file descriptions. Online weather station. San Diego electronic distributors w/search, microbytes, daily computer industry daily newspaper. No download/upload ratios. Download up to two hours on first call. Every call . . . and it's all free.

Technology Transfer Network (TTN); 919/541-5742; 1200-9600 bps; Terminal
    Emulation: VT100, VT102, or ANSI; Voice number: 919/541-5384
TTN is a computer system administered by the U.S. Environmental Protection Agency (EPA) Office of Air Quality Planning and Standards (OAQPS). It contains on-line data bases, downloadable computer programs, bulletins, regulatory information, etc.

> AIRS - Aerometric Information Retrieval System
>
> AMTIC - Ambient Monitoring Technical Information Center
>
> APTI - Air Pollution Training Institute
>
> BLIS - RACT/BACT/LAER Information System
>
> CAAA - Clean Air Act Amendments
>
> CHIEF - Clearinghouse for Inventories and Emission Factors
>
> COMPLI - Stationary Source Compliance
>
> CTC - Control Technology Center
>
> EMTIC - Emission Measurement Technical Information Center
>
> NATICH - National Air Toxics Information Clearinghouse
>
> NSR - New Source review
>
> OAQPS - Office of Air Quality Planning and Standards
>
> SCRAM - Support center for Regulatory Air Models
>
> OMS - Office of Mobile Sources

Triangle Fraternity BBS; 317-872-4305; Merle Newlon, Indianapolis, IN; My fraternity is Triangle Fraternity. We are on 39 campuses in the US and have a mailable alumni membership of about 13,500. Our membership is limited to students in the engineering, physical sciences or architecture studies. Our bulletin board primarily serves our alumni members who access it for jobs or leave messages for one another. You can call in at 317-872-4305.
Merle Newlon, National Secretary; Triangle Fraternity - 8777 Purdue Rd. - Suite 235; Indianapolis, IN 46268 phone: (317)875-9630

US Geological Survey; 703-648-4168;300/1200 bps; Sysop: Jason. This is a public board but full user benefits are not granted until the sysop updates your completed registration. Since this board is paid for by the USGS and many USGS employees use this board, we are interested in any files, happenings, etc. of interest to the geological community in addition to the interests of normal computer users. The three conferences are:

SYSOPS   : For Registered Sysops of Other PCBoards.

dBASE   : For Any Users Interested in dBASE (II,III,+).

CD-ROM : For those interested in CD-ROM Technology.

VA-TECH College of Engineering BBS 703-231-7498
Lots of engineering students, each with a PC, make this an interesting bbs for engineering software.

XYZ Technologies, Inc.; 313-939-4514; 2400 bps; Sysop: Jim Fillmore, Sterling Heights, MI; BBS Software: VBBS, 200Meg; No Subscription, Immediate Validation, No Ratios; ZModem (All); Voice Support Line: (313) 939-9715
XYZ Technologies is a new company (12/91) that does CNC Engraving of CAD files. The board was established to let customers download their CAD files to be engraved which would allow 24-hour access and eliminate the mail delivery delays. We can accept ACAD DWG files or any HPGL plot file from other CAD s-ware. If you are interested in the CAD Engraving then download a copy of the EGRV-INFO.TXT file. It explains everything you need to know about setting up a file to be engraved.
   Since we use ACAD and so do most of our customers we are constantly adding ACAD related files and info to the board. Eventually this will become the local ACAD board.   See You Soon>>>>   Jim Fillmore

"YA! WEBECAD!"; 812-428-3870; 300-19200 bps; Sysop: Don Habegger, Evansville, IN; RIME ->WEBECAD; XYZmodem, Bimodem, Puma, etc; 5:1 Ratio/125k or $20 annual, validation after first call. WildCat!, 420MB, Tomcat! Mail Door, Voice Support Line: 812-428-3927

Even though the name suggests CAD, "WEBECAD" goes much further with the latest in shareware. 420MB with 3000+ files, many of which are AUTOCAD, SHAREWARE CAD, and 40MB graphics library. 400+ files in the games dir. 34 conferences on RelayNetTM including CAD & GRAPHICS. 40+ doors round off the board to make it the largest board in southern Indiana. The board is a personal hobby, but due to the growth I have been forced to ask a subscription fee. Non-subscribing users will have access to all the file directories and RelayNet with limitations. Next yesar the board will be at 1.2GIG and may add a CD-ROM. Give Mr. Petrzelka a call and drop him a message or send one to ->WEBECAD, the Board Rime Address.

18

Switzerland Bulletin Board Systems

In addition to fine chocolate, excellent watches and great skiing, Switzerland may have more bulletin board systems per capita than most countries in the world. While exploring the Internet one of the jewels I encountered was Byte Rider's Dream BBS list of Switzerland. The Byte Rider BBS list is compiled by Mr. Cesar Keller of Zurich, Switzerland and a majority of a recent copy of that BBS list is reproduced in this chapter, courtesy of Mr. Keller, whose cooperation and assistance is greatly appreciated by this author.

The Byte Rider BBS list reproduced in this chapter represents a complete list of Switzerland's 552 online systems available for access during early 1994. Information included in this list goes beyond the scope of a normal BBS listing as data concerning the use of credit card calls and a "yellow pages" directory is also included in the BBS list. When examining the contents of the Byte Rider BBS list readers will note a large number of bulletin boards are accessible via an Integrated Services Digital Network (ISDN) connection or a packet switching X.25 call. This provides you with two additional methods to access bulletin boards in addition to the use of the switched telephone network.

***** BYTE RIDER's DREAM BBS LIST OF SWITZERLAND *****

[=---------------> **CONTENTS** <----------------=]

1. Information and News
2. BBS
    a) Normal Phone Lines
    b) PTT's 156 and 157 Lines
    c) Private & Commercial Systems
    d) PTT's ISDN/SwissNet2 Lines
    e) PTT's TelePac/X.25 Lines
    f) Voice Mailbox Systems / VMB
3. Calling Card & Credit Card calls
4. Dream Yellow Pages
5. Explanation of the strange symbols

[=-------> **1. INFORMATION AND NEWS** <---------=]

Please send me your updates, corrections, ideas and comments. Here's how:

Voice (24h) 01/400 1491
VoiceMail, DreamVMB (24h) . . . . . .   01/451 4446 / Box 555
Modem, Warehouse BBS (24h) 01/492 5157
ISDN, Warehouse BBS (24h) 01/400 1498
E-Mail on internet . . . .   ckeller@avalon.unizh.ch
E-Mail on FIDO-Net. 2:301/807
E-Mail on Ami-Net. 44:8010/407
E-Mail on SL-Net 250:1100/424

Mail (the old, slow kind) . . . .   Cesar Keller, Wydlerweg 17,
                                                           CH-8047 Zurich, SWITZERLAND

Here's where you can find this list each month:

It's available for download from most FIDO-Net nodes in Switzerland.
FIDO-Net: "DREAM"-File-Area or via a file request to 2:301/807 using the "magic" name "DREAM".

Internet: Usenet newsgroup "alt.bbs.lists" or FTP to "satan.ethz.ch", directory anonymous.

2. BULLETIN BOARD SYSTEMS (BBS) / MAILBOXEN / SERVEURS OF SWITZERLAND & FL

```
-----------------------------------------------------------------
-----------------------------------------------------------------
```

[=-------> 2.a) Normal Phone Lines <---------=]

You need a modem and a normal analog telephone line to call a BBS below. You can find rate information in the phone book. To call a BBS from outside Switzerland, dial your international access code plus 41 plus the number without the first 0. For example, from the USA dial 011 41 14925157 or from Germany 00 41 14925157 for my BBS.

[=-----------> ZURICH CITY <-----------=]

Number	Name	Speed	Files	Sysop Comments	Address
01 492 5157	Warehouse BBS	+Z+V	IAMsS	Byte Rider & Hotshot	2:301/807
01 492 5133	Warehouse BBS	H+V	IAMsS	2000mb,	44:8010/407
01 492 5597	Warehouse BBS	+H+V	IAMsS	DreamVMB 555	250:1100/424
01 300 1008	Amiga Microbox	+Z+V	-A--X	Michel Frei,VSDB-Infos	2:301/819
				ISDN/SwissNet	44:8010/514
01 483 0721	CAC-Box	+Z+V	IAmsR	Xaver Aerni/CAC	2:301/709

COMPUTER ANWENDER CLUB ZUERICH

Number	Name	Speed	Files	Sysop Comments	Address
01 401 4046	Dennis' Box	+Z+V	----S	Dennis Iten	
01 422 8622	eternity	+Z+V	----?	Olivier Schraner	

THE METROPOLIS BACKBONE, INTERNET ACCESS

Number	Name	Speed	Files	Sysop Comments	Address
01 431 9649	Eulen BBS	Z+V	i---M	Christoph Lehmann	2:301/710
01 461 0581	Felcom BBS	V	I---W	Marcel Fellmann,1000mb	
01 363 7037	Gepard's Oracle/2	H+V	I---M	Alex Wyss,3000mb,SDN	2:301/802
01 401 2594	Graceland	+Z+V	I---U	Andreas Bundi,425mb	94:100/301
					2:301/711
01 312 1268	Helvetica	+Z+V	-A--X	B. Amsler & A. Glutz	44:8010/512
01 313 0878	Helvetica	+H+V	-A--X	9000mb,8 CD-ROMs,	2:301/723
01 313 0879	Helvetica	+Z+V	-A--X	ISDN/SwissNet,SAN,ADS	39:110/501
+01 241 1539	HIVNet ZH	+V	I--R	Manuel Vincenz,AIDS	2:301/724
01 436 7027	IBM PC-Club Mailbox	H+V	I---M	Dani Heuberger,private	2:301/810
01 381 3252	LakeField-System	HV	IAmsD	Bruno & Erich Crameri	2:301/720
01 381 3253	LakeField-System	Z+V	IAmsD		44:8010/404

Number	Name	Speed	Files	Sysop Comments	Address

NETWORKS: AMIGANET (WORLDWIDE), AMINET, FIDONET   39:110/404

01 302 2541	Lehrer-Mailbox	24	I---?	Fuerrer-Informatik AG	
01 272 4549	/LGX BBS	Z+V	----?	Fredi Keller,Unisys AG	

LINUX, GNU, X-WINDOWS, UNIX FREEWARE

01 372 0700	LIFE	H+V	I---E	Emil Peyer,1500mb	

RELIGION, SWISSLINK, BUECHERVERKAUF, HARDWARE

01 364 3508	Mac City Users	+V	i-M-F	Andreas Feuz & Hans-Peter Kurtz	
01 382 2313	Macworld Online	+V	--M-C	5 lines	
01 303 0488	MTW-Box	+V	----?	Menschen, Technik, Wissenschaft	
01 371 8408	MIG'Dangerous BBS	H+V	iA--X	Mig/Michel Schwab	44:8010/510
01 463 4001	MPC-Mailing System	+Z+V	I--SM	Oliver von Bueren	2:301/701
01 463 8910	MPC-Mailing System	H+V	I--SM	2800mb,5 lines	2:301/702

NOVELLNET, DIV. MS-DOS STUFF, ATARIFILENET, ISDN/SWISSNET

01 272 0663	PD-House	+Z+V	I---J	Erich Jakob,1000mb,ETP AG	
01 363 1930	Programmer's Board	+Z+V	I---E	Roger Gottet,1300mb,2 lines	
01 431 2732	Red Light BBS	24	I---R	Bruno Meier	
01 271 5737	/R/E/M/A/ Net	H	I---W	Reto Mathis,CD-ROM	
01 291 5893	Sexy BBS	24	I---W	Bruno Thoma	
01 240 0196	Sihl Power BBS	+Z+V	I---S	Stefan Guenthner	2:301/823
01 483 0722	Space-Box	+Z+V	IA--R	Xaver Aerni	2:301/715
01 280 3054	Swiss OS/2 BBS	H+V	I---?	Martin Schaefer,485mb	
01 280 3055	Swiss OS/2 BBS	+Z+V	I---?		
01 285 3655	SwissRe Gateways	HV	I---J	Richard Baetschmann	2:301/704
01 285 3593	SwissRe Gateways	HV	I---J		
01 285 3594	SwissRe Gateways	24	I---J		
01 341 1170	Taste Of Paradise	+H+T	-A--X	Jann Six,500mb	44:8010/910
01 342 1160	Taste Of Paradise	+Z+V	-A--X	Amiga & Grafik BBS	39:110/910
01 291 5606	The Best BBS!	+Z+V	I---R	Rolf Taschler,2000mb,2 lines	
				9:412/885, 27:1341/101, 74:4100/704, 2:301/714	
01 482 5586	XF-RAC Box	H+V	---S?	Xaver Aerni	
01 242 1396	Zenith Data Systems	H+V	I---W	Beat Ambord	2:301/820
01 241 5529	Zenith Data Systems	H+V	I---W	ILink/SWISSLink	
01 312 2861	ZEV Mailbox	HV	I---M	Daniel Heuberger,SDN	2:301/805
01 431 2321	Zuerich Live BBS	+Z+V	I---E	Raphael Schmidiger	2:301/801
				Night life, 700mb, ISDN/SwissNet, rschmid@zhlive.spn.com	

[=------------> ZURICH <------------=]

01 885 8015	ACCU	+H+V	-A--D	Urs Utzinger,ISDN	2:301/806
				2:8010/405	

Number	Name	Speed	Files	Sysop Comments	Address
^01 980 4297	AmiCall BBS	+Z+V	iAm-X	Christian Ruf,600mb	2:301/722
				94:100/106, 39:110/506 44:8010/506	
-01*929*1668**Archim-pectori				>>NOT IN SERVICE (now InformationShuttle)	
01 781 3924	Ami BBS	H	I---E	Armin Sommer,CD-ROM,	
01 781 3814	Ami BBS	H	I---E	GIFs,ILink/SWISSLink	
01 761 6885	AST Online BBS	Z+V	I--J	Patrick Oetiker	
	2 lines, for AST customers				
01 781 4223	Aussie BBS	+Z+V	I---E	Oliver Timme,The Music BBS	
	Wait for 8 rings, Home of the Switzerland MIDI Top 10				
01 910 9194	Best Project BBS	Z+V	IAM-J	Marcus Bosshard,6 lines	
01 776 8001	Box4	+Z+V	I-M-F	Andreas Fink,ISDN/SwissNet	
01 776 8002	Box4	H+V	I-M-F		2:301/816
01 946 0959	Computer World BBS	+V	I---E	Marcel Toeltl	
01 946 1202	Computer World BBS	+V	I---E		
01 926 1953	*Cosmo Mailbox	V	I---?	Oliver Rehmann	08:00-02:00
01 946 0547	CTS System	H+V	I---S	Ivo Ruetsche,1600mb	
01 8340143	*Cybernet LAN BBS	+V	I---M	Daniel Tscharner	06:30-22:30
01 742 0236	Dietiker Box	24	I---?	Andreas Spahn	
01 741 1523	Dingo BBS	+Z+V	I--J	Franco Cattarossi	
01 845 0935	Dolphins	+H+T	-A--Z	Hermann Neuhaus	
01 845 0936	Dolphins	+Z+V	-A--Z	PD-Software,ISDN/SwissNet	
*01 734 4889	Euro BBS	+Z+V	I---E	Peter Baumann,860mb >>SOON	
01 786 2044	Etzel Box	H+V	-A--X	Olaf Schaerlinger	44:8010/517
01 803 0396	Fischer Informatik	V	---W	Peter Fischer,200mb	
01 750 6295	FLEAmarket BBS	Z+V	IA--E	Reto Gloor,900mb, SWISSLink	
01 865 6863	FreeStone BBS	+Z+V	I---?	Matthias Cramer	2:301/808.14
01 724 0006	GEC Alsthom BBS	24	I---?	Juerg Friedli	
01 821 3441	Golden Gate BBS	HV	I---E	Jacques Kistler	
01 7800154	*Gorilla Box	Z+V	I---?	Andrew Despont	11:00-01:00
01 701 1522	Graphics Plus BBS	H	I---E	Roger Mella	2:301/813

CAD/DTP, ILINK/SWISSLINK, ISDN/SWISSNET

Number	Name	Speed	Files	Sysop Comments	Address
01 911 0580	GurkBox	Z+V	I---R	R. & T. Gasser,DL-Filme,games	
01 730 8280	Hades, Elcoma	HV	I---?	Cornel Kaufmann,priv.	2:301/814
01 840 0456	Helvetia SBBS	H+V	I---U	Peter Lutz,260mb	
01 724 1686	Hobo's Shack	HV	I---R	Juerg Friedli,SWISSLink	
+01 799 1156	InformationShuttle	+H+T	----M	Christian Meuli	2:301/811
+01 799 1157	InformationShuttle	+Z+V	----M	Archimedes Software	
01 742 0920	Kertamulia Box	24	----R	Adrian Herzig & Daniel Perez	
01 803 0200	Kien-Kun BBS	H+V	I---S	Adriano	
-01*912*0538	**Kuehl Box			>>NOT IN SERVICE	
-01*912*0539	**Kuehl Box			>>NOT IN SERVICE	
01 748 2775	Lady Bird BBS	H+V	I---E	Ernesto Guerber,HSLink support	
01 867 5033	*Lucifer BBS	+Z+V	I---E	Anubis,240mb	22:00-06:30
01 742 0424	MacBox!	24	--M-F	Data Quest AG	

Number	Name	Speed	Files	Sysop Comments	Address
01 742 0496	MacBox!	+V	--M-F	3 lines, voice:01/742 0055	
01 834 1124	MacInTouch	+Z+V	–M-F	4 lines	
01 945 0679	Mailbox Steibrugg	+H+V	I---R	Jack Hanner	2:301/713
01 740 7103	Master Line	24	I---E	Claudio Meier	
01 722 2235	Maxim BBS	+Z+V	I---E	Dino Fiori,1600mb,erotic area	
01 761 2794	McMeier & Son BBS	H+V	I---E	Roland Hausin,6 lines total	
01 761 2737	McMeier & Son BBS	Z+V	I---E	2700mb,UseNet	

ILINK/SWISSLINK, ISDN/SWISSNET, ANNEX, MEDNET, INTERNET

Number	Name	Speed	Files	Sysop Comments	Address
01 865 6178	Milestone	+Z+V	---SI	Aschi & Thedy	
01 750 1220	MusicCall	24	IAMSL	Heinz Bohraus	
01 730 2910	Nevada BBS	HV	I---G	Mr.Export/Marcel Manz	2:301/717
01 730 2913	Nevada BBS	+H	I---G	1250mb,Novell-Net,	
01 730 2914	Nevada BBS	HV	I---G	online doors	
01 955 0451	PD-House Box	H+V	I---?	Rolf Bieri,Shareware,PD	
01 840 5372	ProLine BBS	Z+V	I---E	Gianni Facchinetti	
01 840 5464	ProLine BBS	+Z+V	I---E		
01 7850144	Richterswiler M.S.	+Z+V	I---E	Rene von Euw,CD-ROMs	
01 921 1863	Rowing BBS	H+V	-A--P	IronRower,250mb,sports	
^01 860 7342	RTN Europe	Z+V	I---M	Raphael Bretschneider	2:301/808
01 742 0339	*Sherrif Box	24	I---R	Erol Serifi	18:30-06:00
^01 720 5892	Sphinx BBS	+Z+V	IA--X	Roger Strolz/Rabbit,CD-ROM	
01 945 5077	SwissBase BBS	24	I---J	Hannes Rohner,McAfee support	
01 919 0315	Turicum	+Z+V	-A--?	Caspar Schlegel,Z-Net,chNet,FRAS	
01 817 3127	*Unlimited BBS	+Z+V	I---E	Daniel Aerni,Gotcha	17:00-05:00
01 814 3458	Vortex BBS	24	I---J	Urs Haller & Marco Imber	
01 814 3459	Vortex BBS		Y I---J		
01 921 1191	Zuerisee Mailbox	+H+T	I---R	Marius Appenzeller	
01 921 1350	Zuerisee Mailbox	+Z+V	I---R	1500mb,CD-ROM	73:7411/21
01 923 3577	ZyXEL Support BBS	+Z+V	I---E	Frank Studerus	

[=------------> LAUSANNE <------------=]

Number	Name	Speed	Files	Sysop Comments	Address
021648 0056	Aphrodite BBS	Z+V	I---U	Aphrodite	2:301/313
021648 6587	Aphrodite BBS	+Z+V	I---U	astrology,3000mb,CD-ROM	
021652 3453	Big-Net	24	I---?	IHS Distribution SA	
021652 5090	Big-Net	24	I---?	3 lines	
021648 2862	Bimiko BBS	+Z+V	I---?	Ch. Korber,700mb	2:301/311
+021973 1008	Black Bird BBS	H+V	I---B	Florian Rod	2:301/312
+021973 1007	Black Bird BBS	+Z+V	I---B	ISDN/SwissNet	2:301/317
-021944*0523**	Black Bird BBS		>>NOT IN SERVICE (old number)		
021323 7501	Black Hole BBS	H+V	--M-F	Aurelio Mastropaolo	2:301/821
021311 7516	Black Hole BBS	+Z+V	--M-F		
021803 1919	Contact	24	--M-N	Dancom SA,chatting	

Number	Name	Speed	Files	Sysop Comments	Address
021803 1836	Contact	24	--M-N		
021803 1837	Contact	24	--M-N		
021803 1838	Contact	V	--M-N		
021803 1839	Contact	V	--M-N		
021316 3042	EduServe	+V	--M-F	Yves Croisier,IRDP	
021323 9914	Gismo BBS	Z+V	I---U	JeanChristophe Heger	2:301/314.3
021802 3948	Gnothi Seauton BBS	Z+V	i---M	Michel Roch	2:301/315
021 24 3823	HII BBS	24	I---?	Philippe Huguenin	2:301/315.14
021702 2608	Hotnight BBS	H+V	I---W	F. Bianchi	
	Adult BBS, amateur GIFs, contact				
021869 9817	Logitech BBS	24	I---J	Logitech drivers	
021 20 8831	Mac Univers	24	--M-F	ComputerShop SA	
+021684 0083	OctoPuce BBS	+Z+V	-A--K	Roger Rabbit,UUCP	
-021648*5332	**OctoPuce BBS	>>	NOT IN SERVICE (old number)		
	World BBS support for Perfect-Link BBS - Amiga only				
021653 4344	Pro Online BBS	H+V	--M-C	Burnier Gilles	
021648 5071	Relax	Z+V	I---R	Christophe Peter	2:301/314
021922 1841	Serveur TellSoft	+V	--M-R	Alain Salanon	
021923 6225	SwissLink	+H+V	I-M-C	(this line only >9600 bps)	
021923 6227	SwissLink	+24	I-M-C	4 lines total	
	Graphical international info service for Mac, Windows				
021921 3983	The Black Devil	H	IA--X	Eric Mermod	2:301/316
					44:8010/306
021701 1667	*Trade Wars BBS	+V	I---R	Sebastien Riccio	21:00-06:00
021701 2226	*Underground BBS	+V	I---R	Snake	21:00-02:00

[=-------------> **GENEVE** <--------------=]

Number	Name	Speed	Files	Sysop Comments	Address
022781 5141	CCTI Geneve	H+V	IA--T	Eric Schefer	2:301/327
022781 5189	CCTI Geneve	H+V	IA--T	TI-99/4A	
022320 5688	CCTI Geneve	24	IA--T		
022797 4461	C.I.L	+Z+V	IA--K	Patrick Conconi	
022797 4464	C.I.L	24	IA--K		
022349 9000	Cougar BBS	+Z+V	I---R	Etienne Deschenaux	
022349 9001	Cougar BBS	+Z+V	I---R	20'000mb,ISDN/SwissNet	
022349 9012	Cougar BBS	+Z+V	I—R		
022349 9547	Cyclone PBS	24	--M-N	Cyborg,NLP	
022731 0444	Elex Net	24	I---T	Elex/Magic	
022342 3369	Espace Info BBS	+Z+V	I---R	Gerard Saloukvadze	2:301/326
				52:4100/123, 73:7410/326 102:410/4	
022788 3990	Espace Jeux du GCC	H+V	I---S	Stephane Marquis,games	2:301/321
					102:410/1
022788 4681	Evening Light's BBS	+V	I---R	Tom Nielsen	2:301/324
022788 5616	Evening Light's BBS	+Z+V	I—R		73:741/1
022738 7184	ExYugoNet BBS	H+V	I---R	Vincent Lalieu	2:301/304

Number	Name	Speed	Files	Sysop Comments	Address
022733 2072	FedNet BBS	H+V	I---R	Jean-Paul Lucot	2:301/303
^022779 1943	Flying BBS	+Z+V	I---B	Fabien Voland,2500mb	2:301/308
022301 0460	Geneva MacClub	V	--M-C	>>ONLY with Mac/graph. interface	
022301 0480	Geneva MacClub	+V	--M-C	>>ONLY with Mac/graph. interface	
022757 6573	GoniSoft Comp.Club	+Z+V	I---S	Patrick Wassmer,	
022757 6574	GoniSoft Comp.Club	+H+V	I---S	7 lines total,3000mb,	
022757 6185	GoniSoft Comp.Club	H+V	I---S	Packet AX-25	2:301/320
022364 5343	Grafix, Vertech SA	V	I---T	Peter Werner	
022791 6465	LWF Angel heart	HV	I---O	Stephane Mottier	2:30/20
022344 5132	Micro-Net Zone 022	24	—?		
022751 2914	Oliver's DiveInn/2	+Z+V	IAS-M	Oliver Wagner	2:301/325
	3 lines, ISDN/SwissNet, chNet				44:8010/508
022777 1270	PC Stop BBS	H+V	—R	Serge Sozonoff	
022777 1275	PC Stop BBS	Z+V	—R		
022320 1195	Perokstroika	24	I---?	Fatal Error	
022320 1367	Perokstroika	24	I---?	chatting,4 lines	
022320 1643	*Perokstroika	24	I---?		19:00-09:00
022320 1453	Perokstroika	+V	I---?	>>THIS line only >9600 bps	
022320 1936	Perokstroika	+V	I---?	>>THIS line only >9600 bps	
022771 2054	Schnopoutsse BBS	24	I---W	Gas-Oil	
022364 4808	StarGate One	H+V	I---O	Thomas Baetschmann,K12	2:301/301
					102:410/2
022347 1100	Sun Serveur	+Z+V	I---E	Olivier Junod	
022347 1111	Sun Serveur	H+V	I---E		2:301/323
^022341 5476	The Cobra Line	+H+T	I---B	Cobra/BBS's Canard	2:301/307
022738 9380	The Square	H+V	I---R	Christian Martin	2:301/322
	9:412/122, 12:806/2 52:4100/12				
022362 8313	The Strangler BBS	+Z+V	I---R	Galactica,520mb	2:301/328
022733 8050	Transnet-2	24	I---?	Many infos,X.25	
022733 8060	Transnet-2	1200/75	I---?	CEPT Minitel/Comtel line	

[=-------------> YVERDON <-------------=]

| 024 35 1953 | Le Babillard | +V | --M-F | Christian Pointet,AAPIV | |

[=-------------> CHABLAIS <-------------=]

| 025 72 1058 | Handy BBS Valais | +H+V | -A--P | Jean Perez,3000mb | 2:301/332 |
| 025 72 2058 | Handy BBS Valais | +Z+V | -A--P | 44:8010/205, | 2:301/330 |

[=-------------> SIERRE <-------------=]

| 027 56 3418 | CyberSpace | +H+V | IA--E | ULi,2300mb,2 lines | |

Number	Name	Speed	Files	Sysop Comments	Address

[=---------------> SION <---------------=]

| 027 56 5102 | Compunet BBS | H+V | I---U | Christian Surdez | 2:301/333 |
| | | | | 1200mb | 9:412/1881 |

[=---------------> BRIG <---------------=]

028 24 2253	Ben's Mailbox Brig	H+V	I---M	Bernhard Willa	2:301/708
028 46 6805	*RoTTu-Box	+Z+V	I---B	Damian Heldner	21:00-22:00
028 67 5179	SkyLine	H+V	I---E	John Warren	
028 67 6207	SkyLine	YV	I---E	Evelyne Warren	

[=---------------> BULLE <---------------=]

| 0294 4610 | Dark Angel BBS | +V | I---B | Jean-Claude Schopfer 2:301/314.6 | |

[=---------------> BERN <---------------=]

031921 2215	Amiga-HOBBY-Box	+24	-A--X	Peter Glauser	44:8010/309
031921 2216	Amiga-HOBBY-Box	H+V	-A--X	Australia-board/divers paradise	
031991 5424	AMiGA TEKKNO LiNE	H+V	-A--X	Martin Rytz	2:301/716
031991 3201	AMiGA TEKKNO LiNE	+H+V	-A--X	1260mb	44:8010/301
031991 8179	AMiGA TEKKNO LiNE	+Z+V	-A--X		93:100/1

UUCP, ADS & SKY, 24BIT-GRAFIX, MODULEZ, UTILITIES

031889 1226	ASCII-Link-BBS	+Z+V	I---R	Roger Althaus	
031932 2575	BGB (Baerengraben)	T	I---J	Peter Witschi & Urs Fringeli	
031932 1911	BGB (Baerengraben)	T	I---J	all modems with V.terbo	
031932 2838	BGB (Baerengraben)	H	I---J	3400mb	
031932 2891	Baerengraben I	H+V	I---J	>>FIDO-mail only	2:301/502
031992 9233	Buemplizer Box	+H+V	I---E	Fritz Keller,7000mb,4 lines	
031992 9236	Buemplizer Box	+Z+V	I---E	ZyXEL-only line,4 lines	
031971 0405	Capital BBS	+Z+V	I---E	Beat Jau,4000mb,3 lines	
0319720106	Capital BBS	H+V	I---E		
031889 1271	Comlight BBS	H+V	I---W	M. Ottiger/Comlight AG,2 lines	
031922 1238	Cybernetic Clinic	H	-A--P	Breschi/Martin Schaerer	
031331 6251	FLOATiNG-POiNT BBS	+Z+V	I---S	Nils Kramer	
031331 6781	FLOATiNG-POiNT BBS	+Z+V	I---S	2000mb,DOS,WIN,OS/2	2:301/705
031981 2022	Hewlett-Packard BBS	V	I---?	Response Center Organization,	
031981 2083	Hewlett-Packard BBS	+24	I---?	printer/video drivers,etc.	

Number	Name	Speed	Files	Sysop Comments	Address
031371 7009	HS-Box	H+V	I--SW	Andi Haehlen,MIDI,music	
031 26 2336	Infos/2 Bern	+V	I---?	Martin Stettler	
031765 5661	Kevin Gets Bored BBS	+V	I---W	Rene Maeder,700mb,chat,	
031765 5891	Kevin Gets Bored BBS	+V	I---W	nice ANSI-graphics	
031951 5881	KKB Net	24	I---L	KKB VERSICHERUNGEN	
031951 5882	KKB Net	+24	I---L	8 lines	
031951 5883	KKB Net	+24	I---L		
031951 5884	KKB Net	+24	I---L		
031951 5885	KKB Net	+24	I---L		
031951 2133	KKB Net	HV	I---L		
031731 1432	LOG!C Palace	+H+V	-A--X	Roland Zbinden	2:301/706
					44:8010/507
031741 4100	Mega Power User	24	I---L	Daniel/MPU	
031741 3967	Mega Power User	24	I---L		
-031971*3035	**Meltdown Disaster	>>NOT IN SERVICE			
^031372 4157	Metropolitan Net	+T	I---E	Gerard Vuille,3 lines	
^031372 4159	Metropolitan Net	+H+T	I---E	dBOnline support	
^031372 4187	Metropolitan Net	+H+T	I---E	& distribution	
031971 2762	Neue Gurten Box	24	I---L	Sokrates/Martin Gyger	
031971 6185	Neue Gurten Box	HV	I---L	8 lines,1200mb	
031721 6372	Omni - BBS	H+V	-A--P	Philipp Ruefenacht	44:8010/305
031741 3845	Portner's BBS	+V	—?	Speedway/Daniel Portner	
031952 7817	Rebel's Alliance	+Z+V	I---R	Cyberpunk,-=Gravis Ultrasound=-	
031 24 3617	Seven Eleven	H+V	-A--X	Mark Steiner	44:8010/303
031721 7052	Technobox	H+V	I---U	Christoph Bruegger,1600mb	
031921 5303	The Chata	H+V	IA--?	Remo,2000mb	
031 23 8057	The Church	+H+V	-A--X	Memory	
031889 0969	Vision BBS	+H+V	I---W	Daniel,demos,intros	
031819 6575	Wittwer Box	Z+V	I--J	Housi,3 Lines	
031922 0529	WordPerfect BBS	+V	I---E	WordPerfect support	
031338 3344	Yellow Box	+V	I--J	Peter Balsiger	
031338 9197	Yellow Box	+V	I--J	Info-Center PTT	
031338 9162	Yellow Box	V	I--J		
031338 9005	Yellow Box	24	I--J		
031972 2908	ZoomLine BBS	+V	I---W	Pesche Geiser, FreeNet	

[=---------------> **BIEL** <---------------=]

032 23 5387	Amazing BBS	+Z+V	-A--D	Christoph Dworzak	44:8010/409
032 27 3371	ISB-EIB BBS	H+V	I---E	Mirko Buholzer,Ingenieurschule	
032 27 3312	ISB-EIB BBS	+Z+V	I---E	Biel,SWISSLink,FreeNet	
	internet: info.isbiel.ch				
032 41 0871	MultiServer Network	24	I-M-N	GABUS S.A. Computer	
032 41 0872	MultiServer Network	24	I-M-N	J.-F. Laett	

Number	Name	Speed	Files	Sysop Comments	Address
032 41 0873	MultiServer Network	24	I-M-N	CD-ROM,1200mb,	
032 41 0874	MultiServer Network	24	I-M-N	chatting,French/German,	
+032 41 3413	Redacom AG BBS	H+V	i---E	Support fuer 8051,Log/i/C	

[=---------------> **THUN** <--------------=]

033 43 4839	Amiga Team 2000	+Z+V	-A--X	Roschi & Bruno	
033 45 7075	Mountains BBS	H	----E	Nobody/Rudolf Konrad	
033 54 8888	Shiwa Mailbox	+Z+V	I---W	Peter Gossweiler,375mb,CD-ROM	

[=--------------> **FRIBOURG** <-------------=]

034 45 3078	*Gourmet-CH1	+V	-A--?	Daenu Stocker	22:00-07:00
	{* Erste GASTRO-GOURMET/FRESS & SAUFbox in CH *}				44:8010/408
037 45 2023	Hurricane	+V	--M-C	>>ONLY with Mac/graph. interface	
037 55 1772	Telecri	24	I---O	Jean-Luc Monney	

[=-------------> **NEUCHATEL** <-------------=]

038 41 4081	*Satcom	+V	----?	Marc Schaefer	16:00-22:30
038 42 2071	*CDS Informatique SA	24	I---?	Christian	10:00-22:00
038 21 4064	*NewTech BBS	+24	I---R	Yves Criblez,600mb	19:00-08:00
038 30 3303	Temptation	H+V	IAMSD	Dune,Usenet news	2:301/331

[=---------> **LA CHAUX-DE-FONDS** <---------=]

039 41 2505	Micro-Net Zone 039	24 ---?			
^039 26 1631	Sympa BBS	+Z+V	I---U	Didier Duvanel/Jeans	2:301/334

[=--------------> **LUZERN** <--------------=]

041 42 1919	Berog BBS	+H+V	I---W	Robert Gmeiner	2:301/221
041 41 1941	Berog BBS	+H+V	I---W	4 lines,ISDN/SwissNet,TechNet	
041 66 2616	CCUW Multimedia BBS	+V	I---M	Patrick Reinhart	2:301/608
041 58 8667	Cybertech BBS	Z+V	Ia--E	Alex Marani,CD-ROM	
041 48 6301	Favorite BBS	+V	--M-F	Rene Baeder,2000mb,CD-ROM	
041 55 6059	InformaBox	+Z+V	--M-F	Thomas Ghezzi	

Number	Name	Speed	Files	Sysop Comments	Address
041 85 2955	Lindenberger BBS	Z+V	---SY	Romano Clerici	
041 42 2151	LUMA BBS	H+V	I---W	Bernhard Isenegger	
041 42 2152	LUMA BBS	H+V	I---W	1200mb	2:301/605
041 53 8627	MICS Lucerne	Z+V	I---M	Michael Buenter,OS/2	2:301/601
	Win, Sound, Virnet, ISDN/SwissNet				
+041 52 8692	**MnemoniX SysteM/2	+Z+V	----	Jan Saner,>>mail only	2:301/613
041 71 4522	Nitro BBS	+Z+V	I---W	Josko Vinkovic,CD-ROMs	
041 61 5805	Oberdorfer Mailbox	HV	I--J	Alois Leu	
041 32 9517	Paradize	+Z+V	---SQ	Roland Tobler,Atari	2:301/609
041 57 2258	Panasonic-Mailbox	H+V	I---W	Pius Gloor,1200mb,TechNet	
	John Lay Electronics AG, Panasonic/Technics-Vertrieb				
041 34 8422	Q/G/B-Box H I—W Urs Rusch				
	only for 18 years or older!				
041 61 7992	RenderEye BBS	H+V	-A--?	Ursus Krolzig,graphics,240mb	
+041 95 3671	Sisyphus' Den	+Z+V	I---M	Christian Laubscher	2:301/614
041 51 3928	Solo BBS	H+V	I---W	Rene Grom &	2:301/607
041 51 3943	Solo BBS	H+V	I---W	Rene Mathis,5700mb	
041 74 2287	SpaceLink BBS	+V	I---W	Kuno Stoeckli,RSP,PBEM,Weltraum	
041 43 1201	StarCom Amiga BBS	H	IA--P	Daniel Bucher	44:8010/406
041 43 1202	StarCom Amiga BBS	Z+V	IA--P		
041 43 1203	StarCom Amiga BBS	24	IA--P		
041 76 2989	The Lycaeum	+Z+V	I---U	Chicken,games,demos,coding	
041*76*????	**The Lycaeum	+H+T	I---U	>>SOON ONLINE	
041 37 4714	Waikiki BBS	H+V	IAMSC	Daniela Broennimann/Unixli	
041 37 4715	Waikiki BBS	H+V	IAMSC	340mb	2:301/611

[=--------------> **OBWALDEN** <--------------=]

Number	Name	Speed	Files	Sysop Comments	Address
041 66 2616	CCUW Obwalden	H+V	I---M Patrick Reinhart		2:301/608

[=--------------> **ZUG** <--------------=]

Number	Name	Speed	Files	Sysop Comments	Address
042 64 4991	ARP DATACON	+Z+V	I---E	Raphael Amhof/Marco Bini	
042 64 5187	ARP DATACON	H+V	I---E	Treiber/Aktionen/Fundgrube	
042 64 3932	ByteNet	+V	I---U	Dani Heinecke	2:301/214.1
042 64 3821	SCA Data Box	+V	I---U	Resa Kordi,SCA Computer AG	
042 32 1537	SWW Design Box	H+V	--M-F	Urs Schoen	

[=--------------> **URI** <--------------=]

Number	Name	Speed	Files	Sysop Comments	Address
044 6 4436	Gotthard BBS	+V	I---U	Wilhelm Tell,260mb	
044	2 7514 *The Primus	+H+V	I---U	Roland Gisler/AXl	21:00-24:00

Number	Name	Speed	Files	Sysop Comments	Address

[=--------------> SURSEE <--------------=]

Number	Name	Speed	Files	Sysop Comments	Address
045 71 5252	Wanger Box	+H+V	I---W	Reto Meyer &	
045 71 5250	Wanger Box	+Z+V	I---W	Cyrill Meier	
045 71 5244	Wanger Box	+H+V	I---W	13 lines total	2:301/812

6000mb, TechNet, Intelec, FreeNet, ISDN/SwissNet

[=------------> WINTERTHUR <-------------=]

Number	Name	Speed	Files	Sysop Comments	Address
052232 9442	*Bunny BBS	H	-A--X	Daniel Klotz	17:00-06:00
					44:8010/504
052 41 3500	CCW Mailbox	H+V	I---S	Michel Rimensberger	
+052242 0253	EPBBS	+Z+V	I---R	Eduard Pages	2:301/809
052 53 2056	JOJO BBS	+V	I---?	Uli Josting	2:301/815
052 46 2644	*MCC BBS H -A–P Max Sonderegger				19:00-05:30
					44:8010/505
052222 1948	Pit Stop	+Z+V	I---R	Pit Biernath	2:301/508
052 41 3521	Sky Box	H+V	I---S	TransComm	
052 41 3524	Sky Box	Z+V	I---S	8 lines,ISDN/SwissNet	
052 33 3033	Squirrel Mailbox	HV	I---E	Peter Haessig,5000mb	
052222 1751	Strike Palace	Z+V	-A--X	Roger Hungerbuehler	44:8010/513
052 31 4420	Unicorn-Box	+Z+V	I---R	Roland Gantenbein	

"Fundbox", buy/sell ads

[=------------> SCHAFFHAUSEN <-----------=]

Number	Name	Speed	Files	Sysop Comments	Address
053 24 5458	PIM-Telemail	HV	I---?	Roger,PIM Computer AG,Tele-Inf.	
053 25 0332	SH-Live SBBS	H+V	I---U	Michael Dreier	2:301/214

[=-------------> FRAUENFELD <------------=]

Number	Name	Speed	Files	Sysop Comments	Address
054 43 1879	Jet-Box	Z+V	I---R	Ralf Knoll,JET-Computer	
054 55 2040	MCT-Mailbox	24	I---?	Peter Wehrli	

[=-------------> RAPPERSWIL <------------=]

Number	Name	Speed	Files	Sysop Comments	Address
055 26 1815	Active-Net BBS	+Z+V	I---E Martin Altorfer		2:301/820
055 26 1879	Active-Net BBS	H+V	I---E	ILink,ISDN/SwissNet	2:301/853
055 96 2135	Hoernli BBS	H+V	IA--P	Rolf Graf	44:8010/909
055 42 1800	Sugus BBS	+Z+V	I---E	Michael Helbling	

Number	Name	Speed	Files	Sysop Comments	Address

[=---------------> **BADEN** <---------------=]

Number	Name	Speed	Files	Sysop Comments	Address
056 41 5578	ACCB Brugg	Z+V	I---SY	Reto Thurnherr	2:301/421.9
+056 26 1969	Ascom-Box	+V	I---R	Marcel Stadtmann	2:301/719
056 83 1283	Brother BBS	HV	I---E	Brother,printer drivers	
056 83 5218	CPA BBS	V	I---T	COS Computer Peripherals AG	
056 83 5467	CPA BBS	V	I---T	downloads only on 156-xxxx line	
056 27 2568	Datawave BBS	V	I---E	Adrian Knecht,for customers	
056 27 2683	Elba Info System	HV	I---?	Christian Schmid	2:301/519
056 96 4507	Euro-Soft BBS	H+V	I---R	Roland Furter	2:301/544
056 27 2368	GlBBS Aargau	+Z+V	I---M	Heiner Hirzel	2:301/515
				Hub Aargau - OS2Net	81:441/5
+056 41 2461	*Merlin's Last Rest	+Z+V	I---M	Renato Torti	2:301/612
056 44 5141	Networker BBS	H+V	I---E	Walter Heid,1200mb,FreeNet	
056 94 9848	New Style BBS	+V	I---B	Heinz Lehmann	2:301/520.4
056 26 7762	Octopussy	H	I---R	Rene Rueegg	
056 32 2133	Promigos Hardware BBS	H	-A--X	H.R. Wenger	44:8010/511
056 96 1472	Roni's BBS	Z+V	I---R	Markus Rohner	2:301/511

[=---------------> **WOHLEN** <---------------=]

Number	Name	Speed	Files	Sysop Comments	Address
057 24 4394	City BBS	H	I---W	Romeo Keller,311mb	
057 31 6841	Clipboard BBS	+Z+V	---S?	Bono,240mb	
057 44 3472	GCCS Aargau	+Z+V	I---R	Patrick Oetiker	2:301/818
					52:4100/56
057 33 8003	PC-Lab BBS	H+V	I---W	Charles Rosenberger,3500mb	
057 46 3158	RAPS OS/2 BBS	+Z+V	I---M	Robert Allenspach,OS/2 2:301/512	
057 23 1945	SomyBBS	Z+V	I---W	Rene Sommerhalder	
057 31 8915	The World of...	Z+V	I---R	Bruno Klatzer	

[=------------> **NIEDERURNEN** <------------=]

Number	Name	Speed	Files	Sysop Comments	Address
058 81 1248	Userbox Glarnerland	V	I---?	Erwin Metzger	

[=---------------> **BASEL** <---------------=]

Number	Name	Speed	Files	Sysop Comments	Address
061971 6843	Amiga Magic Box	H+V	-A--D	Manfred Seiler	2:301/707
061971 6847	Amiga Magic Box	+Z+V	-A--D	3000mb	44:8010/102
	Alle Fishes, SKY & ADS, ISDN/SwissNet				39:110/101
+061931 2405	Aviation BBS	H+V	I---W	Hajo Verheyen,ISDN	2:301/230

Number	Name	Speed	Files	Sysop Comments	Address
061841 2003	BaruSoft-BBS	HV	I---R	Walter Triebold,660mb	2:301/222
					77:4161/250
061331 2878	Basler Info System	HV	I---U	Peter Burkhalter	2:301/216
061311 0850	Birs Box Basel	H+V	I---R	Andreas Meyer	2:301/225
061311 0350	Birs Box Basel	Z+V	I---R		2:301/226
^061482 2238	Butsch CD-ROM BBS	HV	IA--A	Mike Butsch,Butsch Infor.support	
061 80 4456	Call me !!	+Z+V	I-MSY	Milbe & Cosinus,420mb	
061383 2123	Caloi-BBS	H+V	I---E	Robert Caloi,8000mb,HAM,shopping	
061921 0777	Chaos Box	+V	I---L	4 lines	
061692 4251	City-Box Basel	Z+V	I---E	Boris Gass,2100mb,CD-ROM	
	Mailboxverbund mit der CommNET BBS Swiss				
061272 2071	ComCon BBS	H+V	I---E	Hans-Werner Schaller	
061821 0021	CommNET BBS Swiss	HV	I---R	Martin Thommen	
	4500mb, 5 lines, ILink/SWISSLink, ISDN/SwissNet				
061321 2210	CompuTell AG	+Z+V	I---R	Gioacchino Franzese	2:301/218
061711 3446	*Data-Box	H+V	I---R	Andres Walther,990mb 07:00-01:00	
					2:301/211
061311 9284	DataComm BBS	+Z+V	I---J	20 lines total	
061311 9193	DataComm BBS	+Z+V	I---J	12 ZyXEL 19200 bps lines	
061311 9273	DataComm BBS	H+V	I---J	5000mb	
061311 9306	DataComm BBS	T	I---J	Chats,Online-Games,Software	
061322 1654	Data-Networks BBS	+V	I---J	Patrick Studer	
061 35 6620	Exitus Mailbox	HV	IA--U	Hansjoerg Watzl/Molchi	
^061721 8212	Fantasy BBS	+Z+V	I---R	Roland Eggenschwiler 2:301/212.5	
061 98 5061	Fenner Mailbox	24	I---U	H.J. Watzl,Fenner Elektronik AG	
061481 6273	Flyconsult+AOPA	H	I---?	Rolf Siegrist,Aviation Mailbox	
061821 4300	Genesis	H	I---W	Philipp Ruegg,Games,Music,MS-DOS	
	Please call with Fax-Modems from 19:00-23:00 only				
061301 3326	Go-Soft BBS	H+V	I---W	Roger Schweizer,2000mb,IBM	
061301 3330	Go-Soft BBS	H+V	I---W		
061301 4044	Go-Soft BBS	+H+V	I---W	>>THIS line only for members	
061 61 2904	Hightech BBS Swiss	+Z+V	I---E	Andreas Jecklin,	
061 61 2558	Hightech BBS Swiss	H+V	I---E	1000mb CD-ROM	
061901 3321	ImproWare	P	---?	10'000mb,	
061901 3342	ImproWare	P	---?	CD-ROMs,UNIX	
061901 3343	ImproWare	+V	---?	internet: root@impch.imp.ch	
061901 3856	ImproWare	+V	---?	ftp,telnet,irc,etc.	
061 61 9925	Input-Box-2000	Z+V	I---R	Garfield/Juerg,1200mb,3 lines	
061811 5492	Ixgate Switzerland	HV	I---?	UNIX,internet mail,Usenet,UUCP	
061731 3483	JAK Mailbox	HV	I---R	Albert Jakubowitsch	
061693 0061	JukeBox	+V	I---L	2 lines,music,KTSI,cooking	
061 67 6408	Le Box	H+V	I---E	Peter Meier,SWISSLink	
061321 5643	LINKSystem LINK-CH1	Z+V	—Z	rleemann@link-ch1.aworld.de	
061911 8166	Mailshop BBS	+Z+V	Ia-sW	Christoph Schneeberger 2:301/270	
061911 8148	Mailshop BBS	+Z+V	Ia-sW		

Number	Name	Speed	Files	Sysop Comments	Address
061711 7421	Miracle Line [HST]	H	-A--D	Michel Clement	2:301/215
061712 1306	Miracle Line [ZyX]	+Z+V	-A--D	SAN,ADS,DLG	44:8010/202
061921 6930	Moulin Rouge	+Z+V	I---U	Tatjana erwartet dich !	
^061 67 6208	Niels Klim BBS	+H+T	I---E	Juerg Loeffler,ILink/SWISSLink	
061 67 6230	Niels Klim BBS	+Z+V	I---E	2200mb,5 lines,ISDN/SwissNet	
061 47 9468	Obi's Mail Box	V	I---U	Heinz Oberli,1600mb	88:4102/422
061941 2202	PC-Info	+H+V	I---E	Ernesto Hagmann,3 lin. 2:301/201	
061 99 6969	Radio Amateur BBS	H+V	I---E	Werner Ludowig,HAMNet	
+061 99 6069	Radio Amateur BBS	+H+V	I---E	2100mb,ISDN/SwissNet	2:301/249
061721 6627	Sky Net	+V	I---?	Robert Nufer,astronomy	
061481 4408	Sunshine BBS	HV	I---R	David Hauser,800mb	2:301/212
					44:8010/204
061275 7310	Suter+Suter BBS	Z+V	I---W	Felix Ohmberger,1000mb,	
061275 7282	Suter+Suter BBS	Z+V	I---W	MSI-Support-Net,FreeNet	
061275 7246	Suter+Suter BBS	Z+V	I---W		2:301/228
061901 4359	The Bunker Box	+24	I---?	La Mamma Crew	
061691 3226	The Life	+Z+V	-A--X	Stefan Kuersteiner	
061811 1482	*Touchforce BBS	+Z+V	I---?	iNVi,350mb	22:00-06:00
061771 0873	Tritscha BBS	+Z+V	-A--X	Marcel Friedli,475mb	44:8010/203
061821 6624	Turbo Box	H	IA-SW	Daniel Mangold	
061302 2828	YaCaN BBS	Z+V	—R	Tobias Gasser	2:301/234
061811 5014	Zottel Box	HV	IA--R	Ueli Jecklin	2:301/220

[=--------------> OLTEN <----------------=]

Number	Name	Speed	Files	Sysop Comments	Address
062 44 3227	AUGS	+Z+V	-A--D	Josef Egloff	44:8010/402
062 44 3882	AUGS	H+V	-A--D	00mb,CD-ROM,Z-Netz	44:8010/401
062 32 7589	*Crystal BBS	+V	I---J	Max Haller	17:00-01:00
062 84 1082	Freeline-Box	H+V	I---E	Thomas Egger,3 lines	
062 97 4522	*Power Graphics BBS	HV	I---R	Walter Baer,300mb	19:00-07:00
					2:301/516
062 52 1328	Savuka-BBS	H	-A--P	Bailoni/Benno Mueller	
062 51 9960	Secret Door BBS	+V	-A--D	Martin Willisegger	2:301/510
	SAN & ADS sowie diverse PD-Disk-Serien				44:8010/411
062 51 1726	The Baboon BBS	HV	I-M-R	Ruedi Kneubuehler	2:301/520
062 51 3401	The Baboon's Kid	Z+V	I-M-R		44:8010/104, 2:301/521
	FidoNet <-> UUCP Gateway Switzerland :			2:301/520.50	
062 76 3662	Xenon Box	Z+V	I---R	Giuseppe Barbagallo	2:301/505

[=----------> OBER-AARGAU/BERN <----------=]

Number	Name	Speed	Files	Sysop Comments	Address
063 66 1463	LemaS	Z+V	I---R Beat Bucher		2:301/503

Number	Name	Speed	Files	Sysop Comments	Address

[=--------------> AARAU <---------------=]

Number	Name	Speed	Files	Sysop Comments	Address
064 37 0036	BeTWeeN THe TiMe	+Z+V	-A--X	TeCHNiQue,1000mb	
064 43 9482	Black-Hole-BBS	+V	I---M	Juerg Schwarz,OS/2	2:301/102
064 24 4687	*Freetime BBS	Z+V	—SQ	Andre Ryser	17:00-24:00
064 56 0200	Hitline BBS	+Z+V	IAM-E	Marcel Aumer,35 lines	2:301/213
064 56 0201	Hitline BBS	+H+V	IAM-E	Ueli Maurer,5 lines	
064 61 4861	Irata-Box	Z+V	—Y		
064 56 3231	Rock BBS	+V	I---W	Daniel Weber,music infos	
064 52 0019	The Emergency Room	+V	—	Paula Moor	2:301/212.22
064 61 3245	W.I.N.SYS.	+V	—J	Hofmann Telecom,economy	
064 22 4602	Wizard's BBS	H+V	I---W	Andre Schwaller	640:130/0
064 47 3046	.oO WoNdErLaNd Oo.	Z+V	IA--E	=PfUsuUs=,1300mb	

[=------------> SOLOTHURN <---------------=]

Number	Name	Speed	Files	Sysop Comments	Address
065 55 3932	Qube BBS	Z+V	I---E	Andreas Cahen,2000mb	

[=--------------> JURA <----------------=]

Number	Name	Speed	Files	Sysop Comments	Address
066 74 4058 *	Phoebus'BBS	+V	—?	Jean-Pierre Chapuis	06:00-01:00

[=-------> ISDN LINES WITH MODEM <-------=]

Number	Name	Speed	Files	Sysop Comments	Address
067 72 1231	Business-Link	+Z+V	I---E	Joachim Wiedemann,3000mb	
067 72 1232	Business-Link	+Z+V	I---E	ISDN/SwissNet	
067 52 1783	Weinland BBS	+Z+V	I---E	Michael Moeckli,ISDN	2:301/822
067 52 1784	Weinland BBS	+H+T	I---E	FreeNet,SWISSLink,OASE 202:202/0	

[=-------------> ST. GALLEN <-------------=]

Number	Name	Speed	Files	Sysop Comments	Address
071 85 2485	Chinchilla Box	+Z+V	I–SU	Werner Haldner,Funk	2:301/421
071 91 2333	Colibri BBS	H+V	I---E	Ruedi Bieg,BUSINESSNet,SWISSLink	
071 25 9061	ComCon Music Box	HV	I---O	Martin Rahm	2:301/341
	Only real names allowed!				
071 72 4421	*Digit BBS	+H+V	-A--X	Thomas	21:00-06:30
					44:8010/906
071 23 5686	EastBBS	H+V	I---E	Bruno Scacchi,1800mb,SWISSLink	
071 20 8130	FAHMail (=Username)	24	—?	Hochschule St.Gallen	

Number	*Name*	*Speed*	*Files*	*Sysop Comments*	*Address*
071 20 8590	FAHMail	3	—?	needs VT100 Emulation	
071 24 0707	Frogy-Box	+Z+V	-A--X	Ralph Kabourek	44:8010/903
071 24 6524	Frogy-Box	H+V	-A--X	>>Press *0 on touch tone phone	
071 71 2787	Inter. Hackerbase	HV	-A--P	Mike Schibli/Superuser,private	
071 23 4713	Killerwal BBS	+Z+V	I---E	Paul Herrmann >>WAIT 30 SECONDS	
071 44 0308	M-Way	+V	IAMS?	Ernst Spitzer	
071 72 8317	Magic-BBS Line 1	+Z+V	I---M	Stefan Widrig,ISDN	2:301/409
	9:412/909,16:200/409,69:410/115,94:100/509,100:410/409,144:4101/409				
071 27 7130	Midnight Special	Z+V	—M	Hansruedi Straub	2:301/418
071 72 5188	Orion Mailbox Sys.	H+V	I---O	Urban Oettli	2:301/103
071 71 5577	Pegasus	H+V	—?	2 lines,Sunshine	
071 71 6074	Pegasus	H+V	—?	2 lines,Dr.Who	071 71 7175
	Pegasus	+24	—?	2 lines,SuperUser	
071 71 6066	Pegasus	+24	—?	4 lines	
	VAX/VMS, Usenet messages, X.25, internet: pegasus.ch				
071 24 2224	Roesslibox	+Z+V	I---U	Michael Huwiler	2:301/406
071 72 6394	Skyline.Host BBS	+Z+V	-A--?	Markus Erlacher	2:301/422
					44:8010/916
071 81 1346	US-Cars	H	I---?	Peter Bersinger,PC-Net	
071 850612	*VideoWorld	H	-A--P	Cody,video games	07:00-22:30
071 71 8392	White Horse BBS	H+V	I---W	Ernst Neuhaus	2:301/408
071 71 8393	White Horse BBS	+Z+V	I---W		
071 72 3374	Wyden-BBS	Z+V	I---U	Harry Hoefinger	2:301/409.2

[=------------> WEINFELDEN <------------=]

Number	*Name*	*Speed*	*Files*	*Sysop Comments*	*Address*
072 22 6527	Carina BBS	+Z+V	-A--X	Roland Zeller	44:8010/907
072 22 3075	Dele-Box	YV	I---U	Rene Mueller	
	VirusKillers, SWISSLink				
072 64 2490*	Maetch-Box	+V	I---U	Peter Kis/Hawk	18:00-20:30

[=------------> GUETTINGEN <------------=]

Number	*Name*	*Speed*	*Files*	*Sysop Comments*	*Address*
072 65 3421	MHS Systems	H+V	IA--M	Matthias Hertzog	2:301/401
^		9		:412/901, 16:200/401, 44:8010/911, 94:100/501	
^				100:410/401, 142:120/201, 144:4101/401	
072 65 3302	MHS Systems	+Z+V	IA--M	2 lines	2:301/402
^				9:412/902, 16:200/402, 44:8010/912, 94:100/502	
^				100:410/402, 142:120/202, 144:4101/402	

Number	Name	Speed	Files	Sysop Comments	Address

[=----------------> WIL <----------------=]

Number	Name	Speed	Files	Sysop Comments	Address
073 51 8565	Amiga Fun-Box	+H+V	-A--X	Gregor Roesli,700mb	44:8010/307
073 51 7840	CBB Mailbox	HV	I---?	CBB-Club	

[=--------------> VADUZ/FL <-------------=]

Number	Name	Speed	Files	Sysop Comments	Address
075233 3801	AUGL Box	H	-A–X	Sven Sauter	
075233 3802	AUGL Box	Z+V	-A--X	1500mb	
075233 3803	AUGL Box	H	-A–X		
075233 3804	AUGL Box	H+V	-A--X		44:8010/905
075373 6479	DataForce	+H+V	iA--X	Jan Schaedler,1300mb	44:8010/908
075373 4926	Empire BBS	24	IA--X	Roman Kuser,620mb	44:8010/904
075373 5984	Empire BBS	+H+V	IA--X		44:8010/901, 2:301/416
075232 6459	Kulturdata Mailbox	24	I---J	Wolfgang Kaufmann,Culture	
075232 4562	Kulturdata Mailbox	12	I---J		
^075373 1513	Maximum Overdrive	+H+V	I---U	Marc Liebigt,1200mb	2:301/407
+075373 6451	News-Net	+V	I---?	download COCONET program here	
+075373 6446	News-Net	+Z+V	I---?	>>ONLY with COCONET program	
075373 6680	OSIS	+V	I---J	Gerald Meier,1200mb,outdials,	

X.25, online shopping, FAX, CD-ROM, internet: sysop@osis.li

[=----------> GRAUBUENDEN/CHUR <----------=]

Number	Name	Speed	Files	Sysop Comments	Address
081947 4232	Blue Water BBS	Z+V	I---U	Patrick Bundi,1000mb	2:301/420
081 27 8044	Buema BBS	+H+V	I---W	Marc-Stefan Buehler	
081 27 8586	Buema BBS	HV	I---W	FreeNet,3000mb	
	5 lines, ISDN/SwissNet, RIP-graphics				
081723 5305	Epcot Box	HV	I---U	Peter Pieth	
081 22 5512	Gizmoz BBS	H+V	iAmsX	Stefan Gluekler,500mb	
081 21 6653	Gizmoz BBS	+Z+V	iAmsX		44:8010/516
^081783 2077	Kickstart BBS	+Z+V	I---E	Peter Moser,support line	
-081783*2096	**Kickstart line #2			>>NOT IN SERVICE (old number)	
081302 7200	New-Line Swiss BBS	+Z+V	IamsW	Roberto Ruga,4 lines,10'000mb	
081 24 6327	Planet Quark	+Z+V	I---M	Ben Schlup	2:301/426
081 22 9245	**Planet Quark	+Z+V	—?	>>mail only	2:301/419

[=------------> ST. MORITZ <-------------=]

Number	Name	Speed	Files	Sysop Comments	Address
082 4 5241	Piz-Box-Engadin	+V	I---E	Andreas Buri,ILink/SWISSLink	
082 2 1627	Powder BBS	Z+V	---SY	John Caprez/Blueblue	2:301/425

Number	Name	Speed	Files	Sysop Comments	Address

[=-----------> **LUGANO/CHIASSO** <----------=]

Number	Name	Speed	Files	Sysop Comments	Address
^091 55 2783	Avalon On Line BBS	+Z+V	I---R	Marco Hardmeier	2:301/342.21
091 56 3668	BBS A.T.E.D.	+V	I---O	Roberto Fisch & Sysop Team	
091 46 5315	Bit Exchange Box	H+V	I---O	Christian Bianchi	2:301/219
091 57 5915	EuroCom	+V	I---R	Cleto Pescia	
091 57 5916	EuroCom	V	I—R		
	GIFs, graphics, programming & science utilities				
091*51*9401	**Firebird BBS	24	I---R	Sergio Puddu,100mb	22:30-08:00
091 68 5110	HB9DHG's BBS	+H+T	I---R	Fulvio Galli	2:301/622
	1200mb, HAM radio				
^091 43 6274	Loce BBS	+H+T	-A--D	Michele Lucini	2:301/281
					44:8010/103
^091 46 1378	Realms of Magic	+H+T	I---S	Mr.Crocodile - [TAC] WHQ	
	660mb, GUS Support, FidoNet, SL_Net, FreeNet,				250:1100/1402
	GamesNet - Hackers, Crackers, CyBuNKs				2:301/807.91
	Where Anarchy Becomes Realithy!				144:4101/422
091 95 4060	The WinCherry BBS	+V	I---?	Manfred Murer,800mb	2:301/256
091 50 5857	Thunder Box	+H+T	I---R	Manuel Wenger,2300mb	2:301/620
	CD-ROMs, using Remote Access 2.01+!			DreamVMB 567, 73:7411/1	

[=------------> **BELLINZONA** <------------=]

Number	Name	Speed	Files	Sysop Comments	Address
^092 26 3924	C.M.C-F.E.S	+H+T	-A--D	Franco Borsa,1700mb	2:301/342
^	Official HB9/TI Radio Club BBS for packet				44:8010/902
^	radio and satellite system, gateway on				39:110/902
^	438.125 MHz (TCP/IP), or ONLINE BBS, AX25				
^	import, AX25: hb9oab@hb9ok, internet: hb9oab@ge.alphanet.ch				
092 25 9433	Espoclub M.BE	V	-A--P	Flavio Esposito	

[=---> **2.b) PTT's "TeleKiosk" (156) and** <----=]

[=---> **"TeleBusiness" (157)** <----=]
Note: Can't be called from outside Switzerland

Number	Name	Speed	Files	Sysop Comments	Address
156 3388	BitLink	HV	I---U	Fr.0.60/m,Martin Stolz,MIDI	
	Asbith Computer AG				
156 3456	Best Project BBS	Z+V	I--J	Fr.0.60/m,Marcus Bosshard	
157 10221	Box4	H+V	I-M-F	Fr.0.80/m,Andreas Fink,3 lines	
156 5686	CPA BBS V I—T Fr.1.00/m,price lists,support				
	COS Computer Peripherals AG				

Number	Name	Speed	Files	Sysop Comments	Address
156 3555	CULTNET	H+V	I---?	Fr.0.60/m,Quasar,1000mb,internet	
	Alive Production GmbH				
156 5051	Free-Box	H+V	I---R	Fr.1.00/m,Windows,MS-DOS,CD-ROM	
156 6610	GigaLine BBS	+Z+V	IAM-E	Fr.1.40/m,GigaRider,5 lines	
157 3035	Hitline BBS	+Z+V	IAM-E	Fr.1.40/m,3 lines	
156 8125	HOTBox BBS	H+V	I---U	Fr.2.00/m,Ilona,Erotic	
156 6067	Kickstart Erotic	+V	I---E	Fr.1.40/m,Peter Moser	
156 ***3007	**Kickstart Shareware	+V	I---E	Fr.1.40/m,Peter Moser >>SOON	
156 2200	Mega Ware Box	+V	I---U	Fr.0.47/m,Heinz	
156 5044	Shareware	+V	I---?	Fr.1.00/m,W.Willaredt,erotic	
156 4010	SoftBox	24	I---?	Fr.0.80/m,Dick Tracy,CD-ROM	
	Sake Timmermans				
156 7949	Software Phone	+V	I---J	Fr.2.00/m,GIFs and PD	
	Software Phone Establishment				
156 6310	Unikat BBS	H+V	I---E	Fr.1.40/m,4500mb,Shareware,GIFs	
	Andry Jan Martin				

[=---> 2.c) Private & Commercial Systems <---=]

Attention! The following systems can only be used by people with accounts on them. Please don't call these systems just for fun and remember that it CAN be illegal to break into a private system or to hack passwords. The area codes 040, 046, 047, 048 & 049 cost the same in whole Switzerland, either Fr.3.00 or Fr.3.60 per hour. Some of these numbers are not reachable from outside Switzerland.

064 45 4056	Aare-News	+Z+V	Christoph Camenzind,ISDN
	internet-server, info@ncc1701.aare.net.ch, Voice:064/45 4051		
156 3400	arCom 400	V	Fr.0.60/min
	PTT's arCom X.400 E-Mail service		
01 273 1028	CompuServe	V	CompuServe Info. Service
	Or Germany: 0049 8966530170 Muenchen, 0049 6920976 Frankfurt		
^	Neumatstrasse, 5703 Seon/AG, Voice:064/55 0491		
031 260871	Datamail/Datastar	12	Data bank,type "RS"
031 26 1333	Datamail/Datastar	3	
01 817 1030	DEC	24	Digital Equipment Corporation
01 241 0026	DunsNet	+24	Dun & Bradsteet's DunsNet,type "INFO"
+01 781 4229	EEIS	V	Excom Electronic Info System
+024 23 2280	EINEV	24	Ecole d'Ingenieurs dr l'Etat de Vaud
01 291 4687	EUnet Mailbox	+V	CHUUG/EUnet, voice:01/291 4580
	internet Mail/USENET/InterEUnet/CIX/Alternet		
01 241 6241	Fides Net	3	
01 422 4100	GEnie	+24	General Electric's Info. Service,
01 422 6821	GEnie	+12	half duplex,type "HHH" after connect,

Number	Name	Speed	Files	Sysop Comments	Address
021617 4511	GEnie	+24		type "XTX99453,GENIE" to register	
021617 5334	GEnie	+24			
022798 5566	GEnie	+24			
061331 8863	GEnie	+24			
+064 46 5016	Haller's BBS	H		Christian Haller,support BBS,ISDN	
071 20 9105	HSG	V		Hochschule St.Gallen	
071 20 8130	HSG	24			
071 20 8590	HSG	3			
092 64 3066	i-Manager Mailbox	+Z+V		For ii-Index-Informatik customers	
01 251 2002	KomETH	V		ETH Zuerich network,	
01 252 4189	KomETH	V		line for NOKIA PMD 9600 modems	
01 257 4811	KomETH	V		X.25: 0228 47911065	
01 256 4851	KomETH	12		internet: ethz.ch	
01 256 4751	KomETH	3			
	#CALL 11 or 111			Infos, main menu (gopher)	
	#CALL 520			ETHics (ETH Library)	
	#CALL e100			ZBIB (Zentralbibliothek, library)	
	#CALL ezinfo or b050			Username: GUEST	
031 46 1376	KTD (Kreisdirektion)	3			
081756 1345	ntb.ch	+V		Neu-Technikum Buchs	
081756 1317	ntb.ch	+V		internet: gusset@ntb.ch	
^01 272 6197	Limmat-Net	+Z+V		Christian Weber,ISDN/SwissNet	
	internet: chris@limmat.net.ch, Voice:01/440 1391				
01 257 4811	NUZ	V		NUZ: Network University of Zurich	
01 257 4411	NUZ	12		internet: unizh.ch	
+052213 0208	OCS-BBS	H+V		Rene Haeberli	2:301/712
+	For customers of Office Computer Systems, voice 052/212 3311				
01 302 8868	SprintNet	V		Support (voice): 155 0846	
031 26 1049	SprintNet	V			
01 261 3006	SWITCH	+V		SWITCH email services,	
01 261 5153	SWITCH	+V		internet/Usenet/UUCP	
01 261 5168	SWITCH	+V			
01 261 8154	SWITCH	+V			
01 252 1339	SWITCH	+V			
01 8300946	UNIGS	V			
01 261 5306	*Zentralbibliothek	24		71O Teilsystem: PUB,<Return>,KATALOG,	
				Help with ESC-1-Return	07:30-20:00
155 1121	VTX	12		PTT's VideoTex (CEPT),free call!	
155 1124	VTX	24		PTT's VideoTex (CEPT),free call!	
	These numbers only work in some places like BASEL (?)				
046 05 1121	VTX	12		Fr.3.00/h (+ 4.20 = Fr. 7.20/h)	
046 05 1124	VTX	24		Fr.3.00/h (+ 6.00 = Fr. 9.00/h)	
	Note: These 046 numbers will soon be out of service too				
04701 1111	VTX	1200/75		Fr.3.60/h (+ 4.20 = Fr. 7.80/h)	

Number	Name	Speed	Files	Sysop Comments	Address
047 04 1111	VTX	1200/75		Fr.3.60/h (+ 4.20 = Fr. 7.80/h)	
106	VTX	V		Fr.3.60/h (+13.20 = Fr.16.80/h!!)	
104	VTX	24		Fr.3.60/h (+ 6.00 = Fr. 9.60/h!)	
104	VTX	12		Fr.3.60/h (+ 4.20 = Fr. 7.80/h)	
105	VTX 1200/75 Fr.3.60/h (+ 4.20 = Fr. 7.80/h)				
	Note: These numbers don't work everywhere yet				
156 2356	VTX	24		Fr.28.00/h,no account necessary	
156 4356	VTX	24		Fr.48.00/h,no account necessary	
01 242 8181	VTX	12		Zurich	
061281 1250	VTX	12		Basel	
061281 1260	VTX	12		Basel	
*047 02	VTX	9600 bps		ISDN/SwissNet (+13.20 = ?)	
156 4660	MTx	H+V		Fr.48.00/h,MEDIAtex's MTx (CEPT)	
156 0249	BTX Germany	1200/75		Fr.28.20/h,BildschirmTex (CEPT)	
156 0349	BTX/ETB Germany	1200/75		Fr.36.00/h,Phone Book (CEPT)	
156 0243	BTX Austria	1200/75		Fr.28.20/h,BildschirmTex (CEPT)	
156 0252	VTX Luxemb.	1200/75		Fr.28.20/h,VideoTex (CEPT)	
156 0314	Teletel France	24		Fr.36.00/h,Teletel 1 & 2 (CEPT)	
156 0314	Teletel France			1200/75 Fr.36.00/h,Teletel 1 & 2 (CEPT)	
156 0415	Teletel France	24		Fr.48.00/h,Teletel 3 (CEPT)	
156 0415	Teletel France			1200/75 Fr.48.00/h,Teletel 3 (CEPT)	
049 04 9111	TelePac	V		Fr.3.00/h,PTT's X.25 network	
049 04 7111	TelePac	24		Fr.3.00/h	
048 03 6111	TelePac			1200/75 Fr.3.00/h	

[=---> 2.d) PTT's ISDN/SwissNet2 Lines <-----=]

"ISDN" means "Integrated Services Digital Network" which is an end to end international digital network for voice/data/fax communication. You need an ISDN-adapter and an ISDN line to call a BBS below. The connection charge is the same as on analog lines. You can find rate information in the phone book.

[=------------> ZURICH CITY <------------=]

Number	Name	Speed	Files	Sysop Comments	Address
01 300 1007	Amiga Microbox	SL	-A--X	M. Frei	44:8010/599, 2:301/861
01 300 1009	Amiga Microbox	IM	-A--X	2 lines,Voice:01/300 1003	
01 310 1015	Helvetica	SL	-A--X	B. Amsler & A. Glutz	2:301/756
01 310 1016	Helvetica	IM	-A--X		44:8010/598 2:301/755
01 440 1397	Limmat-Net	IM	-A--?	Christian Weber	
01 450 1106	MPC-Mailing System	SO	I---M	Oliver von Bueren	2:301/750
01 450 1107	MPC-Mailing System	SO	I---M		2:301/751
01 450 1108	MPC-Mailing System	IB	I---M		2:301/753
01 400 1498	Warehouse BBS	SL	IAMsS	Byte Rider & Hotshot	

Number	Name	Speed	Files	Sysop Comments	Address
01 430 1057	Zuerich Live BBS	V.110	I---E	Raphael Schmidiger	2:301/850
01 430 1058	Zuerich Live BBS	X.75	I---E		2:301/860
01 430 1059	Zuerich Live BBS	SL	I---E		2:301/870
01 430 1056	Zuerich Live BBS	IM	I---E		2:301/880

[=-------------> ZURICH <---------------=]

Number	Name	Speed	Files	Sysop Comments	Address
01 885 8016	ACCU	IM	-A--D	Urs Utzinger	44:8010/405
01 776 8009	Box4	V.110	I-M-F	Andreas Fink	2:301/854
01 997 1018	CTS System	SL	I---S	Ivo Ruetsche,1600mb,SLink	
01 884 6028	Dolphins SL -A–Z Hermann Neuhaus				
01 884 6025	Dolphins	SL	-A--Z		
01 777 8009	Graphics Plus BBS	SO	I---E	Roger Mella	2:301/852
+01 799 1158	InformationShuttle	SL	—M	Christian Meuli,Archimedes	
01 776 1009	McMeier & Son BBS	SO	I---E	Roland Hausin	
01 776 1008	McMeier & Son BBS	SL	I---E		
01 884 1038	ProLine BBS	SL	I---E	Gianni Facchinetti	

[=-------------> LAUSANNE <--------------=]

Number	Name	Speed	Files	Sysop Comments	Address
+021973 1006	Black Bird BBS	X.75	I---B	Florian Rod	2:301/360

[=--------------> GENEVE <---------------=]

Number	Name	Speed	Files	Sysop Comments	Address
0228300025	Cougar BBS	X.75	I---R	Etienne Deschenaux,20000mb,	
0228300026	Cougar BBS	V.110	I---R	Please use CAPI-Fossil-Driver	
0228300027	Cougar BBS	X.75	I---R	"CFOS". Call X.75 with ATB0D	
0228300028	Cougar BBS	V.110	I---R	and V.110 with ATB1D	
022751 8108	Oliver's DiveInn/2			SL IA-SM Oliver Wagner	

[=----------------> BERN <---------------=]

Number	Name	Speed	Files	Sysop Comments	Address
0319940019	Buemplizer Box	SO	I---E	Fritz Keller,7000mb,	
0319940018	Buemplizer Box	SL	I---E	ILink/SWISSLink,FreeNet	
0319740039	Capital BBS	SO	I---E	Beat Jau,ILink/SWISSLink,3000mb	
0319740037	Capital BBS	SL	I---E		
0319740038	Capital BBS	SL	I---E		
0318820029	Comlight BBS	SO	I---W	Martin Ottiger/Comlight AG	

Number	Name	Speed	Files	Sysop Comments	Address

[=--------------> LUZERN <---------------=]

Number	Name	Speed	Files	Sysop Comments	Address
041 70 8119	Berog BBS Mail	SO	I---W	SoLIS-Card	>>ONLINE SOON
041 70 8111	Berog BBS Mail	SL	I---W	SLink-Adapter	>>ONLINE SOON
041 70 8112	Berog BBS Mail	SL	I---W	SLink-Adapter	>>ONLINE SOON
041 70 1048	MICS Lucerne	SL	I---M	Michael Buenter,OS/2	

[=--------------> WOHLEN <---------------=]

Number	Name	Speed	Files	Sysop Comments	Address
057 310010	PC-Lab BBS		I---W	Charles Rosenberger,3500mb	

[=--------------> BASEL <---------------=]

Number	Name	Speed	Files	Sysop Comments	Address
0619730019	Amiga Magic Box Alle Fishes, SKY & ADS	IM	-A--D	X.75,V.110,2 lines	2:301/754 44:8010/150
+061933 1009	**Aviation BBS	IB	I---W	>>mail only	2:301/260
061383 2124	Caloi-BBS	SL	I---E	Robert Caloi,8000mb,HAM,shopping	
061283 5528	CommNET BBS Swiss	SL	-A--D	Martin Thommen,4500mb	
061383 2007	LINKSystem LINK-CH1	IM	----Z	rleemann@link-ch1.aworld.de	
061383 2008	LINKSystem LINK-CH1	IM	----Z	Mailbox fuer Politik & Kultur	
061643 2038	Niels Klim BBS	SL	I---E	Juerg Loeffler,ILink/SWISSLink	
+061923 1009	Radio Amateur BBS	IB	I---E	Werner Ludowig,HAMNet	2:301/250

[=--------------> AARAU <---------------=]

Number	Name	Speed	Files	Sysop Comments	Address
064 45 4057	Aare-News	IM	----?	X.75,	Christoph Camenzind
064 45 4058	Aare-News	IM	----?	V.110	
+064 46 5014	Haller's BBS	IM	-A--?	Christian Haller,support BBS	
064 56 4119	Hitline BBS	SO	I---E	Ueli Maurer,20'000mb	
064 56 4118	Hitline BBS	SL	I---E	Marcel Aumer	
064 56 4117	Hitline BBS	SL	I---E	FreeNet/Fido-Net	
064 56 4120	Hitline BBS	SL	I---E	IBM-BBS OS/2,miro-BBS,2 lines	

[=------> SPECIAL ISDN AREA CODE <-------=]

Number	Name	Speed	Files	Sysop Comments	Address
067 55 1778	Active-Net BBS	SL	I---E	Martin Altorfer	
067 55 1779	Active-Net BBS	SO	I---E		2:301/853
067 41 1419	Berog BBS Mail	SO	I---W	Robert Gmeiner	
067 41 1414	Berog BBS Mail	SL	I---W	SLink-Adapter	
067 58 1389	Buema BBS	SO	I---W	Marc-Stefan Buehler,3000mb,	

Number	Name	Speed	Files	Sysop Comments	Address
067 58 1388	Buema BBS	SL	I---W	FreeNet,5 lines,RIP-gfx	
067 72 1236	Business-Link		I---E	Joachim Wiedemann,3000mb	
067 72 1237	Business-Link		I---E		
067 72 1219	MHS Systems	SO	IA–M	Matthias Hertzog	2:301/450
^				9:411/3, 16:200/450, 44:8010/950, 94:100/550	
^				100:410/450, 142:120/250, 144:4101/450	
+067 72 1218	MHS Systems	SL	IA–M		2:301/451
^				9:411/4, 16:200/451, 44:8010/951, 94:100/551	
^				100:410/451, 142:120/251, 144:4101/451	
067 330401	Shiwa Mailbox	SL	I---W	Peter Gossweiler	
067 51 1501	Sky - Box	SL	I---S	Sky-Box,testing	
067 52 1319	Squirrel Mailbox	SO	I---E	Peter Haessig,5000mb	2:301/752
067 52 1318	Squirrel Mailbox	SL	I---E	Helicopters,ILink/SWISSLink	
067 41 1649	Wanger Box	SO	I---W	Reto Meyer &	2:301/851
067 41 1641	Wanger Box	SL	I---W	Cyrill Meier	
067 52 1788	Weinland BBS	SL	I---E	Michael Moeckli	

[=-------------> ST. GALLEN <-------------=]

| 071 70 6067 | Magic-BBS Line 2 | IB | I---M | Stefan Widrig | 2:301/470 |

SO...MBP SoLIS	IBM internal	2 lines	V110	X75		
SL...SEAL SLink-Adapter	external	1 line	(V110)	(V120)	(X75)	SEAL
SI...SEAL SLink-Adapter	IBM internal	2 lines	(V110)	(V120)	(X75)	SEAL
EL...ELink IBM internal	2 lines	V110		X75		
IM...BSC ISDN Master	Amiga internal	2 lines	V110	V120	X75	
IB...BSC ISDN Blaster	IBM internal	2 lines	V110	V120	X75	

[=-----> 2.e) PTT's TelePac/X.25 Lines <-----=]

To call a system below you need an X.25 line or a TelePac account (NUI with password) so that you can enter TelePac with a modem. To reach a system from outside Switzerland dial 0228 plus the NUA.

NUA	Name	Sysop Comments
46451064	BGB (Baerengraben)	P.Witschi & U.Fringeli,10 llines,64kbps
R 464510003	CompuServe	type "LANGUAGE ENGLISH"R
47911303	CompuServe	
47127015014	ETB	PTT's electronic phone book
4712705000	ETV, VT-100	PTT's new electronic phone book
4712705071	ETV, 7 bits, 127 chars	

NUA	Name	Sysop Comments
4712705081	ETV, 8 bits, 256 chars	
4712705000	ETV, VT-100, Beginner	
4712705003	ETV, VT-100, CP-850	
4712705001	ETV, VT-100, DEC multinational	
47911065	KomETH	ETH Zuerich network
46421111	NUI Server	Statistics,password change,etc.
R 46121005	OSIS	Gerald Meier,online shopping,etc.
475212574	Pegasus	Sunshine,Dr.Who,SuperUser,15 lines
	VAX/VMS, UseNet messages, internet: pegasus.ch	
422411002	VTX Basel	PTT's VideoTex (CEPT)
422412002	VTX Basel	
424103002	VTX Bern	
424103002	VTX Bern	
429102002	VTX Lausanne	
429103002	VTX Lausanne	
435103002	VTX St. Gallen	
435104002	VTX St. Gallen	
450100002	VTX Zuerich	
450101002	VTX Zuerich	
450102002	VTX Zuerich	
450103002	VTX Zuerich	
46821113	Transnet-2	Many infos

[=---> 2.f) Voice Mailbox Systems / VMB <----=]

To call a VMB below all you need is a touch tone telephone.

01 451 4446   Dream System PLUS   Voice   2 lines!
New users press 9, then leave your name and address.
501=Ernst, 500=Reto, 555=Byte Rider, 599=Hotshot, 333=Dennis

[=--> 3. CALLING CARD & CREDIT CARD CALLS <--=]

Since 02/92 the 'Gruene Nummern' (green numbers) are 155-xxxx and not 046-05-xxxx anymore. They can't be called from outside Switzerland. These lines are toll FREE! The call is payed by the owner. They don't work in whole Switzerland yet, but almost (try 046-05-xxxx instead).

To get your own card (for free), call and ask for customer service. At the moment a normal call using PTT after 11pm is cheaper than all companies below.

But a calling card has many other advantages. The following numbers must be called VOICE with a normal telephone.

155	0011	AT&T USA Direct	pay with AT&T calling card (touch tone)
155	1610	Executive TeleCard	pay with MasterCard/VISA (touch tone)
155	0222	MCI Call USA	pay with MCI calling card (voice)
155	5880	MCI Customer Service	to order free MCI card (voice)
155	9777	Sprint	pay with Sprint FONCARD (voice)

[=·········> 4. DREAM YELLOW PAGES <··········=]

+01 312 1268	Helvetica	+Z+V -A--X B. Amsler & A. Glutz	44:8010/512
+01 313 0878	Helvetica	+H+V A--X 9000mb,8 CD-ROMs,	2:301/723
+01 313 0879	Helvetica	+Z+V -A--X ISDN/SwissNet,SAN,ADS	39:110/501

```
++------------------------------------------------------------+
+|              Sysop: Bruno Amsler und Adrian Glutz          |
+|           9 Gigabytes / 26'000 Amiga-Files / 8 CD-Roms     |
+|         Generalvertretung BBS-Software Xenolink CH/D/A     |
+|         Immer die neusten PD-Serien fuer Commodore Amiga.  |
+|          ADS/SAN Filenet / GIF-Pictures / Adult-areas etc. |
+|     Netze: Fidonet/Swiss-Aminet/Int-Amiganet/Internet/SF-Net|
+|     Verkauf: PD-Serien und Hardware von fast allen Herstellern|
+|      Guenstige Memberbeitraege oder Downloaden via Fileratio|
++------------------------------------------------------------4
```

01 492 5157	Warehouse BBS	+Z+V	IAMsS Byte Rider & Hotshot	2:301/807
01 492 5133	Warehouse BBS	H+V	IAMsS 2000mb,	44:8010/407
01 492 5597	Warehouse BBS	+H+V	IAMsS DreamVMB 555,	250:1100/424

```
+--- ================================================== ---+
|            Running Searchlight 3.5 with ANSI & RIP graphics!    |
|     Usernames/Pseudos are allowed, free 1:3 downloads, relaxed & friendly, |
|     no censoring, immediate full access, send E-Mail on FIDO-Net & internet |
|  Home of the DREAM BBS LIST-SEARCHLIGHT SOFTWARE support/dealer BBS- |
|          Thousands of buy/sell/trade ads  CHEAP hardware offers,       |
|        for example modems & Amiga (Commodore, GVP) products       |
+--- ================================================== ---1
```

01 9460547   CTS System   H+V   I---S   Ivo Ruetsche,1600mb

```
* * * * * * * * * * * * * * * * * * * * * * * * * * * * * * * * * * * * * * * * * * * * * *
*                    ISDN/SwissNet, online Bestservice fuer                    *
*              CTS Hardware und Software!     Soundblaster Support,             *
*          Shareware und Drivers fuer Sound- und Videoblaster,                  *
*              ISDN/V.24 SLink-Terminaladapter-Distributor                      *
* * * * * * * * * * * * * * * * * * * * * * * * * * * * * * * * * * * * * * * * * * * * * *1
```

+01 8450935   Dolphins   +H+T   -A- -Z Hermann Neuhaus
+01 8450936   Dolphins   +Z+V   -A- -Z PD-Software,ISDN/SwissNet

```
* * * * * * * * * * * * * * * * * * * * * * * * * * * * * * * * * * * * * * * * * * * * * *
+*          ChNet-Hauptserver              4 Linien (USR/Zyxel/ISDN)       *
+*          UUCP-NEWS & E-Mail             Internet, Fido, Z-,T-Netz        *
+*          Aminet File-Server             Point-Service, Hotline          *
+* * * * * * * * * * * * * * * * * * * * * * * * * * * * * * * * * * * * * * * * * * * * * *
```

01 722 2235   Maxim BBS   +Z+V   I---E Dino Fiori,1600mb,erotic area

```
!!!!!!!!!!!!!!!!!!!!!!!!!!!!!!!!!!!!!!!!!!!!!!!!!!!!!!!!!!!!!!!!!!!!
!!!!!          Insgesamt ueber 3000mb HardDisk-Kapazitaet!           !!!!!
!!!!!             1600mb HD, 2 CD-ROMs, IBM-Soft!                    !!!!!

!!!!!!!!!!!!!!!!!!!!!!!!!!!!!!!!!!!!!!!!!!!!!!!!!!!!!!!!!!!!!!!!!!!5
```

01 840 5372   ProLine BBS   Z+V   I---E Gianni Facchinetti
01 840 5464   ProLine BBS   +Z+V   I---E

```
!!!!!!!!!!!!!!!!!!!!!!!!!!!!!!!!!!!!!!!!!!!!!!!!!!!!!!!!!!!!!!!!!!!!
!!!          V.32bis, 19'200 bps ZyXEL, 1000mb HD,                   !!!
!!!          MS-DOS/Windows/Games, SWISSLink, immer die              !!!
!!!          neusten c't listings/PCMagazine Files, Novell           !!!
!!!          & Turbo Pascal support, viele Door-Games,               !!!
!!!          Hardware zu billigst-Preisen, Online be-                !!!
!!!          stellen/registrieren, grosszuegige Beitrags-            !!!
!!!          Gebuehren! Call soon! Also ISDN/SwissNet                !!!

!!!!!!!!!!!!!!!!!!!!!!!!!!!!!!!!!!!!!!!!!!!!!!!!!!!!!!!!!!!!!!!!!!!4
```

022349 9000   Cougar BBS   +Z+V   I---R Etienne Deschenaux
022349 9001   Cougar BBS   +Z+V   I---R 20'000mb,ISDN/SwissNet
022349 9012   Cougar BBS   +Z+V   I---R

.⁻._.⁻._.⁻._.⁻._.⁻._.⁻._.⁻._.⁻._.⁻._.⁻._.⁻._.⁻._.⁻._.⁻._.⁻._.⁻._.⁻._

.-ZERO COST! FIRST CONNECTION, FIRST DOWNLOADS! OVER 150,000 Share-.
.- /Freeware pgms ONLINE. 500mb USA NEWS/month! FASTEST & CHEAPEST -.
.- FILES SERVICE ON TAPES! Computer peripherals like COLORADO, DAT, -.
.-   MODEMS at BEST prices, delivery 48 hours! VISA, EUROCARD OK!   -.

.⁻._.⁻._.⁻._.⁻._.⁻._.⁻._.⁻._.⁻._.⁻._.⁻._.⁻._.⁻._.⁻._.⁻._.⁻._.⁻._.⁻.0

```
022347 1100   Sun Serveur    +Z+V   I---E Olivier Junod
022347 1111   Sun Serveur    H+V    I---E                        2:301/323
===============================================================
!    3 lignes ZyXEL (19,200 bauds), 1 ligne HST (14,400 bauds)   !
!    Environnements TTY, ANSI ou graphique (RIP).                !
!    Reseaux de messageries FIDOnet et ILink a votre service.    !
!    4 Gbytes (20'000+ fichiers et programmes shareware sont a   !
!    votre disposition), nouveautes chaque jour (MS-DOS, OS/2,   !
!    MS-Windows). Tape service pour Sysp. VISA/EUROCARD/AMEX      !
===============================================================10
```

```
028 67 5179   SkyLine              H+V I---E John Warren
028 67 6207   SkyLine              .YV I---E Evelyne Warren
===============================================================
=            15'000 IBM & Kompatibel Files                  =
=            15'000 Erotik/Porno Gifs                        =
=            Direktimport aus der USA                        =
=    Europaeische Rep. fuer "The InterActive Girls Club"     =
=    Begrenzter GRATIS Zugriff oder Mitgliedschaft           =
=            Online-Registrierung mit VISA                   =
=         -== >>  DIE Mailbox im Wallis  <<==-               =
===============================================================4
```

```
^031372 4157   Metropolitan Net   +T I---E Gerard Vuille,3 lines
^031372 4159   Metropolitan Net   +H+T I---E dBOnline support
^031372 4187   Metropolitan Net   +H+T I---E & distribution
```

^<<<<<<<<<<<<<<<<<<<<<<<<<<<<<<<<<<<<>>>>>>>>>>>>>>>>>>>>>>>>>>>>>>>>

On-Line Datenbanken: City Guide Bern, Inserate-Datenbank (gratis).
Application oriented File Areas / Targa Pictures / Flight-Sim stuff.
LaserDiscs (PAL: d & e / NTSC: e), On-Line Shopping / Infos.
Official Distributor / Support Site: dbOnline by Merlin Systems Inc.
On-Line Database Development/Entwicklung. Eurocard/Mastercard & VISA

^<<<<<<<<<<<<<<<<<<<<<<<<<<<<<<<<<<<<>>>>>>>>>>>>>>>>>>>>>>>>>>>>>0

+041 32 9517   Paradize   +Z+V ---SQ Roland Tobler,Atari   2:301/609
±===
     Atari-Netz NeST, ParaNet, LichtNet, File-Netze EST/AFN/NeST/ADN
        Hints, Tricks, Support - Atari PUR!9 links, Atari-only BBS
==12

052222 1751   Bazzillus BBS   Z+V   IA--X Roger Hungerbuehler   44:8010/513

-                 Bilder-Scan-Service fuer Amiga und IBM   -
---15

052 33 3033   Squirrel Mailbox   HV I---E Peter Haessig,5000mb

<<<<<<<<<<<<<<<<<<<<<<<<<<<<<<<<<<<>>>>>>>>>>>>>>>>>>>>>>>>>>>>>>>>
<<<   8 Lines USRobotics, 2 ISDN/SwissNet: SoLIS + SLINK   >>>
<<<   40'000 IBM-Files / 145 File-Areas / Adult-Area   >>>
<<<   –> Jeden Tag neue Files auf der Box <–   >>>
<<<   MailNets: FreeNet / FIDO / Usenet-internet   >>>
<<<   Online-Registrierung mit VISA   >>>

<<<<<<<<<<<<<<<<<<<<<<<<<<<<<<<<<<<>>>>>>>>>>>>>>>>>>>>>>>>>>>>>>>4

^061482 2238 Butsch CD-ROM BBS HV IA--A Mike Butsch,Butsch Infor.support

0619210777   Chaos Box   +V   I---L 4 lines

+ +

+   Das absolute Chaos unter den kommunikativen Supermaerkten   +
+   +
+   - Spass, Spiel   - Online-Shopping   +
+   - Konferenz, Chat   - Shareware   +
+   - Diskussionsforen - Mekka der FrogyCOMMer   +

+ +

^061311 9284   DataComm BBS   +Z+V   I---J 20 lines total
^061311 9193   DataComm BBS   +Z+V   I---J 12 ZyXEL 19200 bps lines
^061311 9273   DataComm BBS   H+V   I---J 5000mb
^061311 9306   DataComm BBS   !V   I---J Chats,Online-Games,Software

061921 6930   Moulin Rouge   +Z+V   I---U Tatjana erwartet dich !

071 24 2224   Roesslibox   +Z+V I---U Michael Huwiler   2:301/406

```
^##############################################################
^##          Die vielseitige, komfortable Mailbox fuer jedermann...        ##
^##              -+-+-+-+-+-+-+-+-+-+-+-+-+-+-+-+-+-+-+-+—               ##
^##          - Produkte-Info-System (PIS)  - Gravis Ultrasound-Soft        ##
^##          - TrendLimone, InfoThek, etc. - QWK-Offline-Support           ##
^##          - Aktuellste Treiber/Updates  - Message-Boards en masse       ##
^##          - Viel Shareware/PublicDomain - Registrierung von             ##
^##                - Tolle Online-Games (dt.)  FrogyCom !                  ##
^##############################################################?
```

081302 7200   New-Line Swiss BBS   +Z+V IamsW Roberto Ruga,4 lines,10'000mb

```
* * * * * * * * * * * * * * * * * * * * * * * * * * * * * * * * * * * * * * * * * * * *
*          ca. 55'000 Files, neuste SHAREWARE, GRATIS Probelevel,          *
*          GRATIS Inserate, DOS, WINDOWS, Sounds, Spiele, Erotik,          *
*          DTP-Bilder, Cliparts, Schriften, Animationen, Updates,          *
*          Demo+Test Programme, SSV-News, Infos, CDROM, RIPGrafik          *
* * * * * * * * * * * * * * * * * * * * * * * * * * * * * * * * * * * * * * * * * * *3
```

156   8125   HOTBox BBS   H+V I---U Fr.2.00/m,Ilona,Erotic

```
* * * * * * * * * * * * * * * * * * * * * * * * * * * * * * * * * * * * * * * * * * * *
*          GIFs * ANIMs * VIDEOS * CONTACTS * LIVE-CHAT  * AB 18          *
* * * * * * * * * * * * * * * * * * * * * * * * * * * * * * * * * * * * * * * * * * *3
```

[=-> 5. EXPLANATION OF THE STRANGE SYMBOLS <-=]

[=---------------> Status <---------------=]

+01 492 5157   A new BBS! First time on the list.
^01 492 5157   Information has changed since the last list.
*01 492 5157   I couldn't connect or had some other problem.

01　492　5157　*	Not online 24h. But most BBS are online 24h on weekends.
-01 *492*5157**	NOT ONLINE, DO NOT CALL! Last time on the list.
01 *492*5157**	Not yet online, but will be soon.

[=-------------> Modem Types <-------------=]

All following modems with MNP and/or V.42/V.42bis (error correction and compression) and V.21/V.22/V.22bis (300, 1200 and 2400 bps). Example: If a modem with "+H" calls a modem with "+V" you will get a V.22bis (2400 bps) connection with V.42bis or MNP correction/compression. Modems will connect with the fastest protocol that both modems support.

International CCITT standards:

^V	28800 bps V.34		(available soon, known as V.fast)
+V	14400 bps V.32bis		(95% of modern high speed modems)
V	9600 bps V.32		(older or cheap modems)
+24	2400 bps V.22bis		
24	2400 bps V.22bis		(without MNP or V.42/V.42bis)
+12	1200 bps V.22		
12	1200 bps V.22		(without MNP or V.42/V.42bis)
3	300　bps V.21		(without MNP or V.42/V.42bis)

V32turbo, not official but public standard:

T	19200 bps V.32terbo	& V32bis	(many new modems, not really CCITT)
+T	21600 bps AS	& V32bis	(V.32turbo version by USRobotics)
+H+T	21600 bps ASL & 16800 bps HST		(USRobotics Dual Standard 1993/94)

Fast-Class by Rockwell:

F	28800 bps V.FC	(New Rockwell chipset)

HST-protocol (High Speed Technology) by USRobotics:

+H+V	16800 bps HST	& V.32bis	(USRobotics Dual Standard 1992)
H+V	14400 bps HST	& V.32bis	(USRobotics Dual Standard 1991)
HV	14400 bps HST	& V.32	(USRobotics Dual Standard 1990)
+H	16800 bps HST		(USRobotics Courier HST 1992)
H	14400 bps HST		(USRobotics Courier HST 1991)

ZyX-protocol by ZyXEL:

!Z+V	21600 bps ZyX	& V.32bis	(ZyXEL + beta/soon?)
+Z+V	19200 bps ZyX	& V.32bis	(ZyXEL U-1496E+ or U-1496+ LCD)
Z+V	16800 bps ZyX	& V.32bis	(ZyXEL U-1496E or U-1496 LCD)

PEP-protocol by TeleBit:

+P+V	23000 bps TurboPEP	& V.32bis	(TeleBit WorldBlazer)
P+V	1?000 bps PEP	& V.32bis	(TeleBit TrailBlazer,T1000-T3000)

Hayes-protocol by Hayes:

Y	9600 bps Hayes		(Hayes)
YV	9600 bps Hayes	& V.32	(Hayes Ultra)

[=-------> FILES IN DOWNLOAD AREA <--------=]

I	=	IBM files	i =	only a few IBM files
A	=	AMIGA files	a =	only a few AMIGA files
M	=	APPLE Macintosh files	m =	only a few MAC files
S	=	ATARI files	s =	only a few ATARI files

[=-----------> BBS SOFTWARE <-------------=]

A	AmiExpress 2.35	Amiga	Light Speed Technologies
B	RoboBoard/FX 1.08	IBM	Seth Hamilton
C	FirstClass 2.400	Macintosh	SoftArc, Inc.
D	DIALOG Pro BB/OS0.999	Amiga	TelePro Technologies
E	PCBoard 15.0	IBM	Clark Development Company, Inc.
F	TeleFinder 3.1	Macintosh	Spider Island Software
G	GMS-2000 3.0	IBM	Marcel Manz/Nevada BBS
J	The Major BBS 6.12	IBM	Galacticomm, Inc.
K	Perfect-Link BBS 1.04	Amiga	Wild Rabbit Productions
L	DLX	IBM	Inner Loop Software
M	Maximus-CBCS 2.01	IBM (OS/2)	Scott J. Dudley
N	Nova Link Pro	Macintosh	ResNova Software Inc.
O	Opus-CBCS	IBM	Opus-CBCS Development
P	Paragon BBS 2.085	Amiga	Inner Circle Software
Q	QuickBBS ST 1.10c	Atari	DeltaVision Systems
R	Remote Access 2.01	IBM	Continental Software
S	Searchlight BBS 3.5	IBM	Searchlight Software
T	TBBS 2.2	IBM	eSoft, Inc.
U	SuperBBS 1.17	IBM	Risto Virkkala & Aki Antman
W	Wildcat! BBS 3.90	IBM	Mustang Software Inc.
X	XenoLink 1.0 Z.3a	Amiga	Xenomiga Technology
Y	Madness MB System	Atari	Juergen Meyer
Z	Zerberus	IBM,Atari,Amiga	
?	Unlisted software		

```
[=--------------> NETWORKS <---------------=]
```

All the following networks are non-commercial batch networks (mail exchange several times a day - not in real time), using FIDONet compatible software. Data is transferred over normal telephone lines using normal modems. Most nets carry messages and files. To join or use a net, contact a BBS near you.

2:301/xxx	FIDO-Net, United FIDONet of Switzerland (UFS)
2:30/xxx	FIDO-Net Region 30
	Over 20'000 systems worldwide are connected
9:412/xxx	VirNet (virus killers)
15:4020/xxx	DataNetLink (Asia)
15:1200/xxx	AdultNet
16:200/xxx	ZyXELnet (ZyXEL Modems)
27:1341/xxx	SigNet
37:xxx/xxx	ParaNet (Parapsychological Net)
39:110/xxx	AmigaNet (Amiga, worldwide)
42:1301/xxx	SuperNet (SuperBBS)
44:8010/xxx	AmiNet (Amiga, Switzerland)
52:4100/xxx	GlobalNet
67:410/xxx	ParadigmNet
68:2411/xxx	CinemaNet (Movies)
69:410/xxx	GayNet (Homosexual)
73:7411/xxx	RA-Net (Remote Access BBS)
74:4100/xxx	DemNet (Democracy)
81:441/xxx	OS2Net (IBM OS/2)
88:4102/xxx	TopNet
90:xxx/xxx	NeST (Network Atari ST)
91:1100/xxx	Robo-Net (RoboBoard/FX BBS)
93:100/xxx	ImagineNet
94:100/xxx	GrafxNet
100:410/xxx	BorlandNet
101:210/xxx	ChateauNet
101:180/xxx	FrancoMedia
102:410/xxx	Lif-Net
142:120/xxx	SFNet (Science Fiction)
144:4101/xxx	GamesNet
144:xxx/xxx	LichtNet
154:941/xxx	RIPnet (RIP graphics)
177:410/xxx	Box Office (Movies)
202:202/xxx	Oase Net (Shareware)

250:1100/xxx	SL-Net (Searchlight BBS)
640:130/xxx	SwiWN, SwissWildNet (Wildcat! BBS)

Other networks:

ILink/SWISSLink:	Batch network using non-FIDO-Net-compatible software, ILink is worldwide and SWISSLink only in Switzerland.
Zerberus-Netz:	Also called Z-Netz, batch network with most systems in Germany, Austria and Switzerland.
UseNet:	International, non-commercial message network, data is transfered on Internet.
Internet:	Worldwide realtime network, data is transfered on leased lines, satellite links, etc. Includes services such as E-Mail, Usenet news, Telnet, FTP, IRC, Gophers. Millions of systems are connected directly or via UUCP. Addresses look like this: name@address.address.etc or like this: xxx.xxx.xxx.xxx.
UUCP:	Not a network, but a protocol which lets you transport Internet/UseNet data over a modem.
X.25:	Worldwide high speed data lines. In Switzerland it's called PTT's TelePac. X.25 addresses are called NUAs and look like this: 0208057040540.
X.28:	If you want to access X.25 with a modem, you use X.28.

CHAPTER 19

Telephone Numbers To Note

In this chapter readers will find five tables of information, with each table either containing a set of telephone numbers or telephone-number-related information.

The first table in this chapter contains the telephone numbers of information utility systems, Internet access providers and organizations that provide different types of electronic transmission services. Hence, the name of this table is Service and Access Providers.

The second table in this chapter consists of a list of technical support bulletin board systems. This list is provided with the permission of Mr. Gary Barr of Digicom. Information is provided later in this chapter concerning how readers can communicate with the Digicom BBS.

The third table contained in this chapter consists of triple "XXX" codes. You can use those codes to bypass a default long distance provider in the United States to use a different provider by the use of triple "XXX" codes.

The last table in this chapter consists of telephone and fax country codes. Quite often you may have to dial a telephone number but lack the country code. Thus, this table may provide you with a handy reference when you cannot locate the telephone book or fail to get the telephone operator.

Service and Access Providers

Advanced Network and Services (Internet access provider)	1-914-789-5300
Alternet (national Internet access provider)	1-800-4UUNET3
America Online	1-800-827-6364
ANS COO+RE Systems, Inc. (Internet access provider)	1-800-456-8267
Ansnet (national Inernet access provider)	1-914- 789-5300
A2I Communications (Internet service provider)	1-408-293-8078
BARRNet (Internet access provider)	1-415-725-1790
BIX modem: 1-800-695-4882 voice:	1-800-695-4775
CERFnet (Internet access provider serving CA)	1-800-876-CERF
CICNet (Internet access provider)	1-313-998-6103
Colorado SuperNet (Internet access provider serving CO)	1-303-273-3471
CONCERT (Internet access provider serving NC)	1-919-248-1999
Connect	1-408-973-0110
CompuServe	1-800-848-8990
Delphi	1-800-695-4005
Dialog	1-800-334-2564
Dow Jones News Retrieval	1-800-522-3567
Genie	1-800-638-9636
Global Enterprises (Internet access provider)	1-800-358-4437
Institute for Global Communications	1-415-923-0220
Intercon Systems Corp.(Internet access provider)	1-703-709-9890
Interagency (Federaql) E©mail Help Desk	1-816-926-3333
Interagency (Federal) E©mail User's Working Group	1-202-260-7444
Internet Network Information Center:	1-800-365-3642
Internet Society	1-703-648-9888
InterSpan Information Access Service	1-950-1ATT
MCI:	1-800-444-3333
MCI Mail customer support	1-800-444-6245
MichNet (Internet access provider serving Michigan)	1-313-764-9430
MIDnet (Internet access provider)	1-402-472-7600
MRnet (Internet access provider serving Minnesota)	1-612-342-2570
MSEN (Internet access provider serving Michigan)	1-313-741-1120
NEARNET (Internet access provider)	1-617-873-8730
NETCOM (Internet access provider serving CA)	1-408-554-8649
NewsNet	1-800-345-1301
NevadaNet (Internet access provider serving Nevada)	1-702-784-6133
New Mexico Technet (Internet access provider serving NM)	1-505-345-6555

NorthWestNet (Internet access provider)	1-206-562-3000
NSFNET	1-800-456-3000
NYSERnet (Internet access provider serving New York)	1-315-443-4120
OARet (Internet access provider serving Ohio)	1-614-292-0700
PACCOM (Internet access provider serving Hawaii)	1-808-949-6395
Panix (New York Internet access provider)	1-212-787-6160
PC-Link	1-800-827-8532
PREPnet (Internet access provider serving Pennsylvania)	1-412-268-7870
Prodigy membership services	1-800-759-8000
PSCNET (Internet access provider serving north east US)	1-412-268-4960
PSILink (national Internet access service provider)	703-620-6651
Portal Communications (Internet access service provider)	1-408-973-9111
SDSCnet (Internet access provider serving California)	1-619-534-5043
Sesquinet (Internet access provider serving Texas)	1-713-527-4988
SprintLink (Internet access service provider)	1-703-904-2680
SURAnet (Internet access service provider)	1-800-787-2638
THEnet (Internet access provider serving Texas)	1-512-471-5046
World Software Tool & Die (Internet access provider)	1-617-739-0202
UUNET Communications Services (Internet access provider)	1-800-488-6384
VERnet (Internet access provider serving Virginia)	1-804-924-0616
WestNet (Internet access provider)	1-303-491-7260
WiscNet (Internet access provider serving Wisconson)	1-608-262-8874
WVnet (Internet access provider serving West Virginia)	1-304-293-5192

TECHNICAL SUPPORT BULLETIN BOARD SYSTEMS

As the modem has advanced through the years, it is almost a necessary item for commercial & shareware companies to provide a means of technical support through a bulletin board system. This list is to help users find the support BBS's that are available to the public.

This list contains only BBS's operated by Hardware Manufacturers, Commercial Software Companies, and Shareware Software Companies. If you have any support BBS's that you would like to have listed in the next issue of the Tech Support BBS List, you can do one of the following:

1 Call the Digicom BBS and answer the Tech Support BBS Addition Questionnaire.

2 Send Netmail to 1:2310/200 (Gary Barr).

3 Send Private Mail through RelayNet to ->DIGICOM.

4 Fax the form into (812) 474-2264.

5 CompuServe Mail to 70007,4634.

6 By US Mail to Gary Barr, 7624 Syls Drive, Evansville, IN 47712.

You must provide the company name, state of operation, phone number, modem speed & type, your system flags (as follows), and what products the board supports. With that, you'll be listed in the next issue! The flags tracked on the technical support BBS list are indicated below:

Flags:
D - MUST BE AUTHORIZED DEALER
X - PC PURSUIT REQUIRES ADDITIONAL PARAMETERS FOR DIALING
R - MUST BE REGISTERED USER
S - MUST BE REGISTERED USER WITH PRODUCT SERIAL NUMBER

Company/BBS Name	STPCP	Phone number	MDM	FLG	Products supported
3Com	CASJO	408-980-8204	96		Network Cards
3rd Planet Software, Inc	CA	213-841-2260	24		Network Asst Plus
Abacus Concepts	MI	616-698-8106	24		Statview,Supernova Mac
Abaton Technology	CAPAL	415-438-4650	24		Laser Printer,Scanner
Accolade	CASJO	408-296-8800	24		Gaming Software
Acer America	CA	800-833-8241	96		Computers & Monitors
Adaptec	CASJO	408-945-7727	144		Controllers
Addstor	CAPAL	415-324-4077	144		Superstor
Advanced Digital Corp	CASAN	714-894-0893	24		SCSI CTRL,Tape Backups
Advanced Logical Research	CASAN	714-458-6834	144		ALR Computer Systems
All Computer	ONT	416-960-8679	24		Motherboards
Alloy Computer Products	MA	508-460-8140	24		Storage Devices
Allied Telesis	CAPAL	415-964-2994	24		Networking
Alpha Software	MA	617-229-2915	24		Alpha Database
Altima	CA	510-356-2456	24		Laptops
Altsys	TXDAL	214-680-8592	24		Fontographer
Amdek Corporation	CASJO	408-922-4400	24		Monitors
American Megatrends (AMI)	GAATL	404-246-8780	144		AMI BIOS, Motherboards

Company/BBS Name ....STPCP	Phone number	MDM	FLG	Products supported
Apogee Software ....MA	508-365-2359	168		Games,Keen,Secret Agent
Applied Engineering ....TXDAL	214-241-6677	24		Fax/Modem,Fastmath
Artisoft ....AZ	602-884-8648	144		Lantastic Networking
NETWORKArtist Graphics ...MNMIN	612-631-7669	24		Command Center
Ask Sam Systems ....FL	904-584-8287	24		Ask Sam LAN
Asymetrix ....WA	206-451-1173	144		Multimedia Software
AST Research ....CA	714-727-4723	24		Computer Systems
ATI Technologies ....ONT	416-764-9404	144		Video Cards/Modems
AT&T Computer Systems ....NJ	201-769-6397	24		Computers
Automated Design Systems ..GA	404-394-7448	24		Windows Workstation
Award ....CA	408-371-3139	24		Bios
Beagle Bros ....CA	619-558-6151	24		Beagle Works,Time-out
Bestgift Service ....FL	813-978-3044	24		Gift Selection Software
Big State Doors ....TX	512-398-7346	144		BBS Door Software
Blackmond Software ....NM	505-589-0319	96H		Ramail, CCTRX
Boca Research ....FL	407-241-1601	144		Memory Cards,Modems
Borland ....CA	408-439-9096	24		C,Quattro,DBase
Bourbaki ....ID	208-342-5823	24		Fractools
Brightbill Roberts ....NY	315-472-1058	24		LAN Server/Net Remote
Brightwork Development ....NYNYO	914-667-4759	24		Networking Utilities
Brown Bag Software ....CASJO	408-371-7654	168		Powermenu
Buerg Software ....CA	707-778-8944	24		List Software
Buttonware ....WASEA	206-454-7875	144		PCFile,PCCalc,PCWrite
Calcomp ....CASAN	714-821-2359	24		Digitizers
Calera Recognition Systems ..CASJO	408-773-9068	96		OCR Software
Campbell Services ....MI	313-559-6434	24		Ontime Scheduler
Canon Printer Division .....NYHEM	516-488-6528	96		Laser/Bubble Jet PRN-TRS
Canon Printer (Italy) ......ITL	+39-2-58010997	168		Laser/Bubble Jet PRN-TRS
Cardinal Technologies ......PA	717-293-3074	144		Cardinal Modems/Faxs
Cardz ....BC	604-734-5400	96H		Fracterm COMM Software
CBIS, Inc ....GAATL	404-446-8405	24		Network OS
cc:Mail ....CAPAL	415-691-0401	24	C	CC:Mail E-Mail
Central Point ....ORPOR	503-690-6650	144		PC Tools
Certus ....OHCLE	216-546-1508	24		SuperNovi
Cheyenne Software ....NYHEM	516-484-3445	24		Netware Tape Backups
Chipsoft ....CASDI	619-453-5232	24		Memory
Chwatal Development Co ...LA	318-487-0800	144		Ultrabbs
Citizens America Corp ......CAGLE	310-453-7564	24	X	Printers

Company/BBS Name	STPCP	Phone number	MDM	FLG	Products supported
Citrix Systems	FL	305-346-9004	24		Networking Software
Clarion Software	FL	305-785-9172	24		Report Writer
Clark Development Corp	UTSLC	801-261-8976	168		PCBoard BBS Software
Clear Software	MABOS	617-965-5406	24		Clear, All Clear
CNET	CASJO	408-954-1787	24		NetWorking
Coconut Computing Inc	CASDI	619-456-0815	144		Coconet BBS Software
Codenoll	NYNYO	914-965-1972	24		Networking Boards
Colorado Memory Systems	CO	303-679-0650	24		Tape Backups
Columbia Data Products	FLORL	407-862-4724	24		SCSI DRV'S For WD-7000
Communications Research	LA	504-926-5625	24		Terminal Emulators
Compaq Computer Systems	TXHOU	713-378-1418	144		COMPAQ Drivers & Utils
Complete PC	CASJO	408-434-9703	144		Modems,Fax,Scanners
Computers International	CA	213-823-3609	144		ONLINE Shopping Software
Computer Peripherals	CA	805-499-9646	144		Modems
Computer Support	TXDAL	214-404-8652	144		Arts & Letters Software
Computone	GAATL	404-664-1210	24		Intelligent Serial Card
Comtrol	MNMIN	612-631-9310	24		Intelligent Serial Card
Conner International	CASJO	408-456-4415	24		Hard Drives
Core International	FL	407-241-2929	24		Hard Drives
Corel System	ON	613-728-4752	144		Corel Draw
Cornerstone	CASJO	408-435-8943	24		Single/Dual PG Monitor
Corvus System, Inc	CASJO	408-972-9154	24		NET Software
Creative Labs	AZ	405-742-6660	44		Soundblaster Music Card
Cross Communications	CODEN	303-444-9003	44		Cross Connect
Cumulus	OHCLE	216-464-3019	24		Memory, Boards
DAC Software	TXDAL	214-931-6617	24		DAC Easy Accounting
DAK Online Resource Center	CA	818-715-7153	144		All DAK Products
Dariana Technology Group	CASAN	714-994-7410	24		System Sleuth
Darwin Systems	DCWAS	301-251-9206	144	X	Darwin BBS List
Data Access	FLMIA	305-238-0640	24		Dataflex
Datadesk/Prometheus	ORPOR	503-691-5199	96		Keyboards/Trackballs
DataEase Int'l	CT	203-374-6302	24		Dataease,Graftalk
Dataproducts Corp	CA	818-887-8167	96		Dataproducts Printers
Datastorm	MO	314-875-0503	144		PROCOMM Plus
Data Technology	CASJO	408-942-4197	24		HD Controllers
David Systems	CASJO	408-720-0406	24		Networking Hardware
Dayna Communications	UTSLC	801-535-4205	24		Localtalk,E-Net For Mac

Company/BBS Name ......*.STPCP*	*Phone number*	*MDM*	*FLG*	*Products supported*
DCA ....GAATL	404-740-8428	96		CROSSTALK/IRMA
Dell Computer Corp ....TXAUS	512-338-8528	144		Dell Maill Order Clones
Delphi ....CA	800-365-4636	24		DELPHI Online Service
Delrina Technology Inc .....ON	416-441-2752	168		Fax & Forms Software
DeltaComm Development ...NC	919-481-9399	168		Telix COMM Software
Diamond Computer ....CASJO	408-730-1100	24		Video Boards
Digiboard ....MN	612-943-0812	24		Intelligent Serial Card
Digital Communications ....OH	513-433-5080	24		10-Net
Digital Research ....GA	408-649-3443	24		DR DOS
Digital Vision ....MA	617-329-8387	144		Video Imaging
Disk Technician Corporation .CASDI	619-272-9240	24		Disk Technician Gold
Distibuted Processing Tech. ..FLORL	407-831-6432	24		Controller Cards
D-Link Systems, Inc ....CASAN	714-455-1779	144		Network Print Server
DNA Networks, Inc ....PA	215-296-9558	24		MICRONET Network
Dove Computer ....NC	919-343-5616	144		Modems/Fax Boards
DTK ....CA	818-333-6548	24		DTK Motherboards
Dudley Software ....TN	615-966-3574	24		Doorway Software
Dynamic Microprocessor ....NYHEM	516-462-6638	24		Computer CPUS
EagleSoft ....IN	812-479-1310	168		Shoppers Asst,Callaway
Elite Business App's ....MD	410-987-2335	24		Ramjet
Emac/Everex ....CAPAL	510-226-9694	24	X	Trackball,Modem
Emerald Systems ....CASDI	619-673-4617	24		Data Management
Enable Software ....NY	518-877-6316	24		Enable Business Software
Epson America, Inc ....CA	310-782-4531	96		Epson Computer Products
Equinox Systems, Inc ......FLMIA	305-378-1696	24		Multiport COMM Ports
eSoft Inc ....CODEN	303-699-8222	168		TBBS BBS Software
ETS Incorporated ....UTSLC	801-265-0919	144		GUI & Laser Printer Apps
Excalibur ....CASJO	408-244-0813	144		VSUMX Virus Software
Exis ....ON	416-439-8293	144		*TELIX Now by DELTACOMM
EZX Publishing ....TXHOU	713-280-8180	144		EZ-Form, EZ-Diskcopy
Family Scrapbook ....FL	904-249-9515	168		Family Scrapbook
Fifth Generation Systems ....LA	504-295-3344	24		Fastback,London Bridge
Folio ....UT	801-375-9907	24		Mailbag
Foresight Resources ....MOKCI	816-891-8465	24		DRAFIX CADD Software
Frederick Engineering, Inc. ..MD	301-290-6944	24		Datacomm Analyzer

Company/BBS Name ....STPCP	Phone number	MDM	FLG	Products supported
Fresh Technology ....AZPHO	602-497-4235	24		MAP Assist, NETWORK SFTW
Fujitsu America, Inc ....CASJO	408-944-9899	96		Printers,Hard/Floppy Drv
Future Domain ....CASAN	714-253-0432	24		Tape Backups
FutureSoft Engineering .....TXHOU	713-588-6870	24		DYNACOMM
Galacticomm. ....FL	305-583-7808	144		Major BBS Software
GAP Development Company .CA	714-493-3819	144		Gap BBS Software
Gateway BBS. ....SD	605-232-2109	144		Gateway Computers
Gateway Communications ...CASAN	714-863-7097	24		Network Hardware
Gazelle Systems ....UT	801-375-2548	24		Backit,Optune,Q-Dos
GEcho ....KS	316-263-5313	168		Fido Mail Processor
General DataComm Ind .....CT	203-598-0593	144		Modem/Multiplex-ors/LAN
GEnie Information Services. .CA	800-638-8369	24		Genie Online Service
Genoa Systems ....CASJO	408-943-1231	24		Tape Backups
Gensoft Development ......WASEA	206-562-9407	24		SuperCalc
GeoClock ....VA	703-241-7980	144		Geoclock Software
Gibson Research ....CASAN	714-362-8848	24		Spinrite
GigaTrend, Inc ....CASDI	619-566-0361	24		High Capacity Hard Drive
Global Village Comm ....CA	415-390-8397	144		Teleport,Powerport
Goldstar Technologies ......CASJO	408-432-0236	144		Monitors & Compu-ters
Graphic Workshop ....ONT	416-729-4609	144		Graphic Workshop Prg
Great American Software ....NH	603-889-7292	24		One-Write Plus Accnt
Gupta Technologies, Inc ...CAPAL	415-321-0549	24		SQL Windows
GVC Technologies ....NJ	201-579-2380	144		Modems
Hayes Microcomputer ......GA	800-874-2937	144	D R	Modems
Hayes Microcomputer ......GAATL	404-446-6336	144		Modems
Hazard Soft ....OK	405-243-3200	168		Windows Software
HDC Computer ....WASEA	206-869-2418	24		Windows Env Software
Headland Technology ......CAPAL	415-656-0503	24		Computers
Hercules Computer ....CAOAK	510-540-0621	24		Memory Exp, Video Cards
IBM ....NCRTP	919-517-0001	144		IBM Computer Prod-ucts
Intelligent Graphics Corp.. ..CASJO	408-441-0386	24		VM386,Multitasking
IMC Networks ....CASAN	714-724-0930	24		LAN Network Equip-ment
IMSI Software ....CASFA	415-454-2893	24		Desktop Publishing
Infinity Computer Services. ..PA	215-965-8028	24		Bar Code Products
Infochip Systems ....CASJO	408-727-2496	24		Memory
Informix ....MOKCI	913-492-2089	24		Smartware, Informix
InfoShare ....DCWAS	703-803-8000	96H	X	Falken BBS Software
Innovative Data Concepts ...PA	215-357-4183	24		TCXL

Company/BBS Name ....STPCP	Phone number	MDM	FLG	Products supported
Inset Corporation ....CT	203-740-0063	144		Hijaak Graphic Conversn
Insignia Solutions ....CAPAL	415-694-7694	24		Access PC, Soft PC
Intel ....ORPOR	503-645-6275	144		Mathco,Modem,Fax, Chips
Intel Application Support ...CASAC	916-356-3600	144	X	Intel Motherboards
Intracorp ....FLMIA	305-378-8793	24		Travel Partnet
Iomega ....UT	801-778-4400	24		Tape Backups
Irwin Magnetics ....MIAAR	313-930-9380	96		Tape Backups
Jetfax ....CAPAL	415-324-1259	24		Jetfax Boards
Jetform ....ON	613-563-2894	24		Jetform Design
JDR Microdevices ....CASJO	408-559-0253	24		Mail Order Componets
Kent Marsh ....TXHOU	713-522-8921	24		MAC Security Software
Kodiak Technology ....CASJO	408-452-0677	24		Network Hardware
Kurta Corp ....AZPHO	602-243-9440	24	X	Digitizer Boards
LAN Master ....TX	817-771-0233	168		Remote Access Software
LAN Systems ....UT	801-373-6980	24		Networking Hardware
LAN Works ....ONT	416-238-0253	24		Proms
Laser Go ....CASDI	619-450-9370	24		Goscript
Lattice ....ILCHI	708-916-1200	24	X	Lattice Software
Leading Edge ....MA	508-836-3971	144		Computer Systems
Lexmark ....KY	800-453-9223	24		Printers, Keyboards
Liant Software ....WASEA	206-236-6485	24		Language Software
Lightning Communications ..CACOL	714-457-9429	96		Communications Software
Logical Connection ....LA	504-295-3344	24		Logical Connection
Logitech ....CAPAL	510-795-0408	144	X	Mouse,Scanners
Lotus ....MABOS	617-693-7000	24		LOTUS Spreadsheet
Lotus ....GAATL	404-395-7707	24		LOTUS Word Processing
Mace, Paul Software ....OR	503-482-7435	24		Mace Utilities
Madge Networks ....CASJO	408-441-1340	24		Networking Hardware
Magee Enterprises, Inc .....GAATL	404-446-6650	168		Automenu/Treeview
Magitronic Technology .....NYHEM	516-454-8262	144		Motherboards
Magnavox ....CALAN	310-532-6436	144	X	Computers/Monitors
Main Lan ....FLORL	407-331-7433	24		MainLAN
Mannesman Tally ....WASEA	206-251-5513	24		Printer Access
Mansfield Software Group ...CT	203-429-3784	144		Kedit For DOS & OS/2
Manx Software Systems .....NJ	201-542-2793	24		Aztec C
Matrix Technology ....MABOS	617-569-3787	24		Software
Maxi Host Support ....CA	209-836-2402	24		Maxi Host BBS Software
Maxis Software ....CAOAK	510-254-3869	144		SIMEARTH,SIMCITY ,SIMANT
Maxtor/Miniscribe ....CO	303-678-2222	144		Hard Drives

Company/BBS Name ....STPCP	Phone number	MDM	FLG	Products supported
Maynard Electronics ....FLORL	407-263-3502	24		Tape Backups
McAfee Assoc ....CASJO	408-988-4044	168		Virus Protection
Media Vision ....CAPAL	510-770-0968	144	X	Multimedia Products
Micro Display Systems ......MNMIN	612-438-3513	24		Monitors
Microcom ....MA	617-762-5134	24		Carbon Copy, Workmanager
Microdyne ....DCWAS	703-739-0432	24	X	Network Hardware
Micron Technology ....ID	208-368-4530	24		Video Boards
Micronics ....CAPAL	510-651-6837	144	X	Computer, Motherboards
Micropolis Corp ....CA	818-709-3310	24		Hard Drives
Microrim ....WASEA	206-649-9836	24		R:BASE
MicroProse ....MD	301-785-1841	24		Gaming Software
Microsoft ....WA	206-637-9009	144		Word, Windows
Microsystems Software ......MA	508-875-8009	24		Calander Scheduler
Microtech ....CT	203-469-6430	24		MAC Memory
Microtest ....AZPHO	602-996-4009	24		LANport
Mitsubishi ....CASAN	714-636-6216	24		Monitors
Mountain Network Solutions. CA	408-438-2665	24		Tape Backups
Mouse Systems (MSC) ......CAPAL	510-683-0617	144		Mouse
Multi-Tech Systems ....MNMIN	612-785-9875	144		Modems
Mustang Software ....CA	805-395-0650	168		Wildcat, Qmodem, OLX
Mutant Group ....OK	405-372-6621	168		Mutant BBS Software
National Semiconductor ....CASJO	408-245-0671	24		Ethernode, Mainlink
NEC Technologies ....MA	508-635-4706	144		Computer, Printers
NetWorth ....TXDAL	214-869-2959	24		Ethernet Cards
New Media Graphics ......MA	508-663-7612	144		Video Capture Boards
Night Owl BBS ....NY	716-881-5688	168		Night Owl CDRom Disk
NISCA ....TXDAL	214-446-0646	24		Scanners
Norton-Lambert ....CA	805-683-2249	144		Close-up/LAN
Novell ....UT	801-429-3030	144		NOVELL Networking
Novell Desktop Systems .....CA	408-649-3443	24		Computers
Nuiq Software Inc ....NYNYO	914-833-1479	144		Powerboard BBS Software
Number Nine ....MABOS	617-497-6463	96H		Advanced Video
OCR Systems ....PAPHI	215-938-7245	24		Readright
Okidata ....CA	800-283-5474	96		Printers
Omen Technology ....ORPOR	503-621-3746	96		DSZ - Zmodem Protocol
Ontrack Computer Systems ..MNMIN	612-937-0860	24		HD Prep. Software
Open Network ....NYNYO	718-638-2239	24	X	Networking
Orchid Technology ....CAPAL	510-683-0327	24	X	Video Cards
Origin ....TXAUS	512-328-8402	24		Gaming Software
Pacific Data Products ....CASDI	619-452-6329	24		Laser Printer Products

Company/BBS Name ....STPCP	Phone number	MDM	FLG	Products supported
Packard Bell ....CA	818-773-7207	24		Computer Systems
Palindrome ....ILCHI	708-505-3336	24	X	Network Software
Panasonic ....NJNEW	201-863-7847	24		Printers,Scanners, CPUS
Paperback Corporation .....CASFA	415-644-0782	168		Software
Paradise Systems ....CASAN	714-753-1234	144		Video Cards
Patton & Patton Software ....CA	408-778-9697	24		Flow Charting Software
Pentax Technologies ....CODEN	303-460-1637	168		Scanners, Laser Print-ers
Phoenix Technologies ......OK	405-321-2400	144		Motherboard BIOS
Pinnacle Publishing ....WASEA	206-251-6217	24		DGE
Pinpoint Publishing ....PA	707-523-0468	24		Micro Cookbook
PKWare ....WIMIL	414-354-8670	168		PKZIP Compression
PLI ....CAPAL	510-651-5948	24	X	Removable Media
Plus Development ....CASJO	408-434-1664	24		Hard Drives
Practical Peripherals ......CA	805-496-4445	144		Modems
Priam Systems ....CASJO	408-434-1646	24		Hard Drives
Princeton Graphic Systems ..GAATL	404-664-1210	24		Monitors
Prometheus Products ......ORPOR	503-691-5199	144		Fax/Modems
Proteon ....MA	508-366-7827	24		Networking Boards
Public Brand Software .....ININD	317-856-2087	144		Shareware Software
Pure Data ....TXDAL	214-242-3225	144		Networking Boards
Qmail ....TNMEM	901-382-5583	168		QMail Offline Reader
QMS ....AL	205-633-3632	24		Printers
Quadram ....GAATL	404-564-5678	24		Memory Software
Qualitas ....DCWAS	301-907-8030	144	X	386Max & Bluemax
Quantum ....CASJO	408-894-3214	24		Hard Disk Storage
Quarterdeck Office Systems. .CA	310-341-3227	144		QEMM386
Quercus Systems ....CA	408-867-7488	144		REXXTERM
Quess Micro ....CO	719-597-8670	144		Telemagic & Add-ons
QuickBBS ....FLORL	407-896-0494	168		QuickBBS BBS Software
Racal Interlan/Rabbit Soft. ..MA	508-264-4345	24		Networking Cards
Race ....FLMIA	305-271-2146	24		Race User Editors (RA)
Rams' Island Software .....CODEN	303-841-6269	168		Incontext
RelayNet National ....DCWAS	301-229-5623	168	X	Relaynet Mail System
Remote Control Int ....CA	619-431-4030	24		Telemagic
Revelation Technologies ....WASEA	206-641-8110	24		Advanced Revelation
Rix Softworks ....CASAN	714-476-0728	24		Paint Software
Rybs Electronics ....CODEN	303-443-7437	24		Memory Manager
Saber Software ....TXDAL	214-361-1883	144		Saber Network Menu
Salt Air BBS ....UTSLC	801-261-8976	168		PCboard BBS Software
Samsung Info Systems ......NJ	201-691-6238	24		Computers/Monitors
SEAboard ....NJNEW	201-473-1991	96		ARC,SEADOG,AXE
Seagate ....CA	408-438-8771	144		Hard Drives,Con-troller

Company/BBS Name ....STPCP	Phone number	MDM	FLG	Products supported
Searchlight Software ......NYHEM	516-689-2566	96		Searchlight BBS Soft ware
SemWare ....GAATL	404-641-8968	96		Qedit DOS Editor
Sharp ....GAATL	404-962-1788	168		Scanners/Computers
Shiva Corporation ....MABOS	617-621-0190	24		Fastpath 4, Bridges
Sitka Corporation ....CASPA	415-769-8774	24		Tops Network OS
Sierra Online ....CA	209-683-4463	144		Graphic Adventure Games
Sigma Design ....CAPAL	510-770-0111	24	X	Video Board, Monitors
Silicon Valley Computers ....CAPAL	415-967-8081	24		Computers
Sitka ....CAOAK	510-769-8774	24		Flashcard
SMS Technology ....CA	510-964-5700	96H		Hard Disk Controllers
Sofnet ....GAATL	404-984-9926	24		Fax Software
SoftArc Inc ....ONT	416-609-2250	144		Firstclass BBS for MAC
Softklone ....FL	904-878-9884	144		Mirror III, Takeover
Softlogic Solutions ....NH	603-644-5556	24		Disk Optimizer,Double DOS
Softronics ....CO	719-593-9295	24		Softerm PC
Software Products Intl ......CASDI	619-450-2179	24		Open Access, Window-Base
Software Security ....CT	203-329-7263	24		Software Copy Protec-tion
Software Venture ....CAOAK	510-849-1912	24		Microphone Software
Solutions Systems ....MA	617-237-8530	24		Brief Software
SparkWare ....TNMEM	901-382-5583	168		QMAIL Door/Reader
Spectra Publishing ....CASJO	408-730-8326	24		Powerbasic Software
SprintNet ....VA	800-546-1000	24		Networking, PC Pursuit
Stac Electronics ....CA	619-431-5956	144		Stacker HD Software
Star Micronics ....NJNEW	908-572-5010	144		Star Printers
STB Systems ....TXDAL	214-437-9615	168		Video Cards
Storage Dimensions ....CASJO	408-944-1220	144		Storage Devices
Sunrise Software ....GAATL	404-256-9525	24		Sunrise Door Software
Sunriver. ....TXAUS	512-835-8082	24		UNIX Systems
Supermac Software ....CASJO	408-773-4500	24		Spectrum Board,Moni-tors
Supra Corp ....OR	503-967-2444	144		Modems
Sydex ....OR	503-683-1385	24		SHEZ
Symantec ....CASJO	408-973-9598	144		Norton,PCanywhere
Sysgen ....CASJO	408-946-5032	24		Drive Controllers
Systems Compatibility ......ILCHI	312-670-4239	24		Software Bridge, Toolkit
Syquest ....CAPAL	510-656-0473	96	X	Removable Mass Stoage
Swan Technologies ....PA	814-237-6145	144		SWAN Computers
T.A.G. BBS ....MIDET	313-582-6671	168		TAG BBS Software
TEAMate ....CA	213-318-5302	144		Teamate UNIX BBS

Company/BBS Name ....STPCP	Phone number	MDM	FLG	Products supported
Tecmar ....OHCLE	216-349-0853	144		Tape Backups
Telebit ....CASJO	408-745-3803	144		Modems
Telix Support ....ONT	416-439-8293	168		TELIX Comm Software
Template Garden Software ..NYNYO	212-627-5089	96	X	The Documentor
Texas Instruments ....TXAUS	512-250-6112	24		Printers,CPUS
TheSoft Programming ......CAPAL	415-581-3019	24		Thedraw ANSI Software
Thomas Conrad ....TXAUS	512-836-8012	144		Networking Cards
Thumper Technologies .....OK	918-627-0059	24		Ez-Reader
Thunderbyte USA ....TN	615-442-2833	144		Thunderbyte ANTI-Virus
Tiara Computer Systems ....CAPAL	415-966-8533	144		Networking Cards
Timeline Software ....CA	415-892-0408	24		Schedulers
Timeslips ....MA	508-768-7581	24		Timeslips Software
Tops microsystems ....CAOAK	510-769-8774	24		Network OS/Email
TopSoft Software ....KY	502-425-9941	168		BBS Doors,Toped
Toshiba Printer Products ....CASAN	714-581-7600	24		Printers
Trantor Systems ....CAPAL	415-656-5159	24		Parallel Port SCSI
Traveling Software ....WASEA	206-485-1736	144		Laplink, Battery Watch
Trident Microsystems ......CAPAL	415-691-1016	24		VGA Cards
Trius ....MA	508-794-0762	168		ASEASYAS Spreadsheet
True Vision ....ININD	317-577-8783	24		Display Accelerator
TSR Systems ....NYHEM	516-331-6682	24		PALCOM-Paradox Compiler
Turbo Tax ....CASDI	619-453-5232	24		TurboTax Software
Turtle Beach ....PA	717-845-4835	144		Windows Software
Unicorn Software ....ININD	317-784-2147	24		Unicorn Software
US Robotics ....ILCHI	708-982-5092	168	X	Modems
US Sage ....FL	417-331-7433	24		MainLAN Network
Ven Tel ....CASJO	408-922-0988	144		Modems
Ventura Software ....CASDI	619-673-7691	144		Ventura Publisher
Vermont Microsystems ......VE	802-655-7461	24		Hires Video Boards
Video Seven ....CAPAL	510-656-0503	144	X	Video Cards
Virex ....NCRTP	919-419-1602	144		Virus Detection
Visual Business Systems .....GAATL	404-953-1613	24		Video
Volkswriter ....CA	408-648-3015	24		Volkwriter Software
Vortex Systems ....PAPIT	412-322-3216	24		Retrochron Backup
Wacom ....CAPAL	415-960-0236	24		Graphic Tablets
Walker,Richer, & Quinn ....WASEA	206-324-2357	96		TCP/IP Software
Walt Disney Software ......CAGLE	818-567-4027	24		Childrens Software
Wangtek ....CA	805-582-3370	24		Tape Drives
Wantree Development ......MOKCI	913-441-0595	144		Remoteaccess BBS
Weitek ....CASJO	408-522-7517	24		Math CoProc
Western Digital ....CASAN	714-753-1068	144		Controllers,Hard Drive

Company/BBS Name ....STPCP	Phone number	MDM	FLG	Products supported
White Water Systems ....ILCHI	708-328-9442	24	X	Zortech, Actor
Word Perfect Corp ....UT	801-225-4414	144	D S	Wordperfect,Drawperfect
Wordtech ....CASFA	415-254-1141	24		DBXL,Quicksilver
Wyse ....CASJO	408-922-4400	24		Terminals/Computers
Xircom ....CA	818-878-7618	144		Network Adapters
Xyquest. ....MA	508-667-5669	24		Correct Grammer
XTree ....CA	805-546-9150	24		XTREE/XTREE Gold
Zenographics ....CASAN	714-851-3860	24		Pixie, Super Queue
Zoom Telephonics ....MABOS	617-451-5284	144		Modems
Zsoft ....GAATL	404-427-1045	144	S	Paintbrush
ZyXEL ....CASAN	714-693-0762	144		Modems

Modem Parameters:

96H - US Robotics HST Modem   96V - 9600 V.32 Standard Modems
168 - US Robotics Dual Standard   144 - 14.4K V.32/V.42bix Modem
24 - Standard 2400 Modem   24M - 2400 MNP5 Modem

EQUAL ACCESS "TRIPLE XXX" CODES

You can select the long distance carrier to carry your call from any telephone that has an "Equal Access" capability. To do so you enter the digits "10" followed by the three digits assigned to the long distance carrier you wish to use, hence the term "triple XXX" code. After you enter the five digits you would then dial 1+ the telephone number you want to reach. Note that some companies may not provide long distance service from your location. The following table lists for each long distance company their full carrier selection code.

Company	Carrier Selection Code
Allnet	10444
American Network/Savenet	10311
American PTT	10278
American Telephone Exchange	10050
Amptelco Systems	10267

Company	*Carrier Selection Code*
AT&T	10288
ATC Long Distance	10789
BTI	10833
Cable & Wireless	10223
Com Systems	10266
Comex/Chinamerica	10788
CP National	10276
Escondido Telephone Company	10441
ITT	10488
LDDS Communications	10450
Long Distance America	10035
MCI	10222
Metromedia Communications	10488
Republic Telecom	10001
Sprint	10777
Telecom*USA	10852
Telesphere Network	10555
TMC Long Distance	10007
Touch 1 Long Distance	10751
US Telecom	10220

TELEPHONE AND FAX COUNTRY CODES

Ctry Code	*Destination Country*	*Ctry Code*	*Destination Country*
213	Algeria	231	Liberia
684	American Samoa	218	Libya
33	Andorra	41	Liechtenstein
809	Anguilla	352	Luxembourg
809	Antigua	853	Macao
54	Argentina	265	Malawi
297	Aruba	60	Malaysia
274	Ascension Island	960	Maldives
61	Australia	356	Malta
43	Austria	692	Marshall Islands
809	Bahamas	230	Mauritius
973	Bahrain	52	Mexico
880	Bangladesh	91	Micronesia
809	Barbados	33	Monaco

Ctry Code	Destination Country	Ctry Code	Destination Country
32	Belgium	809	Montserrat
501	Belize	212	Morocco
229	Benin	264	Namibia
809	Bermuda	674	Nauru Island
591	Bolivia	31	Netherlands
267	Botswana	599	Nether, Antilles
55	Brazil	809	Nevis Island
809	British Virgin Islands	687	New Caledonia
673	Brunei	64	New Zealand
359	Bulgaria	505	Nicaragua
237	Cameroon	234	Nigeria
None	Canada	967	North Yemen
809	Cayman Islands	47	Norway
56	Chile	968	Oman
86	China	92	Pakistan
57	Colombia	809	Palm Island
506	Costa Rica	507	Panama
357	Cyprus	675	Papua New Guinea
42	Czechoslovakia	595	Paraguay
45	Denmark	46	Peru
809	Dominica	63	Philippines
809	Dominican Republic	48	Poland
593	Ecuador	352	Portugal
20	Egypt	974	Qatar
503	El Salvador	262	Reunion Island
251	Ethiopia	40	Romania
679	Fiji	670	Saipan
358	Finland	685	Samoa
33	France	39	San Marino
596	French Antilles	966	Saudi Arabia
594	French Guiana	221	Senegal
689	French Polynesia	65	Singapore
241	Gabon	677	Solomon Islands
220	Gambia	27	South Africa
37	Germany, East	7	Soviet Union (Moscow only)
49	Germany, West	34	Spain
233	Ghana	94	Sri Lanka
350	Gibraltar	809	St. Kitts
30	Greece	809	St. Lucia
299	Greenland	508	St. Pierre/Miquelon
809	Grenada	809	St. Vincent
671	Guam	597	Suriname
5399	Guantanamo	268	Swaziland
502	Guatemala	46	Sweden
224	Guinea	41	Switzerland
592	Guyana	886	Taiwan

Ctry Code	Destination Country	Ctry Code	Destination Country
509	Haiti	255	Tanzania
504	Honduras	66	Thailand
852	Hong Kong	28	Togo
36	Hungary	809	Trinidad & Tobago
354	Iceland	216	Tunisia
91	India	90	Turkey
62	Indonesia	809	Turks/Caicos Islands
98	Iran	256	Uganda
353	Ireland	809	Union Island
972	Israel	971	United Arab Emirates
39	Italy	44	United Kingdom
225	Ivory Coast	None	United States
809	Jamaica	598	Uruguay
81	Japan	39	Vatican City
962	Jordan	58	Venezuela
254	Kenya	685	Western Samoa
686	Kiribati Island	38	Yugoslavia
82	Korea, South	243	Zaire
965	Kuwait	260	Zambia
266	Lesotho	263	Zimbabwe

SPECIAL OFFER AND CALL FOR ASSISTANCE

The preparation of a comprehensive directory to the electronic highway represents a task that can never be fully accomplished. According to trade press reports, the Internet is growing by over 20 percent per year and the use of different commercial electronic mail systems and bulletin boards is experiencing a similar annual increase.

Since it is anticipated that this will be the first of many future editions of this directory, we are seeking your cooperation and assistance to keep us informed of additions and revisions to information contained in this book. In appreciation of your effort in submitting any updated information, the publisher will inform you of the anticipated publication date of the next edition of this book as well as mail you a coupon entitling you to a discount of 20 percent for the next edition of this book. To receive the coupon and information please send the following information to Gilbert Held, the author of this book. This information can be mailed to Mr. Held at 4736 Oxford Road, Macon, GA 31210 or transmitted to him at his MCI address of GHELD. At a minimum, information to be furnished should include:

1. Type of update: Addition _____   or Revision _____ .

2. Chapter location for addition/revision: _____ and page: _____ .

3. For addition or revision specify:

   Database: _____

   Access method: _____

   Description (if applicable): _____

   _____

4. Your name and postal address::

   _____

   _____

   _____